CAUTION

RADIATION AREA

RADIATION WARNING SYMBOL

ATOMIC ENERGY
ENCYCLOPEDIA
IN THE
LIFE SCIENCES

ATOMIC ENERGY
ENCYCLOPEDIA
IN THE
LIFE SCIENCES

Editor and Major Contributor

CHARLES WESLEY SHILLING, M.D., D.Sc.

Consultant to United States Atomic Energy Commission;
Deputy Director, Division of Biology and Medicine,
United States Atomic Energy Commission, 1955–1960

with the assistance of MIRIAM TEED SHILLING, M.A.

Prepared under the auspices of the
Division of Technical Information,
United States Atomic Energy Commission

W. B. SAUNDERS COMPANY *Philadelphia·London·1964*

Advisory Committee

ELDA E. ANDERSON, Ph.D. (*)
Health Physics Division
Oak Ridge National Laboratory
Oak Ridge, Tennessee

JOHN C. BUGHER, M.D., D.Sc.
Director, Puerto Rico Nuclear Center
University of Puerto Rico
Rio Piedras, Puerto Rico

CYRIL L. COMAR, Ph.D.
Head, Department of Physical Biology
Cornell University
Ithaca, New York

JOHN A. D. COOPER, M.D., Ph.D.
Professor of Biochemistry and Associate Dean
The Medical School
Northwestern University
Chicago, Illinois

EARL L. GREEN, Ph.D.
Director, Roscoe B. Jackson Memorial Laboratory
Bar Harbor, Maine

HARRIS D. LEVINE
President, Delta Instrument Corporation
Formerly USAEC Health and Safety Laboratory

J. NEWELL STANNARD, Ph.D.
Professor of Radiation Biology,
Associate Dean for Graduate Studies
University of Rochester Medical Center
Rochester, New York

SHIELDS WARREN, M.D., D.Sc.
Director, Cancer Research Institute
Professor of Pathology, Harvard Medical School,
at the New England Deaconess Hospital
Boston, Massachusetts

(*) *Deceased.*

v

DEDICATED TO

ELDA E. ANDERSON, Ph.D.

Pioneer in the field of Health Physics

Foreword

THE COMMUNICATION of information and the exchange of ideas govern to a considerable extent progress in any scientific field. In no other field is this more essential than in the application of atomic energy to the life sciences—an area which almost by definition demands that the work involve one or more scientific disciplines.

The Commission staff assisted in the provision of material for inclusion in this book, but the presentation and scientific evaluation are wholly the work of its distinguished author. Dr. Charles W. Shilling in preparing this Encyclopedia for the Commission has attempted to bring together within a single volume the many necessary information ingredients involved as an aid in facilitating this essential communication.

CHARLES L. DUNHAM, M.D.
Director,
Division of Biology and Medicine
U.S. Atomic Energy Commission

Preface

THE ATOMIC ENERGY ENCYCLOPEDIA IN THE LIFE SCIENCES presents
information on the background and present status of the effects and
uses of atomic energy. It largely stresses peaceful uses, and the items
covered were selected as being of interest to those seeking general
information concerning the applications and the effects of atomic
energy in the fields of biology, agriculture and medicine. Combining
features of both a dictionary and an encyclopedia, it is designed to be
useful to high school and college students, to practicing physicians
and to research scientists.

MATERIAL COVERED

Primary emphasis has been placed on material of special interest
to those working in the life sciences; thus the effects of radiation on
living material and the uses of radiation and radioactive isotopes in
medicine, agriculture and biology have been stressed in the various
entries. Physical concepts of importance to biomedicine have been
included, as are items on each of the elements. The problems of
health protection, environmental contamination, waste disposal,
and weapons testing are briefly covered by appropriate items. A
number of items dealing with instruments and their biomedical uses
are included, together with a brief description of relevant aspects of
certain accelerators and reactors. Throughout the work, emphasis
is placed on activity in the United States—this is specially noticeable
in the coverage of atomic energy administrative machinery and the
plants and laboratories doing work in atomic energy.

DEPTH OF TREATMENT

The level and detail of treatment for the more than 1,200 items
in the Encyclopedia varies from a short definition of a physical
science concept to full-length treatment of such items as *treatment
of radiation illness, animal metabolism studies,* or *waste disposal,
radioactive.* However, the limits of a one-volume work definitely re-
strict the depth of treatment for even the most important items.

An attempt has been made to cover each item in a general but concise manner and then to go into additional detail for those who might desire it.

METHOD OF PREPARATION

Most of the entries represent a compilation from a review of the published literature. However, some items represent the personal work and experience of the contributors. In the preparation of the Encyclopedia a number of lists of terms and subjects were combined into a master list of items to be covered. Then for ease of handling and to insure complete coverage these items were grouped in the following 15 units: Radiation; Elements and Radioisotopes; Radiation Biology; Genetic Effects; Somatic Effects; Prevention and Treatment; Accidents; Radioisotope Uses (this was eventually handled in three parts—medical, agricultural and industrial); Health Protection; Environmental Contamination; Waste Disposal; Instruments; Accelerators, Reactors, Power; Weapons; and Administration.

Each unit was completed separately, reproduced and sent to the USAEC for review by experts in the particular subject matter of the unit. The comments were consolidated and the unit reworked before being resubmitted to the Division of Technical Information, USAEC. When all units had been accepted, the items were alphabetized into the master list forming the Encyclopedia.

HOW TO USE THE ENCYCLOPEDIA

All items, including those for cross-reference purposes, are arranged in alphabetical order in the body of the Encyclopedia; thus the reader wishing information on a single item need only locate the item in its alphabetical location. If the reader is interested in the coverage of a broad subject area, this can be obtained by reference to the partial list of contents preceding the first entry. Here items of major interest are arranged under the 15 headings used in writing the original material.

Cross reference is accomplished by using small capitals for a key word leading to another item entry or by actual reference to the full title of the item deemed to be of particular relevance to the material under discussion. For example, cross reference in the body of an item appears in small capitals in the case of the item concerning BIOLOGICAL MODELS . . . "TISSUE EQUIVALENT MATERIAL has been developed and used in the fabrication of the phantom for use in radiation biology . . ." Or at the end of an item there frequently appears a "See . . ." An item included solely for cross reference appears as follows: THERMAL BIOLOGICAL DAMAGE. See FLASH BURN, RETINAL BURN, and THERMAL BURN.

CONTRIBUTORS

Major contributions were made by the following: E. E. Stickley, Ph.D., Associate Professor of Radiology, College of Physicians and Surgeons, Columbia University (instruments); Gould A. Andrews, M.D., Chairman, Medical Division, Oak Ridge Institute of Nuclear

Studies (medicine); Cyril L. Comar, Ph.D., Head, Department of Physical Biology, Cornell University (agriculture); James S. Robertson, M.D., Ph.D., Head, Medical Physics Division, Medical Department, Brookhaven National Laboratory (accelerators and reactors); and Earl L. Green, Ph.D., Director, Roscoe B. Jackson Memorial Laboratory (genetics).

Each of the following individuals contributed one or more items in the special area of interest or concern in the organization which they represented: Dr. Henry Blair; General R. E. Blount, MC, USA; Dr. Howard Boroughs; Dr. John C. Bugher; Dr. Lee E. Farr; Dr. Allen B. Griffen; Mr. Judson Hardy; Dr. Paul S. Henshaw; Dr. David P. Jacobus; Dr. H. A. Kornberg; Dr. Jesse D. Perkinson; Commander John H. Schulte, MC, USN; and Dr. Arnold H. Sparrow.

ACKNOWLEDGMENTS

We wish to thank the Advisory Committee for their generous assistance and helpful criticism. We particularly appreciate the excellent writing of the contributing authors. We are grateful for the valuable help given by Mr. William E. Boardman and Mr. Robert F. Pigeon, the contract representatives of the USAEC Division of Technical Information. Mrs. Katherine E. Weichold of the USAEC Division of Biology and Medicine provided information and documents on numerous occasions. Mr. Paul C. Janaske developed much of the art work. Mrs. Frances Mallard efficiently handled the typing of the manuscript. In addition we wish to thank the many members of the USAEC and its laboratories who provided information, documents, illustrations and helpful comments.

1643 N. Greenbrier St.
Arlington, Virginia

Contents

Although the topics in this book are arranged in alphabetical order, the reader may also be interested in coverage of broad subject areas. In the following table of contents, topics are arranged alphabetically under 15 major-topic headings:

RADIATION

ELEMENTS AND RADIOISOTOPES

RADIATION BIOLOGY

GENETIC EFFECTS

SOMATIC EFFECTS

PREVENTION AND TREATMENT

ACCIDENTS

RADIOISOTOPE USES

HEALTH PROTECTION

ENVIRONMENTAL CONTAMINATION

WASTE DISPOSAL

INSTRUMENTS

ACCELERATORS, REACTORS, POWER

WEAPONS

ADMINISTRATION, LABORATORIES AND ORGANIZATIONS

A-BOMB

Popular term for a nuclear fission or an atomic bomb.

See ATOMIC WEAPONS.

ABCC. *See* ATOMIC BOMB CASUALTY COMMISSION.

ABDOMINAL SHIELDING

Protection of the abdomen with a lead screen. Abdominal SHIELDING experiments have produced the following results:

1. Shielded animals survived at dose rates which killed all the controls.

2. Of the visceral organs, shielding of only the exteriorized spleen leads to survival rates slightly lower than those resulting from total abdominal shielding.

3. Shielding of the exteriorized liver or gut also reduces the mortality rate.

ABERRATIONS, CHROMOSOME, DUE TO IRRADIATION. *See* CHROMOSOMES, RADIATION EFFECTS ON.

ABSORBER

Any substance that takes up energy. A sheet or other body of material placed between a source of radiation and a detector to determine the nature or energy of the radioactive particle or ray; to reduce the intensity of radiation, as in shielding; or to give the radiation some desired characteristic, as in filtering out the soft component from an x-ray beam. The absorber may accomplish its function by true absorption, scattering, or slowing down the particles or rays.

Alpha rays are completely absorbed by a thin sheet of paper; beta rays are stopped by a sheet of aluminum a few millimeters thick. However, gamma rays and x-rays are electromagnetic radiations and are never absorbed completely by any material. The absorption characteristic of a particular material for electromagnetic radiations of a specific quality is generally stated in terms of the thickness needed to reduce the intensity of the transmitted radiation to one-half the incident intensity (HALF-VALUE LAYER).

In a nuclear reactor, a substance that captures neutrons without reproducing them. Useful in control of the reactor and in shielding—but if it is an undesired contaminant, it may reduce the neutron efficiency.

Almost all substances absorb thermal neutrons to some extent; cadmium and boron are especially effective. Boron is used in NEUTRON CAPTURE THERAPY of brain tumors.

See ABSORPTION, ABSORPTION COEFFICIENT, ABSORPTION CURVE, and SELF-ABSORPTION.

ABSORPTION

The process by which the total number of radioactive particles or gamma ray or x-ray quanta emerging from a body of matter is reduced, relative to the number entering, as a result of interaction with the body of matter. In particle radiation, energy is lost by collisions with electrons or nuclei. The kinetic energy of the particles is also reduced or lost, and this process is referred to as moderation, slowing, or stopping (*see* STOPPING POWER). For electromagnetic radiation, energy reduction is due to transfer to electrons by the process of scattering, by the photoelectric effect, and (at voltages greater than 1 Mev) by pair production. In a specific sense, absorption refers to processes by which radiation disappears or is transformed and not merely scattered.

ABSORPTION COEFFICIENT

Measure of the rate of decrease in intensity of a beam of gamma-ray or x-ray photons, or of particles in their passage through a particular substance. The linear absorption coefficient is the fractional decrease in intensity per unit distance covered, and the mass absorption coefficient is the fractional decrease in intensity per unit surface density. The atomic absorption coefficient is the fractional decrease in intensity per number of atoms per unit area. This coefficient is thus equal to the linear absorption coefficient divided by the number of atoms per unit volume, or to the mass absorption coefficient divided by the number of atoms per unit mass.

ABSORPTION CURVE

A graphic presentation of the intensity of transmitted radiation plotted as a function of the thickness of material traversed. Figure A–1 shows the logarithm of the counting rate for various

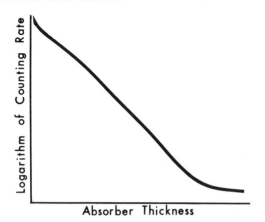

FIGURE A–1. ABSORPTION CURVE. LOGARITHM OF COUNTING RATE FOR VARIOUS ABSORBER THICKNESSES FOR BETA RAYS.

absorber thicknesses plotted against the thickness of absorber for beta rays. Since beta rays consist of particles with a wide range of energies, the absorption curve is not linear. It will be noted that beyond a certain absorber thickness, the counting rate remains constant; this is due to bremsstrahlung radiation.

In terms of radiobiology, the absorption curve depicts the variation in dosage rate with the thickness of absorber.

ABSORPTION OF RADIATION, BIOLOGICAL STUDIES

The absorption phenomena may be studied from either of two viewpoints: (1) By focusing attention on the incident radiation, i.e., examining the manner in which it is decelerated, attenuated, degraded, etc., as the energy is communicated to the medium, or (2) by dealing with the effects on the medium, e.g., the formation of various primary products at different locations during irradiation. These two approaches are not equivalent. It is possible to know the energy lost by a particle in a given time interval without knowing, in detail, the manner in which this energy is acquired by the medium. Also, the energy transmitted to the medium at a certain point is frequently not imparted to the medium at the delivery point.

Absorption of high energy or ionizing radiation in biological material initially gives rise to electrically excited and ionized molecules of several types. These "primary products" are usually unstable and undergo secondary reactions, eventually being converted to stable molecules, returning the system to a thermal equilibrium. Chemical-biochemical equilibrium is reached by interaction of the free radicals with the milieu and with each other to produce a chemical balance. Then follows

a final biological stage, which encompasses the sequential response of the organism to the foreign chemical substances produced by irradiation. These various stages are not clearly delineated, and many of the most challenging problems require studies lying in the borderland areas between the stages.

ABUNDANCE RATIO

The proportion of the various isotopic constituents of an element. This ratio expresses the relative amount (commonly called simply abundance) of a particular isotope as a percentage of the total amount of the element. The natural abundance of each element is given in the discussion of the individual elements. For example, the natural abundance of manganese is furnished 100% by Mn^{55}; therefore the mass number is 55. The atomic weight is determined to be 54.93. The abundance ratio for magnesium is furnished by magnesium of mass numbers 24, 25, and 26. Thus: Mg^{24}, 78.6%; Mg^{25}, 10.1%; and Mg^{26}, 11.3%. The weighted mean gives an atomic weight of 24.32.

See ATOMIC WEIGHT and ISOTOPIC COMPOSITION.

ACCELERATING ELECTRODE

In any device which operates with charged particles, a high-voltage electrode for imparting greater energy to the ions or electrons. Employed in accelerators for the production of high-energy particle streams and in radiation detectors which rely on the collection of ionization released in gases or solids in which the additional energy prevents recombination before complete collection of the signal can be effected.

See ACCELERATORS, RADIATION DETECTORS, and IONIZATION CHAMBERS.

ACCELERATOR

In modern physics the term "accelerator" connotes a device for increasing the velocity and energy of charged elementary particles, e.g., electrons and protons, through application of electromagnetic forces. The VAN DE GRAAFF ELECTROSTATIC GENERATOR, COCKROFT-WALTON ACCELERATOR, CYCLOTRON, LINEAR ACCELERATOR, BETATRON, SYNCHROTRON, SYNCHROCYCLOTRON, and alternating gradient synchrotron are the principal types of accelerators which have been constructed. In most of these devices, charged particles are accelerated as a result of "falling" through electrical gradients and are constrained to follow desired paths by imposition of magnetic fields. In the more powerful machines, the velocities achieved approach the speed of light, and relativistic corrections are essential to assure correct timing of the accelerating impulses. The biological effects of very high-energy particles remain relatively unexplored, but may gain increased interest and importance when space travel becomes a reality.

ACCELERATOR ACCIDENTS

Accidental irradiation has occasionally occurred in the use of an accelerator. For example, in the experimental operation of a new electron linear accelerator, 9 men were exposed to gamma radiation as a result of a faulty electric circuit. Although the dose rate in the target area was 1000 r per hour, the highest exposure was 41 r to one physicist and 400 mr to another; the others received less than 50 mr. No other type of accident appears possible with an accelerator. Cataracts have been found to be associated with accelerator radiation exposure, particularly from neutrons.

ACCELERATOR HAZARDS

High-voltage particle accelerators are used extensively in research laboratories and present some serious hazards and control problems. Most machines are adequately shielded, but since beams of charged particles are frequently brought out through the shield, safety features include an elaborate system of interlocks arranged to interrupt the machine's operation if a person enters the beam area. Indicators with clearly visible lights indicate when the machine is on. Emergency switches are clearly marked. Radiation alarm systems provide warning of dangerous levels of radiation.

All personnel should be carefully indoctrinated in handling the equipment, in regard to hazards involved and safety technique, and should wear personnel-monitoring equipment. Responsibility for safety checks should be clearly fixed, and radiation surveys should be made for each new type of operation. For maintenance work and target handling, the necessary remote control equipment should be available, and shielding should be provided.

ACCIDENTS

Accidents occurring in AEC installations may be conveniently divided into 3 groups: those in no way unique to the use of atomic energy or its products, such as falls, electrocutions, drownings, motor vehicle accidents, etc.; those involving radioactive materials, such as fires, explosions, and environmental contamination; and those resulting in radiation exposure to workers or the general public.

The Atomic Energy Commission rules and regulations set forth the following criteria for Immediately Reportable Accidents and Radiation Exposures:

I. Accidents: (a) Injury or illness of an AEC contractor employee, or a member of the public, where such injury or illness could be attributed to AEC or AEC contractor operations, and which results in: (1) death or imminent death of one or more persons, or (2) injury or illness to five or more persons as the result of one accident; (b) Any accident that the responsible Field Manager or Headquarters Division Director believes to have public information significance; (c) Estimated loss or damage of $5,000 or more of Government property, or estimated costs of $5,000 required for cleaning, renovating, replacing or rehabilitating structures, equipment or property.

II. Radiation Exposures: (a) An injury or illness, diagnosed by a physician, competent in nuclear medicine, as probably resulting from a cumulative or massive exposure to ionizing radiation; (b) A single exposure received over a short period of time in which: (1) the external whole body penetrating radiation exposure is greater than 12 rem, (2) the radiation exposure dose to the skin of the whole body or thyroid is greater than 30 rem, (3) the external radiation exposure dose to the hands and forearms or feet and ankles is greater than 75 rem, or (4) the internal body deposition when averaged over a period of one year exceeds the radiation protection guide; (c) Any radiation exposure which causes an individual's accumulative dose to exceed $5(N-18)$ rem whole body radiation; (d) Whenever there is reason to believe that any member of the general population off-site may have received, as a result of AEC or AEC contractor activities, a radiation exposure greater than those specified for external or internal exposure by Chapter 0524; (e) Any overexposure that the responsible Field Manager or Headquarters Division Director believes to have public information significance.

Twenty-four accidents occurred in AEC facilities during 1962. There were 7 fatalities, none involving radiation. Eight employees received exposures greater than 15 rem (SL–1 reactor emergency).

See ACCELERATOR ACCIDENTS; CRITICALITY ACCIDENTS; INDUSTRIAL ACCIDENTS; INJURIES, RADIATION; RADIATION ACCIDENTS; RADIATION EXPOSURE PERSONNEL RECORD; REACTOR ACCIDENTS; SAFETY RECORD, USAEC; SHIPPING ACCIDENTS; and SL-1 REACTOR ACCIDENT.

ACTINIDE SERIES

Elements of atomic numbers 89 through 103 as follows: actinium, 89; thorium, 90; protactinium, 91; uranium, 92; neptunium, 93; plutonium, 94; americium, 95; curium, 96; berkelium, 97; californium, 98; einsteinium, 99; fermium, 100; mende-levium, 101; nobelium, 102; lawrencium, 103. These elements are grouped under one heading—actinium—in vertical column IIIB in the periodic table on the basis of correlations of their chemical and atomic properties. A similar situation exists in the LANTHANIDE series.

ACTINIDES

Term used to denote elements in the actinide series.

ACTINIUM

From Greek aktinos, beam or ray. Symbol Ac; atomic number 89; a radioactive element with a mass number of 227. Was discovered by the French scientist A. Debierne in 1899 and independently by the German scientist F. Giessel in 1900, in the mineral pitchblende. Since then, other mass numbers (221 through 230) of actinium have been discovered, all radioactive. Actinium-227 occurs in nature as a constituent of uranium ores, 0.15

milligram per ton of pure pitchblende. Actinium-228, known also as mesothorium-2, occurs in the thorium decay series. The actinide series of elements took their name from actinium, as did the actinium decay series.

Ac^{227} has a radioactive half-life of 21.9 years; and with bone as the critical organ, a biological half-life of 200 years and an effective half-life of 19.7 years. It would reach 83% of equilibrium in the body within 50 years. An intense alpha emitter (4.94 Mev), it has potential use as a neutron source.

ACTINIUM RADIOACTIVE SERIES

Table A–1 depicts the decay disintegration chain of the actinium series and the parent-daughter transmutation from uranium-235 (actino-uranium) to lead-207 (actinium D). Named for actinium, the first member of the series to be discovered, although it is not, as originally supposed, the parent of the series.

The table details the name of the element, the

TABLE A–1. ACTINIUM RADIOACTIVE SERIES.

Uranium (Actinouranium)	$(_{92}U^{235}) \xrightarrow[\alpha]{7.13 \times 10^8 \text{ yr}}$	Thorium (Uranium Y)	$(_{90}Th^{231}) \xrightarrow[\beta]{25.6 \text{ hr}}$
Protactinium	$(_{91}Pa^{231}) \xrightarrow[\alpha]{3.43 \times 10^4 \text{ yr}}$		
Actinium	$(_{89}Ac^{227}) \xrightarrow[\alpha \text{ and } \beta]{21.8 \text{ yr}}$		
1.2% α			
Francium (Actinium K)	$(_{87}Fr^{223}) \xrightarrow[\beta]{21 \text{ min}}$		
98.8% β			
Thorium (Radioactinium)	$(_{90}Th^{227}) \xrightarrow[\alpha]{18.4 \text{ days}}$	Radium (Actinium X)	$(_{88}Ra^{223}) \xrightarrow[\alpha]{11.7 \text{ days}}$
Radon (Actinon)	$(_{86}Rn^{219}) \xrightarrow[\alpha]{3.92 \text{ sec}}$		
Polonium (Actinium A)	$(_{84}Po^{215}) \xrightarrow[\alpha \text{ and } \beta]{1.83 \times 10^{-3} \text{ sec}}$		
β ∼ 5 × 10⁻⁴%			
Astatine	$(_{85}At^{215}) \xrightarrow[\alpha]{\sim 10^{-4} \text{ sec}}$		
α ∼ 100%			
Lead (Actinium B)	$(_{82}Pb^{211}) \xrightarrow[\beta]{36.1 \text{ min}}$		
Bismuth (Actinium C)	$(_{83}Bi^{211}) \xrightarrow[\alpha \text{ and } \beta]{2.16 \text{ min}}$		
β 0.3%			
Polonium (Actinium C′)	$(_{84}Po^{211}) \xrightarrow[\alpha]{0.52 \text{ sec}}$		
α 99.7%			
Thallium (Actinium C″)	$(_{81}Tl^{207}) \xrightarrow[\beta]{4.78 \text{ min}}$		
Lead (Actinium D)	$(_{82}Pb^{207})$ Stable end product		

TABLE A–2. COLLATERAL ACTINIUM RADIOACTIVE SERIES.

Protactinium	$(_{91}Pa^{227})\xrightarrow[\alpha]{38\ min}$	Actinium	$(_{89}Ac^{223})\xrightarrow[\alpha]{2.2\ min}$	
Francium	$(_{87}Fr^{219})\xrightarrow[\alpha]{0.02\ sec}$	Astatine	$(_{85}At^{215})\xrightarrow[\alpha]{\sim10^{-4}\ sec}$	
Bismuth	$(_{83}Bi^{211})\xrightarrow{\hspace{2cm}}$	Actinium radioactive series		

corresponding radioelement, the symbol, the type of radiation given off, and the radioactive half-life. In disintegrations in which an alpha (α) particle is emitted, the atomic weight of the daughter element is 4 units less than that of the parent. This is because an alpha particle, on the atomic weight scale, has a mass of 4, and thus the loss of one alpha particle would reduce the weight by 4. On the other hand, since a beta (β) particle is an electron with a negligible mass, the daughter element in this disintegration will have the same weight as the parent. It was found in the THORIUM RADIOACTIVE SERIES that the atomic weights of all members of the series could be represented by 4n, where n is an integer varying from 58 for thorium ($4 \times 58 = 232$, the atomic weight of thorium) to 52 for lead ($4 \times 52 = 208$). In the same way it can be shown that the formula for the actinium series is $4n + 3$. For example, uranium-235 is $4 \times 58 + 3 = 235$, and lead-207 is $4 \times 51 + 3$.

A collateral $4n + 3$ series is also presented in Table A–2. The progenitor is protactinium-227, obtained by the reaction $Th^{232}(d,7n)Pa^{227}$; this decays to bismuth-211 and then enters the actinium series.

ACTINON

A historical term for an isotope of radon ($_{86}Rn^{219}$).

ACTIVATED MOLECULE

An excited molecule produced by the direct reaction of an ion with a neutral molecule. It is possible that such reactions may be quite important in organic systems. For example, two positively charged atoms of bromine may combine with two negatively charged molecules of hydrogen to form two molecules of hydrogen bromide, one of which will be charged:

$$2\ Br_2^+ + H_2 \xrightarrow{\hspace{2cm}} HBr + HBr^+$$

In a similar way:

$$Ch_4^+ + CH_4 \xrightarrow{\hspace{2cm}} C_2H_6 + H_2^+$$

which is of interest since it provides a possible mechanism for the crosslinking of polymers, which is one of the most characteristic reactions of ionizing radiations with macromolecules.

It has been suggested that the activated molecule may react with oxygen, resulting in inactivation; react with another molecule like itself; or return to its normal state. An excited molecule may have an energy of only about 5 ev, and thus it will not play an important role in radiation chemistry.

ACTIVATED WATER

A transient, chemically reactive state created in water by absorbed ionizing radiations. The passage of ionizing radiation through water temporarily produces ions, atoms, free radicals, or molecules in a chemically reactive state. Evidence exists of the presence of free hydroxyl radicals and hydrogen atoms. Since tissues are composed mainly of water, the interaction of radiation and water is of great biological significance.

See ACTIVATED MOLECULE.

ACTIVATION

Process of inducing radioactivity in an element. For example, an element may be exposed to neutrons in a nuclear reactor, to deuterons in a cyclotron, or to other types of radiation, and one or more of the stable isotopes of the element thus exposed are converted (activated) into radioactive isotopes. Most of the artificially produced radioisotopes commercially available are produced by neutron bombardment of a selected target material in a reactor. Activation produces a radioisotope which has the same atomic number as the original element. A typical activation reaction is:

cobalt-59 + neutron $\xrightarrow{\hspace{2cm}}$
                          cobalt-60 + gamma rays.

The physicist calls this nuclear reaction a neutron-gamma reaction and writes it: $Co^{59}(n,\gamma)Co^{60}$. When bombardment of an element results in a different element, the action is called transmutation.

When a nuclear weapon is detonated so that appreciable quantities of neutrons are available for reaction with constituents in the air, soil, or water, induced radioactivity (activation) occurs and many different radionuclides are formed.

In cases of human accidental exposure to heavy doses of neutron irradiation, stable sodium in the serum and tissues is activated and changed to radioactive sodium-24. By careful analysis of the serum sodium it is possible to estimate quite accurately the neutron dose received if the neutron source spectrum is known.

ACTIVATION, NEUTRON. *See* NEUTRON.

ACTIVATION ANALYSIS

Method of chemical analysis based on making radioactive (activating) an element which can then be detected by studying its characteristic radiations and determining its radioactive half-life. Particularly useful in determining the presence of minute traces of elements. A specimen containing a very small quantity of an element may be exposed to neutrons in a nuclear reactor, with one or more of the stable isotopes of the element being activated, i.e., converted into radioisotopes which can then be identified. By using a control sample with a known amount of the element and treating it in the same way, the activation analysis can be made quantitative. For the analysis to be easily conducted, the radioactive half-life of the resulting radioisotope must be conveniently measurable— not too long or too short. In addition, other elements present must not have similar radiation characteristics which would interfere with identification and measurement. The sensitivity of the method, if carried out in a nuclear reactor, depends upon the available thermal neutron flux and on the cross section of the isotopes of the element being studied for radioactive capture of slow or thermal neutrons.

In the biological field, activation analysis has been used to investigate the distribution of gold in the tissues of an animal being studied for rheumatoid arthritis. Used in the physical sciences for analysis of mixtures of rare-earth metals and for estimating traces of gallium and palladium in iron meteorites.

Extensive work has been done at the Oak Ridge National Laboratory in neutron-activation analysis, and it has been possible for this laboratory to determine trace quantities, as indicated by Table A–3. Application for this type of work should be addressed to Union Carbide Nuclear Company, Oak Ridge National Laboratory, Isotopes Sales Department, P.O. Box X, Oak Ridge, Tennessee.

TABLE A–3.   ELEMENTS DETERMINED IN TRACE QUANTITIES BY NEUTRON ACTIVATION ANALYSIS

ELEMENT	SENSITIVITY OF DETECTION (grams)
Bismuth	
Calcium	
Iron	
Magnesium	
Nickel	10^{-6}
Niobium	
Silicon	
Sulfur	
Titanium	
Cerium	
Chromium	
Mercury	
Molybdenum	
Neodymium	
Platinum	
Ruthenium	10^{-7}
Silver	
Strontium	
Tellurium	
Thallium	
Tin	
Zirconium	
Aluminum	
Barium	
Cadmium	
Cesium	
Chlorine	
Cobalt	
Erbium	10^{-8}
Gadolinium	
Germanium	
Hafnium	
Osmium	
Phosphorus	
Potassium	
Rubidium	
Selenium	10^{-8}
Thorium	
Yttrium	
Zinc	
Antimony	
Arsenic	
Bromine	
Copper	
Gallium	
Gold	
Iodine	
Lanthanum	
Palladium	
Praseodymium	10^{-9}
Scandium	
Sodium	
Tantalum	

Table A–3 continued

ELEMENT	SENSITIVITY OF DETECTION (grams)
Terbium	
Thulium	
Tungsten	
Uranium	
Vanadium	
Ytterbium	
Holmium	
Indium	
Iridium	
Lutetium	10^{-10}
Manganese	
Rhenium	
Samarium	
Europium	
Dysprosium	10^{-11}

ACTIVATION CROSS SECTION

The cross section for the formation (activation) of a specified radionuclide is usually expressed in barns. For example, chromium-51 is produced by bombardment with neutrons in a nuclear reactor of chromium-50, for which the thermal neutron cross section is 17 barns. Another example is potassium-42, which is usually produced by $K^{41}(n, \gamma)$ for which the thermal neutron cross section is 1.2 barns.

ACTIVATION METHOD

Analysis by means of activation; commonly used for determining minute traces of elements. It is one of three methods using radioisotopes: tracer analysis or TRACER STUDIES, dilution analysis or DILUTION TECHNIQUES, and ACTIVATION ANALYSIS.

ACTIVITY

Term commonly used for radioactivity. Intensity of emission from a radioactive source expressed in terms of observable effects, i.e., the number of atoms disintegrating in a unit time. Activity often expressed in counts per minute or in roentgens per hour at one meter, etc. Term used to designate a particular radiation component, e.g., the gamma activity of a source. The intensity or strength of a radioactive source.

See SPECIFIC ACTIVITY.

ACUTE RADIATION EXPOSURE

Radiation exposure of short duration, usually a dose delivered in a matter of minutes or hours.

Acute exposure often carries with it the connotation of a heavy or massive dose, although this is not necessarily the case. Frequently it is associated with accidental exposure or with teletherapy treatment of malignancy.

ACUTE RADIATION SYNDROME

Human WHOLE BODY IRRADIATION at a dose level higher than 100 rad of penetrating ionizing radiation may lead to a series of signs and symptoms known as the acute radiation syndrome. The time of onset and the severity depend upon the radiation dose, with early onset and severe response indicating higher doses. The LD_{50} for those not receiving treatment probably is between 450 and 500 rad entrance dose, and for those individuals hospitalized and treated the LD_{50} may be as high as 700 rad. The signs and symptoms of acute radiation syndrome will be presented separately.

Vomiting. Nausea with vomiting is an important clinical entity. For midline doses less than 100 rad, nausea and vomiting seldom occur; at 200 to 400 rad, nausea and vomiting are mild; from 400 to 600 rad, the increase in both incidence and severity is rapid; and above 600 rad, the incidence is about 100%, and vomiting is severe. In general, prolonged, severe, and early vomiting is a serious clinical sign, probably indicating a high dose of radiation. (*See* VOMITING DUE TO IRRADIATION.)

Lymphocytes. A reduction in the number of circulating lymphocytes accompanies exposure to ionizing radiation of 50 rad or more and is therefore an indicator of radiation damage. (*See* LYMPHOCYTES, RADIATION DAMAGE.)

Total White Blood Cell Count. Following exposure to ionizing radiation of 100 rad or more, the count invariably decreases after the first two or three days. The rate of fall is at first rapid and then fluctuates, with depth of depression and time of recovery having some DOSE-EFFECT RELATIONSHIP. A normal total white cell count during the first 24 to 48 hours does not indicate a low exposure, and the degree of depression is often not of itself diagnostic. In radiation illness, as in many other medical conditions, the results of laboratory examinations and the other signs and symptoms must be considered in making either a diagnosis or giving a prognosis.

Diarrhea. One of the symptoms of INTESTINAL DAMAGE, which is diagnostic of a heavy exposure if it occurs during the first few hours. (*See* DIARRHEA DUE TO IRRADIATION.)

Erythema. One of the signs of exposure to radiation may be erythema of the skin (threshold dose ±250r). With doses in the low range, erythema, if it occurs, is late and of little significance;

coming early and well-marked, it probably indicates a high-dose exposure. As a sign, it is not considered alone, but is interpreted along with other signs and symptoms in making a diagnosis.

Body Temperature. There is little evidence that fever is a diagnostic sign except in supralethal dose cases in which it comes early (first two hours) and is high (103° F). Elevated temperature during the usual course of radiation illness probably is related to secondary infection and is not radiation induced.

Bleeding. No signs of bleeding are found in low-dose groups (under 200 rad); small skin and mucous membrane hemorrhages (petechiae), bleeding gums and easy bruising are noted in those exposed to 200 to 400 rad. Hemorrhage as a complication of gastrointestinal tract damage occurs in the third to fifth weeks in persons surviving 400 rad. Hemorrhage is related to the disappearance of platelets from the circulating blood. Hemorrhage resulting from radiation injury is not a sign that is helpful for early diagnosis, but is an indication of a poor prognosis when it occurs late, particularly when severe.

Platelets. The number of platelets circulating in the blood begins to decrease at the end of about a week after irradiation of 200 or more rad. In persons receiving between 400 and 600 rad and surviving until the third to fifth weeks, the platelets may be so low that hemorrhage occurs. Recovery normally takes many months; early recovery is a good prognostic sign. (*See* PLATELETS, RADIATION EFFECTS ON.)

Epilation. One of the effects of a dose of radiation of 300 or more rad. It generally occurs between the seventeenth and twenty-first days—a little later with lower doses. When epilation occurs, it is a significant diagnostic sign.

Fatigue. One of the important clinical signs is fatigue, which in very high-dose exposure may be so severe as to constitute complete debilitation. At lower doses patients talk of a "washed-out" feeling and "weakness." It is impossible to quantitate, but taken with other signs and symptoms provides additional information for diagnosis and prognosis.

Spermatogenesis. Human exposure to 200 r or more of ionizing radiation is known to cause temporary STERILITY. Some information regarding the level of damage may be obtained by needle biopsy of the testicle, but there is not much human data on the effect of radiation on the total sperm count, although viability of sperm can be determined. A constant worry of both the radiation illness patient and his wife is sterility, which is frequently confused with lack of potency. (*See* POTENCY, RADIATION EFFECTS ON.)

ADRENAL GLANDS, RADIATION EFFECTS ON

Following irradiation in the lethal dose range, the medulla of the adrenal gland at autopsy shows loss of lipoid (fat)-staining material and a few small scattered hemorrhages, but few evidences of necrosis (cell death) or severe damage. A depletion of the steroids in the adrenal has been shown to occur following irradiation in the lethal range. But evidence indicates that the "stress" response of the adrenal is important in the development of the ACUTE RADIATION SYNDROME.

The role of the adrenal in modifying the response of an animal to radiation is well established: Adrenalectomized (removal of adrenals) rats or mice show a greatly decreased resistance to radiation.

ADRENALINE (EPINEPHRINE), RESPONSE TO RADIATION

The increased adrenal cortical activity observed following whole body irradiation is not due to direct action on the adrenal glands, but to change in the adenohypophyseal activity. Local irradiation in doses sufficient to destroy tissue produces the typical "alarm reaction" associated with secretion of adrenaline. Secretion from the adrenals has been shown to be related to reaction within a part of the body not irradiated. For example, the response occurs in atrophy of the thymus of a rat subjected to abdominal radiation of 2,000 to 3,700 roentgens (r) but does not occur in animals from which the adrenal glands have been removed (adrenalectomy) 2 to 5 days before. Atrophy of the spleen associated with a 2,800 r dose to the head and neck does not occur after adrenalectomy.

See ENDOCRINE ORGANS, ROLE IN RADIATION SYNDROME.

ADVISORY COMMITTEE FOR BIOLOGY AND MEDICINE

The ACBM is a nonstatutory committee advisory to the U. S. Atomic Energy Commission which reviews the USAEC programs in medical and biological research, and in addition responds to specific requests for guidance on matters of broader interest to the Commission's activities in the fields of health and research. It works closely with the Division of Biology and Medicine in all matters involving their interests. Formed in 1947, it has met on a regular basis since that time. The members as of 1963 are:

Dr. H. Bentley Glass, Chairman; Professor of Biology, Johns Hopkins University, Baltimore, Maryland.

Dr. James G. Horsfall, Vice-Chairman; Director, Connecticut Agricultural Experiment Station, New Haven, Connecticut.

Dr. Fred J. Hodges, Professor and Chairman of Radiology, Department of Radiology, University of Michigan Medical Center, Ann Arbor, Michigan.

Dr. Robert F. Loeb, Bard Professor of Medicine, Columbia University, New York, New York.

Dr. Leonidas D. Marinelli, Associate Director, Radiological Physics Division, Argonne National Laboratory, Argonne, Illinois.

Dr. Carl V. Moore, Professor of Medicine, Department of Internal Medicine, Washington University, Barnes & Wohl Hospital, St. Louis, Missouri.

Dr. James H. Sterner, Medical Director, Eastman Kodak Company, Rochester, New York.

(2 vacancies)

ADVISORY COMMITTEE ON REACTOR SAFEGUARDS

A committee established in 1953 by the USAEC and given statutory Congressional status in 1957. The Committee reviews safety studies, facilitates license applications referred to it, and advises the Commission on the safety aspects of proposed or existing reactor facilities and the adequacy of proposed reactor safety standards. It currently comprises 13 members appointed by the Commission for terms of 4 years each. The members designate their own chairman.

AERIAL MONITORING

Sometimes referred to as aerial radiological monitoring. Monitoring or measuring, by use of low-flying planes or helicopters, the radioactivity on the surface of the ground. It is routine practice to use aircraft equipped with scintillation counters to measure the gamma radiation dose rate of the radioactive cloud (and to take samples) resulting from the test detonation of a nuclear device, and to follow the fallout distribution of the radioactive material.

This technique is the most rapid method of estimating the extent of radiation hazard on the earth's surface. One of the great advantages of such a survey is that it can be made at levels of radiation which might block a survey on foot or by car.

See AERIAL PROSPECTING, AERIAL SURVEYING, and HIGH-ALTITUDE SAMPLING PROGRAM.

AERIAL PROSPECTING*

Also called air-borne exploration, air-borne radiation surveying, and air-borne reconnaissance. From 1952 to 1956 the USAEC conducted air-borne radioactivity surveys in a number of states in a search for uranium ore deposits. It proved to be a rapid, cheap, and effective method with millions of dollars' worth of uranium ore being successfully located. Small planes were used, flying as close to the ground as possible (50 to 75 feet) at speeds of 50 to 120 miles per hour. The gamma detection instrument was of the scintillation type with a large volume crystal.

Copies of maps issued by AEC showing the location of radioactivity anomalies, which do not necessarily indicate the presence of uranium deposits, may be obtained from the Map Division, Library of Congress, Washington 25, D.C., at about $1.00 each, and generally also from AEC depository libraries.

AERIAL SURVEYING

Aerial Radiological Measurements and Surveys (ARMS) have been conducted from the air over 39 areas of the United States to date (1961), including many of the large cities. This program is designed to determine the present normal level of terrestrial radiation, in order to be able to detect any future variation which might result from detonation of nuclear devices in the testing program, from reactor accidents, or from other radiation contamination.

A plane flying 500 feet above the ground carries a scintillation counter, which measures gamma radiation coming from the earth and records the radiation level correlated with the space position of the plane. Instruments and techniques are checked at the Extended Source Calibration Area at the Nevada Test Site where 565 small cesium-137, cobalt-60, and other radioactive isotope sources can be arrayed on an area 2,000 feet square so that they can be "seen" by the aircraft's instruments.

The feasibility of the technique was demonstrated during Operation ARME (aerial radiological monitoring exercise) conducted for the Federal Civil Defense Administration by the USAEC at the Nevada Test Site in 1955.

AEROSOL

Particulates dispersed in air or other gases. These particulates may be either solid or liquid.

*The term AERIAL MONITORING will be reserved for use in connection with fallout and the term AERIAL SURVEYING, for the aerial radiological measurements and surveys (ARMS) program of the USAEC.

In the solid form they may exist in the air as:

1. Dusts, resulting from mechanical size reduction of inorganic or organic solids, with 50 microns (μ) being the upper size limit for air-borne contaminants except under conditions of very high velocities of air motion;

2. Fumes, produced by combustion, condensation, or sublimation of inorganic solid materials— the usual size being less than 1 μ; and

3. Smokes, produced by combustion of organic material, with size usually less than 0.5 μ.

Liquid particulates are usually called mists, which are produced by liquids being atomized, condensed, or entrapped by gases, with a droplet size of 0.1 to 25 μ. Fogs are excessive concentrations of submicron droplets.

AET

Call letters for S, 2-aminoethylisothiouronium bromide hydrobromide, a chemical which gives protection against the effects of radiation if given before exposure. It has the formula:

$$\left[\overset{+}{H_3}N \cdot CH_2 \cdot CH_2 \cdot S \cdot C \overset{\overset{+}{N}H_2}{\underset{NH_2}{\diagup}} \right] 2Br^-$$

See CHEMICAL PROTECTION AGAINST RADIATION INJURY.

AGE AND RADIOSENSITIVITY

Age is one of the factors affecting the radiosensitivity of a cell, tissue, or organism. Rapidly dividing cells have less resistance to radiation than nondividing mature cells, and the embryo is much less able to withstand radiation than the adult organism. The NAS report* says: "Factors Influencing Sensitivity: Very young or very old animals have increased sensitivity to lethal effects, and there is some experimental evidence to indicate that in some species the 50% acute lethal dose (LD_{50}) may decrease progressively with increasing age during adult life, while in other species a decrease in LD_{50} may not be observable until later life."

In the rat, the LD_{50} varies with the age of the animal, increasing from about 400 roentgens (r) in weanling rats to about 700 r in young adults, and then decreasing slowly with increasing age. Young chickens and salamanders are also markedly more sensitive to radiation than the adults. The

*The Biological Effects of Atomic Radiation. Summary Reports. 1960. National Academy of Sciences— National Research Council.

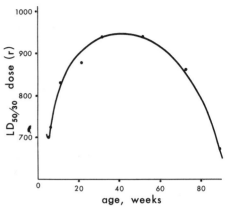

FIGURE A–2. RADIOSENSITIVITY AS A FUNCTION OF AGE.

effect of age in the radiosensitivity of SAS/4 mice is shown in Figure A–2.

The adult Drosophila is much more resistant to radiation than the younger stages: the LD_{50} for 3-hr eggs is 200 r; for 4-hr eggs is 500 r; for 7½-hr eggs is 810 r; and for pupae is 2800 r. Eggs are laid (a few develop) after 8000 r, but eggs laid after exposure to 16,000 r and 32,000 r are not viable. Adult Drosophila are resistant to 64,000 r cobalt-60 gamma rays, but are sterilized.

AGE ESTIMATION, USING CARBON-14

Calculation of the age of a once-living, carbon-containing object by measurement of its carbon-14 content. *See* RADIOCARBON DATING.

AGING DUE TO RADIATION EXPOSURE

A precise definition of aging with a statement of how it can be measured is not possible at present, although extensive animal experimental work is under way to try to determine what constitutes "natural" or physiological aging and how this relates to aging due to radiation exposure. There is evidence that both may be measured in the same units.

There is ample evidence that life expectancy is genetically controlled; as one example, the beetles dying off in the first month of life are probably those of defective biological organization which, although surviving through earlier stages, could not go on living through subsequent stages. It must be stressed that in the light of present knowledge we do not know whether "premature" aging and LIFE SHORTENING from radiation exposure are identical phenomena. In fact, aging may be one process and physiological degradation due to radiation, another.

There is some evidence that the accumulation of

point mutations, either in the germinal or in the somatic tissue, is the principal mechanism of aging (*See* TARGET THEORY). The induction of chromosome breaks and "misunions" by radiation is probably the source of diverse types of tissue change that are suspected of causing aging.

Many late effects following irradiation are also found to be associated with physiological aging. The question arises, does irradiation accelerate the aging process and the development of diseases usually found in aging organisms? Irradiated organs show vascular and connective tissue changes that result in fibrosis of the skin, chronic lung inflammation, kidney damage, and focal fibrosis of heart muscle, lymphoid organs, and endocrine glands. Atrophy and defective development are particularly prominent in skin, lymphoid organs, bone marrow, and gonads. Alterations in pigment deposition are found in the skin and hair. These evidences of aging may be seen following single and repeated doses of radiation in experimental animals.

On the other hand, some characteristic changes used to measure age and aging do not appear to be altered by irradiation. The tensile properties of tail tendons in rats and mice are measurably altered with age, but even a 1100-roentgen dose does not change the elastic behavior from the control group. A typical aging phenomenon is the development of benign hepatoma in CBA mice, but even heavy irradiation does not shorten the time of appearance to less than the normal 1 year in the controls.

The preponderance of evidence points to radiation as causing "premature" aging, although the results of animal research must be applied to human experience with great care.

AGRICULTURE, USE OF RADIOISOTOPES IN

Radioisotopes, as a relatively new research tool, make it possible to obtain certain types of information with more ease and accuracy and to gain new knowledge unobtainable in any other way. The benefits to agriculture may be classified generally as follows:

1. Reduction of losses in production, storage, and distribution due to microbial action, diseases, insects, and weeds.

2. Increase of productivity of land and other resources now in use through better understanding of the life processes, for example, development of optimal feeding and breeding.

3. Development of new areas and resources, for example, through availability of power to provide irrigation facilities and permit exploitation of farm resources.

Although financial estimates are difficult to make, recent studies have indicated that in the United States at least 180 million dollars per year is being saved through the use of radioisotopes in agricultural research. The following outline indicates specific uses to which radioisotopes are being put:

I. Soil and Water
   a. Irrigation, study, and measurement of water sources
   b. Soil composition, aeration, and structure
   c. Chemical analysis of soils for major and minor elements, and availability thereof
   d. Organic decomposition
   e. Nutrient requirements and fertilizers; form, placement, uptake, leaching, sterilization, nitrogen fixation.

II. Plants
   a. Uptake and loss of water and nutrients
   b. Movement within the plant of water, nutrients, and manufactured products
   c. Chemical composition
   d. Photosynthesis, respiration, and enzymatic processes
   e. Synthesis, degradation, and movement of proteins, fats, carbohydrates, vitamins, hormones, and growth substances
   f. Breeding of improved forms
   g. Reproduction
   h. Microbiology, including pathology and fermentation
   i. Environmental factors
   j. Action and residues of fungicides and insecticides
   k. Handling and storage

III. Animals
   a. Nutrition: management problems, requirements, deficiency symptoms, utilization of nutrients, vitamins, tranquilizers
   b. Physiology: lactation, renal function, liver function, gastrointestinal absorption, enzyme action, endocrine function
   c. Genetics and breeding
   d. Reproduction and fetal development
   e. Pathology: microorganisms, cancer, physiological disturbances, insects
   f. Metabolism: carbohydrates, proteins, fats, minerals

IV. Entomology
   a. Insect dispersal and population studies
   b. Disease transmission
   c. Insect physiology
   d. Insect control: radiation, insecticides
   e. Longevity
   f. Parasitology

V. Veterinary Medicine
   a. Diagnostic applications

b. Therapeutic applications
c. Disease processes: infectious, malignant, pathological, physiological
d. Pharmacology
VI. Engineering and Mechanical Processes
a. Thermoradiation and temperature
b. Time and efficiency studies
c. Instrumentation

AGRONOMIC STUDIES. *See* FERTILIZER STUDIES; PLANT BREEDING AND RADIATION; PLANT NUTRITIONAL STUDIES.

AIR-BORNE RADIOACTIVITY

Any radioactive gaseous or particulate matter that is carried by the air within a structure or by the atmosphere surrounding the earth.

See AIR CONTAMINATION, COSMIC RAYS, and FALLOUT.

AIR BURST

The detonation of a nuclear device in the air at a height such that the expanding fireball does not touch the earth's surface when the luminosity is at a maximum, i.e., in the second pulse immediately after detonation. The phenomena associated with the detonation of a 20-kiloton or a 1-megaton nuclear device in the air under standard conditions are presented in the following sketches.

Immediately following the nuclear explosion, a fireball of blinding brilliance is formed, which emits thermal radiation because of its intense heat and initial nuclear radiation resulting from the fission process. For the 20-kiloton nuclear device, as shown in Figure A–3, the fireball will have reached a diameter of 1,460 feet in half a second (maximum size, 1,550 feet). Almost immediately,

a destructive shock wave develops, moving out so that at the end of the first half second it will be 750 feet ahead of the fireball.

When the primary blast wave front strikes the ground, it is reflected as shown in Figure A–4. The reflected blast wave front moves out more rapidly than the primary blast wave front and soon overtakes and fuses with it to form a single front called a Mach front. For a description of these phenomena, *see* BLAST PHYSICAL PHENOMENA. For the 20-kiloton bomb, the Mach effect commences at about 0.35 mile from ground zero at 1.25 seconds after detonation. The blast wave then causes an overpressure on the earth's surface of as much as 16 psi. Thermal and nuclear radiation continues to be emitted from the fireball in significant quantities.

By the end of 3 seconds (see Figure A–5) the Mach front has moved out to 0.87 mile, increasing in height to 185 feet but the overpressure has dropped to about 6 psi. The wind velocity is about 180 mph. Nuclear radiation continues to reach the ground in significant amounts, but the fireball has cooled so that thermal radiation is no longer an important hazard.

At 10 seconds, the Mach front is over $2\frac{1}{2}$ miles from ground zero, the wind velocity is 40 mph and the overpressure has dropped to 1 psi (Fig. A–6). At this distance, other than breaking windows and damaging plaster, wind and pressure are no longer destructive. Nuclear radiation, consisting mainly of gamma rays from the fission products, still reaches the ground. As the still-hot gaseous fireball rises rapidly, air and debris are drawn inward near the surface and upward with the draft, producing strong air currents, called afterwinds (*see* FIREBALL). This helps to form the

20 KILOTON AIR BURST—0.5 SECOND
1 MEGATON AIR BURST—1.8 SECONDS

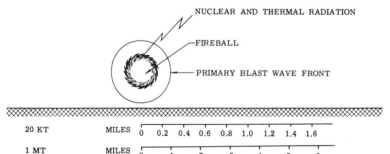

FIGURE A–3. CHRONOLOGICAL DEVELOPMENT OF AN AIR BURST; 0.5 SECOND AFTER 20-KILOTON DETONATION; 1.8 SECONDS AFTER 1-MEGATON DETONATION.

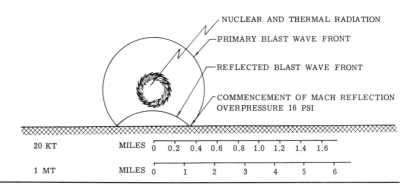

20 KILOTON AIR BURST—1.25 SECONDS
1 MEGATON AIR BURST—4.6 SECONDS

NUCLEAR AND THERMAL RADIATION
PRIMARY BLAST WAVE FRONT
REFLECTED BLAST WAVE FRONT
COMMENCEMENT OF MACH REFLECTION
OVERPRESSURE 16 PSI

FIGURE A–4. CHRONOLOGICAL
DEVELOPMENT OF AN AIR BURST;
1.25 SECONDS AFTER 20-KILOTON
DETONATION; 4.6 SECONDS AFTER
1-MEGATON DETONATION.

| 20 KT | MILES | 0 | 0.2 | 0.4 | 0.6 | 0.8 | 1.0 | 1.2 | 1.4 | 1.6 |
| 1 MT | MILES | 0 | 1 | 2 | 3 | 4 | 5 | 6 |

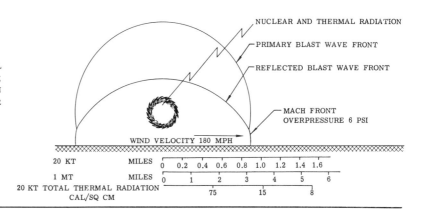

20 KILOTON AIR BURST—3 SECONDS
1 MEGATON AIR BURST—11 SECONDS

NUCLEAR AND THERMAL RADIATION
PRIMARY BLAST WAVE FRONT
REFLECTED BLAST WAVE FRONT
MACH FRONT
OVERPRESSURE 6 PSI
WIND VELOCITY 180 MPH

FIGURE A–5. CHRONOLOGICAL
DEVELOPMENT OF AN AIR BURST;
3 SECONDS AFTER 20-KILOTON
DETONATION; 11 SECONDS AFTER
1-MEGATON DETONATION.

20 KT	MILES	0	0.2	0.4	0.6	0.8	1.0	1.2	1.4	1.6
1 MT	MILES	0	1	2	3	4	5	6
20 KT TOTAL THERMAL RADIATION CAL/SQ CM				75		15		8	

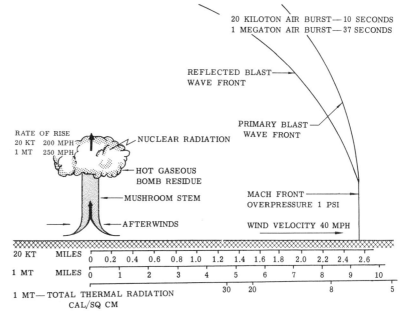

20 KILOTON AIR BURST—10 SECONDS
1 MEGATON AIR BURST—37 SECONDS

REFLECTED BLAST
WAVE FRONT

PRIMARY BLAST
WAVE FRONT

RATE OF RISE
20 KT   200 MPH
1 MT   250 MPH
NUCLEAR RADIATION
HOT GASEOUS
BOMB RESIDUE
MUSHROOM STEM
AFTERWINDS

MACH FRONT
OVERPRESSURE 1 PSI
WIND VELOCITY 40 MPH

FIGURE A–6. CHRONOLOGICAL
DEVELOPMENT OF AN AIR BURST;
10 SECONDS AFTER 20-KILOTON
DETONATION; 37 SECONDS AFTER
1-MEGATON DETONATION.

20 KT	MILES	0	0.2	0.4	0.6	0.8	1.0	1.2	1.4	1.6	1.8	2.0	2.2	2.4	2.6
1 MT	MILES	0	1	2	3	4	5	6	7	8	9	10
1 MT—TOTAL THERMAL RADIATION CAL/SQ CM					30	20			8			5

20 KILOTON AIR BURST—30 SECONDS
1 MEGATON AIR BURST—110 SECONDS

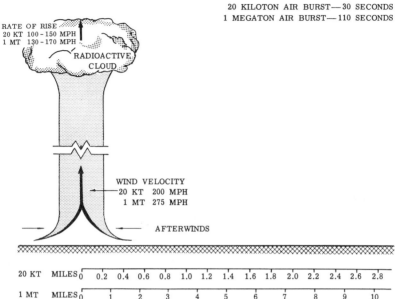

RATE OF RISE
20 KT 100 - 150 MPH
1 MT 130 - 170 MPH

RADIOACTIVE CLOUD

WIND VELOCITY
20 KT 200 MPH
1 MT 275 MPH

AFTERWINDS

20 KT	MILES	0	0.2	0.4	0.6	0.8	1.0	1.2	1.4	1.6	1.8	2.0	2.2	2.4	2.6	2.8
1 MT	MILES	0	1		2		3		4		5		6		7		8		9		10

FIGURE A–7. CHRONOLOGICAL DEVELOPMENT OF AN AIR BURST; 30 SECONDS AFTER 20-KILOTON DETONATION; 110 SECONDS AFTER 1-MEGATON DETONATION.

stem or "cloud column"* as it begins to form the famous mushroom or atomic cloud.

By the time 30 seconds has elapsed, the rising cloud of weapon debris, i.e., fission products and other bomb residues, is beginning to cool and condenses to form the radioactive atomic cloud (Fig. A–7). Within 10 minutes the bottom of the cloud will have attained an altitude of 5 miles. The afterwinds having a velocity of about 200 mph continue to carry dirt and debris up into the cloud. The cloud of fission products, dust, and debris will ultimately be dispersed by the wind but may travel around the world as a measurable entity (see CLOUD, RADIOACTIVE). The radioactive particles at first descend rapidly as local fallout, and then more slowly as "area" or "world-wide" fallout over a period of weeks to years. By the time the cloud has dispersed, little additional nuclear radiation reaches the ground in the vicinity of the detonation.

High-altitude bursts, by a somewhat arbitrary definition, are detonations of nuclear devices at heights in the air above 100,000 feet. There is a progressive decline in the blast energy with increasing height of the burst, but even in this rarefied air, a shock wave is produced, which in the case of one high-altitude shot (TEAK), traveled at an average speed of about 4,200 feet per second (for a distance of about 700 miles from the zero point). A strong flash of light, due to interaction of x-rays with the air, may be seen at great distances. In the TEAK shot, the electronic

excitation of oxygen atoms by the blast wave caused the formation of a large, red, luminous sphere several hundred miles in diameter. High-altitude nuclear explosions over Johnston Island have produced an aurora seen both from Hawaii and Apia Island. "Transmission" of radio waves is disturbed or completely blacked out by disturbances in the ionosphere (that part of the atmosphere from an altitude of about 40 miles to about 250 miles) as a result of a high-altitude burst.

These additional terms are related to the subject of air burst:

Cloud column. The visible cloud of smoke extending upward from the point of burst of a nuclear device. It may extend as far as the tropopause (see ATMOSPHERE) when the shot is an air burst.

Condensation cloud. See FIREBALL.

Height of burst. See separate item.

Scaled height of burst. See HEIGHT OF BURST.

Skyshine. Radiation, particularly gamma rays from a nuclear explosion, reaching a target from many directions as a result of scattering by the oxygen and nitrogen in the intervening atmosphere.

Slant range. The distance from a given location, usually on the earth's surface, to the point at which the explosion occurred.

Transmittance (atmospheric). The fraction (or percentage) of thermal energy received at a given location after passage through the atmosphere relative to that which would have been received at the same location if no atmosphere were present.

---

*Defined later in this article.

Weather changes due to nuclear explosions. There has been speculation concerning the possible influence of nuclear explosions on the weather—energy added to the atmosphere changing existing weather patterns, or the products of the explosion diverting some larger natural store of energy from its original path—and to the interference with transmission of radiant energy from the sun due to debris in the stratosphere. These possible changes may be brought about in the following ways: Falling radioactive debris may produce rain by seeding clouds; electrical conductivity of the air may be altered by the debris. However, apart from localized effects in the vicinity of the test area, there is no known influence of nuclear explosions on the weather.

AIR CONTAMINATION

AIR-BORNE RADIOACTIVITY, or air pollution, may be either gaseous or particulate matter. Radioactive gases are produced by evaporation or volatilization of radioactive material, or a radioactive gas may be a natural decay product, e.g., radon from its parent, radium. Particles dispersed in air (aerosol) may be either liquid or solid. Radioactive mists may result from boiling a radioactive solution in the laboratory. Solid particles may be dusts, fumes, or smokes. Dust hazards may be associated with mining, ore processing, and shaping of radioactive material, or may result from careless handling of radioisotopes in powdered form. Uranium oxide fumes may be produced by burning uranium scrap. Radioactive smoke may result from burning organic radioactive waste. Both gaseous and particulate release occurs in the operation of air-cooled nuclear reactors, but release to the atmosphere is carefully monitored. The gaseous waste is usually filtered to remove particulate matter and is then released to the atmosphere through stack disposal for dilution of the residual concentration of radioactivity in the gaseous waste stream.

The detonation of a nuclear device above the surface produces large amounts of contamination in the air, which returns as fallout.

AIR EQUIVALENT IONIZATION CHAMBER

Ionization chamber for x-rays or gamma rays in which the materials of the wall and electrodes are so selected and the design so constructed as to produce ionization essentially equivalent to that in a FREE AIR IONIZATION CHAMBER. This is possible only over moderate ranges of photon energies. Sometimes called AIR WALL IONIZATION CHAMBER.

AIR MONITORING

Continuous or routine collecting and analyzing of air samples to detect air-borne radioactive contamination. Monitoring devices are often connected with alarm systems to warn of dangerous levels of radiation. Gaseous waste disposed of by stack disposal must be continuously monitored during release to warn of possible contamination of the environment. Briefly, air monitoring is performed for one or more of the following reasons: (1) to detect and evaluate inhalation hazards to workers in a particular area; (2) to constantly watch over operations which might release radioactive substances into the air; (3) to check the effectiveness of various safety and control measures, such as ventilating systems, hoods, and glove boxes; (4) to detect and measure the amount of air-borne radioactivity released from controlled areas. In summary, whenever there is a possibility of air-borne radioactivity in hazardous amounts, the air within, or released from, that region should be monitored.

AIR POLLUTION. *See* AIR CONTAMINATION.

AIR SAMPLING

Collection and analysis of samples of air to determine the level of radioactivity or the presence of radioactive substances. Wherever radioactive materials are used in a form which could lead to the production of dust, fumes, gases, or mists, it is important to collect air samples from time to time. Air sampling is usually part of a radiological survey, and if a hazardous condition is known to exist, continuous or routine AIR MONITORING is required for personnel safety.

The determined level of contamination is compared with the maximum permissible concentration for the radionuclide(s) involved, and measures are instituted to insure safe operation. Air sampling must be carefully performed with several samples (in both place and time) being analyzed before a decision is reached.

There are many different kinds of sampling devices, the selection depending on the particular circumstances: filtration devices, electrostatic precipitators, adsorption devices, impingement sampling devices, thermal precipitation devices, sedimentation devices, condensation devices, and vacuum bottles.

Under the SAMPLING PROGRAM FOR RADIOACTIVE FALLOUT, air samples are collected by the HIGH-ALTITUDE SAMPLING PROGRAM, by collection from the radioactive cloud, and by air samples taken at the earth's surface in various parts of the world. Many samples are taken simply by placing "sticky pans" in the open air to collect particles which fall on them.

AIR WALL IONIZATION CHAMBER

Chamber with outer wall constructed from materials of average atomic number and with sufficient thickness to assure secondary electron equilibrium within the measuring volume, for the quality of radiation being measured, to determine the radiation intensity in air (air dose). Also known as AIR EQUIVALENT IONIZATION CHAMBER.

AIRCRAFT NUCLEAR PROPULSION (ANP)

The ANP Project was the joint Air Force–USAEC effort to develop engines using nuclear power for the propulsion of aircraft. Despite intensive efforts, the feasibility of meeting full military requirements at the current stage of the art was not established, and the project was terminated in March, 1961, by presidential decision. Among the major problems was the weight of shielding necessary to protect the crew from the intensive irradiation.

ALARM SYSTEM

A system whereby a visible or audible signal is actuated when an unusually high level of radiation is detected as a result of malfunction or accident.

Each high-radiation area should be equipped with a warning device such that when an individual enters an area where he might receive a dose of 100 millirem or more in one hour, there would be a conspicuous visible or audible alarm signal, so that both the person entering and the supervisor would be aware of the danger involved. Alarm systems are frequently attached to air monitoring devices if these are designed for continuous operation.

ALKALI METALS

Any metal of the alkali family including cesium, francium, lithium, potassium, rubidium, and sodium.

ALKALINE EARTHS

Barium, beryllium, calcium, magnesium, radium, and strontium, whose oxides have marked chemically basic properties and are therefore alkaline. Also called alkaline-earth metals.

ALLOBAR

A form of an element having a different atomic weight from the naturally occurring form; therefore, a form of element differing in isotopic composition from the naturally occurring form.

ALPHA COUNTER

ION CHAMBER, PROPORTIONAL, GEIGER, or SCINTILLATION COUNTER constructed to respond principally to densely IONIZING PARTICLES; provided with entrance barrier of minimum thickness.

ALPHA DISINTEGRATION

Also called alpha decay. The radioactive transformation of a radionuclide by alpha-particle emission. The daughter decay product is the nuclide having a mass number 4 units smaller and an atomic number 2 units smaller than the original parent radionuclide. The mass number change results because an alpha particle on the atomic weight scale has a mass of 4, and thus the loss of 1 alpha particle would reduce the weight by 4. For example, in the thorium radioactive series (first collateral thorium radioactive series) we note: $_{91}Pa^{228} \xrightarrow{\alpha} {}_{89}Ac^{224} \xrightarrow{\alpha} {}_{87}Fr^{220} \xrightarrow{\alpha} {}_{85}At^{216} \xrightarrow{\alpha} {}_{83}Bi^{212} \xrightarrow{\alpha}$ into the regular thorium radioactive series.

ALPHA EMITTER

A radionuclide that undergoes transformation by alpha-particle emission. In the radioactive series and in their collateral radioactive series, most of the disintegration is by alpha emission. Among the naturally occurring radioelements with atomic numbers greater than 80, there are about 30 alpha-emitting nuclei. There are also 5 naturally occurring alpha emitters with atomic numbers less than 80. With the production of isotopes of higher atomic number by neutron bombardment and by other means, over 100 alpha emitters have been identified.

ALPHA PARTICLE

Symbol: α, $_2\alpha^4$, $_2He^4$. A fast-moving, positively charged, stable group of 2 protons and 2 neutrons, emitted as a single entity in the disintegration of the nucleus of certain radioactive isotopes. It has the same composition as a helium nucleus, but differs in origin and motion. In fact, as it interacts with matter it annexes 2 orbital electrons and becomes a helium atom. The alpha particle has the following characteristics: a subatomic particle; 7,000 times as heavy as an electron; mass, 6.642×10^{-24} grams; atomic mass units, 4.00279; charge, 2 positive; energy 4 to 10 Mev; initial velocity from 1.4×10^9 to 2.2×10^9 centimeters per second; range from 0.3 to 8.6 centimeters in air at $15°$ C and 1 atmosphere; range in tissue, 1 Mev particle–0.0006 centimeter, 5 Mev–0.0037 centimeter; range in aluminum in milligrams per square centimeter for 0.5 Mev particles–0.5, 2 Mev–1.6, and 4 Mev–3.8.

Alpha particles are notable for their high specific

ionization, which for a high-energy particle is almost 1,000 times that of a beta particle. In traveling 1 centimeter in dry air, a rapidly moving alpha particle may create 30,000 to 100,000 ion pairs; one with an energy of 5 Mev will create as many as 40,000 ion pairs per centimeter of its path.

Because of its high specific ionization, the alpha particle dissipates its energy quickly in any medium. A 6-Mev particle will travel about 2 inches in air, and to penetrate human skin would require an energy of 7.5 Mev. Although the path is short, the high specific ionization makes it especially hazardous. The biological damage may be 20 times as great as that for beta or gamma radiation. The relative biological effectiveness for a 5 Mev alpha particle is about 15 and for a 1 Mev particle is about 20. Since, for example, 1 gram of radium emits 3.70×10^{10} alpha particles per second, and since the above characteristics hold, it is obvious that great care should be exerted to prevent inhalation or ingestion of alpha emitters. The damage from external alpha radiation is negligible because of its short range and failure to penetrate the derma (skin).

ALPHA-PARTICLE SPECTRUM

The distribution in energy or momentum of the alpha particles emitted by a pure radionuclide or by a mixture of radionuclides. Each alpha-emitting nuclide yields a characteristic spectrum consisting of one or more sharp lines, each due to a discrete group of monoenergetic particles. In many cases all the alpha particles from a given source have virtually the same range and energy; for example, the discreteness of the range of alpha particles emitted by the nucleus of a radon atom ($_{86}Rn^{222}$) or of a polonium atom ($_{84}Po^{210}$) is very marked. On the other hand some alpha-particle spectra consist of 2 to 13 discrete groups. When more than one group is present, the distribution is said to have fine structure; this results from transitions to more than one nuclear energy state of the product nuclide, with the group of highest energy coming from the ground-state transition. This common type of alpha spectrum is illustrated by the 6 energy groups emitted by thorium C (bismuth, $_{83}Bi^{212}$) with 6.086, 6.047, 5.764, 5.622, 5.603, and 5.478 Mev respectively. The first group constitutes

27.2% and the second group, 69.8% of the alpha particles.

In exceptional cases, lines are found owing to groups that have very low energies (10^{-6} to 10^{-4} Mev) relative to those of the main groups. The particles producing such lines are called long-range alpha particles and result when the emitting nuclei are formed in excited states during the preceding beta disintegration (radium C through radium C' to radium D). For example, radium C' emits a 7.680 Mev alpha particle characteristic of a transition between the ground states of radium C' and radium D, but in addition emits some 12 long-range alpha particles with energies from 8.280 to 10.509 Mev.

ALPHA RAY

A stream of alpha particles. Loosely, a synonym for alpha particle.

ALPHA SCINTILLATION PROBE

Scintillation probe in which the detector phosphor is relatively thin and provides complete absorption for alpha ray particles without protective covering or with a window of least possible absorption.

ALPHA SOURCES

There are about 30 alpha emitters among the naturally occurring radioactive elements with atomic numbers greater than 80. Research with transuranium elements and with accelerator bombardment has added many more, to a total of well over 100 alpha-emitting radioactive isotopes. The first differentiation of alpha rays was done with uranium, the first element whose radioactivity was discovered. (Table A–4 below.)

ALPHA SPECTROMETER

Instrument used to determine the distribution of energies present in a source of alpha particles to establish the spectrum of the rays emitted by a source or generator.

ALPHA STANDARD

A fixed source of radioactive material which emits alpha rays of known energy and quantity.

TABLE A–4. ALPHA SOURCES AVAILABLE COMMERCIALLY

ELEMENT	ISOTOPE	HALF-LIFE	RADIATION (Mev)	FORM
Actinium	$_{89}Ac^{227}$	22 years	α, 4.94; β, .02; γ, .037	Solution
Polonium	$_{84}Po^{210}$	138.4 days	α, 5.3; β, none; γ, .80	Chloride or nitrate
Radium	$_{88}Ra^{224}$	3.64 days	α, 5.68(95%), 5.45(5%); γ, .24	Several
Radium	$_{88}Ra^{226}$	1620 years	α, 4.66; γ, .188	Various

ALPHA SURVEY METER

Portable instrument for detecting contamination by alpha emitters. May be an ionization chamber, proportional counter, or scintillator disk with photomultiplier tube or may be any suitable counter of low background and high sensitivity capable of admitting heavy particles. Those types based on large window ion chamber are generally able to survey for beta or gamma radiations and discriminate by means of additional filters.

ALUMINUM

Symbol Al; atomic number 13; atomic weight 26.98. The name of this element came from the Latin word alumen (alum). A light-weight silver-white metal occurring in almost all ordinary rock formations throughout the earth's crust, aluminum is third in abundance of all the elements (8.1% of the solid crust), exceeded only by oxygen and silicon. It is extracted mainly from bauxite ore. Stable isotope Al^{27} accounts for 100% of the natural abundance of aluminum.

There are several thousand industrial uses for aluminum. The United States alone produces well over 1.5 million short tons a year. Used to acidify soil. It is not essential to life, but is found in trace quantities in man and animals.

There is no evidence of chronic poisoning from the ingestion of aluminum salts. Even in large doses, the only toxic effect is gastric irritation, nausea and vomiting. The LD_{50} of aluminum chloride for the rat (oral dose) is 3,730 milligrams per kilogram of body weight (mg/kg); the oral LD_{50} dose of aluminum nitrate is 4,280 mg/kg.

The five radioactive isotopes are Al^{24}, Al^{25}, Al^{26}, Al^{28} and Al^{29}—all except Al^{26} with short radioactive half-lives. Al^{28} has been found both in soil and in sea water as a result of induced radioactivity from the detonation of a nuclear device. Aluminum-26, an accelerator-produced radioisotope is a beta and gamma emitter; it has a radioactive half-life of about 10^5 years and a biological half-life, with the total body as the critical organ, of 550 days. Useful in studying the movement of aluminum in the soil and its uptake by plants, especially tea, which accumulates relatively large amounts.

AMERICAN STANDARDS ASSOCIATION

The ASA is a nongovernmental organization representing at a national level other groups with a primary interest in establishing standards. The ASA usually does not originate standards, but when a particular standard (ranging from the number of threads for a particular screw to the safety standards for a nuclear reactor) has been rather generally accepted, the ASA establishes a committee to study and to obtain opinions from interested industries and public consumers. If by weighted balloting they find that it is in fact an American standard, they publish it as such. In the case of atomic energy the ASA has been taking a more vigorous role in trying to develop standards relating to safety. The ASA is the official representative of the United States at the International Standards Organization meetings. There are 65 other nations that have similar national standards organizations.

AMERICIUM

Symbol Am; atomic number 95; atomic weight 243; a radioactive transuranic element. Radioactive isotopes of americium having mass numbers 237 through 246 are now known, but Am^{241} was the first to be discovered in 1945 by American scientists G. T. Seaborg, R. A. James, and L. O. Morgan, who named it for the Americas. Americium-241 (alpha emitter, half-life 462 years) is formed by the bombardment of plutonium with neutrons in a nuclear reactor in the following reaction:

$$Pu^{239}(n,\gamma)Pu^{240}(n,\gamma)Pu^{241} \xrightarrow{\beta^-} Am^{241}$$

As will be seen in the neptunium series, Am^{241} yields as its daughter, neptunium-237.

Americium does not occur in nature and has no known biological, medical, or agricultural significance. The maximum permissible concentration for continuous exposure of workers has been determined for $_{95}Am^{241}$ with the critical organ kidney to be 4×10^{-5} microcuries per cubic centimeter ($\mu c/cc$) in water and 2×10^{-12} ($\mu c/cc$) in air for soluble material. Am^{241} has a biological half-life of 200 years, an effective half-life 140 years, and would reach 22% equilibrium in the body in the first 50 years. Because of intense alpha emission (5.54 Mev), it is a potential neutron source.

AMINO ACIDS, STUDIES OF

Amino acids form the building blocks of proteins and are characterized by an amino group in a position alpha to the carboxyl group (R—CH—COOH). Amino acids can be studied
|
NH$_2$
by labeling with carbon-14, tritium, nitrogen-15 or sulfur-35. It is important to know how various amino acids are synthesized in the body, how they are converted into the longer chain complexes and finally into proteins, and how the proteins themselves are broken down. One example from among many is the study of the so-called essential and nonessential amino acids. Man and animals de-

pend on a supply of essential amino acids derived from the dietary intake. For example, a lactating cow was injected intravenously with carbon-14-labeled fatty acid or carbon-14-labeled glucose. When the amino acids in the milk protein from this animal were measured, it was found that only the nonessential amino acids contained appreciable amounts of the carbon-14. This experiment demonstrated that the lactating cow was able to synthesize adequate amounts of the nonessential amino acids but not the essential ones.

Another example is the use of a radioactive label to measure the rate of production of animal protein. Protein synthesis is a slow reaction, and since a weanling 50 g rat can grow about 25 g in a week, one can calculate that this corresponds to about 3 mg per gram of protein per hour, or about 1.4 microequivalents of peptide bond synthesized per gram of original animal protein per hour. It was impossible to measure such a small proportional increase until isotope-labeled amino acids were available. With a carbon-14-labeled amino acid it is possible to measure the incorporation into protein of as little as 0.001 microequivalent.

AMPLIFIER

Circuit for increasing the strength of a signal. For radiation measurements, amplifiers are designed to perform uniformly and with high stability in receiving, enlarging, and relaying pulses in rapid sequence. Their general use is between the detector and the scaler or count ratemeter.

ANEMIA DUE TO IRRADIATION

Anemia, or the reduction in the number or quality of the red blood cells, is not an early manifestation of the ACUTE RADIATION SYNDROME. In general there is no measurable decrease in the number, volume, or hemoglobin content of the circulating red blood cells during the first two weeks, even with lethal doses of radiation. In cases of death within ten days, there may be no evidence of anemia at any time. Following radiation exposure to dose levels between 200 and 500 rad, there is usually a decrease in circulating red blood cells at the end of the second week, with fluctuations for a week or two and slow return to normal by the end of 120 days.

In cases of HEMORRHAGE RESULTING FROM RADIATION INJURY there will be an associated secondary anemia.

Anemia is often classed as one of the chronic effects of irradiation. Aplastic anemia has been reported as a late sequela of WHOLE BODY IRRADIATION, e.g., in Japanese exposed to the atomic bomb at Hiroshima and Nagasaki and in British patients receiving x-ray therapy for disease of the spine.

ANIMAL CELLS, EFFECT OF RADIATION

All living cells are RADIOSENSITIVE, in that serious biochemical or morphological changes, leading at times to death of the cell, will occur if the dose of ionizing radiation is high enough. Cell death may be the result of direct action of radiation on the cell in destroying certain critical cellular components or in seriously disturbing the delicately balanced metabolism of the cell. Cell death may be indirectly caused by toxic products (free radicals) produced by the radiation effects on the water in and around the cells.

From experiments in which only selected portions of cells were irradiated with highly localized beams it appears that the nucleus is much more radiosensitive than the cytoplasm. For example, the nucleus of the egg of the wasp, Habrobracon, was shown to be in the order of a million times as sensitive as the cytoplasm. In alpha-particle irradiation of spores of the fern, Pteris lonigfolia, a lethal effect was observed only when the nucleus was irradiated.

Irradiation of germinal cells causes chromosome breaks and misunions, which in turn lead to dominant lethals affecting the zygotes of the next generation, which in turn are expressed as infertility. Nonlethal damage may result in mutants. The same type of chomosome damage in somatic cells results in varied impairments, abnormalities, and destructive effects which probably underlie the tissue damage associated with the acute radiation syndrome. The chomosome changes may also lead to delayed damage, such as premature aging, leukemia, and malignant disease.

The effect of radiation on cell division has been demonstrated, for example, by the inhibition of mitosis in the neuroblast cells of the grasshopper embryo.

ANIMAL METABOLISM STUDIES

Radioactive isotopes provide the research worker with a technique of unusual scope and flexibility. Two important characteristics of radioisotopes make them particularly valuable:

a. Before radioactive decay, the radioisotope will behave in the system similarly to its stable counterpart.

b. The radiation that it emits upon decay can often be conveniently measured, thus providing an estimate of the amount of radioisotope present. Since radiation can be measured with extreme sensitivity, many studies of animal metabolism can be carried out with normal individuals. For example, cobalt, a micronutrient that occurs in the diet at a level of 0.05 part per million or less, can easily be followed from the diet to the location within a specific tissue of an animal weighing 1,000 lb. without increasing the amount of cobalt in the diet above the physiological level.

The following outline indicates the research and routine uses to which radioisotopes have been put in studies of animal nutrition and animal physiology.

I. Calcium-45
   A. Research use
      1. Estimation of bone accretion and resorption and of the influence of hormones, nutrition, exercise, and physiological status.
      2. Study of formation of teeth.
      3. Determination of the availability of calcium in feedstuffs.
      4. Study of the etiology of milk fever, grass tetany, hypomagnesia, rickets, cage-layer fatigue, gallstones, and urinary calculi.
      5. Study of milk and egg formation and placental transfer.
      6. Study of mechanism of absorption of calcium.
      7. Determination of endogenous calcium as influenced by diet, hormones, and other physiological factors.
      8. Estimation of calcium requirement for various species.
      9. Study of kidney function and its excretory mechanisms.
   B. Routine use
      1. Estimation of the vitamin D content of feeds by a chick or rat assay procedure.
      2. Determination of endogenous calcium in individual animals.
II. Phosphorus-32
   A. Research use
      1. Estimation of bone accretion and resorption and of the influence of hormones, nutrition, exercise, and physiological status.
      2. Study of formation of teeth.
      3. Study of milk and egg formation and placental transfer.
      4. Determination of availability of phosphorus in feeds.
      5. Study of the absorption of phosphorus in the digestive tract, the mechanisms and form in which it is absorbed, and the factors which enhance or reduce utilization.
      6. Estimation of endogenous phos-

phorus as affected by diet, hormones, and physiological factors. Also, the relative contribution of the various phosphorus compounds in the blood and cells of the intestinal tract to the endogenous phosphorus.
      7. Study of the excretory function of the kidney.
      8. Investigation of the formation, turnover, and precursors of the organic phosphorus compounds of bones and soft tissues.
      9. Determination of distribution of labeled pathogenic organisms.
   B. Routine use
      1. Determination of adequacy of blood supply to fractured bone.
      2. Use of therapeutic levels for treating polycythemia.
      3. Use of colloidal phosphate-impregnated sutures to prevent neuromas from developing after neurectomy in horses and other stock.
      4. Assay of feeds for vitamin D content using chicks or rats.
      5. Irradiation of skin tumors and other tumors that accumulate phosphorus.
III. Strontium-85 and Strontium-89
   A. Research use
      1. Contrasted to Ca^{45} to provide a basic understanding of the various selective mechanisms of the body.
      2. Useful as a substitute for calcium-45 in studies of a qualitative nature.
   B. Routine use
      1. Substitute for calcium-45 for vitamin D assays.
      2. Determination of whether or not a bone fracture is healing properly.
      3. Determination of bone accretion or resorption rates in farm animals by external counting.
      4. Irradiation of localized tumors.
IV. Carbon-14
   A. Research use
      1. Study of the metabolic contributions of bacteria, yeast, and protozoa to the nutrition of ruminants and nonruminants. The synthetic, as well as the catabolic, products and mechanisms can be investigated.
      2. Study of the metabolism and distribution of fats, proteins, and carbohydrates within the animal body and the utilization of these for production.
      3. Estimation of rates and mechanisms

of absorption of materials from various parts of the digestive tract.

4. Investigation of the mechanisms of action of such materials as vitamins, hormones, antibiotics, and other drugs.

5. Determination of residual levels and utilization of food additives.

6. Study of the utilization of various carbon sources by animal tissue.

7. Study of excretory mechanisms of the kidney.

8. Study of detoxification mechanisms.

9. Investigation of movement of labeled viruses or bacteria.

B. Routine use

1. Determination of residual levels and utilization of food additives.

2. The use as a criterion for the toxicological effects of new drugs.

V. Sulfur-35

A. Research use

1. Study of utilization of various forms of inorganic and organic sulfur by animals.

2. Study of the formation of amino acids, proteins, and mucopolysaccharides by the body and their subsequent utilization for reproduction, growth, milk production, egg formation, and hair production.

3. Investigation of kidney excretory functions.

4. Study of the detoxification mechanisms involving sulfur.

5. Determination of the sulfur requirement of farm animals.

6. Study of the metabolism of sulfur-containing amino acids and other sulfur-containing compounds.

7. Study of diseases by use of labeled pathogens.

B. Routine use

1. Determination of the "extracellular space" ("sulfate space").

VI. Iodine-131

A. Research use

1. Determination of thyroid function and correlation with desirable production characteristics of farm animals.

2. Use as an aid to selective breeding in regard to a desirable level of thyroid function.

3. Study of absorption and metabolism of fats in the animal body.

4. Determination of the mode of action

of goitrogenic substances, and the mode of action of thyroid hormones.

5. Study of thyrotoxicosis.

6. Estimation of the utilization of iodine from various feed sources.

7. Study of the metabolism of iodine by all farm animals.

8. Determination, with more precision, of the iodine requirements of farm animals.

B. Routine use

1. Determination of thyroid uptake and basal metabolic rate.

2. Estimation of rate of formation of thyroxine.

3. External scanning for thyroid tumors.

4. Determination of plasma volume with I^{131}-labeled albumen.

5. Determination of liver function with I^{131} Rose Bengal.

6. Estimation of circulation time.

7. Application for partial or complete destruction of thyroid gland with massive levels of radioiodine.

8. Determination of the absorption of fats in steatorrhea.

9. Application in kidney function test—I^{131}-labeled Diodrast.

VII. Iron-59

A. Research use

1. Estimation of the iron requirement of farm animals as related to age, sex, nutrition, disease, and hormone status.

2. Determination of the availability of iron from various sources and forms.

3. Study of the absorption, storage, and utilization of iron.

4. Estimation of blood volume of farm animals and the effect of various factors thereon.

5. Study of hemoglobin and enzyme formation.

B. Routine use

1. Determination of iron turnover rates.

2. Determination of blood volumes.

3. Estimation of iron uptake by red blood cells.

VIII. Copper-64

A. Research use

1. Study of the distribution, absorption, and excretion of copper as influenced by age, sex, nutrition, and other physiological conditions and by disease.

2. Study of the function of copper in hemoglobin and enzyme formation.

3. Investigation of the function of copper in the body.
4. Estimation of the availability of copper from various sources.
5. Study of the toxicity of copper.
B. Routine use
1. Localization of brain tumors.

IX. Chlorine-36
A. Research use
1. Study of the absorption, distribution, and excretion as related to the cationic component and the nutritional and physiological status of the animal.
2. Study of acid-base balance, osmotic balance, and kidney excretion in animals.
3. Determination of the "chloride space."

X. Cobalt-57, -58, -60
A. Research use
1. Study of the absorption, distribution, and excretion of cobalt as influenced by chemical form and the nutritional and physiological status of farm animals.
2. Estimation of the utilization of cobalt by bacteria to form vitamin B_{12} or B_{12}-like substances.
3. Study of the absorption, distribution, and excretion of vitamin B_{12}.
4. Determination of the mode and site of action of vitamin B_{12}.
5. Estimation of cobalt and vitamin B_{12} requirement of farm animals.
6. Study of the toxicity of cobalt.
B. Routine use
1. Irradiation of tumors.
2. Determination of efficiency of gastrointestinal absorption of radioactive vitamin B_{12}.
3. Clinical test for pernicious anemia.

XI. Tritium
A. Research use
1. Study of movement and metabolism of many organic compounds and their utilization in milk, egg, or meat formation.
2. Study of the metabolism of rumen or digestive tract organisms to determine their metabolic relation to the host.
B. Routine use
1. Determination of residual levels and utilization of food additives.

XII. Manganese-52, -54
A. Research use
1. Study of the absorption, distribution, and excretion of various forms of manganese in respect to the effect of various nutritional and physiological states of farm animals.
2. Determination of the function of manganese in bone formation.
3. Study of the function of manganese in enzyme systems in the body.
4. Estimation of the minimum requirement of manganese and the effects of toxic levels.

XIII. Potassium-40, -42
A. Research use
1. Study of the factors controlling the preferential sequestering of potassium by the cells.
2. Investigation of the absorption, distribution, and excretion of potassium as affected by nutrition or physiological changes.
3. Study of the function of potassium in acid-base balance.
4. Determination of the mechanisms of potassium excretion by the kidney.
5. Estimation of the requirement for potassium by animals.
B. Routine use
1. Determination of "potassium space" of the body.
2. Estimation of lean body mass.

XIV. Magnesium-28
A. Research use
1. Study of the absorption, distribution, and excretion of magnesium.
2. Investigation of the function of magnesium in various enzyme systems.
3. Determination of the minimum requirement of magnesium by animals.
4. Study of the interrelationship between calcium and magnesium.
5. Study of kidney excretion mechanisms.

XV. Sodium-22, -24
A. Research use
1. Study of the function of sodium in acid-base balance with particular regard to the kidney.
2. Study of the secretion of HCl by the stomach.
3. Study of the relative exclusion of sodium from the interior of cells.
4. Determination of the space into which sodium will penetrate in farm animals and the relation of this to various nutritional and physiological conditions.

5. Study of the action of the adrenal gland and its hormones.
6. Investigation of kidney function and excretion.
B. Routine use
1. Determination of the "sodium space" of the body.

XVI. Zinc-65
A. Research use
1. Study of zinc metabolism and of the effect of nutrition and physiological status.
2. Investigations of the function of zinc in enzyme systems.
3. Determination of the effect of high calcium diets upon zinc absorption.
4. Estimation of the excretion of zinc, particularly by the kidney.
5. Study of the toxicity of zinc.

ANIMAL NUTRITIONAL STUDIES

A general listing of the use of radioisotopes in animal nutrition studies can be found under ANIMAL METABOLISM STUDIES. As an example, there follows a brief discussion of iron absorption, for studies of which essentially three techniques can be used: (1) balance experiments, (2) increases in serum iron shown after a large oral dose, and (3) radioiron measurements. The advantages of the latter are considerable, because small doses of iron comparable to those normally found in the diet can be used, several observations under varying conditions can be made on the same subject, and the experiments are much less time consuming. It has been possible to use a double isotope technique for evaluation of the absorption of iron from two different foods. A subject is given one food, labeled with iron-59, on the first, third, fifth, seventh, and ninth days of observation, and a second compound, labeled with iron-55, on the second, fourth, sixth, eighth, and tenth days. The amount of the two radioisotopes absorbed into the body can then be measured.

Studies of the rate of iron absorption suggest that this element is taken up by the intestinal mucosa, stored temporarily, and then gradually released for hemoglobin synthesis during subsequent days. Various types of experiments, in which radioactive iron has been introduced into different portions of the gastrointestinal tract and autoradiograms made, suggest that the greatest absorption of iron occurs in the stomach and the duodenum. The fact has been established by research showing that iron in the ferrous form is absorbed much more efficiently than in the ferric form. Presumably the latter must be reduced before absorption can occur under physiological conditions.

Measurement of absorption of food iron by conventional means is difficult. However, this can be done with relative ease with radioisotopic iron. Foods labeled with radioactive iron have been obtained by growing vegetables in nutrient solutions containing labeled iron or by injecting the iron into animals for incorporation into the edible animal products. It has thus been possible to compare the absorption of iron from such foods as egg, liver, muscle, enriched bread, and milk in normal subjects and in iron-deficient patients. In general, normal subjects retained 5 to 10% of food iron, whereas iron-deficient subjects retained from 10 to 20%.

ANIMAL PHYSIOLOGICAL STUDIES

A listing of the use of radioisotopes in animal physiological studies can be found under the heading ANIMAL METABOLISM STUDIES. The use of tracer methods for the determination of body fluid composition and for studies of the physiology of circulation are cited as examples. In general the technique is that of isotope dilution; a known amount of labeled material is injected, and after equilibration in the body, a sample is obtained and the concentration of the labeled material determined. From this information and knowledge of the total amount injected, the volume in which the material was diluted can be calculated. For example, red cells can be labeled with chromium-51 in order to obtain the red cell volume in animals. Plasma space can be determined by use of plasma labeled with a dye; however, there seems to be some advantage in using plasma proteins labeled with iodine-131. This method has also been used for determination of the fate of injected artificial plasma substitutes.

The labeled red cell method is valuable in estimating the lifetime of red cells in normal and diseased animals, as well as in the estimation of the time of survival of red cells after transfusion. Total body water can be determined by replacing one or both of the hydrogens of water with the radioisotope tritium.

It has been possible to make simultaneous use of sodium-24, potassium-42, bromine-82, and tritium for body electrolyte studies. The radioisotopes can be measured in the same sample by the use of physical techniques which differentiate on the basis of the type of radiation and the half-life of the radioisotope. Thus from a single injection into an individual, it is possible to determine the following by direct observation:

1. 24-hour exchangeable sodium
2. 24-hour exchangeable potassium

3. 24-hour exchangeable chlorine
4. extracellular water
5. total body water
6. plasma sodium
7. plasma potassium
8. plasma chlorine.

From these observations the following can be calculated:

1. intracellular water
2. extracellular sodium
3. residual sodium
4. extracellular potassium
5. intracellular potassium
6. intracellular potassium concentration
7. lean tissue
8. fat.

ANIMALS, RADIATION RESEARCH WITH

Various types of animals are used to study the numerous parameters dealing with the effects of radiation on human beings. The entire gamut of SOMATIC EFFECTS and of GENETIC EFFECTS has been studied in various living forms other than man.

In a census taken in 1960 of the major laboratories supported by the USAEC, there were 319,535 animals of 25 different types or species being used in biomedical radiation research. This count did not include Drosophila, Habrobracon, Neurospora, paramecia, or any of the many molds and bacteria being used at the time, but it did include the following ordinary laboratory animals:

Mice	266,418
Rats	21,676
Dogs	1,853
Guinea pigs	1,425
Rabbits	1,258
Monkeys	83
Cats	50

Many domestic animals were also being used extensively according to the survey: cattle, burros, swine, sheep, and chickens. In addition there were other types such as gerbils, parakeets, pigeons, ground squirrels, grasshoppers, and rattlesnakes.

ANNIHILATION RADIATION

The radiation produced when a particle and its antiparticle meet. Their positive and negative charges neutralize each other, and they are annihilated with the production of energy in the form of radiation. The most common example is the annihilation of an electron and a positron with the production usually of two photons. The inverse of PAIR PRODUCTION. The conversion of rest mass into electromagnetic radiation: in the above illustration the rest masses are converted into two 0.511-Mev photons.

ANODE

Positively charged electrode in various electrical devices. It is connected to the positive side of the electrical power supply and serves as collection point for free negative charges or ions as in the Geiger or proportional counter, photomultiplier tube, or electrolytic cell and functions as the target in an x-ray, cathode-ray, or betatron tube.

ANOXIA, EFFECT ON RADIATION INJURY.

See OXYGEN, RADIATION SENSITIVITY.

ANTHROPOMETRIC DUMMY

A manikin made according to the size, weight, and proportions of the human body. Anthropometric dummies have been used extensively in studying blast effects associated with the test detonations of nuclear devices. For example, in the 1957 Nevada Test Series, 160-pound anthropometric dummies were exposed at stations where the blast overpressures were 5.3 and 6.9 pounds per square inch (psi). At 5.3 psi, a maximum displacement velocity of 21.4 feet per second was attained in 0.5 seconds, and the dummy was carried 21.9 feet downwind (10 feet per second is considered the threshold for human damage from abrupt decelerative impact following displacement by blast-produced winds). Exposed to 6.9 psi, a standing dummy was hurled 256 feet downwind and 44 feet to the right, further demonstrating the hazard associated with blast effects.

See PHANTOM, BLAST BIOLOGICAL DAMAGE.

ANTIBIOTIC THERAPY IN RADIATION ILLNESS. *See* TREATMENT OF RADIATION ILLNESS.

ANTIBODIES, RADIOACTIVE

Antibodies in which a radioactive isotope is incorporated in or coupled to the molecule. An antibody is desired which will have a preference for localizing in certain tissues or organs. It must preferentially reach an organ in the same manner that iodine-131 localizes in the thyroid gland.

The highly selective localization of a radioactivity-carrying antibody depends on the existence of an antigenic substance available to intravenously administered antibodies. The antigenic substance should be present either solely or in much greater abundance in the tissue in which it is desired to localize the radioactivity. To be therapeutically useful the antibody will have to carry enough radioactivity to destroy the cells containing the antigen. If the antibody is organ-specific, the normal organ cells may have to be sacrificed along with the malignant cells. For example, suppose an antibody could be produced against carcinoma of the prostate gland. It would then carry the radioactivity to this cancerous tissue wherever it is located, and also to the normal prostatic tissue. Thus the normal tissue of the prostate would also be irradiated, but this would be acceptable since the organ is not essential to life.

Antibodies having considerable localizing specificity have been reported for kidney, adrenal, ovary, lung, and small intestine but not at a level to be clinically useful in treating cancer.

ANTICOINCIDENCE CIRCUIT

An arrangement to prevent a counter from recording counts from background or other interfering events, through detecting the extraneous radiation and using the signal therefrom to block operation of the main counting circuit at that time. Especially useful in low-level counting in which a cosmic-ray guard or other background detecting device operates to prevent recording when a cosmic ray passes through the region of the detector.

See COSMIC-RAY GUARD.

ANTIMONY

Symbol Sb (stibium); atomic number 51; atomic weight 121.76. A silver-white, brittle metal occurring in nature chiefly as the sulfide, stibnite (Sb_2S_3). Produced mainly in China, with small amounts in Mexico and Bolivia. Occurs naturally as stable isotopes Sb^{121} (57.25%) and Sb^{123} (42.75%).

Numerous industrial uses include (1) metal products, such as antimonial lead, bearing metal, battery metal, type metal, cable covering, sheet and pipe castings, collapsible tubes and foil, ammunition, and solder, and (2) nonmetal products, such as flame-proofed textiles, paints, ceramic enamels, glass, ammunition primers, and matches.

Its chief biological use is as a therapeutic agent against parasites in animals. Also the various salts of antimony are used in the practice of medicine as antipyretics because they produce sweating, as emetics because they produce vomiting, and as cathartics because of the property of producing intestinal irritation.

Antimony metal poisoning in industry is rare, but cases of illness among workers exposed to fumes have occurred. Stibine gas (antimony hydride, SbH_3) is extremely toxic—concentrations of 1% cause death very quickly and even a 0.01% concentration produces death within a few hours. Tartar emetic (potassium antimonyl tartrate), used in medicine, has been widely studied for its toxic properties. The lethal dose (LD) for oral administration has been found to be: frog, 110 milligrams per kilogram (mg/kg); mouse, 599–666 mg/kg; rabbit, 50–65 mg/kg. For intravenous administration the LD is: mouse, 42 mg/kg; and rabbit, 10–20 mg/kg.

The 27 radioactive isotopes of antimony range in mass numbers from 116 through 136. Antimony-121 and -123 are stable; the others are radioactive. Three radioactive isotopes are available commercially: Sb^{122}, radioactive half-life 2.8 days; Sb^{124}, radioactive half-life 60 days; and Sb^{125}, radioactive half-life 876 days. With bone as the critical organ, they all have a biological half-life of 100 days; their effective half-life is 2.7, 38, and 90 days respectively. The biological use has been largely studies of the distribution and metabolism of antimony. Antimony-124 together with beryllium makes an intense thermal neutron source— as many as 10^{10} neutrons per second being produced.

A number of radioactive isotopes (Sb^{125} through Sb^{136}) have been found as fission products following detonation of a nuclear device. Sb^{122} and Sb^{124} are among the nuclides possibly appearing in sea water following a nuclear detonation contacting the sea. Antimony is one of the fallout radioactive nuclides having biological significance, because radioactivity remains measurable even after one year for Sb^{125}.

AQUATIC ORGANISMS, UPTAKE OF RADIONUCLIDES

Increased amounts of radioactivity affect organisms, both plant and animal, in the marine biosphere in much the same manner they affect terrestrial life. Contamination of bodies of water may result from disposal of radioactive waste or from fallout resulting from the detonation of nuclear devices.

Radioactive materials may become associated with aquatic organisms in the following ways: absorption to surface areas, absorption from surrounding medium, or ingestion as food. Field studies have been conducted of the uptake and accumulation of a variety of radioactive materials by organisms in the Columbia River at the Hanford Operation, and in White Oak Lake at Oak Ridge National Laboratory. In spite of the variety of radionuclides available in these waters, only the few shown in Table A-5 were used by the organisms through their natural food webs.

Although OCEAN DISPOSAL of radioactive waste may cause radioactive contamination, no difficulty has arisen when waste has been packaged and disposed according to the regulations of the USAEC.

TABLE A–5.   ESTIMATED CONCENTRATION FACTORS FOR VARIOUS RADIONUCLIDES IN AQUATIC ORGANISMS.

RADIONUCLIDE	SITE	PHYTO-PLANKTON	FILAMENTOUS ALGAE	INSECT LARVAE	FISH
Na^{24}	CR*	500	500	100	100
Cu^{64}	CR	2,000	500	500	50
Rare Earths	CR	1,000	500	200	100
Fe^{59}	CR	200,000	100,000	100,000	10,000
P^{32}	CR	200,000	100,000	100,000	100,000
P^{32}	WOL†	150,000	850,000	100,000	30,000–70,000
Sr^{90}–Y^{90}	WOL	75,000	500,000	100,000	20,000–30,000

*Columbia River
†White Oak Lake

Even where liquid waste is discharged directly into the sea, contamination of marine life has not been serious.

Because of the constant movement and mixing of the ocean, only local fallout with its relatively larger particles and concentration of radioactivity is of much significance. If the fireball from the detonation of a nuclear device touches the water, 65 to 85% of the fallout may be local, and in addition to the fission products there will be activation of the constituent elements of the sea water. Observations around the Eniwetok test site indicate that of the 3 long-lived fission products, cesium-137, strontium-90 and cerium-144, only the latter is found in marine organisms; by contrast, cesium-137 and strontium-90 are found in land organisms while cerium-144 generally is not. Of the nonfission products, radioisotopes of iron, zinc, cobalt, and manganese were prominent in marine animals but were much less abundant in marine plants, land plants, and land animals.

Because of the remarkable capacity of some marine life to concentrate certain elements, care must be exercised to insure that food contamination does not occur through this aquatic FOOD CHAIN.

AREA MONITORING

Routine or continuous measurement of the level of radiation or of radioactive contamination of any particular area, building, room, or array of equipment. Usage distinguishes between routine monitoring, survey activities, and sampling.

Monitoring is particularly important in a controlled area and in the area immediately outside the controlled area.

Continuous air monitoring is required whenever there is the possibility of hazardous amounts of air-borne radioactivity. Continuous monitoring, with an alarm system to warn of dangerous levels of radiation, is usually used with high-level sources of radiation, such as accelerators, and reactors.

Routine monitoring is also part of any high-level waste disposal activity.

Area monitoring is conducted to record average exposure dose rates in the area; to determine any changes in radiation intensity; to detect spread of contamination; to warn personnel from uncontrolled entry into radiation areas; and to keep responsible supervisors informed of the radiation level.

ARGON

Symbol A (Ar has been suggested); atomic number 18; atomic weight 39.944. A colorless, odorless gas which does not react chemically under standard conditions. From Greek argon, inactive. There are three stable isotopes: A^{40}, which accounts for 99.600% of the natural abundance; A^{36}, 0.337%; and A^{38}, 0.063%. There are five radioactive isotopes. Radioargon as a gaseous effluent from nuclear reactors causes a stack disposal problem.

ARGONNE CANCER RESEARCH HOSPITAL

The Argonne Cancer Research Hospital (ACRH) is operated by the University of Chicago and administered by the medical school and clinics of the university under contract with the U.S. Atomic Energy Commission, Division of Biology and Medicine. In 1948 USAEC approved the establishment of the hospital, which was formally opened in 1953. The hospital has 8 floors with a total area of 102,500 square feet. Two floors with 58 beds are devoted to clinical research, and the remaining 6 floors house high-energy radiation equipment, including a linear accelerator, electronic and machine shops, animal quarters, and conventional research laboratories and offices.

The staff is composed of 58 physicians and scientists and 136 technicians, nurses, and nontechnical laboratory personnel. Undergraduate and graduate medical students and advanced students in the biological sciences at the University of Chicago participate in the ACRH research program.

The purpose and program of the hospital are directed toward the exploitation of high-energy radiation sources in the treatment of malignant disease, the study of the biological effects of radiation, and the use of radioisotopes as tracers in the study of normal and disease states and in the diagnosis and therapy of disease. A view of the type of basic research program conducted at the hospital is afforded by listing the general subject areas of their scientific reports: radioisotopes in therapy and diagnosis; metabolic studies of alkaline earth metals; metabolism of carbon in humans and animals; studies in immunology; biological effects of x-irradiation; studies in hematology; biological effects of steroids; high-energy radiation; depth dose and biological evaluation studies with high-energy radiation; studies on radiation sensitizers; studies in biochemistry; studies on purine metabolism; the use of tracers in biochemistry and pharmacology; and the theory and design of detectors.

ARGONNE NATIONAL LABORATORY

Argonne National Laboratory (ANL) is the direct successor of the wartime Metallurgical Laboratory of the Manhattan Engineer District. One of the primary objectives of that laboratory was to demonstrate the feasibility of a self-sustaining nuclear chain reaction, and this milestone was reached on December 2, 1942, in a reactor under the concrete stands at the University of Chicago's Stagg Field. Another objective was to develop the technology for the production of plutonium and a process for the separation and isolation of this element.

On July 1, 1946, Argonne was established as a permanent laboratory of the USAEC with the University of Chicago as the contractor. The laboratory has continued to perform basic research and to do applied tasks for the USAEC, e.g., the physics design and initial development for the prototype of the submarine Nautilus reactor.

From the beginning, an important ancillary responsibility was to obtain information concerning the hazards involved in the use of radiation and radioactive material. The ANL International School of Nuclear Science and Engineering continues to train foreign scientists and engineers as part of the Atoms-for-Peace program. The following activities are of particular biomedical interest.

Division of Biological and Medical Research. Work in this laboratory was established originally to investigate toxicity and hazards of radiations. Some of these earlier studies contributed in a major degree to the formulation of standards of radiation safety. For example, the presently used maximum permissible concentrations for stontium-89, strontium-90, plutonium-239, carbon-14, and tritium are based on experimental work from this laboratory. The expansion of program is well shown by the subject headings under which their research was presented during a recent meeting in the division: x-ray and gamma-ray toxicity; neutron toxicity; radioelement toxicity; epidemiological radium studies; modification of radiation effects; cancer research; theoretical biology; biophysics; cellular fine structure and related function; biochemistry; plant physiology; mammalian physiology; genetics; and diseases and care of laboratory animals.

The Division of Biological and Medical Research is housed in a relatively new building with ample space and equipment. The staff numbers 178, of whom about 70 are at the scientific level. Construction of facilities for three large additional programs is now essentially complete: the JANUS reactor facility for studies of the immediate and chronic effects of fission neutrons at low dose rates; additional space to house dogs for the study of metabolism and effects of fission products; and additional housing for a program in which the carcinogenic and life-shortening effects of internally emitted radiations and perhaps external beta particle radiation at low-dose levels will be studied on a large scale. Work continues on the significance of the aging process and the formation of cancer in relation to irradiation. Another continuing study of interest is the epidemiological study of the possible effects on humans of radium-226 in the drinking water in a number of Midwest communities. A most important continuing function of the division is the training of other scientists in radiobiological methods and theory.

Special growth chambers (isotope farms) are used for the biosynthesis of plant material in an atmosphere containing controlled amounts of $C^{14}O_2$. Numerous plant constituents, including alkaloids and drugs, have been synthesized in labeled form for a wide variety of studies.

Radiological Physics Division. A relatively small group devoted to the study of some basic problems in the field of biology and medicine are using biophysical techniques. Perhaps their most important area of research is the measurement of the radioelements Ra^{226} and Ra^{228} (mesothorium) in human beings who have been drinking water from deep wells with a radium content of from about 4 μμc per liter to 40 μμc per liter (the maximum permissible concentration for the population as a whole is set at 10 μμc per liter). They are also measuring radioactivity in the humans who are industrially or medically exposed to radium, thorium, and Thorotrast in order to correlate the body content with clinical findings. The measurements are performed by radon breath analysis and by the whole body counter (the iron room) developed by the radiological physics division. Excellent basic work is being done in the field of bone physics in relation to radioactive material in the bone substance.

Meteorological studies are conducted for purposes of local weather prediction and in order to obtain knowledge of the diffusion of gases and dispersal of solid particles in regions around buildings or on uneven terrain. A micrometeorological installation collects continuous records of about 40 atmospheric variables which are studied and summarized. Other fields of interest are basic research in luminescence in liquid solutions irradiated by various means and in other energy transfer mechanisms occurring in the interaction between matter and ionizing particles.

ARMED FORCES RADIATION BIOLOGY AND ATOMIC MEDICINE PROGRAM

Military interest in the field of radiation biology is directed toward the protection of personnel from radiation produced during an enemy attack in which nuclear weapons are used and from the radiation produced by nuclear reactors which are being used by the Armed Forces to generate electrical power for propulsion, operation of equipment, heat, light, etc. Therefore, military research in this field must concern itself with the effects upon man of exposure to single large doses of mixed ionizing radiation produced by a nuclear explosion, the more prolonged exposure to intermediate doses of radiation produced by radioactive fallout, and the continuous occupational exposure to low levels of radiation emanating from shielded nuclear reactors.

In addition, the Medical Departments of the Armed Forces have been charged by law with the responsibility of providing medical care and treatment for military personnel and their dependents. In compliance with this charge, the Medical Departments can and do utilize radiation-generating equipment, radiation sources, and radioisotopes for diagnosis and therapy. The larger medical facilities of each of the Armed Forces can also institute clinical research projects in radiation biology.

Although the assigned responsibilities in this field are the same for all three services, each is treated individually in a description of its specific organization and the method for accomplishing its assigned mission. Variation among the services is

a natural result of their divergence in function; e.g., widely different problems for defense against a nuclear attack are presented by a ship at sea, an operational air base, and a troop training center.

Thus it is necessary for each service to use different approaches to and methods for personnel protection from radiation. To prevent unnecessary duplication of research effort among the three services, the Department of Defense has established the DEFENSE ATOMIC SUPPORT AGENCY (DASA).

See ARMY RADIATION BIOLOGY AND ATOMIC MEDICINE PROGRAM and NAVY RADIATION BIOLOGY AND ATOMIC MEDICINE PROGRAM.

ARMED FORCES RADIOBIOLOGY RESEARCH INSTITUTE

The Armed Forces Radiobiology Research Institute (AFRRI) is located in the National Naval Medical Center at Bethesda, Maryland. Although it is a tri-service research facility and is funded by the DEFENSE ATOMIC SUPPORT AGENCY, it comes under the management control of the Navy Bureau of Medicine and Surgery.

AFRRI is a new research institute. The construction of the facility began in 1959, and the reactor went critical for the first time in 1962. The AFRRI reactor can be operated at a steady-state energy level up to 100 kilowatts. It can also be pulsed to produce a power release of 18 megawatt/second for a period of 13 milliseconds. Utilizing the reactor, AFRRI is capable of simulating radiations generated by a nuclear detonation. Its research scientists can also study the effects of fast neutrons, thermal neutrons, and gamma radiation, singly and in combination, over a wide range of energies and doses.

AFRRI will also have a linear accelerator capable of producing electrons with energies from 10 kev to 30 Mev. When operating at 30 kw, this accelerator can produce 9.6×10^{13} neutrons/second with an energy peak at 2 Mev from a uranium target. When used for gamma irradiation, the linear accelerator will produce a dose rate of approximately 6×10^9 rad/hr at a distance of 3 inches when a 1-gram sample of an element with a high atomic number is used as the target.

Although the primary purpose of research at AFRRI is to study personnel protective measures, the institute has the capacity for research covering the entire field of radiobiology, including nuclear medicine. Because of its ideal location, AFRRI can also produce a variety of short-lived radioisotopes, which are used for research in the other facilities at the National Naval Medical Center and at Walter Reed Army Medical Center.

ARMY RADIATION BIOLOGY AND ATOMIC MEDICINE PROGRAM

Research of the U.S. Army Medical Service in the nuclear field is currently being performed at the following places:

a. Walter Reed Army Institute of Research. Work is being performed on the diagnosis, prevention, and treatment of radiation injury; psychological-behaviorial studies with radiation; metabolic pathways; and the measurement of radioactivity in humans.

b. U.S. Army Medical Research Laboratory, Fort Knox, Kentucky. The biochemical effects of ionizing radiation are under study.

c. U.S. Army Medical Research Unit, Europe. By the use of a whole body counter, the uptake of radioactive material from fallout, metabolic studies, and the measurement of radioactivity in humans are being conducted.

d. Many contractors, nonprofit organizations, universities, and industrial firms are performing research directed by and augmenting the in-service capabilities of the Army Medical Service on the biological effects of ionizing radiation when such radiation is received in acute, repeated, or chronic exposures alone or in combination with other stresses and therapeutic measures.

The Walter Reed Army Institute of Research. The institute has a 9 × 4-inch sodium iodide crystal mounted in a 7-inch thick, iron room connected through 4 balanced, 3-inch photomultiplier tubes to a 400-channel gamma spectrometer. Background of the current facility is 6 counts per minute per channel. The equipment, therefore, serves as a very low-level detection device capable of identifying isotopes by means of the energy of the emitted gamma ray. The device is equipped with a chair for appropriate positioning of humans. Of course, there is equipment for the appropriate positioning of samples. In intimate association with this crystal is a 4π liquid scintillation detection facility capable of holding an entire person or comparably large samples. The detection system consists of toluene containing PPO (2, 5-diphenyloxazole) and POPOP [2, 2-p-phenylenebis(5-phenyloxazole] in association with 30 5-inch photomultiplier tubes and a 2-channel analyzer. This system has also been used in the study of isotopes administered to patients from the Walter Reed General Hospital. In association with this detection equipment there is an array of both standard and nonstandard radiation detection devices suitable for animal and other experimental purposes. A 50,000-watt nuclear reactor for biological research was added in 1962.

The Commanding General of the U.S. Army Research and Development Command is responsible for the over-all management of the Anti-radiation Drug Program. The Walter Reed Army Institute of Research is responsible for the technical management of the program. A master record is kept of chemicals that have been tried against radiation injury, along with a record of all the proposed compounds and a record of the synthetic procedures which have been used to make the appropriate agents. Some biological studies are also conducted at WRAIR. Tests are conducted in bacteria, human cells in tissue culture, mice, dogs, and monkeys. The large variety of agents are also examined with respect to their different physical and biological properties with the hope that these differences will provide an insight into the mechanism of action.

ARSENIC

Symbol As; atomic number 33; atomic weight 74.91; a grey metallic element found largely as arsenide in sulfide ores. Takes its name from Latin arsenicum. Stable isotope arsenic-75 accounts for 100% of the natural abundance. A trace element in human and animal bodies.

Used extensively in agricultural insecticides, in weed killers, and to a lesser extent in the glass industry. Various compounds of arsenic have been used in the treatment of disease for nearly a hundred years, typically arsphenamine (e.g., Salvarsan, arsenobenzene, and arsenobenzol) for intravenous treatment of syphilis and yaws. Arsphenamine has been superseded by a newer, less toxic drug—neoarsphenamine—and even more recently by various forms of penicillin.

In addition to being used as an insecticide and drug, arsenic is of biological interest because of its toxicity. Use of arsenic trioxide as a poison with criminal intent is well known, and its toxicity has been extensively studied. The lethal dose (LD) for arsenic trioxide given orally is as follows: guinea pig, 20-39 milligrams per kilogram (mg/kg); rabbit, 14-30 mg/kg; dog, 30-70 mg/kg; and chicken, 60-150 mg/kg. The LD for intravenous injection for the rabbit is 6 mg/kg and for the dog, 3-5 mg/kg.

There are 10 radioactive isotopes of arsenic with mass numbers 70 through 79, but only 4 have biological, medical, or agricultural significance: arsenic-73, arsenic-74, arsenic-76, and arsenic-77. As[73,74] isotopes (radioisotopes, accelerator-produced, half-life 76 and 17.5 days respectively) have the advantages of high specific activity and low radiocontamination, but are expensive. As[76] has lower specific activity and a shorter half-life (26.8 hours) and costs less, while As[77] has both high specific activity and a short half-life (40 hours) but requires chemical processing to remove the germanium radiocontamination.

Many radioisotopes of arsenic are formed in the atomic fission process, but only As⁷⁷ with its 40-hour half-life is significant, with a slight amount $(1.89 \times 10^{-6}$ megacuries per megaton of fission) remaining at the end of one month. Arsenic-76 is also found in soil and sea water as a result of induced radioactivity following the detonation of a nuclear device.

Arsenic-76 ($_{33}$As^{76}). This beta (β^-) and gamma-emitting radioisotope has a radioactive half-life of 1.1 days; with total body as the critical organ, the biological half-life is 280 days and the effective half-life, 1.1 days. Available commercially as sodium radioarsenate sterile solution for intravenous injection.

The maximum permissible concentration (MPC) for a 40-hour week industrial exposure to As⁷⁶, with the gastrointestinal tract as the critical organ, is 6×10^{-4} microcurie per cubic centimeter (μc/cc) in water and 10^{-7} μc/cc in air. For a 168-hour week (continuous exposure), the MPC for water is 2×10^{-4} μc/cc and for air 4×10^{-8} μc/cc. The maximum permissible burden in the total body is 20 μc.

ASHING PROCEDURES

Depending upon the characteristics and amount of radioactivity present, many samples can be measured directly by counting in the liquid or solid state. Often, however, especially when simultaneous chemical analyses or chemical separations are required, it is necessary to reduce the sample to a homogeneous solution phase for liquid counting, or to oxidize the organic matter completely. Pseudo wet ashing is useful when it is only necessary to produce a homogeneous solution; in this method, small samples of tissue are dissolved in concentrated nitric acid and the solution diluted to volume for direct liquid counting. Conventional wet ashing procedures are frequently based on the Kjeldahl method, which uses concentrated sulfuric acid (occasionally concentrated hydrochloric acid) as the oxidizing agent, and various metallic catalysts; dry ashing methods require a muffle furnace.

The general procedure is to place a dried sample in a platinum, quartz, or porcelain crucible, which is then placed in a cold muffle furnace. The furnace temperature is raised slowly to about 250° C and is held there for several hours, after which the temperature is raised to 500–600° C for the completion of the ashing, which may take several hours more. Precautions must always be taken to assure that the element of interest is not lost during the ashing process by volatilization or by adsorption to the walls of the vessel.

Special methods that involve trapping of gases have been developed for the oxidation of samples for measurement of carbon-14 and tritium.

ASTATINE

Symbol At; atomic number 85; atomic weight 210; a radioactive element discovered in 1940 by American scientists D. R. Corson, K. R. Mackenzie, and E. Segrè while bombarding bismuth-209 with alpha particles in the 60-inch cyclotron at the University of California at Berkeley. They proposed the name from the Greek astatos, unstable, since it is the only member of the halogen group without a stable isotope. There are 20 radioactive isotopes of astatine, At²¹⁶ appearing in the thorium series, At²¹⁷ in the neptunium series, and At²¹⁸ in the uranium series. The radioisotopes are of interest as internal emitters, because they are highly radiotoxic. The maximum permissible concentration of At²¹¹ for a 168-hour week (continuous exposure), with thyroid and ovaries being the critical organs is 2×10^{-5} microcurie per cubic centimeter (μc/cc) in water and 2×10^{-9} μc/cc in air.

ATMOSPHERE

The whole mass of air surrounding the earth— the gaseous envelope. It includes the layer nearest the earth (the troposphere) and an outer layer (the stratosphere) separated by the tropopause as shown in Figure A–8. Contamination of the atmosphere results mainly from the detonation of nuclear weapons but may result from the release of radioactive material from a nuclear reactor or from industrial sources.

See BIOSPHERIC CONTAMINATION, STRATOSPHERIC FALLOUT, and TROPOSPHERIC FALLOUT.

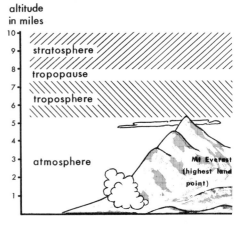

FIGURE A–8. THE AIR MASS SURROUNDING THE EARTH.

ATOM

Smallest unit of matter that exhibits the chemical properties of an element. For example, sodium forms innumerable chemical compounds but can always be identified by standard chemical techniques. Sodium atoms have an internal structure of their own, can be broken up into smaller units, and have various isotopic forms, but these cannot be identified by chemical means.

ATOMIC BOMB

Commonly used to refer to nuclear weapons—either atomic weapons or thermonuclear weapons.

ATOMIC BOMB CASUALTY COMMISSION

A group of scientists organized to study the late effects on man of ionizing radiation, through a long-term study of the survivors who were exposed to the atomic bombs detonated over the Japanese cities of Hiroshima and Nagasaki in 1945. The ABCC is under the direction of the National Academy of Sciences–National Research Council, supported by funds provided by the USAEC.

Within a few weeks after the bombing and the termination of the war with Japan, a United States military medical team was working with the Japanese medical team. A Joint Commission of the Atomic Bomb in Japan was established, composed of military and civilian scientists and working with the Japanese scientists, and began gathering useful data. In 1946, the President approved the establishment of the ABCC (entirely non-military) to continue medical and genetic studies of the late effects of exposure to the nuclear explosion on the survivors of the 2 cities. The ABCC works closely with the Japanese team, which outnumbers the Americans.

The first and most formidable task was to determine the populations to be studied. Finally 100,000 persons were identified on whom all major studies are concentrated. This group contains the majority of the survivors of the 2 cities who were in the proximal zone (within 2,000 meters of ground zero) and are matched by 2 control groups of comparable age and sex. One of the comparison groups is composed of individuals who were in the distal zone (beyond 3,000 meters) and though not exposed to significant radiation were subject to physical and emotional trauma. The other group of controls is composed of present residents of the cities who were not present at the time of the bombing. There are a number of subsamples within this major group, such as the few hundred young people who were exposed in utero to prompt radiation and the medical sample, which is a group of 20,000 who are under continuing active medical surveillance.

Studies to date have revealed a marked increase in the incidence of leukemia among those exposed within the proximal zone; a suggested increase in the incidence of carcinoma; and an increased incidence of cataracts. Genetic effects, except for a suggested shift in sex ratio have been absent so far. No increase has been found in the incidence of abortions, stillbirths, or major malformations among the exposed population when compared with the controls. This study should be continued for many years in an attempt to find answers to many unanswered questions in genetics and to determine the late somatic effects due to ionizing radiation exposure.

ATOMIC CLOUD

Also mushroom cloud. Cloud formed from the fireball of a nuclear device detonation consisting of fission products, solid particles of bomb debris, particles of material sucked up from the surface of the earth, and condensed vapors from the cooling

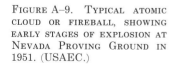

FIGURE A–9. TYPICAL ATOMIC CLOUD OR FIREBALL, SHOWING EARLY STAGES OF EXPLOSION AT NEVADA PROVING GROUND IN 1951. (USAEC.)

fireball. Because of the pressure of the explosion and the intense heat, the rising atomic cloud is carried upward at the average rate for the first minute of 260 mph. It may reach a height of 20 to 25 miles for a megaton-yield bomb and may be a mile or more in diameter, as shown in Figure A–9. After a few minutes the radioactive particles begin to fall back to earth (gravity), the rates depending on their size. This material, which falls out soon after detonation, constitutes local fallout.

See CLOUD, RADIOACTIVE and FIREBALL.

ATOMIC ENERGY

Internal energy of the atom, absorbed when it is formed from its constituent particles and released when it is broken down into its constituent particles. Energy contained in matter by virtue of its mass is given quantitatively by the relationship $E = mc^2$.

In 1902 Pierre and Marie Curie wrote: "Each atom of a radioactive substance functions as a constant source of energy." Rutherford and Soddy in 1903 made the suggestion that all atoms, and not only radioactive atoms, possessed large amounts of energy. We now know that they were speaking of nuclear energy, but even today the terms are used almost interchangeably. In popular usage, atomic energy is nuclear energy released in sufficient quantity to be of engineering interest, particularly in power reactors and large-scale (atomic bomb) releases of energy as a result of disintegration of atomic nuclei.

See NUCLEAR FISSION.

ATOMIC ENERGY ACTS OF 1946 AND 1954

The 1946 Atomic Energy Act, Public Law 585 enacted by the 79th Congress, was the original atomic energy statute. It was passed after a great deal of debate over military versus civilian control. Implemented by Executive Order 9816, effective December 31, 1946, the responsibility for all atomic energy matters was transferred to the Atomic Energy Commission from the Manhattan Engineer District (War Department). The U.S. Government retained a monopoly, in that title to all source materials and special nuclear materials and by-product materials was assigned to the AEC and private ownership of facilities for producing such materials was prohibited. On the other hand, the USAEC was charged with "assisting and fostering private research and development to encourage maximum scientific progress" and also was instructed to disseminate scientific and technical information. The 1946 Act established the congressional Joint Committee on Atomic Energy, the General Advisory Committee, and the Military Liaison Committee.

The 1954 Atomic Energy Act, Public Law 703 enacted by the 83rd Congress, superseded the 1946 Act and together with its amendments constitutes the atomic energy law for the United States. This Act tended to relax government monopoly and provided, under appropriate controls, for private ownership of atomic energy facilities such as research and power reactors, for private leasing of special nuclear materials, and for private access to certain categories of classified information. The Act also established a more liberal patent policy, broadened the policies for international cooperation in the development of peaceful uses of atomic energy, and allowed for exchange of classified information on certain aspects of military applications.

There have been a number of amendments such as the IAEA Participation Act, which provided for United States participation in the International Atomic Energy Agency; the Cooperation with States amendment, which established the responsibilities of the several states in relation to the USAEC; the Indemnification Act, which outlined government liability in the event of a nuclear accident; the Atomic Energy Community Act of 1955 to facilitate the establishment of local self-government in the communities of Oak Ridge, Tenn., and Richland, Wash.; and the Euratom Cooperation Act to provide for cooperation with the European Atomic Energy Community (EURATOM).

Other minor acts and bills have provided annual appropriations, omnibus bills making miscellaneous amendments, and special statutes have been formulated, e.g., providing for construction of the Germantown, Md., headquarters.

ATOMIC ENERGY COMMISSION

The United States Atomic Energy Commission (USAEC) is an independent office of the Federal Government with statutory responsibility for atomic energy matters. The Atomic Energy Act of 1946 established the USAEC as the successor to the Manhattan Engineer District, and the transfer of responsibility became effective January 1, 1947. The basic statute under which the USAEC now operates is the Atomic Energy Act of 1954, as amended.

The policy under which the Commission operates was set forth in the Act to be:

"a. the development, use, and control of atomic energy shall be directed so as to make the maximum contributions to the general welfare, subject at all times to the paramount objective of making the maximum contribution to the common defense and security; and

"b. the development, use, and control of atomic

energy shall be directed so as to promote world peace, improve the general welfare, increase the standard of living, and strengthen free competition in private enterprise."

The Act of 1954 presents detailed findings, purposes, and definitions, which may be summarized very briefly as programs conducted so as to maximize the contribution of atomic energy to the national defense and security and to scientific and industrial progress, and to develop the necessary standards and programs to protect the public from potential atomic energy hazards.

The USAEC conducts its affairs through a headquarters staff located at Germantown, Maryland, about 27 miles northwest of Washington, D.C., through 9 operations offices located throughout the United States, and by contracts with industry and universities to operate research and development facilities and laboratories. (See LABORATORIES OF RADIATION BIOLOGY for a list.)

The headquarters organization consists of the Commission proper, composed of 5 members appointed by the President with the advice and consent of the Senate, and approximately 5,000 staff members organized as indicated in the chart on the end papers of this book. (There are about 2,000 additional staff members in field offices.) Among the approximately 36 divisions and offices, 8 are of primary interest to biomedicine: the Division of Biology and Medicine; the Division of Isotopes Development; the Division of Nuclear Education and Training; the Division of Operational Safety; the Division of Technical Information; and the 3 divisions under the office of the Director of Regulation—Licensing and Regulation, Compliance, and Radiation Standards.

Division of Biology and Medicine. The Division, reporting to the Assistant General Manager for Research and Development, is responsible for all aspects of the program in radiation biology, nuclear medicine, and health physics, whether conducted in Commission-supported laboratories or by contract with universities, hospitals, or research institutions. Under the Director there are 4 Assistant Directors, one each for Administration, Biological Sciences, Medical and Health Research, and Radiological Physics. Each of the Assistant Directors is responsible for 2 or 3 branches. The Assistant Director for Administration with the assistance of the Administrative Branch and the Program Coordination Branch is responsible for all aspects of the administrative and financial programs of the Division. The Assistant Director for Biological Sciences plans, develops, and directs a program of research in biology and environmental sciences. The Biology Branch program includes research on the effects of radiations on man, ani-

mals, plants, and their environment; on the applications of radiation and radioisotopes to the solution of biological and agricultural problems; on the toxicity and metabolism of fission products; and on the comparative genetic effects of different types of radiations on living organisms. The Environmental Sciences Branch sponsors research in the fields of oceanography, geophysics, marine biology, plant and animal ecology, and soils studies.

The Assistant Director for Medical and Health Research is responsible for the medical and health research programs of the Division. The Medical Research Branch conducts a program of research on the mechanism, diagnosis, and treatment of radiation injury and on the application of radioactive isotopes in the diagnosis and treatment of human diseases. It also conducts research on the toxicity of chemicals used within the AEC operations and on the applications of atomic energy products to human diseases. The Civil Effects Branch has a program of laboratory and field projects related to prompt and residual radiation and blast and thermal radiation. The Assistant Director for Radiological Physics with his Fallout Studies Branch and Radiological Physics, Technical Analysis Branch, and Instrumentation Branch conducts a program in the areas of radiological and health physics, atmospheric radioactivity and fallout, and the development and evaluation of radiation detection instrumentation and systems.

Division of Isotopes Development. The DID develops and directs USAEC policies and programs for (1) development and dissemination of technology to accelerate widespread applications of radioisotopes and high-intensity radiation; (2) radioisotopes production, process development, pricing and marketing; and (3) encouraging private enterprise production and distribution of radioisotopes. In short, as the Division's name implies, it is responsible for all aspects of the isotopes development program of the Commission. The office of the Director is assisted by 5 branches: Program Coordination, Isotopes Technology Development, Analysis and Applications, Radiation Development, and Production and Materials.

Division of Nuclear Education and Training. The activities of this newly formed (1962) division are treated separately under EDUCATION AND TRAINING.

Division of Operational Safety (OS). The Director of the OS division is responsible to the General Manager for developing the policies and the requirements for the protection of Government and USAEC contractor personnel, of the public, and of property from all types of hazards resulting from USAEC operations. These policies apply to industrial health, safety, and fire protection, as well as to radiation protection. Each of the 5 branches is responsible for a segment of this over-all safety mission: Health Protection Branch for industrial hygiene and the occupational health and health physics program; the Industrial Safety and Fire Protection Branch for all aspects of industrial safety and fire protection; the Materials Processing Safety Branch for gaseous diffusion plants, normal uranium processing, production of radioisotopes, and management of radioactive waste; the Nuclear Explosives Environmental Safety Branch for nuclear weapons tests, including world-wide monitoring of fallout; and the Reactor Safety Branch for all safety aspects of the operation of reactors.

Division of Technical Information. The activities of this division are covered in detail under the heading TECHNICAL INFORMATION DIVISION, USAEC.

Advisory Bodies. The statutory advisory bodies of the USAEC are: Congressional Joint Committee on Atomic Energy; General Advisory Committee; Advisory Committee on Reactor Safeguards; Patent Compensation Board; Military Liaison Committee and Atomic Energy Labor–Management Relations Panel. Other advisory bodies number 20 to 25 at any one time and include the following of particular interest to biomedical readers: Advisory Committee for Biology and Medicine; Advisory Committee on Isotope and Radiation Development; Advisory Committee on Medical Uses of Isotopes; and Plowshare Advisory Committee.

Operating Philosophy. The USAEC follows the practice of contracting with academic or research institutions and industrial organizations to design, construct, and operate its facilities and to conduct its research and development. Thus, well over 100,000 persons are currently employed by USAEC contractor organizations compared to less than 7,000 on the Civil Service or military payrolls.

The Chairmen of the Commission have been:

David E. Lilienthal	10/28/46–2/15/50
Summer T. Pike	2/16/50–7/10/50
(Acting Chairman)	
Gordon E. Dean	7/11/50–6/30/53
Lewis L. Strauss	7/2/53–6/30/58
Willard F. Libby	7/1/58–7/13/58
(Acting Chairman)	
John A. McCone	7/14/58–1/19/61
John S. Graham	1/20/61–3/1/61
(Acting Chairman)	
Glenn T. Seaborg	3/2/61–

ATOMIC EXPLOSIONS

The explosive release of the energy derived from nuclear fission, fusion, or both. The term may, of course, refer to explosions for the testing of nuclear weapons or to peaceful uses of nuclear explosions or to military action. It is more accurate to speak of nuclear explosions.

ATOMIC MASS

The mass of a neutral atom of a nuclide, usually expressed as atomic mass units.

ATOMIC MASS UNIT

Abbreviation amu. Unit of mass equal to $1/12$ the arbitrary mass assigned to carbon-12 ($_6C^{12}$). The mass of all other atoms is based on a unit which is $1/12$ the weight of the carbon-12 atom. Equivalent to 1.657×10^{-24} gram or 0.999728 atomic weight unit. In terms of energy, an amu is equivalent to 931.162 Mev or 1.49×10^{-3} erg.

ATOMIC NUCLEUS

The positively charged core of an atom in which rests almost the entire mass of the atom but only a minute part of its volume. It has been calculated that the nucleus is only $1/100,000$ the size of the entire atom, but is so dense that a child's marble of the same density would weigh about 36,400,000 tons. The nucleus has a positive electric charge; the electrons, which constitute the outer area of the atom, have a negative electrical charge. The positive and negative charge is usually equal, and thus the normal stable atom is electrically neutral. It is postulated that the orbital electrons move around the nucleus in regular orbits and at high velocities. To illustrate the size of the nucleus and the electron relative to the size of the complete atom, it has been calculated that if the hydrogen atom were expanded so that its one electron moved in an orbit wide enough to circle New York City, the nucleus would be the size of a baseball and the electron about the size of a golf ball.

The nucleus consists of neutrons and protons, together referred to as nucleons. The atomic number (Z) is the number of protons in the nucleus. The mass number (A) is the total number of nucleons, i.e., the protons plus the neutrons in the nucleus. Thus in the carbon atom, $A = 12$ and $Z = 6$; therefore there are 6 neutrons. Figure A–10 shows the concept of the structure of some simple nuclei. It will be noted that for these elements of low atomic weight, the atomic number Z is approximately half the mass number A, and thus these elements contain almost equal numbers of neutrons and protons. With increasing atomic weight the number of neutrons in a stable nucleus

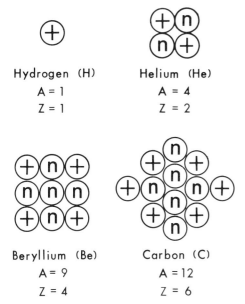

FIGURE A–10. STRUCTURE OF SIMPLE NUCLEI. MASS
NUMBER (A). ATOMIC NUMBER (Z). NEUTRONS (n).
PROTONS (+).

exceeds the number of protons. The atomic number of uranium, for example, is 92 and the mass
number 238, so the nucleus contains 146 neutrons
and 92 protons.

The number of protons in the nucleus of an atom
determines what type of atom it is, i.e., its chemical properties. Thus all atoms containing 8 protons
are oxygen atoms; all those containing 92 are
uranium. A change in the number of protons will
produce a different kind of atom. For example,
cobalt-57 $(_{27}Co^{57})$, $Z = 27$, is the parent of
nickel-57 $(_{28}Ni^{57})$, $Z = 28$, cobalt-57 being the
daughter of iron-57 $(_{26}Fe^{57m})$.

The nucleus is remarkably stable and is immune
from either chemical or physical attack, but it can
be changed by the effects of radiation.

ATOMIC NUMBER

Symbol Z. The number of protons in an atomic
nucleus, or the positive charge of the nucleus
expressed in terms of the electronic charge (e).
The number of electrons outside the nucleus of a
neutral atom and, according to present theory, the
number of protons in the nucleus. For example,
an atom of the element lithium has 3 electrons,
and a nuclear charge equal in amount to three
times the electronic charge—in other words, equal
to three times the charge of the nucleus of the
hydrogen atom. In the same way strontium has
an atomic number of 38 and uranium an atomic
number of 92. All atoms having the same nuclear
charge (atomic number) exhibit the same chemical

properties regardless of the differences they may
exhibit otherwise, such as differences of nuclear
mass and nuclear stability.

The atomic number of all the known elements
is shown in the table accompanying the ATOMIC
WEIGHT entry. The atomic number is written $_3Li^6$
for lithium-6, $_{38}Sr^{90}$ for strontium-90, and $_{92}U^{235}$
for uranium-235.

ATOMIC POWER

Atomic power (or nuclear power) is a general
term used to include all modes of release and use
of nuclear energy on a large scale. These modes
range from use of the uncontrolled rates of energy
release in detonations of fission and fusion bombs
and other nuclear devices such as those being
developed under the plowshare program, to the
highly controlled rate of energy release required
in power reactors for the generation of electricity
and the propulsion of ships. Electricity produced
by nuclear power plants will soon be commercially
competitive in many parts of the world, particularly where coal and oil must be imported. The
ultimate exhaustion of our sources of fossil fuels
at some time in the future may make atomic
power plants one of our major sources of electrical
energy.

See SHERWOOD PROJECT.

ATOMIC SHOT

Popular term used to indicate the detonation of
a nuclear device. Also called atomic explosion or,
more accurately, a NUCLEAR EXPLOSION.

ATOMIC TESTS. *See* NUCLEAR WEAPONS
TESTING.

ATOMIC WEAPON

An explosive military nuclear weapon in which
the energy is produced by nuclear fission. A
thermonuclear weapon is a military nuclear weapon
in which part of the energy is from nuclear fusion.
The fissionable materials used in atomic weapons
are certain isotopes of the elements uranium and
plutonium. U^{235} is the only fissionable isotope that
occurs in nature.

When a free (or unattached) neutron enters the
nucleus of a fissionable atom, it can cause the
nucleus to split into two smaller parts; this fission
process is accompanied by the release of additional
neutrons and large amounts of energy. The complete fission of 1 pound of uranium releases as
much energy as the explosion of 8,000 tons of
TNT (*see* TNT EQUIVALENT). As will be seen in
the discussion of nuclear explosion, if neutrons are
released in greater numbers than they are lost, a

chain reaction may be produced, and if all this occurs in a short enough time and in a contained volume, an explosion may result. The smaller (or lighter) nuclei resulting from the splitting of the original atoms are called fission products.

Since the explosive energy results from nuclear reactions, atomic weapons are in fact nuclear weapons or NUCLEAR DEVICES. The term nuclear devices is used in this book.

ATOMIC WEIGHT

The weighted mean of the masses of the neutral atoms of an element expressed in atomic mass units (amu).

The relative atomic weight scale expresses the average weight of the atoms of an element (of the isotope distribution found in nature) referred to the weight of exactly 12 for the carbon-12 atom ($_6C^{12}$).

TABLE A–6.   RELATIVE ATOMIC WEIGHTS*

ELEMENT	SYMBOL	ATOMIC NUMBER	ATOMIC WEIGHT*
Actinium	Ac	89	227
Aluminum	Al	13	26.9815
Americium	Am	95	(243)
Antimony	Sb	51	121.75
Argon	A	18	39.948
Arsenic	As	33	74.9216
Astatine	At	85	(210)
Barium	Ba	56	137.34
Berkelium	Bk	97	(249)
Beryllium	Be	4	9.0122
Bismuth	Bi	83	208.980
Boron	B	5	10.811
Bromine	Br	35	79.909
Cadmium	Cd	48	112.40
Calcium	Ca	20	40.08
Californium	Cf	98	(251)
Carbon	C	6	12.01115
Cerium	Ce	58	140.12
Cesium	Cs	55	132.905
Chlorine	Cl	17	35.453
Chromium	Cr	24	51.996
Cobalt	Co	27	58.9332
Copper	Cu	29	63.54
Curium	Cm	96	(247)
Dysprosium	Dy	66	162.50
Einsteinium	Es	99	(254)
Erbium	Er	68	167.26
Europium	Eu	63	151.96
Fermium	Fm	100	(253)
Fluorine	F	9	18.9984
Francium	Fr	87	(223)
Gadolinium	Gd	64	157.25
Gallium	Ga	31	69.72
Germanium	Ge	32	72.59
Gold	Au	79	196.967
Hafnium	Hf	72	178.49
Helium	He	2	4.0026
Holmium	Ho	67	164.930
Hydrogen	H	1	1.00797
Indium	In	49	114.82
Iodine	I	53	126.9044
Iridium	Ir	77	192.2
Iron	Fe	26	55.847
Krypton	Kr	36	83.80
Lanthanum	La	57	138.91
Lawrencium	Lw	103	(257)
Lead	Pb	82	207.19
Lithium	Li	3	6.939
Lutetium	Lu	71	174.97
Magnesium	Mg	12	24.312
Manganese	Mn	25	54.9380

Table A-6 continued

Mendelevium	Mv	101	(256)
Mercury	Hg	80	200.59
Molybdenum	Mo	42	95.94
Neodymium	Nd	60	144.24
Neon	Ne	10	20.183
Neptunium	Np	93	(237)
Nickel	Ni	28	58.71
Niobium (Columbium)	Nb	41	92.906
Nitrogen	N	7	14.0067
Nobelium	No	102	(254)
Osmium	Os	76	190.2
Oxygen	O	8	15.9994
Palladium	Pd	46	106.4
Phosphorus	P	15	30.9738
Platinum	Pt	78	195.09
Plutonium	Pu	94	(242)
Polonium	Po	84	(210)
Potassium	K	19	39.102
Praseodymium	Pr	59	140.907
Promethium	Pm	61	(147)
Protactinium	Pa	91	(231)
Radium	Ra	88	(226)
Radon	Rn	86	(222)
Rhenium	Re	75	186.2
Rhodium	Rh	45	102.905
Rubidium	Rb	37	85.47
Ruthenium	Ru	44	101.07
Samarium	Sm	62	150.35
Scandium	Sc	21	44.956
Selenium	Se	34	78.96
Silicon	Si	14	28.086
Silver	Ag	47	107.870
Sodium	Na	11	22.9898
Strontium	Sr	38	87.62
Sulfur	S	16	32.064
Tantalum	Ta	73	180.948
Technetium	Tc	43	(99)
Tellurium	Te	52	127.60
Terbium	Tb	65	158.924
Thallium	Tl	81	204.37
Thorium	Th	90	232.038
Thulium	Tm	69	168.934
Tin	Sn	50	118.69
Titanium	Ti	22	47.90
Tungsten (Wolfram)	W	74	183.85
Uranium	U	92	238.03
Vanadium	V	23	50.942
Xenon	Xe	54	131.30
Ytterbium	Yb	70	173.04
Yttrium	Y	39	88.905
Zinc	Zn	30	65.37
Zirconium	Zr	40	91.22

*Value in parenthesis is the mass number of the most stable known isotope.

ATOMIC WEIGHT UNIT

Abbreviation awu. One-twelfth of the arbitrary mass of carbon-12; identical to the ATOMIC MASS UNIT.

ATOMS-FOR-PEACE AWARD

An award given to that scientist, engineer, individual, or organization that has made the greatest contribution to the peaceful uses of atomic energy.

The award was sparked by a suggestion made by President Dwight D. Eisenhower at the Geneva conference in 1955 and was established by a Ford Motor Company grant of $1,000,000 as a memorial to Henry Ford and Edsel Ford. The award consists of a $75,000 cash honorarium, a gold medal, and a citation. The following have been recipients:

1957—Niels Henrik David Bohr

1959—George Charles DeHevesy

1960—jointly to Leo Szilard, Eugene Paul
Wigner, Alvin Martin Weinberg, and
Walter Henry Zinn
1961—Sir John Cockcroft
1963—jointly to Edwin M. McMillan and
Vladimir I. Veksler

ATTENUATION

In radiation theory, the reduction in the flux
density, or the power per unit area, in relation to
the distance from the radioactive source. It may
be due to either absorption or scattering or both,
but in the best sense it excludes the geometric
decrease of intensity with distance from the source
—INVERSE-SQUARE LAW.

In nuclear physics, the reduction in the intensity
of radiation upon passage through matter due to
a combination of scattering and absorption.

In considering the effects of nuclear weapons,
the reduction of the intensity of radioactive radiation, thermal radiation, or blast by passage through
a suitable medium.

ATTENUATION FACTOR

Measure of the opacity of a layer of material for
the radiation traversing it. It is equal to the
intensity of the incident radiation (I_0) divided by
the intensity of the emergent radiation (I),
i.e., I_0/I. In the usual sense of exponential absorption ($I = I_0 e^{-\mu x}$), the attenuation factor is $e^{+\mu x}$,
where x is the thickness of the material and μ is
the absorption coefficient.

See ATTENUATION.

AUTOLOGOUS TISSUE GRAFTS

Tissue used for treatment of the same individual from which the tissue was taken.

See BONE MARROW GRAFTS.

AUTOPSY ON BODIES CONTAINING RA-
DIOACTIVITY

Special techniques must be used by the pathologist in handling bodies containing treatment
quantities of radioactive isotopes (diagnostic
tracer quantities offer no problem). For example,
care must be used in the removal of brachytherapy implants, such as radon seeds, radium-
containing devices, radioactive gold wires, yttrium
pellets, and other preparations. But since their
location is known from the detailed history of
the patient or can be determined by x-ray, there
should be no danger of undue exposure for the
pathologist.

Radioactive colloidal preparations (gold-198,
yttrium-90) used in the thoracic and abdominal
cavities for the treatment of cancer offer a difficult
problem. For example, 100 millicuries of gold-198
introduced into the abdominal cavity would give
a dose to the gloved hands of about 40 roentgens

per hour. This dose can be reduced to less than
0.15 r/hr by suction removal of fluid and careful
sponging of the organs. Goggles or glasses are
worn to protect the eyes from possible splash of
fluid, and heavy rubber gloves are mandatory.

For details see National Bureau of Standards
Handbook 65, Safe Handling of Bodies Containing
Radioactive Isotopes.

See CADAVERS, RADIOACTIVE, HANDLING OF.

AUTORADIOGRAPHY

A photographic technique which makes it possible to see the location of radioactive materials in
cells and tissues. Ionizing radiations act upon a
photographic emulsion in the same way that light
does. Thus, if a film or emulsion is exposed to an
object containing radioactive material, a photographic image is produced upon development
which shows the location of the radioactivity in
the specimen. The resulting picture or image is
called an autoradiogram, autoradiograph, auto-
gram, or radioautogram.

There are 4 principle techniques used in making
autoradiographs: (a) simple apposition in which
the specimen is pressed against the photographic
emulsion in a darkened laboratory and held for
an exposure period of several days, at which time
the specimen is removed and the film developed;
(b) mounting method in which the sections to be
studied are mounted on the emulsion and remain
permanently bonded during the photographic and
staining processes; (c) coating method in which
the section containing the radioactive material is
covered with a fluid emulsion, which, when it
hardens, forms a permanent bond for further
exposure and processing; and (d) stripping-film
method in which photographic emulsion is stripped
from its base and flattened over the section to be
studied, where it remains in contact. Staining and
processing can be carried out through the film.

The combination of autoradiography with thin
section techniques permits studies of the location
and site of synthesis of specific biological molecules. Since the isotopic tracer used can be introduced in a wide variety of compounds, these
methods provide a link between biochemical and
cytological information. The most useful radioisotope to date has been tritium (H^3). It emits a
short-range beta particle which permits high
resolution (in the order of a micron). Almost all
biological molecules contain hydrogen in relatively
stable positions so that tritium can be used in
many different kinds of studies. Of special note
have been the detailed pictures of chromosomal
replication recently made possible by the use of
tritiated thymidine.

Extensive use of this technique has been made
in metabolic translocation studies in plants to

FIGURE A–11. AUTORADIOGRAPH SHOWING PHOSPHO-
RUS-32 TAKEN UP BY LEAF OF COLEUS PLANT. (BROOK-
HAVEN NATIONAL LABORATORY.)

determine movement of such materials as phos-
phorus-32, sulfur-35, iron-55, and carbon-14.
Figure A–11 shows the movement of phosphorus
into the leaf. Calcium-45 has been used to study
bone growth and development and the deposition
of calcium in relation to metabolic processes.
(*See* BONE STUDIES USING RADIOISOTOPES.) Human
tissues are also studied by use of radioisotopes and
autoradiographic techniques (see Figures A–12 and
A–13). Pathological or disease conditions are also
studied in this manner. Embryonic development
can be studied effectively with autoradiographic
techniques. But the most important work is at the
cellular level at which it becomes possible to de-

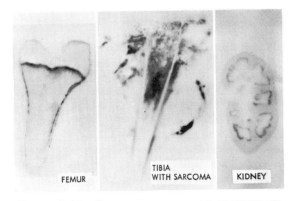

FIGURE A–12. GROSS AUTORADIOGRAMS OF THREE HU-
MAN TISSUES WITH THREE DIFFERENT RADIOISOTOPES
SHOWING NONUNIFORM DISTRIBUTION CHARACTERISTIC
OF MOST RADIOISOTOPES. (MEDICAL DIVISION, OAK
RIDGE INSTITUTE OF NUCLEAR STUDIES.)

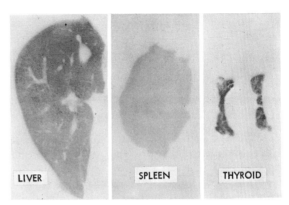

FIGURE A–13. GROSS AUTORADIOGRAMS OF THREE DIF-
FERENT HUMAN TISSUES WITH THREE DIFFERENT RADIO-
ISOTOPES SHOWING THE UNUSUAL GROSSLY UNIFORM
DISTRIBUTION (ON A MICROSCOPIC LEVEL, EVEN HERE IT
WOULD BE NONUNIFORM). (MEDICAL DIVISION, OAK
RIDGE INSTITUTE OF NUCLEAR STUDIES.)

velop correlations between structure, normal function, and pathology.

AVALANCHE

In a pulse-type counter, the voltage on the
accelerating electrode is high enough to give the
ions or electrons sufficient energy to create additional ions by collision. This causes multiplication
of ions at such rate as to create an avalanche of
charged particles which are swept up by the collecting electrode, thus resulting in a pulse greater
than that resulting from normal gas collision.

AVASCULAR NECROSIS OF FEMORAL HEAD, MEASUREMENT

When the neck of the femur is fractured,
phosphorus-32 may be used to help determine the
effectiveness of the blood supply to the head of
the bone. The patient is given an internal tracer
dose of the radioisotope in soluble form, usually
about 200 microcuries intravenously. A short time
later, the radioactivity in the head of the bone is
compared with that in another part of the bone,
either by removing small pieces of bone for radioassay or by inserting a small detector into holes
drilled in the bone. A relatively high level of
radioactivity in the femoral head indicates a good
blood supply and favorable prospects for healing.

See BONE STUDIES and BONE FRACTURES DUE
TO RADIATION.

AVERAGE LIFE

Term used interchangeably with mean life; the
average of the individual lives of all the atoms of
a particular radioactive substance. The actual life
of any particular radioactive atom can have any
value between zero and infinity. However, the
mean or average life of a large number of atoms is
a definite quantity and is equal to 1.44 times the
radioactive half-life.

B

BACKGROUND CORRECTION

Background is the counting rate when there is no radioactive source present in the counting assembly, and is due to the cosmic radiation and radioactivity in the air and surrounding materials. The counting rate of a sample is equal to the observed rate minus the background rate. In general, the smaller the sample count compared to the background count, the more inaccurate will be the results and the greater the length of time required to accomplish the counting. For the counting of very weak samples, the background contribution to the counting error must be minimized by using considerable shielding, and in some instances by use of anticoincidence techniques; under these conditions, the length of counting time will be determined by the statistical accuracy required.

BACKGROUND COUNT

The counts recorded by a radiation detector and scaler from any agent or cause other than a sample under investigation. In general, the background count is simply measured as the counts collected in the absence of any sample and is the total of extraneous events presumed to be included in the gross count indicated during normal sample counting procedures. These counts arise from the background radiation and other causes such as spurious counts related to electrical disturbances, also from radioactivity existing in the materials used in constructing the equipment. An appropriate measurement of the background count is required so that a suitable background correction can be calculated and applied to the observed counting rate when evaluating laboratory measurements, the counts and the counting times being adjusted to provide statistically equivalent data.

BACKGROUND RADIATION

Radiation arising from radioactive material other than the one directly under consideration. Natural radiation is always present, with ever-present effects (counts) in physical apparatus above which a phenomenon must manifest itself in order to be measured. These undesired counts are due to cosmic rays, terrestrial radiation, building materials, or local contaminating radioactivity. In nuclear work with photographic emulsions,

background radiation accounts for developable grains unrelated to the tracks under investigation.

BACKSCATTER

The scattering or deflection of particles or radiation through angles greater than 90° with respect to the original direction of motion.

Backscatter may be important when counting beta particles in an ionization chamber; for beta particles are easily deflected in passing through matter and some originally entering the sample container will be scattered back into the sensitive counting volume. A thick mounted sample may show backscatter of 35%.

Backscatter is important in therapy, for radiation to the underlying tissues scatters back to the skin which is thus irradiated by two components, direct and scattered.

One interesting radiochemistry application is the use of beta rays to determine the properties of substances. Differences in the atomic and molecular composition of the scattering substances give results that can be correlated with other information such as the atomic number of the atoms.

Backscattering has also found application in the industrial use of radioisotopes where thickness gages use the reflection of beta source radiation from material being coated to determine the thickness of the coating being applied to paper, metal, etc.

BACTERIA, STUDIES

Bacteria may be labeled with a radioactive isotope and their movement traced in studies of air-borne infection, homogeneity of bacterial density in the air, and retention and initial distribution in the organs of the body in respiratory route infection.

In a study on air-borne infection of tuberculosis the bacilli were labeled with phosphorus-32 by growth for 5 days in Sauton's media containing 15 μc per ml. of P^{32} as phosphate; the culture was harvested and thoroughly washed; then used in an aerosol. In mice sacrificed immediately after the inhalation exposure, 20% of the total inhaled radioactivity was recovered from the lungs, 60% from the alimentary tract, 15% from the liver and 2% from the kidneys. In mice sacrificed 24 hours later, the radioactivity in the lungs had decreased to one-half, and that in the alimentary tract to one-third, but the radioactivity in the liver and kidneys remained the same.

BAL

Acronym for British anti-lewisite. A chelating agent, 2,3-dimercaptopropanol, used chiefly for stable metal poisoning. It has the formula

$$HS \cdot CH_2 \cdot CH \cdot CH_2OH$$
$$|$$
$$SH$$

See CHEMICAL TREATMENT TO REDUCE RADIOISOTOPE RETENTION.

BARIUM

Symbol Ba; atomic number 56; atomic weight 137.36. A pale yellowish, metallic element belonging to the alkaline earths. Discovered by Swedish chemist Karl Scheele in 1774 and isolated by English chemist Sir Humphry Davy in 1808. Named from Greek *barys*, heavy. Occurs chiefly as sulfate (barite). Georgia and Tennessee are the principal producers.

Metallic barium is of little commercial importance but barite is used extensively in oil-well drilling muds, for lithopone manufacture, for making glass, and in the paint and rubber industries. Several barium salts are used in medicine. For example, barium sulfate is used extensively as a contrast medium in roentgenography of the digestive tract.

The acid-soluble salts of barium are poisonous. Numerous cases have been reported where mistakes have been made such as dispensing barium chloride in place of sodium chloride; or in dispensing the carbonate or sulfide instead of the sulfate for roentgenological purposes. About 200 mg of soluble barium is toxic for man, and about 335 mg/kg of ingested barium chloride is fatal for rats. Barium occurs naturally in foods at levels of usually less than 0.1%. Crop plants may contain 3 to 1,000 parts per million.

There are seven stable isotopes of barium and 14 radioactive isotopes. Ba[131] (half-life 12 days) and Ba[140] (half-life 12.8 days) have the greatest potential biological usefulness. Research has been done on plant uptake and distribution, and on metabolism of barium in animals.

Eleven radioisotopes ((Ba[137m] and Ba[139 through 148]) occur as fission products produced by the detonation of a nuclear device, with Ba[137m] (2.6 minute half-life daughter of cesium-137) and Ba[140] showing measurable contamination at the end of 1 year. Several radioisotopes of barium have also been found in sea water as a result of induced radioactivity from the detonation of a nuclear device. Ba[140] is one of the fission products

for which a routine analysis is made in the high-altitude sampling program.

The maximum permissible concentration (MPC) for a 168-hour week (continuous exposure) for Ba[131] with the gastrointestinal tract as the critical organ is 2×10^{-3} microcuries per cubic centimeter ($\mu c/cc$) in water and 4×10^{-7} $\mu c/cc$ in air. For Ba[140] the MPC is 3×10^{-4} $\mu c/cc$ in water and 6×10^{-8} $\mu c/cc$ in air, with the gastrointestinal tract and bone being the critical organs.

BARN

Abbreviation b. A unit representing the average nuclear cross section, equal to 10^{-24} square centimeter (sq. cm.). The average diameter of a nucleus has been experimentally determined to be about 10^{-12} cm., so the actual area of cross section is approximately 10^{-24} sq. cm. The term barn was a humorous code word at first, for "a cross section of 10^{-24} sq. cm. for nuclear processes was really as big as a barn"; later was universally adopted. Nuclear cross sections are known to vary from 10^{-8} to 10^6 barns but are usually in the range of 0.1 to 10 barns.

BARRICADE SHIELD

A type of portable or movable BARRIER SHIELD for protection from radiation. A typical example, shown in Figure B–1, is made of bricks of lead,

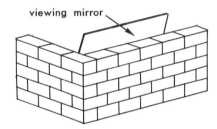

FIGURE B–1. BRICK BARRICADE.

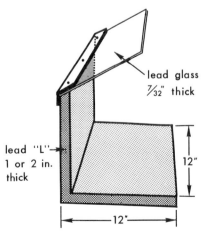

FIGURE B–2. REACH-AROUND BARRICADE SHIELD.

steel or other materials and used when gamma radiation is at too high a dose rate for direct-viewing techniques. Manipulations are carried out with the use of right-angled tongs and the viewing mirror.

A reach-around barricade shown in Figure B–2 allows direct viewing through leaded glass, and is recommended for lower-level sources of radiation (e.g., 160 millirad per hour). Tongs are used to keep the hands at least 12 inches from the source.

BARRIER SHIELD

A wall or enclosure designed to shield the operator from radiation coming from an area in which manipulations are being performed. Figure B–3 shows a wall SHIELD with the operator handling radioactive bottled liquids from a shielded position with remote-control equipment. A barrier shield requires more shielding material than a close shield but permits more flexibility in setting up equipment.

A barrier shield may be easily portable as in the case of the beta barrier (Fig. B–4) made of a transparent plastic sheet (3/8 to 1/2 inch thick) for use in the 10- to 100-millicurie range of high-energy beta emitters. It may have ports for use of manipulators or be narrow for use of tongs around the sides.

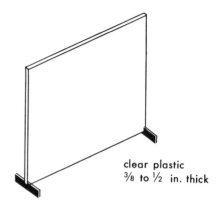

clear plastic
3/8 to 1/2 in. thick

FIGURE B–4.   BETA BARRIER SHIELD.

BASAL CELL CARCINOMA, TREATMENT

A means of treating superficial malignancies by application of destructive amounts of phosphorus-32 to the surface of the lesion. The radio-isotope is in the form of a solution of NaH_2PO_4 absorbed on blotting paper, and dried, or the isotope is placed in a plastic matrix, designed specifically to cover the area to be treated. Doses are 3,000 to 5,000 microcurie-hours per square centimeter. Precautions are taken to avoid direct contamination of the tissues with radioactivity. The relatively short path of the BETA PARTICLE limits sharply the depth to which effective radiation can be delivered. Results are excellent in suitable lesions.

BASE LINE DRIVE

Means for raising or lowering the basal line or lower level discriminator of a pulse height analyzer or gamma spectrometer; employed in obtaining an integral energy spectrum.

BEAM

Flow of electromagnetic radiation or of particles that is essentially unidirectional. In radiology the useful beam is that part of the primary radiation that reaches the subject or patient through the aperture, cone or other collimator. The beam hole, glory hole, is the hole through the shield and often through the reflector of a reactor that permits the escape of a beam of radiation; usually fast neutrons for experimental work.

BEHAVIOR AFFECTED BY RADIATION

Scientists in the United States working with both rodents and primates find that doses in the order of 2,000 roentgens (r) and above to the head are required to induce changes detectable by psychological testing methods. Russian scientists working with conditioned reflexes in experimental

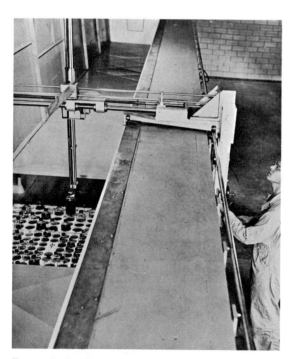

FIGURE B–3.   OPERATOR HANDLING RADIOACTIVE LIQ-UIDS OVER A SHIELDING WALL USING REMOTE CONTROL EQUIPMENT AND MIRRORS. (OAK RIDGE NATIONAL LABORATORY.)

animals have reported changes in responses in rats following several hundred r localized radiation. Claims are made for altered responses following doses below 100 r (as low as 5 r to 20 r). In this connection the NAS-NRC* Committee on Pathologic Effects said, "Doses in the hundreds of roentgens seem to have little measurable effect on adult nervous tissues. Recent reports that subtle functions of the brain are disturbed by doses of a few roentgens still await confirmation."

The widespread use of x-rays for over 60 years and for the past 12 years cobalt teletherapy units for radiation treatment of intracranial neoplasms has accumulated an enormous backlog of experience. In the mature central nervous systems, no specific behavior patterns, sensations or altered functions—motor, sensory or psychological—have been found to accompany or follow such exposure unless the intensity was so high as to damage the central nervous system acutely (e.g., induce pressure signs) or result in symptoms of radiation illness.

Selective irradiation of the cerebral cortex of monkeys with 23 Mev x-ray doses as low as an equivalent 225–900 r from a betatron produced an abnormal electroencephalogram (EEG), which continued to be abnormal even after 2 years. In rabbits epileptiform convulsions followed by a period of ataxia were produced by a dose of 6,000 r to the head. In guinea pigs the pinna reflex threshold is altered 3 hours after exposure of the head to 8,000 r, and 24 hours later the reflex cannot be elicited; but no effect in the pain threshold was evident even after 10,000 r. In the rat, doses to the head above 40,000 r brought on signs of acute rage and hyperactivity which resembled epileptic shock in man.

Behavioral changes following whole body irradiation are more complex etiologically and probably are due more to general somatic damage than to damage to the brain or central nervous system. Acute doses from 200 to 1,000 r caused an abrupt significant depression of volitional running on the exercise wheel. The offspring of rats irradiated with 90 r or more during the final week of pregnancy were significantly poorer maze learners than control animals. In general, irradiation of the whole animal decreases the ability to learn, and if high enough decreases the ability to perform.

One human accident case receiving about 12,000 rad of ionizing radiation to the upper half of the body, and somewhat less to the lower half, illustrates the complex behavioral response following severe somatic damage. The patient showed

---

*NAS-NRC, The Biological Effects of Atomic Radiation Summary Reports, 1960.

immediate signs of profound shock with ataxia, disorientation and semiconsciousness, which developed within the first few hours into severe apathy, prostration and unconsciousness. There were frequent coarse, purposeless movements of the extremities. About 2 hours before death, which occurred about 35 hours after exposure, he developed marked evidence of central nervous system irritation with convulsions and violent body movements.

BERKELIUM

Symbol Bk; atomic number 97; atomic weight 249; a radioactive transuranium element of the actinide series. Discovered in 1950 by American scientists S. G. Thompson, A. Ghiorso and G. T. Seaborg through the bombardment of americium-241 with alpha particles in the Berkeley cyclotron. Named in honor of Berkeley, California. A total of eight radioactive isotopes of berkelium with mass numbers from 243 through 250 have been described. The first to be found, Bk^{243} (decay by orbital-electron capture (EC)), has a half-life of 4.5 hours, but Bk^{247}, alpha emitter, has a half-life of about 7,000 years. Berkelium does not occur in nature. Maximum permissible concentration for 168-hour week (continuous exposure) has been worked out for soluble compounds of Bk^{249} (α, β^-, γ emission) and found to be 6×10^{-3} microcuries per cubic centimeter ($\mu c/cc$) in water and 10^{-6} $\mu c/cc$ in air.

BERYLLIUM

Symbol Be; atomic number 4; atomic weight 9.013. A silver-white, hard, malleable metal of very low density. Discovered as the oxide in beryl and in emerald by French chemist Vauquelin in 1798. Metal isolated independently by Wöhler and by Bussy in 1828. Named from Latin, *beryl*, sea-green jewel. Also called glucinum from Greek, *glykys*, sweet. Occurs as the oxide in beryl (11 to 13%) in the New England states and elsewhere in the world. A crystal weighing about 18 tons was found in Maine. Percent abundance furnished 100% by Be^9. Chemically related to magnesium and aluminum.

Used in industry principally as beryllium-copper alloys, but also as the oxide, as beryllium salts, and to a lesser extent as beryllium-nickel or beryllium-aluminum. Not necessary for animal or plant growth or development. Of interest biologically because of its high toxicity and the industrial hazard to those workers susceptible to beryllium effects. Many workers have been exposed to various types of dusts, fumes and direct contact with no untoward results and yet in susceptible workers clinical manifestations are contact dermatitis, conjunctivitis, rhinitis, bronchitis, and pneumonitis terminating in death in some cases.

In order to insure industrial safety, the U.S. Atomic Energy Commission Advisory Committee on Beryllium Intoxication made the following recommendations:

1. The in-plant atmospheric concentration of beryllium should not exceed 2 micrograms per cubic meter ($\mu g/m^3$) average concentration throughout an 8-hour day.

2. Even though the daily average might be within the above limit, no person should be exposed to a concentration greater than 25 $\mu g/m^3$ for any period of time, however short.

3. In the neighborhood of an AEC plant handling beryllium compounds, the average monthly concentration at the breathing-zone level should not exceed 0.01 $\mu g/m^3$.

In order to have a comparison the following are maximum allowable concentration values for some common industrial toxic dusts and fumes: arsenic 500 $\mu g/m^3$; fluorides 2,500 $\mu g/m^3$; lead 150 $\mu g/m^3$ and mercury 100 $\mu g/m^3$.

Three radioactive isotopes have been identified: Be^7, radioactive half-life 53.6 days; with total body as the critical organ, biological half-life 180 days, and effective half-life 41 days; gamma emitter; is available as one of the radioisotopes, accelerator-produced, and is used to study metabolism and distribution of beryllium in the body.

Beryllium is used with such elements as polonium, plutonium, radium, and antimony as a neutron source. For example, antimony is clad with stainless steel, inserted into a nuclear reactor where it is bombarded with neutrons and becomes radioactive antimony-124. This is then inserted into a beryllium cylinder where the beryllium is irradiated by gamma rays from the disintegration of the antimony; and neutrons are produced by the (γ,n) nuclear reaction—in this case as many as 10^{10} neutrons per second.

BETA BURN

A form of radiation damage to the skin due to actual contact with beta particle emitters, e.g., radioactive phosphorus used in treating skin lesions.

In general, beta burns are similar to those produced by gamma and x-ray radiation, but since the beta particles are less penetrating they produce a more superficial lesion with damage to the epidermis and less damage to the dermis. Consequently beta burns are usually less painful and heal more rapidly.

The development and healing of beta burns

were carefully studied in the Marshall Islanders exposed to fallout in March, 1954. The Rongelap natives were probably exposed to a skin dose from beta radiation from ground contamination of about 2,000 rad at the level of the dorsum of the foot, 600 rad at the hip level and 300 rad at the head. Heavy doses were probably received from actual contact with fallout clinging to the moist skin. During the first two days, itching and burning sensations were noted but no ERYTHEMA was seen (may have been obscured by the dark brown skin). No further symptoms were noted until about 2 or 3 weeks after exposure, when increased pigmentation in the form of dark-colored patches appeared, as shown in the picture of the neck of a young woman (Fig. B–5). Other patients

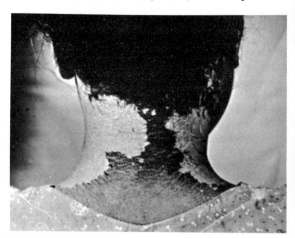

FIGURE B–5. BETA BURN PIGMENTATION ON NECK 1 MONTH AFTER EXPOSURE.

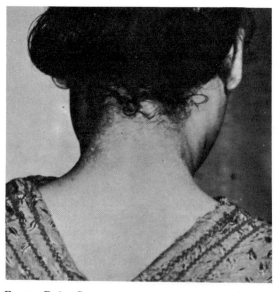

FIGURE B–6. SAME BETA BURN AS SHOWN IN FIGURE B–5, 1 YEAR AFTER EXPOSURE.

developed raised areas (macules, papules and plaques). These lesions appeared on exposed parts of the body in the following order of frequency: scalp (with epilation), neck, foot, and depressions in the forearm, legs and trunk. Some individuals showed blistering with the formation of a dry scab, and a few developed weeping ulcers, but all the lesions healed rapidly leaving very minor or no defects, as seen in the picture of the same young woman one year after exposure (Figure B–6).

As will be seen by noting the Table I–5 accompanying INJURIES, RADIATION, beta burns to the hands are fairly common.

BETA COUNTER

Radiation detector with characteristics especially suited for optimum response to beta rays. May be of ION CHAMBER, GEIGER, PROPORTIONAL or SCINTILLATION type.

BETA DECAY

Disintegration of the nucleus of an unstable nuclide with the spontaneous emission of a beta particle. In this radioactive transformation the mass number remains unchanged but the atomic number changes by ± 1. Increase of atomic number occurs with negative beta particle emission; for example, in the actinium radioactive series, thorium ($_{90}Th^{231}$) decays with the emission of β^- to form protactinium ($_{91}Pa^{231}$). Decrease of atomic number occurs with positive beta particle emission or by electron capture, as, for example, zinc ($_{30}Zn^{65}$) decays with the emission of β^+ and γ and by electron capture (EC) to form stable copper ($_{29}Cu^{65}$).

See BETA PARTICLE and BETA DISINTEGRATION.

BETA DISINTEGRATION

A radioactive transformation of a nuclide where the mass number remains unchanged, while the atomic number is changed by $+1$ or -1. When the ratio of neutrons to protons in the nucleus is such that the nucleus becomes unstable, a neutron may divide into a proton, a negative electron (negatron) and an antineutrino. The proton remains in the nucleus, while the negatron and the neutrino are emitted, carrying off the excess energy. In this case the atomic number is changed $+1$. This is illustrated in Figure B–7 showing the disintegration and transmutation of a carbon-14 nucleus to a nitrogen-14 nucleus by conversion and radiation emission.

In the positive beta emitters, a proton is converted into a neutron and a positron, plus a neutrino. The neutron is held within the nucleus

and the positron ($\beta+$) and antineutrino are emitted. An example of this type is the radioactive decay of cobalt ($_{27}Co^{58}$) into iron ($_{26}Fe^{58}$). There may be an electron capture to satisfy the instability, as in the radioactive decay of argon ($_{18}A^{37}$) into chlorine ($_{17}Cl^{37}$).

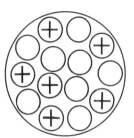

Carbon - 14
Mass number, 14
Atomic number, 6
(6 protons)

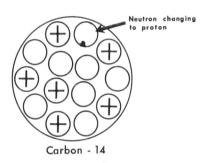

Carbon - 14

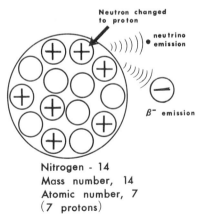

Nitrogen - 14
Mass number, 14
Atomic number, 7
(7 protons)

FIGURE B–7. TRANSMUTATION OF A CARBON-14 NUCLEUS TO A NITROGEN-14 NUCLEUS BY CONVERSION AND RADIATION EMISSION.

BETA EMITTER

A radionuclide that disintegrates by beta particle emission. All beta-active elements existing in nature expel negative particles, i.e., electrons or more exactly negatrons. But in the laboratory a number of radioactive species have been obtained that emit positive beta particles, i.e., positrons.

See BETA PARTICLE and BETA SOURCES.

BETA GAGE

System for determining thickness of materials in the form of thin sheets or coatings, consisting of a beta-ray source and detector.

The beta gage measures thickness essentially by responding to the density of electrons in the path of the beam, through their influence on the attenuation of reflected or transmitted beta rays. The beta gage system is frequently used for determining the thickness of sheet material and to control its manufacturing process. A single unit may be calibrated against a range of standard thicknesses, or a pair may be used with one measuring the beam through a reference standard while the other measures transmission by the material being examined. The device may give a direct indication of thickness or may show the percentage difference between a reference standard thickness and the test material.

Continuous monitor and control applications of the beta gage are made in manufacturing processes for paper, plastic films, rubber, leather, cloth, floor coverings, and thin metal foils. These uses are based on a linear attenuation of the beta-ray beam, with the assumption that composition and density of the material are uniform. Conversely, they can be arranged to measure the density of a material or solution of known composition.

A further important application is in the measurement of thin films on a thick substrate. Since only one face of the thin material is accessible, this is an especially useful measurement technique. Two procedures are used: (1) measurement of the reflected or scattered beta particles themselves; (2) measurement of soft x-rays or bremsstrahlung produced when the beta particles are absorbed in substrate or supporting structure. Backscattering gages are especially valuable for controlling the application of thin lacquer finishes to sheet metal or in measuring metallic coatings as in tin plate or electroplated sheet. Beta rays from titanium-204 allow coatings up to about 30 mg/cm² to be measured; strontium-90 measurement of up to 200 mg/cm².

Beta-gage techniques are also used to indicate and control liquid level in closed tanks, either by tracking a floating source (directly or through the inverse square distance effect) or by the difference of scattering seen at the liquid-gas interface.

See DENSITY GAGING, LIQUID-LEVEL GAGING, and THICKNESS GAGING.

BETA PARTICLE

Symbol β. Charged particle emitted from a nucleus undergoing beta decay. The particle may be a negative electron or negatron, β^-; or a positive electron, positron, β^+. The negatively charged beta particle is actually a high-speed electron ejected from a disintegrating nucleus. The positively charged particle differs from the electron in having equal but opposite electrical properties. The distinction between the beta particle and the ORBITAL ELECTRON is one of origin and energy; it has the same negative charge of 1 unit, and the same mass as the electron.

Beta disintegration is the spontaneous conversion of a neutron into a proton and an electron, plus an antineutrino. In the decay process, the proton remains in the nucleus, but the electron and the neutrino are ejected. In the positive beta emitters, a proton is converted into a neutron and a positron, plus a neutrino, the latter two being ejected.

The mass of the beta particle is 9.1083×10^{-28} gram or 0.000549 atomic mass unit, which is about 1/1837 that of the proton. Beta rays are not monoenergetic in nature, but consist of particles with a wide range of energies. As they pass through matter or an absorber they lose energy by conversion into radiation, and by formation of ion pairs, but largely also because they undergo very marked scattering, with frequent changes in direction, especially when passing through a solid absorber. The beta particle can create as many as 200 ion pairs per centimeter of track in air under standard conditions. The specific ionization for 1 Mev is 6×10^4 ion pairs per centimeter track in tissue. Ionization in tissue also occurs but in traversing matter a beta particle undergoes rapid deceleration and usually penetrates from a few millimeters to 1 centimeter beneath the skin, at most. However, the rapid deceleration is associated with the production of x-radiation, which is an additional hazard (*see* BIOLOGICAL EFFECTS OF RADIATION). Except for its positive charge and shorter life span, the positron has the same characteristics as the negatron.

The penetrating power of beta rays is about 100 times that of alpha rays but only a small fraction of that of gamma rays. A thin sheet of paper will stop an alpha particle, an inch of wood or 1/25 inch of aluminum will stop a beta particle, but it takes several inches of lead to stop gamma rays. The range in aluminum in milligrams per square centimeter is: 0.5 Mev, 111; 2 Mev, 926; and 4 Mev, 2,010. Aluminum is a satisfactory shield for beta particles, and plastics such as lucite may be used.

The beta particles and neutrinos emitted in a

particular disintegration divide the energy and thus both have energy distributions from zero up to a maximum value. In β⁻ decay this maximum value is just equal to the energy difference between mother and daughter atom (not nucleus). In β⁺ decay the energy required to create a negatron-positron pair, 1.022 Mev, must be added to the maximum value to find the atomic energy difference.

The maximum velocities of beta particles range from about 25 to 99% of the speed of light: the corresponding values of maximum energy vary from 0.025 to 3.15 Mev, mostly in the vicinity of 1 Mev.

The range in centimeters in air for beta particles is: for 0.5 Mev, 140; for 2 Mev, 840 and for 4 Mev, 1,600. The range in tissue in centimeters is: for 1 Mev, 0.42 and for 5 Mev 2.2. The half-value layer in tissue in centimeters is: 1 Mev, 0.04; and 5 Mev, 0.4.

See BETA DISINTEGRATION, and BETA-RAY SPECTRUM.

BETA RAY

A stream of beta particles. Loosely, a synonym for beta particle.

BETA-RAY SPECTROMETER

Apparatus for measuring the energy spectrum of beta rays. The beta-particle stream is collimated and directed into a magnetic or electric field, where the degree of deflection will depend upon the speed or energy of the charged particles. Crystal defraction techniques are also used to determine beta-ray energies. Detection and measurement of the rays are accomplished either with photographic registration or ion-chamber technique.

BETA-RAY SPECTRUM

The distribution of energy or momentum of the beta particles emitted in a beta-decay process. The beta-ray spectrum is usually a continuous one and thus differs from most of the other spectra—optical, x-ray, alpha and gamma ray—which are usually line spectra. The continuous spectrum is that produced by the electrons which have been ejected from the nuclei of radioactive atoms. The curves in Figure B–8 show the energy distributions of the continuous beta-ray spectra for pure beta emitters carbon-14 and sulfur-35. In case more than one group is present, a composite spectrum is given. For the tabular data, the type of particle and its maximum energy are shown first. The average energy $\overline{E}_\beta$, of the particles in a group, and of combined groups where more than one is present, is shown next. The intensity of beta rays is shown in percentage of disintegrations. The

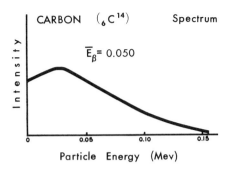

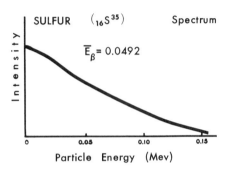

FIGURE B–8. CURVES SHOWING CONTINUOUS BETA-RAY SPECTRUM FOR PURE BETA EMITTERS CARBON-14 AND SULFUR-35.

range in water applies to the maximum energies of the continuous beta-ray spectrum.

The curves may take different shapes but in general if the relative number of particles possessing a particular energy is plotted against the energy, the points will fall on a curve resembling the curve shown for carbon. The end-point maximum energy (E_{max}) varies from 0.025 to 3.15 Mev, with most of them in the vicinity of 1 Mev.

See BETA SOURCES.

BETA SOURCES

At least 90% of all radioactive isotopes are beta emitters. The beta-active elements existing in nature are negative particle emitters (β⁻), but a number of radioactive isotopes have been obtained in the laboratory that are positive particle emitters (β⁺).

In a list of 17 radioactive isotopes in frequent use for medical and biological research, medical diagnosis and treatment, all are beta emitters and the following are pure beta emitters: hydrogen (tritium) ($_1H^3$); carbon ($_6C^{14}$); phosphorus ($_{15}P^{32}$); sulfur ($_{16}S^{35}$); calcium ($_{20}Ca^{45}$); and strontium-yttrium ($_{38}Sr^{90}$-$_{39}Y^{90}$).

In a list of 79 radioactive isotopes used in biology and agriculture, the following 14 are available as pure, or nearly pure, beta (β^-) emitters: arsenic ($_{33}As^{77}$); calcium ($_{20}Ca^{45}$); carbon ($_6C^{14}$); chlorine ($_{17}Cl^{36}$); tritium ($_1H^3$); nickel ($_{28}Ni^{63}$); palladium ($_{46}Pd^{109}$); phosphorus ($_{15}P^{32}$); promethium ($_{61}Pm^{147}$); strontium ($_{38}Sr^{89}$); strontium-yttrium ($_{38}Sr^{90}$-$_{39}Y^{90}$); sulfur ($_{16}S^{35}$); technetium ($_{43}Te^{99}$); and yttrium ($_{39}Y^{90}$).

Of the 10 fission products from the detonation of nuclear devices that are considered to be of biological significance, 2 are pure beta emitters: strontium-89 and strontium-90-yttrium-90.

Table B–1 lists the beta emitters available from the Oak Ridge National Laboratory (*see* RADIO-ISOTOPES AVAILABLE FROM OAK RIDGE).

See BETA-RAY SPECTRUM and RADIOISOTOPE PRODUCTION.

TABLE B–1. BETA EMITTERS AVAILABLE FROM OAK RIDGE

RADIOISOTOPE	HALF-LIFE*	MAXIMUM ENERGY (Mev)
Yttrium-90	64.2 h	2.18
Phosphorus-32	14.3 d	1.701
Yttrium-91	58.0 d	1.537
Strontium-89	50.4 d	1.463
Bismuth-210	5.02 d	1.17
Silver-111	7.5 d	1.04
Palladium-109	13.6 h	0.961
Praseodymium-143	13.95 d	0.932
Thallium-204	4.1 y	0.765
Chlorine-36	3.2×10^5 y	0.714
Strontium-90	25 y	0.61
Technetium-99	2.12×10^5 y	0.29
Calcium-45	164 d	0.254
Promethium-147	2.5 y	0.223
Sulfur-35	87.1 d	0.167
Carbon-14	5.57×10^3 y	0.155
Nickel-63	125 y	0.067
Hydrogen-3	12.46 y	0.01795

*d, day; h, hour; y, year.

BETA SPECTROMETER. *See* BETA-RAY SPECTROMETER.

BETA STANDARDS

Fixed beta-ray source of accurately known energy and intensity, i.e., quality and quantity of beta radiation.

BETATRON

The betatron, invented in 1941, by D. W. Kerst at the University of Illinois, is a machine for accelerating electrons to high velocities by use of a time-varying magnetic-flux linkage within a circular electron orbit of constant radius. The electrons travel in an orbit of fixed radius and the accelerating force depends upon the rapidly changing magnetic flux. The magnetic field is so designed that stray electrons hunt with both an axial and radial oscillation about the equilibrium orbit, and the amplitude of the oscillation decreases with time so that stray particles are brought back to the center of the beam. In commercially available betatrons the electrons achieve energies of 6 to 31 Mev and may be applied directly or used to generate high-energy x-rays. A betatron weighing 350 tons and accelerating electrons to 100 Mev has been built and used.

The betatron was first used for therapy in 1948 at the University of Illinois. Betatron x-rays have high penetration and a correspondingly relatively high depth dose, with little, if any, skin erythema being associated with ordinary therapeutic doses. One advantage of using high-energy x-rays is that, for the same tumor dose, the total integral dose of radiation received by the patient is only about half that when lower-energy x-rays are used.

BEV

The abbreviation Bev represents one billion or 10^9 electron volts.

BEVATRON

A 6 billion electron-volt particle accelerator at the University of California in Berkeley. Protons

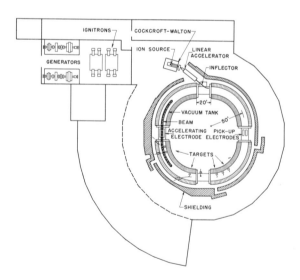

BEVATRON

FIGURE B–9. SCHEMATIC LAYOUT OF BEVATRON AND ANCILLARY COMPONENTS. THE 4 QUARTER-CIRCLE MAGNETS ARE COMPOSED OF MANY LAMINATED C-SHAPED MAGNETS AND ARE SEPARATED BY STRAIGHT SECTIONS 20 FEET LONG, ONE OF WHICH, AS IS INDICATED, HAS THE ACCELERATING ELECTRODES. (COURTESY LAWRENCE RADIATION LABORATORY, UNIVERSITY OF CALIFORNIA.)

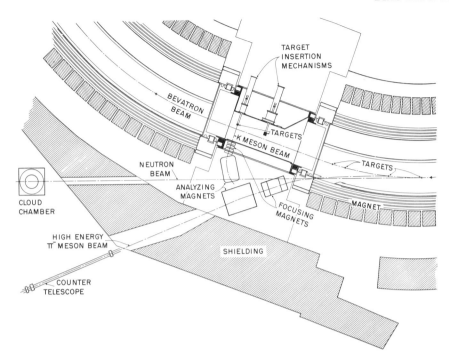

FIGURE B–10. DETAIL OF TARGET LOCATIONS, TARGET-INSERTING MECHANISMS, AND BEAMS FROM THE BEVATRON. (COURTESY LAWRENCE RADIATION LABORATORY, UNIVERSITY OF CALIFORNIA.)

FIGURE B–11. OVER-ALL VIEW OF BEVATRON. (COURTESY LAWRENCE RADIATION LABORATORY, UNIVERSITY OF CALIFORNIA.)

are accelerated to 10 Mev by a Cockroft-Walton machine in series with a linear accelerator before injection into the main unit, which consists of a 10,000 ton nearly-circular magnet having a diameter of about 140 ft. Operating principles are discussed under SYNCHROTRON. Three figures show the schematic layout, detail of the target, and an over-all view of the Bevatron (Figs. B–9, B–10, B–11).

BIAS DISCRIMINATOR

An electronic circuit arrangement frequently employed to reject signal pulses smaller than a selected size. The circuit functions by maintaining a low bias voltage at the amplifier input, which can be overcome only by signal pulses of adequate strength. This part of the circuit is usually located at the input of the main amplifier, following the detector or preamplifier. Its purpose is to minimize spurious and background counts arising from electronic noise or low-level background radiation, or to discriminate against the influence of scattered or degraded radiation from the sample and other nearby sources.

See PULSE HEIGHT ANALYZER.

BILLION ELECTRON VOLTS

Abbreviated Bev, this is a unit of energy equal to 10^9 electron volts (ev).

BINARY SCALER

Scaler device or electronic circuit having a scaling factor of 2 or some power of 2. The basic unit is an arrangement that counts every other pulse which comes to it, thus dividing the pulse rate by 2. Through the use of a number of such binary stages in succession, the counts coming from a detector can be divided by 2,4,8,16,32, . . . , thus cutting the pulse rate down so that a mechanical register can follow and record the count accurately. In using such a scaler, the total count is found by multiplying the register indication by the scaling factor and adding to that number the counts accumulated in the scaler itself, as read off from the indicating lights for each stage as shown in Figure B–12.

See DECADE SCALER; DECIMAL SCALER; and REGISTER, COUNT.

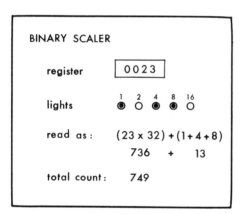

FIGURE B–12. EXAMPLE ILLUSTRATING METHOD OF DETERMINING COUNTS FROM A BINARY SCALER WITH A SCALING FACTOR OF 32.

BINDING ENERGY. *See* ENERGY.

BIO-ASSAY

Also biological assay. A procedure to determine the active power or potency of a substance (drug or compound) by measuring a given effect on plants or experimental animals as test objects. Because of known variations of time-to-time and place-to-place, the substance is tested against a standard preparation of known strength. Radioisotopes are being used in some of the bio-assay determinations. For example, in the assay of vitamin D a method is based on the effect of vitamin D status of a test animal upon the uptake of phosphorus-32 as determined by external meas-urement of radioactivity in the forepaw. Bioassay is also used to study the biological effects of various radioactive materials; for example, measurement of radioactive isotopes in the urine of individuals working with radioactive materials as a measure of ingestion or inhalation of radioactive material.

BIOCHEMICAL PLACEMENT OF RADIOISOTOPES

Because of metabolic activity, many radio-elements are deposited specifically in various tissues. For example, radioisotopes of calcium, strontium, barium and radium tend to accumulate in bone; radioiodine in the thyroid gland; radio-yttrium in parts of bone that are either undergoing active resorption or calcification; radiosulfur in cartilage. Originally there had been the hope that this type of behavior would enable radioisotopes to be used to deliver radiation at specific sites of interest within the body. With the exception of radioiodine, which can be used in some types of thyroid carcinoma, it appears that the localization is not sufficiently specific to permit radiation exposure of the tissue in question without damaging exposure to other tissues of the body. It is possible that in the future labeled organic compounds may be found that will accumulate specifically in tissues of interest—for example, in tumors.

The physical state of the radioisotope preparation is also of importance in determining its ultimate deposition in the tissues. Substances which tend to form colloids, such as yttrium, and some forms of chromium, are deposited in the reticuloendothelial system. Many other radioelements, such as sodium, potassium and cesium, tend to be distributed more uniformly throughout the body.

BIOECONOMIC EFFECTS OF RADIATION

Effects of radiation on the national productivity, conditions of living and total health of the people. A situation index has been postulated which is a function of the interacting effects of public health, fertility behavior and general economy on standards of living of a national population. Radiation is but one of many contributing elements that affect for good or bad the bioeconomic development where standards of living exist in terms of concentrations of people and of their abilities and skills for developing and utilizing things needed for life.

Suppose the entire population is exposed to a radiation dose rate for their lifetime that will lead to decreased vitality, increased morbidity, shortened life span, and genetic damage, we then have a situation in which radiation has a detrimental bioeconomic effect. But if radiation is used constructively in research, in agricultural development, in medical diagnosis and treatment, and in industrial advancement, we have a positive factor tending to increase economic development, productivity, standards of living and health of the population.

BIOENERGETICS

Laws and conditions governing the manifestation of energy in living matter. Such concepts as the TARGET THEORY, latent period, and the question of linearity of response, are concerns of bioenergetics. The term is widely used in relation to energy transformations in metabolism.

BIOGENESIS

The established principle that all living things spring from previously existing living things. Radioisotopes have been used as tracers in studying the origin and interrelationships of various organic compounds, enzymes and coenzymes in biological systems. Labeling permits following the atom through intricate and multiple metabolic pathways, and gives further evidence that this principle is indeed fact.

BIOLOGICAL EFFECTIVENESS OF RADIATION. *See* RELATIVE BIOLOGICAL EFFECTIVENESS.

BIOLOGICAL EFFECTS OF RADIATION

Radiation acts on biological tissue at the molecular level and therefore on the cell and its constituents or on the surrounding oxygenated aqueous media. Thus exposure to ionizing radiation may result in changes in the highly organized molecular system, destruction of certain cellular elements, and altered function or death of the cell.

The biological effect of exposure of a living organism to ionizing radiation depends upon the following factors:

PHYSICAL FACTORS—type of radiation (x-ray, gamma ray, neutrons, alpha particles, beta particles, fission products, etc.); linear energy transfer or ionization density; duration of exposure; intensity of radiation field; shielding, and exposure of whole or part of the body; fractionation of the radiation dose (small divided doses given over a period of time being less damaging than the same quantity of radiation given in a single dose).

EXTERNAL RADIATION—all the above-mentioned physical factors apply to external radiation.

INTERNAL RADIATION—quantity and type of radioisotope retained within the body; and

the EFFECTIVE HALF-LIFE of the radioisotope.

The RELATIVE BIOLOGICAL EFFECTIVENESS of the radiation.

RADIOSENSITIVITY or the sensitivity of a given tissue or organ to the effects of ionizing radiation; and the essentiality of the organ to the life of the organism.

Biological effects may be manifested in the following ways:

SOMATIC EFFECTS, which may be either acute effects, usually called RADIATION ILLNESS; or chronic effects such as early AGING, LIFE SHORTENING, LEUKEMIA or CANCER.

GENETIC DAMAGE due to MUTATIONS passed on to subsequent generations.

A variety of agents and conditions have been tried in an attempt to modify the effect of radiation on biological material. The modifying agents most widely studied are chemical compounds used either before or during irradiation which offer CHEMICAL PROTECTION AGAINST RADIATION DAMAGE. Three physical conditions have been studied extensively: (1) varying the amount of water has shown that dehydrated material is more RADIO-RESISTANT than aqueous material; (2) decreasing the amount of oxygen has shown that anoxia offers protection against the effects of radiation (*see* OXYGEN, RADIATION SENSITIVITY, and ANOXIA, EFFECT ON RADIATION INJURY); and low temperature has been shown to be protective (*see* TEMPERATURE AND RADIATION EFFECTS).

BIOLOGICAL HALF-LIFE

The time required for the total body (or any living tissue or individual organ) to eliminate one-half of the dose of any substance by the regular processes of elimination. This period is about the same for stable and for radioactive isotopes of an element, other factors being equal. The principal methods of elimination are by way of urine, feces, exhalation and perspiration. In general, elimination is much more rapid before a radioisotope is translocated from the blood to a less metabolically active area (bone, for example).

Various factors may affect the removal time, the pattern of distribution, the metabolic fate, and therefore the degree and speed of elimination of a radioisotope. Such factors are: physical (size of particles); chemical (water solubility of material, metabolic affinity of the element); ecological (balance of calcium, iodine, etc.); and physiological (mode of intake, metabolic condition of the organism). Thus, both physical and biological factors affect biological half-life and therefore the toxicity or damage to body tissues from internal emitters.

An isotope may have a very long RADIOACTIVE

HALF-LIFE, but if it is retained in the body for a short time it will have a short biological half-life and a correspondingly short EFFECTIVE HALF-LIFE. Cesium-137, for example, has a radiological half-life of 1.1×10^4 days, but in man has an effective half-life of 17 days (as CsCl). For radium-226 (radioactive half-life 1,622 years) deposited in the bone, the turnover or elimination rate is very slow, and thus the biological half-life is long—44.9 years; and the effective half-life correspondingly long—44.8 years. The total body biological half-life depends entirely upon the behavior of the element in the body; for example, strontium, 1.3×10^4 days; bromine 8 days; calcium 1.64×10^4 days; and germanium 1 day.

There is also a marked difference in biological half-life for the same radioisotope in various organs, for example: for phosphorus-32 it is 1,155 days in the bone and only 18 days in the liver; for iodine-131 it is 138 days in the thyroid and 7 days in the kidneys, liver, spleen or testes; for barium-140 it is 6,500 days in lungs and only 419 days in ovaries.

See individual element entries for biological half-life figures.

BIOLOGICAL HOLE

Cavity in a nuclear reactor to permit placing biological specimens near the active section for experiments on the effects of gamma and neutron irradiation.

BIOLOGICAL MODELS

Numerous physical and mathematical models have been developed to characterize biological phenomena. Of the mathematical models one of the most important is the principle of optimal design which may be stated as follows: for a given set of biological functions which an organism performs, the organism has the possible optimal design from the point of view of economy of material and of energy expenditure which are necessary for the performance of its functions. For example, in line with this principle it was predicted that both the rate of breathing and the pulse rate of animals should vary inversely approximately as the cube root of their masses. The relation is found to be roughly verified within the range from rat to horse.

The problem of cell division has been approached by developing as many mathematical theories and models as possible and then subjecting them to test. In the diffusion drag model such factors as critical cell size, elongation theory, oxygen consumption, oxygen concentration and rate of metabolism have been carefully considered. But no completely satisfactory model explaining

cell division has yet been developed, although certain functions are well described by models limited to that particular function.

Models dealing with excitation and conduction in peripheral nerves have been much more successful, for nerve conduction is the example par excellence of communication in biology. The nervous system is composed of information sources or detectors; their signals must be encoded for transmission and decoded at the receiver. Of course, noise may be introduced at any stage but mathematical models quite accurately describe the function of the various parts of this system. The present work on the information capacity of the neuronal link, and in developing models to elucidate the function of the central nervous system is very promising.

Information theory has been used to treat the genetically controlled specificity of proteins, and is thoroughly entrenched in working with the problem of the DNA-RNA-protein code.

In the nonmathematical sense biological models of several kinds have been developed. BODY COMPOSITION has been carefully determined and the chemical standard man information is routinely used in biochemistry and radiation biology. TISSUE EQUIVALENT MATERIAL has been developed and used in the fabrication of the phantom for use in radiation biology and in medical therapy using radiation. The ANTHROPOMETRIC DUMMY is a type of biological model used in studies of blast biological damage.

BIOLOGICAL PROTECTION

Attempts on the part of the organism itself to modify radiation injury; to compensate for damage to part of the body; or to prevent death of the organism, and promote recovery from irradiation through cellular repair, restoration or regeneration.

One of the earliest demonstrations of biological protection on the part of the body was furnished by SHIELDING the legs of a guinea pig while irradiating the rest of the body. The protected, and thus undamaged, bone marrow of the lower legs took over for the entire body and furnished the necessary blood elements, and the usual hemorrhagic picture of the acute radiation syndrome was not seen. Further extensive research on shielding parts of the body during irradiation has confirmed the biological protection activity of the total body.

Recovery from a sublethal dose of radiation is in itself evidence of biological protection, in that the undamaged cells carry out the necessary body functions, while repair, regeneration and restoration are taking place, restoring the total organism to apparently normal condition.

Biological protection is also afforded following

sublethal irradiation, by injection of biological materials such as spleen extracts, bone marrow cell suspensions, subcellular fractions of the spleen, ground bone, and various homologous, heterologous and autologous cell suspensions.

BIOLOGICAL RESEARCH

The most important use of radioisotopes in biology is as tracers; i.e., as labels for elements or compounds studied in biological systems. Radioisotopes may also be used to tag whole organisms; for example, in insects for investigations of populations and movement. Activation analysis is a special technique involving the induction of radioactivity to allow detection and measurement of certain elements; this procedure may be applied to biological problems, especially trace element metabolism. Another highly specialized technique is the dating of fossils on the basis of measurements of natural radioactivity and determinations of specific activity.

In most of these research methods, the radiations produced by radioisotopes are of value because they can be detected and measured, but not because of any biological effects they produce; indeed, such effects are to be avoided in tracer experiments. However, in another group of uses, the effects of radiations on living tissues are the object of study. Such research often yields information of general biological importance in addition to data or radiation effects as such. For example, genetic studies based on radiation are of broad application.

See AMINO ACID STUDIES; ANIMAL METABOLISM STUDIES; ANIMAL NUTRITIONAL STUDIES; ANIMAL PHYSIOLOGICAL STUDIES; BLOOD STUDIES; BLOOD CELL STUDIES; BONE STUDIES; CARBOHYDRATE STUDIES; CELLULAR STUDIES; EMBRYONIC DEVELOPMENT STUDIES; ENTOMOLOGICAL STUDIES; FAT DIGESTION AND ABSORPTION MEASUREMENT; INTERMEDIARY METABOLISM STUDIES; MEMBRANE PERMEABILITY STUDIES; PLANT BREEDING AND RADIATION; PLANT PHYSIOLOGICAL STUDIES; PLANT REGULATOR STUDIES; POLLEN STUDIES; PROTEIN STUDIES; VIRUS STUDIES; and VITAMIN STUDIES.

BIOLOGICAL SHIELD

A shield used to reduce the intensity of radiation transmitted to an amount permissible physiologically, and to protect personnel from the effects of particles or radiation. This term is generally used in connection with nuclear reactors.

BIOPHYSICS

The physics of biological processes or phenomena. The physical interpretation of body functions; e.g., the eye as an optical instrument; the ear as an acoustic instrument; dynamics of bones, joints and muscles; osmosis in vital processes such as secretion and respiration; bioluminescence (emission of light by living organisms such as the firefly and luminous fungi); explanation of nerve responses in terms of electrical current; the study of brain and central nervous system function in terms of computer technology, etc. Currently studies are being done at the cellular and subcellular level using physical science techniques to explore the function of the living cell. Cybernetics or the science of communication and control in the animal and in the machine is closely related to biophysics.

Also closely related is the use of physical techniques in medical practice: diathermy; electrotherapy; and the application of x-ray and other radioactivity to the diagnosis and treatment of illness. However, biophysics is much more than the application of physical techniques to biology. A biophysicist is one who works in the field of biophysics.

BIORADIOLOGY. *See* RADIOBIOLOGY.

BIOSPHERIC CONTAMINATION

The biosphere is the sphere of living organisms, which in their activity penetrate the atmosphere, or gaseous envelope around the earth; the hydrosphere or aqueous phase of the atmospheric envelope and surface of the earth; and the lithosphere or solid part of the earth. Radioactive contamination of the biosphere which is therefore of great biological significance may occur from radioactive fallout, testing of nuclear devices, disposal of radioactive waste, accidental release of radioactive material from a nuclear reactor, use of radioactive isotopes in medical or agricultural activity, and industrial uses of radioactive materials.

Extensive programs sampling air, rain water, sea water, snow and soil are conducted to determine the extent of biospheric contamination.

See FOOD SAMPLING, MILK SAMPLING, MONITORING PROGRAM FOR RADIOACTIVE FALLOUT, and SAMPLING PROGRAM FOR RADIOACTIVE FALLOUT.

BIOSYNTHESIS

Incorporation of a radioisotope into the metabolic compounds of an organism by providing the radioisotope in the nutrients or substrate from which the organism builds its structure. Labeled organic compounds may be prepared by chemical synthesis as well as by biosynthesis but since many biological metabolites are very complex, the biological synthesis is often most convenient. Plants may be grown in an atmosphere of carbon-14-labeled carbon dioxide ($C^{14}O_2$), and thus the

C^{14} enters into the metabolism of the plant and becomes incorporated into various metabolites produced. This has been accomplished on a large scale in the ISOTOPE FARM. Sulfur-35, phosphorus-32 and other radioisotopes may be incorporated into the plant through the soil. Some of the more important types of materials which have been labeled include sugars from crop plants, oil from soy beans, drugs from medicinal plants, vitamins from bacteria, yeasts and molds, and fatty acids and pigments from algae.

Animals may be injected with radioactive compounds which are metabolized and become part of the metabolites produced. For example, by administering cobalt-60 to sheep, it was possible to demonstrate the biosynthesis of a vitamin-B_{12}-like compound both in the gastrointestinal tract and in the tissues. By administering iodine-131 to animals it is possible later to separate the thyroid hormones or the protein complex. Isotopes of carbon, nitrogen and hydrogen have been used to determine the origins and the manner in which certain large complex molecules are assembled. The following are examples of such biosynthesis: purines, sterols, porphyrins, polysaccharides, phosphatides and proteins. Rates of synthesis and breakdown, biological half-life, and pathways of excretion can be studied with such labeled material.

BISMUTH

Symbol Bi; atomic number 83; atomic weight 209.00. Discovered by Valentine in 1450. Takes its name from German *weisse masse*, white mass, later Wismuth. Occurs naturally as stable isotope Bi^{209} (100% abundance) in Bolivia and Saxony, frequently with other ores. Does not occur naturally in biological materials to any significant extent. It is relatively nontoxic—continued dosage of 5 to 10 mg/kg daily produced kidney damage in rabbits, but 40 to 50 mg/kg in one dose injected intramuscularly was tolerated.

Salts of bismuth are used extensively in medicine: as a soothing protective to irritated mucous membranes in digestive disorders; as a treatment for syphilis; and as an opaque liquid suspension to be ingested for making x-ray contrast pictures of the gastrointestinal tract.

Twenty different radioactive isotopes have been isolated, from Bi^{198} through Bi^{215} but Bi^{210} is the only one with biological and medical significance. One of the radioisotopes of bismuth appears in each of the uranium, thorium, actinium and neptunium decay series.

Bismuth-210 $(_{83}Bi^{210})$. This beta (β^-) emitting radioisotope, has radioactive half-life of 5.02 days; with kidney as the critical organ, biological

half-life of 6 days; and effective half-life of 3 days. Occurs as the daughter of lead-210 and is the parent of polonium-210. $Pb^{210} + Bi^{210}$ is highly radiotoxic. Employed in early studies of velocity of blood flow, bismuth-210 is now largely replaced by other radioisotopes, particularly sodium-24.

BLAST

The detonation of a nuclear device, like the detonation of a high explosive such as TNT, results in the sudden formation of a pressure or shock wave, called a blast wave in the air and a shock wave when the energy is imparted to water or earth. In a nuclear explosion of a fission weapon (atomic weapon), about 50 per cent of the energy is released in the form of blast and shock, as shown in Figure B–13.

For details of blast effects *see* BLAST BIOLOGICAL DAMAGE; BLAST PHYSICAL DAMAGE; and BLAST PHYSICAL PHENOMENA.

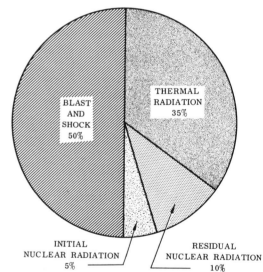

FIGURE B–13. DISTRIBUTION OF ENERGY IN A TYPICAL AIR BURST OF A FISSION WEAPON IN AIR AT AN ALTITUDE BELOW 100,000 FEET.

BLAST BIOLOGICAL DAMAGE

Damage from blast resulting in impairment of physiological function. Blast injury to a biological target, including man, is dependent on three factors: (1) the pressure wave (and negative after-wave) from a detonation in soil, air or water (*see* AIR BURST, SURFACE BURST, UNDERGROUND BURST, and UNDERWATER BURST); (2) movement of materials e.g., missiles, carried along by the blast winds; and (3) the interaction of these 2 with the target and its environment.

Biological damage may be associated with primary blast effects, missiles (secondary blast effects), displacement (tertiary blast effects) or miscellaneous blast effects.

Primary Blast Effects. These are due to overpressure and the reflection from blast waves (*see* BLAST PHYSICAL PHENOMENA). Eardrums, the sinuses and lungs (air-containing and therefore easily compressible spaces) are most likely to suffer damage from pressure changes. Air bubbles picked up by the blood (air embolism) circulating through a damaged lung can prove fatal. Other severe effects include lung hemorrhage, heart failure from lack of oxygen, and rupture and bleeding of internal organs. Biological damage depends upon the rate, character and magnitude of the rise and fall of pressure measured in pounds per square inch (psi) and the duration of the pulse. In general, shock tube* experiments have shown that mammalian material tolerates slowly rising overpressures much better than those developing almost instantaneously; and overpressures of long duration are likely to be less damaging than pressure pulses of short duration. This relationship is shown for nearly 100 per cent mortality for dogs in Table B-2.

TABLE B-2. FAST-RISING, SHORT-DURATION OVERPRESSURE REQUIRED FOR NEARLY 100 PER CENT MORTALITY IN DOGS

MAXIMUM STATIC OVERPRESSURE (psi)	OVERPRESSURE DURATION (msec)
216	1.6
218	1.6
125	4.1
85	8.6
79	10.3

Secondary Blast Effects (Missiles). Secondary blast effects result from blast-moved objects (missiles) which cause damage by striking the biological target. The hazard depends on missile size, shape, composition, mass and velocity. Missiles which penetrate vital organs can cause death. Missiles which do not penetrate can still produce serious injury similar to the effects from the blast wave: i.e., chest injuries can damage the lung; skull fractures can result in concussion and brain hemorrhage; blast pressure on the abdomen may result in rupture and hemorrhage of internal organs; and bone fractures and crushing injuries may be caused by falling objects, such as portions of buildings. Experimental work with animals and

---

*Described at end of this item.

human cadavers has furnished information on most aspects of missile damage. For example, a 10-gram glass fragment traveling with a velocity of 115 ft/sec has only a 1% probability of penetrating the abdominal wall of a dog (180 ft/sec, 50%; 335 ft/sec, 99%). Thus an impact velocity of 115 ft/sec for a 10-gram glass fragment has been chosen as the threshold for human casualties for various fragments of this weight. Again, experimental work with cadavers has shown that for a 10 pound missile, the minimum impact velocity associated with skull fracture is 14.6 ft/sec (9.9 mph), while the maximal without fracture was 23.1 ft/sec.

Tertiary Blast Effects (Displacement). Tertiary blast effects are those caused by displacement of the biological target when it is hit by the blast wave and winds. Severity of effects depends on the amount of acceleration and the speed of deceleration, and in particular on the type of surface hit and the portion of the body making first contact. Animal experiments indicate that the deceleration impact which causes 50% mortality in mice, guinea pigs and rabbits is 38, 44, and 31 feet per second, respectively. Extrapolation to man suggests that an impact velocity of 27 ft/sec (18 mph) would cause death of half the individuals. In another study of speed of movement which causes bone fractures at the moment of impact, it was learned that the threshold for fracture of the heel, foot and ankle bones lay between impact velocities of 11 and 16 ft/sec (another study gave values of 12 to 13 ft/sec, i.e., 8 to 9 mph). The data have led to a tentative criterion of 10 ft/sec as a threshold velocity below which very few casualties or serious injuries would be likely to occur.

Miscellaneous Indirect Blast Effects. These result from ground shock, dust and heat associated with the blast wave. Damage from ground shock would be much the same as for displacement and impact against heavy objects. Dust in very high concentration can cause suffocation, depending on the duration of exposure and the size and concentration of particles. Heat produced by blast presents the same problems as heat from other sources.

Injuries may be due to any or all the blast effects discussed above. The extent of injury a group may experience is well illustrated by a summary,† prepared by the Lovelace Foundation, of the "various types of injuries involved in the Texas City experience in which about 560 persons

---

†Biological Blast Effects. Progress Report AEC Contract No. AT(29-1)-1242, Lovelace Foundation for Medical Education and Research, Albuquerque, New Mexico.

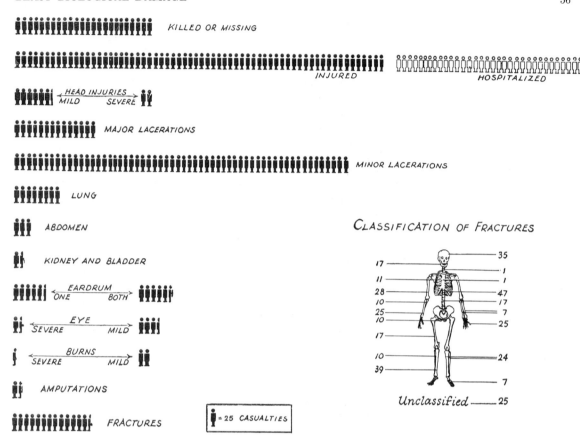

FIGURE B–14. HUMAN CASUALTIES FROM TEXAS CITY EXPLOSION. (LOVELACE FOUNDATION FOR MEDICAL EDUCATION AND RESEARCH, ALBUQUERQUE, NEW MEXICO.)

were killed or missing, 800 cases hospitalized and between 3,000 or 4,000 other less serious casualties occurred (see Fig. B–14). The disaster illustrates very well the catastrophic character and nature of blast injuries and, if multiplied several fold, illustrates many of the biomedical consequences of large-scale nuclear blast delivered to an unprotected urban or suburban area."

The report further summarizes what is known about blast biological damage: "A summary of the interrelations between the several tentative criteria adopted to estimate the thresholds of human injury from blast phenomena in terms of ranges and areas involved is given in Figure B–15 for 1 Mt and in Figure B–16 for the 10 Mt surface bursts. To a great extent, of course, the 2 figures reflect the arbitrary choice of criteria, but each serves to show the ranges from ground zero at which primary, secondary and tertiary blast casualties will begin. Stated another way, one can

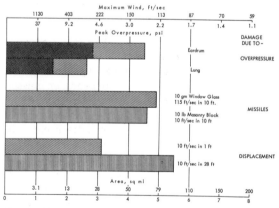

FIGURE B–15. ESTIMATED SPATIAL EXTENT OF BIOLOGICAL DAMAGE DUE TO BLAST (COMPUTED FOR 1 MT SURFACE BURST AT SEA LEVEL). (LOVELACE FOUNDATION FOR MEDICAL EDUCATION AND RESEARCH, ALBUQUERQUE, NEW MEXICO.)

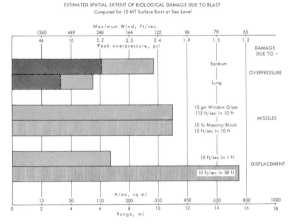

FIGURE B–16. ESTIMATED SPATIAL EXTENT OF BIO-
LOGICAL DAMAGE DUE TO BLAST (COMPUTED FOR 10 MT
SURFACE BURST AT SEA LEVEL). (LOVELACE FOUNDA-
TION FOR MEDICAL EDUCATION AND RESEARCH, ALBU-
QUERQUE, NEW MEXICO.)

say that, inside the ranges shown for each effect,
blast-related casualties will progressively increase
in number.

"In general, Figures B–15 and B–16 indicate a
trend implying that the potential hazard from displacement is more significant than missile damage
and that missile damage, in turn, is more im-

portant than primary blast injury. To be sure,
conditions at the time of exposure will be critical,
and no doubt entirely unpredictable for an unin-
formed and unprotected population under nuclear
attack."

The situation is much more complicated as the
result of a nuclear explosion in which the injury
may be due to thermal radiation and ionizing
radiation as well as to blast. It is estimated that,
among the surviving casualties on the first day in
Hiroshima, blast accounted for the largest percentage of injuries (Table B–3). Many persons
received two or more types of injuries, but in considering mortality in first-day injured survivors
for Hiroshima, thermal radiation was the major
cause of death (Table B–4). Cause of immediate-
death statistics as a result of the atomic bombing
are not available for either Hiroshima or Nagasaki.

The shock tube is a hollow cylindrical or rec-
tangular duct in which a shock wave is generated.
It is used for the purpose of investigating, through
experimentation with anesthetized animals, the
biological effects of concussion phenomenon. These
are similar to those produced by a blast from an
atomic explosion, including reflection, refraction,
diffraction, Mach stem formation, etc. Existing
tubes vary from several feet to 250 feet in length,
and utilize compressed gas (or solid or gaseous
explosives) for the generation of shock.

TABLE B–3. MODERATE AND SEVERE INJURIES IN SURVIVING CASUALTIES ON THE
FIRST DAY, HIROSHIMA. (FROM "MEDICAL EFFECTS OF THE ATOMIC BOMB IN JAPAN"
BY ASHLEY OUGHTERSON AND SHIELDS WARREN.)

TYPE OF INJURY	MODERATE INJURIES			SEVERE INJURIES			ALL INJURIES	
	NO.	PER CENT	% OF ALL INJURIES	NO.	PER CENT	% OF ALL INJURIES	NO.	% OF ALL INJURIES
Blast	22,190	42.1	48.9	23,166	32.1	51.1	45,356	36.3
Heat	17,483	33.1	41.7	24,439	33.9	58.3	41,922	33.6
Ionizing radiation	13,095	24.8	34.3	24,562	34.0	65.2	37,657	30.1
Total	52,768	100.0	42.2	72,167	100.0	57.8	124,935	100.0

TABLE B–4. MORTALITY IN FIRST-DAY INJURED SURVIVORS AT HIROSHIMA.

TYPE OF INJURY	INJURIES			MORTALITY*				
	TOTAL INJURIES	SEVERE INJURIES	MOST SEVERE INJURIES	NO.	% OF INJURIES	% OF SEVERE INJURIES	% OF MOST SEVERE INJURIES	% OF ALL DEATHS
Blast	45,356	23,166	29,012	3,475	7.7	15.0	12.0	18.4
Heat	41,922	24,439	31,202	9,776	23.3	40.0	31.3	51.7
Ionizing radiation	37,657	24,562	30,686	5,649	15.0	23.0	18.4	29.9
Total	124,935	72,167	90,900	18,900	15.1	26.2	20.8	100.0

*All survivors who died are assumed to have had single injuries.

BLAST PHYSICAL DAMAGE

Blast damage is due to displacement or distortion of objects or structures, and may result in complete destruction of a building or only broken windows. Objects may be hurled through space and be damaged when they strike the earth or another object, or the object struck may be damaged by the impact. Glass, wood splinters, bricks and other objects hurled through the air by the "blast wave"* form exceedingly destructive missiles.

The destructive force of the blast wave is directly related to "overpressure" and "dynamic pressure" developed by the blast wave. Table B–5 gives a few examples of the relationship between overpressure in pounds per square inch and the physical damage which results. (*See* DAMAGE CRITERIA.)

TABLE B–5.   RELATION BETWEEN OVERPRESSURE AND PHYSICAL DAMAGE

TYPE OF STRUCTURE	OVERPRESSURE (psi)	PHYSICAL EFFECTS
Window glass	0.5	Shatters
Houses, wooden	1–2	50% damage
Houses, wooden	4–5	Destroyed
Houses, brick	5	Destroyed
Reinforced concrete	4–6	Moderate damage
Motor vehicles	2–3	Light damage
Motor vehicles	10–15	Severe damage

The behavior of an object or structure exposed to blast from a nuclear explosion depends upon "loading" or the forces which result from the action of the blast pressure; and the response or displacement or distortion of the object. For example, Figure B–17, "diffraction loading" tends both to displace and to distort. The air blast (*see* Mach front in BLAST PHYSICAL PHENOMENA) traveling in a horizontal direction strikes perpendicular to the face of the building (a in Figure B–17) and as the wave strikes the overpressure is produced all along the face of the building (b). In (c) the wave has moved along the sides of the building, and in (d) it has reached the rear. By this time the pressure on the front has dropped somewhat and it is building up along the sides and rear; and by (e) it is equal on all sides and on top, dropping off rapidly as the front moves on—in fact in the negative phase the pressure may drop below ambient pressure and the winds be reversed. During the entire positive phase of the air pressure wave the structure will also be subjected to the dynamic pressure loading

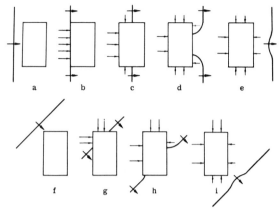

FIGURE B–17.   STAGES IN THE DIFFRACTION OF A BLAST WAVE BY A STRUCTURE WITHOUT OPENINGS (PLAN VIEW).

or "drag loading" caused by the strong transient winds behind the shock front. Also the various forces may strike an object at various angles (see f,g,h,i, of Figure B–17); and in the case of an air burst the pressure may be exerted primarily on the roof of a building or top of an object, as was observed in buildings in Japan near the zero points.

The response of an object depends upon the yield of the weapon, the type of burst (AIR BURST, SURFACE BURST, UNDERGROUND BURST or UNDERWATER BURST), the height of burst, the distance from ground zero, plus all the structural characteristics of the object. The strongest structures are heavily framed steel and reinforced-concrete buildings, whereas the weakest are probably certain shed-type structures having light frames, long beam spans, and large surfaces (*see* DAMAGE CRITERIA). Most frame houses (Fig. B–18) are designed to withstand lateral loadings due to moderately strong winds only, so when struck by the blast from a nuclear explosion they disintegrate (Fig. B–19).

The following are related terms:

Blast loading.   The force exerted on an object by the air shock wave striking and flowing around it. It is a combination of overpressure (or diffraction) and dynamic pressure (or drag) loading.

Blast wave.   *See* BLAST PHYSICAL PHENOMENA.

Diffraction.   See separate item.

Diffraction loading is the force (or loading) on the structure during the envelopment process.

Drag loading.   The force on an object or structure due to the transient winds accompanying the passage of a blast wave. Whereas diffraction loading is effective usually for only a fraction of a second (while the blast wave is enveloping the structure) the drag loading for a 1-megaton nuclear explosion lasts for about 2 seconds at a distance of 1 mile. It is a lateral (or translational) force acting upon the structure.

---

*Terms in quotes, plus other related terms, are defined at the end of this discussion.

FIGURE B–18. WOOD-FRAME HOUSE BEFORE A NUCLEAR EXPLOSION, NEVADA TEST SITE.

FIGURE B–19. SAME WOOD-FRAME HOUSE AS SHOWN IN FIGURE B–18 AFTER NUCLEAR EXPLOSION (5 PSI OVERPRESSURE) AT NEVADA TEST SITE.

Dynamic pressure. See BLAST PHYSICAL PHENOMENA.

Impulse. See BLAST PHYSICAL PHENOMENA.

Loading. Force on an object or structure or part of a structure.

Overpressure. See BLAST PHYSICAL PHENOMENA.

Shock wave. See BLAST PHYSICAL PHENOMENA.

BLAST PHYSICAL PHENOMENA

Following the detonation of a nuclear device, the expansion of intensely hot gases at extremely high pressures in the fireball causes a "blast wave"* to form in the air, which moves outward

---

*Terms in quotes, plus other related terms not treated separately in the work, will be defined either later on in this item or under BLAST PHYSICAL DAMAGE.

at high velocity. The main characteristic of this wave is that the pressure is highest at the moving front and falls off toward the interior region of the explosion. This "overpressure" also steadily decreases as the blast wave travels out away from its source. When the "shock front" has traveled a short distance, the pressure behind the front drops below that of the surrounding atmosphere and the negative phase of the blast wave forms.

These general effects are graphically shown in Figure B–20, on a light structure, a tree and a dog. At the right on the graph the numeral 1 represents the time of detonation, and for a short time (4 seconds for a 1-megaton burst at 1 mile distance) there is no change in the ambient pressure. When the shock front arrives (numeral 2 on the right in

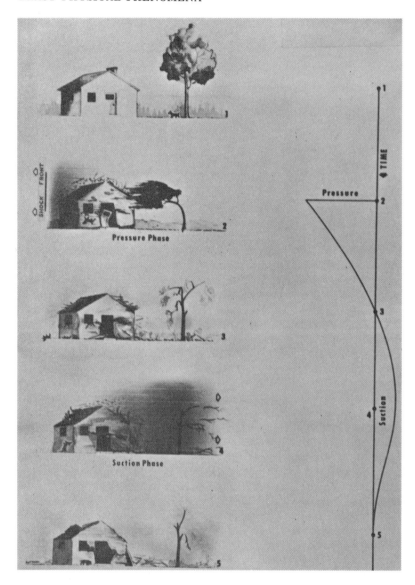

FIGURE B-20. VARIATION OF PRESSURE WITH TIME AT A FIXED LOCATION AND EFFECT OF BLAST WAVE PASSING OVER A STRUCTURE.

the figure) the peak overpressure will develop almost instantly and a strong wind commences to blow away from the explosion. At this moment both "diffraction loading" and "drag loading" are being exerted on all objects. Duration of this phase is roughly 1/2 to 1 second for a 20-kiloton weapon and 2 to 4 seconds for a 1-megaton explosion, and represents the positive (or compression) phase of the blast wave. With the end of this period we arrive at point 3 where the pressure is again the original or ambient atmospheric pressure. As the pressure in the blast wave continues to decrease, it goes below the normal atmospheric pressure and the negative or suction phase of the blast wave takes over as indicated by numeral 4 in the figure. The period from 3 to 5 may be several seconds and for most of this period the transient wind blows back toward the direction of the explosion. This negative phase is not associated with much damage—most of the damage results from the positive phase. As indicated in the picture opposite numeral 5, the winds have ceased and the damage is over except for the secondary destruction by fire which often follows.

So far the destructive effects have been related only to peak overpressure but "dynamic pressure" must be considered also, for it is a function of the velocity of the wind and the density of the air caused by the shock front. For a great variety of types of buildings, the degree of blast damage depends largely on the "drag" force (see BLAST PHYSICAL DAMAGE) associated with the strong winds accompanying the blast wave. It is generally dependent on the peak value of the dynamic pressure and its duration at a given location. Like the peak shock overpressure, the peak dynamic pressure decreases with increasing distance from the zero point (*see* GROUND ZERO), but at a different rate. Table B–6 gives some indication of the corresponding values for peak overpressure, peak dynamic pressure, and maximum wind velocities

TABLE B–6.   OVERPRESSURE, DYNAMIC PRESSURE, AND WIND VELOCITY IN AIR AT SEA LEVEL

PEAK OVERPRESSURE (lbs/sq in)	PEAK DYNAMIC PRESSURE (lbs/sq in)	MAXIMUM WIND VELOCITY (miles/hr)
200	330	2,080
150	223	1,778
100	123	1,414
72	80	1,170
50	40	940
30	16	670
20	8	470
10	2	290
5	0.7	160
2	0.1	70

in air at sea level. For very strong shocks the dynamic pressure is larger than the overpressure, but below 69 psi overpressure the dynamic pressure is smaller. This is graphically shown in Figure B–21.

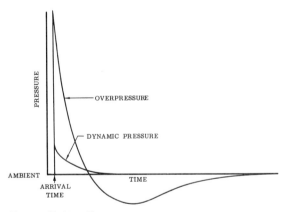

FIGURE B–21.   VARIATION OF OVERPRESSURE AND DYNAMIC PRESSURE WITH TIME AT A FIXED LOCATION IN THE LOW-PRESSURE REGION.

When the primary or "incident blast wave" from an explosion in air strikes a more dense medium such as the earth's surface a "reflected wave" is formed. Four stages of growth of the blast wave are shown in Figure B–22 (t_1 through t_4) together with the development (dotted line) of the reflected wave. As these 2 waves move out, the reflected wave overtakes the incident wave and

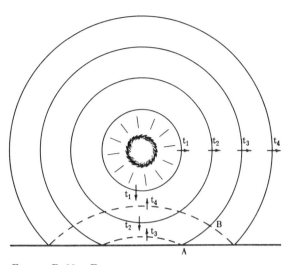

FIGURE B–22.   REFLECTION OF BLAST WAVE AT THE EARTH'S SURFACE IN AN AIR BURST; t_1 TO t_4 REPRESENT SUCCESSIVE TIMES.

together they form the "Mach stem" (*see* MACH EFFECT for graphic presentation), which moves out and up until it disperses.

A number of factors modify the general physical phenomena of a nuclear burst, the most important being the type of burst: air blast, surface burst, underwater burst or underground burst. The general description of blast physical phenomena in this item applies to air blast, and here the height of burst is an important modifying factor, as are the meteorological conditions and the type of terrain over which the explosions occur. The type and yield of the nuclear weapon is, of course, crucial.

The following terms are related to the subject of blast physical phenomena:

Blast scaling laws. Formulas which permit calculation of the characteristic properties of the blast wave (e.g., overpressure, dynamic pressure, time of arrival, etc.) from an explosion of any given energy, if those for another energy are known.

Blast wave. The shock wave from an explosion transmitted through air. Also air blast.

Blast yield. The portion of the total energy of a nuclear detonation that is identified as the blast or shock.

Breakaway. The onset of a condition in which the shock front (in the air) moves away from the periphery of the expanding fireball produced by the detonation of a nuclear device or weapon.

Direct shock wave. Shock wave traveling through the material in which the explosion occurred, without having encountered an interface. Also incident blast wave.

Dynamic pressure. The air pressure which results from the mass of air flow (or wind) behind the shock front of a blast wave. It is equal to the product of half the density of the air through which the blast wave passes and the square of the particle (or wind) velocity behind the shock front as it impinges on the object or structure.

Free air overpressure. Also free air pressure. The unreflected pressure in excess of atmospheric or ambient pressure created in the air by the incident shock of an explosion.

Height of burst. See separate item.

Impulse (per unit area). The product of the overpressure (or dynamic pressure) from the blast wave of an explosion and the time during which it acts at a given point. Specifically, it is the integral, with respect to time, of the overpressure (or dynamic pressure), the integration being between the time of arrival of the blast wave and that at which the overpressure (or dynamic pressure) returns to zero at the given point.

Incident blast wave. The blast or shock wave, produced by the detonation of a nuclear device, traveling in the same media in which it was produced, and before being overtaken by the reflected wave. Also called direct shock wave.

Induced shock wave. The shock wave induced in a medium when a shock wave traveling in another material crosses the boundary between the two. For example, when the shock wave produced in air strikes the earth some of the energy is expended in producing a shock wave in the earth's surface.

Mach effect. Can best be explained by reference to the series of sketches in Figure B–23. The incident and reflected waves are represented in (a) at a point fairly close to ground zero, while (b) represents a later stage, further from ground zero, illustrating that the reflected wave is traveling faster than the incident wave and is thus catching up (this is due to the fact that the reflected wave is traveling through air that has been heated and compressed by the passage of the incident wave). In (c) a stage is represented where the reflected shock wave has overtaken and fused with the incident shock wave to form a single shock front called the "Mach stem." The meeting point of the 3 is called the "triple point."

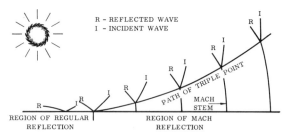

FIGURE B–24. OUTWARD MOTION OF THE BLAST WAVE NEAR THE SURFACE IN THE MACH REGION.

As the reflected wave continues to overtake the incident wave, the triple point rises and the height of the Mach stem increases as shown in Figure B–24. At a point above the triple point an aircraft would experience 2 shocks while nearer the surface of the earth there would be but 1 shock felt. The behavior of this fused or Mach shock is the same as for shock fronts in general.

Mach region. The region for a given height of burst in which the Mach stem has formed along the surface.

Mach stem. Shock front formed by the meeting of the incident and reflected shock fronts from an explosion. The term is usually used with reference to an air-propagated blast wave reflected at the earth's surface.

Overpressure. The transient pressure, usually expressed in pounds per square inch, exceeding the ambient pressure, manifested in the shock (or blast) wave from an explosion. The variation of the overpressure with time depends on the energy yield of the explosion, the distance from the point of burst, and the medium in which the weapon is detonated. The peak overpressure is the maximum value of the overpressure at a given location and is generally experienced at the instant the shock (or blast) wave reaches that location.

Precursor pressure wave. The pressure wave which moves ahead of the main blast wave of a nuclear explosion.

Reflected pressure. The pressure along a surface at the instant a blast wave strikes the surface.

Reflected shock wave. When a shock wave traveling in a light medium (e.g., air) strikes the interface between this medium and a denser medium (e.g., ground), part of the energy of the shock wave is expended in producing an induced shock wave in the denser material, but the remainder of the energy results in the formation of a reflected shock wave which travels back through the less dense material. As they travel out together there is a point at which this primary shock wave meets the reflected shock wave and together they move out as the Mach front or Mach stem.

Reflection factor. The ratio of total pressure to

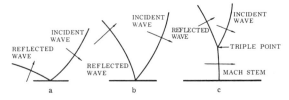

FIGURE B–23. FUSION OF INCIDENT AND REFLECTED WAVES FORMATION OF MACH STEM.

incident pressure produced in air by a nuclear detonation.

Rise time. The time interval from arrival of the blast wave to the time of peak overpressure in the blast wave.

Scaling law. See separate item which includes blast scaling law.

Shock. Term used to describe a destructive force moving in air, water or earth caused by the detonation of a nuclear device.

Shock front. Boundary at which the medium being traversed by a shock or blast wave undergoes abrupt changes in velocity, pressure and temperature.

Shock wave. The steep frontal compression or pressure discontinuity rapidly advancing through a medium as the consequence of a sudden application of pressure. Its form depends on the magnitude of the pressure and the displacement of the medium as the wave progresses. In soil, the shock wave is commonly referred to as the ground shock; in water, the water shock; and in air, the air blast. The shock wave is divided into 2 separate phases, a positive and a negative. The positive or compression phase is the first during which the pressure rises abruptly to a level considerably higher than normal atmospheric pressure, then declines rapidly. The duration of the positive phase is usually about half that of the subsequent negative phase. The negative or rarefaction or suction phase is the second phase, during which the ambient pressure is reduced below atmospheric pressure.

Triple point. Intersection of the incident, reflected and fused shock fronts produced by an explosion in air. See "Mach effect" above.

2 W concept. Concept that the detonation of a nuclear device of energy yield W on the surface of the earth produces blast phenomena identical to those produced by a device of twice the yield or 2 W in free air, i.e., away from any reflecting surface.

BLAST SHELTER

A shelter designed to protect against damage from blast, ground shock, thermal radiation, initial nuclear radiation, and fallout radiation. Such complete protection is difficult to attain, but structures of special design located undergound can withstand blast overpressures of 100 pounds or more per square inch. They can also protect against initial ionizing radiation, and the installation of a suitable ventilating system, as well as chemical and biological materials, adds protection against fallout. Blast-arresting devices must be installed in both intake and exhaust ducts so that mechanical damage will not occur. Entryways to the shelter must have special construction so that the doorway will

be blast resistant. But even such shelters will be damaged if they are close to ground zero of a megaton shallow underground burst or surface burst.

A design for a group shelter was tested by the Civil Effects Test Group (*see* CIVIL DEFENSE) at the Nevada Test Site and found to furnish 100% protection against fallout radiation and in addition to withstand blast overpressures of 576 pounds per square foot (4 psi). (For comparison purposes, conventional dwellings are designed to withstand external blast pressures of 20 to 30 lbs./ft.^{2} or about 0.17 psi). It is claimed that with modest redesigning, this shelter could withstand 35 psi.

All shelters must have certain minimum facilities for a stay of several weeks: ventilation, lighting, food, water, sanitary facilities, clothing, blankets, and first-aid and medical supplies.

BLOOD, RADIATION EFFECTS ON

Determination of the effects of radiation on whole blood is a complex problem because of the interrelationships between: (1) blood plasma and body fluid, (2) the cellular content of the blood (ERYTHROCYTES, LEUKOCYTES and PLATELETS) and (3) the HEMATOPOIETIC SYSTEM.

In vitro studies of radiation effects cannot take into consideration the homeostatic influence of the human body with its tendency to maintain stability of the normal body state. WHOLE BODY IRRADIATION or PARTIAL BODY IRRADIATION if by a dose sufficient to injure blood cells will also injure the hematopoietic tissues (blood-forming organs). A new approach has been perfected for studying the effects of irradiation on the blood circulated at a constant rate through a radiation field outside the body (extracorporeal irradiation) and then back into the body. In this way lymphocyte production, life span and fate have been studied, and it has been found that this type of radiation outside the shielded and nonirradiated body will produce a prompt drop in the number of circulating lymphocytes, i.e., lymphopenia, which persists for weeks.

Mature circulating cells are relatively RADIORESISTANT requiring radiation in the whole body lethal dose range in order to kill them. The various blood cell precursors are much more RADIOSENSITIVE with bone marrow irradiation showing the lymphocyte precursors most sensitive, granulocytes next, and erythrocytes being least sensitive.

Blood plasma is highly radioresistant with no predictable changes in its constituents having been found to date. HEMORRHAGE RESULTING FROM RADIATION INJURY is a secondary effect related to the destruction of platelets with associated reduction in BLOOD COAGULATION time, or to damage to the BLOOD VESSELS which allows the blood to escape from the circulating system.

BLOOD CELL STUDIES

Radioisotopes are largely responsible for a new era in hematology. Although the emphasis was formerly on descriptive studies of blood cells, there is now increasing information on the formation and survival of the various cell types. Much of this new information comes from radioisotopic tracer studies. Each cell arises as a result of mitosis, undergoes maturation, perhaps is stored near the site of formation, and finally enters the blood stream. From here it may migrate into fixed tissues or be destroyed by a variety of mechanisms. The technique of microscopic AUTORADIOGRAPHY, which makes possible the identification of single labeled cells, has played an important role in these studies.

See RED CELL LIFE SPAN MEASUREMENT.

BLOOD CELLS, RADIATION EFFECTS ON.

See CYTOLOGICAL CHANGES DUE TO RADIATION; ERYTHROCYTES, RADIATION EFFECTS ON; LYMPHOCYTES, RADIATION DAMAGE; NEUTROPHIL LEUKOCYTE, RADIATION DAMAGE; and PLATELETS, RADIATION EFFECTS ON.

BLOOD COAGULATION

Radiation exposure, of a magnitude great enough (over 175 rad, whole body irradiation) to cause a reduction in the number of circulating platelets (thrombopenia) leads to a diminished prothrombin utilization, to a deficiency in clot retraction, and to loss of capillary wall integrity. At very low platelet levels with almost no prothrombin conversion, the blood-clotting (blood coagulation) time becomes greatly prolonged, and hemorrhage develops. Bleeding rarely becomes severe until platelet counts are less than 20,000 per cubic millimeter. Intravenous injection of platelets will decrease blood coagulation time and prevent hemorrhage.

BLOOD COUNT, RADIATION EFFECTS ON.

See ANEMIA, DUE TO RADIATION; ACUTE RADIATION SYNDROME; LEUKOCYTE CHANGES DUE TO RADIATION; LYMPHOCYTES, RADIATION DAMAGE; NEUTROPHIL LEUKOCYTE, RADIATION DAMAGE; and PLATELETS, RADIATION EFFECTS ON.

BLOOD FORMATION, RADIATION EFFECTS ON. *See* HEMATOPOIETIC SYSTEM, EFFECTS OF RADIATION ON.

BLOOD PLATELETS, RADIATION EFFECTS ON. *See* PLATELETS, RADIATION EFFECTS ON.

BLOOD STUDIES

Many aspects of the blood are studied with radioisotopes. The total blood volume and its main components, the red cell mass and plasma volume, are measured by radioisotopic dilution techniques. The dynamics of formation, survival and destruction of blood cells have been elucidated by TRACERS, special methods having been devised for studying red cells, leukocytes and PLATELETS, using radioisotopes. Many plasma constituents have also been investigated with radioisotope tracers, for example, serum proteins, electrolytes, food components, hormones and vitamins.

See specific blood constituents.

BLOOD TRANSFUSION IN RADIATION ILLNESS. *See* TREATMENT OF RADIATION ILLNESS.

BLOOD VESSELS, RADIATION EFFECTS ON

Local irradiation can induce vascular changes such as swelling of endothelial cells, deterioration of elastic fibers, degeneration of muscle cells, thrombosis and varying degrees of fibrosis, sclerosis, obliteration and occlusion. However, such vascular changes require radiation doses greater than the minimal whole body lethal dose for mammals, and the changes usually do not develop for several weeks. Capillaries are more radiosensitive than arteries or veins but even they require several thousand roentgens (r) for demonstrable damage. Some of the effects of local radiotherapy of tumors are believed to be, in part at least, the result of radiation damage to vessels in the stroma.

Vascular fragility and increased capillary permeability are two of the causes of hemorrhages occurring late in the course of RADIATION ILLNESS.

See CIRCULATION, RADIATION EFFECTS ON; and VASCULAR SYSTEM, RADIATION EFFECTS ON.

BLOOD VOLUME MEASUREMENT

Techniques using the dilution principle are used for measuring blood volume. A known amount of radioactivity is injected intravenously; after time for mixing in the blood stream, a sample is withdrawn and assayed. The total injected radioactivity divided by the final radioactivity per unit volume gives the total volume in the body. For measurement of the plasma volume the tracer material is usually iodine-131-labeled human serum albumin. For determination of red cell volume the label—usually chromium-51 or phosphorus-32—is applied in vitro to a sample of cells which are then injected.

Total blood volume is measured by adding the red cell and plasma volumes obtained separately, or, less accurately, by determining one or the other and estimating the total on the basis of the relative volumes of cells and plasma in a sample of venous blood.

Blood volume studies are used clinically to evaluate preoperative patients and to determine the magnitude of alterations in anemia, polycythemia and burns.

See CARDIAC OUTPUT MEASUREMENT, ISOTOPE DILUTION, PLASMA VOLUME MEASUREMENT, and RED CELL MASS MEASUREMENT.

BODY BURDEN. *See* MAXIMUM PERMISSIBLE BODY BURDEN.

BODY COMPOSITION

From an anatomical point of view, the human body can be carefully dissected, parts weighed and measured and the organs and tissues composing the body identified. The total body can be ashed or individual organs can be removed and ashed and the chemical composition determined. These methods are laborious and have been carried out on limited numbers of bodies; however, agreement has been reached as to the composition of the standard man.

The body composition proportion of fat, water and lean muscle mass can be determined by several methods in vivo without disturbing any metabolic function. By volume dilution techniques using radioisotopes it is possible to estimate quite accurately such physiological entities as the red-blood-cell volume, plasma volume, lymph volume, extracellular space, and body water. Also, the volumes of fluid through which other materials of biological interest are apparently distributed can be estimated, i.e., chloride space, bromide space. Total exchangeable sodium and total exchangeable potassium can be determined by measuring the mass of the element which equilibrates with an injected tracer dose.

Activation analysis has provided another approach to the quantitative estimation of body composition. By exposing biological material (blood, organ tissue, etc.) to thermal neutrons in a reactor, induced radioactivity results in certain elements in the biological material. By an analysis and measurement of the radioactivity emitted, or by radiochemical separation and measurement, the amount of a given element in the tissue being analyzed can be calculated. By these methods it was shown that the blood contains trace amounts of gold. Iodine in the thyroid tissue has been determined, as well as sodium and potassium in muscle; and the cobalt, iron and zinc content of various human tissues has been measured.

Body composition information is essential for a number of health physics, radiobiology and medical activities.

BONE DISEASES DUE TO RADIATION

Skeletal damage may occur from either external radiation or radiation following internal deposition of radioactive isotopes. The effect is related to the dose—in growing children and in young animals a dose of 100 to 200 roentgens (r) may cause temporary impairment of growth due to suppression or damage to cartilage growth, whereas it takes over 1,000 r in an adult bone to cause necrosis which would lead to BONE FRACTURES. BONE TUMORS have been shown to occur after a latent period of from 12 to 30 years and from an accumulated internal dose of over 1,100 rad from radium and about 50 rad from mesothorium.

See BONE MARROW, RADIATION EFFECTS ON, and SARCOMAS DUE TO RADIATION.

BONE FRACTURES DUE TO RADIATION

External radiation of 1,000 roentgens (r) to a localized area has been known to result in necrosis and subsequent spontaneous fracture of ribs, neck of the femur, and of the jaw in human patients. The organic matrix of bone is relatively resistant to radiation, but in the radium dial painter cases some of those most severely poisoned showed necrosis of the mandible, maxillae and temporal bones with subsequent fracture. Animal experimental work has shown that injection of various radioactive isotopes of heavy elements may lead to necrosis and pathological fracture, particularly of the long bones.

See BONE DISEASES DUE TO RADIATION, and BONE TUMORS RESULTING FROM RADIATION.

BONE MARROW, RADIATION EFFECTS ON

Bone marrow is particularly susceptible to irradiation, with a drop in circulating lymphocytes being detectable after a single exposure of 25 roentgens. In the acute radiation syndrome the early findings of leukopenia (reduced numbers of white cells), and the later development of anemia (reduced numbers of red cells) are directly related to damage of the hematopoietic tissue, of which bone marrow is an important component.

Bone marrow damage appears shortly after irradiation and is demonstrated by early degeneration of the red blood cell (erythropoietic) precursors. The white blood cell (granulocytic) precursors degenerate at the next most rapid rate, and the precursor for the platelets (megakaryocyte) degenerates last, usually by the fifth or sixth day after a mid-lethal (LD_{50}) radiation dose. Mitosis or cell division is diminished or temporarily stopped and therefore cell production is correspondingly diminished. Figure B–25 shows

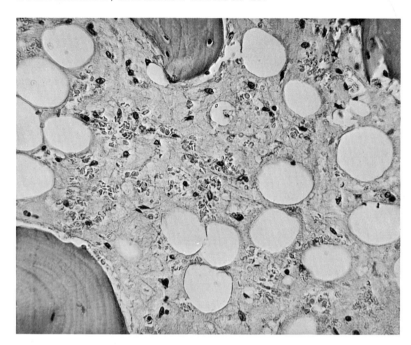

FIGURE B–25. BONE MARROW FROM A SWINE WHICH DIED 11 DAYS FOLLOWING TOTAL BODY EXPOSURE TO IONIZING RADIATION FROM THE ATOMIC BOMB TESTS AT BIKINI. NOTE THE MARKED CELLULAR DEPLETION AND ABSENCE OF BLOOD CELL FORMATION. RETICULAR CELLS, FAT CELLS, ERYTHROCYTES AND BONE SPICULES ARE APPARENTLY UNHARMED. (OFFICIAL U.S. NAVY PHOTOGRAPH.)

bone marrow with marked cellular depletion and the absence of hematopoiesis in a swine which died 11 days following whole body irradiation exposure to ionizing radiation from a test detonation of a nuclear device.

At doses below the LD_{50} the damage to the bone marrow is less and the decrease in the circulating blood cells is less. At doses over the LD_{50} the rate at which the cells diminish remains about the same but the duration of the depression in cellular production is greatly lengthened. Spontaneous recovery of bone marrow function is unlikely after a surface dose exposure to 800 roentgens or more.

The severity and course of radiation illness can be markedly altered by shielding the long bones (i.e., bone marrow) during irradiation, with acute symptoms being altogether absent unless the dose is high. Bone marrow therapy, or the intravenous injection of bone marrow cells, has been reported to have been used successfully in treating cases of accidental radiation exposure.

The effect of radium on bone marrow is minimal for it remains incorporated within the crystals of the bone mineral, mainly within the lamellae of compact bone, and its very short-range alpha particles do not reach the bone marrow. In fact, among the radium dial painter cases there have been no cases of leukemia, although there have been some cases of osteogenic sarcoma. The same type of distribution within bone structure is also found for strontium-90, which with its short-range beta particles will probably not damage bone marrow in man.

External radiation involving bone marrow, has resulted in an increased incidence of LEUKEMIA.

BONE MARROW GRAFTS

Used in the treatment of radiation illness and giving promise of being useful for other medical applications. Some years ago it was discovered that shielding the spleen of an animal given radiation at a high dose to all the rest of the body would greatly promote recovery. This technique served especially to improve recovery of the hematopoietic tissues. Somewhat later it was shown that bone marrow cells injected into a heavily irradiated recipient would allow survival after doses otherwise fatal. For some time after this development it was not clear whether the injected cells acted by furnishing an obscure chemical factor needed for recovery or whether they served as a graft of precursor cells for blood formation. A group of ingenious experiments proved that the donor cells served as a true graft and that this was their main mode of action. Soon it became apparent that the genetic and immunological relationship between donor and host was of great importance in experiments of this type. These relationships are the basis for the following classification of grafts:

Autologous. Tissue returned to the identical, or almost identical individual from which it came.

Isologous. Donor and host of same genetic make-up, as in highly inbred strains of mice. (In human patients, grafts between identical twins.)

Homologous. Donor and host from different

genetic strains of same species (this would include all human grafts not involving identical twins).

Heterologous. Donor and host of different species.

These studies in experimental animals showed that isologous grafts not only allowed survival of the acute damage produced by high doses of radiation, but also resulted in prolonged maintenance of health. Homologous and heterologous marrow yielded fairly good protection from immediate radiation deaths; the initial "take" of these was made possible by the temporary suppression of the immune reactions of the host by irradiation. However, many of the animals protected by this foreign marrow died within a relatively short time of a peculiar disorder that came to be known variously as secondary disease, homologous disease, or foreign bone marrow disease. It is characterized by weight loss with good food intake, by failure of hair growth, and by abnormalities of lymphatic tissues. It is believed to be due to an immune or antigen-antibody reaction between donor and host. A major portion of this reaction may involve the donor cells as producers of antibody and the host as antigen. It was found possible to avoid this complication, in some circumstances, by using donor tissue from fetal sources; this tissue is too immature to have developed its own genetic identity and is immunologically adaptable to the environment of the host.

These studies in animals have suggested important possible uses of the marrow graft procedure in human beings, for treatment of accidental radiation injury and, combined with intentionally administered radiation, for therapy of certain diseases. Only rarely is it possible to attempt isologous grafts from an identical twin. Autologous grafts have limited application but some success has been reported. In the majority of human graft attempts, homologous donors are used; most of these attempts have failed, not with the picture of secondary disease, but, rather, with lack of evidence of a primary take.

In one group of patients injured in a reactor accident in Yugoslavia and treated in Paris by French physicians, there was evidence that a successful temporary homologous graft was achieved. In patients intentionally irradiated for disease a few other homologous grafts have been reported, and an even smaller number of examples of what appears to be secondary disease have been described.

Bone marrow therapy should probably be given to persons injured in radiation accidents at doses expected to be otherwise lethal but not high enough to produce rapid neurological or gastrointestinal deaths. In the absence of an identical twin, homologous donors are used, selected according to special criteria. It is not believed necessary to give the marrow within the first hours or even the first one or two days after exposure, and so there is time for careful preparation. Further efforts to develop additional medical applications for marrow grafts are under way.

BONE SAMPLING

The analysis of human and animal bone samples for their content of radioactive isotopes. Usually considered in relation to the strontium-90 (Sr^{90}) content of bone, as an end result of food contamination due to fallout from the testing of nuclear weapons. Because in the final analysis the amount of Sr^{90} in human bone is a crucial problem in connection with fallout from weapons testing, the USAEC established an extensive world-wide bone sampling program in 1955 which operated through 1960. Bone samples are also obtained at autopsy to study the effect of radium deposition, e.g., in the radium dial painter cases.

The following facts should be used in interpreting bone sampling data:

1. Strontium is chemically similar to calcium and is metabolized into bone in much the same manner.

2. There is a discrimination factor of between 2 and 4 for man, in favor of bone deposition of calcium instead of strontium when both are available.

3. The strontium-calcium ratio is the usual method of considering bone content of Sr^{90}.

4. The strontium unit (micromicrocuries of strontium-90 per gram of bone calcium—$\mu\mu c$ Sr^{90}/g Ca) is frequently used to express content.

5. The maximum permissible concentration (MPC) for Sr^{90} is 4×10^{-6} μc/cc of water for occupational exposure, and the maximum permissible body burden is 20 μc.

6. The United Nations Scientific Committee on Effects of Atomic Radiation calculated that 1 $\mu\mu c$ Sr^{90}/g Ca is equivalent to a dose of 1 millirem (mrem) per year to the bone marrow.

7. The radiation dose to the skeleton from natural radiation is approximately 125 mrem per year.

8. Adult bone changes about 3.5% per year. Bone formed prior to testing will take many years to come into equilibrium.

9. Bones of children of age 2 years are about in equilibrium with their diet, at least 80%.

10. A long bone (leg or arm) taken at autopsy or in the case of amputation, is representative for ashing and analysis.

Based on the bone sampling and analysis program of the USAEC the following findings and predictions briefly summarize available information:

1. Based on an analysis of bone samples from 1,339 adults and 370 children from 35 world-wide stations, the population-weighted mean average as of January, 1958 was 0.52 μμc Sr^{90}/g Ca, and the weighted average of the adult population was 0.19. Based on bone samples from skeletons of 47 children, age 0 to 9 years, in North America, the average concentration was 0.8 μμc Sr^{90}/g Ca.

2. If equilibrium levels are assumed, dietary differences are taken into account, no more testing after 1958 is assumed, and maximum fallout will be reached in 1962 to 1965, the estimates given in Table B–7 are pertinent.

TABLE B–7. ESTIMATED AVERAGE MAXIMUM STRONTIUM-90 EQUILIBRIUM BONE LEVELS DERIVED FROM BONE ANALYSES

REGION	μμc Sr^{90}/g Ca	
	1958	At Maximum
United States of America	4	6
Western Population	3	5
20°N–60°N Latitude	5	8
Far Eastern Population	6	10
Weighted World Average	4	7

3. An estimate based on all nations testing through 1958 placed 11 μμc Sr^{90}/g Ca as the upper limit of foreseeable contamination of milk in New York City. A child deriving his calcium from dairy sources may then be expected, on this basis, to develop a bone level of 5.5 μμc Sr^{90}/g Ca, which will deliver a dose of radiation of about 5.5 mrem per year to the bone marrow, i.e., about 5% of that due to natural radiation.

4. Ten bone samples taken from states adjoining the Nevada Test Site up to 1958 showed from 0.6 to 12.0 μμc Sr^{90}/g Ca.

5. All the predictions will have to be revised in the light of the Soviet tests in the fall of 1961. It is estimated, for example, that a 100-megaton detonation (25 megatons of fission) might produce roughly half as much world-wide, stratospheric fallout as all previous tests of all nations prior to the November 3, 1958, moratorium.

BONE SEEKER

Any element that localizes in the body preferentially in bone. The skeleton, including marrow, of the standard man weighs 10,000 grams and constitutes 14.2% of the weight of the total body. Bone tissue consists grossly of 3 fractions: inorganic fraction (bone ash), the organic matrix 30% (proteins), and inorganic fraction 45%. Elements of interest in bone tissue are phosphorus, sulfur, calcium, sodium and potassium.

Radioactivity may enter the body as particulate matter or gas either through ingestion of radioactive material or by inhalation of radioactive material. Biological effects of internally deposited radioisotopes depend largely upon the organ or tissue in which they are concentrated, i.e., the critical organ. Bone is the critical organ for a number of radioisotopes, the best known of which are radium and strontium-90. Radium, as a bone seeker, became known as a hazard because of the RADIUM DIAL PAINTER CASES, where the end result in a few of the cases has been osteogenic sarcoma. Strontium is important because it is the most biologically significant component of stratospheric fallout. Other radionuclides of fallout interest as bone seekers are yttrium-91, barium-140 and cerium-144. The potential hazard from bone-seeking radionuclides is enhanced because of the slow removal.

National Bureau of Standards Handbook 69 lists the following radionuclides for which the critical organ is bone: phosphorus-32, calcium-45,-47, nickel-59,-63, strontium-89,-90, yttrium-91, zirconium-93, niobium-93m, tin-113, antimony-125, barium-140, cerium-141,-144, neodymium-144, promethium-147, samarium-147,-151, europium-154,-155, gadolinium-153, terbium-160, thulium-170,-171, radium-223,-224,-226,-228, actinium-227,-228, thorium-227,-228,-230,-232,-234, natural thorium, protactinium-230,-231, uranium-232,-233,-234,-235,-236, neptunium-237, plutonium-238,-239,-240,-241,-242, americium-241,-243, curium-243,-244,-245,-246, berkelium-249, californium-249,-250,-252.

See BONE DISEASES DUE TO RADIATION; BONE FRACTURES DUE TO RADIATION; BONE MARROW, RADIATION EFFECTS ON; BONE TUMORS RESULTING FROM RADIATION.

BONE STUDIES

The mineral metabolism of the skeleton has been widely studied for many years. Within recent times, however, new impetus has been given to such studies because of (a) the availability of new techniques based on radioisotopes for the study of bone structure and metabolism, and (b) recognition that the skeleton retains certain radioisotopes such as strontium-90 which have become distributed throughout the biosphere as a result of environmental contamination. The most useful radioisotopes for research are calcium-45, phosphorus-32, and strontium-85; short-lived calcium-47, only recently available, has many advantages.

The techniques of study usually involve ad-

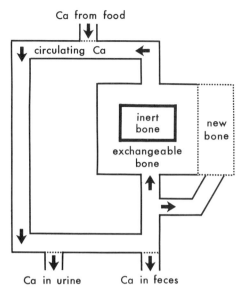

FIGURE B-26. SIMPLE MODEL OF CALCIUM ION MEASUREMENT IN THE BODY.

ministration of the radioisotope to the organism and measurement of deposition in the skeleton by radio-assay of a bone sample, by autoradiography of bones, or by external counting of the body. Important subject areas are the mechanism and sites of deposition of substances within the skeleton, the dynamics of bone mineral, the formation and resorption of bone, the modes of growth and remodeling of the skeleton, and the relationship with disease conditions, endocrine function and vitamins.

Bone consists of the bone mineral, or bone crystal, and an organic matrix. The bone crystals contain calcium phosphate and hydroxyl ions arranged in an hexagonal structure that gives an x-ray pattern characteristic of the apatite minerals. The organic matrix is comprised of collagen fibers, between which occur the mucopolysaccharide, chondroitin sulfate. Certain substances pres-

ent in blood tend to be deposited in relation to the organic matrix; these include beryllium, carbon, magnesium, phosphate, sulfur, lanthanide rare earths and actinide rare earths. The surface ions of the bone crystals are in equilibrium with the body fluids bathing these crystals and certain ions in the blood may become associated with the bone crystals by exchange processes. These include fluorine, phosphate, calcium, strontium, magnesium, radium, lead, hydrogen, sodium and uranium. A simple model which depicts calcium ion movement in the body is shown in Figure B-26. As shown, circulating calcium in the blood comes into contact with surfaces of a certain portion of the bone mineral, and exchanges with the surface calcium. Also calcium enters the skeleton by the formation of new bone. Calcium from the diet enters the blood from the gastrointestinal tract, and calcium is lost from the body by urinary and fecal excretion.

Figure B-27 demonstrates the relationship between the deposition of calcium-45 in bone and the anatomical structure. The autoradiogram is of a longitudinal section of a metatarsal bone of a young calf. It is noted that the nature of the calcium-45 deposition is characteristic of the anatomical region as follows:

a. There is a heavy and relatively diffuse deposition below the epiphyseal plate;

b. The subperiosteal accumulation is characterized by a sharp line of deposition related to the narrow layer of growth cells;

c. The area of endochondral growth shows a linear deposition which is distinguished from the periosteal deposition by the spottiness of the former;

d. The region of trabecular bone shows a more generalized spotty distribution at a lower intensity than the areas already mentioned;

e. The compact bone of the shaft shows much lower density of calcium-45. Recent evidence indicates, however, that these regions of low intensity

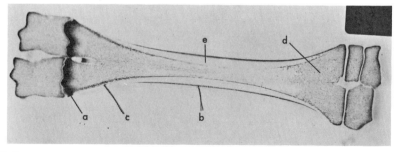

FIGURE B-27. Ca^{45} AUTORADIOGRAM OF METATARSUS OF 1-MONTH-OLD CALF SACRIFICED 7 DAYS AFTER ADMINISTRATION. (A) HEAVY DEPOSITION BELOW EPIPHYSEAL PLATE; (B) SHARP SUBPERIOSTEAL DEPOSITION; (C) SPOTTY DEPOSITION IN AREA OF ENDOCHONDRAL BONE GROWTH; (D) TRABECULAR BONE; (E) COMPACT BONE OF SHAFT. (COMAR, "RADIOISOTOPES IN BIOLOGY AND AGRICULTURE.")

may account for a considerable portion of the total amount of calcium-45 deposited in the skeleton because of the greater amount of this type of bone. It appears that the deposition in these areas involves a long-term exchange process.

BONE TUMORS RESULTING FROM RADIATION

Bone tumors have developed in humans following ingestion of radium and mesothorium, as in the radium dial painter cases. However, many of these women are still in normal health, and after many years none has been found with a sarcoma in whom less than 0.4 microcurie of radium, plus an undetermined amount of mesothorium, was left in the body.

Tumors, mostly osteogenic sarcomas, have been demonstrated to develop in laboratory animals following injection of such radioactive isotopes as phosphorus-32, strontium-89 and -90, yttrium-90, cerium-144, radium-226, mesothorium, radiothorium and plutonium. These experimentally produced sarcomas appear after a long latent period —following injection, for example, of 0.5 microcuries per gram in rabbits (3.6×10^{-4} rad dose accumulated in 1 year); there are frequently multiple lesions; they are both dose-dependent and time-dependent; there is no linear relation between dose and response; and the findings are consistent with the existence of a threshold dose below which sarcomas are not induced (1,000 rad accumulated dose in 1 year for mice).

External radiation has been shown to produce bone tumors—a single dose of 3,000 r gamma to a rat knee joint, or a single whole body exposure of 660 r to a rat. However, no cases appear in the literature of bone tumors arising from chronic external radiation. In fact none was produced experimentally in mice, rats or guinea pigs from daily dosage rates of as much as 8.8 r per day. Bone tumors, again osteogenic sarcomas, have developed in human cases following irradiation of benign bone lesions. Tumor development in normal bone is extremely rare, however, as a result of radiation doses used in radiotherapy—only 2 reports of osteogenic sarcoma in the ribs after radiation following mastectomy, in spite of the many thousands of such treatments given.

See BONE DISEASES DUE TO RADIATION, and BONE FRACTURES DUE TO RADIATION.

BORON

Symbol B; atomic number 5; atomic weight 10.82. Discovered in 1808 by English chemist Davy, and independently by French chemists Gay-Lussac and Thenard. An extremely hard non-metallic substance found in nature as a mixture of two stable isotopes, B^{10} (18.8%) and B^{11} (81.2%).

Boron has a high cross section for thermal neutron capture (755 BARNS for the natural mixture and 4,010 barns for the isolated B^{10} component). Based on this feature boron-10 has an important medical use in NEUTRON-CAPTURE THERAPY for the treatment of cancer, particularly malignant glioblastomas of the brain. It has been used in studies of plant cell maturation and differentiation.

Certain boron compounds are toxic—pentaborane and decaborane vapors present a serious health hazard in manufacture and use. Boric acid if taken internally is toxic, with the fatal dose in infants being 5 to 6 grams.

Boron has 2 radioactive beta-emitting isotopes: B^8 (half-life 0.46 sec, β^+) and B^{12} (half-life 0.027 sec, β^-). The biological half-life of boron is 12 hours with total body as the critical organ.

BRACHYTHERAPY

The use of solid or encapsulated radioisotopic sources on the surface or at a short distance from the area to be treated. Brachytherapy is not always distinguished from the use of similar sources for INTERSTITIAL or INTRACAVITARY therapy which are essentially the same as brachtherapy except that the sources are inserted into tissues or into body cavities.

Brachytherapy yields a very high radiation dose to a localized surface area but the fall off of dose with depth is quite pronounced. This form of treatment is used for certain accessible cancers and for some superficial nonmalignant diseases.

See TELETHERAPY.

BRAGG-GRAY PRINCIPLE

The concept that a small gas-filled cavity in an irradiated medium will experience the same radiation intensity as would the material it replaces; useful in dosimetry, especially in designing radiation measuring instruments.

BRAIN STUDIES

Several different approaches to the study of the brain take advantage of radioisotope techniques. Most of these are experimental and are not widely used in medical practice.

The blood flow to the brain has been measured with krypton-85, a radioactive gas that is absorbed from the lungs. The patient breathes a mixture of gases in a closed system; included in the gas is a known amount of Kr^{85}. Blood returning from the brain is studied by collecting repeated samples from both jugular veins and analyzing these for Kr^{85}. On the basis of these values and the total amount of Kr^{85} taken into the body during the period of study, the blood flow to the brain is calculated. Normal values are about 50 cc per 100 g of brain tissue per minute, with considerable variation on either side of this figure.

The metabolic incorporation of organic compounds into the fatty substance of the brain has been studied with carbon-14 and tritium-labeled compounds.

Studies of an entirely different type use spheres containing pure beta emitters, yttrium-90 or palladium-109. These are inserted into the brain substance of experimental animals to produce localized destruction; the neurological consequences, in terms of localizing brain functions, are the main object of the investigation.

See BRAIN TUMORS, LOCALIZATION.

BRAIN TISSUE, RADIATION EFFECTS ON

Animal experimentation indicates the occurrence of late RADIONECROSIS in the brain after selective irradiation of the head at dose levels of 4,000 roentgens (r) and higher. In primates exposed to doses up to 5,000 r from 22 Mev x-rays, acute effects of inflammation, edema and hemorrhages occurred in the irradiated part of the brain, which cleared but was followed weeks or months later by selective degeneration of myelin; at higher doses the end result was necrosis of brain tissue.

Radionecrosis of the human brain has been found to follow heavy therapeutic irradiation for brain tumors. There was a long latent period and in all cases vascular damage was marked and the necrotic area occurred almost entirely in the white matter. Two cases receiving approximately 7,000 r to the brain had latent periods of 5 and 6 years, and 2 cases receiving about 12,000 r showed signs of damage 9 and 10 months later respectively. Whether the brain damage is a primary effect of radiation exposure or is secondary to vascular damage has not been definitely settled.

Following death from acute radiation illness resulting from whole body irradiation, the brain appears normal. The dura and pia often contain petechial hemorrhages and there may be some extravasation of blood into the subarachnoid space. Microscopically there may be a few perivascular hemorrhages. In deaths due to 2,000 or 3,000 r whole-body irradiation, the major damage appears in the hematopoietic tissue and in the gastrointestinal tract; the brain and other portions of the central nervous system appear to have relative radioresistance.

PITUITARY GLAND IRRADIATION or radiohypophysectomy by the use of 340-million volt focused protons has proved to be a successful method of removing the pituitary (26,000 rads over 3 weeks). This treatment has been used in breast carcinoma.

See CENTRAL NERVOUS SYSTEM, RADIATION EFFECTS ON.

BRAIN TUMOR BED IRRADIATION

An experimental procedure using radioisotope-impregnated sponges, was designed to supplement the surgical treatment of brain tumors. Colloidal forms of gold-198 and phosphorus-32 (chromic phosphate) are held by gelatin or starch sponges. These sponges may be inserted against brain tissue at the site of previous removal of a brain tumor. The radioisotopes stay on the surface of the tissue but their radiations produce an intense local destructive effect which, under some circumstances, may have a beneficial effect.

See BRAIN TUMORS, LOCALIZATION.

BRAIN TUMORS, LOCALIZATION

Methods for the preoperative detection of brain tumors have been the subject of extensive research efforts. Because of disturbances in the permeability of blood vessels in and around tumors, they concentrate some radioisotopes more than does surrounding normal brain tissue. Often the concentration in the tumor is not sufficiently high to make detection easy and special equipment has been devised to record slight differences. Sometimes nonmalignant lesions such as abscesses are difficult to distinguish from tumors. The radioisotope preparations commonly used are iodine-131-labeled human serum albumin, arsenic-74 as sodium arsenate, and mercury-203-labeled Neohydrin. The labeled drug is given intravenously and, at intervals of from 1 hour to 2 days, measurements are made of the radioactivity in the head region, using manual or automatic scanning, or photoscanning.

In spite of limitations, these tests, if skillfully done, will reveal a high proportion of all brain tumors, with little risk or discomfort to the patient. These methods do not replace other diagnostic procedures, but supplement them. Figures B–28 and B–29 show graphically the method of locating

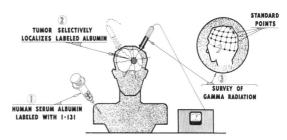

FIGURE B–28. METHOD OF LOCATING BRAIN TUMORS WITH IODINE-131-TAGGED HUMAN SERUM ALBUMIN. MULTIPLE COUNTERS CAN BE USED FIXED IN STANDARD POSITIONS. BY THIS TECHNIQUE TUMORS CAN BE DEMONSTRATED. (USAEC-1D-154A.)

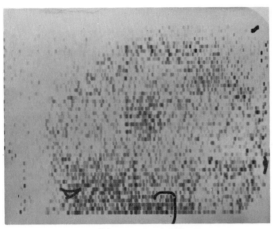

FIGURE B–29. RADIOISOTOPE SCAN SHOWING BRAIN TUMOR. TUMOR SHOWS AS A DENSE AREA JUST TO THE FRONT OF CENTER OF THE PATIENT'S SKULL. NOTE THE EYE AND EAR LINES FOR ORIENTATION. (COURTESY MEDICAL DIVISION, OAK RIDGE INSTITUTE OF NUCLEAR STUDIES.)

brain tumors and a scan of the left side of the patient's head. The tumor shows as a dense area just to the front of the center of the patient's skull.

BRAIN TUMORS, TREATMENT. *See* NEUTRON CAPTURE THERAPY.

BREATH ANALYSIS. *See* RADON BREATH ANALYSIS.

BREMSSTRAHLUNG

German word meaning, braking (or slowing down) radiation. The production of electromagnetic radiation by the acceleration that a fast-charged particle (usually an electron) undergoes when it is deflected by another charged particle (usually a nucleus). The spectral distribution is continuous, continuous x-rays from an anticathode bombarded by high-speed electrons being a prominent example. For very energetic electrons (approximately above 50 Mev), energy loss by radiation far exceeds that by ionization as a stopping mechanism in matter; this process is sometimes called outer bremsstrahlung.

Inner bremsstrahlung is a process occurring infrequently in beta disintegration and resulting in the emission of a photon of energy between zero and the maximum energy available in the transition.

Very weak electromagnetic radiation with a continuous spectral distribution is sometimes observed from beta-active substances; this is due to one or both types of bremsstrahlung.

In the synchrotron when electrons traveling at maximum energy strike the target they produce highly penetrating, i.e., short wave-length x-rays (bremsstrahlung) of equivalent energy. In the passage of cosmic rays through air (or other matter), the electrical interaction of electrons with atomic nuclei results in the formation of bremsstrahlung x-rays.

BROMINE

Symbol Br; atomic number 35; atomic weight 79.916. A brown liquid, volatilizing at room temperature to a red vapor, which is suffocating and extremely irritating to the eyes, nose and throat. Discovered by Balard in 1825. Named appropriately from Greek *bromos*, stench. Occurs as the bromide in sea water (0.188% Br), in the mother liquor from the salt wells of Michigan, Ohio and West Virginia, and in POTASSIUM deposits of Germany and France. United States commercial material is largely recovered from brines and sea water. Its natural abundance is in stable isotopes Br^{79}, 50.52% and Br^{81}, 49.48%.

Bromine is used commercially in the manufacture of lead-tetraethyl, in various other chemical processes (76 organic compounds of bromine may be listed), and in the manufacture of a poison gas. Many different bromides are used in medicine as sedatives to lessen nervous irritability and excitability, to inhibit vomiting, and to lessen attacks of various convulsive conditions. It is found in all living matter as a TRACE ELEMENT but is not considered essential.

Bromine is highly toxic. Burns of a deep, penetrating nature followed by persistent ulceration result from contact with liquid bromine. One thousand parts per million in air are rapidly fatal; 40 to 60 parts per million are highly irritating to the upper respiratory passages and dangerous even for short exposure; the maximum concentration allowable for one-half hour is 4 parts per million. About 875 mg/kg of sodium bromide ingested daily by rats produced death in 20 days.

There are 14 radioactive isotopes, three of which (Br^{80m}, Br^{80} and Br^{82}) may be produced in sea water as a result of the detonation of a nuclear device in contact with the sea.

Bromine-82 ($_{35}Br^{82}$). Half-life 1.5 days; with total body as the critical organ, biological half-life 8 days, effective half-life 1.3 days; beta (β^-) and gamma emitter. Potassium bromide (KBr^{82}) is available commercially and is used in biological research to study the metabolism, movement and distribution of bromine. Radiobromine is also used to label organic compounds and dyes for biological and agricultural studies. Potassium radiobromide is also available as a sterile solution used in medical research. It has been suggested as a possible radioisotope for use in medical treatment.

Maximum permissible concentration for soluble material, total body as the critical organ for occupational exposure 40-hour week is 8×10^{-3} microcuries per cubic centimeter (μc/cc) in water and 10^{-6} μc/cc in air. For a 168-hour week (continuous exposure) 3×10^{-3} μc/cc in water and 4×10^{-7} μc/cc in air.

BROOKHAVEN MEDICAL RESEARCH RE-ACTOR. *See* MEDICAL RESEARCH REACTOR.

BROOKHAVEN NATIONAL LABORATORY (BNL)

BNL is located at the former Camp Upton near the center of Long Island on a 3,500-acre tract of land. The laboratory was established in 1947 as a cooperative venture, particularly for the use of large and expensive types of equipment, and for concentrating scientific manpower for the successful prosecution of nuclear research. BNL is operated by Associated Universities, Inc., a non-profit educational corporation, whose governing Board of Trustees is made up of one representative scientist and an administrative officer from each of the 9 sponsoring universities: Columbia, Cornell, Harvard, Johns Hopkins, Massachusetts Institute of Technology, Princeton, University of Pennsylvania, University of Rochester, and Yale.

The plant, equipment, the large machines and other special facilities make this laboratory unique as a place to conduct nuclear energy research: a large research nuclear reactor; the first accelerator to deliver particles over a billion electron volts, i.e., the 3-Bev Cosmotron (proton synchrotron); the Alternating Gradient Synchrotron, a 30-Bev proton synchrotron; a new high-flux research reactor; a nuclear reactor especially designed for clinical neutron irradiations (*see* MEDICAL RESEARCH REACTOR); a gamma field; a gamma greenhouse; a gamma forest; the High Intensity Radiation Development Laboratory; a chemistry hot laboratory; and many other facilities.

At present (1963) the laboratory employs more than 2,600 persons, of whom 400 are scientists and 700 technical personnel. In addition, in accordance with laboratory policy, over 400 scientists and graduate students participate intermittently in the Laboratory's research program with members of the regular staff. An important feature of the scientific staff is the considerable number of scientists from other countries who come to work for one or more years, to learn the methods, to utilize the special facilities, and to collaborate in advancing technical knowledge in their special field of work. In the summer the laboratory provides additional research and training opportunities for about 125 scientists and 150 students.

The stated objectives of the BNL, as part of the USAEC nation-wide program are: (1) to seek new knowledge in the nuclear and other related sciences; (2) to encourage appropriate use of its facilities by qualified scientists of universities and other laboratories, and industrial research groups; (3) to assist the Atomic Energy Commission in the solution of specific problems; and (4) to aid in the training of scientists and engineers in nuclear science and technology.

Of the many activities at BNL the three of most direct biomedical interest are the Biology Department, the Health Physics Division and the Medical Department.

Biology Department. During its 14 years of operation the department has maintained a basic cooperative research program with special arrangements for visiting scientists, graduate students and postdoctoral appointments. The department is probably best known for its gamma field, gamma greenhouse and the fundamental research being done on plants. Thus, the activities of the Biology Department center on the special facilities available and include studies of the biological effects of radiation and the use of isotopes for the elucidation of basic problems in biology. Increasingly the problems are being investigated by the methods of molecular biology with studies on protein structure, enzyme kinetics, the molecular structure and function of antibodies, the molecular structure of chromosomes and its relation to the mutation process. This approach has served to add knowledge concerning the nature of radiation-induced mutations, the ultimate nature of the mechanism of radiation damage in plants and animals, and the details of the basic reactions involved in photosynthesis. Each year the Biology Department sponsors a symposium on a topic of current interest in biology. The Department has been prolific in the publication of scientific articles.

Health Physics Division. This Division performs monitoring studies in connection with operation of the various facilities of BNL; handles the problems of disposal of radioactive waste; operates a decontamination reclamation center where items ranging from hand tools to 2,000-gallon tanks are decontaminated; and conducts research on various health physics problems, particularly those dealing with dosimetry. For example, the Division did a complete analysis of the health physics and radiation protection problems associated with the operation of the BNL Alternating Gradient Synchrotron and established safety factors and operational requirements. An integrated radiation monitoring, alarm and evacuation control system was designed and established for a complex of 4 critical assembly facilities. The Division also took a leading role in determining the dosimetry and setting up the radiation safety standards for operating the new BNL Gamma Forest for long-term ecological studies of the effect of irradiation of plants and animals in their natural environments. Basic studies in radiation biology are also conducted.

Medical Department. The research program of the Medical Department of BNL is based on studies contributing to better understanding of physiologic processes in man, and is oriented toward increasing knowledge of the effects of radiation in the human being. The Department has a large, new and well-equipped laboratory, a unique research hospital, and the first nuclear reactor designed primarily for medical research and therapy. A corps of full-time, regular staff members having "tenure" or "indefinite" appointments comprises the continuing scientific staff. Other scientists are appointed for specific terms in keeping with the general BNL policy of encouraging rotation, as well as extensive collaboration with scientists from other institutions.

The Medical Department is administratively organized into 7 divisions—Hospital, Biochemistry, Experimental Pathology, Physiology, Microbiology, Medical Physics and Industrial Medicine—all operating as a single functional unit. This Department also takes advantage of the special devices and extensive facilities available at BNL. The availability of the medical research reactor has stimulated studies designed to test the feasibility of utilizing this instrument not only for medical research but also for therapy, particularly of malignancy. The research objectives in this phase of the program may be said to center on development of an understanding of the interaction between components of living cells and ionizing radiations. Clinical studies have been designed to elucidate a number of disease states such as blood dyscrasias, diseases of the nervous system, hypertension and diabetes. Research is also conducted on radioactive tracer methodology from the standpoint of mathematical, biochemical, physiological and clinical approaches. Tracer studies using tritiated compounds at the organ, tissue and cellular level have been conducted. Research with the whole body counter has included studies of persons contaminated by accident, occupational exposure or fallout, or with patients who have received radioactive materials in the course of diagnosis or treatment. The Medical Department has been active in studying the Marshall Islanders who were accidentally irradiated by fallout. The conclaves on nuclear medicine for departmental chairmen of the various departments of the medical schools of the United States and Canada have been most effective in developing and disseminating information on the use of nuclear science and technology in the medical sciences and in the teaching of medical personnel.

BUBBLE CHAMBER

An instrument using superheated liquid to display the tracks of ionizing particles. Conceived and developed by the American physicist D. A. Glaser, working at the University of Michigan in 1952. He received the Nobel Prize in Physics in 1960 for this work. The density of the liquid under pressure is at least a hundred times as great as the supersaturated vapor of even pressurized cloud chambers; hence, the stopping power is good and tracks, including those of particles of high energy, are reasonably short.

Although normally a liquid will boil when its temperature reaches the boiling point it is possible to superheat it if the vessel has no rough surfaces and is clean. Then, when exposed to nuclear radiation, the resulting ions act as nuclei for the production of small bubbles along the path of the ionizing particle. These bubbles, spaced about a hundredth of an inch apart, form a fairly continuous track, which can be photographed against a dark background (Fig. B–30). The bubbles (from which the chamber gets its name) are analogous to the small droplets of liquid in the cloud chamber.

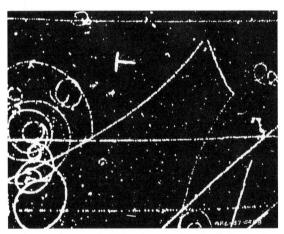

Figure B–30. A catalyzed nuclear reaction recorded in a hydrogen bubble chamber at the University of California Radiation Laboratory.

Ordinary ether was the first liquid employed but subsequently liquid hydrogen, liquid nitrogen, isopentane and other liquids have been employed for different studies. The first chambers were small (a few hundred cubic centimeters volume) but a liquid-hydrogen chamber of over 500 liters capacity is now in use. The operation is similar in some respects to the expansion cloud chamber. The liquid in a smooth glass or glass-lined vessel is compressed to several atmospheres (23 for isopentane) then heated to well over the boiling point. The pressure is suddenly released, thus becoming sensitive to demonstrating the passage of ionizing particles. The operation can be timed so that a flash of light permits photographs to be taken on a moving film. It has the drawback of not being continuously sensitive as are nuclear emulsions, but has been most useful in the study of charged particles of very high energy.

BUREAU OF MINES

The Bureau of Mines, an agency of the U. S. Department of the Interior, works with the USAEC in investigating methods for radioactive waste disposal, and conducts hazards evaluation work on pyrophoric and potentially explosive reactor materials.

See EXPLOSIONS, RADIOACTIVE MATERIALS; and FIRES, RADIOACTIVE MATERIALS.

BURIAL GROUND

Also called graveyard. Site of land disposal and burial, radioactive waste.

BURNS, RADIATION

The first obvious harmful effects to human beings noted shortly after the discovery of x-ray were radiation burns of the skin, followed by ulcers and late cancer in some cases. Radiation damage to human skin can be caused by various types of radiation exposure.

BETA BURNS result from skin contact with beta particle emitters and may be seen in industrial accidents, or as the result of fallout.

FLASH BURNS result from thermal radiation, for example, that produced by the detonation of a nuclear device.

ERYTHEMA may result from a mild beta burn or from exposure to other ionizing radiation, ultraviolet radiation, or thermal radiation.

Ionizing radiation may produce severe skin damage if the dose is high enough (at least 300 roentgens). The damage may vary from simple erythema to massive blister formation, but these burns never show the charring seen with severe thermal flash burns.

BURST.

See AIR BURST, SUBSURFACE BURST, SURFACE BURST, UNDERGROUND BURST, and UNDERWATER BURST.

BYPRODUCT MATERIAL

"Any radioactive material (except special nuclear material) produced in a nuclear reactor or otherwise yielded in or made radioactive by exposure to radiation incident to the process of producing or utilizing special nuclear material." This definition from the Code of Federal Regulations (CFR), Title 10 Atomic Energy, Part 30 Licensing of Byproduct Material, includes more than 900 radioactive isotopes of over 100 elements.

The law is also specific about how byproduct material will be handled. For instance, Public Law 703 of the 83rd Congress, Atomic Energy Act of 1954 says in Chapter 8, Byproduct Material: "No person may transfer or receive in interstate commerce, manufacture, produce, transfer, acquire, own, possess, import, or export byproduct material, except to the extent authorized. . . . The Commission is authorized to issue general or specific licenses to applicants seeking to use byproduct material for research and development purposes, for medical therapy, industrial uses, agricultural uses, or such other useful applications as may be developed. The Commission may distribute, sell, loan, or lease such byproduct material as it owns to licensees with or without charge. . . ."

See LICENSES FOR BYPRODUCT MATERIAL.

C

CADAVERS, RADIOACTIVE, HANDLING OF

Handling bodies containing radioactive material requires care and special techniques on the part of the embalmer. However, a diagnostic tracer dose of a radioactive isotope presents no hazard; and neither does a body containing less than 30 millicuries of radioactivity from any of the commonly used radioactive materials except radium, which may be released for embalming without question. For the extreme case of a patient dying a few hours after receiving 150 millicuries of gold-198 in the abdominal cavity, the absorbed dose rate by anyone standing close to the abdomen may be as much as 0.3 rad per hour, but even here only a fraction of the permissible dose will be received in 2 hours. Removal of ascitic or pleural fluid should be done with care, and the fluid should be flushed directly into the sewer. Any beta-ray emitter deposited in a body cavity will deliver only insignificant radiation outside the body. A body having recently received iodine-131 may have appreciable quantities in the blood and urine, which should be handled carefully as the ascitic or pleural fluids were. Precautions must be taken to prevent inhalation or ingestion of the radioisotopes.

If the body is to be cremated without embalming no handling precautions are necessary, and there will be no radiation hazard from either stack gases or ash, if all the bodies handled per year do not contain a total of over 200 millicuries of iodine-131, and 2,000 millicuries of all other radioisotopes, except radium.

For further details see National Bureau of Standards Handbook 65, Safe Handling of Bodies Containing Radioactive Isotopes.

See AUTOPSY ON BODIES CONTAINING RADIOACTIVITY.

CADMIUM

Symbol Cd; atomic number 48; atomic weight 112.41. A silver-white metal found chiefly in zinc ores and as the sulfide in greenockite. Discovered by Stromeyer in 1817. Named from Greek *kadmia*, earth. Natural abundance furnished by 8 stable isotopes.

Used commercially as a protective coating of steel, in certain bearing alloys for engines, for pigments and in chemicals.

Foods contain about 1 part per million (ppm) of cadmium; and crop plants range from 0.02 to 2 ppm. No indication that it is required for either plant or animal growth. Lethal dose (LD) for cadmium chloride by subcutaneous injection: frog 30 milligrams per kilogram (mg/kg), mouse 20 mg/kg, rabbit 25-50 mg/kg, and cat 25-40 mg/kg. About 15 ppm in food produces mild poisoning in humans. Food poisoning from cooking in cadmium-coated vessels caused 689 reported cases of poisoning in the period 1941–46. Seventy per cent of the personnel of a U.S. destroyer were incapacitated in one outbreak. Occupational poisoning due to inhalation of fumes is extremely hazardous, with a mortality rate of about 15%. Mass poisoning of 23 individuals resulted when a cigarette ash ignited some finely divided powder; there were no fatalities but several victims had stormy convalescences and disability in one case lasted 2 months.

Twenty-two radioactive isotopes of cadmium have been identified; 16 occur as fission products resulting from the detonation of a nuclear device. Cd^{115m} (half-life 42.6 days, β^- and γ emitter) and Cd^{118} (half-life 50 minutes, β^- emitter) are both significant components of radioactive fallout since appreciable amounts remain at the end of 1 year. The maximum permissible concentration for Cd^{115m}, soluble material, for a 168-hour week (continuous exposure) with liver as the critical organ is 0.01 microcurie per cubic centimeter ($\mu c/cc$) in water and 10^{-8} $\mu c/cc$ in air. Insoluble material in the lung is also 10^{-8} $\mu c/cc$ in air.

Cd^{115} (radiological half-life 2.2 days, β^- and γ emitter) and Cd^{115m} are both available commercially and have been used to study cadmium distribution in biological materials and foods.

Cd^{109} (radiological half-life 470 days; with liver as the critical organ, biological half-life 200 days, effective half-life 140 days; pure γ emitter) is available as an accelerator-produced radioisotope. It is carrier-free and has been used to study metabolism of cadmium in animals. Also has been used as a low-energy teletherapy source for a small hand-held device for use in treating eye or skin conditions.

CALCIFICATION STUDIES. *See* BONE STUDIES.

CALCIUM

Symbol Ca; atomic number 20; atomic weight 40.08. Discovered by English chemist Sir Humphry Davy in 1808. Since it occurs in nature in rocks, especially in limestone, it takes its name from Latin *calx*, lime. It is a mixture of 6 stable isotopes.

Calcium is an intimate part of the metabolic processes of all living matter. The biochemical standard man is 1.5 to 2.2% calcium or 1,300 grams per 70 kilograms. Intake levels for the daily needs of various species give an idea of its importance to life: man, 0.9 gram (g); rat, 40 milligrams (mg); laying hen, 3 g; sheep, 4 g; 100-lb pig, 12 g; and cattle, 17 g. There are increased requirements for all species during pregnancy and lactation. The plasma level of calcium in most species ranges from 9 to 10 mg/100 ml (milliliter), toxicity symptoms being observed at levels of 15 mg/100 ml or above.

Four beta-emitting radioactive isotopes of calcium have been made and identified: Ca^{39}, β^+, half-life 1.06 seconds; Ca^{45}, β^-, 164 days; Ca^{47}, β^- (also gamma), 4.8 days; Ca^{49}, β^-, 8.5 minutes; and in addition a fifth radioisotope, Ca^{41} which decays by orbital-electron capture with a half-life of 1.1×10^5 years.

The detonation of a nuclear device coming into contact with the earth's surface will lead to induced radioactivity, which in the case of calcium may have biological significance. The amount of radioactive calcium will depend upon the amount of calcium in the soil. Assuming an average soil which contains 4% calcium by weight, and assuming that 10^{26} neutrons per megaton of yield were captured in the soil, the radioactivity (microcuries per megaton yield) would be as shown at the bottom of this page.

Of the 9 nuclides usually found in the soil from induced radioactivity, only iron-55 shows significant radioactivity at the end of one year.

Calcium-45 ($_{20}Ca^{45}$). A pure beta (β^-) radioisotope with a radioactive half-life of 164 days; with bone as the critical organ, biological half-life 1.6×10^4 days, effective half-life 162 days; particle radiation maximum energy of 0.256 Mev and average β^- energy ($\overline{E}\beta$) of 0.077 Mev; intensity 100% and range in water of 0.061 cm.

Ca^{45} is widely used in human, animal and plant research. Its most extensive use is in animal physiology, as will be seen by the following tabulation of "current and expected uses" of the isotope in farm animals:

A. Research Use
1. Estimation of bone accretion and resorption; influence of hormones, nutrition, exercise and physiological status.
2. Study of formation of teeth.
3. Determination of the availability of calcium of feedstuffs.
4. Study of the etiology of diseases such as milk fever, grass tetany, hypomagnesia, rickets, cage-layer fatigue, gallstones, and urinary calculi.
5. Study of milk and egg formation; placental transfer.
6. Study of mechanism of absorption of calcium.
7. Determination of endogenous calcium as influenced by diet, hormones, and other physiological factors.
8. Estimation of calcium requirement for various species.
9. Study of kidney function and its excretory mechanisms.
B. Routine Use
1. Estimation of the vitamin D content of feeds by a chick or rat assay procedure.
2. Determination of endogenous calcium in individual animals.

Medical use either in research or diagnosis is not as extensive, but there is an appreciable use in metabolic studies. A difficulty in using calcium-45 with human patients is the relatively long half-life of 164 days. This problem is solved with the present availability of calcium-47 (β^- and γ emitter) with its half-life of only 4.8 days, which is being used increasingly in place of Ca^{45} in studies of skeletal metabolism in humans.

The maximum permissible concentration in air for calcium-45 is 3×10^{-8} µc/cc (microcuries per cubic centimeter); and in water 5×10^{-4} µc/cc for continuous consumption. The maximum permissible body burden is 65 µc, the critical organ being bone.

RADIOACTIVITY IN SOIL Mc/MT

NUCLIDE	HALF-LIFE	Immediately	1 hr	1 day	1 month	1 year
Ca^{45}	164 days	47.4	47.4	47.4	41.5	8.95
Ca^{49}	8.5 minutes	174,300	21,400	—	—	—

CALIBRATION

Procedure to establish the response and to verify the scale of a radiation-measuring device by comparing, under identical conditions, with the response of a standard or absolute instrument. Also, evaluation of the rate of disintegration of a radioactive standard source.

For x-rays or gamma-rays the free-air ionization chamber is commonly used as the standard instrument, since the roentgen unit is defined in terms of the ionization produced in air. Valid calibration also requires that the energy of the radiation be specified and, in many cases, the dose rate as well. Secondary standard instruments such as the condenser r-meter are calibrated in this way and are then used to calibrate x-ray or cobalt-60 sources in routine service. Survey meters are calibrated in similar fashion. Alpha-ray and beta-ray instruments for laboratory or survey use are customarily calibrated by measuring their response to alpha standards and beta standards for which the rates of emission have been established separately by physical or chemical means.

CALIFORNIA, UNIVERSITY OF

Various branches of the University of California have maintained an interest in atomic energy since the early days of the Manhattan Engineer District. At present the following USAEC-supported activities are managed or run by the University:

DAVIS RADIOBIOLOGY PROJECT, UNIVERSITY OF CALIFORNIA; DONNER LABORATORY, UNIVERSITY OF CALIFORNIA, BERKELEY; E. O. Lawrence Radiation Laboratory, Berkeley Branch; E. O. Lawrence Radiation Laboratory, Livermore Branch; RADIOLOGICAL LABORATORY, UNIVERSITY OF CALIFORNIA SCHOOL OF MEDICINE, SAN FRANCISCO; LOS ALAMOS SCIENTIFIC LABORATORY; UCLA LABORATORY OF NUCLEAR MEDICINE AND RADIATION BIOLOGY.

CALIFORNIUM

Symbol Cf; atomic number 98; atomic weight 251; a radioactive transuranium element of the actinide series. Discovered in 1950 by the American scientific team of S. G. Thompson, K. Street, Jr., A. Ghiorso and G. T. Seaborg through the bombardment of curium-242 with alpha particles in the University of California's 60-inch cyclotron. Named in honor of the State of California. A total of 11 radioactive isotopes of californium, with mass numbers 244 through 254, have been identified. Californium-245 ($_{98}Cf^{244}$), the first to be discovered, decays by alpha particle emission with a half-life of 45 minutes. Californium does not occur in nature and has no known biological, medical or agricultural significance.

Cf^{249} (α and γ emitter) has a radioactive half-life of 4.7×10^2 years; with bone as the critical organ, biological half-life 200 years, effective half-life 10 years; and would reach 22% of equilibrium in the body within 50 years.

Cf^{250} (α emitter) has a radioactive half-life of 10 years; with bone as the critical organ, biological half-life 200 years, effective half-life 10 years; and would reach 97% of equilibrium in the body in 50 years. The maximum permissible concentration (MPC) with bone as the critical organ, for soluble material, for a 168-hour week (continuous exposure), is 10^{-4} microcuries per cubic centimeter ($\mu c/cc$) in water, and 2×10^{-12} $\mu c/cc$ in air.

CANCER, DUE TO RADIATION.

See CARCINOGENESIS, RADIATION; CARCINOMA, DUE TO RADIATION; CO-CARCINOGENS; SARCOMA DUE TO RADIATION; and TUMORS DUE TO RADIATION.

CANCER RESEARCH INSTITUTE

The Cancer Research Institute of the New England Deaconess Hospital, Boston, Massachusetts, is one of the major research efforts supported by the USAEC. As early as 1937, its director, Dr. Shields Warren, was doing research work in radiobiology, particularly as related to the effects of exposure to x-rays. During the intervening years the work has broadened to cover the following areas, as indicated by the Institute's table of organization: biochemistry, biophysics and radiation protection, biostatistics and administration, clinical contacts, experimental pathology, hematology, radiobiology, and x-ray diffraction. The staff totals 58 persons of whom 23 are scientists.

As an example of the basic research, the experimental pathology program has brought international recognition of the potency of ionizing radiation as an experimental tool in the embryology of the central nervous system, and has focused attention on the importance of guarding the developing fetus from undue radiation exposure.

CANCER TREATMENT.

See BASAL CELL CARCINOMA; BRACHYTHERAPY; BRAIN TUMOR BED IRRADIATION; CHONDROSARCOMA, TREATMENT; COLLOIDAL AND LARGE PARTICLE RADIOISOTOPES FOR MEDICAL USE; INTERSTITIAL IMPLANTS; INTERSTITIAL INJECTIONS; INTRACAVITARY USE OF RADIOACTIVE COLLOIDS; LEUKEMIA, TREATMENT; MALIGNANT LYMPHOMAS, TREATMENT; MEDICAL TREATMENT; MULTIPLE MYELOMA, TREATMENT; NEUTRON CAPTURE THERAPY;

PITUITARY GLAND IRRADIATION; RADIOTHERAPY; TELETHERAPY; and THYROID CANCER, TREATMENT.

CAPTURE

Process by which an atom or atomic nucleus acquires an additional particle; for example, the capture of electrons by positive ions, or of electrons by nuclei, or of neutrons by nuclei.

Radiative capture is a nuclear capture process resulting in the emission of electromagnetic radiation only (gamma ray). Examples are the (n,γ) and (p,γ) nuclear reactions.

ELECTRON CAPTURE is a radioactive transformation of a nuclide of a given mass number and atomic number to another nuclide with the same mass number but an atomic number one unit lower: $_{26}Fe^{55} + {}_{-1}e^{0}$ (electron) $\longrightarrow {}_{25}Mn^{55}$. Usually called orbital-electron capture, since the captured electron usually comes from one of the electron shells surrounding the nucleus. If the electron comes from the K shell, the process is called K-electron capture; if it comes from the L shell, L-electron capture.

NEUTRON CAPTURE has great significance in the production of radioactive isotopes, in the effects from the detonation of a nuclear device, and in induced radioactivity.

Capture gamma rays are those emitted immediately after a neutron capture of the (n,γ) type.

Capture cross section is the cross section effective for radiative capture.

CARBOHYDRATE STUDIES

Carbohydrates (hydrates of carbon) are the aldehyde or ketone derivatives of polyhydrate alcohols, the chief members of the group being the starches and sugars. Of all foodstuffs, carbohydrates are used the most for energy sources by organisms. Pentoses and hexoses are obtained in large quantity from animal and plant sources. Glucose, a hexose, is perhaps the most important of all carbohydrates. Before availability of radioisotopes, the study of intermediary carbohydrate metabolism was limited to measurement of what organic compounds entered the body, what compounds could be found in various tissues and fluids, and what compounds were excreted. Understanding of how carbohydrates were converted in the body was attained only by tedious effort and brilliant deduction.

Radioisotopes have shown readily that many constituents of the body are continuously being built up and broken down, and that these processes are cyclic in nature. Energy is required for synthetic processes to take place, and the energy released upon degradation must be trapped in order to be used by the cell. The chemical compounds most frequently serving for the transfer of energy between degradative and synthetic processes are the high-energy phosphate compounds such as adenosine triphosphate (ATP). The general laboratory approach involves the administration of isotopic compounds and the subsequent isolation, purification and measurement of possible synthetic or degradation products. Rigorous isolation procedures and a wide application of degradation methods to allow assignment of the label to specific carbon atoms within the molecule have allowed increasingly detailed interpretations of the mechanisms involved.

An example of carbohydrate studies using radioisotopes is the citric acid cycle, discovered by Krebs, which is the primary pathway by means of which oxidation occurs in animals. The occurrence of this cycle in animal tissues was confirmed in many details by the use of radioactive carbon (C^{14}). Substances such as glucose, which can be converted to acetic acid, are oxidized by this pathway, which may be represented as follows:

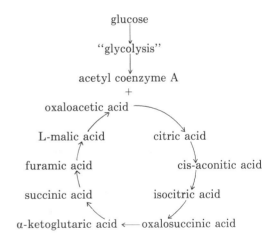

The citric acid cycle

CARBON

Symbol C; atomic number 6; atomic weight 12.011. Carbon, either free or combined in numerous forms, occurs extensively in the earth's crust, in all living matter, and in the atmosphere. Its name comes from Latin *carbo*, charcoal. Carbon occurs free as diamonds and as graphite; combined, as carbonate rocks, such as limestone; as hydrocarbons in petroleum, natural gas and coal; in the air as an oxide, carbon dioxide (CO_2), which is in part produced by the oxidation of foods by man and animals and given off through respiration; and as a constituent of all plant and animal life. The standard man (biochemical) is 18% carbon—12,680 grams per 70 kilograms.

Carbon has myriad uses depending upon its form: diamonds as jewels and for cutting and abrasive material; graphite in lubricants and as an electrical conductor; activated carbon to remove odor from water; coke and wood charcoal as fuels; and many others. Carbon-12 has been officially adopted as the standard for atomic weights, replacing oxygen.

The two stable isotopes of carbon are C^{12} which accounts for 98.892% of the abundance and C^{13}, yielding 1.108%. The 4 radioactive isotopes are: C^{10}, a beta (β^+) emitter with a half-life of 19.1 seconds; C^{11}, β^+, 20.4 minutes; C^{15}, β^-, 2.4 seconds; and C^{14}, β^-, 5,760 years.

Carbon-14 ($_6C^{14}$). A pure beta-emitter with the very long radioactive half-life of 5,760 years; with bone as the critical organ, biological half-life 40 days; effective half-life 40 days; is probably the most important of all radioisotopes.

It changes by decay to stable nitrogen-14 with the emission of β^- of a maximum energy of 0.156 Mev and a range in water of 0.029 cm. It is formed as a result of neutron interaction with nitrogen [N^{14} (n,p—neutron proton) C^{14} reaction] as follows:

$$_7N^{14} + _0n^1 \longrightarrow {}_6C^{14} + {}_1p^1$$

Carbon-14 is formed naturally as the result of cosmic-ray bombardment of the nitrogen in the atmosphere and is present in atmospheric carbon dioxide in fixed or equilibrium concentrations. By this action carbon-14 is produced in nature in amounts estimated from 7 to 10 kilograms per year.

It is also produced as a result of nuclear weapon explosions, for all nuclear weapons involve in their nuclear reactions the production of neutrons, and some of these neutrons escape to the outside environment, where they are captured by nitrogen nuclei in the air to form carbon-14 by the same reaction noted above. In U.S. weapons tests, approximately 2×10^{26} ATOMS of carbon-14 are formed per megaton of total (not fission alone) yield for air bursts. Expressed in activity units, 2×10^{26} atoms of carbon-14 represent about 20,000 curies, or expressed in weight units approximately 4.7 kilograms. There is a factor of uncertainty of 2, and, in addition, for surface bursts, this number should be divided by 2 because about one-half the escaping neutrons would be captured in surface materials rather than escaping into the air. The total number of carbon-14 atoms produced by the detonation of 174 megatons of nuclear explosives and released into the at-

mosphere from all U.S. tests up to the suspension of atomic tests on 31 October, 1958, is estimated to have been 25×10^{27} atoms. If this amount of carbon-14 were mixed throughout the world atmosphere only, the total tropospheric concentration would be 1 3/4 times the natural equilibrium concentration. However, mixture with the surface layers of the oceans will reduce the concentration to a level of 1 1/3 times the natural concentration.

Carbon-14 may also be produced artificially in nuclear reactors, usually by irradiation of boron nitride or beryllium nitride pellets, beryllium serving essentially as an inert carrier. Chemical treatment separates the product from the carrier.

Carbon, including carbon-14, since it is an integral part of all living matter, has great biological significance. It exists in the atmosphere as radioactive carbon dioxide and as such takes part in the over-all carbon cycle of the earth, mixing with ocean water and with the biosphere (plants and animals) and entering man's body. Because carbon-14 appears to have been produced at a constant rate for millions of years, it now exists on earth essentially in a constant quantity: whatever is made each year compensates, approximately, for what decays.

Carbon-14 is used extensively in tracer experiments both in plants and animals. It has been used so widely as a label for so many organic compounds in biological experiments that it would be almost impossible to enumerate them individually. The Isotope Index (Scientific Equipment Co., P.O. Box 19086, Indianapolis 19, Indiana) lists about 780 commercially available C^{14}-labeled compounds.

Compounds such as C^{14}-labeled carbonate, bicarbonate, acetate, amino acids, ascorbic acid, adrenalin, codeine, digitoxin, and ergosterol have been given through routes such as oral, intraperitoneal, intravenous, and skin, for metabolic studies using rats, mice, guinea pigs, rabbits and other laboratory animals. Biosynthesis of uric acid has been studied in pigeons, lactose formation has been studied in goats, and radioactive silk has been produced by injecting a C^{14} compound into silkworms.

Innumerable plant studies have been performed using C^{14}-labeled compounds, but by far the most striking use is in the isotope farm, a specially constructed greenhouse where plants are grown in a carbon dioxide atmosphere where CO_2 is labeled with carbon-14 to make $C^{14}O_2$. The plant uses the $C^{14}O_2$ and is thus effectively labeled and ready for animal metabolic studies. For example, when it was desired to determine how an animal metabolized soybean oil, it was a simple matter to grow soybeans in a radioactive carbon dioxide atmosphere, thus incorporating C^{14} throughout the beans and effectively labeling the soybean oil for tracer metabolic studies.

The well-known carbon dating work of Dr. Willard F. Libby (for which he received the Nobel prize in 1960) took advantage of the fact that carbon-14 is present in atmospheric carbon dioxide in fixed (i.e., equilibrium) concentrations and also that all living matter takes up carbon as an intimate part of its organic matter. Therefore, when an organism dies, it ceases to take up carbon dioxide, and from the moment of death, the amount of carbon-14 present in its system will begin to diminish at the rate fixed by the isotope's decay half-life (5,760 years). In every organism there is also present a known proportion of stable carbon-12. Thus one has only to measure the proportion of carbon-14 to carbon-12 at a given time to estimate the time since death occurred. Advantage has been taken of this fact to do archeological/geological dating or age estimation. It should be noted that the chemistry and counting are extremely difficult and a very special laboratory and techniques are essential.

Since carbon is an intimate part of all living matter, and since radiation is known to be deleterious, it follows that radioactive carbon is a potential hazard to man, for in his body it emits radiation that can affect living cells detrimentally. The genetic hazard may also be important, since C^{14} as a part of organic molecules is incorporated into the genetic material, deoxyribonucleic acid (DNA). In addition to radiation, C^{14} is constantly undergoing change—transmutation—by decay to another element, nitrogen, of different chemical characteristics, and this change in itself may possibly be deleterious to living cells.

CARCINOGENESIS, RADIATION

Human medical experience and extensive animal experimentation have provided ample proof that various types of radiation have carcinogenic (cancer-producing) properties. External radiation, or irradiation from internal emitters, has induced, or as a CO-CARCINOGEN helped to induce, tumors of the blood-forming organs, leukemia; the skin and subcutaneous tissue, carcinoma; the skeleton, sarcoma; the lung, carcinoma; and various malignant processes of other organs and tissues of the body.

There always is a long induction period—in cancer from 10 to 20 years and in leukemia from 5 to 10 years. Clinical experience shows that malignant tumor induction is an infrequent, and definitely not an invariable or inevitable result of even severe radiation exposure, leukemia is the most probable end result of heavy whole body

irradiation, but even here the incidence is low. (See Table L–2 in LEUKEMIA DUE TO RADIATION.)

Local external irradiation of an area or organ must be at a dose level of 1,000 roentgens (r) or more, and must result in local tissue destruction (ulcers, etc.) before cancer is produced. Radioactive elements (plutonium; radium; strontium-89, -90) deposited in the skeletons of animals have produced bone tumors and have been observed in radium poisoning in man. Ten microcuries of strontium-90 appear to have equivalent carcinogenic effect of about 1 microcurie of radium.

Whole body exposure to external ionizing radiation has been shown to be carcinogenic, but here the incidence of tumors, the type and their site are highly dependent on the genetic inheritance of the animal, and there is wide species and strain variation. The only large-scale human experience was in the atomic bombing of Hiroshima and Nagasaki. The irradiated survivors have shown an increase in the incidence of leukemia.

In general, the circumstances in which ionizing radiation has been shown to induce malignant disease in humans have been the following:

a. Continued irradiation for long periods of time to normal structures such as skin, bone, lungs, hematopoietic system and lymphoid structures. Examples are the early radiologists developing cancer of the hands; radium dial painters developing sarcoma of the long bones; and cancer of the lung in the cobalt miners of Schneeberg and the uranium miners of Joachimsthal.

b. Heavy irradiation of normal structures such as skin and bone marrow beyond the power of these tissues to recover. An example is the development of leukemia following the therapeutic x-ray irradiation of patients with severe arthritis of the spine.

c. The therapeutic irradiation of precancerous lesions such as nodular goiter or giant-cell tumors of bone, resulting in malignant changes in the condition.

d. Acute irradiation of the whole body as in accidents and in the Japanese bombing cases.

CARCINOMA DUE TO RADIATION

Clinical experience and animal experimentation provide ample evidence that carcinoma (cancer) is one of the late or chronic effects of radiation exposure. Within a decade following the discovery of x-rays, carcinoma of the skin developed in a number of persons who had experienced severe radiation lesions as a result of occupational exposure or in the course of x-ray treatment. Carcinoma of the lung developed in miners of radioactive ores; and carcinoma of the mouth developed in some radium dial painters.

Local irradiation of 1,000 roentgens or more is required to produce carcinoma, and even then it appears that local tissue destruction (ulcers, etc.) must occur prior to malignant change. There is always a long induction period of 10 to 20 or more years in man, following exposure before carcinoma develops.

See CARCINOGENESIS, RADIATION; CO-CARCINOGEN; SARCOMA DUE TO RADIATION; and TUMORS DUE TO RADIATION.

CARCINOMA, TREATMENT.   *See* BASAL CELL CARCINOMA, TREATMENT; and CANCER TREATMENT.

CARDIAC DISEASE, TREATMENT

Certain patients with heart disease may be benefited by treatment with the radioactive isotope iodine-131. The orally administered radioiodine is picked up by the thyroid gland, where it partially destroys the functioning tissue, thus reducing the total hormonal output of the gland, leading to a reduction in the metabolic rate. This, in turn, reduces the workload on the heart. The treatment is used for certain selected cases of angina pectoris (heart pain) and persistent congestive heart failure. Enough radioiodine is usually given to completely destroy the function of the thyroid—usually doses of 10 to 30 millicuries, which may need to be repeated; the patient is then maintained on carefully controlled small doses of thyroid hormone as partial replacement therapy to prevent severe manifestations of hypothyroidism. Beneficial results are reported in the majority of properly selected patients. Less commonly, certain other patients with cardiac arrhythmias are treated similarly.

CARDIAC OUTPUT, MEASUREMENT

The cardiac output, which is the amount of blood pumped out by the heart per unit time, has been measured with sodium-24, with phosphorus-32-labeled red cells, and most commonly with iodine-131-labeled human albumin. A tracer dose of the albumin is injected rapidly intravenously and a continuous recording is made of the level of radioactivity over the heart or in a tube containing a stream of arterial blood. See Figure C–1. This recording will show a sharp peak as first passage of the radioactivity through the heart occurs, sometimes a secondary peak, and will eventually reach a plateau after complete mixing in the blood stream. The area under the curve for a single passage time is determined. This area, when related to the level after mixing, is the basis for calculating cardiac output in terms of total blood volume. Normal values are about 1.3 blood vol-

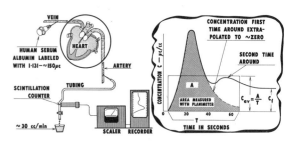

FIGURE C–1.   METHOD OF DETERMINING CARDIAC OUTPUT USING IODINE-131-LABELED HUMAN SERUM ALBUMIN. INJECTED ACTIVITY = HEART OUTPUT DURING $T \times C_{av}$ = TOTAL BLOOD VOLUME $\times C_f$.

$$\text{FLOW RATE} = \frac{C^f}{C_{AV}} \times \frac{V}{T} \text{ LITERS/MINUTE.}$$

(USAEC-1D-157A.)

umes per minute. To obtain a result in liters, total blood volume is calculated with the same dose of tracer.

See BLOOD VOLUME, MEASUREMENT.

CARRIER

An isotope or an element mixed with a radioactive isotope of the same element in order to obtain a quantity sufficient for chemical handling. Or a chemically similar element added to a radioactive trace of another element in order to carry it through a chemical or physical process. This tracer technique is used, for example, in studying the transuranic elements where the quantities available are usually very small (generally a few millionths of a gram). If a ponderable amount of thorium is added as a carrier to a solution containing a tracer amount of neptunium, and the total is chemically processed, it is found that the precipitate contains essentially all the neptunium activity. In a similar way bismuth acts as a carrier for polonium, iron for uranium X, and barium for radium. When the substance is a different element from the trace it is called a nonisotopic carrier. Such a carrier can usually be separated from the radioelement chemically if desired.

If no carrier is present or added, the radioactive material is said to be CARRIER-FREE.

The term carrier has at least 6 connotations in chemistry and physics and 1 in medicine (disease carrier), so the word must be used carefully and in context.

Figure C–2 represents samples of a radioisotope with varying amounts of stable carrier. Some isotopes, like radioactive iodine, can be obtained in practically carrier-free states and others, like radioactive gold, are usually obtained diluted with a relatively large amount of stable element.

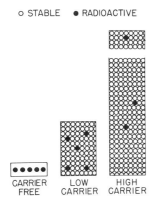

○ STABLE ● RADIOACTIVE

CARRIER FREE   LOW CARRIER   HIGH CARRIER

Figure C–2. Carrier principle. (Courtesy Medical Division, Oak Ridge Institute of Nuclear Studies.)

CARRIER-FREE

Term used to denote a radioactive isotope of an element in pure form, i.e., essentially undiluted with stable isotope carrier. Usually refers to minute quantities used in tracer studies. For example, a diagnostic iodine preparation is described as containing "carrier-free sodium radioiodide (I^{131})."

CASCADE

Any connected arrangement of separative elements whose effect is to multiply the isotope separation created by the individual element. For example, a bubble plate tower is a cascade whose elements are the individual plates; a plant consisting of many towers in series and parallel is a cascade, the elements of which may be considered to be either towers or individual plates.

The ideal cascade is the theoretical minimum number of separative elements necessary to perform a given separation.

A square cascade is one in which the circulation is the same in each stage.

In the process of disintegration a series of gamma-ray photons may be emitted simultaneously. For example, Na^{24} decays to an excited state of Mg^{24}, which in turn decays to the stable ground state of Mg^{24} by emitting two gamma-ray photons in cascade.

A cascade shower is a type of cosmic-ray shower.

A cascade particle is a negatively charged hyperon which decays into a lighter neutral hyperon and a negative pi-meson.

CASCADE SHOWER

Type of cosmic-ray shower initiated when a high-energy electron (many billions of electron volts) produces one or more high-energy brems-strahlung photons in its passage through matter. Each of these highly energetic photons produces a positron-electron pair, each particle carrying off half the excess energy. In the first generation, one primary electron thus produces two secondary electrons. Each of these secondaries can behave in a similar manner, so that there is a very rapid multiplication of the number of particles—hundreds or even thousands of electrons and positrons. This cascade shower builds up until the level of energy is so low that photon emission and pair production can no longer occur.

CATARACTS, RADIATION-INDUCED

Opacities of the crystalline lens of the eye and of the capsule of the lens are known to result from exposure to ionizing radiation.

X-rays, particularly in extensive radiation therapy involving the eye, have been found to produce cataracts, but large doses (threshold dose being 600 to 1,000 roentgens) appear to be necessary; therefore, ordinary diagnostic medical use of x-rays and the usual use of x-rays in industrial radiography do not present a hazard.

By 1948 it was noted that 5 nuclear physicists with a mean age of 31 had developed incipient cataracts. In January 1949, these plus 6 other physicists were examined and 10 were found to have cataracts; 3 cases were severe with definitely impaired vision and required operation, 4 cases were moderate, and 3 were minimal. They had exposed their eyes directly during the operation of a cyclotron, and had received, over periods of 10 to 250 weeks, an estimated median dose of fast neutrons of 50 n*; the range of doses was 10 n to 135 n. Human accidental exposure information and animal experimentation have definitely shown that fast neutrons are much more efficient in producing lens opacities than are x-rays; in fact, fast neutrons of 2- to 3-Mev mean energy have an RBE of 9 for induction of mild opacities in mice and greater than 9 for production of threshold lens damage.

There have been a number of careful examinations of the eyes of the Japanese survivors of the atomic bombing of Hiroshima and Nagasaki. For example, an intensive investigation was made of 3,700 exposed and nonexposed persons 6 to 8 years after exposure. The investigators found 154 survivors with posterior subcapsular polychromic plaques large enough to be visible with the ophthalmoscope. These presumably radiation-induced pathologic changes in the lens did not in general impair vision significantly, and in most cases vision was correctable to normal with prop-

*An n has energy equivalent to 1 roentgen.

erly fitted glasses. Of the approximately 8,000 exposed survivors of Hiroshima and Nagasaki who have been examined during the last 10 years, 10 cases of severe cataract have been found, about 25 cases of slightly impaired vision due to posterior polychromatic plaques, and perhaps 200 cases with minimal changes in the lens detectable only by competent slit-lamp examination. One can only conclude that there has been negligible loss of vision to date due to the atomic bombing.

The Marshallese inhabitants of Rongelap atoll who received the highest calculated radiation exposure (260 r) from fallout following the detonation of a nuclear device have been carefully examined several times by an ophthalmologist using slit-lamp examinations and photographic recordings of the cornea and the lens; no lesions ascribable to ionizing radiation have been seen. It appears that either neutrons or very large doses of gamma or x-rays are necessary to cause lens damage.

The lens is histologically such a simple structure that its possible ultimate response to any trauma or injury is limited almost exclusively to cataract formation. In addition to radiation injury, many other types of injury and metabolic disease result in the production of opacities. Cataracts are known to be associated also with general physiological aging.

CATHODE

Negatively charged electrode such as the electron-emitting surface in an x-ray tube, betatron, or ordinary electronic vacuum (valve) tube. Its function is normally to hold or give off negative charges or to attract and collect positive charges.

CATHODE-RAY TUBE HAZARDS

Any gas-discharge tube or vacuum tube in which electrons are subjected to electrical potential drop of 20 kilovolts (kv) or more may produce x-rays. If the voltage is under 30 kv the amount may be negligible, but if it is above 30 kv, radiation levels should be carefully determined. Cathode-ray oscilloscopes, radarscopes, rectifier tubes, high-voltage power tubes, and klystrons and magnetrons operating in high-power radar equipment are quite likely to produce x-rays to a varying degree, and adequate shielding should be provided.

See TELEVISION, RADIATION.

CAUTION SIGNS, LABELS, AND SIGNALS

The USAEC prescribes* that wherever there is any radiation hazard the approved RADIATION

---

*Federal Register, Title 10—Atomic Energy; Chapter 1—Atomic Energy Commission, Part 20—Standards for Protection Against Radiation.

WARNING SYMBOL and the appropriate caution signs shall be displayed. In addition to the standard signs such as

CAUTION

RADIOACTIVE MATERIAL

licensees are encouraged to provide on or near such signs additional information to aid personnel to minimize radiation exposure.

See RADIATION AREA.

CAVE

Protective enclosure for the storage of radioactive substances, designed to diminish radiation in the surrounding space to a safe level; generally constructed of heavy shielding materials such as lead (Pb), steel, or concrete.

See HOT CELL.

CELL CULTURE

Growth of mammalian cells in tissue culture. By very careful techniques it has been possible to plate a known number of cells and observe colony formation from single cells. Many types of cell have been thus cultured. This is an excellent tool for use in radiobiology, particularly for studying the effects of various types of radiation at the cellular and subcellular level (remembering that a cell thus grown is not directly comparable with a normal cell actually growing in the human body). In one experiment, human cells were given various doses of x-ray and the formation of macrocolonies was scored as the normal cell survival end point; the mean lethal dose with this criterion was 96 roentgens. Cells that did not form macrocolonies did one of two things: they formed microcolonies and after 4 or 5 cell divisions they lysed; or they formed giant cells. With 800 to 1000 r almost a pure culture of giant cells was obtained—cells with 10 times the volume of a normal human cell. Many other end points have been studied. This tool has great possibilities in elucidating the effects of radiation on individual cells.

CELL DIVISION, RADIATION EFFECTS ON

Mitosis, the process of cell division which prevails in the organic world, consists of 5 recognizable stages: (1) interphase, a preparatory stage; (2) prophase, during which centrioles move apart and fibers appear between them, forming a spindle; chromatic materials become condensed, contract and become visible as chromosomes, whose number is constant for each species, 46 being the number for human beings; (3) metaphase, during which the chromosomes migrate toward the center of the spindle and arrange themselves in the plane of the equator; (4) anaphase, during which one set of daughter chromosomes moves toward one pole and the other set toward the opposite pole; and (5) telophase, during which each chromosome grouping forms into a cell nucleus and division of the cytoplasm occurs, separating the two nuclei and culminating in the formation of two new cells.

Exposure to ionizing radiation during any of the stages of cell division may result in abnormal mitosis. This may originate from the effects of irradiation upon the spindle mechanism or upon the chromosome complex but ordinarily upon both simultaneously. The most common effect, following doses of 200 to 800 roentgens (r), is a delay in the onset or an inhibition of mitosis, particularly in all cells whose nuclear membrane is intact, i.e., during interphase through mid-prophase. Mitosis is normally not inhibited in cells whose nuclear membrane is disintegrated at the time of irradiation and whose spindles have formed or have begun to form or to function, i.e., during late prophase through anaphase.

Radiation exposure may result in a prolonged period of time being required for completing the mitotic process. Early prophases may regress to the interphase appearance and along with regular interphases fail to enter division for a period of 12 to 15 hours, even in tissues which normally show constant and rapid proliferation. Following this period of radiation-produced inhibition there usually is a wave of mitotic activity with large numbers of cells dividing simultaneously.

Fragmentation of chromosomes and a lagging of chromosome fragments in the equatorial plate may also be seen. Presumably both the inhibition of spindle formation and the production of aberrant spindle types may be attributed to changes in the extranuclear centriole and aster mechanism in animal cells, or in the transparent protoplasm of the nucleus and the cytoplasm on opposite sides of the nucleus in plants. Chromosome modifications provide abnormal appearances in the spindle figures. Cells irradiated in late prophase show, at later stages, nodal thickening of the chromosomes, clumping, lateral adhesions, and changes indicating pyknosis (degeneration of cell with chromatic material condensed to a solid mass). Heavy pyknotic masses among the chromosomes ordinarily indicate necrosis of the cell after irradiation doses in excess of 800 r. At the succeeding anaphases and telophases, fragmentation, bridging, and unequal distribution attributable to centromere misfunction frequently appear.

Daughter cells may be formed with chromosome excesses or deficiencies. (See Figure C-3, which shows abnormal chromosomes as the result of

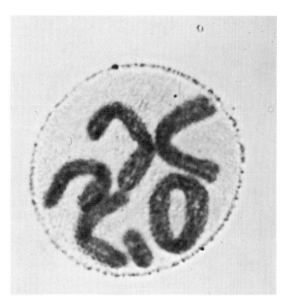

FIGURE C–3. ABNORMAL CHROMOSOMES AS A RESULT OF RADIATION. ONE IN THIS CELL IS COILED. (COURTESY OF THE BROOKHAVEN NATIONAL LABORATORY.)

radiation.) When chromosome replication has approached completion, or is complete at the time of irradiation, mitotically arrested cells may become complete tetraploids (4 sets of homologous chromosomes) and thereafter persist as such, barring concomitant deleterious chromosomal aberrations and related causes of degeneration and death. Such polyploidy (more than 2 full sets of homologous chromosomes) is less frequent than aneuploidy (having an unbalanced set of chromosomes), in which individual whole chromosomes may be retained in duplicate in one daughter cell and be totally absent in the other. Survival of either type of cell depends upon the genic constitution of the aberrant element. When aneuploid cells are viable, their proliferation gives rise to sectors of aberrant tissue whose size and extent depend upon the stage in development at which the aneuploidy occurs. Whole body aneuploidy for certain small chromosomes is frequent in man and Drosophila.

Heavy exposure to ionizing radiation may result in multipolar cell division, as seen in Figure C–4. This is a pathological form of cell division in which the spindle has 3 or more poles, leading thus to formation of a corresponding number of nuclei and daughter cells with varying amounts of chromatin materials.

Somatic crossing over, and hence recombination, may be induced by irradiation, resulting in mosaicism (different genetic constitution in adjacent tissues), which is produced by homozygosis. Ionizing radiation has an apparently contradictory

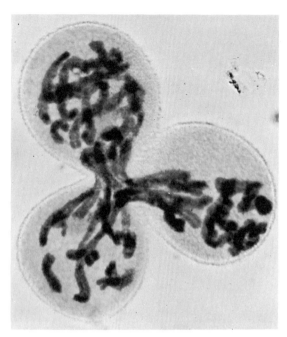

FIGURE C–4. MULTIPOLAR CELL DIVISION AS A RESULT OF RADIATION. ALSO MANY ABNORMAL CHROMOSOMES. (COURTESY OF BROOKHAVEN NATIONAL LABORATORY.)

Primary oocytes give rise to 4 daughter cells in an analogous fashion, but only 1 becomes a mature ovum.

Radiation exposure may affect any stage in the process of cell division and development in the same way as in mitosis. Figure C–5 shows a composite of the first meiotic anaphase of cells of Trillium erectum; a normal cell is seen above, and below a cell with bridges and fragments after irradiation with 50 r of x-rays at early pachytene phase. Figure C–6 shows Drosophila (fruit flies) with abnormal, rudimentary wings; they are offspring of males who received internal irradiation through ingestion of radioactive phosphorus.

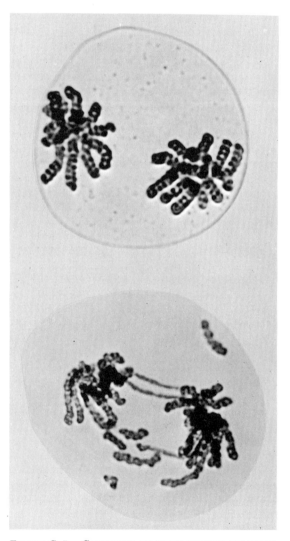

FIGURE C–5. COMPOSITE OF FIRST MEIOTIC ANAPHASE OF CELLS OF TRILLIUM ERECTUM. ABOVE, A NORMAL CELL, AND, BELOW, A CELL WITH BRIDGES AND FRAGMENTS AFTER IRRADIATION WITH 50 r OF X-RAY AT EARLY PACHYTENE PHASE. (MAGNIFICATION: 2000 ×.) (COURTESY OF A. H. SPARROW AND R. F. SMITH, BROOKHAVEN NATIONAL LABORATORY.)

effect on crossing over and hence on recombination, as shown in the study of Drosophila. The effect is to increase the frequency of crossing over in some chromosome sites and to decrease it in others. The most likely explanation of the different effects is that radiation promotes crossing over in the region of a centromere and in heterochromatic segments, but decreases it elsewhere. Some part of the decrease at regions remote from centromeres is probably a consequence of interference arising from the enhanced crossing over near the centromeres and in the heterochromatin.

Chromosomal miscarriages of all types may occur long after the irradiation. In insects, irradiated egg cytoplasm may cause the loss of either maternal or paternal chromosomes even after many cleavages have occurred. Inhibition of cytoplasmic separation of daughter cells may occur after irradiation, forming syncytial cells (a multinucleate mass of protoplasm produced by the merging of cells).

Meiosis is a special type of cell division occurring during the maturation of sex cells. Meiotic cell division involves a change from the diploid chromosome number (2n) of the parent cell to the haploid number (n) of the 2 daughter cells. Two successive nuclear divisions occurring rapidly (essentially meiosis then mitosis) give rise to 4 spermatids, which in turn give rise to 4 functional sperm, each containing n chromosomes.

FIGURE C–6.   DROSOPHILA WITH
ABNORMAL, RUDIMENTARY WINGS.
OFFSPRING OF IRRADIATED MALES.
(COURTESY OF BROOKHAVEN
NATIONAL LABORATORY.)

See CHROMOSOMES, RADIATION EFFECTS ON; GEN-
ETIC DEATH; GENETIC EFFECTS, RADIATION; GO-
NADS, RADIATION EFFECTS ON; and MUTATION,
RADIATION INDUCED.

CELLS, RADIATION EFFECTS ON

No living cells are completely resistant to
radiation. Cell damage may vary from alteration
in a single molecule in the cell which could be
repaired at once to complete lysis or destruction
of the cell. Observable changes may be classified
as direct or indirect depending on whether an
ionizing particle strikes the cell at the point of
damage (*see* TARGET THEORY), or the damage is
due to highly reactive substances (free radicals)
formed in the aqueous environment and later
reacting with the cell. Structural damage refers to
demonstrable pathological changes in the form of
the cell or its constituents, e.g., chromosome
breaks or pyknosis or shriveling of the cell.
Damage may be classed as somatic (*see* SOMATIC
EFFECTS, RADIATION-INDUCED) when it occurs in a
cell of the body, as distinct from genetic (*see*
GENETIC DAMAGE FROM RADIATION), which occurs
from damage to the reproductive cells (ovum and
sperm). Damage to chromosomes in somatic cells
may lead to cancer or, if damage is to reproductive
cells, to less-than-normal offspring. If chromosomal damage is severe enough it may lead to cell
death or failure of cell division (mitosis). Figure
C–7 illustrates the types of cell damage associated
with irradiation.

As early as 1904 two French scientists developed
a "law" which in general stated that radiation (in
their case x-rays) is more effective on cells in active
mitosis or division; that cells with a larger number
of divisions required before maturity are more
radiosensitive; and that cells are more radioresistant in proportion to the degree of morphologic
and physiologic differentiation. Younger or gen-
erative cells of a given tissue are more sensitive
to radiation than mature, functioning cells. For
example, the more rapidly dividing bone marrow
precursor cells are more sensitive than the adult
circulating cells. An exception to this is the
extremely sensitive small lymphocyte (*see* LYMPH-
OCYTES, RADIATION DAMAGE).

At any given time between the beginning of
irradiation and complete recovery, the amount of
radiation effect within the cell will be the amount
of initial effect minus the amount of recovery

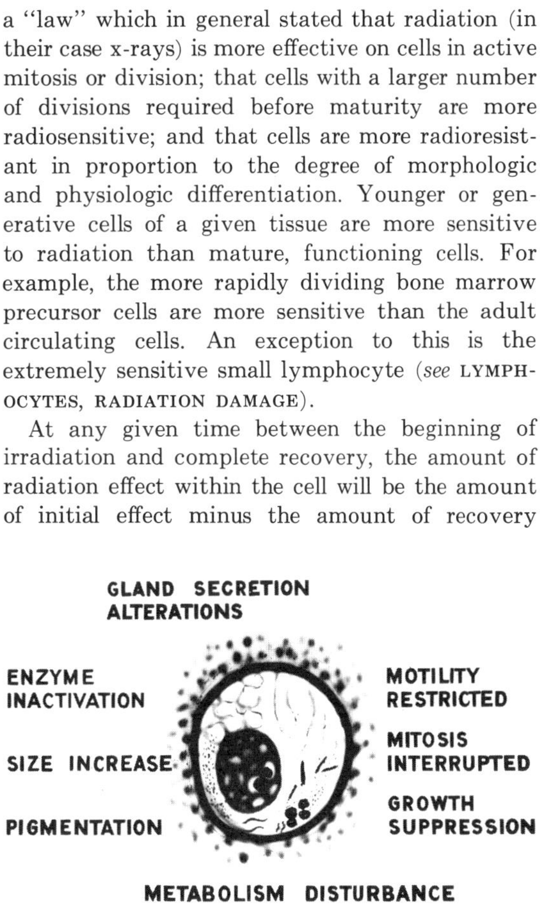

GLAND SECRETION
ALTERATIONS

ENZYME
INACTIVATION

MOTILITY
RESTRICTED

SIZE INCREASE

MITOSIS
INTERRUPTED

GROWTH
SUPPRESSION

PIGMENTATION

METABOLISM DISTURBANCE

FIGURE C–7.   TYPES OF CELL DAMAGE ASSOCIATED WITH
IRRADIATION.

which has occurred. This remaining amount is called the residual effect.

There is a marked difference in the radiosensitivity of the nucleus and of the cytoplasm of a cell, as shown by the following experiments: A few dozen protons directed to the chromosomes produced "stickiness," whereas tens of thousands of protons to the cytoplasm of the cell had no visible effect on the chromosomes; in alpha (α) radiation of newly laid eggs of Habrobracon the nucleus was inactivated by one α particle, but it took about 16×10^6 α particles for an LD_{50} when the cytoplasm was irradiated; and exposure of Drosophila eggs showed a ratio of 1 to 185 when the anterior nuclear portion was irradiated compared with irradiation of the posterior non-nuclear portion.

The type and amount of radiation are important. In one experiment on cells of frog eyes in vivo α rays were found to produce twice as much damage as gamma (γ) rays; thermal neutrons were found to be 2.5 times as effective as x-rays in reducing the first division of irradiated fern spores; and in irradiation of grasshopper neuroblasts, α particles were more effective, x-rays next, and beta (β) particles least effective in inhibition of mitosis. The dose rate has been shown to be an important factor, e.g., in both male and female mice the number of observed mutations is two to three times as great when a single dose is given compared with the same dose given distributed over weeks or months.

Environmental factors have a positive effect both on original response and on subsequent repair. Anoxia reduces radiosensitivity, and increased oxygen tension—up to about 21 volumes per cent at the time of irradiation—increases radiosensitivity (see OXYGEN, RADIATION SENSITIVITY). Decreasing the temperature reduces radiosensitivity (see TEMPERATURE AND RADIATION EFFECTS).

See CYTOLOGICAL CHANGES DUE TO RADIATION.

CELLULAR STUDIES

Radioisotope procedures, particularly autoradiographic techniques, permit observations on specific cells from among many. Thus, it is possible in the true sense of the word to study cellular function at the cell level. For example, experiments have been able to demonstrate the time of synthesis of deoxyribonucleic acid (DNA) in relation to the mitotic cycle. The success of the experiments was dependent upon resolution adequate to distinguish activity in single cells or cell parts and on removal of all radioactivity from the cell except that which was in the compound of interest. In this study, plant cells were grown in a medium containing phosphorus-32 and autoradiograms were made. The slides were treated so that the only P^{32}-containing compound left was expected to be DNA. This was further proved by the fact that when the sections were treated with deoxyribonuclease, which destroyed the DNA, no autoradiograms were obtained. It was shown that in this particular plant the synthesis of DNA occurred during interphase. Similar studies with rats have shown that newly formed deoxyribonucleic acid is found in tissues where divisions are numerous. The incorporation of P^{32} into individual nuclei has also been detected and related to the time of chromosome reproduction. It is suggested that deoxyribonucleic acid constitutes a permanent framework of the chromosome.

CENTRAL NERVOUS SYSTEM, RADIATION EFFECTS ON

The central nervous system (CNS) is the most radioresistant organ system in mammals. Within the component parts of the CNS, the brain is more radiosensitive than the spinal cord and peripheral nerves. No alteration in structure or function of monkey spinal cord was found after exposure to gamma radiation for 24 hours at the rate of 135 roentgens (r) per hour.

The Committee on Pathologic Effects of the NRC* in writing on the CNS said, "The adult nervous system may be affected by ionizing radiations in several ways. In the course of conventional cancer therapy, when parts of the nervous system must be exposed, several thousand roentgens may permanently injure the blood vessels of the brain or spinal cord, leading to ischemic damage. Many thousands of roentgens when delivered rapidly may quickly destroy certain elements in the central nervous system or, in other instances, so derange the function of vital centers as to cause death at once. Doses in the hundreds of roentgens seem to have little measurable effect on adult nervous tissue."

In acute radiation illness 3 general types of death resulting from whole body irradiation are: hematopoietic, gastrointestinal and central nervous system types. For the highest doses death results from damage to the CNS. For the rat this level is above 10,000 r; for the guinea pig the level is about 6,000 r; and for man whole body exposure to ionizing radiation above 1,000 r produces symptoms referable to the CNS such as convulsions.

---

*National Academy of Sciences–National Research Council. The Biological Effects of Atomic Radiation. Summary Reports. 1960.

See BEHAVIOR AFFECTED BY RADIATION; BRAIN TISSUE, RADIATION EFFECTS ON; and NERVOUS SYSTEM, RADIATION EFFECTS ON.

CERENKOV DETECTOR

Device to detect and measure the energy of high-speed particle radiations, utilizing the Cerenkov radiation to detect the passage of particles through emission of the characteristic Cerenkov light. By the addition of mirrors and cameras to record and measure the angle between the emitted light and the original particle beam, the energy of the particles can be determined.

CERENKOV RADIATION

When a very fast particle passes through a transparent solid or liquid medium at a velocity exceeding the velocity of light in that medium, the interaction produces an electromagnetic radiation called Cerenkov radiation. This is analogous to the shock wave emitted by an object traveling through air faster than the speed of sound.

CERIUM

Symbol Ce; atomic number 58; atomic weight 140.13. The most abundant of the rare earth metals, occurs in monazite sand, cerite and allanite. Discovered by Swedish chemists Berzelius, Klaproth and Hisinger in 1803 and named for the asteroid Ceres discovered two years before. Four stable isotopes furnish the natural abundance.

The cerium subgroup of the rare earth metals consists of elements lanthanum, cerium, praseodymium, neodymium, promethium, samarium, scandium, and europium.

Used industrially for lighter flints, tracer bullets, pyrotechnics, for polishing lenses, and for alloy in various types of metals.

Does not occur naturally to any significant degree in living materials. Insoluble salts are considered nontoxic, and soluble salts are only slightly toxic.

There are 18 radioactive isotopes of which 13 appear as fission products produced by the detonation of a nuclear device. Several of these have such biological significance in connection with fallout that the entire series is presented in the accompanying table. (The total number of radionuclides demonstrated as fission products is about 450.)

Cerium-139 ($_{58}Ce^{139}$). Radioactive half-life 140 days, gamma emitter, one of the radioisotopes, accelerator-produced. It does not appear to have any advantage over cerium-144 for biological and medical use.

Cerium-143 ($_{58}Ce^{143}$). Half-life 33 hours, beta (β-) and gamma emission. A fission product, which, together with its daughter praseodymium ($_{59}Pr^{143}$), is a biologically important component of fallout because of its bone-seeking quality and its abundance at 1 month (see accompanying table).

Cerium-144 ($_{58}Ce^{144}$). Radioactive half-life 290 days; with bone as the critical organ, biological half-life 1,500 days; effective half-life 243 days; beta (β-) and gamma emission. A fission product in a nuclear detonation and in reactor operation. With its daughter praseodymium ($_{59}Pr^{144}$, half-life 17.5 min., intensive beta (β-) and gamma emitter) is one of the most biologically important radionuclides in radioactive fallout (see Table C–1). One of the 7 nuclides for which stratospheric filter samples are analyzed routinely as part of the USAEC sampling program.

TABLE C–1. CERIUM FISSION PRODUCT ABUNDANCE

NUCLIDE	T 1/2	MAX. Mc/MT	TIME AT MAX.	Mc/MT AT 1 HR.	Mc/MT AT 1 DAY	Mc/MT AT 1 MO.	Mc/MT AT 1 YR.
Ce¹⁴¹	32.5d	38.9	23.8h-1.45d	4.13	38.9	21.35	0.0162
Ce¹⁴³	33h	843.0	2.40h	764.0	540	0.00445	a
Ce¹⁴⁴	290d	3.72	2.15m-2.13d	3.72	3.72	3.48	1.567
Ce¹⁴⁵	1.8h	12,400	1.47m	8,540	1.350	a	
Ce¹⁴⁶	14.6m	73,600	28s	4,185	a		
Ce¹⁴⁷	9s*	3,320,000	3s	a			
Ce¹⁴⁸	7s*	2,625,000	1s	a			
Ce¹⁴⁹	3.5s*	2,725,000	0	a			
Ce¹⁵⁰	2.5s*	1,900.000	0	a			
Ce¹⁵¹	2s*	637,000	0	a			
Ce¹⁵²	1.5s*	1,199,000	0	a			
Ce¹⁵³	1.5s*	257,000	0	a			
Ce¹⁵⁴	1s*	76,600	0	a			

Abundance of various times up to 1 year, given in terms of megacuries per megaton of fission (Mc/MT). A factor of 10^{26} fissions per MT used in calculations. T 1/2 is half-life; * indicates it is estimated. Letter "a" indicates values less than 1 curie/MT.

Ce^{144}-Pr^{144} together are extremely important in the handling and reprocessing of irradiated fuels, accounting for about three fourths of the beta activity and one third of the gamma activity given off by fission product wastes during the first year of decay. They are now being separated from fission product wastes and are available for large-scale uses.

Ce^{144} is the energy source in the nuclear battery being developed for satellite power. (*See* SNAP PROJECT.) Ce^{144}-Pr^{144} has been used for metabolic studies in animals and for radioassay. The maximum permissible concentration for a 168 hour week (continuous exposure) for soluble Ce^{144}, with bone as the critical organ, is 0.08 microcuries per cubic centimeter ($\mu c/cc$) in water and 3×10^{-9} $\mu c/cc$ in air. The half-time pulmonary retention of $Ce^{144}O_2$ for the rat was found to be 80 days.

CESIUM

Symbol Cs; atomic number 55; atomic weight 132.91. An alkali, silver-white metal, softest of all metals, tarnishes instantly on exposure to air and ignites spontaneously, reacts vigorously with water. First metal discovered by Bunsen and Kirchhoff using the spectroscope (1860). Because of the two bright blue spectral lines it was named from the Latin, caesius, sky blue. Occurs as the oxide in pollucite and lepidolite. Natural abundance furnished 100% by Cs^{133}. Occurs in earth's crust at about 7 parts per million (ppm) and in sea water at about 0.002 ppm.

Industrial uses: construction of photoelectric cells; a "getter" in radio tubes because of its affinity for oxygen; in ceramics; and for infrared searchlights in military use. Occurs in traces in animals and plants, but is not considered an essential element. Toxicity relatively low. May be used in thermoelectric fuel cells, proposed for ion rockets.

Twenty-two radioactive isotopes have been identified. Eleven may be fission products resulting from the detonation of a nuclear device or produced in the operation of a nuclear reactor. Cesium-134, radioactive half-life 2.3 years, and cesium-137 are commercially available. Cs^{137} is the most important of the cesium radionuclides.

Cesium-137 ($_{55}Cs^{137}$). Radioactive half-life 33 years, effective half-life 17 days (as CsCl), beta (β^-) emitter. Important in radioactive fallout, for at the end of 1 year 0.0910 megacurie per megaton of fission is still present, and also because it is the principal source of gamma rays through its daughter barium-137m, radioactive half-life 2.6 minutes, gamma energy 0.662 Mev, which decays by isomeric transition (IT). Cs^{137} is one of the radioisotopes routinely analyzed for in high-altitude samples. Cs^{137} falling upon and entering the soil is bound up to about 99% and is not taken up by the plant. Thus, only direct contamination of plants eaten by the cow (or man) is responsible for entry into the food chain. Most of the ingested cesium is found in the body muscle mass, where it turns over rather rapidly, reaching equilibrium in a few months. Excreted in the cow's milk as well as the urine. Thus the major source of Cs^{137} in our diet comes from meat and milk. However, as long as the contamination is not greater than it was during our period of testing of nuclear weapons, the internal radioactive contamination from Cs^{137} will remain relatively insignificant. As a soft tissue internal emitter it is a potential genetic hazard.

As fuel residue gross fission products are allowed to age, Cs^{137} and Sr^{90} emerge as the principal source of radiation in the mixture. Thus the separation and removal of Cs^{137} from the mixture will go a long way toward solving the waste disposal problem. The Oak Ridge Fission Product Development Laboratory for separation of various isotopes from gross fission products is producing large quantities of Cs^{137} for use. One of the applications considered is as a massive radiation source.

The use of Cs^{137} as a teletherapy source has been carefully investigated since 1955 and it has been found to have a few advantages over cobalt (Co^{60}) sources and multivolt x-ray for selected types of therapy. It will not replace Co^{60} but in the larger hospital clinics may be added as one type of available teletherapy for malignancy. Also used in industrial radiography as a radiation source.

The maximum permissible concentration of soluble material for a 168-hour (continuous exposure) week with the total body as the critical organ is 2×10^{-4} microcuries per cubic centimeter ($\mu c/cc$) in water and 2×10^{-8} $\mu c/cc$ in air.

CHAIN REACTION

A reaction in which one of the agents necessary to the reaction is itself produced by the reaction so as to cause like reactions. In the neutron-fission chain reaction, a neutron plus a fissionable atom causes a fission resulting in a number of neutrons which in turn cause other fissions. Fissionable material such as uranium-233, uranium-235, or plutonium-239 will react as follows: Neutron + uranium-235 $\longrightarrow$ fission fragments + 2 or 3 neutrons + energy. Thus the fact that, on the average, more than one neutron is emitted per fission, leads to the possibility of a chain reaction in a mass of fissionable material. The minimum requirement is that for each nucleus undergoing fission, there must be produced, on the average, at least one neutron that causes fission of another nucleus.

Whether the chain reaction remains steady, dies down or builds up depends upon the rate of production of neutrons and the rate of loss of neutrons to reactions other than fission of another nucleus.

A system in which the fissionable and nonfissionable materials are so arranged that the fission reaction can be controlled is called a nuclear reactor; a system in which the chain reaction builds up at an explosive rate is an atomic bomb. The rate at which the energy builds up is the important aspect for an explosive chain reaction. It can be calculated that it would require 1.45×10^{22} fissions, and hence the same number of neutrons, to produce 0.1 kiloton equivalent of energy. Starting with 1 neutron it would take about 51 generations to produce the required number of neutrons. A generation is the time interval between each two stages of the fission chain, and one generation for fast neutrons is about a one-hundred-millionth part of a second, i.e., one hundredth of a microsecond. The release of 100 kilotons of energy would require 1.45×10^{25} neutrons, and this number would be attained in about 58 generations. It is seen, therefore, that 99.9 per cent of the energy of a 100-kiloton fission explosion is released during the last 7 generations, i.e., in a period of roughly 0.07 microsecond. Extremely high temperatures will have been attained by the 50th generation (about half a microsecond time), with a nuclear explosion resulting. The neutrons will then escape and the self-sustaining reaction ends.

CHELATING AGENTS. *See* CHEMICAL TREATMENT TO REDUCE RADIOISOTOPE RETENTION.

CHEMICAL DOSIMETER

Detector having quantitative response to ionizing radiation, based upon alteration of a chemical property or composition, usually observable by titrimetric or colorimetric means. Dosimeters are prepared in forms for practical use in various ways, the most common being a sealed quartz glass vial containing the liquids which comprise the sensitive chemical system. Alternatively, films or sheets are formed by milling the chemicals into intimate mixture in a plastic monomer which is then processed and rolled into a sheet of suitable thickness. Also, massive blocks of gel-like or waxlike material with a uniform distribution of the dosimeter substance have been used to develop full-scale three-dimensional display of the radiation pattern throughout the exposed block. The system is made up of a chemical or mixture of chemicals sensitive to ionizing radiations. The ionization and the activation induced by the passage of the radiation through the chemicals causes and allows changes

to occur which are observable by ordinary means. Most commonly the result is a change in the visible color of the material, resulting from alteration of the chemical binding, different valence states, or modification of the electronic field within the molecular structure in such a way that the transmission of light is changed in spectral characteristics or intensity. Other chemical attributes have also been employed on occasion.

See FERROUS-SULFATE CHEMICAL DOSIMETER.

CHEMICAL EXCHANGE, ISOTOPIC

The exchange, without net chemical reaction, of an atom bonded to one molecule, with similar atoms in other molecules. This presents one of the problems in the use of the tracer technique, for the radioactively tagged atoms may not follow the usual chemical reaction.

Suppose, for example, that we tagged ethyl alcohol, C_2H_5OH, with H^3 on the OH hydroxyl portion of the molecule and then studied its fate in the body. We would fail completely because the hydrogen atom of the OH structure exchanges freely with other H atoms, and in a short time the H^3 would be widely distributed without any relation to any chemical reaction. Care, effort and ingenuity are required to select the right isotope and molecules. Exchange takes place with either stable isotopes or radioactive isotopes.

CHEMICAL PROCESSING, RADIOACTIVE WASTE

The processing, for final disposal, of radioactive waste by chemical methods. Such standard methods of concentration as incineration of solid waste and evaporation of liquid waste are actually chemical processes. Disposal into the soil of low-level activity liquid waste involves both physical and chemical reactions.

Reprocessing of spent fuel elements and the associated fission product waste disposal is also a chemical process. The removal of long radioactive half-life radioisotopes such as strontium-90 and cesium-137 depends upon chemical reactions. Purification of reactor coolant water for a nuclear-powered ship entails a chemical reaction in the use of ion exchange resins.

The standard process of water softening by lime-soda treatment chemically removes radioactive contamination. Other processes involving precipitation, co-precipitation, flocculation and adsorption have been used for removal of radioactive ions from liquid waste.

By far the most encouraging possibility for ultimate disposal is to chemically fix the waste in a solid carrier so that the possibility of migration of activity into the environment is eliminated or reduced to acceptable limits. According to one procedure, the actual fission products in the wastes would be sorbed to an inert solid carrier and then heated or fired to yield a ceramic. The incorporation of fission products into glass is an example of this approach. Several "conversion-to-solids" methods are under study, including the use of fluidized beds, heated pots, radiant heated spray columns and rotary kilns. As noted, in some cases glass-forming materials are added to the waste for the purpose of providing a really nonleachable final product.

CHEMICAL PROTECTION AGAINST RADIATION INJURY

Such protection has been demonstrated with several compounds. When these chemicals are in the body during exposure, they reduce the acute damaging effects of radiation on tissues. (These substances are quite distinct from those that reduce the radiation dose by facilitating excretion of radioisotopes.) (See CHEMICAL TREATMENT TO REDUCE RADIOISOTOPE RETENTION.)

Several groups of protective chemicals are known, major ones being those with free sulfhydryl groups, i.e., CYSTEINE and GLUTATHIONE, and those with both a free sulfhydryl and a basic amine group, i.e., CYSTEAMINE and AET. The most effective of these will approximately double the dose of radiation that can be survived. Protection against late radiation effects is not complete and varies with different agents. A deficiency of oxygen in the tissues is known to have a protective effect, and some of these compounds exert their action by producing oxygen deficiency. This is believed to be the mechanism of action of the amines; that of the sulfhydryl groups is more complex and is not entirely understood.

Since, to be effective, these chemicals must be given before exposure to radiation, their usefulness in military or accident situations appears very limited. Furthermore, they are in themselves very toxic at doses required to give good radiation protection. They have served, however, to greatly enhance knowledge of radiation effects and they offer promise of additional value in the future.

See HORMONES IN RELATION TO RADIATION INJURY.

CHEMICAL RADIATION DETECTORS

Systems in which a measurable chemical property is altered in a uniform and reproducible way under the action of ionizing radiation; these may be liquid or solid, ordinarily a mixture of the component liquids sealed inside a small glass or quartz vial, but sometimes made in the form of plastic sheet impregnated with the sensitive chemicals.

See CHEMICAL DOSIMETER.

CHEMICAL SYNTHESIS

The introduction of a radioactive isotope into the molecule to be traced by some form of chemical or biological action. One of the steps in tracer technique. The particular radioactive isotope being used will determine the synthetic method: with a short radioactive half-life it may be necessary to sacrifice yield to gain time; conversely, with an expensive, long half-life radioactive isotope yield would take precedence over speed and convenience. Because of the extreme dilution in which most of the labeled molecules must be detected, a high specific activity is wanted. Moreover, in general most syntheses are time consuming, hence radiation hazards must always be considered. Much of the work is done in caves or special cabinets, and with remote control equipment.

Many of the more frequently used compounds are commercially available with tagged or labeled molecules.

CHEMICAL TRACER

A chemical with properties similar to those of the substance being studied and which when mixed with it homogeneously will enable the determination of the distribution, location and action of the substance being studied. There are also physical tracers, radioactive tracers, and isotopic tracers.

See TRACER.

CHEMICAL TREATMENT TO REDUCE RADIOISOTOPE RETENTION

Sometimes the amount of radiation dose received by the body from an internal radioisotope can be reduced by decreasing the absorption or increasing the excretion of the radioisotope. (These methods are quite different from those that provide CHEMICAL PROTECTION by reducing the biological effectiveness of a given dose of radiation.)

Absorption of a radioisotope may be reduced by binding it in an insoluble form in the gastrointestinal tract, an example of which is the use of aluminum hydroxide to bind radiophosphorus. Sometimes it is possible to saturate the body with the element in stable form and thus prevent binding of much of the radioactive form; the clinical example of this is the use of stable iodine to prevent retention of radioiodine. An adequate supply of stable calcium tends to reduce but not to eliminate the absorption of radiostrontium.

Chelating agents are substances that tend to grasp certain elements and carry them from the body. Given orally, they may prevent absorption, and given intravenously or intramuscularly, they tend to carry the elements out of the body by way of the urinary tract. One of these agents that has been used chiefly for stable metal poisoning, but could also be used for radioactive metals, is BAL. Somewhat more efficient complexing or chelating agents are EDTA and DTPA. Another agent that has proved useful is zirconium citrate; when injected it helps prevent retention of radioactive heavy metals and fission products. Its mode of action is not entirely understood. The chelating agents and zirconium citrate are more effective if they can be given before the undesirable radioisotope enters the body. They are more practical for acute problems than for chronic low-level exposures.

CHLORINE

Symbol Cl; atomic number 17; atomic weight 35.457. A pale greenish yellow gas; one of the halogen elements. Discovered by Swedish chemist Scheele in 1774, but identified as an element by English chemist Davy in 1810. Named from Greek *chloros*, greenish yellow. Found in nature only in the combined state, chiefly as common salt (NaCl) in sea water, salt beds, and salt brines. It is the twelfth most abundant element. Its natural abundance is supplied by the stable isotopes Cl^{35}, 75.4%, and Cl^{37}, 24.6%.

Chlorine is used commercially as a disinfectant, for purifying drinking water, for bleaching purposes, and in the preparation of many chemicals. It combines directly with nearly all elements; 88 organic compounds of chlorine can be listed.

Occurs as the chloride in all living material and is considered essential for both animal and plant growth and development. A recommended nutrient solution for plants contains 0.177 parts per million; crop plants contain about 0.2 to 2%. Animal intakes vary widely and usually exceed needs. About 5 milligrams per day is considered adequate for rats. Chlorine constitutes 0.15% of the chemical composition of the standard man or 105 grams per 70 kilograms.

Chlorine gas has a strong odor, is irritating to the eyes and throat and is highly toxic. Concentrations of 3.5 parts per million (ppm) can be detected by odor; 15.1 ppm cause throat irritation; 30.2 ppm cause lung irritation and coughing; 40 to 60 ppm cause edema of the lungs; and 1,000 ppm is invariably fatal. Used in World War I as a poison gas.

Radioactive isotopes Cl^{33}, Cl^{34}, Cl^{36}, Cl^{38}, Cl^{38m}, and Cl^{39} have been identified. Three of these, Cl^{36}, Cl^{38m} (half-life 1.0 second) and Cl^{38} (half-life 37.5 minutes) are among the nuclides which may possibly be induced in both soil and sea water as the result of neutron bombardment associated with the detonation of a nuclear device.

Chlorine-36 $(_{17}Cl^{36})$. Radioactive half-life $3.03 \pm 0.03 \times 10^5$ years, effective half-life 29 days, pure beta (β^-) emitter. Available commercially, usually produced by neutron bombardment of stable Cl^{35} (n,γ). Decays (98.3%) by beta emission to stable argon-36, and 1.7% by electron capture to stable sulfur-36. Used in biological and agricultural research for: study of the absorption, distribution and excretion as related to the cationic component and the nutritional and physiological status of the animal; for study of acid-base balance, osmotic balance and kidney excretion in animals; and for determination of the "chloride space." Used in medical research for studies of the distribution, movement, metabolism and excretion of chlorine.

Because of the long half-life the radioactivity in soil and water at the end of 1 year is found to be 0.00019 megacurie per megaton of the original fission. Maximum permissible concentration for 168-hour week (continuous exposure) with total body as the critical organ is 8×10^{-4} microcuries per cubic centimeter ($\mu c/cc$) in water and 10^{-7} $\mu c/cc$ in air.

CHONDROSARCOMA, TREATMENT

These malignant tumors arising in cartilage, tend to take up inorganic sulfur, as does normal cartilage. When sulfur-35 is injected intravenously as sulfate a considerable concentration occurs in these tumors and it may produce a definite but limited therapeutic effect. This radioisotope has only a beta emission and has a relatively long radioactive half-life (87.2 days) for internal use. A large portion of each dose is excreted promptly in the urine; thus a high total dose is required. Therapeutic doses of 100 millicuries or more may be given repeatedly.

CHROMATOGRAPHY

Procedure by which different materials are spatially separated on an absorbent by their differential solubility in the mobile liquid phase and the fixed phase on the absorber. Accomplished in a column with the solution of different substances being passed through an absorbent. Gas chromatography separates material which is in the gas phase. Paper chromatography has been extensively developed. All three types of chromatography are made more accurate and quantitative by the use of radioisotopes.

See ELECTROPHORESIS.

CHROMIUM

Symbol Cr; atomic number 24; atomic weight 52.01. A grayish metal, hard, and capable of taking a brilliant polish. Occurs in nature in many parts of the world as chromite in chrome iron ore. Natural abundance furnished by 4 stable isotopes. Discovered by French chemist Vauquelin in 1797. Named from Greek *chroma*, color.

Commerically important as an essential component of high-speed steel, many of the engineering steels, stainless steels, and many corrosion-resistant alloys. Also used extensively in chemical industry. Only hexavalent compounds show toxic properties (mild). Recent reports indicate that it may function as an essential micronutrient.

Four radioactive isotopes have been identified, of which chromium-51 is important medically.

Chromium-51 ($_{24}Cr^{51}$). Radioactive half-life 27.8 ± 0.1 days, effective half-life 22 days, biological half-life 616 days with thyroid or kidneys as the critical organs. Decays by electron capture (EC). No positrons are emitted in the decay. The disintegration energy of 0.756 Mev is carried off chiefly by neutrinos. Usually produced by neutron bombardment of Cr^{50}, neutron, gamma (n, γ) nuclear reaction. Used extensively in medical diagnosis and in research in the study of red cell mass and red cell survival. The advantage over other labels is that the Cr^{51}-labeled cells have a half-survival time of from 30 to 39 days in the normal adult, and in vitro the bond is so stable that the half-time of elution of the chromium from the red cell is 77 ± 12 days.

CHROMOSOMES, RADIATION EFFECTS ON

The most readily observed effect of radiation upon chromosomes is nonlocalized "stickiness." The degree and extent of the resulting adhesions increase with the radiation dose, and range from chromatid adhesion through whole chromosome adhesion and finally through clumping of the entire nuclear mass.

Chromosome breakage, although occurring spontaneously, is greatly increased by certain chemical compounds and by ultraviolet and ionizing radiation. Chromosome radiosensitivity, as measured by this type of aberration frequency, varies with the state of the chromosomes at the time of exposure, e.g., interphases are less sensitive than later mitotic and meiotic stages (*see* CELL DIVISION, RADIATION EFFECTS ON). The radiation effects upon the chromosomes probably are brought about through the chemical action of free radicals, rather than by direct action as ionization or excitation in the target molecule, as postulated by the TARGET THEORY.

As will be shown later, the broken ends may rejoin in the original sequence, remain open, or if 2 breaks (4 ends) exist simultaneously in a cell, may reunite in a new arrangement. Through such breakage and rearrangements the genetic structure of an irradiated nucleus may be greatly modified. Genes or blocks of genes may be lost, duplicated, triplicated, inverted, moved to a new position in the same chromosome or translocated onto a different chromosome.

A mutational change may occur at the site of a break or a mutation-like event called position-effect may result from rearrangement of gene sequences. In addition to the possibility of breakage leading to a recognizable genetic change, the effect can also be lethal to a cell or, if transmitted by an egg or sperm, lethal to the resultant zygote or embryo.

The frequency of chromosome breakage and of resultant aberrations increases with increasing dose and, as is true for mutation, there is no threshold dose. The shape of the dosage response curve (DOSE-EFFECT RELATIONSHIP) depends upon many factors such as type of aberration, type of radiation, ionization density, dose rate, stage and nature of material irradiated, and upon many environmental factors such as temperature, concentration of oxygen, etc. So far, no method of preventing chromosome breakage in irradiated cells has been discovered, but the yield per rad can be considerably reduced by appropriate treatment of the organisms before, during or after exposure to radiation. (*See* CHEMICAL PROTECTION AGAINST RADIATION INJURY.)

Somewhat paradoxically, chromosome breakage and aberration are thought by many to lead both to a reduced rate of cell division or even cell death, and also to be associated in certain cases with an increased resistance or greater viability in certain tumor cells. Recent work also has shown that certain congenital human diseases can be attributed to the loss or addition of part or all of one chromosome. When one further considers that certain beneficial plant mutations are also associated with radiation-induced chromosome aberration, it readily becomes evident that chromosome structural changes are an extremely important response of living cells to ionizing radiation.

The breakage and reattachment of chromosomes are independent events which are separated in time; and when reattachments occur, the broken ends may have become separated in space through movement, however small. Most chromosome breaks are considered to undergo restitution, or reattachment at the original matching points, whereas only a relatively small portion achieve entirely new associations of the broken ends. The

number and location of chromosome breaks determines the types of aberrations which may be
induced by irradiation. The basic simple breakage
aberrations may be classified as follows:

1. The single break. A single break in a
chromosome results either in restitution or in reduplication as follows:

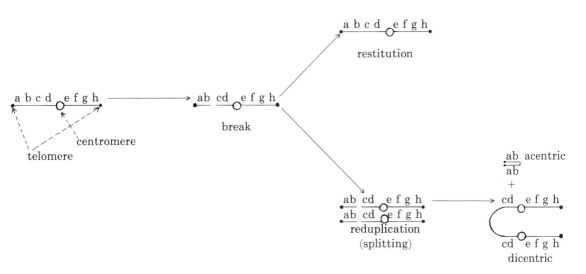

2. Two breaks. A, When two breaks occur in
a single chromosome the consequences may be
inversion, or 180° rotation of the segment which
lies between the breaks; or deletion of an acentric
fragment:

B, When two breaks occur, one in each of two chromosomes, a reciprocal translocation may be formed:

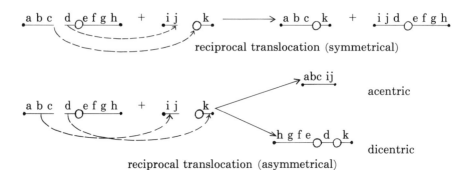

reciprocal translocation (symmetrical)

reciprocal translocation (asymmetrical)

3. Three breaks. A, When three breaks occur in a single chromosome, inversions and deletions may be produced as in the two-break situation; but a new type of aberration is also possible, transposition of either segment which is bounded by two breaks into the third break:

transposition

B, When the three breaks occur two in one chromosome and one in another, the transposition will result in the insertion of a portion of one chromosome into the other:

insertion

C, When three breaks occur one in each of three chromosomes, a progressive translocation may occur:

progressive translocation

More than three breaks may permit an un-limited variety of complex aberrations, combining the basic types and often superimposing one upon another. For all aberrations, deleterious effects often may be ascribed to gene mutations which may accompany the breaks.

CHRONIC EFFECTS, RADIATION

The long-term, delayed or chronic effects of irradiation which have been observed in animals and which may occur in man are the following:

Shortening of life span (*see* LIFE SHORTENING DUE TO RADIATION EXPOSURE).

Early aging (*see* AGING, DUE TO RADIATION EXPOSURE).

Increased incidence of leukemia (*see* LEUKEMIA DUE TO RADIATION).

Increased incidence of benign and malignant tumors (*see* CARCINOMA, DUE TO RADIATION; SARCOMAS; and TUMORS).

Lowered fertility (*see* FERTILITY).

Sterility (*see* STERILITY DUE TO RADIATION).

Cataracts (*see* CATARACTS, RADIATION-INDUCED).

Genetic damage (expressed as an increased incidence of mutations) (*see* MUTATION, RADIATION INDUCED).

Impaired growth rate.

Cardiovascular and renal diseases.

Anemia.

CHRONIC EXPOSURE, RADIATION

Radiation exposure of long duration, accomplished either by protraction or fractionation (*see* DOSE). The period of time may be months to years. Natural radiation, background radiation and environmental radiation, as well as industrial radiation exposure, are usually considered to be types of chronic exposure.

See CHRONIC EFFECTS, RADIATION.

CIRCULATION, RADIATION EFFECTS ON

Functional changes involving cardiac output, arterial blood pressure, blood flow and blood vessel diameter require an exposure to several thousand roentgens (r) of ionizing radiation. Five thousand r to the head of an anesthetized dog does not alter blood pressure, cerebral blood flow or oxygen consumption. Functional changes involving the diameter of blood vessels and blood flow in rabbits' ears and bats' wings require radiation exposures of 10,000 r or more.

Cardiovascular changes in dogs given whole body doses of 1,000 r of x-ray do not become evident until about 12 hours before death, and the blood volume is well maintained up to the last day. Whole body doses of 400 r or less have no effect on either cardiac output or arterial blood pressure in dogs.

Massive doses of whole body irradiation cause serious circulatory embarrassment in both experimental animals and in man. For example, one worker (Case K in CRITICALITY ACCIDENTS) was accidentally exposed to between 3,900 and 4,900 rad, the upper part of the body receiving the greater portion. He immediately lost consciousness

and within about 20 minutes developed such severe cardiovascular shock that death seemed imminent. His radial pulse and blood pressure were at first unobtainable, but his apical heart rate was 160 per minute. When finally obtained, the blood pressure was 80/40 and pulse still 160. Hypotension continued, in spite of supportive fluid therapy, for about 6 hours. Death occurred 35 hours after exposure.

Tissue destruction involving alteration in the vascular bed, fragility of the vascular walls, occlusion, and the late manifestation of fibrosis can seriously embarrass circulation and produce degenerative changes in the tissues supplied by the damaged vessels. Hemorrhaging can lead to circulatory embarrassment and ultimate cardiac failure.

CIRCULATION TIME, MEASUREMENT

Radioisotopes are valuable for measurement of the circulation time—the interval required for blood to flow from one point to another in the vascular system. A tracer dose, such as a small volume of iodine-131-labeled albumin, chromium-51-labeled red cells, or sodium-24 chloride solution are injected intravenously and time is recorded from the moment of injection. A detector placed over the heart or a blood vessel as in Figure C–8, announces the arrival of the labeled material; the interval that has elapsed since injection is an indication of rate of flow.

See CARDIAC OUTPUT, MEASUREMENT.

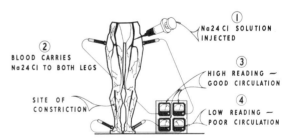

FIGURE C–8. METHOD FOR DETECTING NORMAL AND RESTRICTED BLOOD CIRCULATION BY INJECTING SODIUM-24 AND MEASURING ITS APPEARANCE IN OTHER PARTS OF THE BODY. THIS METHOD PERMITS RAPID LOCATION OF ARTERIAL CONSTRICTION WITH LITTLE DISCOMFORT TO THE PATIENT. (USAEC-1D-174.)

CIVIL DEFENSE

Defined* as "all of those activities and measures designed or undertaken (1) to minimize the effects upon the civilian population caused or which would be caused by an attack upon the United States or by a natural disaster, (2) to deal with the immediate emergency conditions which would

---

*Civil Defense Glossary. H-25-2 (Handbook) U. S. Civil Defense. Federal Civil Defense Administration.

be created by any such attack or disaster, and (3) to effectuate emergency repairs to, or the emergency restoration of, vital utilities destroyed or damaged by any such attack or disaster.''

The Office of Civil and Defense Mobilization (OCDM), formerly responsible for civil defense, has been reconstituted as a small staff agency, called the Office of Emergency Planning, to assist the President in coordinating assigned functions.

The responsibility for the fallout shelter program has been (1961) assigned to the Secretary of Defense. Responsibilities for related preparedness programs in health, food, manpower, transportation, and other needs have been assigned to other appropriate federal departments and agencies, who will work cooperatively with state and local agencies.

The following appear frequently in the literature pertinent to civil defense problems:

Civil Effects Exercises (CEX). These were individual research studies conducted by USAEC as part of the nuclear weapons testing program, under Civil Effects Test Operations by the Civil Effects Test Group.

Civil Effects Test Group (CETG). A USAEC and Civil Defense group organized to take advantage of nuclear weapons testing to accumulate technical and scientific data valuable for civil defense activities. For example, during Operation PLUMBBOB, the CETG conducted 58 projects connected with 21 nuclear explosions. Six general areas were studied: fallout radiation; prompt gamma and neutron radiation; blast effects on structures; blast biology; radiological countermeasures and training; and instrumentation of weapons effects. Data were accumulated concerning the consequences of blast; thermal, neutron and gamma radiation; and fallout on people, food, drink, conventional structures, shelter, utilities, transportation, and community services.

Civil Effects Test Operations. A program conducted by the CETG through which information, resulting from weapons tests, essential to nonmilitary defense (civil defense) is sought, obtained, proof-tested, and applied.

Emergency Broadcast System. EBS replaced "Conelrad" on August 5, 1963. In an emergency, all non-EBS stations will advise their listeners to tune in to local EBS stations and then they will go off the air. The designated EBS stations will stay on the air during their assigned hours of operation and will broadcast at their usual frequencies and power. To assure that vital emergency broadcasting is not interrupted by fallout exposure to operating personnel, protection is being built into key operating areas of EBS stations.

CLEAN WEAPON

A nuclear weapon so designed and detonated as to produce less residual nuclear radiation than the detonation of a normal nuclear weapon of equivalent yield. A weapon so constructed that its major energy component is from the nuclear fusion reaction (*see* THERMONUCLEAR REACTION and THERMONUCLEAR WEAPON) is relatively "clean," since the proportion of fission yield, and associated fission products from a nuclear fission reaction, would be relatively low. Other aspects being the same, a weapon detonated high in the air would be relatively clean since there would be a minimum of induced radioactivity, e.g., no tower materials and none of the elements of the earth's surface. However, even if a pure fusion (with no fission) weapon should be developed and detonated high in the air, there still would be radioactivity produced by the formation of carbon-14 by transmutation from nitrogen-14 in the air as a result of neutron bombardment.

A "dirty" weapon can be produced by "salting" a normal weapon, i.e., adding significant quantities of certain elements, possibly enriched in specific isotopes, so as to produce additional induced radioactivity. This would be done in radiological warfare. By its nature, a fission device (atomic weapon) is "dirty."

A salted weapon, therefore, is a nuclear weapon which has, in addition to its normal components, certain elements or isotopes which capture neutrons at the time of the explosion and produce radioactive products over and above the usual radioactive weapon debris.

CLEARANCE STUDIES

In medical tests, clearance is a statement of the rate of transfer of a substance from one compartment of the body into another—for example, the rate of removal of iodine from the blood stream by the thyroid gland. The procedure is used as a measure of the functional activity of the organ causing the removal. The clearance is often reported as the volume of blood that would have to be completely cleared of the substance to provide the amount transferred per unit time. (This does not mean that the organ removes all the substance with one passage of blood; partial clearance of a larger volume is what actually takes place.) For the determination it is necessary to measure the total amount cleared for a given period of time and the concentration (often a changing value) in the compartment from which it is removed.

$$\text{clearance in liters per minute} = \frac{\text{milligrams removed}}{\text{milligrams per liter of blood} \times \text{number of minutes in study}}$$

Radioisotopes, because they are so suitable for measurement in blood, thyroid and urine, have proved very valuable in clearance studies. The clearance of radioactive iodine by the thyroid and kidney is a typical example of this type of study. Radioiodine is also used as a label for such substances as Diodrast and Hippuran; their clearance is used as an index of kidney function.

CLOSE SHIELD

A radiation shield that fits closely around the container of radioactive material or other source of radiation. Lead, concrete or steel pigs are excellent examples, as are shielded syringes—plastic shields for beta emitters, and closely fitted lead shields for gamma emitters. Clear plastic shields allow visibility and are protective up to, for example, 10 millicuries of phosphorus-32. Such plastic shields have been used with beakers, flasks, centrifuge tubes, serum tubes, and similar items, and allow for safe handling by hand. Close shields utilize a minimum of shielding material and permit visibility and ease of handling, but the amount of activity which can be handled with safety is strictly limited. Particular care is needed to guard against doses to the operator from scattered radiation.

See SHIELD.

CLOTHING DECONTAMINATION

Clothing worn in contaminated areas is removed and delivered to the laundry facility where it is carefully monitored. In a typical installation it may be divided into 3 groups: (1) no detectable activity—laundered in an uncontaminated laundry; (2) low-level contamination, defined as: 2 milliroentgen per hour gamma, 9 millirad per hour beta, and 50 disintegrations per minute (dpm) per 12 square inches for fixed alpha; or removable alpha of 1 dpm/in.^{2} and removable beta-gamma (wipe method), 4,000 dpm/in.^{2}—must be laundered in separate equipment; and (3) high-level contamination, which is anything over the low-level values—soaked in 3% citric acid or versene, rinsed, dried and counted; if the level is not reduced suitably for ordinary low-level laundry, clothing is retreated or discarded.

See PROTECTIVE CLOTHING.

CLOTHING, PROTECTIVE. *See* PROTECTIVE CLOTHING.

CLOUD CHAMBER

An instrument with a chamber containing air or other gas saturated with vapor (water or other vapor) used in the demonstration of the tracks produced by the passage of ionizing particles. The path of a single ionizing particle (alpha or beta particle) can be seen as a white streak of mist, sometimes several centimeters in length, which can be photographed and studied. A great deal of information has been obtained in this way as to the nature and movements of particles and the interactions between particles and matter. Perhaps the most significant effect of this discovery is to provide the most convincing evidence of the reality of the atom.

The fundamental principles of the cloud chamber were discovered by English physicist C. T. R. Wilson, in 1896, who demonstrated the path of a single ionizing particle in 1911. Early cloud chambers were known as Wilson cloud chambers. In 1927 he received the Nobel prize for physics in consideration of this work. Although there have been numerous modifications, the general principles, as depicted in Figure C–9 remain much the same. A vessel containing air saturated with water vapor is put under pressure by means of a piston activated by compressed air from a supply line with a valve which can be suddenly opened allowing the pressure to fall and the saturated air to expand instantaneously. The air will be cooled as a result of the expansion and will become supersaturated. If an ionizing particle enters the chamber either immediately before, during or immediately after the expansion, the trail of ions it leaves will act as condensation nuclei and a line of fine droplets will form, called a cloud track. This track can be visualized as a white line in a strong penetrating light from the side (see Figure C–9). With two cameras at right angles, a three-dimensional permanent photographic record can be made similar to the one shown in Figure C–10 of the tracks produced by alpha particles.

This "expansion chamber" has been modified by using ethyl or propyl alcohol or a mixture of

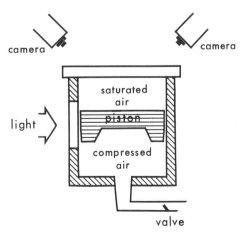

FIGURE C–9.   WILSON CLOUD CHAMBER.

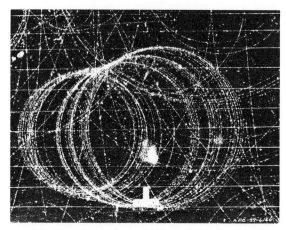

FIGURE C–10. CLOUD CHAMBER PHOTOGRAPH SHOWING
A NUMBER OF ELECTRON-POSITRON PAIRS BEING FORMED
IN THE GAS OF THE CHAMBER AND A TROCHOID PATTERN
FORMED BY AN ELECTRON SPINNING IN THE MAGNETIC
FIELD. (UNIVERSITY OF CALIFORNIA, BERKELEY.)

alcohol and water to saturate the air. Argon has
been used instead of air. Pressures have been used
from below to well above atmospheric. The operation of the piston has been made automatic so as
to produce pressure and rarefaction at regular
intervals. Automatic cameras are timed with the
piston and the entire mechanism has been constructed so as to function automatically when
triggered by Geiger counters placed at the top and
bottom of the chamber and responding to a cosmic
ray (for example) passing through both counters
and chamber.

Since the expansion chamber is intermittent in
its operation, a device known as a diffusion cloud
chamber has been developed which is continuously
sensitive to ionizing particles. Essentially, the diffusion chamber is a vessel containing air or other
gas which is kept cold at the bottom and warm at
the top. Near the top is a trough of volatile liquid
(usually methyl alcohol) which vaporizes in warm
air and continuously diffuses to the cold bottom
region, where the vapor pressure is low, causing
condensation. In between, the air is supersaturated
and conditions are right for demonstrating and
photographing the track of an ionizing particle.
This device can be used at atmospheric pressure
or put under pressure of several atmospheres;
continuous photography can be added.

The range of the particle can be measured; by
counting the drops, specific ionization can be
determined; and particles can be distinguished.
The alpha particle gives a short, dense track and
has the highest specific ionization; the beta particle leaves a track that is diffuse and tortuous. A
proton and a meson can also be identified.

See BUBBLE CHAMBER and NUCLEAR EMULSION.

CLOUD, RADIOACTIVE

A concentration of air-borne radioactive debris
carried in the troposphere or stratosphere. This
cloud of material originates from the atomic cloud
and stem resulting from the detonation of a
nuclear device above ground and is carried by the
prevailing winds (in the United States usually in
an easterly direction) in the same latitude as the
point of origin, although it diffuses both laterally
and vertically over a fairly wide front. British
scientists report that on the average the tropospheric cloud from a shot at Nevada Test Site
crosses England on the 5th day after detonation
and thereafter every 4 to 7 weeks as it circulates
around the world until it dissipates, usually by the
third time. This radioactive cloud is responsible
for tropospheric fallout which is brought to earth
by gravity or the scavenging effect of precipitation.

See FALLOUT PATTERN.

COAST AND GEODETIC SURVEY, U.S.

The U.S. Coast and Geodetic Survey, an agency
of the Department of Commerce, is responsible
for conducting surveys of U.S. territorial waters
for the purpose of determining the safety of
licensed ocean disposal, radioactive waste.

COBALT

Symbol Co; atomic number 27; atomic weight
58.94. A silver-white metal, harder and stronger
than iron or nickel. Discovered by Brandt in 1735.
Named from the German, kobold, goblin or evil
spirit. Occurs as arsenide and sulfide associated
with iron, nickel, copper and silver minerals.
Natural abundance 100% Co^{59}.

Used in stellite-type alloys and in carbide-type
alloys. Used as the bonding material in cemented
tungsten carbide tool and die fabrication. Also
used in the production of magnets. Used as a soil
dressing in areas where cobalt deficiency produces
disease in sheep and cattle. Ruminants require
about 0.1 milligram per day of cobalt per 100
pounds of body weight. Also required by other
animals to satisfy vitamin B_{12} needs. Crop plants
range from 0.03 to 0.4 part per million on a dry-
weight basis. Toxicity is very low. Elimination is
very rapid.

Twelve radioactive isotopes have been identified.
Co^{57}, Co^{58} and Co^{60} may be produced in sea water
by neutron bombardment associated with the
detonation of a nuclear device. Not significant in
residual radiation. Co^{60} is the most significant of
the radioisotopes, but cyclotron-produced Co^{56}
with its half-life of 80 days is being increasingly
used in biological and medical research.

Cobalt-60 ($_{27}Co^{60}$). Radioactive half-life 5.26
± 0.02 years; effective half-life 9 days; beta and

gamma emitter. Usually produced in a nuclear reactor by neutron bombardment of Co^{59} by the following reaction: $Co^{59}(n,\gamma)Co^{60}$. Decays to stable isotope nickel-60. Particle radiation type $\beta_{\bar{1}}$, intensity about 100%. There are two types of beta (β^-) radiation, almost 100% of the intensity being produced by type $\beta_{\bar{1}}$, which has a maximum energy of 0.314 Mev and a range in water of 0.082 centimeter (cm); type $\beta_{\bar{2}}$ has an intensity of about 0.01%, energy 1.48 Mev and range 0.67 centimeter. There are also two types of gamma electromagnetic radiation; type γ_1, photo intensity about 100%, has an energy of 1.173 Mev producing a dose rate at 1 meter of 0.63 milliroentgen (mr) per millicurie per hour (mc-hr); type γ_2, energy 1.332 Mev, dose rate 0.70 mr/mc-hr.

Used extensively in biological, agricultural and medical research and in medical therapy. The teletherapy use of Co^{60} is the most significant; there are about 500 Co^{60} teletherapy machines in use in the world, largely for the radiation treatment of malignancy. This is remarkable when it is realized that the idea of Co^{60} teletherapy was first put forth in 1948, with an estimate of a 10-curie cobalt machine; the range now is from a few hundred millicuries up to a 60,000-curie source.

Also used as a gamma source for animal exposure for study of radiation effects; for irradiation extermination of the screw worm fly; in gamma field studies in agriculture; in radiography, where its rays can penetrate up to 6 inches of steel; for food irradiation to produce sterilization or to enhance food preservation.

Co^{60}, Co^{57} and Co^{58} are used extensively in biological research and in medical research, diagnosis and treatment. Some of the more common uses are: irradiation of tumors—teletherapy use; determination of efficiency of gastrointestinal absorption of radioactive vitamin B_{12}; clinical test for pernicious anemia; study of the absorption, distribution and excretion of cobalt as influenced by chemical form and the nutritional and physiological status of farm animals; estimation of the utilization of cobalt by bacteria to form vitamin B_{12} or B_{12}-like substances; study of the absorption, distribution and excretion of vitamin B_{12}, determination of the mode and site of action of B_{12}, and estimation of the cobalt and B_{12} requirements; study of the toxicity of cobalt.

The importance of cobalt-60 is seen from the current estimate of about a million curies produced in both the United States and Canada and beginning production in other countries.

Maximum permissible concentration for a 40-hour work week for Co^{60} with the total body as the critical organ is 4×10^{-3} microcuries per cubic centimeter (μc/cc) in water and 4×10^{-7} in air; for a 168-hour week (continuous exposure) 10^{-3} μc/cc in water and 10^{-7} μc/cc in air.

CO-CARCINOGEN

An agent which increases the effect of a carcinogen (cancer-producing substance) by direct concurrent local effect on tissue is called a co-carcinogen.

Clinical observations in man and extensive animal experimentation have shown conclusively that radiation is a general or nonspecific carcinogen and induces or acts as a co-carcinogen in inducing tumors in almost all tissues of mammals, irrespective of species. Thus, ionizing radiation is classified with ultraviolet radiation, coal tar products, and a great variety of other chemical agents known to be carcinogenic in their action.

A true radiomimetic is by definition carcinogenic, and if present with radiation would be a co-carcinogen.

See CARCINOGENESIS, RADIATION, and CARCINOMA DUE TO RADIATION.

COCKROFT-WALTON ACCELERATOR

Named for the British physicists J. D. Cockroft and E. T. S. Walton, it is a voltage-multiplier type of particle ACCELERATOR used to produce beams of charged particles with energies in the range of 3 Mev. Starting with charged particles such as protons, alpha particles (helium nuclei), deuterons (deuterium nuclei), etc., and a high-voltage transformer, the voltage is generated by a voltage multiplier system consisting of a number of condenser pairs connected through switching devices (vacuum tubes).

The Cockroft-Walton has the advantage of simplicity, and provides fairly large ion currents at constant voltage. The maximum energies are low compared to other accelerators but many of these machines are used in physics laboratories for experimental work requiring moderate potentials. They are also used in the injection system of high-energy particle accelerators such as the bevatron.

COINCIDENCE CIRCUIT

Electronic arrangement which records a count only when signals from 2 or more detectors arrive simultaneously. In low-level counting experiments, interference from cosmic rays is eliminated by surrounding the counting device with a ring of Geiger tubes connected to inactivate the low-level counter for the instant when a cosmic ray goes through the region, causing coincident counts in the Geiger ring.

COINCIDENCE CORRECTION

At high counting rates, a radiation detector is unable to record those counts which fall too closely together because of the random nature of radioactive emission. It is necessary to correct for counts lost during the dead time intervals by use of a relationship as shown for a typical case in Figure C–11.

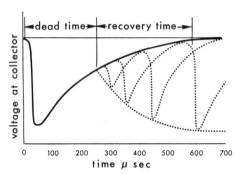

FIGURE C–11. COINCIDENCE CORRECTION.

COINCIDENCE COUNTING

Method for detecting or identifying particular radioactive materials, also for calibration of their absolute disintegration rate, by counting two or more characteristic radiation events which occur together or in a specific time relationship to each other. This method for identification of isotopes is of great significance in activation analysis and similar problems of counting isotopes in the presence of others when simple pulse height analysis or energy discrimination cannot distinguish them. A simple arrangement for beta-gamma coincidence counting is shown in Figure C–12. Note also the application of a coincidence ring or cosmic ray guard to eliminate background counts of cosmic origin in low-level counting techniques.

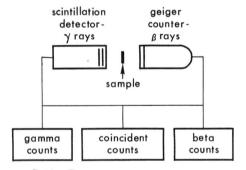

FIGURE C–12. DIAGRAMMATIC PRESENTATION OF CO-INCIDENCE COUNTING.

COLD STERILIZATION. *See* FOOD PRESERVA-
TION.

COLLATERAL RADIOACTIVE SERIES

Radioactive elements arranged so as to show the decay chain, i.e., parent-daughter relationship. They are associated with the naturally occurring ACTINIUM, THORIUM and URANIUM RADIOACTIVE SERIES, and with the artificially produced NEPTUNIUM RADIOACTIVE SERIES. The collateral radioactive series have different parents, but they become identical with the regular series when they have a member in common.

COLLECTOR ELECTRODE

Electrical element in an ionization chamber which collects the ionized particles from the defined measuring volume. May be either positive or negative. Usually surrounded by a guard ring at the same electrical potential to insure uniformity of electrical field conditions in the sensitive volume.

Also, any terminal which serves to collect electrons or ions in a detector or amplifier element.

COLLIMATOR

System of slits or apertures to control the path of radiation, especially by eliminating radiation not traveling in the desired direction; attached to a radiation source to limit the field of irradiation (to define the irradiation in teletherapy), or to a radiation detector for the purpose of limiting its view or the geometrical region of sensitivity to which the detector responds (as in SCANNING, RADIOISOTOPE). Materials of construction may be lead, tungsten, or other substances to suit the particular characteristics of the radiation being controlled. Collimator design is also subject to requirements of equipment weight and expense and to necessity for maneuverability and avoidance of interfering with other related manipulations.

See FOCUSING COLLIMATOR.

COLLOIDAL AND LARGE PARTICLE RADIOISOTOPES FOR MEDICAL USE

Many radioisotopes can be prepared (with the addition of other chemicals) as radioactive colloids for medical use. In this form the elements lose much of their biologic individuality and their localization and behavior depends largely on particle size. When injected into a solid tissue or into a body cavity, part of the colloid remains adherent to the first tissue with which it comes in contact. That portion that reaches a blood vessel or lymphatic channel, or any colloid that is injected directly into such vessels, tends to be removed by the reticuloendothelial cells of lymph nodes, liver, spleen, and bone marrow. The radioisotopes most commonly used in this form are gold-198, phos-

TABLE C–2. COLLOIDAL AND LARGE PARTICLE RADIOISOTOPES FOR MEDICAL USE

ROUTE OF INJECTION	LOCALIZATION OF COLLOID AND ITS RADIATION	CLINICAL USE
Directly into tumors and adjacent tissues	At site of injection or in lymph nodes draining this area	Treatment of cancer of prostate, certain other tumors, under special conditions
Into body cavities	Chiefly on surfaces lining cavity	Treatment of fluid accumulations caused by cancer; to reduce cancer spread in cavities
Intravenously	In liver, spleen, and bone marrow	Treatment of leukemia of certain types, and related diseases
Into lymphatic channels	In lymph nodes nearest to site of injection	To locate and irradiate lymph nodes (experimental)

phorus-32, and yttrium-90. Table C–2 summarizes some of the clinical information.

Colloids are also used diagnostically; for example, in scanning the liver.

More limited use has been made in medicine of radioisotopes produced in the form of still larger particles that tend to lodge in the first capillary bed they encounter after intra-arterial injection. An example of such particles is that prepared from carbon and coated with gold-198. These have been used experimentally in the treatment of cancer. They do not show much tendency to localize in the tumor; their distribution is in a whole organ or in a portion of an organ, depending on the arterial vascular pattern and the site of injection. These large particles have as yet had very limited practical usefulness.

Figure C–13 demonstrates three modes of administration: (a) Interstitial; direct injection into tumors or adjoining tissues; some remains at the site of injection, some reaches regional lymph nodes and some goes to liver and spleen. (b) Intracavitary (left pleural); most remains in cavity, some goes to lymph nodes, liver and spleen. (c) Intravenous; goes chiefly to liver, spleen and, although not indicated in the drawing, to the bone marrow.

THERAPEUTIC USES OF COLLOIDAL GOLD[198]

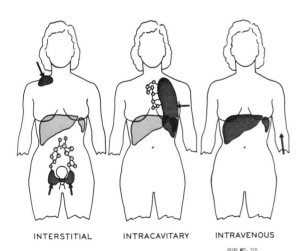

INTERSTITIAL   INTRACAVITARY   INTRAVENOUS

ORINS MED. DIV.

FIGURE C–13. THREE MODES OF ADMINISTERING COLLOIDAL RADIOISOTOPES: (A) INTERSTITIAL BY DIRECT INJECTION INTO TUMOR OR ADJACENT TISSUES; SOME REMAINS AT THE SITE OF INJECTION, SOME REACHES REGIONAL LYMPH NODES AND SOME GOES TO LIVER AND SPLEEN; (B) INTRACAVITARY (LEFT PLEURAL) INJECTION; MOST REMAINS IN CAVITY, SOME GOES TO LYMPH NODES, LIVER AND SPLEEN; (C) INTRAVENOUS, GOES CHIEFLY TO LIVER, SPLEEN AND BONE MARROW. (COURTESY MEDICAL DIVISION, OAK RIDGE INSTITUTE OF NUCLEAR STUDIES.)

COLLOIDS, RADIOACTIVE

Some carrier-free radiotracers in solution behave like colloids rather than true solutes and therefore have been called radiocolloids, although it is not to be inferred that radioactivity is a cause of colloid formation. Radiocolloids may be detected by such procedures as dialysis, ultrafiltration, diffusion, electrophoresis, adsorption, and autoradiography. The following elements are known to form radiocolloids under appropriate conditions: barium, beryllium, bismuth, cerium, lanthanum, lead, magnesium, niobium, plutonium, polonium, protactinium, scandium, thorium, tin, titanium, yttrium, and zirconium. Colloid formation is promoted by (a) use of solvents in which the tracer (see TRACER STUDIES) tends to hydrolyze or form an insoluble compound; (b) foreign particles in the solution, (c) presence of certain electrolytes, (d) increased age of solution. Radiocolloids behave differently in biological systems than do ions of the same radioisotope, and it has been shown that the distribution of many radiocolloids in animals is dependent on particle size. The localization of radiocolloids in the reticuloendothelial system, especially the bone marrow,

spleen and liver, has been utilized for the therapeutic delivery of radiation to these sites.

See COLLOIDAL AND LARGE PARTICLE RADIOISO-
TOPES FOR MEDICAL USE.

COLORADO STATE UNIVERSITY ANIMAL RESEARCH LABORATORY

A joint project of the U. S. Public Health Service
and the Colorado State University to establish a
specific pathogen-free dog colony for the study of
the biological effects of low-level radiation. The
initial purpose of the laboratory will be to establish a large population of test animals. These will
be studied by selected physiological measurements
so that their normal characteristics will be known
throughout their lives. After these normal characteristics are established and the colony attains
adequate size, which is expected to be 2,000 animals in 3 to 4 years, the animals will be studied
for their response to low-level radiation. In this
manner it is hoped that important new knowledge
about the long-term biological effects of low-level
radiation will be obtained.

Plans call for the area to be completely isolated.
Within 65 acres more than a thousand 15- × 30-
foot dog pens will be built. The colony is to be
handled as a specific pathogen-free colony; all
animals will be taken by cesarean section, separated from the dams, and hand-fed and placed
within the colony in isolation.

COLUMBIUM. *See* NIOBIUM.

COMPARTMENTAL ANALYSIS

Compartmental analysis of biological systems is
the development of models which reproduce the
kinetics of tracer distribution. The term "compartment" may refer to a physiological volume limited
by membranes or barriers such as the plasma, the
red blood cell, or specific tissues. The term "compartment" may also be used in the chemical sense
referring, for example, to the body water, the
phospholipids, or cholesterol. When a radioactive
tracer element is introduced into a biological
system, it produces a change in the isotopic consti-
titution of a chemical species. The effect of this
change is measured by observing the fate and
equilibrium distribution of the tracer. Compartmental analysis is then used to develop a model of
kinetic behavior and provides a method for interpretation of tracer experiments. The model should
be created on the basis of the best known biological features of the system, and should be rigor-
ously tested to ensure that it does conform to the
biological system. Analogue computers are most
helpful for detailed consideration of alternate
models rapidly and decisively.

An example of the use of compartmental analysis
is in studies of the formation of labeled cholesterol
from labeled body water. It was shown that the
average life of a cholesterol molecule in man was
about 12 days, and that the half-time for synthesis
of the cholesterol pool was about 8 days. It was
also shown that body water cannot be the direct
precursor of all the hydrogen in the cholesterol
molecules.

COMPTON EFFECT

The elastic scattering and increase in wave
length of x-ray photons interacting with an
orbital electron to produce a recoil electron and a
scattered photon of energy less than the incident
photon. Named for the United States physicist A.
H. Compton, who in 1923 found that when x-rays
fall on carbon or other material of low atomic
weight, the scattered radiation contained some
rays of longer wave length. He deduced that the
effect was produced as indicated in Figure C–14,
with the wave length of the scattered radiation
changed by an amount corresponding to the angle
of scattering of the electron. The same interaction
can be produced by a gamma-ray photon.

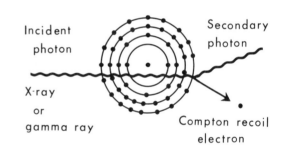

FIGURE C–14. COMPTON EFFECT. A PARTICLE OF
X-RAY (OR GAMMA-RAY) ENERGY COLLIDES WITH AN
ELECTRON IN MATERIAL OF LOW ATOMIC WEIGHT, WITH
RESULTANT INCREASE IN WAVE LENGTH OF THE SECOND-
ARY OR SCATTERED X-RAYS AND SIMULTANEOUS RECOIL
OF THE STRUCK ELECTRON.

CONCRETE SHIELD

Concrete is frequently used in the construction
of a shield against radiation because of its convenience, availability, and low cost compared with
alternative substances (lead, steel, etc.), and also
because in many cases the shield may be a structural wall as well; e.g., hot cells designed for handling megacurie quantities of 1-Mev gamma emitters are up to 5 feet thick. The density of concrete
(see Table C–3) contributes to its shielding effectiveness and the high hydrogen content (from its
bound water) helps slow down neutrons.

The usual aggregate (gravel or crushed stone)
in the concrete mix (Portland cement, sand, aggre-

gate and water) may be replaced by iron ore, steel scrap or shot, and the sand may also be replaced by more dense material as shown in the accompanying table, which gives the specific gravity in grams per cubic centimeter and the density in pounds per cubic foot for a number of different types of concrete.

TABLE C–3. SPECIFIC GRAVITY AND DENSITY OF VARIOUS TYPES OF CONCRETE

TYPE OF CONCRETE	SP. GR. g/cc	DENSITY lb/cu ft
Limestone-plasterer's sand	2.2	140
Gravel-sand	2.4	152
Barytes-barytes sand	3.4	215
Magnetite-magnetite fines	3.65	228
Barytes-iron shot	4.15-4.30	260-268
Ferrophosphorous-ferrophosphorous fines	4.7	293
Metallic iron-iron shot	5.9-6.18	370-385

CONDENSER r-METER

The standard secondary calibration instrument, widely used to measure the output of x-ray machines and other sources of radiation. Also known as r-meter or thimble chamber. The complete instrument is portable (Fig. C–15) and is equipped with one or more condenser chambers, usually constructed with air-equivalent wall for measurement of exposure dose, together with a charger-reader which includes voltage source and fiber electrometer. Customarily provided with a calibration factor determined by comparison with a primary standard free air chamber, giving response characteristics in terms of roentgen units for various qualities of x- or gamma radiation.

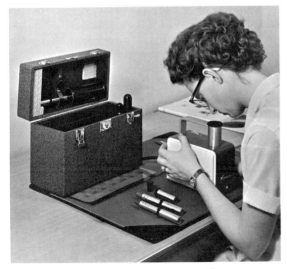

FIGURE C–15. CONDENSER r-METER. (COURTESY OF VICTOREEN INSTRUMENT COMPANY.)

CONTAMINATION ACCIDENTS

Occurrences in which the environment and animals or human beings become contaminated with radioactive material. These accidents usually are the result of environmental contamination from a radioactive powder or liquid, and individuals may be contaminated externally and, perhaps, internally through respiration or ingestion of the material. Radioactive fallout, although contaminating the environment, is not considered a contamination accident.

Five illustrative accidents are presented:

1. A sealed metal capsule, containing a neutron source (polonium-beryllium powder) used for instrument calibration, ruptured during handling, and contamination resulted when the powder spread and was tracked throughout the building. Several workers were exposed beyond maximum permissible dose levels. The cost of decontaminating the building plus the value of lost-work time totaled more than $30,000.

2. The skin of an employee's hands was contaminated when a plutonium-bearing organic solution deteriorated his rubber gloves. About 100 milligrams of plutonium were removed at once by intensive scrubbing of the hands, but 2 months elapsed before the final 200 micrograms of radioactive material were removed or eliminated by natural body processes. However, careful bio-assay several months later indicated that the internal deposition of soluble plutonium remaining did not exceed 5 per cent of the maximum permissible dose or body burden.

3. An excessive internal dose of plutonium was received by an employee when doing maintenance work on plutonium-contaminated equipment. He was wearing protective clothing and a gas mask and no leaks were detected, but routine monitoring disclosed that the employee's clothing and some skin surface were contaminated. Biological tests showed a deposition of plutonium about 1 1/2 times the maximum permissible dose.

4. During the production of metallic thorium in a laboratory, liquid waste containing more radioactivity than was anticipated was discharged into a city sewer. Mesothorium was the principle contaminant, but was removed in the sludge of a "complete treatment" sewage process, to the extent that the effluent water was potable.

5. Air-borne iridium-192 contamination of an industrial laboratory in Texas occurred when 2 employees were handling iridium-aluminum pressed pellets. Two pellets each containing about 35 curies of iridium-192 disintegrated into particle form, and although the operation was being performed in a hot cell, the material became air-borne and contaminated the laboratory and the clothing

of the employees. One of the employees carried radioactive material home on his clothing, contaminating his car and house. Actual radiation exposures received by the employees due to the accident were less than the maximum permissible dose for occupational exposure, but the emotional impact of the contaminated home developed into an incident of national interest.

See WOUND CONTAMINATION.

CONTAMINATION, RADIOACTIVE

Deposition of radioactive material in any place where it may harm persons, spoil experiments, or make products or equipment unsuitable or unsafe for some specific use. A condition in which an undesirable radioactive substance is mixed with a desired substance. In reactor engineering: radioactive material on the walls of vessels in used-fuel reprocessing plants; radioactive material that has leaked into a reactor coolant.

See RADIOCONTAMINATION.

CONTAMINATION SURVEY

Determination of the presence of radioactive material in any place where it is not desired, particularly where it may vitiate the results of an experiment or be a hazard to personnel.

See SURVEY.

CONTOUR METHODS

Representation of the degree of contamination from the detonation of a nuclear device, using contour lines to connect points of equal radiation dosage or dose rates.

See FALLOUT PATTERN, ISODOSE LINES, and ISOINTENSITY CONTOURS.

CONTROL (electronic). *See* GAIN CONTROL.

CONTROLLED AREA

An area in which the occupational exposure of personnel to radiation or radioactive material is under supervision (usually of a health physicist— *see* HEALTH PHYSICS), and is carefully monitored for radioactivity.

COPPER

Symbol Cu; atomic number 29; atomic weight 63.54. A yellowish red metal, soft, malleable and ductile. Its discovery dates from prehistoric times. Probably the first metal to be used, it is said to have been mined for over 5,000 years. Named from Latin, cuprum, from the island of Cyprus. Occurs as the free metal widely distributed over the earth. Natural abundance is furnished by two stable isotopes: Cu^{63}, 69.1%, and Cu^{65}, 30.9%.

Because of its workability and corrosion resist-

ance, copper is the second most extensively used metal (iron first). Commonly used as an electrical conductor and as a constituent of various alloys (brass and bronze). Copper amalgam is used as a dental cement. Considered an essential element to growth and development in both animals and plants. Daily food intake for man is about 2 milligrams (mg). Sheep, cattle and swine consume about 5 mg/day/100 pounds body weight. About 0.1 mg/day is optimum for rats. A recommended nutrient solution for plants contains 0.0127 part per million. The chemical standard man contains 0.00015% of copper, or 0.105 gram per 70 kilograms body weight.

Fifteen radioactive isotopes have been identified, 6 of which may occur as fission products from the detonation of a nuclear device. None have radioactive fallout significance.

Copper-64 $(_{29}Cu^{64})$. Radioactive half-life 12.80 hours; with brain as the critical organ, biological half-life 800 days; effective half-life 12.7 hours; decays by electron capture and by beta (β^- and β^+) and gamma (γ) emission.

Used in studies of animal metabolism and distribution. Radioactive copper thiocyanate has been tried in the localization of brain tumors. Radio-Copper Edathamil Sterile Solution, the EDTA chelate of radiocopper is available commercially. Radio-Cupric Acetate is also available in sterile solution for medical activity. The maximum permissible concentration for a 168-hour week (continuous exposure) for soluble material with the gastrointestinal tract as the critical organ is 3×10^{-3} microcuries per cubic centimeter ($\mu c/cc$) in water and 7×10^{-7} $\mu c/cc$ in air.

CORPUSCULAR RADIATION

Radiation consisting of particles (corpuscular emissions) such as alpha and beta particle radiation, or rays of mixed or unknown type, as cosmic radiation. Nonelectromagnetic radiation.

See RADIATION.

CORTISONE IN TREATMENT OF RADIATION ILLNESS. *See* TREATMENT OF RADIATION ILLNESS.

COSMIC RADIATION

Penetrating radiation resulting from cosmic rays reaching the earth from outer space. The radiation is so penetrating that all the organs of the body receive a practically uniform dose, which is equal to the dose rate in air. For example, one study found the gonad dose, the osteocyte dose and the mean marrow dose were each 28 millirems per year.

Table C–4 illustrates the effect of both altitude

TABLE C–4. EFFECTS OF ALTITUDE AND LATITUDE UPON INTENSITY OF COSMIC RADIATION

ALTITUDE (METERS)	INTENSITY ION PAIRS/CM³: SEC		DOSE RATE MRAD/YEAR	
	At 50° latitude	Near equator	At 50° latitude	Near equator
0	2.8	2.4	41	35
1,500	4.5	3.0	66	44
3,050	8.8	6.1	128	89
4,580	18	12	263	175
6,100	34	23	500	340

and latitude upon the intensity of cosmic radiation. (The figures in this table are the upper limits.)

Cosmic rays constitute one of the natural radiation sources to the body as a whole, terrestrial radiation contributing 47, cosmic radiation 28 and atmospheric radiation 2 millirems per year. Because of its great penetrating power and its extent, even at sea level, cosmic radiation is extremely important in any consideration of the biological effects of radiation.

COSMIC-RAY COUNTERS

Arrangement of radiation detectors, usually of the Geiger or proportional types, and having high efficiency for radiations of great energy. Customarily mounted or distributed in an appropriate geometric fashion, connected by coincidence circuits, providing a telescopic or orientation effect to indicate the direction of travel of the cosmic ray.

See ANTICOINCIDENCE CIRCUIT, COINCIDENCE COUNTING and COSMIC-RAY GUARD.

COSMIC-RAY GUARD

An arrangement of detectors surrounding the region of a sensitive radioactivity measuring experiment, designed to preclude registration of extraneous counts. The guard may be of the cosmic ray coincidence ring (see Figure C–16) or other suitable type, such as the gas flow "umbrella counter," and is ordinarily connected in anticoincidence with the experimental detector. Of general use in low-level counting procedures.

See ANTICOINCIDENCE CIRCUIT, COSMIC-RAY COUNTERS and LOW-LEVEL COUNTING.

COSMIC RAYS

Highly penetrating radiation from extraterrestrial sources reaching the entire surface of the earth. First shown to come from outer space by the United States scientist Millikan in 1925, who called this radiation "cosmic rays." First suspected around 1900 because of the discharge of electroscopes in air made free from all known ionizing influence. Additional evidence was the increase in the rate of discharge as the electroscope was carried to higher altitudes.

Cosmic rays are commonly spoken of as if they were a single type of radiation, but they are actually very complex, and because of their interaction with matter, their nature changes as they pass through the atmosphere. Studies have shown two components of cosmic rays: the hard (primary) component and the soft (secondary) component. The hard component consists mainly of mesons, a small number of protons and a still smaller number of nuclei of heavier atoms like carbon, nitrogen, oxygen and iron. In addition there are a few neutrons, electrons and photons.

The soft (secondary) component constitutes about 20% of the total cosmic radiation at sea level and 50° geomagnetic latitude. This component is made up essentially of about equal proportions of positrons, negative electrons (negatrons) and photons with energies less than 200 Mev. There are in addition a small number of slow mesons, neutrons, protons and heavier particles. Much of the soft component is the result of interaction with the atmosphere.

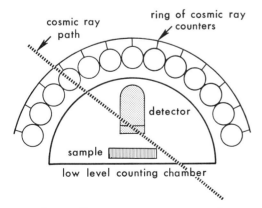

FIGURE C–16. COSMIC-RAY GUARD IN THE LIBBY ARRANGEMENT, USED IN ANTI-COINCIDENCE TO ELIMINATE COSMIC RAY BACKGROUND COUNTS IN LOW LEVEL PROCEDURES.

The hard component consists of radiation of tremendously high energies, of the order of 10^{12} to 10^{15} electron volts. The penetrating power of these rays is enormous. To traverse the entire earth's atmosphere is equivalent to penetrating 1 meter thickness of lead; but in addition the rays have been detected under water and underground in mines at distances equivalent to 1,400 meters of water. Only particles with many billions of electron volts of energy could penetrate to such depths.

The intensity of cosmic rays increases strongly with altitude and increases with increasing geomagnetic latitude as a result of the effect of the earth's magnetic field.

Study of cosmic rays has led to the identification of the positron, several types of mesons, nuclear disintegrations (stars) and other striking effects.

COSMIC RADIATION is of great significance to all living matter as a potential source of radiation damage.

See CASCADE SHOWER.

COSMOTRON

A 3-billion electron-volt proton synchrotron at Brookhaven National Laboratory (see Figure C–17). Protons are injected into the main unit at an energy of 3.6 Mev from an electrostatic generator. The main unit consists of an 1,800-ton doughnut-shaped magnet about 75 feet in diameter. The protons are accelerated by an electrical field each time they cross a gap in the magnet. Since the cycle time (one revolution) shortens as the velocity increases, production of a continuous stream of particles is not possible with this device. Instead, it is pulsed every 5 seconds. Nuclear fragments produced when the 3-Bev protons strike a target are observed on photographic film or by the use of cloud chambers, bubble chambers and electronic counters. These observations have contributed to the understanding of the structure of the atomic nucleus and of the characteristics of fundamental particles.

High-energy protons are of special interest in

FIGURE C–17. THE COSMOTRON, A SYNCHROTRON THAT ACCELERATES PROTONS IN A CIRCULAR PATH TO SPEEDS APPROACHING THE VELOCITY OF LIGHT. IN THIS ACCELERATION PROCESS, THE PROTONS ATTAIN AN ENERGY OF 3 BILLION ELECTRON VOLTS, AND ARE THEN DIRECTED AT A TARGET. THE FRAGMENTS OF THE RESULTANT NUCLEAR COLLISIONS ARE STUDIED BY PHOTOGRAPHIC METHODS. TO THE REAR OF THE COSMOTRON IS THE EXPERIMENTAL AREA, INTO WHICH PROTON BEAMS CAN BE DEFLECTED TO THEIR TARGETS. WHEN IN OPERATION, THE COSMOTRON IS SURROUNDED BY HEAVY CONCRETE SHIELDING BLOCKS (NOT SHOWN IN THIS ILLUSTRATION) TO PROTECT PERSONNEL FROM RADIATION HAZARDS. (COURTESY OF BROOKHAVEN NATIONAL LABORATORY.)

space medicine because of their occurrence in solar flares and the consequent hazards to voyagers in space. In pursuit of this interest, mice and rabbits have been exposed to a beam of 2.2 Bev protons in studies of the relative biological effectiveness of this type of radiation for various tissues.

COUNT RATE METER

Radiation detector with electronic circuit and indicator which shows continuously the average rate of occurrence of ionizing events. Devices of this kind are widely used both in radiation survey or monitor instruments and in laboratory or clinical measurements. The typical "Geiger counter" instrument used in field work is of light weight and readily portable, depending on batteries for power; it is usually of low or moderate precision. For clinical work in the dynamic observation of organ function or extensive scanning of in vivo isotope distribution, the precision must be good and the response fast. Other uses run the full range of engineering and research applications. The response interval or integrating time is ordinarily adjusted to suit the specific purpose at hand.

When accurate and reliable performance is required, the circuit must first convert the initial pulses to uniform size, following which the averaging function can be accomplished by delivering the pulses into an intermediate storage capacitor. Different counting rates can be accommodated by switching to capacitors of appropriate size. Within limits, it is also possible to change the integrating interval by adjustment of circuit constants. It is necessary to make a judicious selection of these factors if adverse statistical effects and fluctuations are to be avoided.

COUNTERS

General designation applied to all RADIATION DETECTION INSTRUMENTS or SURVEY METERS which detect and measure radiation in terms of individual ionizing events, either as the accumulated total or the time rate of occurrence. Also used in reference to the mechanical or electromechanical COUNT REGISTER used to record the output of a SCALER. Sometimes designates the individual radiation detector element, especially the Geiger and proportional types of gas detection devices or scintillation detectors.

COUNTING EFFICIENCY

This term is sometimes used with reference to the detector alone, in which case it signifies the detector's ability to respond to radiation passing through its sensitive volume. When so used, the efficiency factor is commonly regarded as the probability that a count will be recorded when radiation falls on the detector.

In the general sense, counting efficiency denotes the over-all ability of a radiation counter device to detect and record the radioactivity of a sample, expressed as the fraction or percentage of the actual disintegrations in the sample which are counted. The counting efficiency is specified for a given specific set of experimental conditions, for a particular detector and scaler, and for fixed geometrical relationship between sample and detector. While the efficiency might be computed from a complete analysis of the geometrical and performance factors of the set-up, it is more commonly determined by calibration using standard or reference sources of known activity. Component factors making up the total efficiency figure include the true response efficiency of the detector itself, the geometrical relationship defining the fraction of the radiation which can reach the detector, the size and shape of the sample, the sample thickness because of its influence through scattering and absorption processes, loss by absorption in materials lying between the sample and the sensitive volume, including air and entrance window, and the general interference through scattering on the surrounding structures. Those factors of the efficiency which relate to absorption, scattering, and counter response are markedly dependent upon the energy of the radiation and on its nature, whether alpha, beta, gamma, or neutron.

COUNTING PLATEAU.   See PLATEAU, COUNTING.

COUNTING RATE

The average number of counts recorded in a unit of time, found by dividing total counts collected by the time over which the count was made. Commonly expressed as counts per minute, sometimes counts per second.

CRATER

Or bomb crater. The pit, depression, or cavity formed in the surface of the earth by a surface burst or a shallow underground burst following the detonation of a nuclear device. Its size and shape depend upon the type of soil, the depth to which the bomb penetrates and the yield. For example, it is estimated from test results that if a 1-megaton nuclear weapon were dropped from the air and penetrated into the surface of sandy soil to a depth of 50 feet before exploding, the resulting crater would be about 300 feet deep and nearly 1,400 feet across. This means that about 10 million tons of earth and rock would be hurled upward from the earth's surface by the explosion.

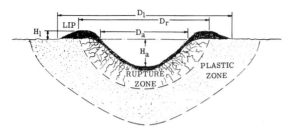

FIGURE C–18. CHARACTERISTIC DIMENSIONS OF THE CRATER IN A SURFACE BURST.

A number of terms are used in describing a crater. Figure C–18 will help to elucidate them.

The apparent crater is the visible surface of the depression or hole left in the ground after the explosion. The true crater includes the volume extending beyond the apparent crater where a definite shear has occurred. The diameter of the apparent crater is represented by D_a, and the true crater by D_t.

The crater depth is the maximum depth of the crater measured from the deepest point of the pit to the original level of the ground.

The crater radius is the average radius of the crater measured at a level corresponding to the original surface of the ground.

Lip height is the height above the original surface to which earth is piled around the crater formed by an explosion.

The zone immediately beneath the crater where there are innumerable radial cracks of various sizes, resulting from increased density and stresses, is called the rupture zone.

Below the rupture zone is the plastic zone in which there is no visible rupture but the soil is compressed to a greater density and permanently deformed.

In a very deep underground burst, there normally will be no rupture of the surface and thus no crater.

CRITICAL EXPERIMENT

Experiment in which fissionable material is gradually assembled until the arrangement will support a self-sustaining chain reaction. Usually its purpose is to determine the operating and control features and the critical size of a proposed or new nuclear reactor. It is carried out at essentially zero power and such quantities as critical mass, temperature coefficient of reactivity, and control rod effectiveness are measured. In such testing CRITICALITY ACCIDENTS have occurred when the reactor went supercritical and went out of control momentarily. Accidents involving supercriticality have also occurred during demonstrations and during supposedly routine operations.

CRITICAL MASS

That amount of fissionable material (uranium or plutonium) which will just support a self-sustaining chain reaction. A mass of fissionable material which loses neutrons more rapidly than they are formed within the mass is subcritical, will not sustain a chain reaction and will not explode. In order to produce an explosion, the material must be made supercritical, i.e., larger than the critical mass, in a time so short as to preclude a subexplosive change in the configuration, such as by melting.

Obviously a critical mass of material cannot be maintained, transported, or stored; so until the desired moment of detonation a nuclear device cannot contain a piece of fissionable material that is as large as the critical mass for the given conditions. On the other hand, material must be available so that at the moment of detonation it may be made supercritical.

One method of accomplishing this is in a nuclear weapon designed to bring two or more pieces of fissionable material, each less than a critical mass, together very rapidly thus forming one piece that exceeds the critical mass. This is achieved in a gun-type weapon in which a high explosive is used to blow one subcritical piece of material from the breech end of the gun into another subcritical piece firmly held in the muzzle end.

Another approach, the implosion weapon, achieves supercriticality by strongly compressing the fissionable material. The material is at the center of a sphere and surrounded by an arrangement of fabricated shapes which consist of ordinary high explosive. The compression is achieved when the inwardly directed implosion wave reaches the center and compresses the fissionable material; nuclear explosion results.

CRITICAL ORGAN

That organ the irradiation of which results in the greatest insult to the total body. It is almost always the organ showing the greatest concentration of an internally deposited radioisotope, and thus the one contributing the most to the INTERNAL IRRADIATION HAZARD.

The critical organ is determined by the following criteria:* "(1) the organ that accumulates the greatest concentration of radioactive material; (2) the essentialness or indispensability of the organ to the well-being of the entire body; (3) the

---

*National Bureau of Standards Handbook 69, "Maximum Permissible Body Burdens and Maximum Permissible Concentrations of Radionuclides in Air and in Water for Occupational Exposure." U. S. Department of Commerce.

organ damaged by the entry of the radionuclide into the body; and (4) the RADIOSENSITIVITY of the organ, e.g., the organ damaged by the lowest dose. Theoretically all of these considerations are taken into account through the use of RBE factors, the basic standards and the methods of calculation."

The critical organ concept is intimately related to the MAXIMUM PERMISSIBLE BODY BURDEN, and to the MAXIMUM PERMISSIBLE CONCENTRATION (MPC). In the present state of our knowledge the organ calculated to have the lowest MPC value is the most likely choice as the critical organ. For insoluble radionuclides the critical organs are either the lungs or the gastrointestinal tract. For soluble material any organ may be involved but the most frequently involved, other than the total body, are gastrointestinal tract with reference to the stomach, small intestines, upper large intestine or lower large intestine; kidney, liver, bone, spleen, testes, ovary, adrenal, skin, muscle, prostate, thyroid, pancreas, heart, and brain.

CRITICAL SIZE

The size of a system containing fissionable material in which the number of neutrons produced in the fission process just balances those lost by capture and leakage. Critical size is not fixed but depends upon a number of factors: the geometry of the configuration—a sphere is the most efficient, but its surface area and volume are important factors; the type of fissionable material and the degree of enrichment; the amount of impurities— some elements such as boron and cadmium have extremely high cross sections for the capture of neutrons; the type and arrangement of any moderator present; the nature of the reflector; and other factors. Thus, one might define critical size as any one of a set of physical dimensions of the core and reflector of a nuclear reactor maintaining a critical chain reaction, the material and structure of the core and the reflector having been specified.

Critical size relates both to controlled chain reaction in a nuclear reactor and to the chain reaction produced in the detonation of a nuclear weapon.

CRITICAL MASS is closely related and is simply that amount of material necessary to attain criticality.

A system is said to be critical when it will sustain a chain reaction. If it is smaller than critical size it is said to be subcritical. To accelerate the fission chain reaction the size must be supercritical.

See CRITICAL EXPERIMENT.

CRITICALITY ACCIDENTS

Critical experiments are essential for information in 4 important areas: reactor design; weapons-systems design; criticality limits on processing operations; and basic physics data. A number of accidents have occurred not only during experimental activity but during demonstrations, and also during supposedly routine operations.

The first fatality from a criticality accident occurred in 1945 when a scientist was performing a critical mass study by stacking blocks of tamper material around a mass of fissionable material. He dropped a block of tamper material directly on top of the set-up; the mass went critical with the "blue-glow" and a dose of radiation calculated as 480 r of 80 kev x-ray plus 110 r gamma ray, which proved fatal to the operator.

The most recent criticality fatality (1958) associated with a routine operation occurred when a worker (Case K) was routinely mixing an emulsion in a 225-gallon stainless steel tank. He added a dilute solution containing plutonium-bearing solids and nitric acid; as he started the mixer a "blue flash" occurred and he received a calculated 12,000 rads ($\pm 50\%$). The dose varied from approximately 12,000 rad to the upper abdomen to less than 100 rad to the lower extremities, which might be averaged to 4,500 rad of whole-body radiation. Two other workers in the area received 130 rad and 35 rad respectively. The operator found his way outdoors but when his fellow workers got to him (within a minute or two) he was disoriented and ataxic, and complained only, "I'm burning up, I'm burning up!" Thinking it was a chemical accident they gave him a shower; he had to be held up for he was unable to stand alone. When the nurse arrived about 10 minutes after the accident she found him in severe shock and virtually unconscious but "with a nice pink skin." Although not realized at the time, this was erythema, already evident from the massive radiation dose. When he arrived at the medical center about 20 minutes after the accident he was semiconscious and incoherent. His blood pressure and pulse were at first unobtainable but later were found to be 80/40 and 160, respectively. He was retching and vomiting and within 10 minutes after arrival had a propulsive, watery diarrhea. His body surface gamma-ray reading was 15mr/hr and his vomitus and feces were radioactive. In spite of heroic efforts he died in 35 hours in a state bordering on mania (brain damage). (Journal of Occupational Medicine, Vol. 3, No. 3, March, 1961: a special supplement covering all details.)

A nuclear excursion of the order of 10^{19} fissions occurred in a process equipment waste tank as a result of the accidental transfer of about 200 liters of uranyl nitrate solution containing about 34 kg of enriched uranium from critically safe process storage tanks to a geometrically unsafe waste tank.

TABLE C–5. REPORTED CRITICALITY ACCIDENTS RESULTING IN LOST-TIME INJURIES

DATE	LOCATION	NUMBER INVOLVED	SOURCE OF INJURY	NATURE OF INJURY	EXPOSURE 80 KV X-Ray	Gamma Ray	DAYS LOST
8/21/45	Los Alamos	Two	Chain reaction in experimental critical assembly	(1) Fatality (2) No clinically diagnosed injury	(1) 480 r (2) 31 r	110 r 1 r	†6,000* 60
5/21/46	Los Alamos	Eight	Chain reaction in experimental critical assembly	(1) Fatality (2) Skin rash, loss of hair and other symptoms	(1) 930 r (2) 390 r	114 r 26 r	6,000* 70
				(3) Skin rash and other symptoms	(3) †	†	†
				(4) No clinically diagnosed injury	(4) 185 r	10.7 r	14
				(5) No clinically diagnosed injury	(5) 140 r	8.7 r	18
				(6) No clinically diagnosed injury	(6) 55 r	4.4 r	4
				(7) No clinically diagnosed injury	(7) 43 r	3 r	4
				(8) No clinically diagnosed injury	(8) 33 r	2.41 r	4
6/2/52	Chicago	Four	Manual withdrawal of control rod from reactor	No clinically diagnosed injury	190 rem 160 rem 70 rem 12 rem		23 23 34 23
6/16/58	Oak Ridge (Y-12 Plant)	Eight	Criticality accident caused by draining enriched uranium in drum of water	‡	461 rem 341 rem 428 rem 413 rem 298 rem 86 rem 86 rem 29 rem		83 83 83 83 83 34 65 41
12/30/58	Los Alamos	One	Criticality accident	Fatality	12,000 ± 50% rem		6,000*

*6,000 days lost charged for each fatality.

†Information not available; employee had received termination notice prior to accident.

‡Three employees not requiring prolonged hospital care exhibited mild changes in blood elements but showed no symptoms of injury. The five employees requiring longer hospitalization showed significant decreases in blood elements and other clinical and laboratory findings characteristic of more severe radiation damage, such as mild nausea and vomiting, and indications of possible hemorrhagic complications, although no bleeding actually occurred.

Seven persons received whole-body exposures ranging up to 6 rem; of these two received skin exposures of 50 rem and 32 rem. Fourteen others received negligible exposure. No medical treatment was required. Neither fission neutrons nor prompt gamma radiation penetrated the 4-foot thick concrete deck over the tanks; exposure was from gamma rays and beta particles carried by the vented air and gas.

Table C–5 lists 5 criticality accidents involving lost-time injuries from 1945 through 1958.

CROP IMPROVEMENT, USING RADIATION

Ionizing radiation can induce changes in genes and chromosomes which may result in altered characteristics in later generations. In plants the vast majority of such sports or mutants are deleterious or neutral, but a few are beneficial or potentially beneficial. Within a few years after the discovery of the mutagenicity of x-rays in 1926, investigators in several countries began to search for potentially useful induced mutations. However, except in Sweden, the efforts along this line were of a minor nature until after World War II, when the advent of nuclear energy gave a boost to radiobiology in general and radiation genetics in particular.

Plants have been irradiated during various stages in their life cycles to produce mutations. Seeds and pollen are commonly irradiated but embryos, seedlings and whole plants as well as cuttings and scions have also been exposed. Effective radiations include all types of ionizing radiations and the facilities used vary from small x-ray machines to large gamma fields or nuclear reactors.

During the last 10 years, hundreds of geneticists and plant breeders in many different countries have used ionizing radiation to produce new variability and many of them have then used the induced mutations in further breeding programs. Useful induced mutations have been reported in many cultivated plants (or in some cases have already been introduced into commercial channels). The potential economic value of these new forms varies considerably, but in some the increased values of a single crop may run into millions of dollars per year.

The need for new variability differs greatly in different crops and correspondingly so does the probable usefulness of radiation-induced mutations. It is worth while to use mutation breeding in plants in which (1) little-known variation exists, (2) life cycles are long, (3) asexual propagation can be used, (4) degenerative changes may be useful, e.g., in ornamentals, (5) normal methods of hybridization are difficult or inadequate. There is no longer any doubt that crop improvement can be facilitated by radiation-induced mutations. A vast array of mutations can be readily produced in most plants. Their identification, isolation, testing and recombination with other desirable genes is often complex and time-consuming. Further, it is often not clear whether the use of radiation is more or less efficient in any given instance than the older standard methods of plant improvement.

Examples are: disease-resistant barley, oats and wheat and higher yields for radiation-induced mutants of barley, oats, wheat, peanuts, peas, sesame and oil mustard.

See PLANT GENETICS AND RADIATION.

CROSS SECTION, NUCLEAR

Symbol σ. The probability, per unit flux and per unit time, that a certain event or reaction will occur. The cross section of a nucleus for a given process, such as the cross section for the scattering of charged particles, or the cross section for the absorption of certain particles, or for the absorption of radiation such as gamma rays. Used in this sense, cross section is a measure of the probability of the occurrence of a given process. It is expressed as the effective area that the nucleus presents for the reaction. For example, if I is the number of incident particles striking in a given time a square centimeter (sq cm) area of target material containing N target nuclei (or atoms), and A is the

number of these nuclei which undergo interaction in the specified time, then the nuclear cross section, expressed in sq cm per nucleus, is defined by

$$\sigma = \frac{A}{NI} \text{ sq cm per nucleus.}$$

The activation cross section is the cross section for the formation of a specified radionuclide. Used most frequently for neutron-induced reactions.

Capture cross section refers to the probability that a nucleus will capture an incident particle, i.e., the cross section effective for radiative capture.

Differential cross section is the cross section for a nuclear process leading to emission of photons or particles at a specified angle relative to the direction of incidence. May be expressed in terms of either unit plane angle or unit solid angle.

Macroscopic cross section refers to the cross section per unit volume or per unit mass.

Microscopic cross section is the cross section of one atom or molecule.

Stopping cross section is a synonym for atomic stopping power.

The total cross section is the sum of the separate cross sections for all processes by which the particle can be removed from the beam; that cross section effective for removal of an incident particle from a beam.

Cross sections also include the cross section for fission, for neutron capture, for elastic scattering, for Compton collision, and for ionization by electron impact.

Experimental values for nuclear cross sections are usually about 10^{-25} to 10^{-23} sq cm per nucleus, although values down to 10^{-32} sq cm per nucleus have been measured and those as high as 10^{-20} sq cm are known. Since the average diameter of a nucleus can be taken to be about 10^{-12} cm the average area of cross section is 10^{-24} sq cm. Since this represents the order of magnitude of many nuclear reaction cross sections, it has been chosen as a unit and called a barn.

Cross sections are frequently in the range of 0.1 to 10 barns but are known to vary from 10^{-8} to 10^6 barns for different reactions. A famous example is xenon-135, which has an absorption cross section for 3.5 million barns for slow neutrons.

CRYSTAL DETECTOR

A device sensitive to radiation because of specific characteristics of its crystal structure; especially one whose electrical conduction changes under irradiation.

See RADIATION DETECTOR.

RADIONUCLIDE	RADIOACTIVE HALF-LIFE (years)	BIOLOGICAL HALF-LIFE (years)	EFFECTIVE HALF-LIFE (years)	% EQUILIBRIUM REACHED IN 50 YEARS
Cm²⁴³	35	200	30	69
Cm²⁴⁴	18.4	200	17	87
Cm²⁴⁵	2×10^4	200	200	16
Cm²⁴⁶	6.6×10^3	200	190	16

CUBE ROOT LAW

A scaling law applicable to most blast physical phenomena. It relates the time and distance at which a given blast effect is observed to the cube root of the energy of the explosion (yield). This means that a thousandfold increase in energy will increase the range for a particular kind of damage by a factor of roughly 10; i.e., if a 1-kiloton-energy device exerts direct blast biological damage of a given type at 1 mile, a 1-megaton-energy device would exert similar blast biological damage at 10 miles.

CURIE

Symbol c. A unit of radioactivity measurement defined as the quantity of any radioactive nuclide in which the number of disintegrations per second is 3.700×10^{10} (recommended by the International Commission on Radiological Units, July, 1953). Named for Marie and Pierre Curie for their discovery of radium, and earlier defined as the quantity of emanation (radon) from or in equilibrium with 1 gram of radium.

Multiple units of the curie are: kilocurie, 1 thousand curies; and megacurie, 1 million curies. Fractions of a curie are: millicurie, 1 thousandth; microcurie, 1 millionth; and picocurie, 1 millionth of a millionth.

The International Commission on Radiological Units and Measurements (ICRU) in their report 10a of 1962 (published as National Bureau of Standards Handbook 84) suggested that the term "activity" be used for the transformation rate of a radionuclide, and that the curie be made its unit; i.e., that the curie be redefined as a unit of activity and not as a quantity of a radioactive nuclide, and that it be $3.7 \times 10^{10} s^{-1}$.

CURIUM

Symbol Cm; atomic number 96; atomic weight 247; a radioactive transuranic element of the actinide series. Curium-242 (Cm²⁴²) was discovered in 1944 by American scientists G. T. Seaborg, R. A. James and A. Ghiorso, as a product obtained by alpha particle bombardment of plutonium-239. Named in honor of Marie and Pierre Curie. Pure compound of Cm²⁴² obtained in 1947 by action of neutrons on americium-241. Curium-242 is an alpha particle emitter with a half-life of 162.5 days. Because of the intensity of the alpha (α) emission (6.110 Mev), has potential use as a neutron source and as a concentrated heat source for batteries. Other radioactive isotopes of curium have mass numbers 238–241 and 243–249. Curium does not occur in nature. Maximum permissible concentrations (MPC) have been determined for 5 curium radioisotopes. For example, for Cm²⁴², for a 168-hour week (continuous exposure), with the gastrointestinal tract as the critical organ, the MPC is 2×10^{-4} microcuries per cubic centimeter (μc/cc) in water and 5×10^{-8} μc/cc in air.

Four radionuclides of curium do not reach equilibrium in the body within 50 years (critical organ, bone). (See table above.)

CUTIE PIE

Manhattan project code name for an ionization type radiation survey meter. The name has been retained; widely used to explore for possible radiation hazards and to evaluate exposure levels in the field or laboratory. Usually made to respond to beta and gamma rays, with a movable filter window to discriminate between them (see Figure C–19). Derived from an early type, with pistol grip, completely self-contained and powered by batteries.

CYCLOTRON

First described in 1931 by its inventors, E. O. Lawrence and M. S. Livingston, is a type of particle ACCELERATOR in which repeated accelerations through intermediate (10^5v) voltages are used to achieve high-particle kinetic energies (10^7ev). In the cyclotron the ionized particles to be accelerated are introduced into the space between 2 hollow, evacuated, semicircular electrodes called "dees" from their shape. The dees are mounted between the poles of a large electromagnet (see Figure C–20). The particles are attracted into the dee of opposite electrical charge and within the dee are constrained to move in a semicircular path by electromagnetic field, and thus return to the accelerating gap between the dees. During this time the electrical gradient across the gap has been

FIGURE C–19. CUTIE PIE SUR-
VEY METER. INSET SHOWS DETAIL
OF SELECTIVE FILTERS. (COUR-
TESY OF TECHNICAL ASSOCIATES.)

FIGURE C–20. WORKER RE-
MOVING RADIOACTIVE TARGET
AFTER BOMBARDMENT IN 60
INCH CYCLOTRON AT BERKELEY.
THE DEES ARE IN THE CENTER
OF THE PICTURE, THE MAGNET
POLES BEING LOCATED ABOVE
AND BELOW. (COURTESY OF
LAWRENCE RADIATION LABORA-
TORY, UNIVERSITY OF CALI-
FORNIA.)

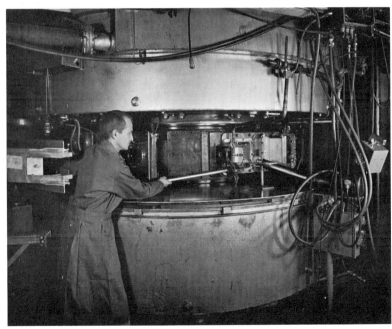

reversed so that the particles are attracted into the second dee, and so on. Each time the particles cross the gap, they receive an acceleration corresponding to the voltage across the gap. Within the dees the radius of their path is directly dependent upon their velocity, so they tend to spiral outward as their velocity increases. The increased path length exactly corresponds to the increased velocity (below relativistic velocities, i.e., velocities approaching the speed of light) so the gap-to-gap time is constant. Thus, the frequency of alternation of charge across the gap may be kept constant, and a steady stream of particles may be accelerated. When the velocities become relativistic, design modifications are necessary to synchronize the accelerating impulses, and the machine becomes known as a synchro cyclotron.

Fast neutrons produced by a cyclotron have been used in experimental cancer therapy, but the unsatisfactory late results have discouraged further attempts of this application. Taking advantage of the rise in the linear energy transfer rate which occurs at the ends of the tracks of heavy particles, protons and deuterons accelerated in cyclotrons have been used to produce sharply defined lesions at preselected depths in tissue. This technique makes it possible to study the effects of deletion of single layers of cells in the brain.

CYSTEAMINE, EFFECT ON RADIATION INJURY

A chemical compound, 2-mercaptoethylamine, with the formula $HS \cdot CH_2 \cdot CH_2 \cdot NH_2$, used in CHEMICAL PROTECTION AGAINST RADIATION INJURY.

CYSTEINE, EFFECT ON RADIATION INJURY

An amino acid, 1-2-amino-3-mercaptopropanoic acid, with a free sulphydryl group used in CHEMICAL PROTECTION AGAINST RADIATION INJURY. Its formula is $HS \cdot CH_2 \cdot CH \cdot CO_2 H$

$$NH_2$$

CYTOLOGICAL CHANGES DUE TO RADIATION

The changes in cell structure and function as a result of irradiation are covered under the following items: BLOOD, RADIATION EFFECTS ON; BONE MARROW, RADIATION EFFECTS ON; CELLS, RADIATION EFFECTS ON; and HEMATOPOIETIC SYSTEM, RADIATION EFFECTS ON.

D

DAMAGE CRITERIA

Damage level or degree of damage resulting from the blast effects associated with the detonation of a nuclear device has been established under three categories.*

1. Slight or light damage. A level of damage such that only moderate repair is necessary for the continued use of the damaged item. In a building, for example, this would mean broken windows, slight damage to roofing and siding, and cracking of curtain walls.
2. Moderate damage. Level of damage which requires major repairs before structure or object can be used for its intended purpose.
3. Severe damage. Damage which completely impairs designed function of a target so that it cannot be used or repaired economically. For a structure or building, collapse is generally implied.

Damage criteria have been set for many of the common types of structures and objects, some examples of which are shown in tables D–1, D–2, D–3, and D–4. The damage will depend upon many characteristics of both the nuclear device

and the object being considered; the tables present only an average situation. For details see Glasstone's "The Effects of Nuclear Weapons—1962."†

Damage criteria have also been established for personnel under the title Atomic Damage Template (ADT) System, which is a system for prediction and assessment of damage using a series of templates showing radii of effects and safe distances for troops for detonations of particular yield and height-of-burst combinations.

Various terms relating to the problem of damage from blast and shock are briefly defined:

Soft target. One that is relatively easily damaged.

Hard target. One constructed or designed to withstand the effect of nuclear explosion.

Ductility. The ability of a material or structure to absorb energy (withstand a force or load) inelastically without failure. Materials which are brittle have poor ductility and fail easily. Structural steel has the property of ductility to a considerable extent.

Elastic range. The range in which a material, after stress, will recover its original form once the loading or force has been removed.

---

*A number of terms related to damage criteria are defined in the opposite column and on page 118.

†For sale, Superintendent of Documents, U.S. Government Printing Office, Washington 25, D.C. Price $3.00.

TABLE D–1. MOTOR EQUIPMENT (CARS AND TRUCKS)

DAMAGE	NATURE OF DAMAGE
Severe	Gross distortion of frame, large displacements, doors and hood torn off, need rebuilding before use
Moderate	Turned over and displaced, badly dented, frame sprung, need major repairs
Light	Glass broken, dents in body, possibly turned over, but immediately usable

TABLE D–2. PARKED AIRCRAFT

DAMAGE	NATURE OF DAMAGE	OVERPRESSURE PSI	
Severe	Major or depot-level maintenance required to restore aircraft to operational status	Transport plane	3
		Light craft	2
		Helicopters	3
Moderate	Field maintenance required to restore aircraft to operational status	Transport plane	2
		Light craft	1
		Helicopters	1.5
Light	Flight of aircraft not prevented, although performance may be restricted	Transport plane	1
		Light craft	0.5
		Helicopters	0.5

TABLE D–3. SHIPS

DAMAGE	NATURE OF DAMAGE
Severe	Ship is either sunk or damaged to the extent requiring rebuilding
Moderate	Ship is immobilized, requiring extensive repairs, especially to shock-sensitive components or their foundations, e.g., propulsive machinery, boilers and interior equipment
Light	Ship may still be able to operate, although there will be damage to electronic, electrical and mechanical equipment

TABLE D–4. FORESTS

DAMAGE	NATURE OF DAMAGE	EQUIVALENT STEADY WIND VELOCITY MPH
Severe	Up to 90% of trees blown down; remainder denuded of branches and leaves. Area impassable to vehicles and difficult on foot	130–140
Moderate	About 30% of trees blown down; remainder have some branches and leaves blown off. Area passable to vehicles only after extensive clearing	90–100
Light	Very few trees blown down; some leaves and branches blown off. Area passable to vehicles	60–80

Plastic range. The stress range in which a material will not fail when subjected to a force. It will not recover completely, however, so that permanent deformation results when the force is removed.

Plastic deformation. The deformation from which an object, upon which force has been exerted, does not recover.

DARK CURRENT

In a photoemitting or photoconducting radiation detector, the dark current is the output signal current measured when the detector is not exposed to radiation. This current arises from low-level thermal and electronic noise effects, which are increased by defects in the materials or assembly.

DAUGHTER

Nuclide formed in the radioactive decay of a radioactive nuclide (called the PARENT). Also called a decay product. For example, yttrium-90 is the daughter of strontium-90.

DAVIS RADIOBIOLOGY PROJECT, UNIVERSITY OF CALIFORNIA

The Radiobiology Project, School of Veterinary Medicine, University of California at Davis, conducts 2 large beagle-dog projects for the Division of Biology and Medicine of the USAEC.

A lifetime study of "The Effects of X-radiation on Work Capacity and Longevity of the Dog" was started in 1951 with a colony of purebred beagles. Exposure schedules set up 3 groups (sham radiation control, 100 roentgens [r] and 300 r of

x-ray) and 7 subgroups for each radiation exposure (25 r at 28-day intervals, 25 r at 14-day intervals, etc.). The average age of the colony of 264 beagles is 3,003 days (31 Jan., 1962), so that the aging syndrome, as well as the chronic effects of radiation, is beginning to show. The most significant changes are an increased incidence of mammary tumors, the highest number of tumors occurring in the 300-r group; cardiac disease with an incidence of 6.8% in the 100-r group, 2.9% in the 300-r group, and 4.7% in the controls. Skin deterioration is also noted. An associated study demonstrated that a single median lethal dose of whole-body irradiation (x-ray) to 60 purebred female beagles did not interfere with their reproductive activity. The MLD/30 days for this group was 260 r (midline air dose).

In 1957 a second long-term project was undertaken on "The Effects of Continual Strontium-90 Ingestion during the Growth Period of the Beagle and Its Relation to Radium-226 Toxicity." In 1962 this study was not at a stage at which definitive results were available, but data collected during the first 18 months indicate that the beagle discriminates against strontium in a manner similar to other species; the observed ratio ($OR_{bone\text{-}diet}$) is 0.4 to 0.5.

DEAD TIME

When a pulse is formed and collected in a Geiger counter, a time interval must elapse before the tube can be ready to detect and count another ionizing event. This interval is the dead time of the detector; radiation events occurring within this span of time will not be counted. For ordinary types of Geiger counter this interval is something like a few thousandths of a second; superior types of detector may be able to recover from this "moment of paralysis" in a fraction of a millisecond. When the ionizing radiation events are occurring at a rather slow rate, few of the counts will be lost for this cause. As faster counting rates are encountered, however, the fraction of time that the detector is disabled becomes greater and greater, so that a dead time correction must be made to make up for the counts which may have been lost. For counting rates which are relatively high in relation to the recovery abilities of a particular counter, the correction required becomes large and must be accurately computed (although electronic circuits are available which can do this automatically and instantaneously). For moderately rapid counting rates, a simple approximation formula is adequate; it is a statement of the proportion of counts possibly lost based on the expectation that the ionizing events will occur in a statistically random pattern in time.

See COUNTING EFFICIENCY, COINCIDENCE CORRECTION and RESOLVING TIME.

DEAD TIME CORRECTION.   *See* COINCIDENCE CORRECTION.

DECADE SCALER
Pulse recording circuit having a scaling factor of 10.

See DECIMAL SCALER.

DECAY, RADIOACTIVE.   *See* RADIOACTIVE DECAY.

DECAY CONSTANT
Symbol λ. Also called the radioactive constant or the disintegration constant. The fraction of the number of atoms of a radioactive nuclide which decay in unit time. The decay constant is a specific and definite property of any given radioelement and is independent of its chemical combination or physical state. The decay constant is used in the equation

$$N = N_0\ e^{-\lambda t},$$

relating the number of atoms of a radioactive species to the number of atoms present at a given time, where N_a is the initial number of atoms present, and N is the number of atoms present after some time, t. A related constant, RADIOACTIVE HALF-LIFE, equal to 0.693 divided by λ, is commonly used as an alternative to the decay constant. The relation between the decay constant λ and radioactive half-life, $T_{\frac{1}{2}}$, is

$$T_{\frac{1}{2}} = \frac{0.69315}{\lambda}.$$

DECAY CURVE
Curve showing the relative amount of a radioactive substance remaining after any time interval. A simple decay curve is shown in the chart (Figure D-1) for a radioactive isotope with a half-life of 3 hours and with initial activity equal to 16 millicuries.

The amount of radioactivity present at any given time is essential information for biological and medical research, for diagnosis and for medical treatment. This information may be obtained for any radioactive isotope by use of the following formula:

$$A_2 = A_1 e^{-0.693\frac{t}{T_{\frac{1}{2}}}}$$

FIGURE D-1. SIMPLE DECAY CURVE FOR A RADIOACTIVE ISOTOPE WITH A HALF-LIFE OF 3 HOURS AND WITH INITIAL ACTIVITY EQUAL TO 16 MILLICURIES.

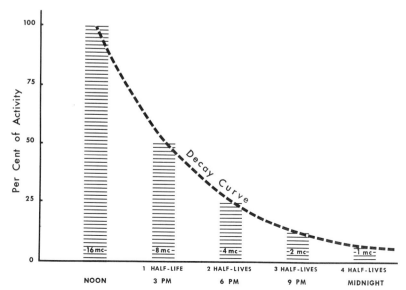

where A_2 = activity to be determined, A_1 = known initial activity, e = 2.7183, 0.693 = a constant, t = elapsed time (from A_1 to A_2) expressed in the same units as $T_{\frac{1}{2}}$, $T_{\frac{1}{2}}$ = radioactive half-life of the element.

The calculation may be made with a slide rule which has log and log-log scales. Set the hairline on 0.500 on the log-log scale (usually labeled LL00); locate the half-life on the left half of the B scale and set this point under the hairline; to determine the decay factor, slide the hairline to the left along the B scale so that it coincides with the elapsed time in question; the decay factor may then be read from the log-log scale. If the reading runs off the left end of the scale, move the hairline to the right of the half-life and locate the elapsed time on the right half of the B scale—the decay factor should then be read from the log scale (usually labeled LL0).

For a sample containing several radioactive substances the compound decay curve is the sum of the simple decay curves of the individual substances.

See RADIOACTIVE DECAY.

DECAY PRODUCT

A radioactive or stable nuclide formed by the radioactive decay or disintegration of a radioactive nuclide, formed either directly or as the result of successive transformations in a radioactive series.

See DAUGHTER.

DECIMAL SCALER

An electronic impulse counter which uses a circuit arranged to count signal pulses from 0 to 9, resetting itself to 0 on the next pulse and at the same time triggering the succeeding decade or register. Succeeding scales are arranged to read

FIGURE D–2. DECIMAL SCALER (BELOW) AND TIMER (ABOVE) WITH CONTROLS USED IN PRESET COUNT AND PRESET TIME PROCEDURES. (COURTESY OF BAIRD-ATOMIC, INC.)

tens, hundreds, thousands . . . of events. Originally these were contrived by modification of binary scaler techniques; newer types of direct transfer scaling tubes called dekatrons now perform the whole scale-of-ten function within a single tube envelope. Figure D–2 shows a decimal scaler used with an electronic timer.

DECONTAMINATION

Physical removal of radioactive contamination to a contained or controlled location. The type and methods of decontamination depend upon the type of contaminant and the objects being decontaminated. (*See* PERSONNEL DECONTAMINATION, CLOTHING DECONTAMINATION, EQUIPMENT DECONTAMINATION, and LABORATORY DECONTAMINATION.)

Decontamination of the outside surfaces of buildings and grounds may be required in the

TABLE D–5. FALLOUT DECONTAMINATION PROCEDURES ON LAND SURFACES

PROCEDURE	APPROX. REDUCTION FACTOR
Plowing (to depth of 8 inches)	3
Bulldozing or grading (to depth of 4 inches)	4
Fill (clean dirt to depth of 6 inches)	5
Scraping (to depth of 4 inches with concurrent removal of exhumed dirt)	10

TABLE D–6. DECONTAMINATION USING FIRE HOSING METHOD*

SURFACE	APPROX. REDUCTION FACTOR
Concrete	10
Wood	30
Metal	30
Roofing	30

*Data from U.S. Naval Radiological Defense Laboratory, San Francisco, California.

event of heavy radioactive fallout following the detonation of a nuclear device. Structures may be washed with a fire hose to remove fallout particles, taking care that the run-off does not accumulate and form hazardous levels of radiation. Radioactive fallout material may be sealed with asphalt or covered with earth. Tables D–5 and D–6 provide estimates of reduction in gamma radiation intensity after various decontamination procedures.

DECONTAMINATION FACTOR

Test methods are designed to compare the relative effectiveness of various methods and conditions for different contaminants and for different surfaces. In order to have working rules to indicate effectiveness of surfaces in resisting contamination and of methods of decontaminating, the following factor is one of several developed to express quantitatively the effectiveness of any given procedure:

$$\text{Decontamination factor} = \frac{\text{initial activity}}{\text{final activity}}$$

DEFENSE ATOMIC SUPPORT AGENCY (DASA)

DASA is an agency of the U.S. Department of Defense which coordinates the ARMED FORCES RADIATION BIOLOGY AND ATOMIC MEDICINE PROGRAM. DASA approves, supervises and financially supports research in nuclear weapons effects among the 3 services (Army, Navy, Air Force) and awards contracts to universities and civilian laboratories for research beyond the capabilities of Service facilities.

See ARMY RADIATION BIOLOGY AND ATOMIC MEDICINE PROGRAM and NAVY RADIATION BIOLOGY AND ATOMIC MEDICINE PROGRAM.

DEGENERATIVE PHENOMENA

Irradiation may cause cell damage leading to cell degeneration and ultimate cell death. The nucleus of the cell, especially during mitosis, is more RADIOSENSITIVE than the cytoplasm. Initiation of mitosis may be temporarily inhibited, but if already started, mitosis continues. Abnormal mitoses, broken chromosomes, and lagging and clumping of chromosomes have been noted. Cytoplasm may become vacuolated. Nuclei, e.g., of fibroblasts, may become large and pleomorphic, and the cytoplasm may swell. Sensitivity and changes vary with cell types. Nuclear pyknosis, shrinking and karyorrhexis are ultimate results of radiation.

More general degenerative phenomena may be noted such as demyelination (destruction of the myelin sheath of nerve tissue) or atrophy of the skin.

See CELLS, RADIATION EFFECTS ON.

DELTA RAYS

Secondary electrons which have acquired enough energy to cause further ionization, released in matter by the action of a primary radiation.

DEMOGRAPHY, USE IN STUDY OF RADIATION EFFECTS

Natural radiation in the environment (75 millirad per year in normal regions) apparently has little measurable effect upon mankind. How an over-all increase in the level of radiation would affect the well-being of the population is not known.

It is, however, well established that accidental exposure of single individuals to radiation of a dose level of 100 roentgens (r) or more affects the somatoplasm in a detrimental way (*see* SOMATIC EFFECTS). Radiation illness and death may occur if the dose is high enough (LD_{50} for man is 450 r). Chronic effects of radiation also take their toll in lessened function and death in some cases. Germ plasm may be affected by radiation in a detrimental way through the production of mutations leading to the development of less-than-normal offspring or to death of the reproductive cells.

The stamina and vigor of population groups is determined by the ability to do work, resist disease, perform mental functions, reproduce—in fact, species survival depends upon such ability. Genetic quality and somatic quality combine in a living generation to determine individual and thereby group vigor. In addition, individuals and groups have a certain reserve capacity available to call upon for endurance, defense, and repair of injury in the struggle against disease, injury and adverse environmental conditions. What level of increasing radiation will affect this reserve and alter the group vigor is unknown, but studies in radiation biology make it evident that a fewfold increase over the present level of natural radiation need not be disastrous or even detrimental if natural selection is allowed to operate.

See POPULATIONS, RADIATION EFFECTS ON.

DENSITOMETER, PHOTOGRAPHIC

Instrument for measuring the amount of exposure recorded by photographic film through measuring its optical density; operates by sending a light beam through the film (at the point of interest) and measuring the fraction of light transmitted; calibration is in units indicating the (developed) density of the film.

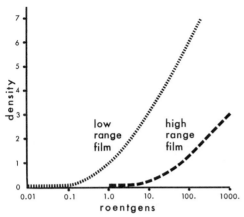

FIGURE D–3. DENSITY CHARACTERISTICS OF PHOTO-
GRAPHIC FILM TO COBALT-60 RADIATION. TYPICAL D VS.
LOG E CURVES.

DENSITY, PHOTOGRAPHIC

Amount of darkening of photographic film; taken to indicate the amount of exposure when used in a FILM BADGE as read from an appropriate characteristic curve (see Figure D–3). Measured as the logarithm of the opacity of the processed film, the opacity being the ratio of the light incident to the light transmitted. Photographic densitometers are customarily calibrated directly in terms of this function.

DENSITY GAGING

The measurement and/or automatic control of the density of a liquid, powder or solid by using a radioactive isotope density gage. Used in processes involving evaporation or dilution, mixing or fractioning, thickening or foaming, and in such industries as the chemical, food, mining, petroleum and pharmaceutical. Measurement of density to 0.1% is common. Two operations serve to illustrate the many industrial uses: cigarette density control, and packing of medicinal capsules.

The accompanying diagram (Fig. D–4) shows

the method of controlling the firmness of the pack of tobacco as the cigarette is being made. A strontium-90 source is mounted so that the radiation passes through a standard and also through the cigarette being made and is absorbed, depending on the density of each. The radiation which passes through each is then picked up in the ionization chambers, and the electrical control unit instructs the machine to adjust the amount of tobacco being fed so that the density of the cigarettes matches the density of the standard.

Continuously controlled filling of capsules for medicinal use is also done with density gaging. Each capsule is automatically checked as it passes by on an endless belt, and those capsules not properly filled are rejected. The principle involved is illustrated in Figure D–5.

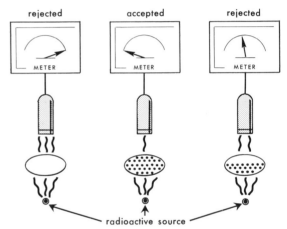

FIGURE D–5. STRONTIUM-90 SOURCE USED IN QUALITY CONTROL OF CAPSULE CONTENT.

Other pharmaceutical uses of density gaging are the following: in process measurement of uniformity and thoroughness of mixing; automatic in process separation of liquids of different densities (to within 0.01 specific gravity units); continuous in process measurement and control of percentage

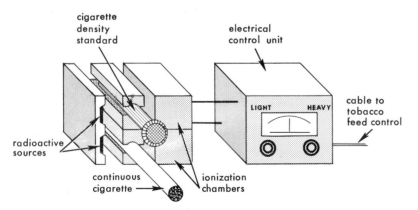

FIGURE D–4. GAGING CIGA-
RETTE FIRMNESS WITH RADIO-
ISOTOPES.

of solids in suspensions; continuous in process measurement and control of specific gravity; measurement of consistency of semisolids (ointments and creams); and grinding powders to a predetermined density.

DEOXYRIBONUCLEIC ACID (DNA). *See* NUCLEIC ACID STUDIES.

DEPARTMENT OF COMMERCE, U.S.

An agency of the U.S. government whose primary interest in atomic energy is centered in the NATIONAL BUREAU OF STANDARDS and in the OFFICE OF TECHNICAL SERVICES.

DEPARTMENT OF DEFENSE (DOD)

A department of the U.S. Government composed of the armed forces (Army; Navy, including naval aviation and the Marine Corps; and the Air Force) whose mission is to support and defend the United States against its enemies, and to safeguard the internal security of the country.

The task of development and testing various types of nuclear devices is the joint responsibility of the DOD and the USAEC (*see* JOINT TASK FORCE). They also work together in the development of nuclear power suited to the various needs of the 3 services. A number of research programs in the area of atomic energy are either jointly or independently sponsored by the DOD.

In the DOD the atomic energy program is the responsibility of an assistant to the Secretary of Defense who reports directly to the Secretary of Defense. He provides advice and assistance on atomic energy matters to other officials of the DOD as required, and coordinates with other DOD departments having related functions. He is also chairman of the Military Liaison Committee to the USAEC.

See ARMED FORCES RADIATION BIOLOGY AND ATOMIC MEDICINE PROGRAM and DEFENSE ATOMIC SUPPORT AGENCY.

DETECTION INSTRUMENT

Apparatus or device embodying a detector and related equipment to measure or analyze the response of the detector for the purpose of determining the nature or the quantity of the events detected.

See RADIATION DETECTION INSTRUMENTS.

DETECTOR

Material or device which is sensitive to radiation and has the capability of developing a response signal suitable for measurement or analysis.

See RADIATION DETECTORS.

DETECTOR PROBE

Movable assembly, including radiation detector, used to find areas where radiation is present and to make localized measurements; sometimes incorporates preamplifier; variously contrived for specific requirements in medical applications, health physics surveying, or commercial purposes (such as geological prospecting): e.g., radioisotope scanners, thin surgical instruments, and extension detectors in survey meters. Figure D–6 shows a standard type used in measuring iodine uptake in thyroid.

See SCINTILLATION SCANNER.

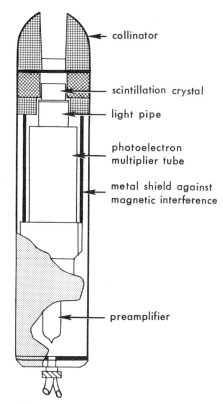

FIGURE D–6. DIAGRAM SHOWING COMPONENTS OF A DETECTOR PROBE.

DEUTERIUM

Isotope of hydrogen; atomic number 1; mass number 2 ($_1H^2$); constitutes about 0.02% of natural hydrogen. Named from Greek *deuteros*, second. Deuterium oxide (D_2O), heavy water. High concentrations (over 30%) of D_2O in body water have been shown to be toxic. D-labeled compounds have been used in biological tracer studies.

See FUSION, NUCLEAR, and THERMONUCLEAR WEAPON.

DEUTERON

Nucleus of a deuterium (heavy hydrogen) atom. A positive charge of 1 unit and a mass of approximately 2 units on the atomic weight scale indicates that a deuteron (d) contains a proton and a neutron.

DIAGNOSTIC METHODS

Radioisotopes, because they can be detected and measured accurately, are highly useful for diagnostic tests. The fact that radioactive atoms generally behave the same as stable atoms of the same element makes it possible to study many biochemical processes by means of appropriately chosen radioactive tracers. Diagnostic information may be derived from the amount and location of the radioisotope in the body, its rate of movement, on the amount in blood, urine or feces. Common examples include the study of thyroid function with iodine-131, the measurement of red cell survival with chromium-51, the assessment of iron utilization with iron-59, and the confirmation of pernicious anemia with cobalt-57-labeled vitamin B_{12}.

See MEDICAL DIAGNOSIS.

DIARRHEA DUE TO RADIATION

Diarrhea is part of the symptom complex of the gastrointestinal syndrome in radiation illness, and usually indicates INTESTINAL DAMAGE. In patients who have been accidentally (*see* RADIATION ACCIDENTS) exposed to whole-body irradiation in the dose level of 400 to 600 roentgens (r) there may be diarrhea during the third or fourth week. In the 600- to 800-r group the gastrointestinal syndrome dominates the picture, and diarrhea during the third or fourth week almost invariably occurs and is severe, frequently complicated by bleeding. For example, an accident patient who received 718 rad whole body had abdominal pain and cramps accompanied by diarrhea on the twenty-fifth day, which increased in severity until the twenty-eighth day, when a massive intestinal hemorrhage occurred. Death occurred on the twenty-ninth day. Diarrhea immediately following a single dose of whole-body radiation usually indicates that a supralethal dose has been received.

Diarrhea—thin, mucoid or bloody—is common after radiation therapy involving the abdominal region. The intestinal mucosa may show hyperemia, edema and fibrinous exudate with a granular surface that bleeds readily. This mild reaction lasts 2 to 3 weeks. The occurrence of diarrhea during radiation therapy does not necessitate cessation of treatment, since it is usually easily controlled by drugs, e.g., paregoric.

Multiple intestinal ulcerations are not uncommon in late radiation reactions and may lead to diarrhea. They become progressively destructive with perforation and fistula formation. Most lesions are in the rectum and sigmoid, with the ileum the most frequent site in the small bowel.

DIET IN TREATMENT OF RADIATION ILLNESS. *See* TREATMENT OF RADIATION ILLNESS.

DIFFERENTIAL ENERGY SPECTRUM

Data or graph which displays an energy spectrum in terms of the numbers of detected gamma rays or particles which have energies lying within each selected energy interval throughout the full energy range reported. Such a plot represents the mathematical differential of the accumulated count curve, which is known as the INTEGRAL ENERGY SPECTRUM.

DIFFERENTIAL PULSE HEIGHT ANALYZER

One which develops and presents energy spectrum data as numbers of events occurring in each particular channel or selected energy interval.

DIFFRACTION

Phenomenon produced by the interruption and spreading of waves (light, sound, pressure, electromagnetic) around and past one or more opaque objects. Various types of apparatus, diffraction gratings, and crystals have been used to study wave motion and wave lengths.

Light and sound waves have been extensively studied, as have x-rays. Electrons and neutrons have also been studied by diffraction techniques.

A blast wave from the detonation of a nuclear device, when striking an object, is diffracted around and envelops the object or structure.

DIFFUSION STUDIES. *See* MEMBRANE PERMEABILITY STUDIES.

DILUTION TECHNIQUES. *See* ISOTOPE DILUTION ANALYSIS.

DISCRIMINATION FACTOR

The ratio of 2 elements in the diet divided by the ratio in the body (or bone); e.g., discrimination factor for Sr^{90} with respect to Ca is:

$$\frac{Sr^{90}/Ca \text{ (diet)}}{Sr^{90}/Ca \text{ (bone)}} = 2 \text{ to } 4 \text{ in the adult.}$$

Strontium is metabolized in the animal body and human body in a manner similar to metabolism of calcium; exposure occurs largely as the result of ingestion of Sr^{90} along with the calcium in the diet; therefore study of the Sr^{90}/Ca ratio is important.

TABLE D–7.   COMPARATIVE USE OF STRONTIUM AND CALCIUM

ANIMAL	DIET		BODY	
	STRONTIUM*	CALCIUM	STRONTIUM*	CALCIUM
Rat	100	100	28	100
Mouse	100	100	35	100
Rabbit	100	100	22	100
Sheep	100	100	24	100
Goat	100	100	29	100
Cow	100	100	18	100
Man	100	100	25 or 50	100

The reduction in the Sr/Ca ratio for animals is shown in table D–7, in which it is seen that animals raised on a diet containing equal parts of strontium and calcium retained in their bodies about 1 part of strontium per 4 parts of calcium, i.e., 25 to 100 parts.

The values for man are probably not less than 2 or greater than 4; i.e., as noted in the table, if the diet contains 100 Sr* to 100 Ca, then the body would contain 25 to 50 Sr* to 100 Ca.

The physiological processes responsible for the differential behavior of calcium and strontium, i.e., that tend to move calcium in preference to strontium, are (a) absorption from the alimentary tract, (b) urinary excretion as a result of more efficient tubular reabsorption of calcium than of strontium, (c) secretion from blood into milk, and (d) movement from blood of the mother to the developing fetus. Also there is less discrimination in young animals than in adults.

Experimental evidence indicates that if the diet of a lactating cow or goat contains 100 parts of Sr per 100 parts of Ca, then the milk will contain about 11 or 12 parts of Sr per 100 parts of Ca. About 95% is excreted in the feces (percentage of daily dose per day), 1.5% in the urine, and about 0.9% appears in the milk. This means that each quart of milk contains about 0.1% of the amount of strontium-90 eaten daily by the cow.

DISCRIMINATOR

Electronic circuit which functions to select signal pulses by accepting or rejecting them according to their pulse height or voltage. Used to delete extraneous counts or background, or as the basis of energy spectrum analysis. Figure D–7 shows the discrimination action in a typical case, where it eliminates the noise signals from the true counts from radioactive iodine.

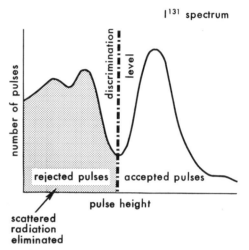

FIGURE D–7.   DISCRIMINATOR ACTION TO ELIMINATE NOISE AND OTHER UNWANTED SIGNALS FROM THE TUBE COUNT.

DISCRIMINATOR, PULSE HEIGHT

An electronic circuit which selects and passes signal pulses of strength between selected minimum and maximum amplitudes fixed by the control settings. Frequently the simpler circuits provide only the minimum criterion; however, pulse height analyzers and multichannel analyzers provide a range of successive pulse height channels for counting.

DISEASE STUDIES

For studies of disease mechanisms a wide variety of isotopic procedures have been used. In heart disease, changes in electrolytes and body fluids are measured with tracers of such elements as sodium, potassium and chlorine; recently tritium has been used as a tag for the hydrogen of water. In an effort to understand arteriosclerosis, organic compounds tagged with carbon-14 are used to learn of the formation and destruction of

*Indicates radioactive form.

cholesterol. Many other metabolic pathways are studied by the tracer technique.

Several types of compounds labeled with radioisotopes are used to measure the effectiveness of gastrointestinal absorption. Suitable isotopic methods have been devised for the study of the function of specific organs, especially the thyroid gland, heart, lungs, liver and kidneys.

Although these techniques are already highly valuable, it appears that only a beginning has been made in applying radioisotopes to the problems of clarifying disease mechanisms.

DISINTEGRATION. *See* RADIOACTIVE DISINTEGRATION.

DNA (deoxyribonucleic acid). *See* NUCLEIC ACID STUDIES.

DONNER LABORATORY

Donner Laboratory, Donner Pavilion and Crocker Laboratory, located on the Berkeley Campus of the University of California, provide the primary physical facilities for the Biology and Medicine Program of the Lawrence Radiation Laboratory under contract with the USAEC. Funds for these buildings were given to the University by the Donner Foundation (1941, 1952, 1953), the Crocker Foundation (1936) and other interested donors to extend the pioneering studies of 1935 on the biological effects of heavy particles (neutrons), and on the use of radioactive tracers in research, diagnosis and therapy which were initiated as a result of the development of the early cyclotrons. Further support for these studies was received under the Manhattan Engineer District, and they were continued and extended as the Biology and Medicine Program of the Radiation Laboratory upon the formation of the AEC. Donner Pavilion, constructed in 1954, provides investigative hospital facilities for intensive metabolic studies on unsolved medical problems, and also is utilized in the investigation of the beneficial uses of radioisotopes and high-energy heavy particles in research, diagnosis and therapy. A new group of buildings designated as the biomedical complex funded by the AEC was started in 1961 with construction of the Animal Bioradiological Laboratory and will provide for the needed expansion of the biomedical program.

The combined scientific staffs number about 65 persons. The program of the Donner Laboratory covers a wide range of subjects on which basic research is conducted: radiobiology; space radiobiology; metabolism of bone seekers; modification of effects of radiation; cancer research; tracer studies; erythropoietin; blood cells and ferro-

kinetics; physiology; circulation and body composition studies; biochemistry; nervous system; structure and function of the cell; genetics; photosynthesis; radiation chemistry; biophysics, medical physics, and health physics; methodology and instrumentation.

Donner Laboratory has the many accelerators of the Lawrence Radiation Laboratory available for use in biomedical studies. These include the 184-inch synchrocyclotron, the heavy ion linear accelerator (HILAC) and the 88-inch cyclotron. The 900-Mev alpha particle beam of the 184-inch synchrocyclotron is used for pituitary irradiation in the investigation of the hormonal control of certain malignant and metabolic diseases, direct irradiation of tumors and the production of lesions in the central nervous system in investigation and therapy. The HILAC is used to investigate the effect of heavy ions on biological systems. The 88-inch cyclotron will soon be available for use in the production of radioisotopes of short half-life and penetrating heavy ions for biomedical studies.

A training and teaching program in the fields of radiation, tracers, biophysics, medical physics and radiation health includes the formal program of teaching and research leading to the degrees of Master of Science in bioradiology and Doctor of Philosophy in biophysics or medical physics as a part of the University group training in these fields.

DOSAGE CRITERIA

Historically, the first dosage criterion was x-ray-produced erythema of the skin, called an HED unit, an acronym from human erythema dose. Many other units for describing dose have been developed, roentgen (r), rad and rem being commonly used at present.

The following additional factors are important in considering dosage criteria: dose rate, length of time of exposure, the part or volume of the body irradiated, the type of radiation and its RELATIVE BIOLOGICAL EFFECTIVENESS, and the RADIOSENSITIVITY of the tissue or organ being irradiated.

Dose rate takes into consideration the amount of radiation emitted per unit of time, often expressed in roentgens per hour (r/hr). Length of exposure time is important in determining dosage criteria, for if a 50 r/hr dose rate is delivered for 6 hours, the total accumulated dose delivered would be 300 r. The time elapsing between doses is also important, for it has been shown that the fractionated or divided dose, when compared to a single dose of the same magnitude, produces less biological damage, owing to recovery and repair factors.

Biological damage depends also upon the part

and amount or volume of the body irradiated. For example, an absorbed dose of 1000 r ionizing radiation to the hand would produce no serious effects, but the same type and amount of radiation to the whole body would probably produce death. Whether the part of the body being irradiated is particularly radiosensitive or is essential to life is also important.

The type of radiation (alpha, beta, gamma, x-ray, neutron, cosmic-rays, etc.), and its relative biological effectiveness (RBE) have a direct bearing on dosage criteria. For example, the RBE for alpha particles is probably 10; i.e., it is 10 times more effective biologically than gamma rays with their RBE of 1.

Based on these criteria, PERMISSIBLE DOSE and MAXIMUM PERMISSIBLE DOSE figures have been established.

DOSE

Also referred to as dosage. The accumulated or total quantity of radiation. According to current usage, the radiation delivered to a specified area of the body or to the whole body. Units used in specifying the dose are roentgen for x-rays or gamma rays, and rep or rem for beta rays.

Absorbed dose. The amount of energy imparted to matter by ionizing particles per unit mass of irradiated material at the point of interest. Usually expressed in rads. The same absorbed dose of different kinds of radiation does not, in general, produce exactly the same biological effect, for different types of radiation have a different relative biological effectiveness (RBE).

Absorbed dose rate. See DOSE RATE.

Acute dose. Radiation absorbed during an acute exposure, i.e., a single exposure of short duration. The acute dose results in more biological damage than a divided or fractionated dose.

Air dose. X-ray or gamma-ray dose expressed in roentgens delivered at a point in free air. In radiological practice it consists of the radiation of the primary beam and that scattered from surrounding air. Measured using the free-air or air-wall ionization chamber.

Chronic dose. Radiation absorbed during a chronic exposure, i.e., a fractionated dose or a protracted dose.

Critical organ dose. The absorbed dose of ionizing radiation in a critical organ of the body. The critical concept is used in determining the maximum permissible body burden and the maximum permissible concentration.

Cumulative dose. Total dose resulting from repeated exposures to radiation of the same region, or of the whole body. Careful records are kept on industrial workers' exposure to make certain that

they do not exceed the limits set by the RADIATION PROTECTION GUIDES (RPG).

Depth dose. Radiation dose delivered at a particular depth beneath the surface of the body. It is usually measured in roentgens or rads, and expressed as percentage of surface dose or of air dose.

Dose-effect relationship. See separate item.

Dose equivalent. The dose equivalent (DE) is the product of absorbed dose, D; quality factor, (QF); dose distribution factor, (DF); and other necessary modifying factors; i.e.,

$$(DE) = D \, (QF) \, (DF)$$

where QF is the linear-energy-transfer-dependent factor by which absorbed doses are to be multiplied to obtain, for purposes of radiation protection, a quantity that expresses on a common scale for all ionizing radiation, the irradiation incurred by exposed persons; and DF is used to express the modification of biological effect due to nonuniform distribution of internally deposited isotopes. The unit of dose equivalent is the rem. It is numerically equal to the dose in rads multiplied by the appropriate modifying factors.

Dose rate. See separate item.

Dose-response relationship. Used interchangeably with dose-effect relationship.

Emergency dose (radiation workers). An accidental or emergency dose of 25 rems to the whole body or a major portion thereof, occurring only once in the lifetime of the person, which does not have to be included in the determination of the total accumulated industrial exposure status of the worker, as defined under the MAXIMUM PERMISSIBLE DOSE (MPD) standards or the more recent RADIATION PROTECTION GUIDES (RPG).

Exit dose. Dose of radiation at the surface of the body opposite to that on which the beam is incident, resulting from radiation emerging after having traversed the body.

Exposure dose. Dose delivered to a point within a sizable amount of biological material, consisting of both direct radiation attenuated by traversing the material, and of scattered radiation from the biological material. Even though measured in the tissue, it is still an exposure dose, for it is measured in terms of ionization in the air contained within the measuring instrument. This roentgen dose can be converted into an absorbed dose by changing it into rads by application of a small correction factor.

Fractionated dose. Dose administered in divided, relatively small units given daily or at longer intervals. In general, divided doses, when compared with the total accumulated dose given at one time, show much less biological damage, owing to recovery and repair factors. For example, the effect of dose fractionation on the incidence of leukemia in x-irradiated mice is shown in the following: 1,000 r total dose; when 25 r were given daily, 10 out of 18 mice (10/18) developed leukemia; for 125 r weekly, 12/20; 250 r fortnightly, 3/18; 50 r daily, 14/20; 250 r weekly, 9/19; and 500 r fortnightly, 4/15.

Genetic dose. See separate item.

Infinite integrated dose. See separate item.

Integral dose. Sometimes called volume dose. A measure of the total energy absorbed by a patient or other biological object during radiation exposure. Usually expressed in gram-roentgens, or gram-rads, which is a unit equal to 100 ergs.

Lethal dose. See separate item.

Maximum permissible dose (MPD). See separate item.

Median lethal dose (MLD). See separate item.

Medical dose (radiation workers). Radiation exposures resulting from necessary medical and dental procedures which need not be included in the determination of the total accumulated industrial exposure status of the worker, as defined under the maximum permissible dose (MPD) standards.

Percentage depth dose. Amount of radiation delivered at a specified depth in tissue, expressed as a percentage of the amount delivered at the skin surface, or as a percentage of the air dose.

Permissible dose. See separate item.

Protraction dose. Dose of radiation administered over a relatively long time (weeks or months) at a low dose rate.

Radiation dose. A general term which needs to be further qualified according to one or more of the following characteristics of radiation: type of radiation, alpha, beta, gamma, x-ray or neutron; external or internal radiation exposure; penetrating or nonpenetrating; partial body or whole body; acute or chronic exposure; or the poorly defined terms, high-level or low-level exposure.

Radiation protection guides (RPG). See separate item.

Skin dose. Defined as the dose on the skin at the center of the radiation field. It is the sum of the air dose, plus back scatter, with the addition of the exit dose from other parts, if this is significant. For more definitive data see BETA BURN, and SKIN, RADIATION EFFECTS ON.

Surface dose. Dose of radiation measured in roentgens or rad at the surface of a structure. It is the sum of the air dose plus the dose due to back scattering from the structure, and is, except for the possible addition of exit dose, equivalent to skin dose.

Threshold dose. Minimum dose that will produce a detectable degree of any given effect. The earliest dose measurements were based on the production of erythema of the skin, i.e., a threshold dose.

Tissue dose. Dose received by the tissue in the region of interest. The tissue dose includes both the direct air dose attenuated by passage through the intervening tissue and the radiation scattered by the tissue. Expressed in roentgens for x-rays and gamma rays, and in reps for other ionizing radiations. These may be converted into rads, which is the more appropriate term.

Tolerance dose. An obsolete term, replaced by permissible dose. It was based on the assumption that an individual can receive such a dose of radiation without any harmful effects.

Units of dosage. The first unit of dosage was the HED, which stood for either human erythema dose or Hauteinheintsdosis. Other units of x-ray dosage were suggested and adopted locally, but in 1928 by international agreement the roentgen (r) was adopted as the standard for x-rays and for gamma rays. Other presently used units are the rad (radiation absorbed dose) and the rem (roentgen equivalent, man).

See DOSAGE CRITERIA.

DOSE-EFFECT RELATIONSHIP

The relation between the size of the dose and magnitude of the radiation effect being measured. The factors which determine the relation are relatively simple in radiation chemistry, when compared with interpretation of the relation in biological response where the effect measured is the end-result of many changes. In general, the biological effect depends primarily upon the total dose, its RELATIVE BIOLOGICAL EFFECTIVENESS, the portion of the body receiving the dose, and the amount of tissue, within broad limits, included in the beam.

There are individual differences in RADIOSENSITIVITY within a species, as well as species differences. It takes 1,800,000 roentgens (r) to inactivate the tobacco mosaic virus, while after an exposure to only 400 r half of the human population exposed probably would die if untreated.

The biological effects of radiation in relation to the dose of radiation depend upon what function is being measured. Threshold erythema may be caused by about 300 r to the skin, while severe erythema requires about 10,000 r. In rabbits a maximum decrease of about 25% in the lymphocyte count was detected in 24 hours after an exposure to but 25 r. Permanent sterility in the human male follows an exposure of 500 r, and in the female of 300 r. Temporary sterility is asso-

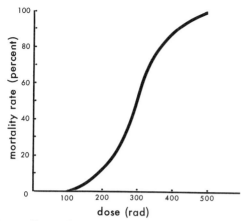

FIGURE D–8. DOSE-RESPONSE CURVE WITH ACUTE MORTALITY PLOTTED AGAINST X-RAY RADIATION DOSE. ($LD_{50}/30$ IS 300 RAD.)

ciated with exposure to about half this amount, and in a number of individuals with acute RADIATION ILLNESS recovery of fertility has been complete. For complete sterilization the screw worm fly requires 5,000 r, the Drosophila 16,000 r and the powder post beetle 32,000 r. The $LD_{50}/30$ varies from 250 for the guinea pig to 300,000 for paramecium (see RADIOSENSITIVITY for table).

A dose-effect curve is often constructed which relates the dose of radiation to the effect produced. Acute mortality versus radiation dose (see Figure D–8) will illustrate the type of curve commonly seen in a response to a drug dosage as well as to the lethal effects of radiation. The S-shaped curve is characteristic, a few individuals dying at relatively low doses, most dying at intermediate doses, and a few others surviving even at very high doses.

DOSE RATE

Also referred to as dosage rate. Radiation dose delivered per unit of time. Also, the amount of ionizing radiation absorbed by biological tissue per unit of time. Commonly used to indicate the level of radioactivity in a contaminated area. Usually expressed in roentgens per hour. Dose rate is measured by some type of dosimeter.

Dose rate is an important biological consideration, for it has been shown in mice that the biological effect is dependent not only on total dose, but also on dose rate. For example, when a given dose of gamma rays is distributed over weeks or a few months, the observed mutations may be but a half or a third of the number observed when the same dose is given in a single short exposure.

The absorbed dose rate is the quotient of ΔD by Δt, where ΔD is the increment in absorbed dose in

time (Δt), and Δ represents the appropriate averaging procedure necessary to take into consideration the fact that, in general, radiation fields are nonuniform in space and also may be variable in time.

$$\text{Absorbed dose rate} = \frac{\Delta D}{\Delta t}$$

A special unit of absorbed dose rate is any quotient of the rad by a suitable unit of time (rad/d, rad/min, rad/h, etc.).

DOSIMETER

Any instrument which combines a radiation detector element with an appropriate measuring system to provide means for determining quantity of radiation dose delivered or absorbed. There is an endless variety of such instruments to accommodate the broad range of radiation types, exposure situations, and specific purposes for which the radiation dose information is needed, ranging from personnel dosimeters for field use to precise standards for laboratory calibration.

See FILM BADGE, POCKET DOSIMETER, PERSONNEL MONITORING.

DOSIMETER, CHEMICAL. *See* CHEMICAL DOSIMETER.

DOSIMETER, POCKET. *See* POCKET DOSIMETER.

DOSIMETRY. *See* RADIATION DOSIMETRY.

DOUBLE LABELING. *See* MULTIPLE LABELING.

DRUG STUDIES. *See* PHARMACOLOGICAL STUDIES.

DRY BOX. *See* GLOVE BOX.

DUST HAZARDS

Dust containing radioactive particles may be produced and released to the air in mining, ore processing, milling, or shaping of radioactive materials; by industrial use of radioisotopes in solid or powder form; and by careless housekeeping or poor industrial hygiene. Inhalation of radioactive material is one of the most important routes for entry of hazardous material into the body. Radiation monitoring is carried out for all operations which might release radioactive dust.

See AEROSOL and AIR CONTAMINATION.

DYNODE

An electrode in a photomultiplier tube situated

between the emitting and collecting electrodes and supplied with an intermediate voltage to accelerate the incident electron stream and provide multiplication upon bombardment by secondary emission. Common photomultiplier tubes carry about 10 dynodes and achieve electron multiplication of the order of a million. Dynodes also serve similar acceleration purposes in other devices using streams of charged particles.

DYSPROSIUM

Symbol Dy; atomic number 66; atomic weight 162.51. Discovered by French chemist Leroy de Boisbaudran in 1886. Its name is derived from a Greek word meaning hard to speak with. A member of the yttrium subgroup of the rare earth metals. Its natural abundance is furnished by 7 stable isotopes, and there are 8 radioactive isotopes.

ECOLOGY. *See* RADIOECOLOGY.

EDTA

Abbreviation for ethylenediamine tetraacetic acid. Trade names are Sequestrene and Versene. A chelating agent acting on divalent and trivalent cations. The affinity for trivalent ions such as Fe^3, Al^3, Ga^3, and rare earth cations, in general exceeds that for divalent ions such as Mg^2, Ca^2, Sr^2, etc. Individual differences in affinity for specific ions make possible highly selective separations. The formula for EDTA is

$$NaO_2C \cdot H_2C \qquad\qquad CH_2 \cdot CO_2Na$$
$$\diagdown \qquad\qquad \diagup$$
$$N \cdot CH_2 \cdot CH_2 \cdot N$$
$$\diagup \qquad\qquad \diagdown$$
$$NaO_2C \cdot H_2C \qquad\qquad CH_2 \cdot CO_2Na$$

EDUCATION AND TRAINING, USAEC

The USAEC sponsors and supports an extensive program in education, training and information designed to assist individuals, organizations and educational institutions in implementing their programs and courses in various aspects of nuclear science and technology. This program helps to implement one of the USAEC's principal functions, i.e., maximizing the contribution of atomic energy to scientific, technical and industrial progress.

The educational activities of the USAEC are administered by the Division of Nuclear Education and Training in the headquarters organization. The division has the following 4 branches: (1) Grants and Materials Loan Branch with major responsibilities for nuclear equipment grants, loans and grants of nuclear materials, and university research reactor assistance; (2) Institutes and Fellowships Branch, which is responsible for institutes and seminars, fellowships, course operation, manuals, textbooks, teaching aids, technical information on education, nuclear newsletter, and educational TV; (3) Program and Policy Development Branch with responsibility for policies and plans, program integration and coordination, new AEC programs, technical conferences and meetings, educational trends, research progress and implications, policy papers and education speeches, and technical review; (4) Administration and Appraisal Branch, responsible for organization and staffing, budget and fiscal, education surveys, major systems and procedures, management projects, comprehensive reports and presentations, administrative and office services, administrative liaison and program appraisal.

Implementation of the education and training program is being achieved through a number of channels, of which the following are of most interest to the life sciences: (1) fellowships, (2) faculty training, (3) equipment grants and loans, (4) traveling teachers program, (5) lecturers for radiation biology and atomic medicine, and (6) special training courses and activities.

Fellowships. The fellowships available from the USAEC support both the individual recipient and the host university, and are directly related to the need for trained scientists, technicians and engineers in the nuclear science field. The following fellowships are currently being offered to qualified applicants:

Health Physics. Provides 60 to 70 first-year fellowships per year for specialized training in health physics; 20 to 30 may be renewed for a second year, leading to a master's degree. Academic training at one of 8 universities—California, Harvard, Kansas, Michigan, Puerto Rico, Rochester, Vanderbilt and Washington—followed by 3 months training at Argonne National Laboratory, Brookhaven National Laboratory, Hanford Atomic Products Operation, National Reactor Testing Station, Oak Ridge National Laboratory or the Lawrence Radiation Laboratory, Berkeley. Administered by ORINS.*

Advanced Health Physics. Provides up to 3 years' graduate training for the degree of Doctor of Philosophy to candidates qualified by prior schooling and experience. Training at university of choice. Five new appointments per year. Administered by ORINS.

Industrial Hygiene. Provides one-year graduate academic training in industrial hygiene at Harvard, Cincinnati, Michigan, Pittsburgh or Wayne State. Eight to 12 fellowships per year. Administered by ORINS.

Industrial Medicine. Provides one or two years of academic and in-plant training to physicians. Six to 8 trainees per year. Administered by University of Rochester, Atomic Energy Project, for

*Oak Ridge Institute of Nuclear Studies, P.O. Box 117, Oak Ridge, Tennessee.

training at one of 4 medical schools having an industrial medicine curriculum (Cincinnati, Harvard, Pittsburgh, Rochester).

Nuclear Science and Engineering fellowships are also offered. Administered by ORINS.

Faculty Training. Various types of institutes in radiation biology have been in operation since 1956, supported jointly with the National Science Foundation. The NSF pays the student stipend, family allowance and travel allowance, while the USAEC pays the cost of instruction, equipment and materials, including a kit of equipment which each successful candidate may take back to his high school or college to make his teaching more effective. In addition to summer institutes which have been conducted since 1956 for both high school and college teachers, in-service sessions conducted nights and/or Saturdays were started in 1960, and academic-year sessions for college teachers on leave for one year were started in 1961.

Institute training is also being offered in radioisotope techniques and radiation phenomena for physical and engineering teachers. Major emphasis has been at the college and university level. Since a student's interest must be aroused and his attention directed toward a scientific or engineering career before he enters college, increasing emphasis is being placed on reaching the high school science teacher.

Equipment Grants and Loans. The USAEC started an equipment grant program in 1957 for educational institutions to assist them in obtaining nuclear instrumentation and related equipment to increase the instructional scope in radiation biology and use of radioisotopes in biology and medicine. The USAEC similarly administers a grant program in the engineering and physical sciences. Also various nuclear materials, such as radionuclide sources, enriched uranium, heavy water, and graphite are made available on loan.

Science Demonstration Lecture Program. This program is designed to stimulate interest and competence in science among high school students, teachers, educational consultants, supervisors and foreign country educators. Through a series of lectures, laboratory experiments and demonstrations, discussions and tours of Oak Ridge facilities, the participant acquires a working knowledge of the current scientific development which they introduce into the scientific programs of their institutions or others that they are called upon to visit.

Lecturers for Radiation Biology and Atomic Medicine. With support from the USAEC and the NSF the American Institute of Biological Sciences provides lecturers in radiation biology and other specialties to colleges and universities (and a few high schools). In several schools this program has stimulated a "science emphasis week" or a "science-in-life" program for the entire student body.

Special Training Courses. The USAEC sponsors, and through its national laboratories operates, a number of special training courses open to foreign students as well as to United States citizens:

Radioisotope Techniques Courses. These are the most widely known and attended of any of the special training courses. They are conducted at the Oak Ridge Institute of Nuclear Studies.

See TRAINING, RADIOISOTOPES.

International Institute of Nuclear Science and Engineering. Advanced training courses are given in 5 areas of interest: Reactor Science and Technology, Engineering Research and Development, Physical Science Research and Life Science Research, and Engineering, Administration and Operation of Nuclear Facilities. Participant appointments are available for 16- to 32-week courses in Reactor Science and Technology, and Engineering Research and Development, or for a 16-week program in Engineering, Administration and Operation of Nuclear Facilities given only in the spring semester. Affiliate appointments at an advanced level for 2 terms or longer are available for Physical Science Research and Life Science Research, as well as for applied research and development in the science and technology of reactor systems and in the various areas of nuclear engineering.

See REACTOR TRAINING.

Reactor Operation Supervision. A 1-year course is given at the ORNL.

Reactor Hazards Evaluation. A 1-year course is given at ORNL.

Radiochemical Analysis Techniques. Training in these techniques is available at the USAEC HEALTH AND SAFETY LABORATORY.

Puerto Rico Nuclear Center. See separate item for details of their numerous courses.

Special courses for state and local employees have been initiated in an effort to prepare the states to take over licensing and inspection activities in the use of radioactive material.

Other Activities. *Research Training.* All USAEC university contractors are encouraged to employ undergraduate and graduate students on their research programs.

USAEC Laboratories Research Training. All the laboratories take undergraduate, graduate and postgraduate students for special training. Several hundred foreign students receive research on-the-job training each year in USAEC laboratories.

Visits to USAEC Laboratories. Visitors are welcome in the laboratories at any time, but on Thomas A. Edison's birthday a special occasion is made for high school students and their teachers.

Information Activities. (a) The headquarters USAEC, Division of TECHNICAL INFORMATION, and its Oak Ridge Extension furnish technical information at both scientific and popular levels.

(b) The American Museum of Atomic Energy, the Mobile Radioisotope Laboratory and various traveling exhibits handled by the OAK RIDGE INSTITUTE OF NUCLEAR STUDIES are also potent educational forces.

EFFECTIVE HALF-LIFE

Time required for the radioactivity from a given amount of a radioactive element or a radioisotope, deposited in the tissues or organs of an animal or man, to diminish by 50% as the result of the combined action of radioactive decay, and loss of the material by biological elimination.

Effective half-life (T) is defined in terms of the RADIOACTIVE HALF-LIFE (T_{rad}) of the radioactive substance itself, and the BIOLOGICAL HALF-LIFE (T_{biol}) of the substance in a given organ or in the total organism, by the following expression:

$$T = \frac{T_{biol} \times T_{rad}}{T_{biol} + T_{rad}}$$

It is of importance in determining the extent of tissue exposure from internal emitters.

Figure E–1 explains the relations between

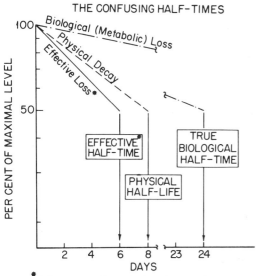

THE CONFUSING HALF-TIMES

* Unfortunately Biological is often used as synonymous with Effective.

FIGURE E–1. REPRESENTATION OF THE HALF-LIVES (HALF-TIMES) FOR IODINE-131 AFTER MAXIMAL UPTAKE IN THE THYROID GLAND. (MEDICAL DIVISION, OAK RIDGE INSTITUTE OF NUCLEAR STUDIES.)

physical or radioactive half-life, biological half-life (half-time) and effective half-life (half-time) for iodine-131 after maximal uptake in the thyroid gland.

See individual elements for effective half-life figures.

EFFICIENCY.   *See* COUNTING EFFICIENCY.

EINSTEINIUM

Symbol Es; atomic number 99; atomic weight 254; a radioactive transuranic element of the actinide series. Found in the coral debris from the vicinity of the thermonuclear test explosion of November, 1952, at Eniwetok Atoll, and announced by the USAEC on February 1, 1954. The element was isolated and identified by scientists at the Los Alamos Scientific Laboratory, the Argonne National Laboratory and the Radiation Laboratory, University of California, Berkeley. Named in honor of Albert Einstein. Eleven radioactive isotopes with mass numbers from 246 to 256 are known. Of these, einsteinium-254 ($_{99}Es^{254}$, α emitter, half-life 270 to 300 days) may be obtained in sufficient quantity for research. Does not occur in nature.

ELECTRICAL FIELD

This term indicates a region or space where the voltage or electrical potential changes from one place to another. In such a region free electrical charges or charged particles are accelerated, as in high-energy particle accelerators and in radiation detectors which utilize ion collection, gas multiplication or avalanche discharge.

ELECTRODE

General name for a terminal or element in an electrical system, especially in electronic or electrolytic devices. Electrodes serve as points or surfaces for emitting, collecting, converting or controlling streams of ions or electrons. Particular functions are performed by electrodes known as anode, cathode, dynode, photocathode.

ELECTROMAGNETIC RADIATION

The emission and propagation of electromagnetic waves, i.e., energy from the entire electromagnetic spectrum. Oscillating electric and a similar magnetic field, inextricably connected, each depending on the other for its existence. The propagation of electric and magnetic stresses through space with the speed of light. This includes not only visible light, but also radiofrequency, infra-red, ultraviolet, x-ray and gamma-ray radiation.

The term "radiation" or "radiant energy," when

TABLE E–1. THE ELECTROMAGNETIC SPECTRUM

TYPE OF RADIATION	FREQUENCY RANGE (CYCLES PER SEC.)	WAVE LENGTH RANGE (CENTIMETERS)	PHOTON ENERGY (ELECTRON VOLTS)
Cosmic rays	Greater than 10^{22}	Less than 10^{-12}	Greater than 10^8
Gamma rays	3×10^{18} to 3×10^{21}	10^{-8} to 10^{-11}	10^4 to 10^7
X-rays	3×10^{16} to 3×10^{22}	10^{-6} to 10^{-12}	10^2 to 10^8
Ultraviolet	7.5×10^{14} to 3×10^{18}	4×10^{-5} to 10^{-8}	5 to 10^2
Visible	4×10^{14} to 7.5×10^{14}	7.6×10^{-5} to 4×10^{-5}	2 to 5
Infra-red	10^{11} to 4×10^{14}	0.3 to 7.6×10^{-5}	1 to 10^{-3}
Radiowaves	10^4 to 10^{11}	3×10^6 to 0.3	10^{-3} to 10^{-10}
Electric waves	0 to 10^4	0.3 to 3×10^6	10^{-10} to 10^{-13}

unqualified, usually refers to electromagnetic radiation.

Vibrating electric charges which set up alternating electric and magnetic fields at right angles to each other and to the direction of propagation, which pass on the energy from one portion of the ether to the next as an electromagnetic wave.

See ELECTROMAGNETIC SPECTRUM.

ELECTROMAGNETIC SPECTRUM

The electromagnetic radiations arranged on an energy, a wave length or a frequency scale. The spectrum is divided into several arbitrary divisions, including 4 of particular interest in atomic and nuclear science: cosmic rays, gamma rays, x-rays and ultraviolet light. Table E–1 gives the known data (approximate) on the various divisions.

See ELECTROMAGNETIC RADIATION.

ELECTROMETER

An instrument capable of measuring minute quantities of electrical current. These instruments have high sensitivity and do not disturb or drain the circuit they are measuring. Most electrometers in common use depend upon complex electronic circuitry to achieve the requisite sensitivity and the degree of stability needed to sustain the reliability of response necessary in precision measurement. Some types are specifically intended for use in balanced circuits where the unknown signal is balanced to the null point against a known and controlled potential source. In other instances the electrometer has been refined for the direct measurement of electrical current to the level of micro-microamperes (10^{-12} amp), through use of especially developed vacuum tubes of the so-called electrometer types, in conjunction with sealed resistor components of high megohm values.

ELECTRON

An elementary particle which is a constituent of every neutral atom. Its electric charge may be either positive or negative, but the term "electron" is commonly used for the negative particle, also called the negatron. The positively charged electron is called a positron. In the normal state, matter is electrically neutral; thus the normal atom consists of a positively charged nucleus surrounded by a sufficient number of electrons (negatrons) so that their total negative charge is equal to the positive charge on the nucleus. A negatively charged body is thus one which contains more electrons than in the normal or neutral state; a positively charged body is one with fewer electrons than in the neutral state. The classic experiment of rubbing glass with silk demonstrates that electrons pass from the glass to the silk, giving the glass a positive charge and the silk a negative charge. It follows that a positive ion is an atom or group of atoms which has been deprived of one or more of its electrons, and a negative ion is an atom or group of atoms which has acquired additional electrons.

The electron charge (e) equals 4.8×10^{-10} statcoulombs or electrostatic units, or 1.6×10^{-19} coulombs. Its mass (m_e) is 9.1083×10^{-28} grams (g), or 0.000549 atomic mass unit (amu). Thus, 1837 electrons are required to equal the mass of an atom of hydrogen.

An electron ejected from an atom, molecule or surface as a result of a collision with a charged particle is called a secondary electron.

An electron which is gained, lost or shared in a chemical reaction is called a valence electron.

An orbital electron may be captured by its nucleus. This electron capture is a type of radioactive decay, and the electron is designated by the electron shell from which it is captured as K-electron capture, L-electron capture, etc.

ELECTRON CAPTURE

Abbreviation EC. A mode of radioactive decay of a nuclide in which a bound electron is captured by and merges with its nucleus, thus forming a new nuclide with the mass number unchanged, but the atomic number decreased by 1. A bound electron ($_{-1}e$) is taken up, and a proton (p) is transformed to a neutron (n) within the nucleus, and a neutrino (ν) emerges having energy equal to the difference between the disintegration energy and the original binding energy of the electron. By formula it is expressed:

$$_1p^1 + _{-1}e \longrightarrow _0n^1 + \nu$$

An example is vanadium + electron capture = titanium:

$$_{23}V^{49}_{26} \longrightarrow _{22}Ti^{49}_{27}$$

The relation may be shown thus:

	proton	+ electron	$\longrightarrow$ neutron	+ neutrino
mass	1	0	1	0
charge	+1	−1	0	0

The phenomenon described above is called orbital-electron capture. The electron is usually captured from the first quantum level nearest to the nucleus, i.e., the K level. Thus the term "K-electron capture" or "K-capture" is often used when the atomic shell occupied by the electron captured is known. Capture from the L level is also known.

In a metal it may be a conductivity electron. Capture of unbound electrons by nuclei has not been observed.

ELECTRON DENSITY

Average number of electrons in unit volume of a material; product of the number of atoms present per unit of volume times the number of electrons associated with each atom.

ELECTRON MICROSCOPE

An instrument which uses electrons in a manner analogous to that in which the ordinary microscope uses visible light. Whereas optical lenses produce the light image, focusing effects are achieved with electrons by application of magnetic lens systems. The initial collimated and uniform stream of electrons plays upon the prepared thin specimen beyond which the pattern of transmitted electrons is magnified by the lens system and displayed on a fluoroscopic screen or recorded in a photographic emulsion. Since electrons used in this way have wave lengths about a thousand times smaller than the wave lengths of ordinary light, the electron microscope is able to present an image of objects of the size of the larger molecular structures.

Figure E–2 compares the arrangement and function of the electron microscope with the

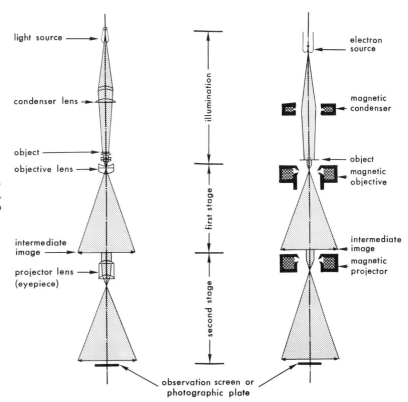

FIGURE E–2. SCHEMATIC REPRESENTATION OF THE OPTICAL SYSTEMS OF THE LIGHT AND ELECTRON MICROSCOPES.

light source

condenser lens

object

objective lens

intermediate image

projector lens (eyepiece)

illumination

first stage

second stage

electron source

magnetic condenser

object

magnetic objective

intermediate image

magnetic projector

observation screen or photographic plate

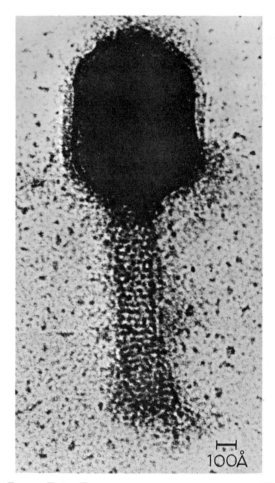

FIGURE E–4. ELECTRON MICROGRAPH SHOWING A T2 BACTERIOPHAGE PARTICLE, MAGNIFIED 720,000 TIMES, MADE AT MASSACHUSETTS GENERAL HOSPITAL.

familiar light microscope. Figure E–3 shows a typical electron microscope installation in the laboratory. Figure E–4 is an electron micrograph of a T_2 bacteriophage particle, magnified 720,000 times. The micrograph shows the precisely arranged "head," its "sheath" covering, and tail-fiber components, all of which are built of a few molecules. Recently perfected techniques permit selective irradiation of the "head" region alone with electron microbeams scaled down to molecular dimensions.

ELECTRON SPIN RESONANCE SPECTROMETER

Instrument combining magnetic field and microwave techniques to provide specific information about the molecular structure of materials, through measurements delineating the characteristic spin resonance patterns of the unpaired electrons related to free radical formation. Fre-

quency or wave length spectrums thus found have been used to follow structural changes produced in biologically significant molecules, as for instance in radiation damage effects in proteins and nucleic acids.

ELECTRON VOLT

The ev is a unit of energy used in calculations in connection with ionization or excitation of atoms or molecules. The kinetic energy an electron acquires when it is accelerated in a vacuum in an electric field produced by a difference of potential of 1 volt. One electron volt = 1 ev = 1.602×10^{-12} erg, or = 1.602×10^{-19} joule. One atomic mass unit (amu) = 931.2 million electron volts (Mev). Multiple units of the ev frequently used in nuclear physics are kilo-electron-volt (kev) for 1000 ev; million electron volts (Mev) and billion electron volts (Bev). Electron volt should not be abbreviated to simply volt.

ELECTROPHORESIS

Movement of colloidal particles suspended in a fluid medium, under the influence of an electric field. The differential migration of solutes due to the application of an electrical current provides a means of resolution of mixtures. Positive material (metallic oxides and hydroxides, basic dyestuffs) migrate to the cathode; negative material (metals, sulfur, metallic sulfides, acid dyestuffs) migrate to the anode.

Electrophoresis may be used separately, combined with PAPER CHROMATOGRAPHY or as paper electrophoresis without chromatographic separation. Equipment is now available for electrophoresis which operates on the continuous-flow principle; the most important of its many advantages is that relatively large amounts of materials can be separated. Paper electrophoresis has been used to study sugars, serum and body fluids, and lipids. The use of radioisotopes extends the sensitivity by facilitating the detection and estimation of the separated components. Autoradiography can be used to identify the radioactive labeled molecules separated by paper electrophoresis.

ELECTROSCOPE

A simple instrument which can detect and measure the quantity and sign of an electric charge, widely used to display the passage of ionizing radiation. In ordinary use the instrument is given an initial charge; when it is then exposed to a field of ionizing radiation, the charge is progressively neutralized and a measurement is effected by visually observing the displacement of an electrode which indicates the electrical potential or voltage remaining on the electrodes. Electroscopes operate generally by application of the principle of balancing electrostatic forces against mechanical forces, e.g., using spring torsion fibers or stretched fibers to oppose the repulsion of accumulated electrical charge. Early electroscopes are typified by the gold-leaf variety, which was used, in a variety of forms, in much of the pioneering work in this field. Later important uses are characterized by the Lauritsen electroscope, which served as a standard radioactivity assay instrument and in the present-day reading pocket dosimeter. The outstanding ruggedness and stability of the fiber electroscope provide significant advantages, especially in portable and personnel monitoring applications. Other electroscopes are important components of precision laboratory standard apparatus, where they function as null or balance indicators of the highest sensitivity and least disturbance of the quantities being measured. An early type is shown under GOLD-LEAF ELECTROSCOPE.

ELEMENT

A form of matter made up of a collection of atoms which cannot be decomposed into, or produced from, any simpler units by means of chemical reactions; but which may change into other units by radioactive processes. A substance all of whose atoms have the same atomic number or the same nuclear charge.

In the fifth century B.C. the Greek philosopher Empedocles spoke of all matter as composed of four elements: fire, earth, air and water. Later Aristotle considered all matter as containing only one primordial substance, hyle, but this could vary according to its content of the four "principles," hot, cold, dry and moist. In 1789 the French chemist Lavoisier advanced the modern concept, setting forth a list of 33 alleged elements, of which 20 are still regarded as separate elements. By 1819 the Swedish chemist Berzelius had increased the number to 50, and we now recognize 103 elements, of which 90 are known to exist naturally. An alphabetical list of the known elements is included as a table under ATOMIC WEIGHT.

Elements may be grouped into an ascending series according to their atomic number (Z). Such a grouping may be seen by reference to the table accompanying RADIOACTIVE ISOTOPES and STABLE ISOTOPES. The nuclear charge determines the chemical properties of the element, i.e., the types of chemical reactions into which the element enters with other elements or substances.

Atomic weight of each element was for many years regarded as the most important distinguishing characteristic. In fact, atomic weight was used to arrange the elements according to the periodic law into the periodic table. Emphasis was also placed on the physical and chemical properties of the elements in arranging the table.

The atom is the smallest particle of an element which is capable of entering into a chemical reaction. If one considers maintaining the identity of the element as the criterion, the atom may be considered indivisible. But atoms have properties in addition to nuclear charge, such as mass and stability, which means that an element may have more than one type of atom, even aggregates of them. These are called isotopes, which may be stable isotopes or radioactive isotopes; some elements have both.

Compounds are substances containing more than one constituent element and having properties, on the whole, different from those which their constituents had as elementary substances. The composition of a given pure compound is perfectly definite, and is always the same no matter how that compound may have been formed. Some are simple, such as water with only hydrogen and oxygen, while others are complex, such as the amines or the cyanides.

Since it would be difficult to have a different sign for each element, the use of the initial letter or letters of the name of each element was used as a symbol to designate the element in chemical formulae, e.g., $C_{12}H_{22}O_{11}$, meaning 12 atoms of carbon, 22 atoms of hydrogen and 11 atoms of oxygen in sucrose sugar.

ELEMENTARY PARTICLE

A term loosely applied to the electron; neutrino; neutron; positron; proton; positive and negative mu mesons; positive, negative and neutral pi mesons; positive, negative and neutral V-particles, and other particles not yet thoroughly investigated.

EMANATION

Historical name for radon, $_{86}Rn^{222}$.

EMBRYO, EFFECTS OF RADIATION ON.

See FETUS, RADIATION EFFECTS ON.

EMBRYONIC DEVELOPMENT STUDIES

Autoradiography has been of special advantage in the study of embryology, primarily because of the difficulty of precise dissection of newly developed organs and their small mass. The usual procedure is to administer the radioisotope to the pregnant animal and some time thereafter to make histological sections and autoradiograms from the embryo. In the case of birds, radioactive material has been injected directly into the egg or into the veins of the embryo. Figure E–5 shows the appearance of sulfur-35 in a 20-day-old rat embryo. It can be seen that there was considerably more deposition in the skeleton than in other tissues, and that the cartilage showed a higher concentration than did the calcified or calcifying regions.

Other studies of embryonic development have been done with sulfur-35 in the rabbit fetus, with iodine-131 in the chick and hamster, with phosphorus-32 in the frog, and with copper-64 in the chick. Radioiodine studies have been particularly helpful in determination of the beginning of thyroid function in the frog, rat, mouse and chick. In the chick, for example, radioactive calcium has been used extensively to study bone development in the embryo.

Figure E–6 shows an autoradiogram of a metatarsal bone from a newborn sheep whose mother had received radioactive calcium about 3 weeks before birth. The dark areas of the bone indicate the size of the bone at the time of administration of the radioisotope. The lighter areas indicate the amount of growth that had taken place in the 3-week period. Figure E–7 indicates schematically the behavior of calcium in the mother-fetus relation. Dietary calcium enters the circulating fluids of the mother, where some of it is incorporated into the exchangeable bone of the mother by exchange reactions, and some into new bone of the mother by accretion. Some of this calcium is excreted in the urine and feces of the mother, and some crosses the placental barrier to enter the circulating fluids of the fetus. In the fetus this calcium is then used to form new bone and also

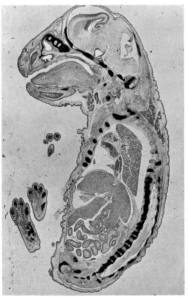

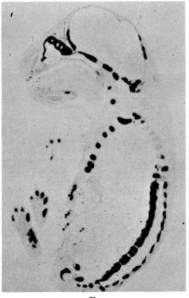

FIGURE E–5. AUTORADIOGRAPHIC APPEARANCE OF S³⁵ IN A 20-DAY-OLD RAT EMBRYO. *A*, STAINED SECTION. *B*, SHOWING SELECTIVE DEPOSITION IN CARTILAGE. (COURTESY OF DOMINIC D. DZIEWIATKOWSKI.)

A   B

enters into some of the exchangeable sites of bone. It is noted that the pool of exchangeable bone in the fetus is much greater proportionally than that in the mother. Also the rate of new bone formation in the fetus is proportionally greater than that in the mother.

EMULSION, NUCLEAR. *See* NUCLEAR EMULSION.

ENDOCRINE GLAND STUDIES

Radioisotopes have added greatly to the knowledge of the thyroid gland and have contributed in lesser degree to understanding of other endocrine organs. (*See* THYROID FUNCTION STUDIES, THYROID SCANNING and HORMONE STUDIES.)

The role of the pituitary gland is studied indirectly when radioiodine tests are done with and without pituitary thyroid-stimulating hormone (TSH). When there is deficient function of the thyroid gland, it is possible to determine by this method whether the defect is in the thyroid itself or whether the pituitary is producing too little TSH. (*See* PITUITARY GLAND IRRADIATION.)

The parathyroid glands influence the behavior of calcium and phosphorus in the body, and radioisotopes of these elements have been used in experimental studies of the parathyroids, but practical clinical tests have not yet been devised.

The adrenal glands influence the movement of sodium and potassium, which have been investigated with Na^{24} and K^{42}. Steroid hormones produced by the adrenals, ovaries and testes have been studied by labeling techniques.

The internal secretion of the pancreas, insulin, has also been radioactively tagged.

ENDOCRINE ORGANS, RADIATION EFFECTS ON

In general, endocrine tissues are remarkably radioresistant. External radiation of the thyroid of the rat with 17,200 roentgens (r) produces only negligible changes. Although the reproductive cells of the testis are destroyed by very low doses (300 r) of radiation, the endocrine tissue is not altered histologically by doses up to 100,000 r of gamma radiation. In the pancreas 5,000 r are required to alter the α cells of the islets of Langerhans, whereas the β cells tolerate 20,000 r before any change is noted. Radiation in the lethal dose range is required to cause alteration of the adrenal glands. The pituitary gland is remarkably resistant, although a beam of directed, energetic electrons will alter its function so as to increase the ACTH content of blood within an hour. This effect will continue for at least 24 hours.

See ADRENAL GLANDS, RADIATION EFFECTS ON;

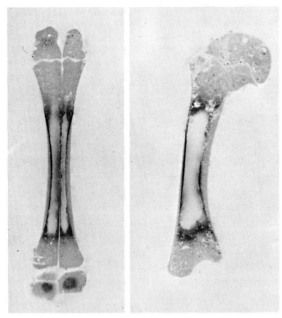

FIGURE E–6. AUTORADIOGRAM OF BONE OF NEWBORN SHEEP WHOSE MOTHER HAD RECEIVED Ca^{45} 3 WEEKS BEFORE BIRTH. (MEDICAL DIVISION, OAK RIDGE INSTITUTE OF NUCLEAR STUDIES.)

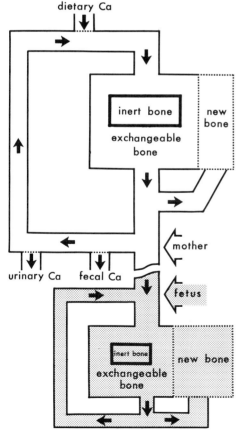

FIGURE E–7. SIMPLE MODEL OF CALCIUM MOVEMENT IN MOTHER AND FETUS.

GONADS, RADIATION EFFECTS ON; TESTES, RADIATION EFFECTS ON; and THYROID, RADIATION EFFECTS ON.

ENDOCRINE ORGANS, ROLE IN RADIATION SYNDROME

Radiation injury has been shown to produce certain nonspecific effects mediated through the adrenal gland, e.g., lymphopenia. These effects are identical with those produced by other stress agents, triggering the "alarm-reaction" or producing the "stress-syndrome," to which the adrenal cortex responds. (See ADRENAL GLAND, RADIATION EFFECTS ON; and ADRENALINE, RESPONSE TO RADIATION.)

Although definite proof is meager, it is possible that other endocrine processes also concerned with regulatory functions in the body can be affected by doses of a few hundred roentgens. Alterations in the function of the thyroid in the uptake and release of radioiodine have been described following doses in the LD_{50} range. These changes may be mediated through the pituitary, which responds in an attempt to correct the hormonal imbalance associated with radiation damage.

In general, however, endocrine organs have remarkable radioresistance; destruction of their function requires a dose of radiation several times the lethal dose if given as whole-body irradiation to a mammalian organism.

ENERGETICS

Science of conditions and laws governing manifestation of energy: in biology, as energy affects living matter (bioenergetics); in radiation, the various methods of energy transfer.

ENERGY

Symbol E. From the Greek *en*, in, and *ergon*, work. Capacity to do work. There are many kinds of energy; some of extreme importance in the field of atomic energy will be briefly considered in alphabetical order.

Atomic energy is the internal energy absorbed by the atom when it is formed and released when broken into its constituent parts.

Binding energy of a particle is the energy required to remove the particle from a system. Binding energy of a system is the energy required to disperse the system into its constituent parts. The electron-binding energy is the energy required to separate an electron from an atom. In the same way the proton- or neutron-, or alpha-particle-binding energy is that required to remove a single proton, neutron or alpha particle from a nucleus. The binding energy, E_B, of a nucleus is the difference between the sum of the masses of the Z protons and N neutrons in the free state and the mass of the nucleus containing the $A = Z + N$ nucleons.

Degradation of energy refers to the fact that changes in form of energy take place in the direction of increasing entropy and thus lesser availability.

Energies in atomic studies are now usually expressed in electron volts (ev) using kev (1,000 ev) and Mev (1,000,000 ev) as indicated. The word "quantum" is often used; e.g., the energy quantum for a gamma ray having a wave length of 10^{-10} cm would be 1.24 Mev.

Excitation energy is the energy required to change a system from its ground state to an excited state.

Explosive energy is demonstrated by the uncontrolled fission process making possible nuclear weapons or atomic bombs. The fusion process and the associated thermonuclear explosions or hydrogen bombs are also examples of explosive energy. This is measured in millions of tons of TNT equivalent.

"Imparted energy." The energy imparted by ionizing radiation to the matter in a volume is the difference between the sum of the energies of all the directly and indirectly ionizing particles which have entered the volume and the sum of the energies of all those which have left it, minus the energy equivalent of any increase in rest mass that took place in nuclear or elementary particle reactions within the volume. This quantity, energy imparted to matter, in a given volume is identical with the quantity often called integral absorbed dose in that volume.

Ionizing energy is the average energy given up by an ionizing particle in producing an ion pair in a gas. For air it is about 33 ev.

Kinetic energy is the most obvious way in which a body can manifest energy, i.e., to be in motion. The kinetic energy of a body is determined by its mass, m, and its velocity of motion, v, according to the following formula:

$$\tfrac{1}{2} mv^2.$$

Luminous energy is the value of radiant energy in terms of its ability to produce brightness, and is expressed in terms of sensory response or visual perception.

The famous mass-energy equation of Albert Einstein, $E = mc^2$, is fundamental to the entire subject of atomic energy. It shows that there is an exact equivalence between energy and mass, and it points to the possibility of releasing large amounts of energy by the conversion of mass.

Nuclear energy is the energy released in nuclear

reactions and may be controlled as in the production of nuclear power or uncontrolled as in the atomic bomb.

Nuclear potential energy is the average total potential energy of all the nucleons in a nucleus due to the specifically nuclear forces between them, but excluding the electrostatic potential energy.

A *photon* is a definite quantum of radiation energy moving with the speed of light.

Potential energy is inherent in a body if by virtue of its position or state it is capable of doing work. Potential energy and kinetic energy are the two categories into which mechanical energy is divided. For example, the water impounded behind a dam has potential energy, but if it is released, the potential energy is converted into kinetic energy of motion.

Radiant energy is energy which is transferred by electromagnetic waves (radio, visible light, x-rays and gamma rays) without corresponding transfer of matter.

In a nuclear reaction the *reaction energy* is equal to the sum of the energies of the reactants minus the sum of the energies of the products.

Solar energy as measured at the surface of the earth averages about 1.34×10^6 ergs per square centimeter per second. The direct illumination from the sun is about 6,500 foot-candles. Many attempts have been made to use directly solar energy for the production of power. The energy from the sun as well as the stars is from a thermonuclear reaction of either the carbon cycle type or the proton-proton chain type, depending on the temperature.

ENERGY DEPENDENCE

In instrumentation the characteristic response of a radiation detector to a given range of radiation energies or wave lengths, as compared with the response of a standard free air ionization chamber.

ENERGY DISCRIMINATION

The selection of signal pulses accepted by a counter on the basis of the energy of the radiation being detected. This function is usually accomplished by adjustable or selected bias levels incorporated in the amplifier circuit, which prevent the passage or counting of signals derived from radiations with too much or too little energy for the established selection or discrimination criteria.

See PULSE HEIGHT ANALYZER.

ENERGY SPECTRUM

The distribution of the intensity or quantity of radiation presented as a function of its energy, which can be expressed in terms of electron volts, wave length, or frequency.

See ALPHA-PARTICLE SPECTRUM, BETA-RAY SPECTRUM and GAMMA-RAY SPECTRUM.

ENERGY TRANSFER

Within the same molecule (intramolecular) energy transfer can occur by the conversion of the electronic excitation into vibrational and oscillational energy; the molecule behaves as if it were at a much higher energy, and the irradiated substance undergoes changes similar to those occurring during decomposition due to heat (pyrolysis). Energy transfer is not restricted to excitational energy and is encountered also with ionizations. A number of experiments have shown that the site of the chemical reaction is not necessarily identical with the site of the initial deposition of energy (e.g., the site of ionization) within the molecule. The physical mechanisms involved are not well understood, but the phenomenon is of importance.

Energy of excitation can also be transferred intermolecularly, i.e., from one molecule to another even when they are not in contact. In this way an electronically excited molecule can raise another molecule to an excited level. For example, energy taken up by the solvent contributes by an energy transfer involving excited solvent molecules to the fluorescence phenomenon in solutions of scintillators in nonreactive organic solvents.

In the use of a protective agent, as in CHEMICAL PROTECTION AGAINST RADIATION DAMAGE, the protection can occur by energy transfer or by repair of an unstable intermediate.

ENIWETOK MARINE BIOLOGICAL LABORATORY

A small marine biological laboratory on Parry Island at Eniwetok Atoll, completely equipped as a permanent base for studies on radioactive contamination, and for all types of ecological, physiological and radiobiological studies on marine organisms, and for biological collecting. Constructed, equipped and operated with support of the USAEC and with essential laboratory services supplied by the University of Hawaii. Available to any scientist whose work can be advantageously conducted on a central Pacific Ocean atoll.

Coral reefs represent stable natural communities with a history of thousands of years of constant adjustment between organisms and environment. Many studies are possible; e.g., a food chain study disclosed that a healthy reef had a production rate of about 74,000 pounds of glucose per acre per year, which exceeds man's best agricultural efforts in most parts of the world.

ENIWETOK PROVING GROUND

The Marshall Island U.S. nuclear weapons testing area in the Pacific Ocean, including Eniwetok and Bikini Atolls. First used for testing nuclear weapons in the spring of 1946 and thereafter until the moratorium in 1959. Although it will remain available if needed by the USAEC, it was made available to the U.S. Department of Defense on 1 July, 1960 as part of the terminal facilities of the Pacific Missile Range.

See PACIFIC TESTING AREAS.

ENTOMOLOGIC STUDIES

In the United States insects cause a loss estimated at about 4 billion dollars per year. For the important insects it is necessary to understand the entire life history, food habits, dispersal, mating behavior, parasites, predators and other biological aspects; then economic control can be carried out by capitalizing on the weakest link, or the most vulnerable point, using quarantines, environmental control, crop practices, insecticide treatment, baits, traps, predators or parasites. The detailed biology of many insects has become understood only through the use of radioisotopes.

The common methods of labeling involve the use of phosphorus-32, cobalt-60, zinc-65, strontium-89 or iodine-131. Numerous studies have been carried out on insect dispersal and flight range. Population studies have been made possible by releasing a known number of radioactive-labeled insects in an area, collecting them and then calculating the ratio of marked recaptures to unmarked naturally occurring insects; it is thus possible to calculate the size of the actual population. Radioactive labeling has also been used to study habitat, feeding habits, natural control by predators, and parasitic relationships. Entomological studies have been done on labeled flies, ticks, mosquitoes and other insect pests.

The insect transmission of animal and plant diseases has been studied by using radioactive-tagged insect vectors, or tagged viral, bacterial, protozoan or nematode pathogens. The nutrition, physiology and biosynthesis of compounds by insects have been studied, using radionuclides of minerals and of carbon-14 and tritium to investigate organic compounds. Table E–2 gives results of studies with orchard insects.

New knowledge about the action of control chemicals has been gained by tagging portions of insecticides, fumigants and repellents. These data have led to the planning of more efficient chemicals, especially among the toxic phosphorus esters, by taking advantage of the differences found between the metabolic pathways in insects and higher animals.

In the United States about 300 million pounds of toxic insecticides per year are used, the residuals of which may represent a hazard to the population. Studies of such residuals by means of radioisotope techniques have led to increased public safety.

See SCREW WORM FLY ERADICATION.

TABLE E–2. DISPERSAL OF RADIOACTIVE MARKED ORCHARD INSECTS

INSECT	ISOTOPE	NO. RELEASED	LONGEVITY	MAXIMUM DISPERSAL (km)
Plum curculio				
Conotrachelus nenuphar	P^{32}	62	Up to 120 d	0.11
,, ,,	Co^{60}	705	Up to 8.5 months	0.27
,, ,,	Zn^{65}	23	Up to 120 d	0.041
,, ,,	Sr^{89}	175	3 d	0.123
,, ,,	I^{131}	86	—	0
Oriental fruit fly				
Dacus dorsalis	P^{32}	—	Up to 40 d	—
Fruit fly				
Drosophila melanogaster	P^{32}	20,000	—	3.84
Mediterranean fruit fly				
Ceratitis capitata	P^{32}	944	—	32.0
Cherry fruit fly				
Rhagoletis cingulata	P^{32}	2,010	Up to 42 d	0.287
Walnut husk fly				
Rhagoletis completa	P^{32}	15% of natural population	—	14.4

ENVIRONMENTAL CONTAMINATION

Contamination of the surrounding environment with radioactive material. Term usually used in connection with contamination from waste disposal, or as a result of fallout from the detonation of a nuclear device. May also describe the contamination of a building from accidental release of radioactive material. Environmental contamination may result from release of gaseous or particulate matter from the stack of a nuclear reactor.

The fallout fission products of biological importance in environmental contamination are usually listed as iodine-131, barium-140, lanthanum-140, strontium-89 and strontium-90, and cesium-137.

See ENVIRONMENTAL RADIATION.

ENVIRONMENTAL RADIATION

Man-made radiation produced as a result of industrial use of radioisotopes; use of radioisotopes in agricultural, biological, medical and physical research; therapeutic and diagnostic medical use of radioisotopes and x-rays; from fallout as the result of testing of nuclear devices; and from possible accidental release from a nuclear reactor.

The National Academy of Sciences–National Research Council reported that the average person residing in the United States receives a total accumulated gonadal dose of about 3 roentgens over a 30-year period from man-made sources, largely through the medical use of x-rays and fluoroscope. This calculation did not include radioactive fallout.

See NATURAL RADIATION.

ENVIRONMENTAL SURVEY

Determination of the level of radiation in a given area (room, building or surrounding environment) arising from or caused by natural radiation; radioactive contamination; fallout; or the presence of a radioactive source; x-ray machine or accelerator.

Careful environmental surveys coupled with detailed ecological studies are made in connection with the selection of the site for construction of a nuclear reactor. One of the most extensive environmental studies ever undertaken has recently been completed in Alaska.

An environmental survey of the intensity of radiation in various parts of the United States was conducted by scientists of the USAEC Health and Safety Laboratory during the summer of 1957. Their measurements included cosmic radiation, terrestrial radiation, and in some cases radiation due to tropospheric fallout. Their figures for natural radiation indicated a range of about 70 to 175 millirads per year as an external radia-

tion dose rate. The terrestrial component contributed in a range of 4 to 12 microroentgens per hour. The intensity of cosmic radiation at various altitudes is shown in table E–3.

TABLE E–3. INTENSITY OF COSMIC RADIATION

ALTITUDE (IN FEET)	INTENSITY (MICROROENTGENS PER HOUR)
Sea level	4.0
1,000	4.7
2,000	5.4
3,000	6.2
4,000	7.1
5,000	8.1
6,000	9.1
8,000	11.7
10,000	14.6
12,000	18.0
14,000	21.0

ENZYME STUDIES

Research on enzymes making up the complex metabolic pattern of the living organism can be classified into (a) the actions brought about by enzymes, (b) the quantitative aspects of enzymatic reaction, (c) nature of enzymes themselves, (d) the mechanisms of enzymatic catalysis. Isotopes have found considerable use in studies of enzymes, particularly carbon-14, phosphorus-32, deuterium, tritium and oxygen-18. A simple example of an early study was the use of phosphorus-32 to demonstrate that the enzymatic conversion of glucose monophosphates was accomplished without the exchange of ester phosphate with radioactive inorganic phosphate. Through the use of carbon-14, and phosphorus-32-labeled hexosephosphates, a better understanding was obtained of the mechanism of action of phosphoglucomutase. It was shown that the transfer of a phosphate group from carbon-6 to carbon-1 of a glucose molecule involves glucose-1:6:diphosphate as an intermediate. Deuterium or tritium has been widely used to study the stereospecificity of enzymatic transfer of hydrogen, particularly with reference to the diphosphopyridine nucleotide-linked enzymes.

Isotopes have also been invaluable in the evaluation of alternate metabolic pathways. Radioisotopes have been used to determine the composition of enzymes; e.g., it was a relatively simple matter to show that the element molybdenum was a nondialyzable component of xanthine oxidase by administration of radioactive molybdenum to a dairy cow, and subsequent isolation of the enzyme from the milk, which is a good source of xanthine oxidase. From these experiments it was also possible to calculate that the molar ratio of flavine to molybdenum was 2:1.

ENZYMES

Proteins which catalyze reactions occurring in biological systems. Knowledge of enzymes and their function is essential to understanding the processes of life. Isotopes, particularly carbon-14, phosphorus-32, deuterium and tritium, have been used extensively in studying the mechanisms of biological (enzymatic) reactions.

All enzymes in pure solution are inactivated when irradiated, and the dose-response curve (see DOSE-EFFECT RELATIONSHIP) is nearly always exponential, indicating that one reaction by a radical is sufficient to produce inactivation. Pure enzyme solutions react to irradiation in a completely different way from enzymes in physiological media, indicating that there are mechanisms operating in tissue extracts that provide protection against the inactivating effects of ionizing radiations. For example, a 95% inhibition of enzyme action occurs as a result of irradiation of pure solutions of glutamic dehydrogenase with 5,000 roentgens (r) as compared with unirradiated controls. However, the addition of 1% liver extract completely prevents this inhibition, and 50% protection is afforded by the addition of liver extract in a concentration of only 1:10,000. Liver extracts or liver homogenates have been irradiated with 5,000 r and with 20,000 r, and enzyme activity measurements on 12 different enzymes contained in the extract showed no inhibition in any instance. In the intact organism it appears that enzymes are also extremely radioresistant.

EPIDEMIOLOGY STUDIES

In research on the spread of infectious diseases, radioisotopic tracer techniques have proved of value. The reproduction rates and distribution of bacteria and viruses have been approached by this method. (See BACTERIA STUDIES and VIRUS STUDIES.) In addition, certain animals that transmit disease are studied with the tracer technique; e.g., mosquitoes that carry malaria have been labeled with a small amount of a radioisotope, and their population and range thus studied. Radiation has also been used to control insect vector organisms as in the case of the SCREW WORM FLY ERADICATION.

EPILATION DUE TO RADIATION

External penetrating ionizing radiation of 200 rad or more may cause loss of hair on the body and head on the fourteenth to twenty-first postexposure day; earlier with higher doses, and later with lower doses. The development of epilation thus indicates the probability of radiation illness requiring hospitalization; however, it does not have much prognostic significance.

Epilation and skin damage are also caused by beta radiation; e.g., 64 Marshall Islanders received about 175 rad ionizing radiation and several hundred rad beta radiation to their skin from heavy "snow-like" fallout from the detonation of a test nuclear device. Epilation and lesions of the skin (burns, radiation) developed in 90% of the Rongelap group (see MARSHALL ISLANDERS), beginning about 12 to 14 days after exposure. In the less heavily irradiated group on Ailinginae, 69 rad whole-body irradiation and moderate "mist-like" fallout, the lesions did not appear until 20 days after exposure and were less severe. Among the 157 Marshallese on Utirik with 14 rad whole body and no fallout observed, there were no skin lesions and no epilation. Epilation was more extensive and severe among the children, as illustrated in the picture (Fig. E–8, A) of a 7-year-old girl with epilation of the scalp 28 days after the fallout ex-

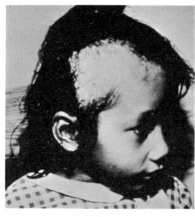
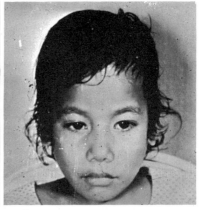

A   B

FIGURE E–8.   A, EPILATION OF THE SCALP OF A 7-YEAR-OLD MARSHALLESE GIRL 28 DAYS AFTER EXPOSURE TO FALLOUT FROM THE TESTING OF A NUCLEAR WEAPON. B, THE SAME MARSHALLESE GIRL SHOWING REGROWTH OF HAIR 3 1/2 MONTHS LATER.

posure. The same girl (Fig. E–8, *B*) illustrates the regrowth of hair 3 1/2 months later.

EPIPHYSIS, RADIATION EFFECTS ON

In growing children the epiphysial or growth area of the long bones is particularly susceptible to radiation. Three or four hundred roentgens to the epiphysial area may cause swelling and disarrangement of cartilage cells, and damage to the ingrowing blood vessels. This leads to suppression of mitotic activity and thus cessation of growth, which may be permanent if the dose has been large.

See BONE DISEASES DUE TO RADIATION.

EPITHELIUM, RADIATION EFFECTS ON.

See SKIN, RADIATION EFFECTS ON.

EQUILIBRIUM, RADIOACTIVE. *See* RADIO-
ACTIVE EQUILIBRIUM.

EQUIPMENT DECONTAMINATION

Removal of radioactive contamination from equipment. Small pieces of laboratory equipment and glassware are cleaned by immersion in mineral acids (HCl, HNO_3, H_2SO_4); strong oxidizing solutions (chromic acid cleaning solution); a complexing agent (sodium citrate, Versene); or a household detergent. The solutions should be at raised temperatures, and frequently items may need to be left for some time or be treated several times. Immediate action is imperative to prevent contamination from becoming fixed, which makes it increasingly difficult. Larger pieces of equipment may be handled by hoist or crane and dipped into a tank and then rinsed. Rust must be removed, and at times sandblasting may be necessary to eliminate the contamination.

ERBIUM

Symbol Er; atomic number 68; atomic weight 167.27. A member of the yttrium subgroup of the rare earth metals. Discovered by Swedish chemist Mosander in 1842. Named for Ytterby, Sweden. Its natural abundance is furnished by 6 stable isotopes in such minerals as xenotime, fergusonite, gadolinite and exonite. There have been 7 radioactive isotopes identified.

ERYTHEMA

In radiobiology, a morbid redness due to congestion of the capillaries of the skin, as a result of irradiation. The production of erythema was the first-used criterion of a radiation dose. This led to the unit called the human erythema dose (HED). A threshold dose producing erythema was experimentally determined to be 289 roentgen equivalents, physical (rep), to the surface of the skin,

and erythema appeared after a latent period of 7 to 19 days. The standard erythema dose is 700 roentgens, and the height of the reaction occurs in about three weeks.

See DOSE, and DOSE-EFFECT RELATIONSHIP.

ERYTHROCYTES, DEVELOPMENT STUDIES

The development and maturation of red blood cells in the bone marrow have been studied with radioisotopes. Thymidine, a precursor of DNA (deoxyribonucleic acid), is taken up in the nuclei of cells that are capable of division. When this substance, labeled with tritium (H^3), is given intravenously to human beings, aspiration of bone marrow shows prompt labeling of early stages of the red cell series, up to and including polychromatophilic normoblasts. The next stage in maturation, the orthochromatic normoblast, is not labeled until somewhat later; this suggests that these more mature cells do not undergo division and that when they are seen with a label, they have undergone some maturation since they took in the radioisotope. The maximal labeling of the red cell precursor cells in general is seen about 12 to 24 hours after the thymidine has been given.

Radioiron (Fe^{59} and Fe^{55}) is also used to study red cell formation in the bone marrow. It is taken up chiefly in cells forming hemoglobin; in general this is at the intermediate and later stages of development up to and including the reticulocyte. Once incorporated in the hemoglobin of the cell, the radioiron stays there during the life of the cell.

These studies with radioactive thymidine and radioiron indicate a fairly rapid and orderly maturation (within a few days) of the red cell from its most primitive recognizable precursor cell in the marrow. Studies of this sort take advantage of the techniques of microscopic autoradiography to demonstrate the presence of the label in individual cells.

In the circulating blood, erythrocytes are studied with several labels. Microscopic autoradiography is less used, and serial radioassay of blood samples is usually performed.

See RED CELL LIFE SPAN, MEASUREMENT and FERROKINETICS STUDIES.

ERYTHROCYTES, RADIATION EFFECTS ON

Destruction of the adult circulating erythrocytes or red blood cells requires whole-body doses of radiation in the supralethal range. However, after acute whole-body irradiation in the 200 to 500 rad range there is destruction of the red cell-forming tissue and red cell precursors (erythroblasts) evident by the second week, with regeneration beginning in the fifth or sixth week. But since human red cells have a life of about 120 days, the cessation of production does not cause a significant drop in the circulating red cells before regeneration ensues. Thus the red blood cell count shows only a slight drop even with exposure to as much as 400 to 500 rad whole-body exposure. There is then a slight reduction in the volume of red cells as measured by the hematocrit, with a slow return to normal by the end of about 120 days. When death occurs within the first few days, there may be no measurable drop in the number of circulating red blood cells.

ERYTHROPOIETIN

A substance, found in the blood plasma and urine of mammals, that plays an important role in controlling the rate of formation of red blood cells. Certain factors that stimulate red cell production, such as anoxia and some types of anemia, are believed to exert this effect by increasing the amount of erythropoietin formed. The site of its formation is not definitely known; the pituitary gland and the kidneys are possible sites. The chemistry of this substance is also yet to be clarified; more than one component may be involved. It is demonstrated and measured by means of bioassay procedures in experimental animals.

In total body irradiation the anemia is not believed to be caused by a deficiency of erythropoietin, but rather by inability of the bone marrow to respond to it. When erythropoietin is injected into irradiated animals, there is an impaired and delayed response, as compared with normal animals.

ESTRADIOL, USE TO REDUCE RADIATION INJURY

A female sex hormone, β-estradiol (estrogenic steroid, 1,3,5-estratriene-3-17β-diol) which, if given before irradiation, has been shown to have a protective effect in reducing or preventing radiation injury. It has the following formula:

See HORMONES IN RELATION TO RADIATION INJURY.

ESTROGENS, USE TO REDUCE RADIATION INJURY

A generic term for female sex hormones, some of which, if given before irradiation, have been shown to have a protective effect in reducing or preventing radiation illness.

See ESTRADIOL, USE TO REDUCE RADIATION INJURY and HORMONES IN RELATION TO RADIATION INJURY.

EURATOM

The European Atomic Energy Community (EURATOM) is a supranational organization activated in 1958 by Belgium, France, the German Federal Republic, Italy, Luxembourg and The Netherlands to develop the European nuclear industry by providing financial and technical resources. It supplements the national programs of its member states.

EUROPEAN NUCLEAR ENERGY AGENCY (ENEA)

ENEA was established in 1958 as a special agency of the Organization for European Economic Cooperation, charged with implementing the program in the atomic energy field. It has participated in the joint operation of experimental reactors, in a pilot facility for reprocessing irradiated fuel, and has proposed several conventions which have been adopted by the OEEC.

EUROPIUM

Symbol Eu; atomic number 63; atomic weight 152.0 A member of the cerium group of rare earth metals. Discovered by Demarcay in 1906 and named for Europe. Exists in small amounts in various minerals as stable isotopes Eu^{151}, 47.77%, and Eu^{153}, 52.23%.

Fourteen radioactive isotopes have been identified, of which 8 occur as fission products associated with the detonation of a nuclear device. Biological significance in fallout is shown by Eu^{155} with 0.00681 megacurie per megaton of fission (Mc/MT) still remaining at 1 year, and by Eu^{156} with 0.0637 Mc/MT remaining at 1 month (*see* CERIUM fission product abundance table).

Has not been found to occur naturally in living matter.

EXCHANGE REACTIONS

An isotopic exchange reaction, as a special case of exchange, may be defined as a chemical reaction in which the atoms of a given element interchange between two or more chemical forms of the element. Examples of isotopic reactions are as follows:

(1) Simple exchange due to electrolytic dissociation:

$$2PbCl_2 + 2Pb^*(NO_3)_2 \rightleftharpoons 2Pb^{+2} + 4Cl^- + 2Pb^{*+2} + 4NO_3^-$$

$$PbCl_2 + Pb^*Cl_2 + Pb(NO_3)_2 + Pb^*(NO_3)_2$$

(2) Electron transfer:

$$Fe^{+2} + Fe^{*+3} \rightleftharpoons Fe^{*+2} + Fe^{+3}$$

(3) Atom transfer:

$$I^{*-} + CH_3I \xrightarrow{\text{Ethyl alcohol}} I^- + CH_3I^*$$

(4) Solid-fluid reactions:

$$\text{Bone crystal } ^-Ca + Ca^{*+2} \rightarrow \text{Bone crystal } Ca^* + Ca^{+2}$$

(5) Solid-gas reactions:

$$BaCO_3 + C^*O_2 \xrightarrow{H_2O \text{ vapor}} BaC^*O_3 + CO_2$$

These types of reactions have provided much valuable information on reaction rates, bond strengths, and molecular rearrangements in structure.

In biological studies, however, the radiotracers are most often used to provide information on metabolic processes, and if the radioactive element becomes incorporated in a metabolic product merely by exchange, which requires no energy production, then the studies do not provide any evidence for synthesis of product. Therefore, in biological studies, corollary experiments must always be run to make sure that the observations truly represent the result of metabolic properties, and are not the result of physical exchange. An example of the simple corollary experiment is to poison the biological system with an enzymatic inhibitor; if the results observed are due to physical exchange, then the poison would be expected to have no effect.

Ion exchange methods have also been most useful for separations, concentrations or purifications of substances. The process as usually carried out involves the reversible interchange of ions between a solution and a particular solid material, such as an ion exchange resin, which consists of a matrix of insoluble material interspersed with fixed ions of opposite charge. The applications of ion exchange are as follows:

1. Removal of impurities or interfering substances, e.g., the removal of metal contamination from adenosine triphosphate (ATP) preparations, or of strontium-90 from milk.

2. The concentration of trace constituents; an example of this is the isolation of radioisotopes from urine in amounts sufficient for radioassay.

3. Separation of materials: a large-scale application has been in the separation, concentration and purification of the small but highly radioactive masses of fission products from reactor operations.

4. Determination of properties of complex ions,

such as the dissociation constants for the radium citrate complex.

EXCHANGEABLE BODY POTASSIUM, MEASUREMENT

Potassium-42 is used in an isotope dilution method, the dose for man being about 25 microcuries. After administration, equilibrium of the trace element is generally attained in about 20 hours, so that determinations are usually carried out on 24-hour samples, urine being the sample of choice. It is possible to compare the 24-hour exchangeable body potassium with that of the total body, because natural potassium contains radioactive K^{40}, which can be determined with a whole-body counter. Comparative measurements show that the potassium-42 dilution technique underestimates the total body content by about 15%. Normal values are about 45 milliequivalents per kilogram of body weight in young men, and 35 milliequivalents per kilogram in normal women, the difference being due mainly to the relatively large muscle mass in the male.

EXCHANGEABLE BODY SODIUM, MEASUREMENT

Sodium-24 is used in an isotope dilution method, the dose for man being about 25 microcuries. Sodium-24 reaches an apparent equilibrium in 12 hours in normal subjects, but takes about twice as long in patients with edema, ascites or other abnormal fluid accumulations. The results from sodium-24 experiments represent about 70% of the sodium actually present in the body of adults, the balance being present in bone in a form that is not readily exchangeable. The average value for total exchangeable sodium is about 43 mEq per kilogram of body weight for adult males, and about 40 mEq per kilogram for females, with considerable individual variation due to differences in body fat content and nonuniform dietary intakes.

EXCITED STATE

Condition of a nucleus, an atom or a molecule having higher energy than the ground state.

Excitation is the addition of energy to a system changing it from its ground state to an excited state. Excitation of a nucleus, an atom or a molecule can result from absorption of photons or from inelastic collisions with other particles or systems.

Radioactive isotopes may be excited.

EXCRETION PATHWAY STUDIES

Isotopic labeling is especially convenient for determination of pathways of excretion from the body of molecules and elements. The total excretion is easily measured simply by collection of the excretion and radioassay. The values obtained can then be compared with the known dietary intake in order to give a value for percentage retention.

With minerals there has always been a difficult question of how much of the mineral appearing in the feces represented that which had passed through the gastrointestinal tract unabsorbed, and presumably was of no use to the animal, and how much was absorbed and later secreted into the intestinal tract for excretion. With phosphorus-32 and calcium-45 it has been possible to estimate the so-called endogenous losses of these elements in man and domestic animals by labeling the body pool and determining the relative contributions of the body and the unabsorbed element to the fecal excretion, using the isotope dilution principle. When such data are available, it is then possible to estimate (a) the proportion of the element in the diet that is unavailable to the animals, and, conversely, the net digestibility; (b) the maintenance requirement; and (c) the actual body losses as they may be affected by such variables as dietary levels and age.

In the study of utilization of organic molecules, the problem is somewhat simpler, because these are often broken down in the body. For example, using cholesterol labeled with carbon-14, it was demonstrated that this substance was absorbed via the intestinal lymphatics into the general circulation. The principal end-products were found in the bile and feces. In the rat, about 90% of the carbon-14 derived from injected cholesterol was recovered in the bile, and of this, over 90% was identified as being in the bile acids.

EXPLOSIONS, RADIOACTIVE MATERIAL

In addition to their destructive force, explosions associated with radioactive material spread contamination. For example, a thorium explosion occurred during a routine operation consisting of burning thorium metal for conversion to thorium oxide in order to reduce the fire potential during subsequent shipment. A small amount of the metal in the form of a wafer had been fired in a tray in a hood, and the employee, wearing protective equipment, took a piece of thorium metal about the size of a golf ball from a drum containing 30 to 40 pounds of the material. There was an immediate sharp explosion, followed at once by a second, heavier blast. Nine employees were injured, four requiring hospitalization and one dying 5 weeks later. Property damage was about $125,000, but contamination was limited to the explosion room and the ventilating system.

A plutonium explosion in a dry box sprayed two employees with flying debris, causing contaminated minor abrasions and cuts. One employee had 0.4 microgram of plutonium deposited in an abrasion wound of the face, and another required a surgical amputation of the end of his little finger because of deposition of 0.5 microgram of plutonium in a cut.

Radioactive materials dissolved in nitric acid have exploded during the process of evaporation, apparently from organic contamination. Sealed drums containing radioactive liquid waste have exploded and spread contamination widely over storage areas.

In the transportation of nuclear weapons, a crash would not lead to a nuclear explosion, but might cause the burning or detonation of the non-nuclear high explosive components, and the spread of the radioactive contents of the nuclear weapon. In order to prepare for this or other major radiological types of emergency, the USAEC took the lead in organizing the Interagency Committee on Radiological Assistance with membership of 13 federal agencies, which have worked out a detailed Interagency Radiological Assistance Plan.

See FIRES, RADIOACTIVE MATERIAL.

EXPOSURE

Exposure to ionizing radiation is frequently classified according to the time (DOSE RATE) during which the irradiation takes place, i.e., ACUTE EXPOSURE, subacute exposure (not frequently used as a separate division) and CHRONIC EXPOSURE. Acute exposure usually refers to doses delivered over a period of hours or days. Subacute doses are those delivered in days or weeks. Chronic exposure refers to doses delivered over months to years.

Exposure may also be modified by such terms as external or internal, penetrating or nonpenetrating, high-level or low-level, and partial body or whole body.

EXPOSURE LIMITS. *See* MAXIMUM PERMISSIBLE CONCENTRATION, MAXIMUM PERMISSIBLE DOSE and RADIATION PROTECTION GUIDES.

EXTERNAL COUNTING

Measurement of radioactivity in a subject by using a probe detector outside the body, as in thyroid uptake studies, kidney function tests, or in scintiscanning; also refers to whole-body counting. Generally means the procedure carried out with the living subject.

EXTERNAL QUENCHING

Electronic circuit for pulse-type gas counter which quenches the detector by automatically lowering voltage each time a pulse is delivered.

EXTERNAL RADIATION

Man is constantly exposed to radiation from external sources:

1. Natural radiation sources are cosmic rays and terrestrial radiation. The National Academy of Sciences (NAS) reported in 1956 that the average American would receive 4.3 roentgens (r) gonadal dose over a 30-year period from natural radiation.

2. The medical use of x-ray (roentgenographic, photofluorographic and fluoroscopic examinations) is estimated to contribute a per capita mean bone marrow dose of 50 to 100 millirem per year. The NAS study estimated the medical use of x-ray would give a gonadal dose of 3.0 r for the average American over a 30-year period.

3. Industrial use of x-ray and of radioisotopes contributes to external radiation, as does the use of nuclear reactors, accelerators, etc.

4. Testing of nuclear weapons contributes to external radiation through initial nuclear radiation, induced radioactivity, and fallout. If weapons testing were to continue at approximately the same level as the 5 years prior to the 1956 NAS report, the average gonadal dose would be 0.1 r in a 30-year period.

EXTRACELLULAR WATER

Extracellular water includes plasma water, interstitial water, collagen or connective tissue water, and finally transcellular water, which can be reached only by an indicator that passes through or is processed by cells. This includes the cerebrospinal fluid, water in the gastrointestinal tract, and the aqueous humor of the eye. A suitable indicator must diffuse rapidly into all these various compartments without appreciable loss by metabolic processes, and must not be retained to any significant extent in the cells. Indicators such as inulin, sucrose and mannitol, which are large molecules, have been used, and tend to give the lowest figures because they do not cross the cell membranes. Radioactive sulfate has also been used and gives a value similar to that from inulin. Radioactive sodium has also been used, but with time penetrates into the cells and exchanges with sodium in bone. Bromine-82 reaches effective equilibrium between 4 and 6 hours, and thereafter the apparent volume of distribution does not change significantly for at least 48 hours. Various considerations lead to the conclusion that the 24-hour distribution of bromine-82 as bromide ion, multiplied by a correction factor of 0.9, gives a value for extracellular water which is less open to criticism than that given by other methods.

EXTRAPOLATION IONIZATION CHAMBER

Ionization chamber in which one or more physical factors (e.g., electrode separation, collecting volume, gas pressure) can be varied, providing means for radiation at different values of the variable, to allow extrapolation to some desired value of the parameter under study (e.g., 0 thickness of chamber, infinitely small collecting volume, or to simulate the absorbing mass of biological receptors).

Extrapolation measurements are carried out to derive values for the radiation intensity in situations impossible to measure directly. Interesting radiobiological situations which must be evaluated in this way include the deposition of energy in very thin layers, as in the skin, and the delivery of radiation into living structures of extremely small volume, such as individual cells. Data obtained for various values of the controlled variable are treated graphically or analytically, by extrapolation of the plotted curve or the derived equation into the region desired. Typical extrapolation experiments have used chambers with adjustable interelectrode spacing (for skin surface dosimetry), with variable wall thickness (for surface build-up or back scatter factors), and with control over the pressure of the ionizing gas (for extrapolation to a very small irradiated mass).

EYE LESIONS DUE TO RADIATION

Eye injuries associated with exposure to radiation from the detonation of a nuclear device may be due to thermal radiation or ionizing radiation.

RETINAL BURNS and flash burns are two types of thermal radiation injury, but in the Hiroshima and Nagasaki survivors these did not present serious problems.

Keratitis (an inflammation of the cornea characterized by lacrimation, photosensitivity, pain and redness) occurred in some persons. In a study of 1,000 cases chosen at random, from those who were in the open and within 6,600 feet of ground zero, only 42 gave a history of keratitis appearing within the first day, and an additional 14 cases were reported as appearing within the first month. Nuclear or ionizing radiation may have been a factor in these later cases. In spite of serious face burns in a number of cases, there was no permanent opacity of the cornea in any of the 1,000 cases examined 3 years after the detonation.

CATARACTS, RADIATION INDUCED and iris atrophy may be seen as late effects (3 to 5 years) resulting from large single doses of radiation.

Physicists working with accelerators, improperly shielded x-ray operators, and patients whose eyes cannot be completely shielded may suffer radiation conjunctivitis.

F

FALLOUT

The process of the return to earth of radioactive particulate matter which has been carried up into the atmosphere by the detonation of a nuclear device, also any resulting radioactive particulate contamination of the ground, buildings, etc.

Fallout is frequently referred to in relation to the area of the atmosphere in which it is carried: close-in, near-in or LOCAL FALLOUT coming back to the surface of the earth in the immediate vicinity of the detonation; TROPOSPHERIC FALLOUT or fallout coming from the radioactive cloud (see CLOUD, RADIOACTIVE) being moved as a result of meteorological conditions in the troposphere; and STRATOSPHERIC FALLOUT resulting from material carried into the stratosphere by the force of the explosion.

Fallout is sometimes also classed according to RESIDENCE TIME immediate or early, coming down directly from the atomic cloud; intermediate, being carried for a few hours to a month or more in the troposphere; and delayed, being held for a few months to 5 years in the stratosphere.

The amount or extent of radioactive fallout depends on the type of device; the size or yield of the "bomb"; the method of detonation; and for the local situation, the meteorological conditions. A fission device produces fission products which constitute most of the radioactivity in fallout, but a fusion reaction does not in itself produce radioactive material (except that induced by neutron activation). All other factors being equal, the amount of fallout is related directly to the fission yield. A device detonated in a sealed tunnel or cave produces radioactive material which usually remains contained in the cavity and thus does not cause a fallout problem. A device detonated high enough in the air so that the fireball does not touch the earth's surface produces only very small particles and very little local fallout. A nuclear explosion occurring at or near the earth can result in a much greater mass of material thrown into the air and consequently a heavy local fallout. As an example, the high-yield thermonuclear explosion at Bikini Atoll during Operation CASTLE on March 1, 1954, was close to a coral surface and fallout contamination was significant over an area of about 7,000 square miles. Owing to meteorological conditions the FALLOUT PATTERN or heavily contaminated area was roughly cigar-shaped, extending about 20 miles upwind and 220 miles downwind, with a maximum width of about 40 miles. The scavenging effects of rain and snow are significantly related to the amount of fallout, frequently resulting in hot spots.

Distribution or fallout pattern is determined by yield, height and location of the detonation, and by meteorological conditions.

Dose rate and total accumulated dose from fallout depend not only upon the amount of radioactive fallout but also upon the factor of radiation attenuation.

In the process of detonation of a nuclear device, for every megaton of fission yield about 110 pounds of intensively radioactive material are formed, consisting of approximately 200 radionuclides of 35 elements. Fortunately many of them have an extremely short radioactive half-life and thus have little significance other than in local fallout. The nuclides remaining after one hour postdetonation decay approximately by a factor of 10 for every seven-fold increase in time after H + 1.

The fallout radionuclides presenting the major biological hazard from the standpoint of internal irradiation hazard are:

1 day to 1 week: iodine-131, barium-140, lanthanum-140, and molybdenum-99.

1 week to 1 month: iodine-131, barium-140, lanthanum-140, praseodymium-143, yttrium-91, zirconium-95, strontium-89, and cerium-144.

1 month to 1 year: cerium-144, zirconium-95, yttrium-91, iodine-131, niobium-95, barium-140, and strontium-89.

1 year to 70 years: strontium-90, cerium-144, cesium-137, and ruthenium-106.

Various federal agencies conduct fallout sampling programs and a monitoring program for radioactive fallout.

The National Academy of Sciences–National Research Council reported in 1956 that the average individual residing in the United States had been receiving a radiation dose for the previous 5 years, such that if weapons testing were continued at the same rate for 30 years he would receive an accumulated gonadal dose of 0.1 roentgen (r), with an uncertainty factor of 5; i.e., the dose probably would be greater than 0.02 r and less than 0.50 r. With the Russian, British and French testing an additional factor of perhaps 3 must be added so that if all testing were continued for 30 years the gonadal dose might be 0.06 or 1.5 r.

FALLOUT ATTENUATION

The reduction of FALLOUT radioactivity results from: radioactive decay of the component radionuclides; vertical distribution and holding (residence time); horizontal spread; and, from the standpoint of the individual, shielding or fallout shelter can reduce the radiation dose.

Radioactivity as measured one minute after detonation decreases by a factor of over 6,000 in the first 24 hours. For a period of time up to 200 days, there is a decrease by a factor of ten for every seven-fold increase in time measured from the end of the first hour. For example, if we take the radiation intensity at one hour as the reference point of one, then 7 hours later the intensity will have decreased to one-tenth; at 49 hours it will be one-hundredth, etc. This is graphically presented in Figure F–1.

The relative dose rates at various times after a nuclear explosion are given in Table F–1. If the actual dose rate is measured for any given time after detonation, it is possible from this table to obtain the dose rate for any other time by simple proportion.

TABLE F–1. RELATIVE DOSE RATES IN ROENTGENS PER HOUR FOR VARIOUS TIMES AFTER A NUCLEAR EXPLOSION (EXTERNAL GAMMA)

HOUR	RELATIVE DOSE RATE
1	1,000
2	440
3	270
5	150
7	100
10	63
20	27
40	12
49	10
100	4.0
200	1.7
343	1.0
600	0.46
1,000	0.25

Vertical distribution of radioactive debris from a "shot" into the various parts of the atmosphere and the residence time there afford time for decay, while the horizontal spread reduces the concentration in any one place.

The dose attenuation factors afforded by shielding in a regular frame house or a special fallout shelter are shown in Table F–2.

TABLE F–2. ATTENUATION FACTORS AFFORDED BY SHIELDING

TYPE OF STRUCTURE	APPROXIMATE ATTENUATION FACTOR FOR GAMMA RADIATION FROM FALLOUT
Frame house:	
First floor	2
Basement	10
Multistory, reinforced concrete:	
Lower floors (away from windows)	10
Basement (surrounded by earth)	1,000 +
Shelter below grade:	
3 feet of earth	1,000 +

The attenuation of radiation dose is due largely to the absorption of radioactivity by the materials of house or shelter, but also to the factor of distance from the radiation source (fallout material outside the house), where the intensity varies as the inverse square of the distance from a point source.

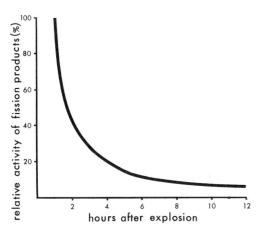

FIGURE F–1. RATE OF DECAY OF FISSION PRODUCTS (ACTIVITY TAKEN AS 100 AT 1 HOUR AFTER DETONATION).

FALLOUT PATTERN

If there were no air movement, radioactive material from the detonation of a nuclear device would descend from the atomic cloud to the earth as LOCAL FALLOUT, deposited in a circle around ground zero. Since there is always some air movement, the pattern of fallout is usually somewhat cigar-shaped as shown in Figure F–2.

The shape and dimensions will be determined by wind velocities and directions at all altitudes between the ground and the radioactive cloud. Also, because of time and decay factors, and because of decreasing fallout deposited as the cloud moves along, there will be a series of dose-rate contours or isodose lines, as shown in Figure F–3.

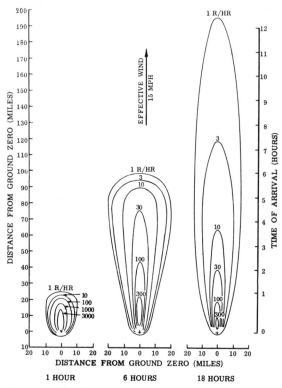

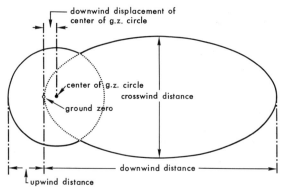

FIGURE F–2. GENERALIZED FALLOUT PATTERN.

FIGURE F–3. DOSE-RATE CONTOURS FROM EARLY FALL-OUT AT 1, 6, AND 18 HOURS AFTER A SURFACE BURST WITH 1 MEGATON FISSION YIELD (15 MPH EFFECTIVE WIND SPEED).

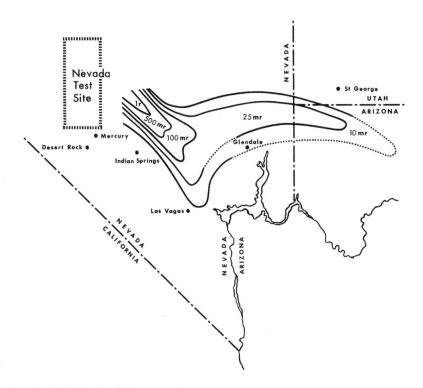

FIGURE F–4. ACTUAL MEASURED CONTOURS SHOWING EFFECTIVE BIOLOGICAL DOSE FROM FALLOUT.

TROPOSPHERIC FALLOUT patterns may vary greatly from the predicted pattern owing to wind and weather with its SCAVENGING effect. The rugged, irregular terrain makes prediction additionally difficult at the USAEC Nevada Test Site. This is illustrated in Figure F–4 which gives the dose-rate contours in roentgens (r) and milliroentgens (mr) for a shot fired on March 23, 1955. It illustrates the irregularity of an actual compared with a schematic contour.

See CONTOUR METHODS and ISOINTENSITY CONTOURS.

FALLOUT SAMPLING. *See* SAMPLING PROGRAM FOR RADIOACTIVE FALLOUT.

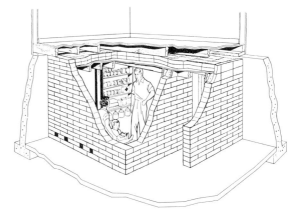

FIGURE F–5.   BASEMENT CONCRETE BLOCK SHELTER.

FALLOUT SHELTER

A shelter designed to protect its occupants against hazards of overexposure to FALLOUT radiation from the detonation of a nuclear weapon.

Several types of family fallout shelters* have been designed and others are under consideration to protect against radioactive fallout:

Aboveground Double-Wall Shelter affords no protection against blast, but reduces radiation inside to at least 1/100 of that out-of-doors. Practical for areas in which underground shelters are not feasible because of water level or rocky terrain.

Basement Concrete Block Shelter affords no protection from blast, but reduces fallout intensity to at least 1/200 of that out-of-doors. Easy to construct (Fig. F–5) but is hazardous if the house catches fire.

Underground Reinforced Concrete Shelter reduces radiation levels to 1/5000 or less of that out-of-doors. Resistance to blast probably significant but not yet tested. This concrete shelter can be built as an additional room attached to a basement entrance if topography is right.

Preshaped Metal Arch Shelter reduces radiation to 1/500 of levels outside. Protects against blast overpressures of 30 psi and is estimated to offer 90% assurance of survival beyond 1 1/2 miles

*The Family Fallout Shelter MP-15. Office of Civil Defense Mobilization.

from ground zero under 5-megaton bombing (Fig. F–6).

All shelters must have certain minimum facilities for occupancy of several weeks: ventilation, lighting, food, water, sanitary facilities, clothing, blankets, first-aid and medical supplies.

FAST NEUTRON

An arbitrary division of neutron energy usually considered to be greater than 0.1 Mev. In this frame of reference: thermal neutrons average 0.025 electron volt (ev); epithermal, few hundredths ev up to 100 ev; slow neutrons, general class up to 100 ev; intermediate neutrons from 100 to 100,000. Neutrons released in the fission process are originally all fast neutrons. The (n,p) type of nuclear reaction is common for fast neutrons.

FAT DIGESTION AND ABSORPTION MEASUREMENT

Impaired absorption of fat is a frequent result of diseases of the intestinal tract; until the advent of radioisotopes it was tedious and unpleasant to measure fat digestion and absorption in man. This information can now be obtained on a routine basis with radioiodine-labeled triolein (a neutral fat) and oleic acid (a fatty acid). A test meal is

FIGURE F–6.   PRESHAPED METAL SHELTER.

prepared in the form of an emulsion containing the labeled material—a dose of 5 microcuries or less is adequate if assays are to be made of feces only; at least 10 times this dose is needed if blood assays are also to be done. Feces are collected for several days after the meal and blood samples hourly for 6 hours. Normally the plasma lipid radioiodine level rises during the 6-hour period to reach a level indicating that 12% of the dose is in the blood stream, and the total fecal assays indicate an excretion of less than 8%. In disorders of digestion and absorption the blood levels are low and fecal levels are high. If there is a general disorder of the digestive tract both triolein and oleic acid will be poorly absorbed; if the deficiency is limited to pancreatic enzyme, the oleic acid will be well absorbed, the triolein not.

FEDERAL RADIATION COUNCIL

The Federal Radiation Council was established by Executive Order 10831, August 14, 1959, and also by Public Law 86–373, effective September 23, 1959, amending the Atomic Energy Act of 1954. The membership consists of the Secretary of Health, Education, and Welfare, the Chairman of the Atomic Energy Commission, the Secretary of Defense, the Secretary of Commerce, the Secretary of Labor, the Secretary of Agriculture, or their designees, and such other members as shall be appointed by the President. The Special Assistant to the President for Science and Technology, or his designee, also is authorized to attend meetings, participate in deliberations, and advise the Council.

A major function of the Council is to ". . . advise the President with respect to radiation matters, directly or indirectly affecting health, including guidance for all Federal agencies in the formulation of radiation standards and in the establishment and execution of programs of cooperation with States . . ."

The Secretary of Health, Education, and Welfare was designated by the President as the first Chairman of the Council. With the aid of a technical committee consisting of designees of the Council members and an appointed Secretary of the Council, work has been completed and Staff Report No. 1 of the Federal Radiation Council, entitled "Background Material for the Development of Radiation Protection Standards," was published on May 13, 1960. Staff Report No. 2 under the same title appeared in September, 1961. Staff Report No. 3 is entitled, "Health Implications of Fallout from Nuclear Weapons Testing Through 1961" and appeared in May, 1962.

See RADIATION PROTECTION GUIDE.

FERMI AWARD

An award, honoring the late Enrico Fermi, established in 1956 under the statutory authority granted in the Atomic Energy Act of 1954, Section 157.b(3) which states, in part, that: "The Commission may also, upon the recommendation of the General Advisory Committee, and with the approval of the President, grant an award for any especially meritorious contribution to the development, use or control of atomic energy." The award consists of a medal, citation, and up to $50,000 (tax exempt) which may be given to a single individual or divided among two or more individuals. Recipients of the award have been:

1956 Dr. John von Neumann. "In recognition of his scientific contributions to the theory of fast computing machines and for his original contributions to their design and construction."

1957 Dr. Ernest O. Lawrence. "For his development of the cyclotron and his other contributions to the development of atomic energy and nuclear physics."

1958 Dr. Eugene P. Wigner. "For his outstanding contributions in the fields of nuclear and theoretical physics, development of nuclear reactors and practical development of nuclear energy."

1959 Dr. Glenn T. Seaborg. "For discoveries of plutonium and several additional elements and for leadership in the development of nuclear chemistry and atomic energy."

1960 No award made.

1961 Dr. Hans A. Bethe. "In recognition of his outstanding contributions in the fields of nuclear and theoretical physics which helped to establish the foundations of nuclear physics and nuclear technology; in the applications of atomic energy for the betterment of mankind, in weapons technology and as a teacher and a leader of men."

1962 Dr. Edward Teller. "For contributions to chemical and nuclear physics, for leadership in thermonuclear research, and for efforts to strengthen national security."

1963 Dr. J. Robert Oppenheimer. "In recognition of outstanding contributions to theoretical physics and scientific and administrative leadership not only in the development of the atomic bomb, but also in establishing the groundwork for the many peaceful applications of atomic energy."

Dr. Enrico Fermi was granted an award of merit in 1954 and given $25,000 for his contributions to basic neutron physics and his achievement of the controlled nuclear chain reaction.

See ATOMS FOR PEACE AWARD and LAWRENCE MEMORIAL AWARD.

FERMIUM

Symbol Fm; atomic number 100; atomic weight 253; a radioactive transuranic element of the actinide series. Announced in 1954, first found in 1953 in coral debris following the thermonuclear test explosion of November, 1952, at Eniwetok Atoll. Isolated and identified by scientists at the Los Alamos Scientific Laboratory, the Argonne National Laboratory, and the Radiation Laboratory, University of California, Berkeley. Named in honor of Enrico Fermi. Seven radioactive isotopes of fermium, in mass numbers of 250 through 256, have been made. Fermium does not occur in nature.

FERROKINETICS STUDIES

The term "ferrokinetics" usually refers to the plasma iron turnover rate, the red cell iron turnover rate, and the movement of iron in or out of tissues. The plasma iron turnover rate is a measure of the iron entering or leaving plasma per unit of time, and can be calculated from the rate at which a small transferrin-bound tracer dose of iron-59 leaves the plasma. Normally half the labeled iron disappears in 80 to 100 minutes. The interest in plasma iron turnover rates arises from attempts to use this value as a measure of the rate of red cell formation. It appears that the plasma iron turnover rate does provide an index of the rate of erythropoiesis, but should not be regarded as providing quantitative information.

When tracer doses of radioiron enter the body, the isotope is utilized for hemoglobin synthesis in an amazingly prompt and complete fashion. Tagged hemoglobin can be identified in the peripheral blood within 4 to 8 hours, and from 70 to 100% of the injected dose is found in the circulating hemoglobin within 7 to 14 days. After a tracer dose of iron-59, counts can be made over the surface of the body with a scintillation counter, and the radioactivity in the bone marrow, liver, spleen and other tissues can be compared. In this way the greater uptake by the liver and spleen can be detected when extensive extramedullary hemopoiesis is occurring in these organs. Mathematical models have been developed for the transference of iron in the several pools, and these studies suggest that a portion of the iron that goes to the bone marrow from the plasma constitutes a labile pool, part of which is unused and returned to plasma. It has also been calculated that the rate of hemoglobin synthesis is about 6 grams of hemoglobin per day in the normal individual. It is estimated that approximately two-thirds of the iron enters the marrow each day and is used for hemoglobin synthesis, while one-third is fed back to the plasma. Radioactive techniques have also been used to demonstrate relative completeness of conservation of hemoglobin iron.

FERROUS SULFATE CHEMICAL DOSIMETER

A commonly used type of chemical dosimeter which utilizes the oxidation of ferrous sulfate in dilute acidic solution under the action of ionizing radiation, the consequent color change being observed quantitatively.

FERTILE MATERIAL

Material capable of being transformed into a FISSIONABLE MATERIAL by capture of a neutron. Common examples are thorium-232 and uranium-238. Also the cases in which the nucleus is capable of capturing a neutron and, after existing as an intermediate element of relatively short half-life, becomes a fissionable nucleus, for example, uranium-233 from thorium-232, and plutonium-239 from uranium-238.

FERTILITY. *See* REPRODUCTION, ANIMAL, RADIATION EFFECTS ON.

FERTILIZER STUDIES

Soil-plant relationships, soil fertility and fertilizer use have been under active study for many years. The amounts of certain essential elements available to growing crops can be estimated with relative accuracy and ease through the use of radioisotope tracer procedures in the laboratory and greenhouse and in the field. Such studies have shown where fertilizers should be placed, at what time in the growing season they should be employed, the age at which the plant absorbs the greatest amount, and the leaching or movement that may take place in the soil after application.

Most of the early work utilizing radioisotopes has dealt with the phosphorus problem, because of the importance of this element, and also because the radioisotope P^{32} has a number of desirable characteristics from the standpoint of experimentation, such as its relatively short half-life and strong beta emission. Other radioisotopes, however, are becoming of increasing use to provide information on the macronutrients such as calcium, sulfur, and potassium, as well as on the micronutrients such as chlorine, cobalt, copper, iron, manganese, molybdenum, and zinc.

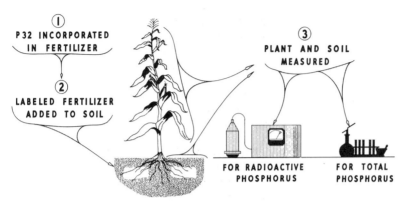

FIGURE F–7. STUDY OF PHOS-
PHATE FERTILIZER UPTAKE US-
ING RADIOACTIVE PHOSPHORUS
(P³²) AS A TRACER. FIXATION
CAN BE DETERMINED BY THE
SOIL, UPTAKE BY PLANT AND
PROPER TYPE AND PLACEMENT
OF FERTILIZER. (USAEC-1D-
179.)

Following are some general conclusions that illustrate how radioisotopes have been an important aid in finding out how to obtain maximum value from applied fertilizers. By use of P^{32} it was shown, for example, that superphosphate and ammonium phosphate provided about the same amount of phosphorus to various crops, and that tricalcium phosphate supplied much less phosphorus than did the other two compounds (method of study shown in Fig. F–7). From the standpoint of placement, it was found that in sandy loam, surface-applied phosphorus was utilized to a much greater extent by alfalfa than that placed 3 or 6 inches deep. Peanuts have been found to require a source of calcium in the peg zone, in addition to calcium near the roots. Evidence has been forthcoming to show that crops differ in ability to obtain nutrient elements from similar sources. For instance, milkweed and alfalfa were found to take up considerably more phosphorus from the same soil than did beets, oats, or perennial rye grass. It has also been shown that a greater proportion of the applied nutrients in the fertilizer is used during the early stages of growth.

Iron deficiencies which affect fruit crops in some types of soil have been shown to be caused by the presence of bicarbonate ion in such soil. Radioisotopes have also been used to show that cobalt, manganese, molybdenum, and copper are readily absorbed by plants and translocated from roots to leaves. Manganese absorption by plants has been shown to be reduced by iron and other heavy metals.

It is important to know the extent of activity of the root systems of crop plants to gain information on the volume of soil from which the plant can obtain the nutrients and water that it requires. A simple method for the study of rooting systems and habits utilizing P^{32} is illustrated in Figure F–8. The procedure consists in injecting radiophosphorus into the soil at specific locations relative to the plant, and determining the amount taken up

by the plant at different times by analysis of leaf or root tissue. A typical injection pattern as used in the study of cotton and tobacco is shown. This design required 20 different placements and therefore 20 different plants for one complete experiment. The following types of information were obtained:

a. the time of arrival of the roots at a given location in the soil, which is a measure of the over-all growth and rate at which the root expands through the soil volume;

b. the seasonal and soil effects on the root pattern;

c. the time and manner of plant competition which may lead to spacing recommendations;

d. the effects of depth of tillage;

e. the relative importance of various root segments for nutrient uptake;

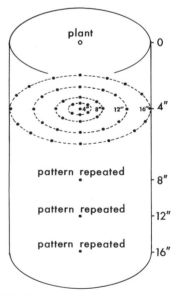

FIGURE F–8. RADIOPHOSPHORUS INJECTION PATTERN
USED FOR STUDY OF THE ROOT DEVELOPMENT OF COTTON
AND TOBACCO.

f. the efficiency of the root system of a given species in utilizing added fertilizer under given conditions.

FETUS, RADIATION EFFECTS ON

The effect of radiation on the mammalian embryo and fetus varies with the amount of radiation and with the time of irradiation. For the mouse, it is convenient to divide the term of pregnancy into 3 approximately equal parts. During the first third, the effect of radiation is to kill the embryos. In mice, for example, 200 roentgens will kill about 80% of embryos at this stage. The percentage killed increases with an increasing dose of radiation.

During the second third of pregnancy, when the major organs are being developed, a wide range of abnormalities may be induced, singly or in combination. Many of these will be so severe as to cause death immediately after birth, even if the embryo survives to the end of pregnancy. The abnormalities include imperfect development of skeletal parts, viscera, and body size.

Irradiation during the last third of pregnancy produces fewer skeletal abnormalities but more neural abnormalities (see Fig. F–9).

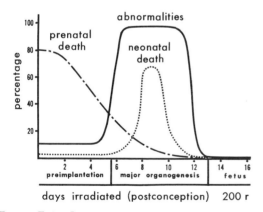

FIGURE F–9. INCIDENCE OF FETAL ABNORMALITIES AND OF DEATH IN MICE IRRADIATED WITH 200 r AT VARIOUS STAGES IN THEIR PRENATAL DEVELOPMENT.

For human beings much less is known though there can be no doubt that irradiation of the embryo or fetus may produce abnormalities. The term of human pregnancy may be approximately equated to the term of mouse pregnancy by comparing stages of development, rather than by subdividing the period of time into thirds.

FIBER ELECTROSCOPE

The type of electroscope commonly employed in direct reading pocket dosimeters or in portable calibration instruments.

See ELECTROSCOPE and CONDENSER R-METER.

FILM BADGE

Personal DOSIMETER to detect and record radiation exposure. It consists of photographic films and holders incorporating an arrangement of special filters, to be worn by radiation workers for a period of a week to a month. The combination of ·filters and film types (Fig. F–10) is contrived to provide a record of the exposure to radiations of different kinds, through measurement of photographic density and nuclear tracks in specified areas of the film after processing.

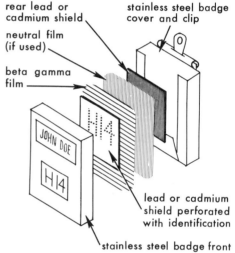

FIGURE F–10. FILM BADGE DISASSEMBLED TO SHOW HOLDER, PHOTOGRAPHIC FILMS, AND FILTERS.

FILM LIBRARIES

As part of its information and education program, the USAEC maintains 10 domestic motion picture libraries* from which qualified borrowers throughout the United States and Canada may obtain 16-mm sound-track films that explain various aspects of atomic energy. There are over 90 films listed in the "Popular Level Film List" suitable for nonprofessional audiences. In the publication, "Motion Picture Film Library, Professional Level" there are over 100 films listed suitable for professional audiences.

---

*Films are also distributed by the USAEC Liaison Offices at American embassies in Tokyo, Brussels, London, and Buenos Aires, and by the United States Information Agency.

These films may be obtained for short-term loan
as follows:

IF YOU LIVE IN	SERVICE AREA	ADDRESS YOUR REQUEST TO
Alaska, Oregon, Washington	#1	Director, Information Division U.S. Atomic Energy Commission Hanford Operations Office P.O. Box 550 Richland, Washington
California, Hawaii	#2	Assistant to the Manager U.S. Atomic Energy Commission San Francisco Operations Office 2111 Bancroft Way Berkeley 4, California
Nevada, Arizona, New Mexico, Texas, Oklahoma	#3	Director, Division of Information U.S. Atomic Energy Commission Albuquerque Operations Office P.O. Box 5400 Albuquerque, New Mexico
Montana, Utah, Idaho	#4	Assistant to the Manager for Information U.S. Atomic Energy Commission Idaho Operations Office P.O. Box 2108 Idaho Falls, Idaho
Colorado, Wyoming, Nebraska, Kansas	#5	Director, Information Division U.S. Atomic Energy Commission Grand Junction Operations Office Grand Junction, Colorado
North Dakota, South Dakota, Minnesota, Iowa, Missouri, Wisconsin, Illinois, Michigan, Indiana, Ohio	#6	Information Assistant to the Manager U.S. Atomic Energy Commission Chicago Operations Office 9800 South Cass Avenue Argonne, Illinois
Arkansas, Kentucky, Tennessee, Louisiana, Mississippi	#7	Public Information Officer U.S. Atomic Energy Commission Oak Ridge Operations Office P.O. Box E Oak Ridge, Tennessee
Pennsylvania, New York, Vermont, New Hampshire, Maine, Massachusetts, New Jersey, Rhode Island, Connecticut	#8	Director, Public Information Service U.S. Atomic Energy Commission New York Operations Office 376 Hudson Street New York 14, New York
Delaware, Maryland, Virginia, District of Columbia, West Virginia, Canada	#9	Deputy Chief Audio-Visual Branch, Division of Public Information U.S. Atomic Energy Commission Washington 25, D.C.
North Carolina, South Carolina, Alabama, Georgia, Florida	#10	Assistant to the Manager for Public Education U.S. Atomic Energy Commission Savannah River Operations Office P.O. Box A Aiken, South Carolina

FILTER

In radiology, a device that selectively transmits radiations of different types or of different energies. A primary filter is a sheet of material, usually metal, placed in a beam of radiation to absorb, as far as possible, the less penetrating components, which are damaging to the skin and superficial tissues. A secondary filter is a sheet of material of low atomic number relative to that of the primary filter, placed in the filtered beam of radiation to remove characteristic radiation produced in the primary filter. In medical radiographic installations good practice demands that the total filtration permanently in the useful beam shall be not less than 2.5 millimeters of aluminum equivalent. (See National Bureau of Standards Handbook 76.)

The term is also widely applied to many kinds of devices that permit selectively the passage through them of certain kinds of matter. Filters of various types are used in stack disposal of radioactive gaseous waste, and in the laboratory for filtration of the radioisotope hood effluent.

Filters are commonly used in devices for air sampling.

Filters are also used in radiochemistry to separate finely divided solids from fluids.

FILTRATION

The removal of some components of a heterogeneous beam of radiation by passage through a sheet of material. The filtering effect of any substance depends on its absorption coefficients for photons of various energies.

The removal of particulate matter from either air or a liquid.

See FILTER.

FIRE STORM

Stationary mass fire, generally in built-up urban areas, generating strong, inrushing winds from all sides; the winds keep the fires from spreading while adding oxygen to increase their intensity. This phenomenon has been observed in large forest fires and following incendiary bombing of cities in World War II. Approximately 35% of the energy released in the detonation of a nuclear device is thermal radiation, thus combustible material may be ignited and a fire storm such as the one in Hiroshima may result. It has been estimated that in Hiroshima materials on the ground immediately below the burst were heated to about 5,400° to 7,200° F, and even at 4,000 feet from ground zero the temperature exceeded 2,900° F. Thousands of fires broke out, eventually covering an area of about 4.5 square miles; the fire storm was created with wind velocities of 30 to 40 mph. The fires

burned themselves out by evening of the same day. Many of the casualties both dead and injured were the result of burns, both flame and thermal burns (*see* FLASH BURNS).

An ordinary conflagration may develop into a fire storm.

FIREBALL

Also called ball of fire. The visible, luminous sphere of hot gases formed by a NUCLEAR EXPLOSION. In the fission of uranium (or plutonium) in the detonation of a nuclear device enormous amounts of energy are liberated in a fraction of a millisecond and in a confined space. Thus, all parts of the device are raised to a temperature of tens of millions of degrees and completely vaporized. Large amounts of energy, mainly soft x-rays, are released, which are absorbed within a few feet of atmosphere, producing the visible fireball.

Immediately after it forms, the fireball begins to increase in size and engulfs the surrounding air. The diameter of about 440 feet is reached within 0.7 millisecond after the detonation of a 1-megaton device, increasing to a maximum of 7,200 feet in 10 seconds. From the moment of detonation the fireball rises; at 10 seconds it is rising at the rate of 250 to 300 ft./sec. Its growth and rise are accompanied by a temperature and pressure decrease, causing a lessening of luminosity. After one minute, having risen approximately 4.5 miles from the point of burst, it has cooled to the extent that it is no longer visible.

In the detonation of a 1-megaton nuclear device the fireball may be as much as 5,800 feet across at its maximum brilliance in the second pulse. In tests conducted at the Nevada Test Site (energy yields less than 100 kilotons) the glare in the sky, at dawn, was visible as far as 400 miles away. To an observer 60 miles away the fireball of such a device would be 30 times as brilliant as the sun at noon (see Fig. F–11).

Because of the intense heat of the fireball, rock, soil and other material in its vicinity (surface burst) will be vaporized and taken up into it, thus adding greatly to the radioactive fallout (see Fig. F–12).

As the fireball increases in size and cools, the radioactive cloud becomes evident. This radioactive cloud or atomic cloud, contains the radioactive fission products, uranium (or plutonium) that did not fission, the weapon casing and other materials, including that sucked into it. It has the toroidal circulation shown in Figure F–13.

Afterwinds or high-wind currents at the earth's surface and moving toward the center of the burst will carry along surface particles to be sucked up

FIGURE F-11. BALL OF FIRE FROM AN AIR BURST IN THE MEGATON-ENERGY RANGE, PHOTOGRAPHED FROM AN ALTITUDE OF 12,000 FEET AT A DISTANCE OF ABOUT 50 MILES. THE FIREBALL IS PARTIALLY SURROUNDED BY THE CONDENSATION CLOUD. (USAEC.)

FIGURE F-12. FIREBALL AND DIRT CLOUD SUCKED UP BY THE AFTERWINDS IN A LOW AIR BURST.

nuclear detonation in a very humid atmosphere. It is also called the Wilson cloud since it resembles the cloud observed in the Wilson cloud chamber. Rapid cooling of the initially heated air surrounding the fireball during the negative pressure phase of the shock wave (see BLAST PHYSICAL PHENOMENA) causes the moisture in the air to condense and form a cloud. The cloud is dispelled within a second or so when the air pressure returns to normal and the air warms again.

The fireball begins to emit thermal radiation at once in the form of ultraviolet, visible and infrared rays (see ELECTROMAGNETIC SPECTRUM). For a typical fission weapon air burst about 85% of the total energy released is in the form of heat (kinetic) energy, composed of 50% producing BLAST

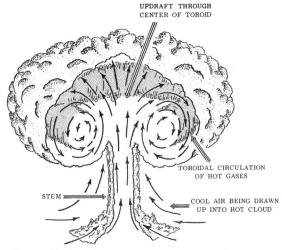

FIGURE F-13. CUTAWAY SHOWING ARTIST'S CONCEPTION OF TORIDIAL CIRCULATION WITHIN THE RADIOACTIVE CLOUD FROM A NUCLEAR EXPLOSION.

into the fireball as it rises, and these will become radioactive through attachment of weapon residue and to a lesser extent by induced radioactivity.

A condensation cloud consisting of mist or fog may temporarily surround the fireball following a and shock with the remaining 35% appearing as thermal radiation (heat and light rays). About 5% of the total energy goes into initial nuclear radiation; and the remaining 10% of the total energy represents that of the residual (or delayed) nuclear radiation which is emitted over a period of time. This is due almost entirely to the radioactivity of the fission products present in the weapon debris after the explosion.

FIRES, RADIOACTIVE MATERIAL

A number of fires have occurred involving radioactive materials, particularly plutonium, uranium and thorium. In addition, a number of metals used in atomic energy activities are encountered in forms that may be highly pyrophoric; zirconium, hafnium, sodium, magnesium, calcium and potassium. Fires not only destroy property but when radioactive material is involved, contamination of the environment usually occurs. Fires in radioactive "scrap" (solid waste) have also occurred and have spread contamination. A few examples follow:

A fire occurred when plutonium turnings were being sealed in a plastic bag. During the 6-second electronic heat-sealing cycle, the masked operator observed a growing brown spot on the bag and white smoke inflating it. The sealer was shut off and the operators left the area. Carbon dioxide fire extinguishers had little effect, and the fire burned itself out. Decontamination cost approximately $20,000.

A uranium scrap fire occurred in a 500-pound drum of normal uranium in the form of 3-pound discs. Before it could be put out the fire spread to 9 of the 50 other drums in the storage area; 31 were removed before the intensity of the fire prevented further moving. Water finally brought the fire under control. Damage was slight. The other 10 drums did not ignite.

A spontaneous fire occurred in a drum of thorium metal pellets being transported by truck. The drum was pushed from the truck and burned out after 2 1/2 hours.

Several days after a heavy rain, a fire of unknown origin took place in an open bin filled with zirconium (not radioactive) scrap turnings, chips, plates, rods, etc. Shortly thereafter other bins not adjoining the first flared up. Material in all bins soon became involved and 159,000 pounds of zirconium burned.

Radioactive sodium in a hot cell for chemical tests started to burn when a leak developed in the apparatus. The fire was extinguished with a special powder, but some contamination was spread, and one person received a little more than 1-r radiation dose.

Fire was discovered in a metal mesh cage used for the storage of dry contaminated waste which had been used with nitric acid to clean up contamination. Spread of contamination was slight and no injuries resulted.

Glove box (or dry box) fires occur and are often associated with the spread of radioactive contamination.

See EXPLOSIONS, RADIOACTIVE MATERIALS and REACTOR FIRES.

FISH AND WILDLIFE SERVICE

The U.S. Fish and Wildlife Service is a unit within the U.S. Department of the Interior, which has primary interest in atomic energy activities as they relate to radioactive contamination and the uptake of fission products by fish, algae, and other forms of marine organisms, and by various forms of terrestrial wildlife. The contamination may be related to radioactive fallout or to radioactive waste disposal.

FISSION

Splitting of a nucleus into two more or less equal fragments. Fission may occur spontaneously or may be induced by capture of bombarding particles. Neutrons and gamma rays are usually produced in addition to fission fragments.

When a free or unattached neutron enters the nucleus of a fissionable atom, it usually causes the nucleus to split into two parts. In this process large amounts of energy are released. The nuclei which result are called "fission products."

See NUCLEAR FISSION and FISSION PRODUCTS.

FISSION COUNTER

Radiation pulse detector of the proportional counter type in which a foil or film of fissionable material is incorporated to make it respond to neutrons. The kind of fissionable material is selected to show various kinds of neutrons (U^{235} for response to slow neutrons, U^{238} for neutrons of energy above 1/2 Mev, others as required for special ranges). The operation is otherwise similar to the alpha counting technique.

FISSION PRODUCTS

About 200 different radioactive isotopes (including radioactive daughters) of some 35 light elements (atomic numbers 30 through 64) are formed as initial fission product nuclei in the detonation of a nuclear device. There are 40 or more different ways in which the nuclei of uranium and plutonium can split when fission occurs, so that 80 or more different fragments are produced. All these products are involved in the problem of radioactive fallout. From the standpoint of long-term, world-wide, or stratospheric fallout it is generally agreed that strontium-90 and cesium-137 are potentially the most important hazards to man. For shorter periods of time following the detonation strontium-89, iodine-131, barium-140, and cerium-144 are considered to have biological interest (*see* CERIUM for table of Fission Product Abundance). Because of their bone-seeking properties the following are of biological interest from the tropospheric fallout point of view: strontium-89; yttrium-91; zirconium-95—niobium-95; barium-140—lanthanum-140; cerium-143—praseodymium-143; cerium-144—praseodymium-144; and neodymium-147—promethium-147. Table F–3 lists the principal radioactive isotopes present at various periods after the detonation.

An enormous amount of radioactivity is produced in the detonation of a nuclear device; 1 minute after detonation a nominal yield nuclear bomb (equivalent to 20 kilotons of TNT) has created 8.2×10^{11} curies gamma activity. From even a 1-kiloton explosion, it has been postulated that at 1 minute after detonation the radioactivity is comparable to that from 100,000 tons of radium. This radioactivity comes from about 0.11 pound of fission products formed for each kiloton of fission energy yield.

Fortunately it decays rapidly. A rule of thumb is that radioactivity will decrease ten-fold for every seven-fold increase in time after detonation. For example, if the radiation intensity at 1 hour after the explosion is taken as a reference point, then 7 hours after the explosion the intensity will have decreased to one-tenth; at $7 \times 7 = 49$ hours it will be one-hundredth; and at $7 \times 7 \times 7 = 343$ hours the activity will be one-thousandth of that at 1 hour after the burst. This is shown graphically in Figure F–14.

If there is postulated complete mixing of the various fission products the decay activity can be expressed by the formula $A = A_1 t^{-1.2}$, where A_1 is the activity at one unit of time after the detonation and t is time.

Fission products are also produced in the operation of a nuclear reactor. A waste disposal problem exists in handling and disposing of these fission products. At present a plant at the USAEC Oak Ridge National Laboratory is separating out certain of the fission products that may be used

TABLE F–3. PRINCIPAL FISSION PRODUCTS

ISOTOPE	HALF-LIFE	PER CENT CONTRIBUTION TO FISSION PRODUCT ACTIVITY		
		After 1 week	After 1 month	After 1 year
Strontium ($_{38}$Sr^{89})	53 d	2.1	6.4	2.6
Strontium ($_{38}$Sr^{90})	28 y			1.9
Yttrium ($_{39}$Y^{90})	64.2 h			1.9
Yttrium ($_{39}$Y^{91})	57 d	2.4	7.2	4.0
Zirconium ($_{40}$Zr^{95})	65 d	2.4	7.6	7.1
Niobium ($_{41}$Nb^{95})	35 d		3.7	15.3
Molybdenum ($_{42}$Mo^{99})	68.3 h	10.0		
Ruthenium ($_{44}$Ru^{103})	39.8 d	1.9	5.4	
Ruthenium ($_{44}$Ru^{106})	1 y			2.4
Rhodium ($_{45}$Rh^{103m})	57 m	1.9	5.3	
Rhodium ($_{45}$Rh^{106})	30 s			2.4
Tellurium ($_{52}$Te^{132})	77.7 h	7.0		
Iodine ($_{53}$I^{131})	8.1 d	6.2	4.0	
Iodine ($_{53}$I^{132})	2.4 h	7.2		
Xenon ($_{54}$Xe^{133})	5.27 d	12.1	3.1	
Cesium ($_{55}$Cs^{137})	30 y			1.5
Barium ($_{56}$Ba^{137})	2.6 m			1.5
Barium ($_{56}$Ba^{140})	12.8 d	8.8	11.1	
Lanthanum ($_{57}$La^{140})	40 h	9.3	12.8	
Cerium ($_{58}$Ce^{141})	32.5 d	4.8	11.1	
Cerium ($_{58}$Ce^{144})	290 d		1.8	26.0
Praseodymium ($_{59}$Pr^{143})	13.7 d	8.0	11.4	
Praseodymium ($_{59}$Pr^{144})	17.5 m		1.9	26.1
Neodymium ($_{60}$Nd^{147})	11 d	4.1	4.3	
Promethium ($_{61}$Pm^{147})	2.6 y			5.7
Promethium ($_{61}$Pm^{149})	54 h	1.7		
Total accounted for.		89.9%	97.1%	98.3%

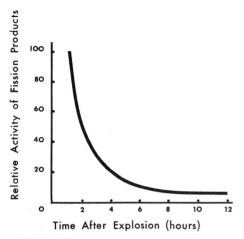

FIGURE F–14. FISSION PRODUCT DECAY. RADIOACTIV-
ITY DECREASES TEN-FOLD FOR EVERY SEVEN-FOLD
INCREASE IN TIME AFTER DETONATION.

commercially. Zirconium-95 is being considered and cesium-137 is being used as a massive radiation source, for example in teletherapy. Strontium-90, cerium-144 and promethium-147 are being developed as possible power sources. Technetium-99 is of interest because of its chemical properties, for it has been shown that the corrosion of iron can be significantly inhibited when as little as 5 parts per million are added to circulating water. Chemical removal of the above fission products (some of which are of long half-life) will materially simplify the waste disposal problem. See FISSION PRODUCTS, WASTE DISPOSAL.

Mixed fission products are not of value in biological research for it is almost impossible to interpret measurements of such an uncertain mixture of activities.

See OAK RIDGE NATIONAL LABORATORY; RADIO-NUCLIDES OF BIOLOGICAL INTEREST (BOMB); and RADIONUCLIDES PRODUCED IN AIR, WATER, AND SOIL (BOMB).

FISSION PRODUCTS, WASTE DISPOSAL

The major problem in the disposal of radioactive waste from the operation of a reactor is in fuel reprocessing and in handling the FISSION PRODUCTS that have been separated from the spent fuel elements. In fact, the magnitude of the waste disposal problem associated with chemical processing far outweighs the problems of the operation of a reactor and is potentially a greater hazard to public safety. As the nuclear power program builds up, the disposal of fission products in a manner that will not be injurious to health will need to have particular attention also in relation to waste disposal economics.

Spent fuel elements are now removed from reactors and shipped to one of the major USAEC processing sites: Hanford Works, Washington; Savannah River Plant, South Carolina; or Chemical Processing Plant at Arco, Idaho. They are cooled for 90 days to allow decay of radioisotopes with short radioactive half-lives. Processing is initiated by dissolving the fuel jackets and then the fuel elements in appropriate chemicals. Plutonium and uranium are separated from the other fission products, purified by solvent extraction, and then processed to usable forms. During these steps radioxenon and radioiodine are discharged, but the aqueous waste from the first solvent extraction cycle may still contain more than 99% of the fission products. Current processing methods produce from 0.5 to 5 gallons of liquid waste per gram of uranium processed; the radioactivity levels vary over a range from tens to several thousand curies per gallon of waste. Subsequent operations produce lower-level aqueous wastes (LIQUID WASTE) which are handled by conventional treatment methods such as evaporation, ion exchange, etc., with the effluent being discharged to the ground and/or surface streams. Resulting SOLID WASTES are disposed by LAND DISPOSAL AND BURIAL, or OCEAN DISPOSAL.

In considering the hazard factors of effective half-life, maximum permissible concentration, and general biological significance, strontium-90 always emerges as the fission product of most concern. Removal of Sr^{90} plus 3 years of storage achieves a hundred-fold hazard reduction. After a 3-year storage period cerium-144 is the radioisotope with the greatest activity, but after this period cesium-137 becomes most hazardous. A further reduction in hazard can be achieved by removal of Cs^{137}, but the remaining material is still too highly radioactive to be discharged directly to the environment. Long-term tank storage followed by packaging in 55-gallon sealed drums for either ocean or land disposal is the present method.

Chemical processing is now being tried. The Oak Ridge Fission-Product Development Laboratory is separating out 6 radioisotopes that have commercial significance: strontium-90, zirconium-95, technetium-99, cesium-137, cerium-144, and promethium-147. Removal of these radioisotopes materially reduces the hazard as well as the required holding time. The highly radioactive liquid waste may then be chemically incorporated into some solid form, such as a ceramic cake which can be safely buried.

See WASTE DISPOSAL, RADIOACTIVE.

FISSION YIELD. See YIELD.

FISSIONABLE MATERIAL

Material having the property of capturing neutrons and thereupon splitting into 2 particles possessing great kinetic energy. Uranium-235 (natural abundance 0.7%) is the only naturally occurring fissionable material; but uranium-238 (abundance 99.3%) is a fertile material which can be converted by neutron irradiation to plutonium-239, a second fissionable material, and thorium-232, a fertile material, which can be converted to uranium-233, making a third fissionable material. Used as nuclear reactor fuels, and in the construction of nuclear devices.

FLASH BLINDNESS

Temporary loss of vision due to flooding the eye with a very intense light, such as the brilliant light produced by the detonation of a nuclear device. At 0.7 millisecond after detonation the fireball from a 1-megaton nuclear bomb would appear 30 times as brilliant as the sun at noontime to an observer 60 miles away on a clear day. Among the survivors in Hiroshima and Nagasaki there were many cases of temporary flash blindness, occasionally lasting up to 2 or 3 hours, but in all cases this was a temporary condition and visual acuity was completely regained.

See RETINAL BURNS.

FLASH BURN

A skin burn due to THERMAL RADIATION. A flash burn can be distinguished from a fire or flame burn by the profile nature of the flash burn, i.e., the burn occurs on the unshielded parts of the body exposed in a direct line with the origin of the thermal radiation (it is milder under even the thinnest fabrics). A flame burn may involve any or all parts of the body, and tends to be much deeper in skin penetration.

Of the injured survivors of the bombing of Hiroshima and Nagasaki 65 to 95% experienced burns (40,000 fairly serious burn cases in Hiroshima), and flash burns were by far the most common. Examples of profile burns were numerous: a man writing at a window had his hands and forearms badly burned but since the rest of his body was shielded by the window frame it was unburned; a man wearing a cap had a sharp line of demarcation on the side of his face where the cap covered the forehead. Clothing usually protected but in some cases of heavy irradiation burns occurred through the clothing. Here the color absorption effect came into play, with the black pattern showing superficial skin burns whereas the white-covered portion remained normal, as in Figure F–15 showing a patient who had on a kimono of black and white when the flash came.

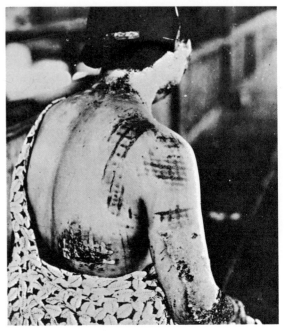

FIGURE F–15. PATIENT'S SKIN BURNED IN A PATTERN CORRESPONDING TO THE DARK PORTIONS OF THE KIMONO WORN AT THE TIME OF EXPOSURE.

The severity of the burns in Japan ranged from mild erythema to charring of the outermost layers of the skin. Unlike low-temperature contact or flame burns there was no accompanying edema and even in the cases of charring the depth of damage was much less for flash burns. However, apart from other injuries, including prompt radiation (initial nuclear radiation accounts for about 5% of the energy of a typical air burst), the flash burns experienced by those Japanese within a mile of ground zero without protection, would probably have proved fatal. Even out as far as 12,000 feet there were thermal radiation burns severe enough to require treatment.

Burns of moderate second degree or first degree usually healed within a month but the more severe burns and those that became infected required much longer. Many left scars; keloid formation was quite common.

FLOW COUNTER, GAS

1. A gas pulse-type counter for detection and measurement of ionizing radiation, operated in either the proportional or the Geiger region, through which the counting gas flows continuously in and out of the counting volume. Among the special advantages of this type of instrument is the possibility of using a minimum or even zero thickness window between the sample and the counting volume, since the window or other seal

needs only to sustain a slight excess over the ambient atmospheric pressure. A bubbler is included in the exit gas line to indicate the rate and continuity of flow of the gas during counting. The thin window or no-window arrangement has particular value in measurements on samples containing the weakest beta-ray emitting substances, including tritium, carbon-14, and sulfur-35, which are certainly among the most significant of tracer isotopes in biological and medical experimentation.

The gas flow principle also avoids the problem of depleting the counting ability of the radiation-sensitive constituents in the gas. For counting in the Geiger region, a gas is used which contains compounds to aid in the quenching process, the mixture sometimes being referred to as Q-gas. Proportional counting is carried out with another mixture with enhanced stability characteristics, called P-gas.

2. A counter for measuring continuously the radiation present in a constantly flowing gas sample, as in a metabolic experiment or in the exhaust gas of a device such as a nuclear reactor. These are generally adjusted to respond to specific energies of radiation, for purposes of identifying the active constituent in the flowing gas sample.

FLOW MEASUREMENTS

Two types of flow measurements are made with radioactive isotopes. Speed of flow is measured by injecting a small amount of radioactive material into the flowing liquid and then by use of two detection instruments, located some distance apart, marking the time of passage of the radioactive tracer. The volume of flow is calculated by multiplying the time of passage between the 2 counters by the volume capacity of the pipe line between the 2 points.

Another use of radioactive tracers is in marking the interface between 2 different oil products being put through the same pipe line. A radioactive tracer, as shown in Figure F-16, marks the boundary. No sampling is required, and yet separation of the types of oil is made possible with a minimum of loss.

FLUOR

Fluorescent substance, used in scintillation techniques for radiation detection. There is a very wide range of actual and potential materials that can be used. Some are relatively pure compounds with only imperfections in the crystal lattice to trap the energy; with others the crystal structure is modified by the addition of impurities, e.g., zinc sulfide with 1 part per million silver atoms, or silicates activated with beryllium.

See FLUORESCENCE and PHOSPHOR.

FLUORESCENCE

The emission of light (electromagnetic radiation) by a material as a result of the absorption of energy from radiation, either electromagnetic or particulate, provided the emitted light ceases within about 10^{-8} seconds when the exciting light or radiation is cut off. Fluorescence may be considered as LUMINESCENCE which ceases 10^{-8} seconds after the excitation stops. It was described by the French physicist Becquerel in 1896 as a result of his work with a uranium salt.

The term may refer to the radiation emitted, as well as to the emission process.

X-ray fluorescence is characteristic x-radiation emitted as a result of absorption of x-rays of higher frequency.

A fluorescent screen is material coated with a fluorescent substance emitting visible light when irradiated with ionizing radiation.

Fluorescence yield is the probability that an atom whose electronic structure is excited will emit an x-ray photon rather than an Auger electron in the first transition.

See PHOSPHORESCENCE.

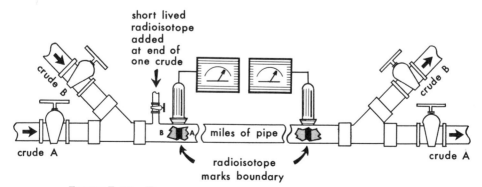

FIGURE F-16.   TRACING OIL FLOW IN PIPE LINES USING RADIOISOTOPES.

FLUORINE

Symbol F; atomic number 9; atomic weight 19.00. A pale yellow, poisonous, very active gas. A member of the halogen family of elements. Discovered by Swedish chemist Scheele in 1771, but not isolated until 1886, by French chemist Moissan. Named from Latin, *fluo*, flow. Occurs as fluorspar or calcium fluoride and as cryolite or sodium aluminum floride. The stable isotope F^{19} supplies 100% of the natural abundance.

Over half the fluorine is used in the steel industry, the second largest use is in the manufacture of hydrofluoric acid, while the glass industry uses fluorspar as an opacifier and as a flux. Fluorides are of significance in the prevention of tooth decay. Fluorine is not a constituent of living material. It is highly toxic from the standpoint of inhalation or ingestion. Hydrofluoric acid causes burns on the skin.

Of the 3 known radioactive isotopes F^{20} may possibly be induced in sea water following the neutron bombardment associated with the detonation of a nuclear device in contact with the sea; and reactor-produced F^{18} is useful in biological work, in studying fluorine metabolism, and in work with insecticides and insect physiology.

FLUOROSCOPE

An instrument consisting of a fluorescent screen suitably mounted with respect to an x-ray tube for ease of observation and protection. Used extensively in medical diagnosis for indirect visualization of internal organs in the body. Also used in industrial practice for x-ray observation of internal structures in apparatus or in masses of metal. The fluorescent screen is a sheet of material coated with a fluorescent substance (commonly barium platino-cyanide) which emits visible light when irradiated with ionizing radiation. Fluoroscopy is x-ray examination by means of a fluoroscope. A photofluorograph or fluorograph is a photograph of an image produced on a fluorescent screen.

FLUX

In nuclear physics, the product nv, where n is the number of particles per unit volume and v is the mean velocity.

For particles, the number passing through a given area per unit time.

For electromagnetic radiation, the energy per unit time, passing through a given surface area. *See* NEUTRON FLUX.

FOCUSING COLLIMATOR

Focused shielding nose piece for a detector especially for use in isotopic localization procedures; designed to have discretely limited region from which radiation is received. Used with probe detectors especially in uptake measurements (thyroid, etc.) and for in vivo scanning procedures.

See COLLIMATOR.

FOLIAR FEEDING OF PLANTS

Roots are commonly considered as the principal organs through which plants absorb nutrients. Radioactive mineral nutrients, however, supplied to leaf, stem, and fruit surfaces are shown to be readily absorbed as measured by subsequent assay on nontreated parts. A remarkably high percentage (40 to 95%) of the applied nutrient is often absorbed within a few days or hours, and significant contributions to the nutritional needs of distant plant organs, such as roots, may be made after a single spraying treatment. Many crops pass through critical periods when nutrient demands are high, and when availability from soil sources is low. It has been shown by radioisotopes that during these critical periods leaves can supplement the function of the root as the nutrient absorbing tissue; for example, the application of phosphorus to the leaves of plants represents the most efficient method of fertilizer placement yet devised (Fig. F–17).

Phosphorus-32, potassium-42, sulfur-35, and the stable isotope nitrogen-15 are readily taken up by aerial plant tissues, and transport from the site of entry to other plant parts is rapid.

In contrast, calcium-45, strontium-89, -90, barium-140, iron-55, and ruthenium-103, although readily absorbed by leaves and fruit, move little, if at all, from the site of entry. Urea is widely used for nitrogenous fertilizations, through leaf application, and carbon-14-labeled urea has been employed to study its behavior.

A proved method is now available for treatment of fruit trees by application of nutrients to the trunk and branches during the dormant and early spring seasons. In addition, flowering and fruiting

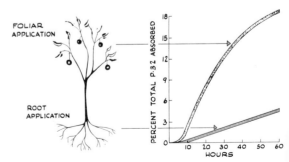

FIGURE F–17. STUDIES OF FERTILIZER UPTAKE BY ROOTS AND FOLIAGE USING RADIOACTIVE PHOSPHORUS (P^{32}) AS A TRACER. (USAEC-1D-277A.)

can be controlled by foliar sprays of hormone-like materials so that, for example, it is possible to adjust pineapple production with fields ripening in succession as desired. All these applications have been greatly aided by the use of radioisotopes.

FOOD AND AGRICULTURE ORGANIZATION (FAO)

A United Nations specialized agency interested in the use of radioactive isotopes in agricultural activity; in the use of radiation in food preservation and sterilization; and in related aspects of the peaceful uses of atomic energy.

See AGRICULTURE, USE OF RADIOISOTOPES IN; FOOD PRESERVATION; and NUCLEAR EXPLOSIONS, PEACEFUL USES OF.

FOOD AND DRUG ADMINISTRATION

An agency of the U.S. Department of Health, Education and Welfare whose functions relating to atomic energy include monitoring of foods, with the exception of milk, on a routine basis for radioactive contamination from fallout. FDA is also concerned with use of radioisotopes in applications to control quality in food and drug processing; applications of radiation to drug and food preservation and sterilization; standardization of radiopharmaceuticals; labeling requirements; and introduction of radioactive materials in food products (*see* FOOD PRESERVATION).

FOOD CHAIN

The pathways by which radioactive material from fallout producing biospheric contamination can reach man or animals. The major terrestrial pathways are illustrated by the accompanying diagram:

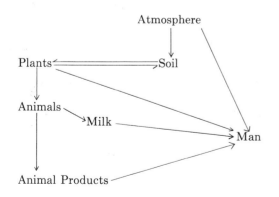

For ease of future reference they may be summarized as follows:

    a. atmosphere to man;
    b. atmosphere to plant to man;
    c. atmosphere to soil to plant to man;
    d. atmosphere to plant to animal to milk to man;
    e. atmosphere to soil to plant to animal to milk to man;
    f. atmosphere to plant to animal to animal products to man;
    g. atmosphere to soil to plant to animal to animal products to man.

Five radionuclides of importance in environmental contamination considered in relation to food chain movement are:

Iodine-131: Because of the relatively short radioactive half-life (8.07 days) only pathways (a) and (d) are significant:

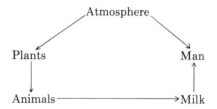

Barium-140: Again, because of the short half-life (12.8 days) only pathway (d) is significant:

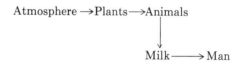

Strontium-89 and -90: Pathways (b), (c), (d), and (e) are important:

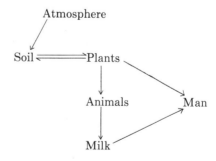

Cesium-137: Because it is fixed in soil and markedly unavailable to plants and because cesium is deposited in both animal muscle tissue and milk, the important pathways are (b), (d), and (f):

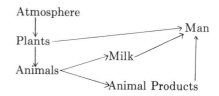

Consideration of the most likely pathways for the movement of radioactive contamination enables the intelligent establishment of a sampling program for radioactive fallout. For example, in considering the same 5 radionuclides the samples of importance for monitoring are:

Iodine-131: Plants, milk, thyroid tissue (animal).

Barium-140: Plants, milk.

Strontium-89, -90: Soil, plants, milk, dairy products, bone (animal), aquatic food.

Cesium-137: Plants, milk, dairy products.

The following are factors that determine the importance of and modify the food chain pathways:

1. Soil characteristics and climatic conditions.
2. Plant cover, e.g., heavy roots may delay strontium reaching soil for dilution with soil calcium.
3. Management, e.g., plowing depth, fertilization, barn feeding versus pasture.
4. Dietary habits, e.g., proportion of milk in diet, amount of leafy vegetables.
5. Food technology, e.g., washing of foods.
6. Time pattern of contamination, e.g., at short times after detonation of a nuclear device, the shorter-lived radionuclides are of more significance—iodine-131, barium-140, and strontium-89. As time goes on, strontium-90 and cesium-137 become more important.

During active fallout contamination of leafy vegetables is an important pathway; as fallout diminishes, the soil reservoir pathway becomes relatively more important.

An interesting and graphic example of food chain radiocontamination is furnished by a laboratory experiment*. The water plant Elodea was grown for 7 days in a solution containing the radioactive isotope phosphorus-32, (500 ml of water and 10 μc P^{32}). It was removed, washed, counted (250 counts per minute [cpm]), radioautographed (see Fig. F–18), shredded, and fed to guppies. One guppy was used after 48 hours to make a radioautograph as shown in the accompanying picture (Fig. F–19). A whole-body count of 450 to 500 cpm was recorded. The guppies were then fed to Egyptian mouth breeders with the result as shown in Figure F–20. The whole-body count in this case was about 500 cpm.

---

*Reported by Robert Starrett at an AEC-NSF Radiation Biology Summer Institute at Adelphi College.

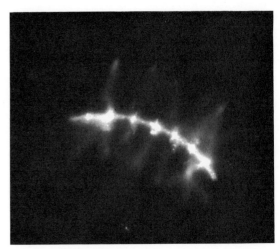

FIGURE F–18.   ELODEA WITH ABSORPTION OF P^{32}.

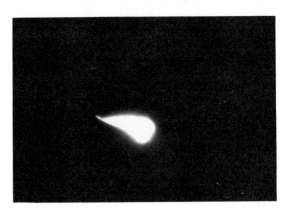

FIGURE F–19.   GUPPY AFTER INGESTION OF ELODEA.

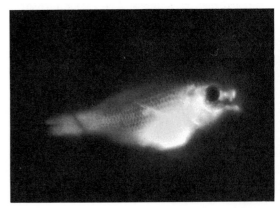

FIGURE F–20.   EGYPTIAN MOUTH BREEDER AFTER INGESTION OF GUPPIES.

This illustration highlights the fact that the food chain contamination may be from fallout to ocean to plankton to fish to man.

See FOOD CONTAMINATION.

FOOD CONTAMINATION

Contamination with radioactive materials of substances intended for use as food for man or animals. Usually considered in relation to fallout from the detonation of a nuclear device. Although more than 200 radionuclides are thus produced only a few are significant in food contamination: iodine-131, barium-140, strontium-89, strontium-90, and cesium-137. Other radioactive materials are of lesser or no importance in the FOOD CHAIN because of: (a) low fission abundance, (b) short radioactive half-life, (c) poor absorption by plants, (d) poor absorption within the animal or human body, or (e) non-entry into the food chain.

Plants are basic to the food chain, supplying nearly all man's food either directly or indirectly. They obtain most of the nutrient material through the root system, and thus most radionuclides are taken up by the roots. In order to be assimilated they must be soluble in water, and thus some radionuclides are not a hazard. For example, the amount of plutonium-239 may be greater than that of strontium-90 or of cesium-137, but plutonium is taken up from soil to plant in a ratio of only 1 part in 10,000. There is a similar discrimination factor in the human intestinal tract— for every 10,000 to 100,000 parts of plutonium in food only 1 part is absorbed into the body.

Plants do absorb some radioisotopes through leaves and stems (aerial parts); in fact this foliar absorption of strontium-90 and cesium-137 has been demonstrated under experimental conditions for wheat, potatoes, beans, cabbage, and sugar beets. Radioisotopes may also be adsorbed to the plant. This was the case of the iodine-131 in the Windscale reactor accident where the food chain contamination was from reactor stack to atmosphere to pasture grass to cow to milk which had to be dumped to prevent contamination of humans.

Contamination of milk from the Russian series of 1961 indicated in one locality 530 micromicrocuries of iodine-131 per liter of milk. A physician normally prescribes 5 millicuries of iodine-131 for thyroid treatment in the case of heart disease. To get the same amount of iodine in the thyroid gland a person would have to drink several million quarts of milk at one time. The milk sampling program is part of a continuous FOOD SAMPLING program.

Wheat samples from 9 states show strontium-90 levels ranging from 14 to 198 micromicrocuries ($\mu\mu$c) per kilogram of wheat. The maximum permissible concentration for continuous consumption for strontium-90 in water is 800 $\mu\mu$c per kilogram of water for occupational exposure and 1/10 this amount or 80 $\mu\mu$c for so-called population exposure. If nothing but the whole wheat grain were eaten

it would thus be possible to get an MPC at the population exposure level. But whole wheat bread ranged from 16 to 56 $\mu\mu$c per kilogram and white bread ranged from 8.5 to 16 $\mu\mu$c, so if nothing but bread were eaten as the complete diet it would still be impossible to get even an MPC.

The USAEC food sampling program measured strontium-90 levels in vegetables from 12 areas in the United States, collected from May to November, 1959, and found that strontium-90 ranged from 2.1 to 48.0 $\mu\mu$c per kilogram in cabbage; 0.8 to 8.2 in potatoes; 9.2 to 178.2 in soybeans; and 9.1 to 96.4 in wheat.

Food in cans will not be contaminated if the can is washed prior to opening. Careful washing of vegetables will remove much of the adsorbed radioactive contamination. Washing lettuce reduced strontium-90 contamination by 60%, while paring carrots brought a reduction of 87%.

See SAMPLING PROGRAM FOR RADIOACTIVE FALLOUT and FOOD SAMPLING.

FOOD PRESERVATION

The commercial and beneficial potential of preservation of foods by radiation has led to extensive research programs sponsored by several Federal agencies. The Department of Defense has concentrated largely on high-dose radiation sterilization of foods, while more recently the Atomic Energy Commission has supported research on low-dose radiation pasteurization, or extended shelf-life, of refrigerated foods. The major advantages of radiation preservation can be listed as follows:

1. Decrease of food losses. Since there is no question that insect life can be destroyed without adverse effects, a decrease of food losses by insect control holds considerable promise.

2. Improved flavor and texture. Since most present-day processed foods have a characteristic texture and taste brought about by heat treatment, it is quite likely that radiation preservation, which can be done with but a rise of a few degrees in temperature, will lead to improved texture and taste.

3. Increased variety in food selection. Some tropical fruits, for example, are not permitted into this country because of the infestation with insect pests. A program of radiation sterilization would make it possible to lift such quarantines.

4. Decreased cost of food handling. The storage life of potatoes can be extended from 8 to 15 months, thereby spreading the year's crop for a longer distribution time. The inhibition of sprouting in onions has also been achieved. The shelf-life of many meats and vegetables can be extended considerably.

5. Wider distribution of perishables. It would become possible to ship perishables to peoples of the world who do not have refrigerators and refrigerated handling facilities.

6. Control of certain food-borne diseases. There is little question but that worm and food parasites, such as trichina, can be controlled by irradiating the suspected food at low dosages. It is expected that other pathogenic micro-organisms can also be destroyed by radiation.

The requirements for commercial feasibility of food preservation are as follows:

1. Action on contaminating organisms. The treatment must in fact kill or slow down the growth of bacteria, parasites, insects, and other contaminating organisms in food. The dosage required varies, but it appears that:

    a. at 12,000 rad potatoes (Fig. F–21) and onions are inhibited from sprouting;

    b. at 25,000 rad worms, flukes, and insects are killed;

    c. at 200,000 rad most micro-organisms are killed, resulting in pasteurization;

    d. at 4 to 6 million rad the most resistant of bacteria are killed, resulting in sterilization.

2. Wholesomeness of product. The irradiated food must not be toxic to man. At the present time, a group of 22 foods including fruits, vegetables, meats, and dairy products has been tested in acute and chronic toxicity investigations with 4 animal test species, and in limited studies with man. Evaluations have been made on the basis of growth, food consumption, reproduction, lacta-tional performance, longevity, and carcinogenicity. Over-all results are not yet available. The problem of induced radioactivity in food is dependent upon the energy of the source used for irradiation. Low-energy gamma sources, such as cobalt-60, are considered incapable of inducing measurable radioactivity. High-energy (24 Mev) electron sources can induce the production of certain radioisotopes in food, all of which would be at levels less than the natural radioisotopes of potassium and carbon.

3. Acceptable flavor, odor, and appearance. The treatment must not adversely affect the taste, odor, texture, and appearance of food. Foods differ in their response to ionizing radiation as far as these qualities are concerned. Milk, for example, develops undesirable flavor changes at 100,000 rad, whereas dried prunes are capable of withstanding over 3 million rad. Foods that tend to develop undesirable odors and flavors at pasteurizing doses of about 200,000 rad are those such as bananas, crab meat, oranges, butter, milk and cheese; others that are not adversely affected include luncheon meat, beef, carrots, cole slaw, peas, and mackerel. Foods that are apparently relatively resistant are asparagus, bacon, green peas, beef liver, broccoli, chicken, cod fish cakes, corn beef, halibut, ham, pork, pork sausages, sweet potatoes, and waffles.

4. Economic feasibility. The order of magnitude of cost estimates at present indicates that such procedures may become economically feasible. It is most likely that the ultimate decision will depend upon such factors as the wholesomeness and taste of the product.

FOOD RADIATION. *See* FOOD PRESERVATION.

FOOD SAMPLING

A program of sampling foodstuffs for their radioactive content is being conducted by the USAEC, the Public Health Service (USPHS), the Food and Drug Administration (FDA), and the Department of Agriculture (DA). This food sampling program is part of the SAMPLING PROGRAM FOR RADIOACTIVE FALLOUT and includes sampling of many different types of food in the United States with the milk sampling program being the most extensive.

An international food sampling program was inaugurated by the USAEC in 1956 to study the distribution of radiostrontium in foodstuffs and the importance of such factors as geographic location, calcium content of soils, and local dietary habits. Of prime importance was determination of major sources of calcium in the diet of various national groups. The first two countries studied

FIGURE F–21. INHIBITION OF SPROUTING IN POTATOES BY IRRADIATION. PHOTOGRAPHED 8 1/2 MONTHS AFTER EXPOSURE TO GAMMA RAYS. TOP ROW, LEFT, NO IRRADIATION; CENTER, 1,250 ROENTGENS (r); RIGHT, 5,000 r; BOTTOM ROW, LEFT, 20,000 r; CENTER, 80,000 r; RIGHT, 106,250 r. (BROOKHAVEN NATIONAL LABORATORY.)

TABLE F–4. CALCIUM, POTASSIUM, AND RADIONUCLIDE CONTENT OF FOODS

SAMPLE	Ca (gm/kg)	K (gm/kg)	Sr^{89}	Sr^{90}	Ba^{140}	Cs^{137}	Ra^{226}
			(micromicrocuries per kilogram)				
Eggs	0.695	1.369	—	3.0	0	2.0	0.52
Fruits	0.178	2.484	—	3.7	2.0	63.0	—
Cereals	0.480	1.368	—	12.4	0.0	110.0	0.12 to 0.60
Dairy products	4.836	—	61.0	39.0	0.0	21.0	0.0
Seafoods	0.335	—	0.0	0.2	0.0	25.0	—
Meats	0.172	3.483	0.0	1.0	0.0	160.0	0.10
Leafy vegetables	0.508	3.404	21.0	3.9	12.0	49.0	0.0
Instant coffee	1.900	44.280	31.0	19.0	0.0	19.0	0.0
Instant tea	0.150	45.320	150.0	60.0	0.0	890.0	0.0
Mixed nuts	0.727	6.975	0.0	8.2	0.0	350.0	2.23
Rice	0.196	0.811	0.0	1.2	0.0	95.0	0.0
Milk (1958 av.)	1.145	0.0	55.0	8.5	24.0	75.0	0.0

were the Philippines and Turkey. This program was expanded in 1957 to include Latin America where samples of wheat, flour, potatoes, and green vegetables were collected in Chile, Argentina, Peru, Brazil and later from Venezuela, Bolivia, Ecuador, and Guatemala. Emphasis again was on primary calcium foods. In Turkey the foods (wheat, wheat products, beans, and milk products) collected in 1957 showed 1 to 5 micromicrocuries of strontium-90 per gram of calcium. In the Philippines foodstuffs (legumes, cereals, vegetables, fruit, meat, fish, eggs, coconut rice, evaporated milk) collected February–March, 1957 showed 4 to 12 micromicrocuries of strontium-90 per gram of calcium.

In order to establish a base-line, the FDA, in a food sampling program, collected from various parts of the United States and other nations over 1,000 food samples grown prior to the first atomic bomb tests in 1945. Analysis revealed no strontium-90. In samples grown between 1945 and 1957 there was found: (1) No measurable contamination of fruits and vegetables; (2) some contamination of fish and shellfish; (3) increased contamination with strontium-90 in powdered milk and cheese; and (4) marked contamination of tea. Samples of food produced from 1957 to April, 1959, showed increase in radioactive contamination over that found in 1957 analyses and in addition contamination of fresh vegetables, animal forage (alfalfa), and wheat.

Various foods shown in Table F–4 were all purchased on the Cincinnati market in 1958 and analyzed by various techniques for their calcium, potassium, strontium-89 and -90, barium-140, cesium-137, and radium-226 content. Variation from these levels will be found in specific situations but these are typical examples of fallout contamination in a nuclear device testing year.

Marine food products (see AQUATIC ORGANISMS) have been monitored on a number of occasions. As an example, following an underwater defense test detonation in the eastern Pacific in the spring of 1955, the USAEC in cooperation with the FDA monitored 49,514,000 pounds of anchovy, mackerel, and tuna caught off the California and Mexico coasts. No health hazard was found.

FRACTIONATION

Breaking up a total dose of radiation into small fractions of low intensity given daily or at longer intervals of time. Divided doses generally show less biological damage than the same total dose given at one time.

See DOSE.

FRANCIUM

Symbol Fr; atomic number 87; atomic weight 253. A radioactive element with the chemical properties of an alkali metal. The radioisotope with mass number 223 (half-life 21 minutes, β⁻ and α emitter) is the longest lived isotope. Discovered in 1939 by Mlle. Marguerite Perey of the Paris Radium Institute and named for her native land. Formed in the actinium decay series from the branched disintegration of actinium-227, the radioiosotope Fr^{223} thus occurs in nature. There are 7 other radioactive isotopes.

FREE AIR IONIZATION CHAMBER

The primary standard instrument for x- and gamma-ray dosimetry providing direct measurement of radiation in terms of the roentgen unit. Free air chambers are maintained in the national laboratories of several countries, where they are used for standardization of radiation sources and for calibration of secondary standard dosimeters such as the condenser r-meter. This device operates

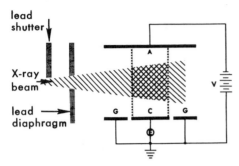

FIGURE F–22. FREE AIR IONIZATION CHAMBER. X-RAY
BEAMS CONTROLLED BY DIAPHRAGM AND SHUTTER. E,
ELECTROMETER; C, COLLECTING ELECTRODE; G, GUARD
RING ELECTRODE; A, ACCELERATOR ELECTRODE; V,
VOLTAGE SOURCE.

by collecting the ionized particles produced by
radiation in an accurately defined volume of free
air, the quantity of electricity being measured in
a precise electrometer circuit. It is then possible
to make an absolute determination of the exposure
dose in terms of the roentgen unit or "r" through
knowledge of the current or electric charge, the
size of the collecting volume, the temperature and
the pressure of the air. The design of the free air
chamber (Fig. F–22) must assure that the collection volume is strictly defined and known; that
complete collection of the ionization is accomplished; and that no part of the structure interferes
with the radiation beam. To these ends, the
collecting electrode is surrounded by a guard ring
electrode, the electrical field is uniformly graded
through the aid of a grid wire cage, and the electrodes are spaced well clear of the path of the
radiation.

See CALIBRATION.

FREE RADICALS

Chemical entities carrying a lone (unpaired or
odd) electron, produced by the ionization of water
or a gas. They are extremely reactive and consequently have a very short lifetime in an aqueous
solution, 10^{-5} seconds or less. Irradiation of pure
water results in the liberation of the very highly
reactive radicals, the uncharged H and OH. The
uncharged free radicals are written with a dot to
designate an unpaired electron (e.g., OH·) These
radicals tend to lose or gain another electron so
as to have an even number and become stable
ions, e.g., the OH· radical on capturing an electron
becomes the extremely stable OH^- ion. These hot
radicals can act either as oxidizing or reducing
agents, or can impart their energy to some point
in a molecule. In addition, the radicals can combine to form such highly reactive compounds as
HO_2, H_2O_2, and O_2.

There are two general concepts of action of
radiation on chemical systems: direct action by
ionization or excitation in the target molecule
(target theory); and indirect action by transfer
of energy through free radicals. In irradiation of
dry material, the major effect is direct. In very
dilute solutions of essentially pure materials all
the effect is mediated indirectly through radicals
liberated by the water. In biological objects both
direct action and indirect action are operative,
with the indirect free radical effect predominating.

FUSION, NUCLEAR

Coalescing of 2 light nuclei to form a heavier
nucleus, with an energy release of the difference
between the sum of the nuclear binding energies
of the products and the sum of the binding energies of the two light nuclei. An example is:

$$_1D^2 + {}_1D^2 \longrightarrow {}_2He^3 + {}_0n^1 + 3.22 \text{ Mev},$$

where two deuterium molecules interact to produce
helium, a neutron, and energy.

See THERMONUCLEAR REACTION and THERMO-
NUCLEAR WEAPON.

G

GADOLINIUM

Symbol Gd; atomic number 64; atomic weight 157.26. Member of the cerium subgroup of the rare earth metals. Separated by Marignac in 1880, and by Lecoq de Boisbaudran in 1886. Named after Finnish chemist J. Gadolin, an early worker in the rare earth field. Seven stable isotopes furnish the natural abundance, and there are 7 radioactive isotopes.

Gd^{159} and Gd^{161} are fission products. The maximum permissible concentration for a soluble compound of Gd^{159} (half-life 18.0 hours, β^- and γ emission) with the gastrointestinal tract as the critical organ for a 168-hour week (continuous exposure) is 8×10^{-4} microcuries per cubic centimeter ($\mu c/cc$) in water and 2×10^{-7} $\mu c/cc$ in air.

GAGING

The most common industrial application using radioactive isotopes is in gaging. Radioisotope gages are used in 3 principal applications: THICKNESS GAGING, the measurement of density or DENSITY GAGING, and LIQUID-LEVEL GAGING.

See BETA GAGE.

GAIN

The amplification factor of an electronic circuit. Gain is usually determined as the ratio by which the circuit increases the strength or voltage (sometimes the power) of a signal pulse.

GAIN CONTROL

A variable element or component in the circuit of an amplifier which can be adjusted to provide different amounts of gain or amplification factor. It is usually a variable resistor or potentiometer in the control grid or cathode connection of a vacuum tube or transistor, although other circuit components may also be used for the purpose.

GALLBLADDER, RADIATION EFFECTS ON

Following exposure to ionizing radiation in the lethal-dose range, hemorrhages are sometimes found in the wall of the gallbladder, and edema of the wall is often very extensive. The epithelium of the gallbladder may show partial desquamation, but this is not considered a specific manifestation.

GALLIUM

Symbol Ga; atomic number 31; atomic weight 69.72. A very rare metal with the unusual property of melting at a point slightly above room temperature. Found in traces in many zinc blendes and nearly always in bauxite. Discovered in 1875 by Boisbaudran. Named from Latin, *Gallia*, France. Its natural abundance is furnished by two stable isotopes, Ga^{69}, 60.2% and Ga^{71}, 39.8%.

Used commercially in high-temperature thermometers, and as a constituent of alloys in dental fillings. Of interest biologically because of its tendency to accumulate in bone, and medically for its possibilities in diagnosis and treatment of bone cancer using Ga^{72} (radioactive half-life 14.3 hours, effective half-life 0.14 hours, β^- and γ emitter) which is available commercially. Very mildly toxic.

There are 16 radioactive isotopes, 11 of which may be produced in the fission process during the detonation of a nuclear device. None have fallout significance.

GALVANOMETER

Instrument for detection and measurement of very small quantities of electricity.

GAMMA COUNTERS

Radiation counters of any type with response characteristics enhanced for efficient counting of energetic electromagnetic radiation.

GAMMA FIELD

Any area subject to radiation from an unshielded or lightly shielded source of gamma rays may be so termed. In current biomedical research in the United States the term is used frequently to identify a 10-acre radiation field established in 1953 at the Brookhaven National Laboratory, where growing plants can be exposed to gamma radiation from a centrally located 2,000- to 4,000-curie, cobalt-60, radiation source. The accompanying picture, Figure G–1, shows the arrangement by which growing plants may be exposed to varying degrees of radiation for periods varying from a day to several years. Normally the source is in the raised position inside a steel pipe for 20 hours daily irradiation, and is

FIGURE G–1. AERIAL VIEW OF THE 1953 GAMMA FIELD AT BROOKHAVEN NATIONAL LABORATORY. THE DARK AREA INDICATES PROGRESS OF IRRIGATION FOR THE DAY.

FIGURE G–2. SEDUM ALBOROSEUM PLANTS GROWN IN GAMMA FIELD FOR 16 WEEKS. DOSAGE INDICATES NUMBER OF ROENTGENS PER DAY OF EXPOSURE. (COURTESY BROOKHAVEN NATIONAL LABORATORY.)

lowered for 4 hours into an underground shielded container so that work may be done on the plants in the field.

In an attempt to determine the effects that different chromosome numbers have on radiosensitivity in plants, Sedum alboroseum, a small border plant, was grown with plants of different ploidy exposed to varying degrees of radiation. (See Fig. G–2.)

A somatic mutation developed during growth in the gamma field is shown in Figure G–3 of a

dahlia bloom from a plant exposed to 118 roentgens per day.

Plant breeders from all over the world have cooperated with the Biology Department of Brookhaven in the development and breeding of beneficial mutants resulting from radiation. One of the most successful is a new type of pea bean, Sanilac, which in 1960 provided added income of over $5,000,000 to Michigan farmers. Many new types of flowers, fruit trees, grains, and vegetables have been developed through irradiation of plants

FIGURE G–3. A SOMATIC MUTATION, WHITE PETALS ON A NORMALLY RED FLOWER, AS THE RESULT OF EXPOSING THE DAHLIA TO 118 ROENTGENS GAMMA RADIATION PER DAY. (COURTESY BROOKHAVEN NATIONAL LABORATORY.)

in the gamma field, or irradiation of seed in a nuclear reactor.

GAMMA RAY

Symbol, γ. Type of electromagnetic radiation emitted by a nucleus in an excited state, which permits the nucleus to go to a state of lower energy, or to its ground state, i.e., state of lowest energy. A quantum of electromagnetic radiation emitted by a nucleus, each such photon being emitted as the result of a quantum transition between two energy levels of the nucleus. Discovered by French physicist P. Villard in 1900.

The GAMMA-RAY SPECTRUM, part of the electromagnetic spectrum, has the following characteristics: frequency, 3×10^{18} to 3×10^{21} cycles per second; wave length, 10^{-8} to 10^{-11} centimeters; and energy of 10^4 to 10^7 electron volts. Gamma rays cannot be deflected in a magnetic field as will be seen in Figure G–4, which Marie Curie included in her doctoral thesis, published in 1903. Her experiment was set up so that all 3 types of rays would emerge as a narrow vertical beam from a deep hole in a block of lead. When a strong magnetic field was applied in a direction perpendicular to and out of the plane of this paper, the positively charged and relatively heavy alpha particles were slightly deflected to the right and the negatively charged and light beta particles were deflected more widely to the left, while the gamma rays, having no electrical charge, were not deflected.

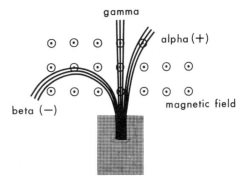

FIGURE G–4. ACTION OF ALPHA, BETA, AND GAMMA RAYS IN A MAGNETIC FIELD. GAMMA RAYS ARE NOT DEFLECTED.

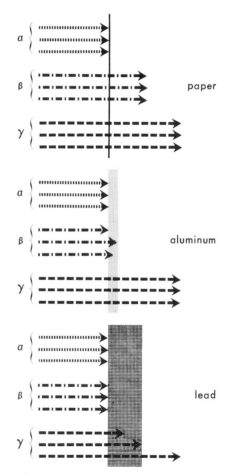

FIGURE G–5. RELATIVE PENETRATING POWER OF ALPHA, BETA, AND GAMMA RADIATION.

As shown graphically in Figure G–5, alpha particles are completely stopped by a few sheets of paper, beta particles are absorbed by a few millimeters of aluminum, but gamma rays have great penetrating power and may not be completely stopped or absorbed by several centimeters of lead.

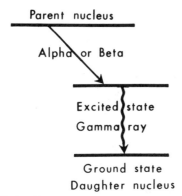

FIGURE G–6. EMISSION OF GAMMA RADIATION IN RADIOACTIVE DECAY.

In their passage through matter gamma rays lose their energy, i.e., are absorbed, in several ways. One important way for gamma rays of low energy to be absorbed by absorbers of high atomic weight is the photoelectric effect, where the radiation causes electrons to be ejected from atoms or molecules. The second important method of absorption is the Compton effect, in which a gamma-ray photon collides with a free or loosely bound electron and loses some of its energy. A third way in which gamma rays lose their energy is in the formation of positron-electron pairs (see PAIR PRODUCTION). The electrons ejected or the pairs produced cause the secondary ionization of matter.

In alpha and beta decay, the radioactive transition often leaves the daughter nucleus in an excited state and, as will be seen in Figure G–6, the excess energy is emitted as gamma radiation. Positive beta emission is invariably accompanied by gamma radiation resulting from the annihilation of positrons which have been slowed down by interaction with electrons in matter.

Internal conversion may occur with the entire energy of the gamma ray being transferred to one of the orbital electrons.

Gamma rays may produce nuclear reactions of the following types: (γ,n), (γ,p), $(\gamma,2n)$, $(\gamma,n2p)$, (γ,α), and others. In 1934 it was shown that the gamma radiation from thorium C, with an energy of 2.62 Mev, could cause the disintegration of a deuterium nucleus thus:

$$_1H^2 + \gamma \longrightarrow {}_1H^1 + {}_0n^1.$$

The binding energy of a neutron in beryllium of mass number 9 is low enough so that the (γ,n) reaction may be produced:

$$_4Be^9 + \gamma \longrightarrow {}_4Be^8 + {}_0n^1.$$

Highly energetic rays produced by particle accelerators can bring about numerous other types of nuclear reactions, even as complex as the transmutation of oxygen-16 to carbon-11, which would indicate the following reaction: $O^{16}(\gamma,3n2p)C^{11}$, in which 5 nuclides are ejected. Twenty-five-Mev gamma rays can break up a carbon-12 nucleus into 3 alpha particles.

Gamma rays are used for the production of neutrons through the neutron reaction, i.e., the (γ,n) type. Two such reactions are: $H^2(\gamma,n)H^1$ and $Be^9(\gamma,n)Be^8$ (see NEUTRON SOURCES).

The detection of gamma rays and measurement of their intensity is accomplished by the use of radiation detection instruments of the GAMMA COUNTER group, the GAMMA SPECTROMETER, GEIGER-MUELLER COUNTER and others.

Gamma rays and x-rays, although of different origin, have precisely the same characteristics. They penetrate and pass through matter in the same way, and therefore can be used for medical diagnosis of a fracture, for example, and can also be used for industrial radiography. Both are used in teletherapy in medical treatment (see COBALT).

Because of their penetrating power and secondary production of ionization, gamma rays are a great potential radiation hazard. Like x-rays they cause radiation damage of cells and tissues, produce radiation illness, and if the exposure is great enough lead to death of the organism.

In recording the gamma sources of radiation, nuclear fission must be considered, either controlled in a nuclear reactor or uncontrolled in the detonation of a nuclear device (see GAMMA-RAY SOURCES).

The problem of absorption and shielding is much more complex and difficult for gamma rays than for alpha or beta particles.

GAMMA-RAY SOURCES

The most prolific source of gamma rays is nuclear fission associated with the detonation of a nuclear device.

In the first minute after detonation of a nominal yield nuclear bomb 8.2×10^{11} curies of gamma activity are produced. These gamma rays are produced largely through neutron bombardment of elements in the air, soil, water or in the elements associated with the bomb itself, by the (n,γ) nuclear reaction. The initial nuclear radiation constitutes about 5% of the energy distribution in a typical air burst of a nuclear device and the residual nuclear radiation about 10%. Although the radioactivity of the initial fission fragments usually consists of negatively charged beta particles, this disintegration is almost always accompanied by gamma radiation in the transition from the excited state to the ground state. In a few cases gamma radiation only is emitted.

Similar reactions occur in the controlled situation of the nuclear reactor. For example the Oak Ridge National Laboratory (ORNL) Graphite Reactor, in which most of the radioactive isotopes shipped from Oak Ridge are produced, has a gamma emission of approximately 10^6 roentgens per hour. The hard gamma-emitting radioisotopes available from Oak Ridge for use in research, and in medical diagnosis and treatment, are listed in Table G–1.*

TABLE G–1. HARD GAMMA EMITTERS AVAILABLE FROM OAK RIDGE NATIONAL LABORATORY

RADIOISOTOPE	HALF-LIFE*	ENERGY† (Mev)
Sodium-24	15.0 h	2.754
Gallium-72	14.2 h	2.51
Lanthanum-140	40 h	2.50
Iridium-194	19 h	2.1
Antimony-124	60 d	2.11
Arsenic-76	26.6 h	1.2
Praseodymium-142	19.3 h	1.59
Silver-110m	270 d	1.516
Potassium-42	12.7 h	1.51
Europium-152, -154	12.7 y; 16 y	1.40
Cobalt-60	5.27 y	1.33
Bromine-82	35.87 h	1.312
Iron-59	45.1 d	1.289
Tantalum-182	112 d	1.223
Scandium-46	85 d	1.12
Zinc-65	245 d	1.12
Rubidium-86	18.6 d	1.08
Rhodium-106 (Ru^{106})	30 s	1.045
Cesium-134	2.3 y	0.794
Tungsten-187	24.0 h	0.78
Zirconium-95	65 d	0.754
Niobium-95	35 d	0.745
Cerium-144		
Praseodymium-144	290 d	0.696
Barium-137m (Cs^{137})	2.6 m	0.662

*h, hour; d, day; y, year; m, minute; s, second.

†The energy given in each case is the maximum gamma energy which occurs to an extent of 5% or more.

GAMMA-RAY SPECTRUM

The distribution of the intensity of the various functions of gamma rays along a continuum. Located as part of the electromagnetic spectrum with the following characteristics: frequency range in cycles per second, 3×10^{18} to 3×10^{21}; wave length range in centimeters, 10^{-8} to 10^{-11}; energy in ergs, 2×10^{-8} to 2×10^{-5}, or in electron volts, about 10^4 to 10^7. Although the x-ray spectrum

*A catalog and price list of radioisotopes (special material and services) available from Oak Ridge may be obtained from Union Carbide Nuclear Co., Oak Ridge National Laboratory, Isotope Sales Department, P.O. Box X, Oak Ridge, Tennessee.

overlaps the gamma-ray spectrum on both ends in the electromagnetic spectrum, the term gamma-ray spectrum is reserved for describing the radiation emitted by nuclei.

See DOSE RATE; ELECTROMAGNETIC SPECTRUM; and SPECTRUM.

GAMMA SPECTROMETER

Instrument that determines the energy spectrum of gamma radiation; used to identify nuclides present in a source of radiation by their gamma-ray emission. Also used medically or in other investigations to differentiate the localization of different radioactive materials.

See PULSE HEIGHT ANALYZER.

GAS AMPLIFICATION

When the accelerating electrical field in a gas counter is sufficiently high, the electrons that are set free in response to the passage of ionizing radiation can acquire enough energy to cause the release of additional ions upon collision with the molecules of the counting gas; this effect is called the gas amplification or the gas multiplication.

See DELTA-RAY.

GAS COUNTER

Radiation counters which can be classed as gas counters include Geiger or Geiger-Mueller counters, proportional counters, and, in rare instances, ionization chambers. In all cases the counting function of the device depends upon collection of the ionization directly developed in the detecting gas volume by the passage of the radiation, or by observing other effects associated with its passage. To illustrate the various aspects of gas counting, Figure G–7 shows the relationship between response of the detector, in terms of the electrical charge collected from the passage of a single ionizing event, as it depends upon the potential or voltage applied to the accelerating and collecting electrodes.

When the collecting voltage is increased, starting from zero, the amount of charge collected rises steadily until it reaches a level where all the ionization produced directly by the initial event is fully and completely collected. This value of the voltage where the response flattens out is called the saturation voltage; further increase of the collecting voltage serves only to collect the ionized particles more rapidly. Since the collection of each ion neutralizes the collecting voltage in part, in radiation fields of high intensity it becomes necessary to raise the voltage if saturation conditions are to be maintained. However, at higher voltages the increased speed or energy acquired by the ions during collection eventually gives them the capa-

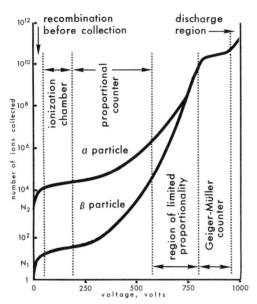

FIGURE G–7. VOLTAGE CURRENT CHARACTERISTIC CURVE FOR A GAS COUNTER.

bility of ionizing other gas atoms when they collide. This phenomenon is called gas amplification and it becomes a greater factor as the collecting voltage is further increased. At a particular voltage and for a particular type of radiation, the gas amplification factor will be a constant. In a properly designed counter, this fact can be utilized to analyze radiations on the basis of their initial energy, or in a converse way it can be used to discriminate between different kinds of radiation. The region of the characteristic curve where this relationship holds is called the proportional region; a counter operating in this region is a proportional counter. Further increase of the collecting voltage leads into a new type of response which can be enhanced by designing the accelerating electrode or collecting element to provide a zone in which a sharp rise of voltage exists. High acceleration in the zone surrounding a sharp collecting point or fine collecting wire produces a catastrophic avalanche of ions, delivering a massive electrical pulse to the collecting wire. When this occurs, the size of the pulse is not in proportion to the initiating event; this is the "Geiger" effect. The voltage at which Geiger-type counting becomes established is called the Geiger threshold; it is followed by a range or plateau over which the counting rate increases slowly. If the voltage is raised significantly beyond this range of steady increase, the rapid rise of counting rate and resultant high-ion current causes a continuous discharge to set in. If this is allowed to occur, the electrode surfaces of the counter are damaged and the counter may even be destroyed. It is to be noted that, in ordinary service over an extended life, the plateau

of a Geiger counter become shorter, until eventually stable operation can no longer be maintained.

Gas counters have been designed for many routine and special applications, by modifying the shape and arrangement of electrodes and by using special materials to enhance response to particular radiations. They have been made small enough to be used as surgical probes exploring for radioactive concentrations in the brain. Some have been filled with gases having specific response to neutrons. Others were made with walls of the heavy metal bismuth to improve response to energetic gamma rays. Still others are filled each time with a new sample of radioactive gas mixed into the counting gas itself.

See FLOW COUNTER, IONIZATION CHAMBER; PROPORTIONAL COUNTER; GEIGER COUNTER; GEIGER-MUELLER COUNTER.

GAS COUNTER, INTERNAL

A counter which is designed for radioactive gas samples mixed in with the counting gas. Both Geiger-Mueller and proportional techniques are used in this way. An important advantage accrues

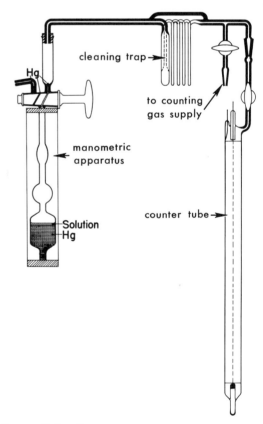

FIGURE G–8. GAS COUNTER WITH SAMPLE MIXED INTO COUNTING GAS. HERE GAS SAMPLE IS PREPARED IN MANOMETRIC APPARATUS, PASSED THROUGH CLEANING TRAP, AND MIXED WITH COUNTING GAS IN COUNTING TUBE. (COURTESY DR. DONALD VAN SLYKE.)

from the intimate mixture of sample and counting gas in that there is no absorption loss between the source of the ionizing event and the mechanism of the detector; this allows the counting of the weakest of radiations. Figure G–8 shows a counter tube developed by Van Slyke for carbon-14 studies. The gas sample can be measured directly from the manometric apparatus into the tube and appropriate gases added for either proportional or G-M counting. Similarly useful for tritium, sulfur-35, and other weak radiations.

See P-GAS and Q-GAS.

GAS FLOW COUNTER. *See* FLOW COUNTER, GAS and GAS COUNTER.

GAS MASKS. *See* RESPIRATORS.

GASEOUS WASTE

Radioactive gases or air-borne radioactive particles which emanate as waste products from air-cooled reactors, incinerators, radio-chemical hoods, glove boxes, ventilation systems, various mining, machining, and metallurgical operations, and from accidental stack releases, e.g., the Windscale incident.

Gaseous fission products from uranium-235 thermal fission are: bromine-82, -83, -84, -85; krypton-85, -87, -88, -89; iodine-129, -131, -132, -133, -134, -135; and xenon-131m, -133m, -133, -135m, -135, -137, -138. After 90 days of cooling, chemical processing of fuel elements results in the release of gases containing radioactive isotopes of krypton, xenon, and iodine; and of particles including strontium, yttrium, cesium, ruthenium, and radioactive iodides. Argon-41 is emitted from the stacks of air-cooled reactors. Carbon-14 may also be formed during reactor operations.

Radioactive aerosols and particulate matter ranging in size from 0.05 micron to 20 microns may occur in gaseous wastes, and are produced in various chemical, machining, and metallurgical operations.

Aerosols and particulates are collected by coagulation, filtration, scrubbing, and precipitation. Gases may be separated by adsorption, scrubbing, or solvent extraction. Continuous monitoring during the discharge of gaseous waste is necessary in order to guard against the possibility of environmental contamination.

See STACK DISPOSAL.

GASTROINTESTINAL BLEEDING, MEASUREMENT

Chromium-51 may be used for a sensitive and quantitative measurement of bleeding from the gastrointestinal tract. The patient is given intravenously red blood cells (his own or from a donor) that have been labeled in vitro with the isotope. Subsequently, feces are collected and assayed for radioactivity. Small amounts may be present normally, probably derived from the fraction of the isotope no longer bound to red cells, but amounts equivalent to more than 5 ml of blood per day are abnormal and indicate hemorrhage into the gastrointestinal tract.

GASTROINTESTINAL TRACT, RADIATION EFFECTS ON

The gastrointestinal syndrome is a symptom complex of anorexia, nausea, vomiting, and diarrhea seen occasionally in patients with radiation illness who have been exposed to whole body irradiation in the 200 to 400 roentgen (r) dose group, more frequently in the 400 to 600 r group, and is the predominant syndrome in the 600 to 800 r group. (*See* VOMITING DUE TO RADIATION and DIARRHEA DUE TO RADIATION.) It is also seen in x-ray therapy of abdominal malignancies.

Following cessation of mitosis the earliest gross changes in INTESTINAL DAMAGE DUE TO RADIATION are edema, degeneration, and necrosis of the mucosal epithelial cells. These early changes are responsible for the gastrointestinal symptoms of the acute radiation syndrome. Functional effects include depression of pepsin and acid secretion by the stomach, increased mucus production by the small intestine and colon, and impaired intestinal absorption. There is more physiologic than morphologic response in the salivary glands, with dryness of the mouth a common symptom.

Chronic radiation injuries appear 6 months to a year after exposure and consist of chronic mucosal ulceration, often with secondary bacterial infection. Perforation and fistula formation may occur. Traction diverticula have been noted in the esophagus following radiation.

GEIGER COUNTER

The original type was a "point" counter which utilized the highly concentrated electrical field surrounding a needle point to produce the pulse or avalanche initiated by the passage of ionizing radiation. Later modified into the more common form which is properly called GEIGER-MUELLER COUNTER. The principles of operation are discussed under GAS COUNTER.

GEIGER COUNTING

Commonly used to refer to counting of ionizing radiation events by Geiger-Mueller counter techniques; in general speech, no longer limited to strict reference to the archaic Geiger tube or Geiger point counter.

GEIGER-MUELLER COUNTER

A gas discharge pulse counter for ionizing radiation, being an improvement of the Geiger counter. It utilizes the same principle of pulse formation by ionizing rays in a strong electric field but achieves more reliable performance by using a long thin wire in place of the pointed collector electrode of the original counter. Usually the outer electrode is cylindrical in shape (see Fig. G–9), with the wire stretched along the axis to act as both accelerating and collecting electrodes. The operating curve of a good Geiger-Mueller counter is shown in Figure G–10, representing the counting rate observed from a given source in relation to the voltage applied across the tube. Characteristic features

illustrated in the graph include the starting voltage, the Geiger threshold, the plateau and its slope, and the tendency to go into continuous discharge when the applied voltage is raised too high.

In addition to the appropriate electrodes, the essential features of a G-M tube include a suitable counting gas, the characteristics of which must provide first for the pulse mechanism and then for a quenching or clearing action to terminate each individual pulse. The mechanical structure which supports the electrodes and contains the gas is sometimes contrived to provide further special applications. Thus the G-M tube appears in a wide variety of forms (see Fig. G–11). To detect beta rays, it may have a thin wall or end window. For energetic gamma rays, the shell or outer electrode is sometimes constructed of heavy elements to enhance secondary electron production, thus improving the response. For alpha particles (and very weak betas) it may be made with a completely open window, since these particles have so little penetrating power; this type provides for a continuous flow of counting gas.

Another way of counting weakly ionizing radiations is to introduce them as gases into the counting gas itself, as in the Van Slyke carbon-14 counter. The counting gas may also be modified to provide response to particular radiations, as by the addition of boron trifluoride for the counting of neutrons. The G-M tube is limited in its speed of operation; each counter has a resolving time interval while the counter registers one pulse and gets set for the next event. (Proportional and scintillation detectors are much faster.) Some of the gases which are used deteriorate in service. The electrode surfaces may also deteriorate from heavy or improper use, giving rise to spurious counts. In general, these are fragile devices.

THE GEIGER-MÜLLER COUNTER

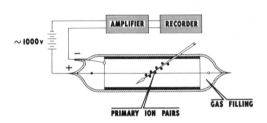

MATERIALS AND FILLING SUITABLE FOR α, β, γ, OR NEUTRONS

THIN CENTRAL WIRE GIVES HIGH FIELD FOR AVALANCHES

I OR 1,000,000 PRIMARIES GIVE SINGLE PULSE

USAEC-ID-194A

FIGURE G–9. GEIGER-MUELLER COUNTER.

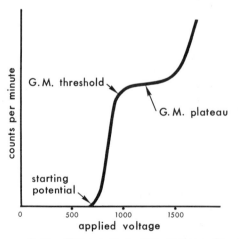

FIGURE G–10. TYPICAL CHARACTERISTIC OF A GEIGER-MUELLER COUNTER.

TYPES OF GEIGER-MÜLLER COUNTERS

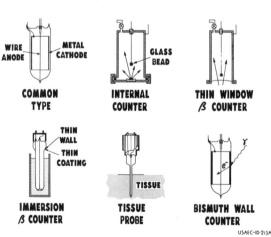

USAEC-ID-213A

FIGURE G–11. VARIOUS TYPES OF GEIGER-MUELLER COUNTERS.

GENETIC DAMAGE, RADIATION. A popular term used to indicate GENETIC EFFECTS, RADIATION.

GENETIC DEATH

A genetic death is the failure of a given gene or genotype to be transmitted to progeny because of the death or sterility of the bearer of the gene or genotype. The death or sterility may be due to a dominant or recessive mutation and its effect may occur at any stage from the zygote to the prereproductive age. In a broader sense, the term also includes the failure to survive and reproduce due to the genetic makeup even though other organisms of the same makeup survive and reproduce. That is, an organism with a given mutant gene may have a 90% chance of surviving and reproducing; the 10% that fail to do so undergo genetic deaths.

GENETIC DOSE

This term refers to irradiation that affects embryos (see FETUS, RADIATION EFFECTS), GONADS, or germ cells in such a manner that individuals that have not yet been conceived might have an altered genetic constitution. The genetic dose for an individual may come from: natural radiation, environmental radiation, medical exposure, and fallout. The genetic dose to an individual begins at the time of that individual's conception and ceases with the end of his reproductive period. During developmental stages of life, all irradiation of the gonads contributes to the genetic dose in direct proportion to its intensity times its relative biological effectiveness, but after the onset of the reproductive period additional radiation contributes to genetic dose only in relation to the proportion of the individual's children who have not yet been conceived.

Only a small proportion of the genetic dose received by an individual can result in effects that are limited to that individual's children. These are changes that result in dominant lethality or dominant sterility. Almost all the genetic dose will be distributed among the descendants of the individual down to an infinite number of generations, but in such a manner that the greatest effect will be, on the average, in the first generation, and slightly lesser effects will occur in each subsequent generation. Thus, the genetic dose for an individual is diluted, in time, throughout the whole population, and so the important concept for the community is the average genetic dose, i.e., the average of the genetic dose for all of the individuals in a given population. Use of this concept has resulted in a general acceptance of the principle that some individuals in a population might receive relatively large genetic doses, provided that the proportion of such persons is not large so that the average genetic dose remains small. Methods for keeping genetic doses small include gonadal shielding and the employment of older persons in tasks that might result in gonadal exposure. A general failure to recognize the problem of genetic dose has resulted in extremely limited acceptance of these measures.

Taking into consideration the necessary compromise between deleterious effects and social benefits, the International Commission on Radiological Protection suggested that the genetic dose to the whole population from all sources except natural radiation and the essential diagnostic use of the x-ray should not exceed 5 rem for the reproductive lifetime.

See POPULATIONS, RADIATION EFFECTS ON.

GENETIC EFFECTS, RADIATION

Various types of radiation (alpha, beta, gamma, x-ray, neutron, and ultraviolet light) can produce mutations (see MUTATION, RADIATION INDUCED) in the genes of living cells. The effect has been found in all animals and plants where controlled experiments have been performed. The nature of the gene change or mutation is the conversion of an existing gene to a new stable state, endowed with the ability to produce different effects on the descendants.

The rate of induction of mutations in spermatozoa in mice, flies, and other organisms increases linearly (see LINEARITY) with increasing doses of radiation, at least for doses of 25 roentgens (r) or more which have been investigated. The number of mutations is considered to increase in direct proportion to the genetically significant radiation exposure, even at low levels; and the damage is considered to be cumulative. There does not appear to be a threshold dose of radiation such that doses below it will not induce mutations. However, the observable mutation rate of spermatogonia and oöcytes appears to depend upon the radiation dose rate, chronic irradiation producing fewer mutations than the same amount of acute irradiation.

There are large differences between species in the induced mutation rates, based upon experimental studies using quite large doses of radiation. For example, the rate is about 1.5×10^{-8} per roentgen per locus for fruit-fly spermatogonia and about 21.3×10^{-8} per roentgen per locus for mouse spermatogonia exposed to acute radiation. There are probably also large differences between loci of a single species, in both natural and induced mutation rates.

A doubling of the natural rate of human mutations probably would occur with an additional dose of 10 to 80 roentgens per generation. Some authorities believe that this could be tolerated, but since most facts point to the danger of radiation exposure, such exposure should be reduced whenever and wherever possible; medical and industrial procedures that increase radiation exposure to large human populations should be carefully weighed, taking into consideration such benefits or hazards as each may have.

There are a number of complicating factors in trying to assess the damage to a population from a given amount of radiation exposure. In the first place, among 4 or 5 children with measurable defects out of each hundred live births, one or two are probably the result of intra-uterine trauma. Of the mutations some are due to causes other than radiation and of those due to radiation, some are due to natural radiation.

The technique for detecting the genetic effects of radiation consists of comparing the incidence of mutations in descendants of irradiated individuals with the incidence among the descendants of those not irradiated. If the incidence is higher in the treated group, the radiation is said to have induced some mutations. It cannot always be known with certainty which specific mutation was induced by the experimental radiation and which was "natural."

In considering genetic effects it is imperative that consideration be given to natural selection as a factor in the continual transmission of a given mutated trait.

GEOLOGICAL SURVEY, U.S.

The U.S. Geological Survey, an agency of the U.S. Department of the Interior, works closely with the USAEC in survey work on radioactive waste disposal to the environment; in domestic uranium exploration, especially in aerial prospecting; and in determining environmental contamination from radioactive fallout by aerial monitoring.

GEOMETRY, RADIATION

A nuclear physics term referring to the physical relationship and symmetry of the parts of a radiation detection assembly. A term used commonly in instrumentation for counting and scanning. Counting efficiency is closely related to geometry. The term is often used to indicate the percentage of rays leaving a sample which reach the sensitive volume of the counter; thus a gas sample contained within a counter would have 100% geometry, whereas a solid sample in the usual internal counter arrangement might approximate 50% geometry.

The radiation geometry factor is the average solid angle at the source subtended by the aperture or sensitive volume of the detector, divided by the complete solid angle (4π).

Good geometry refers to an arrangement of radiation source and detecting equipment such that the use of finite source size and finite detector aperture introduces little error.

Poor geometry is an arrangement such that the angular aperture between the source and detector is large, thus introducing into the measurement of the energy of the particle a comparatively large uncertainty for which a correction may have to be made. Poor geometry may be deliberately used: for example, to give a distinction between scattering and absorption.

By assuming that tissues, organs, and bodies have symmetrical forms and can be represented by geometrical models such as spheres and cylinders, it is possible to calculate geometrical factors (g factors) useful in predicting radiation intensity at a given point. Closely related is the use of a phantom for determining the depth dose likely to result from a given type of radiation. Another form of geometry is the development of isodose curves to indicate the depth dose distribution of radiation. The standard man radiation equivalent manikin also takes geometry into consideration.

GEOMETRY, SAMPLE

The space relationship between radioactive sample and detector or counter, defining the solid angle available for collection. Sample geometry is said to be "four-pi" (4π) when the sample is completely surrounded by counting space. When the counter can collect all radiation emanating from one side of a plane sample, the geometry is "two-pi" (2π). Smaller geometries are sometimes expressed in percentage of the total sphere instead of in solid angular measure. Effective counting geometry can be established by comparing actual measurement with the theoretical or absolute activity of a known sample or standard.

See COUNTING EFFICIENCY.

GERMANIUM

Symbol Ge; atomic number 32; atomic weight 72.60. A silver-white, lustrous, hard, brittle metal. Discovered by Winkler in 1886. Named from Latin, *Germania*, Germany. Predicted by Mendelyeev in 1871 as an element with properties resembling silicon. Found in several sulfide ores and in coal ash. Natural abundance furnished by 5 stable isotopes. Most important commercial use is in the manufacture of germanium diodes and transistors. Carefully studied and found to be non-toxic. There are 15 radioactive isotopes, 13 of which may be produced as fission products in the detonation of a nuclear device. None have significance in radioactive fallout.

GLASS DOSIMETER

Miniature rod or plate of activated glass which responds quantitatively to ionizing radiation, either in its ability to fluoresce under ultraviolet (FLUOR) or thermal (thermoluminescent) stimulation or by an increase in optical density.

GLOVE BOX

An enclosed laboratory bench or work space for carrying out manipulations under controlled conditions. A major purpose of such equipment is to maintain radiological safety, or to keep all moisture away from materials which must be stored or handled in the dry state.

The principal physical features of the glove box or DRY BOX as seen in Figure G–12, include a transparent panel for observing the work, built-in gloves with long sleeves installed in appropriate front-panel space, and interlocked doors through which materials and tools are admitted or removed. The box is generally fitted with laboratory facilities such as electric outlets, gas and air lines, and mechanical handling devices.

FIGURE G–12. GLOVE BOX. NOTE REMOTE HANDLING TOOLS, GLOVE APERTURES (CLOSED) AT EACH SIDE OF OBSERVING WINDOW, ACCESS DOOR AT RIGHT END, VENTILATING AND CONTROL EQUIPMENT AT TOP. WITH APPROPRIATE CONTROL OF ATMOSPHERE, USED ALSO AS DRY BOX. (COURTESY OF ALLIED ENGINEERING & PRODUCTION CORP.)

GLUTATHIONE

A tripeptide, γ-L-glutamyl-cysteinylglycine, with a free sulfydryl group used in CHEMICAL PROTECTION AGAINST RADIATION INJURY. It has the formula:

$$HO_2C \cdot CH \cdot CH_2 \cdot CH_2 \cdot \overset{\overset{\textstyle O}{\|}}{C} \cdot NH \cdot CH \cdot \overset{\overset{\textstyle O}{\|}}{C} \cdot NH \cdot CH_2 \cdot CO_2H$$

$$\underset{NH_2}{|} \qquad\qquad \underset{CH_2 \cdot SH}{|}$$

G-M COUNTER, G-M TUBE

Common terms for GEIGER-MUELLER instruments.

GOLD

Symbol Au; atomic number 79; atomic weight 197.0. A metallic element which occurs mainly as the free metal. Widely distributed in nature, principally in rock or alluvial deposits but not in living material. Extensively used in the arts and in coinage. Also used in dentistry and has some medical significance.

Although gold is relatively non-toxic, effects have occurred from intraperitoneal administration of 23 to 50 mg/kg of gold as the chloride.

The stable isotope Au^{197} accounts for 100% of the naturally occurring abundance. There are 17 radioactive isotopes of which Au^{198} has the chief medical significance.

Following nuclear detonations associated with the sea two nuclides of gold may be produced: Au^{198} and Au^{196} The amounts would be insignificant, since the percentage by weight of natural Au in sea water is only 4×10^{-10}.

Gold-198 $(_{79}Au^{198})$. A short-lived beta $^-(\beta^-)$ and gamma $^-(\gamma)$ emitting radioisotope of gold usually formed from gold-197 by the neutron-gamma (n,γ) reaction. Its decay half-life is 2.7 days; with total body as the critical organ, biological half-life 120 days, effective half-life 2.6 days.

Gold-198 with an activation index of 9,500 heads the list of nuclides having practical therapeutic potentialities. Radiogold is used in medical research and frequently in the treatment of disease, particularly cancer. Radioactive gold needles and beads are placed in the tissues (INTERSTITIAL IMPLANTS) in order to irradiate a specific area. Colloidal radiogold is also placed in such areas as the abdominal or thoracic cavity where it irradiates the cavity lining and by destroying cellular material acts to reduce or prevent the fluid formation which is so distressing to cancer patients. Commercially produced Aurcoloid is a sterile radiogold colloid that provides 30 to 50 mc/ml

(γ) Au[198] with a specific activity of 4 to 5 mc/mg Au.

Maximum permissible concentration for a 40-hour work week for a soluble compound with the gastrointestinal tract as the critical organ is 2×10^{-3} microcuries per cubic centimeter ($\mu c/cc$) in water and 3×10^{-7} $\mu c/cc$ in air; for a 168-hour week · (continuous exposure) 5×10^{-4} $\mu c/cc$ in water and 10^{-7} in air.

GOLD-LEAF ELECTROSCOPE

A simple device of historical interest in early studies on static electricity; directly useful for investigating phenomena associated with ionizing radiation. The deflection of the gold leaf away from its supporting electrode, shown in Figure G–13, is extremely sensitive to small changes of

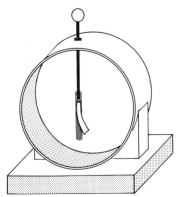

FIGURE G–13.   GOLD LEAF ELECTROSCOPE.

the electrical charge on it. Ionization produced by radiation passing through the air neutralizes some or all of the charge, the consequent leaf movement measuring the effect.

GONADS, RADIATION EFFECTS ON

The gonads, i.e., the ovaries in the female and the testes in the male, are radiosensitive. The ovaries, in all experimental animals and in the human, are highly sensitive to radiation, with the ova and their precursor oöcytes being particularly radiosensitive. Temporary sterility may be induced in female mammals by doses less than 200 roentgens (r), and permanent sterility by doses exceeding 300 r. In insects, complete sterility may be induced by doses less than 1,000 r. Genetic anomalies induced by ovarian irradiation are directly comparable in kind to those induced in the testes, and either the ova or the sperm can transmit the altered genetic material which may result in a mutation. Mutations and aberrations of the haploid chromosome system result from irradiation of ova in all animals. Since the ova and precursor follicular cells are highly radiosensitive, irradia-

tion leads to either temporary or permanent sterility, depending on the dose. Radiation sufficient to prevent development of the primary follicles causes complete sterility, since oöcytes once destroyed are not replaced.

The testes in mammals are visibly damaged by radiation exceeding 300 r. Irradiated male mice show normal fertility in an initial period of 3 or 4 weeks. The fertile period is followed by one of sterility, the duration of which varies with the radiation dosage; spermatogonia and spermatocytes disappear from the testes, whose tubules become thin and empty. A third period begins 6 to 8 weeks after irradiation, characterized by the regeneration of spermatogonia from the primordia in the lining of the tubules. Spermatogenesis is resumed, and the renewed fertility continues until the death of the animal. After dosages exceeding 1,000 r, the sterility is usually permanent and no regeneration occurs. The production of androgen is not diminished at any time.

In the short-lived insects (represented by Drosophila and Habrobracon) structural modification or damage in the testes is not known, presumably because the time required for degeneration and regeneration exceeds the remaining part of the life span of the animals. Irradiation of larvae, whose testes are in the imaginal disc stage, may result in permanent degeneration and sterility, although normally functioning adult testes are usually formed. Mutations, as well as complex chromosome aberrations involving more than a single strand for each of the involved chromosomes, indicate that genetic modifications occur in diploid spermatogonial cells and primary spermatocytes as well as in haploid mature sperm. Diploid cells of the insect testes are not known to survive radiation exceeding 2,000 r, while mature sperm survive and are functional after doses exceeding 10,000 r.

Although spermatogenesis is usually blocked, and may be permanently stopped, by irradiation, in insects the minimum dose at which this occurs is not known. In mammals, represented by the mouse, x-ray dosages in excess of 300 r are known to interrupt spermatogenesis temporarily and there is some evidence to indicate that 50 r is approximately the minimum dose at which this occurs.

In all organisms, spermatogonia are most sensitive to radiation. Spermatocytes, spermatids, and spermatozoa are highly resistant. In the mouse, irradiated spermatogonia fail to transform into spermatocytes and rapidly degenerate until no gonial cells are detectable in histological preparations. At doses exceeding 1,000 r of x-rays permanent sterility may remain and no gonial regeneration occurs. At doses below 1,000 r gonial regeneration is completed 6 to 8 weeks after irradiation, followed by regular spermatogenesis and nearly normal fertility. Irradiated spermatocytes and spermatids complete their meiotic and spermioteleotic processes to form functional spermatozoa. Irradiated spermatozoa may appear to be unharmed, except for nuclear aberrations, and show regular motility and fertilization capacities.

Aside from the changes in genes and chromosomes of sperm exposed to radiation, the principal effects of high doses of irradiation on sperm are loss of motility, increased incidence of abnormalities (coiled tails, head and tail separations), and death. The effect varies with the intensity and duration of the radiation. In dogs, for example, 3.0 r/wk of x-rays may reduce the sperm count to less than 10% of normal after 50 weeks of irradiation.

In mammals, testicular regeneration after irradiation may progress to completion, with the formation of functional spermatozoa. Regeneration may also result in testes in which only a sharply delimited partial return to normal function is evident; for example, spermatids may be produced, but no spermatozoa; spermatozoa may be found, but fail to become motile; or spermatozoa may be found, only a fraction of which become motile.

Gene mutations and chromosome aberrations may be produced in any irradiated cells of the testis, regardless of their nature or their state at the time of irradiation. Most of the regularly recovered genetic changes are those that occur in spermatozoa that are mature and present in vast quantities at the time of irradiation. Genetic changes in other cells are recovered and detected only with the use of specialized techniques and proper timing of the procedures.

In Drosophila, crossing over is normally limited to females; it is readily induced in males by irradiation.

GRAM ATOMIC WEIGHT

Or gram atom. The mass in grams numerically equal to the atomic weight.

GRAM-RAD

A unit of integral absorbed dose, equal to 100 ergs.

See RAD.

GRAM-ROENTGEN

A unit of integral dose; the real energy conversion when a dose of one roentgen is delivered to one gram of air (about 84 ergs). The unit is employed, however, to describe total energy absorption by the patient in the course of therapy. The quantity obtained by integrating gram-roentgens throughout a region is called the integral dose (see DOSE). Thus, the integral dose, measured in gram-roentgens, resulting from irradiation of a patient with 1 roentgen of x-rays, will vary with the quality of the radiation, the size of the fields, and the thickness of the part.

GROUND STATE

Condition of lowest energy of a nucleus, an atom, or a molecule; the stable state. Other states are termed excited states.

See ISOMERIC TRANSITION.

GROUND ZERO

Abbreviation GZ; the point on the earth's surface immediately below (or above) the point of detonation of a nuclear device. Ground zero is sometimes called the hypocenter of the explosion.

For a burst over (or under) water, the point is generally called surface zero.

Zero point is defined as the location of the center of a burst at the instant of detonation, whether it be in the air, on the surface, or beneath the surface of the ground or water, thus differing from ground zero and surface zero. In the case of a contact surface burst (see SURFACE BURST) ground zero and zero point are one and the same.

The term air zero is used to designate the point in space at which a detonation occurs; it is thus a measurement of the height of burst above the earth's surface.

GROWTH CHAMBER. *See* ISOTOPE FARM.

GUN-TYPE WEAPON. *See* CRITICAL MASS.

H

HAFNIUM

Symbol Hf; atomic number 72; atomic weight 178.50. Most of the zirconium metals contain small amounts (usually 0.5 to 3%) of hafnium; alvite contains about 20%. Discovered in 1922 by Coster and Hevesy in the mineral zircon of Norway. Named for Hafnia, Copenhagen. Its natural abundance is furnished by 6 stable isotopes and there are 9 radioactive isotopes. Hafnium-181 (Hf[181], half-life 46 days, β^- and γ emitter) is available commercially. Hafnium is chemically and apparently physiologically quite similar to zirconium. No biological, medical, or agricultural uses have been identified.

HALF-LIFE, BIOLOGICAL. *See* BIOLOGICAL HALF-LIFE.

HALF-LIFE, EFFECTIVE. *See* EFFECTIVE HALF-LIFE.

HALF-LIFE, RADIOACTIVE. *See* RADIOACTIVE HALF-LIFE.

HALF-THICKNESS

Also known as half-value layer. The thickness of any given absorber that will reduce the intensity of a beam of radiation to one-half its initial value. It may be expressed in units of length or of mass per unit area. The initial intensity is successively weakened with each layer of absorber (3 centimeters of lead reduce incident intensity of 1 Mev gamma rays by a factor of 10; another 3 cm by another factor of 10 or to 0.01). Since absorption is exponential, some fraction, however weak, is transmitted by the last layer. Thus for practical problems such as quick shielding estimates some value such as half-thickness is both useful and necessary.

Engineering texts should be consulted for tables and graphs necessary to calculate gamma shielding requirements, but as an example Table H–1 listing half-thickness values in centimeters for gamma radiation is included here.

TABLE H–1. HALF-THICKNESS FOR GAMMA RAYS

ENERGY (Mev)	CENTIMETERS			
	Water	Concrete	Steel	Lead
0.5	7.37	3.81	1.09	.41
0.6	8.13	4.06	1.17	.48
0.8	9.14	4.57	1.35	.69
1.0	10.16	5.08	1.52	.89
1.2	11.18	5.59	1.67	1.04
1.4	11.94	6.10	1.83	1.17
1.6	12.70	6.60	1.96	1.27
1.8	13.46	7.11	2.13	1.37
2.0	14.22	7.62	2.26	1.45
2.2	14.99	7.87	2.41	1.52
2.4	15.75	8.13	2.51	1.55
2.6	16.51	8.64	2.54	1.57
2.8	17.02	8.89	2.79	1.60
3.0	17.78	9.14	2.79	1.60

Table H–2 lists the half-thickness for the most energetic of the gamma emissions for 10 radioactive isotopes in frequent use in medical activity.

TABLE H–2. HALF-THICKNESS FOR MEDICAL RADIOISOTOPES

ELEMENT	RADIO-ISO-TOPE	ENERGY (Mev)	HALF-THICKNESS (cm)	
			Water	Lead
Sodium	$_{11}Na^{22}$	1.277	11.0	1.07
Sodium	$_{11}Na^{24}$	3.85	20.2	1.48
Potassium	$_{19}K^{42}$	1.53	12.1	1.21
Chromium	$_{24}Cr^{51}$	0.321	0.60	0.20
Iron	$_{26}Fe^{59}$	1.29	11.1	1.09
Cobalt	$_{27}Co^{60}$	1.332	11.3	1.11
Zinc	$_{30}Zn^{65}$	1.114	10.3	0.98
Rubidium	$_{37}Rb^{86}$	1.078	10.2	0.96
Iodine	$_{53}I^{131}$	0.724	8.4	0.67
Gold	$_{79}Au^{198}$	1.089	10.2	0.97

If the absorption is exponential, the half-thickness $(d_{\frac{1}{2}})$ is related to the appropriate (linear or mass) absorption coefficient (μ) as follows:

$$d_{\frac{1}{2}} = \frac{\int n\ 2}{\mu} = \frac{0.693}{\mu} = 0.693 \int$$

where $\int$ is the mean free path.

HALF-VALUE LAYER

In radiology, the thickness of any particular material necessary to reduce the dose rate of an x-ray beam to one-half its original value.

See HALF-THICKNESS and RANGE.

HALOGENS

Member elements of the closely related chemical family of group VIIA of the periodic table: fluorine, chlorine, bromine, iodine, and astatine. Salt-like compounds are formed with sodium, i.e., haloid salts: sodium bromide (NaBr); sodium chloride (NaCl); sodium fluoride (NaF); and sodium iodide (NaI). These elements lack just one electron to make a closed outer shell.

HAND AND FOOT COUNTERS

Monitoring device arranged to give rapid radiation survey of hands and feet of personnel working with radioactive materials, to detect radioactive contamination. Typical installation, as in Figure H–1, is situated at passageway from working area into decontamination or dressing rooms.

FIGURE H-1. HAND AND FOOT COUNTER, A STANDARD PIECE OF HEALTH MONITORING EQUIPMENT. (COURTESY BROOKHAVEN NATIONAL LABORATORY.)

HANDBOOKS.
See NATIONAL BUREAU OF STANDARDS HANDBOOKS.

HANDLING TECHNIQUES

Since direct contact with radioactive material is hazardous, various techniques with associated equipment have been developed for the safe handling of radioisotopes and radioactive materials. As the level of radiation and/or the need for contamination control increases, the need for radiation protection also increases and handling becomes more difficult, the techniques more complex, and the equipment more expensive.

Increasing the distance is one method of reducing the dose rate, for the intensity from a given source of radiation per unit of time is reduced as the square of the distance. Tongs, forceps, remote-control unit-process equipment (pipettes, liquid samplers, etc.), and remote-control equipment (clamping, threading, magnetic handling, pneumatic, and electromechanical devices) serve to provide distance from the source.

Shielding provided by all types of shields from the lead-impregnated rubber gloves and apron of the radiologist to the 5-foot-thick concrete shield wall of the hot cell serves to provide the essential radiation protection.

However, even with the most elaborate equipment the hazard of overexposure depends largely upon the development of and adherence to prescribed safe operating rules and procedures. Short cuts must be avoided. Training, dummy runs, trial procedures with low-activity sources, and use of monitors are important if excessive irradiation is to be avoided.

HANFORD WORKS

A USAEC-supported plutonium production and research facility located on the Columbia River at Hanford, Washington; operated by the General Electric Company (Hanford Atomic Products Operation, HAPO). The Hanford Works was established by the wartime Manhattan Engineer District.

The Biology Operation is one of the research components of the Hanford Laboratories, in which about 1,400 scientists and supporting personnel are employed. Hanford's Biology program, which engages about 100 people, is oriented toward supplying biological information needed for the improvement of radiation protection practices and toward contributing to the basic understanding of the effects of radiation. Chief emphasis is placed on studies of the metabolism and toxicity of internal emitters in plants and animals.

One of the early investigations at Hanford was concerned with the toxicity to sheep of daily ingested iodine-131. This experiment, started in 1950 and, on a reduced scale, still continuing, constitutes the most extensive study in which an internal emitter has been fed daily to large animals over several generations in order to establish a safe level of daily ingestion.

Because of its physiological similarity to humans, the miniature pig is being employed in a number of current studies, including extensions of the I^{131} study and a major study of the toxicity of daily ingested strontium-90.

A large, pure-bred beagle colony is employed in inhalation research designed to define the toxicity of inhaled plutonium oxide and other radioactive particles, to devise means for estimating body burdens of inhaled radioactive particles, to determine the effect of particle size on pulmonary deposition, and to find ways to hasten clearance of radioactive materials from the lungs (see INHALATION OF RADIOACTIVE MATERIAL and LUNG CLEARANCE).

Other internal emitter work, mostly employing small animals, has been concerned with the measurement of metabolic parameters required in the establishment of permissible limits (see MAXIMUM PERMISSIBLE CONCENTRATION) for plutonium, ruthenium, tritium, cesium, zinc, and several other radionuclides. Special emphasis has been placed on the study of the effect of unabsorbed radionuclide irradiation of the gastrointestinal tract, and on methods for removing internally deposited radionuclides.

In the field of plant nutrition, studies have been made of radionuclide uptake from the soil and of methods for influencing this uptake. In both plant and animal studies emphasis has been placed on the interrelationships of pairs of similar elements, notably calcium to strontium and cesium to potassium.

Fish are used as "monitors" to insure the safety of reactor effluent water and as test organisms in the study of basic radiation effects. In the field of radioecology, studies are made of the effects of radiation on aquatic and terrestrial populations and of the transfer of radionuclides among members of ecological communities. Research at the cellular level includes studies looking toward the development of new radiation protective agents, and studies of the effect of radiation on membrane permeability and on the blood-forming organs.

H-BOMB

Abbreviation for hydrogen bomb. See THERMONUCLEAR WEAPON.

HEALTH AND SAFETY LABORATORY

HASL, located at 376 Hudson St., New York,

New York, is operated directly by the Atomic Energy Commission, responsible administratively to the Manager of the New York Operations Office (NYOO), and for direction of its scientific program to the Director of the Division of Biology and Medicine (DBM) in the USAEC Washington Headquarters.

Historically, a Medical Division was established in the NYOO in 1947 to deal with various contractor problems in industrial hygiene and industrial medicine. Two of the early studies dealt with toxicity and improved safety controls necessary in handling beryllium and uranium. As the interest, competence, and activity of the staff became more diverse the name was changed in 1949 to the Health and Safety Division and the group increasingly worked with industrial laboratories to aid in maintaining adequate control of air-borne dusts, direct radiation hazards, and fire and safety.

In 1953 the name was changed to the Health and Safety Laboratory and it came under the DBM for scientific direction. At present there is a staff of about 100 persons organized with an Administrative Branch, a Statistical Branch, and 4 Divisions: Analytical, Health Protection Engineering, Instrumentation, and Radiation Physics. The Analytical Division analyzes environmental and biological samples to assist in the definition of hazards within mining, milling, and production facilities for uranium, beryllium, thorium, radium, radon, and other materials. This division also conducts an extensive analytical program for the determination of the levels of strontium-90 and other radionuclides occurring in samples of soil, vegetation, milk, animal and human bones, water, and air as a result of contamination from radioactive fallout. The Health Protection Engineering Division actively assists in the design and selection of fire protection, industrial safety, and health protection systems and equipment for USAEC contractors, using or processing radioactive, toxic, or otherwise hazardous materials. They also perform operational surveys to assure satisfactory hazard control. The Instrument Division has been in the forefront in designing, developing, and constructing radiation detection and measuring instruments. The Radiation Physics Division carries out analytical and experimental evaluations of all types of problems relating to radiation safety, and also undertakes fundamental studies in the areas of radiation dosimetry.

HASL has been active in education and training for both United States and foreign scientists.

HEALTH PHYSICS

The profession or science of radiation protection in all its aspects, centered principally in technology, but also including philosophy, teaching, organization, and administration. The term has come to mean not only radiation protection, but also radiation hygiene and radiation control and safety. Some of the areas of concern to health physics are: (1) development of the principles of radiation protection; (2) application of these principles to practical situations, e.g., conducting radiation surveys, setting up and operating monitoring programs, developing specifications for adequate shielding, overseeing waste disposal, and assisting in setting up potentially hazardous experiments; (3) devising techniques of dosimetry and setting up methods of handling the problems of safe dosage; (4) helping in setting up and operating adequate training programs; and (5) developing and administering an adequate radiological safety program for proper safe handling of radioactive material. In short, the purpose of health physics is to insure the protection of personnel who either are ignorant of the hazards of radiation or are too preoccupied with other duties to pay attention to them.

The USAEC offers fellowships in health physics and in advanced health physics. The practitioners are called health physicists.

See EDUCATION AND TRAINING, USAEC; INDUSTRIAL HYGIENE; INDUSTRIAL MEDICINE; OCCUPATIONAL MEDICINE; RADIOLOGICAL HEALTH; and RADIOLOGICAL PHYSICS.

HEART, RADIATION EFFECTS ON

The heart is relatively radioresistant, although late in the course of fatal radiation illness the cardiac muscle is often spotted with hemorrhages of various sizes. In a rapidly developing fatal case in man (*see* the case of K in CRITICALITY ACCIDENTS) there were numerous petechial hemorrhages and small ecchymotic areas in the pericardium and in the heart muscle. Microscopic examination showed severe edema and beginning degeneration of the muscle fibers. The cellular exudate between the muscle fibers indicated a true interstitial myocarditis.

HEART STUDIES

Up to the present, heart studies have been chiefly indirect, having to do with the movement of blood through the organ. Investigations bearing directly on the condition of the heart muscle are at a preliminary stage and are not clinically practical.

The size of the blood pool within the heart can be shown by giving intravenously a dose of 300 to 400 microcuries of serum albumin labeled with radioiodine. A scan made over the heart region any time within the first few hours after the radioiso-

tope is given will show an area of increased activity due to the blood pool. This technique will usually distinguish between an enlarged heart and a collection of fluid around the heart in the pericardial sac. These two conditions are both associated with an apparent large heart shadow on routine chest x-ray. With the radioisotopic study, if the heart is truly enlarged, the blood it contains will give a large image in the scan record, while if there is a pericardial effusion the scan will usually show an image of small or normal size.

This same procedure will also show the presence of a large blood pool in an aneurysm or abnormal enlargement of the aorta, the great artery that leaves the heart. A solid tumor in the mid-chest region that might give a similar appearance on x-ray will not yield a positive scan record.

In congenital abnormalities of the heart, radioisotopic methods can serve to show abnormal passages (or shunts) between the chambers of the heart. Normally the blood enters the right side of the heart, is pumped through the lungs (pulmonary circulation), returns to the left side of the heart, and is pumped out to the rest of the body (systemic circulation). If there is a shunt allowing blood to go directly from the right to the left side of the heart, a tracer such as radioiodine-labeled albumin will appear with abnormal rapidity in the systemic arteries, since some of it bypasses the lungs. A dose in the neighborhood of 25 to 100 microcuries is adequate for such studies and the measurements can be made over the two sides of the heart, over peripheral arteries, or on blood drawn rapidly from appropriate sites. Another technique for diagnosing such a shunt is to inject intravenously a solution of the radioactive gas krypton-85. Virtually all of this gas leaves the blood on its first passage through the lungs, but if some of the blood is reaching the left side of the heart without traversing them, an abnormally large amount of the Kr[85] will appear in the systemic arterial blood.

The demonstration of shunts in the opposite direction, flowing from the left to the right side of the heart, is somewhat more complicated and usually requires the introduction, by way of major vessels, of tubes directly into the chambers of the heart for the collection of blood samples. One technique requires the patient to inhale the radioactive gas Kr[85] (in air containing 0.1 to 0.4 millicurie per liter); the concentration of the gas is measured in samples drawn quickly from the heart. Since the gas is absorbed in the pulmonary circulation the concentration in the right side of the heart is very low (during the early period before recirculation). In the presence of a shunt from left to right the early concentration in blood from the right side is abnormally high; the extent of the shunt can even be quantitated on the basis of this level.

In a very different study, an effort has been made to determine the blood flow in the arteries that carry blood to the heart muscle, the coronary vessels. A dose of radioiodine-labeled human serum albumin is injected rapidly intravenously while a detector is in place over the region of the heart. A recording system that is rapidly responsive to changes in radioactivity levels shows a sharp rise with the first entrance of the labeled material into the heart. As the radioactive material leaves the heart, on the downward phase of the activity curve, a small secondary rise is noted; this is believed due to the radioisotope in the coronary vessels. The size of this peak may be related to the caliber of the vessels. This test would be of great practical value if it could be shown to be a reliable test for coronary circulation.

See CARDIAC DISEASE, TREATMENT; CARDIAC OUTPUT MEASUREMENT; and CIRCULATION TIME MEASUREMENT.

HEAVY WATER

Popular name for deuterium oxide (D_2O). Water (H_2O) in which the hydrogen of the water molecule consists of heavy hydrogen of mass 2. Heavy water has a density of 1.108 gram per cubic centimeter (g/cc) compared to 1.000 g/cc for ordinary water. Heavy water freezes at $3.82°$ C and boils at $101.42°$ C, compared to $0°$ C and $100°$ C for ordinary water. Density 1.1076 at $20°$ C.

Used as a moderator in certain types of nuclear reactors. Has been used in biological and medical research with such diversified findings as the following: depresses ascites tumor growth in mice; adversely affects growth of tissue culture cells; adversely affects the growth of mice fed 25% D_2O for 3 weeks; changes bacteriophage replication; causes polio virus in D_2O media to multiply at higher temperature; and deuterated green algae have been shown to be useful in photosynthesis studies.

HEIGHT OF BURST

The altitude of the point of burst of a nuclear weapon measured directly to the surface beneath. The height or distance above the earth at which a nuclear weapon is detonated is intimately related to all weapon effects: blast, thermal radiation, and nuclear radiation. For example, the 2 factors determining the extent of the blast physical damage and the blast biological damage, at a given distance from ground zero, are the energy yield and the height of burst. Fallout will be far less if

the height of burst is such that no large amounts of dirt or water are sucked up to become part of the radioactive cloud. The amount of thermal radiation falling on an object, other factors being equal, varies inversely as the square of the distance from the explosion, so the greater the height of burst, the less thermal energy is received. Initial nuclear radiation is affected by height of burst in the same manner as thermal radiation.

The scaled height of burst for blast effects, for a particular detonation, is the height of burst which compares with the height of burst for a 1-kiloton weapon. It is usually expressed as some function of the yield, and is determined by dividing the actual height of burst by the appropriate function of the yield:

$$\text{Scaled height of burst} = \frac{\text{Actual height of burst}}{W^{\frac{1}{3}}},$$

where W is the yield expressed in kilotons.

HELIUM

Symbol He; atomic number 2; atomic weight 4.003. A colorless, odorless gas. Named from Greek *helios*, sun, because it was first found in 1868 by the English astronomers Lockyer and Frankland in the gas surrounding the sun. In 1895 discovered by the Scottish chemist Ramsey in mineral clevite. Also occurs in some natural gases. Four wells in Texas have produced 55 million cubic feet of helium. Two stable isotopes, He^3 and He^4, account for its natural abundance, with He^4 furnishing almost 100%.

Used because of its lightness and therefore lifting power for inflating airships and balloons and as a replacement for nitrogen in the gas mixture for deep-sea divers. Also used in nucleonics and rocket research. Density 0.1785 gram per liter compared to hydrogen, 0.0899 (inflammable); oxygen 1.42904; and argon 1.784.

No biological, medical, or agricultural usefulness. Only one radioactive isotope, He^6 (half-life 0.82 second, β^- emitter).

HEMANGIOMAS, TREATMENT

Hemangiomas are benign tumors made up largely of blood vessels. They may occur in deep tissues and in bone but are most commonly found in the skin. There are several different types including those that are commonly called birthmarks. Some hemangiomas fade or disappear spontaneously with the passage of time. If treatment is needed, careful use of radiation is sometimes advisable and this may be given by use of radioisotopes. For very superficial hemangiomas phosphorus-32 or strontium-90 surface applications are made. For deeper ones, x-ray therapy, radium, or radon implants can be used. The radiation doses required are usually much less than those used for malignant tumors.

HEMATOLOGY

Although strictly speaking "that branch of biology which treats of the morphology of the blood and blood-forming tissues," the word hematology is usually used to indicate the laboratory tests involving blood chemistry, blood cell, and bone marrow cell studies. In studying the acute radiation syndrome, or in diagnosing radiation illness, hospital routine hematology includes: total red blood cell count; platelet count; hemoglobin and hematocrit determinations: white blood cell total count; differential counts for total lymphocytes and total neutrophils; bone marrow cell studies; thymidine uptake; mitotic indices; and sodium-24 content of the blood if activation by neutron bombardment of the normal blood sodium-23 is suspected.

See BLOOD COUNT, RADIATION EFFECTS ON.

HEMATOPOIETIC SYSTEM, RADIATION EFFECTS ON

The body organs and structures, such as bone marrow, spleen, and lymph nodes, which produce blood cells are radiosensitive, showing evidence of damage from exposure to 50 to 100 roentgens (r). This radiosensitivity of the myeloid and lymphoid tissues may be demonstrated within a few hours by the effect on circulating white blood cells. The rate of disappearance of cells from the circulation is a function of the natural survival of the cell, the individual radiosensitivity, and the damage to the precursor cells. Lymphocytes disappear first

following irradiation (*see* LYMPHOCYTES, RADIATION DAMAGE); then there is a drop in the granulocytes (*see* NEUTROPHIL LEUKOCYTE, RADIATION DAMAGE); next the erythrocytes (*see* ERYTHROCYTES, RADIATION EFFECTS ON); and finally the platelets (*see* PLATELETS, RADIATION EFFECTS ON). Disappearance is due to non-generation, hence lymphocytes with a 2-day life disappear first, etc. Figure H–2 presents actual values in an accidental case.

Examination of the blood-forming organs shows early destruction of precursors, destruction of cells, and suppression of mitosis. For example in bone marrow, shortly after irradiation, there is cell destruction of the erythropoietic precursors, loss of mitotic activity, then loss of granulocytic precursors, and last, loss of the cells that give rise to the blood platelets—in the mid-lethal range of radiation this occurs by the fifth to sixth day. For doses in this range, the marrow may become (within one to two weeks) virtually acellular. Only primitive hematocytoblasts, fibroblasts, and blood vessels are left.

Regeneration and return to normal of bone marrow and other elements of the hematopoietic system depend upon the level of exposure, the type of treatment given, and the individual's radioresistance. In the mid-lethal range (400 to 600 r) regeneration may occur in 6 weeks; for lethal levels (700 to 800 r) the probability of spontaneous recovery of the bone marrow is unlikely. When regeneration takes more than 6 weeks, recovery is unlikely.

Heavy exposure of the blood-forming organs to radiation increases the incidence of leukemia due to radiation experimentally in mice, and also appears to increase the incidence in humans.

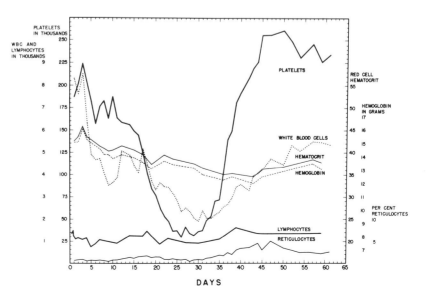

FIGURE H–2. AVERAGE BLOOD VALUES IN 5 MEN EXPOSED TO 236 TO 365 RAD TOTAL BODY RADIATION IN THE Y-12 ACCIDENT. (COURTESY MEDICAL DIVISION, OAK RIDGE INSTITUTE OF NUCLEAR STUDIES.)

HEMATOPOIETIC SYSTEM STUDIES

The hematopoietic system consists of the circulating blood cells and platelets, and the tissues that form them—the bone marrow, spleen, and lymph nodes. The system also includes the mechanisms for removal of the dead circulating elements, about which much has yet to be learned. Information on this subject is included under the following topics, all studied with radioisotopes: LEUKOCYTES, PLATELETS, BLOOD CELLS.

Additional types of studies involve measurements made outside the body with local detectors or scanners, after gamma-emitting isotopes have been administered. These supplement the measurements made directly on samples of blood or on blood and marrow cells. For example, the localization of iron-59 in the marrow after intravenous injection can be determined with a detector over the sacrum. As the iron leaves the marrow in newly formed red blood cells, decreasing activity in the marrow will be shown. Similar counts made over the spleen may show the extent of this organ's activity in the breakdown of red blood cells labeled with either chromium-51 or iron-59.

An interesting demonstration of the extent of the functioning marrow has been made with colloidal gold-198 given intravenously followed by a scan of the whole body. The radiogold is deposited in reticuloendothelial cells of the marrow and the distribution of these is believed to be the same as that of the hematopoietic cells in the marrow. (This procedure also shows the liver and spleen where there are many reticuloendothelial cells.)

HEMORRHAGE RESULTING FROM RADIATION INJURY

Bleeding was not noted following exposure to less than 200 rad in a careful study of 31 known human radiation injury cases. Between 200 and 400 rad exposure most patients exhibited some hemorrhagic phenomena, such as gingival (gums) bleeding, nosebleed (epistaxis), or hemorrhage into the skin (petechiae, ecchymosis, purpura); but none of these were serious. Above 400 rad exposure all patients showed evidence of hemorrhage, and if they lived into the third to fifth week there was intestinal bleeding. One patient (whole body irradiation treatment for leukemia) who had received from 400 to 600 rad died as the result of uncontrollable menstrual bleeding (menorrhagia); and one patient in the 600 to 1,350 rad range died from uncontrollable vomiting of blood (hematemesis) and coughing of blood (hemoptysis). In experimental exposure in dogs the most common site of hemorrhage is the pericardium, followed in descending order of frequency by the gastrointestinal tract, lungs, pleura and mediastinum, pharynx, skin, bladder, and kidneys.

Cause of the hemorrhagic syndrome has been shown to be a progressive decrease in the number of platelets in the circulating blood (thrombopenia) which is time- and dose-dependent, and leads to a quantitative deficiency in clot retraction, prothrombin utilization, and capillary integrity. In severe cases the blood-clotting time becomes so prolonged that trauma, ulcerations, and infections can bring on hemorrhage. Platelet transfusions will prevent bleeding or stop bleeding that has commenced. In human cases bleeding does not occur at platelet levels above 20,000 per cubic millimeter.

See ACUTE RADIATION SYNDROME and PLATELETS, RADIATION EFFECTS ON.

HETEROLOGOUS TISSUE GRAFTS

Tissue transplants where donor and host are of different species. *See* BONE MARROW GRAFTS.

HIGH-ALTITUDE SAMPLING PROGRAM

A stratospheric or high-altitude atmospheric sampling program to determine the amount and type of radioactive material (gaseous and particulate) in the stratosphere as a result of the detonation of a nuclear device. The Department of Defense and USAEC conducted the program in order to provide insight into the circulation in the stratosphere, and to contribute to the evaluation of the fallout hazards from a nuclear explosion.

The sampling was carried out by the use of unmanned balloon ascents to altitudes up to 115,000 feet, where samples were taken by collecting a whole-air sample in a special balloon, by electrostatic precipitation, or by filtration. The most widely used was the "ash can" particulate filter system.

With the whole-air samples, analysis was made of the concentration of carbon-14, carbon dioxide, and tritium. The filter samples were examined for total activity and for the quantity of barium-140, zirconium-95, cerium-144, cesium-137, strontium-89, and strontium-90.

The collection of an adequate sample by balloon is exceedingly difficult for the particles are probably less than 1/10 micron in diameter (i.e., less than 4 millionths of an inch), and the total mass of strontium, for example, collected by the best method is seldom more than a micromicrogram (i.e., 1/1,000,000,000,000 of a gram). Airplanes can sample 10 to 100 times as much air with high efficiency but are limited in altitude to about 70,000 feet.

HIROSHIMA

At 0815, August 6, 1945, the first atomic bomb to be used in combat was dropped, as an air burst, detonated at about 1,850 feet, over the Japanese city of Hiroshima. The bomb's fissionable material was uranium-235 and had a yield of approximately 20 kilotons (TNT equivalent).

Hiroshima was an important seaport and military base on the SW coast of Honshu. Its terrain was flat; its buildings were predominantly of wood-frame construction; and the civilian population of about 255,000 were completely surprised by the attack.

The zero point (see GROUND ZERO) was almost directly over the center of the city. In the proximal zone (within 2,000 meters, or 1.24 miles of ground zero) destruction was almost completely due to the blast effect and thermal radiation with an associated fire storm. Only a few reinforced concrete structures withstood the blast and fire. In the intermediate zone (between 2,000 and 3,000 meters, or 1.2 and 1.86 miles) the damage was heavy but out toward 3,000 meters houses were not beyond repair. Beyond 3,000 meters (the distal zone) the damage consisted largely of broken windows and dislodged doors and roofs.

About 60% of the population were within 1.2 miles (2,000 meters) of ground zero. The casualties within this proximal zone are show in Table H–3. Beyond this distance there were very few deaths on the first day. Those that did occur were due to injuries and burns, and not to direct thermal radiation or ionizing radiation. The casualty-distance curves indicate that the point at which the chance of death was 50% was 0.77 mile. By the middle of November, 1945, the deaths were approximately 64,000 or about 25% of the total population of the city.

TABLE H–3. ESTIMATED CIVILIAN CASUALTIES WITHIN 2,000 METERS OF GROUND ZERO

DISTANCE FROM GROUND ZERO (meters)	EXPOSED POPULATION (number)	SURVIVORS (number) (20 days)	SURVIVORS (per cent of those exposed)
0–499	6,230	220	3.5
500–999	24,950	4,240	17.0
1,000–1,499	45,270	21,910	48.4
1,500–1,999	67,900	53,030	78.1
Total	144,350	79,400	55.0

Blast and thermal radiation were directly or indirectly responsible for almost all of the first-day deaths, and for most of the injuries to the first-day survivors. The 50% point for injury or death was 1.30 miles.

The burns of the survivors were largely flash burns, occurring out to a distance of 2.79 miles, but blistering beyond 2.05 miles was rare.

The air-dose-distance has been calculated to have been about 900 rad at 1,000 meters from ground zero, 120 rad at 1,500 meters, and 15 rad at 2,000 meters. Remembering that the median lethal dose for man is considered to be 450 rad of whole body irradiation, it is evident that the radiation hazard to the survivors was confined to the proximal zone. Those few individuals in the proximal zone who survived the blast and thermal radiation (only 20.5%) developed severe and usually fatal acute radiation illness. Those between 1,000 and 1,500 meters also developed the acute radiation syndrome, but in this zone apparent recovery generally occurred within 2 months. Beyond 2,000 meters overt symptoms of radiation damage were very few.

The delayed effects are being carefully studied under the auspices of the ATOMIC BOMB CASUALTY COMMISSION. The group being studied over the intervening years is the combined population of 60,000 Hiroshima and NAGASAKI citizens who survived within 2,000 meters from ground zero, and were living in the two rebuilt cities in 1950. Of these, a most significant subgroup consists of approximately 25,000 who were within 1,500 meters, 7,000 of whom experienced major symptoms of irradiation (epilation, purpura, or oropharyngeal ulcerations). Much of the present-day knowledge of chronic radiation effects such as cataract, leukemia, cancer, genetic effects, and in utero damage to the embryo and fetus has been developed by detailed study of survivors from these cities.

HISTOPATHOLOGY OF RADIATION DAMAGE

Observable microscopic pathologic changes in cells and tissues following radiation exposure. The changes are usually nonspecific and resemble those produced by other injurious agents, e.g., change in staining quality, increase in size of cells, edema, hyperemia, etc. However, since the damage varies with the type and dose of exposure, and with the sensitivity of the tissue, it is often possible to identify radiation damage by the pattern of tissue response. (See RADIOSENSITIVITY, and RADIORESISTANCE.)

Illustrations of radiation histopathology will be found in the presentations under various body organs: ADRENAL GLANDS, BLOOD, BONE MARROW, BRAIN TISSUE, etc.

HIT THEORY. See TARGET THEORY.

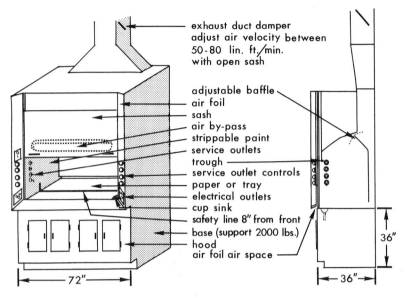

exhaust duct damper
adjust air velocity between
50-80 lin. ft./min.
with open sash

adjustable baffle
air foil
sash
air by-pass
strippable paint
service outlets
trough
service outlet controls
paper or tray
electrical outlets
cup sink
safety line 8" from front
base (support 2000 lbs.)
hood
air foil air space

72"

36"

36"

FIGURE H–3.   RADIOCHEMICAL
FUME HOOD.

HOLMIUM

Symbol Ho; atomic number 67; atomic weight 164.94. Named from Latin *Holmia*, Stockholm. A member of the yttrium subgroup of the rare earth metals. Discovered by Cleve in 1879. Occurs in such minerals as xenotime, fergusonite, gadolinite, and euxenite. Natural abundance 100% by stable isotope Ho^{165}. There are 9 radioactive isotopes. None have been found to have any biological, medical, or agricultural value.

HOMOLOGOUS TISSUE GRAFTS

Tissue transplants from one individual to another of different genetic strains of the same species. *See* BONE MARROW GRAFTS.

HOOD

For handling radioactive material at elevated temperatures where gases may be emitted and for radiochemical work in general a specially designed radioisotope hood, or radiochemical fume hood, is necessary. Figure H–3 illustrates various features of a satisfactory type of hood. Adequate ventilation is necessary; for example, 100 to 200 ft/min (linear velocity) in the maximum open position of the door.

See GLOVE BOX and RADIOISOTOPE WASTE DISPOSAL.

HORMONE STUDIES

Hormones, distinct chemical substances produced by one gland or organ, act in a specific manner on the function of other organs of the body. Hormones are produced mainly by the glands of internal secretion—the ductless or endocrine glands; but may also be produced by glands of external secretion. Table H–4 gives the glands and their hormones.

TABLE H–4

GLAND	HORMONE
Adrenal	
Medulla	Epinephrine
Cortex	Deoxycortisone, cortisone, corticosterone
Gonads	
Ovaries	Estrin or estradiol (follicular hormone)
	Progestin (corpus luteum hormone)
Testes	Testosterone (androsterone)
Pancreas	Insulin
Parathyroid	Parathyroid hormone
Pituitary	
Anterior lobe	Growth hormone
	Thyrotropic (thyroid-stimulating)
	Adrenocorticotropic (adrenal cortex-stimulating)
	Gonadotropic (gonad-stimulating)
	Lactogenic (milk gland-stimulating)
Posterior lobe	Pituitrin, composed of
	Oxytocin (uterine-stimulating)
	Vasopressin (pressor substance)
Thyroid	Thyroxine

The use of radioactive isotopes has greatly facilitated the study of the function of the glands and their secretions; for example, information about the thyroid hormones has increased greatly as a result of the use of radioactive iodine, the advent of improved chromatographic techniques, and the combination of these methods with autoradiography. A sequence of events in the formation of thyroid hormones can be presented although many details are lacking, particularly about the enzymes in the gland that make these reactions possible. Trapping of iodide in the thyroid is followed by its oxidation to iodine. The amino acid tyrosine is iodinated to form monoiodotyrosine and diiodotyrosine. Oxidative coupling of two molecules of diiodotyrosine yields one of thyroxine. Triiodothyronine is formed either from thyroxine with the loss of iodine or from the coupling of one molecule of monoiodotyrosine with one of diiodotyrosine. These organic iodine compounds are found in conjugated form in thyroglobulin, the large molecule substance that makes up the "colloid" that is seen in histological sections to occupy the thyroid acini. The main hormonally active substances released into the blood stream normally are thyroxine and triiodothyronine. The latter is present in much smaller amounts but is more active per milligram than thyroxine. Both substances travel in association with plasma protein fractions in the blood stream. They play an important role in the metabolic activity of the body; considerable fractions of them are metabolized in liver and kidneys.

Insulin is the hormone secreted by the pancreas; although it does not normally contain iodine as a vital part of its structure (as do the thyroid hormones) it has been labeled with radioiodine and its distribution and behavior have thus been studied by means of the tracer technique. Tagged insulin was shown to penetrate the cell and was found concentrated in certain portions of the cytoplasm. Largest concentrations were in liver, kidney, and muscle. After intravenous injection the labeled hormone remains present in the blood at much higher levels in diabetics taking insulin than in normal persons; this suggests that in the former group an active plasma-binding mechanism may be present.

See ENDOCRINE GLAND STUDIES and STEROID STUDIES.

HORMONES IN RELATION TO RADIATION INJURY

The endocrine organs are among the radioresistant tissues. Adrenal cortical atrophy and abnor-

mally large quantities of corticoids in the urine of heavily irradiated individuals occur as part of a nonspecific stress reaction.

Many hormone preparations have been given to experimental animals both before and after radiation illness in an effort to determine whether they have any effect on survival. Some conflicting results have been reported; the actions of these materials are quite complex and clear-cut results are not always obtained. Estradiol and other estrogens have been shown to have a definite protective effect if given before irradiation. The benefit appears to be related to an action of the hormone on the hematopoietic system and best survival is obtained if the irradiation is given while the white blood cell count is depressed by the hormone. When estrogens are given after exposure, variable results are reported. Other hormones— ACTH (adrenocorticotropic hormone), cortisone, androgens (male sex hormones), somatotropic (growth) hormone—have all given variable results without consistent benefit. Experimental administration of hormones has not proved of value in treatment of the radiation syndrome.

Late effects of radiation in animals sometimes include cancer arising in endocrine glands. In some instances the incidence of such cancers can be reduced by giving adequate replacement therapy —that is, by giving as medication the hormones needed to reduce the demand on the damaged endocrine gland.

See ENDOCRINE ORGAN, RADIATION EFFECTS ON.

HOT

Commonly used colloquial term meaning relatively more radioactive than some adjacent area which may be referred to by the antonym, cold, i.e., having little or no contact with radiations.

HOT CELL

A well shielded completely enclosed room-like space where radioactive materials of the highest activity range (curie to megacurie quantities) are handled by remote control. Usually directly connected with a cave storage space for highly radioactive materials. Figure H–4 shows an operator handling radioactive isotopes with remote manipulators and looking through a thick shield window into the hot cell.

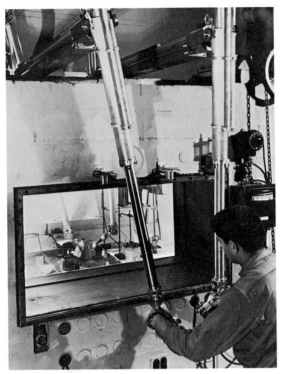

FIGURE H–4. HOT CELL PROCESSING OF RADIOISO-
TOPES. (OAK RIDGE NATIONAL LABORATORY.)

HOT LABORATORY

A specially designed laboratory for working with radioactive materials where the activity is so high that special precautions in both construction and handling are necessary. Working spaces should be easily decontaminated, i.e., have plastic coverings or strippable paints that can be easily removed. Adequately ventilated hoods are essential. There should be a dry box or glove box for small-scale operations. A cave for safe storage should be available; and if high-level activity work is necessary a hot cell should be part of the laboratory. All work must be performed with proper protective clothing and protective equipment, and with adequate protective shielding. All surfaces, tables, walls, floor, benches, etc., must be of nonabsorbent washable material. Strippable paints are frequently used in such installations.

See LABORATORY DESIGN.

HOT SPOT

A local geographical area where environmental contamination levels are higher than average for the surrounding areas. Hot spots may encompass many square miles, and are formed when an air mass or cloud containing a high concentration of radioactive particles becomes part of rain or snow.

Usually associated with "close-in" fallout and TROPOSPHERIC FALLOUT.

Rain droplets tend to form around particulate matter in the air and carry it down to the ground. The highest concentrations of radioactive material may be expected in contamination clouds from recently detonated nuclear devices. Therefore hot spots are more likely to be observed in the United States during testing operations at the Nevada Test Site. One of the most striking examples of this occurred around Mandan, North Dakota, on the day after the Diablo shot was detonated. There had been no measurable radioactivity in the rain that fell the day before the shot; but a heavy rain the following day washed out enough radioactive debris from the cloud passing over North Dakota to yield a contamination of 22 millicuries per square mile, which resulted a month later in an increase of strontium-90 in milk to a total of 30 micromicrocuries per gram of calcium.

The term "hot spot" is also used to describe areas in a body tissue, such as lung or bone, where much higher than average concentration occurs. These areas are usually small but much controversy revolves around their significance in the evaluation of radiation hazards, since the radiation dose around such a "hot spot" may be of an order of magnitude higher than the average for the organ.

HYBRIDIZATION AND RADIATION

The process of producing progeny (called hybrids) from crosses between inherently unlike strains, either different species or different strains of the same species. Plant hybrids are more easily propagated (bulbs, cuttings, grafts) than are animal hybrids. In recent years it has been demon-

FIGURE H–5. HYBRID PRODUCED AFTER IRRADIATING THE GAMETES PRIOR TO CROSSING. IRRADIATION OF EITHER MALE OR FEMALE GAMETES OF THIS PLANT, GENUS BRASSICA, WAS EFFECTIVE. (COURTESY DR. ROY DAVIES, A.E.R.E., HARWELL, ENGLAND.)

strated that ionizing radiation can be used to facilitate the production of hybrids between closely related species which otherwise could not be crossed successfully. One such case, shown in Figure H–5, was the production of visible hybrids of the plant genus Brassica by irradiation of either male or female gametes. A number of other crosses apparently were not successful even though a similar technique was employed. It seems too early to predict how important this method may be in general in facilitating hybridization between otherwise incompatible parental lines.

HYDROGEN

Symbol H; atomic number 1; atomic weight 1.0080. A colorless, odorless, tasteless, nontoxic gas. First recognized as a distinct element by the English physicist Cavendish in 1766. Named by Lavoisier from Greek, *hydro*, water, and *genes*, forming. Occurs chiefly combined with oxygen in water, with carbon in hydrocarbons, with other elements in acids and bases, and with carbon, oxygen, and nitrogen in a vast variety of organic substances. Natural abundance furnished by 2 stable isotopes: H^1, 99.9849%; and H^2, 0.0151%.

Because it is lightest of all gases it is used to inflate balloons. Also used as a reducing agent for high-temperature flames and in welding. Great quantities are used for the fixation of nitrogen from the air in the Haber ammonia process and for the hydrogenation of fats and oils. Occurs throughout living material. The biochemical standard man contains 10.0% or 7,000 grams of hydrogen per 70 kilograms of body weight.

An isotope with an atomic weight of 2 ($_1H^2$), commonly called deuterium, was separated by the American scientist Harold C. Urey in 1932. One part (by weight) of deuterium is found present in ordinary water along with 5,000 parts by weight of isotope 1 or ordinary hydrogen (sometimes called protium).

Tritium ($_1H^3$) is the only radioactive isotope of hydrogen, and is used extensively in biological and medical research.

See FUSION, NUCLEAR; and THERMONUCLEAR WEAPON.

HYDROGEN BOMB

Term commonly applied to a thermonuclear weapon, i.e., a nuclear weapon in which a portion of the explosive energy is furnished by nuclear fusion.

HYPERTHYROIDISM TREATMENT

The use of iodine-131 for hyperthyroidism is one of the most important therapeutic applications of internally administered radioisotopes. It is the preferred form of treatment for many patients with this disease, particularly those who do not have nodular goiters and who are over 40 years of age. Because of possible long-delayed undesirable effects there has been some hesitancy to treat younger patients who are suitable for surgical therapy; it is now believed that these fears are unfounded. Especially in patients who have had previous thyroid surgery or who have heart disease or other complicating disorders, radioiodine is the preferred treatment regardless of age.

A single treatment dose of from 4 to 8 millicuries may be all that is needed, but some patients require two or more doses to control the disease. The benefit usually begins to become apparent within a few weeks, but several months may elapse before the full effect is noted.

Certain patients with nodular goiters are also suitable for radioiodine treatment; they usually require larger doses than those with diffusely enlarged thyroid glands.

HYPOCENTER. A term sometimes used for GROUND ZERO.

HYPOTENSION AFTER RADIATION

A decrease in diastolic and systolic blood pressure occurs in most individuals after high (200 rad +) whole body radiation exposure. The decrease is usually transient, returning to normal in a few days, but may occasionally remain chronically depressed. Hypotension is thought to be part of general systemic depression rather than a specific effect. Hypertension has been found to be associated with experimentally produced radiation nephritis. Attempts at treating hypertension with irradiation have been unsuccessful.

I

ICRP. *See* INTERNATIONAL COMMISSION ON RADIOLOGICAL PROTECTION.

ICRU. *See* INTERNATIONAL COMMISSION ON RADIOLOGICAL UNITS AND MEASUREMENTS.

IMMUNE REACTION FOLLOWING IRRADIATION

It has been demonstrated in several species of mammals that total body irradiation depresses the immune mechanism with impairment in the ability to produce antibodies in response to an antigen. In rodents this effect is usually most pronounced during the first 1 or 2 days after exposure. Recovery begins promptly but may not be complete for many weeks. The depression in the immune mechanism may be produced by doses from about 100 roentgens up to levels that are lethal; the depression tends to be more pronounced with the larger doses. The response to a genetically closely related antigen is more easily impaired by irradiation than that to a distantly related one.

The inadequate function of the immune mechanism may play a part in the susceptibility to infection that occurs after irradiation. The effect has great significance in that, with high doses of irradiation, it makes possible the survival of homologous tissue grafts (bone marrow, kidney) that would otherwise be promptly rejected.

IMMUNOLOGICAL STUDIES

Radioactive tracer techniques, in addition to fluorescent microscopy and tissue culture, have provided a major stimulus for research in various branches of immunologic investigation, especially in studies on:

a. the fate of antigens in vivo;

b. the synthesis and degradation of antibodies;

c. the interaction between antigen and antibody in vivo, especially in relation to hypersensitivity lesions; and

d. the physical and chemical aspects of antigen-antibody interaction in vitro.

Iodine-131-labeled foreign serum proteins have been used extensively in studies of the fate of antigens. Another type of isotopically-labeled antigen is the combination of a haptene bearing an isotope label with a carrier protein, usually carbon-14 or sulphur-35 in the form of anthranilic

or sulfanilic acid. A third type of labeled antigen is that produced by a metabolic incorporation of the radioactive tracer into the antigen; examples are protein antigens that are naturally synthesized in the presence of labeled amino acids, viruses in a medium containing isotopes, and polysaccharides synthesized in part from labeled simple sugars. For these studies, the isotopes most frequently used have been sulphur-35, carbon-14, and phosphorus-32.

Following injection of the radioactive serum protein antigen, there is rapid equilibration throughout the body, and radioactivity is found in many tissues and organs. There is then a latent period during which time the antigen is broken down at the same rate as homologous serum protein. A sudden increase in the rate of disappearance of the radioactive antigen indicates that newly formed antibody has entered the circulation, has formed complexes with the circulating antigen, and is being rapidly removed. It has been demonstrated that the antibody is formed "de novo" from the available amino acid pool by the reticuloendothelial and lymphoid tissues.

IMPLANTATION THERAPY. *See* INTERSTITIAL IMPLANTS.

IN VITRO STUDIES

In vitro means "in glass" and is used to refer to procedures performed with test tubes, particularly when these are contrasted with tests done in living animals (*see* IN VIVO STUDIES). A great variety of radioisotope tests are done in vitro, and these involve many areas of the biological and chemical sciences. Most are based upon the fact that radioisotopes can be measured accurately when they are present in very small amounts. Sometimes radioactive reagents are used in simple chemical tests; thus the amount of a precipitate may be measured by making radioactive one of the elements in it. Isotope dilution analysis is a method for measuring the amount of a constituent that cannot be completely separated from a mixture. A known amount of the same compound, tagged in one element, is added to the mixture. Partial chemical separation is then carried out; the percent recovery for the labeled material also applies to the stable form, and by using this information along with the weight of stable material recovered, one can calculate the total weight originally present in the mixture.

Certain biological reactions involving very small amounts of material are made possible by radio-isotopes—for example, studies of the capacity of blood plasma to bind with iodine-131-labeled triiodothyronine, one of the hormones of the thyroid gland. Living cells may be studied in vitro with radioisotopes, and many metabolic observations have been made on such preparations.

IN VIVO COUNTING. See EXTERNAL COUNTING.

IN VIVO STUDIES

In vivo or surface measurement is based on the fact that radioisotopes emit radiation that can traverse the tissues and be measured outside the organism. The primary advantage is that a continuous measurement on the intact organism is available during the course of the experiment, and the same organism can be used repeatedly for observations.

The main types of metabolic research undertaken by the in vivo method are as follows:

a. Sodium-24: circulation times, blood flow through the heart, absorption from ointments, and dissolving of coated capsules.

b. Iodine-131: thyroid function, location of metastases, the fate of antithyroid compounds.

c. Phosphorus-32: circulation times, selective uptake in tumors.

d. Strontium-85 and calcium-47: accumulation in bone tumors and fractures.

INCOHERENT SCATTERING

SCATTERING of particles or photons in which the scattering elements act independently of one another, so that there are no definite phase relationships among the different parts of the scattered beam.

INDIUM

Symbol In; atomic number 49; atomic weight 114.82. A rare silver-white metal, softer than lead, malleable, ductile and crystalline. Discovered in 1863 by Reich and Richter by the use of the spectroscope. Named for its indigo blue spectrum. Found in very small amounts in zinc blende, tungsten, tin, and iron ores. Natural abundance furnished by 1 stable isotope; In^{113}, 4.23%; and 1 radioactive isotope, In^{115}, 95.77%.

Indium is used extensively in metallurgy and has been used in medicine in treatment of trypanosomal and spirochetal diseases. Also used in dental alloys. Relatively nontoxic.

Thirty-one radioactive isotopes have been identified; 16 of these may occur as fission products following the detonation of a nuclear device. Of these, In^{118} is of interest in radioactive fallout with 0.000616 megacurie per megaton of fission at the end of 1 year. None of the radioisotopes has any known usefulness.

INDUCED ACTIVITY IN AIR, WATER, AND SOIL (BOMB). See RADIONUCLIDES PRODUCED IN AIR, WATER, AND SOIL (BOMB).

INDUCED RADIOACTIVITY

Radioactivity produced in an element by bombardment with neutrons, protons, alpha particles, etc. This induced radioactivity is the result of one of two types of NUCLEAR REACTION, i.e., either TRANSMUTATION or ACTIVATION. Both these reactions are important in the production of artificial radioactive isotopes by neutron bombardment of elected target materials in a nuclear reactor. The process of neutron capture by an atomic nucleus is involved in both the transmutation and activation reactions. Induced radioactivity can also be produced by bombarding an element with either high-energy deuterons or protons in a cyclotron or other type of accelerator, where almost all the reactions are of the transmutation type.

Induced radioactivity is the basis for activation analysis used to detect the presence of trace quantities of elements. Also used as a measure of the level of accidental exposure by analysis of a blood sample for the presence of radioactive sodium. In the same manner a metal object (gold wrist watch), worn by an individual who has been accidentally exposed, can be analyzed for induced radioactivity and the neutron flux estimated.

A nuclear explosion with its massive release of neutrons produces large amounts of induced radioactivity in the various elements constituting the air, water, and earth with which the neutrons come in contact. This remains as residual nuclear radiation (see RADIONUCLIDES PRODUCED IN AIR, WATER, AND SOIL (BOMB)).

See ACTIVATED MOLECULE and ACTIVATED WATER.

INDUSTRIAL ACCIDENTS

Accidents and their associated injuries are common to all industrial activities; and in spite of all precautions, industrial accidents have occurred in USAEC facilities and in work conducted by contract.

One method of evaluating industrial accidents is by determining industrial injury frequency rates based on the number of lost-time injuries per million man-hours of employment. As will be seen in Table I–1 the USAEC showed a reduction of 20% in its injury rate from 1959 to 1960, with a drop from a rate of 2.17 in 1959 to 1.71 in 1960. There was an increase in 1961 to 1.97 per million man-hours worked and again a slight increase in 1962 to 1.98.

TABLE I–1. USAEC INDUSTRIAL INJURY FREQUENCY RATES

TYPE OF WORK	1959	1960	1961
Production	1.14	0.73	0.94
Research	1.94	1.57	1.83
Services	3.05	2.30	2.65
Cost-plus construction	4.64	4.23	4.73
Lump-sum construction	16.72	13.35	13.36
Architect-engineering	2.05	1.48	0.96
Government	2.14	0.69	1.56
All	2.17	1.71	1.97

It is of interest that the USAEC rates have always been much lower than those reported by 42 industries in the United States to the National Safety Council (NSC). The annual average for 1960 for the NSC was 6.04 compared to 1.71 for the USAEC. The total number of workers injured in USAEC plants and laboratories for five years is as follows:

TABLE I–2. USAEC TOTAL EMPLOYEES AND NUMBER INJURED

YEAR	TOTAL EMPLOYEES	NUMBER INJURED
1960	120,919	411
1959	117,953	511
1958	121,053	534
1957	117,094	451
1956	115,610	577

The total lost-time injuries since the beginning of the nation's atomic energy program with the Manhattan Engineer District (the forerunner of the USAEC) in 1943 through 1960 was 6,573, of which 35 were radiation injuries.

From 1943 through 1962 the total number of fatalities was 237, which is about half the number that would have occurred had the atomic energy program had the same rate as reported by the NSC. Only 7 fatalities occurred in 1962, none due to radiation. Of the 237 fatalities, 6 were the result of radiation exposure, and the balance were typical industrial accidents: falls (52), electric shock (36), motor vehicles (32), mobile equipment

(cranes, bulldozers) (27), falling objects (23), burns (13), aircraft (7), trench cave-in (9), and miscellaneous (33).

No matter how it is compared, the SAFETY RECORD, USAEC is an enviable one.

INDUSTRIAL HYGIENE

The nonmedical aspects of industrial health and safety, including safety engineering, air pollution, toxicology, etc. It now includes emphasis on radiological hazards in relation to other industrial hazards. Special fellowships in industrial hygiene are awarded by the USAEC.

See EDUCATION AND TRAINING, USAEC; HEALTH PHYSICS; INDUSTRIAL MEDICINE; OCCUPATIONAL MEDICINE; and RADIOLOGICAL HEALTH.

INDUSTRIAL MEDICINE

The medical aspects of the health and safety of industrial workers, including treating diseases incurred in industrial activity. The role of radiological hazards in industrial medical practice is now being emphasized, but the field is much broader than radiation hazard evaluation alone. Special fellowships in industrial medicine are awarded by the USAEC.

See EDUCATION AND TRAINING, USAEC; HEALTH PHYSICS; INDUSTRIAL HYGIENE; OCCUPATIONAL MEDICINE; and RADIOLOGICAL HEALTH.

INDUSTRIAL RADIOGRAPHY

Radium and x-ray have been used for years in industrial radiography. The radioactive isotopes cobalt-60, cesium-137, and iridium-192 are now replacing radium and x-ray in many applications, for they have a number of advantages, such as greater versatility and reliability and the possibility of on-the-spot inspection without dismantling the object. Moreover, sources may be obtained of various sizes and shapes, and radioisotope sources furnish high activity at a low cost. A typical way of using a radioisotope source for radiographic inspection is shown in Figure I–1.

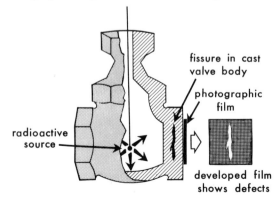

FIGURE I–1. RADIOGRAPHY USING COBALT-60.

INDUSTRIAL USE OF RADIOISOTOPES

Radioactive isotopes provide an important peaceful benefit of atomic energy in their industrial applications, which make it possible to carry out many manufacturing and research processes more easily, quickly, and cheaply. Principal industrial uses of radioisotopes are in DENSITY GAGING, FLOW MEASUREMENT, FOOD PRESERVATION, INDUSTRIAL RADIOGRAPHY, LEAK LOCATION, LIQUID-LEVEL GAGING, RADIATION STERILIZATION, THICKNESS GAGING, and TRACER INDUSTRIAL APPLICATION.

The chief benefits are reduced waste, lower labor costs, greater product quality control or product uniformity, and the solution of other previously insoluble or costly-to-solve production problems. Over 3,500 gages utilizing radioactive material have been licensed by the USAEC. About 2,000 of them are in use in the cigarette industry and the others principally in rubber and tire, plastics and adhesive, paper and allied products and in the sheet metal and pharmaceutical industries.

INFINITE INTEGRATED DOSE

Also infinity dose. The dose of radiation a person would receive as a result of continued exposure (i.e., remaining at a given position in a radiation field) for an infinite time. This applies especially to fallout.

INFORMATION SERVICES. *See* TECHNICAL INFORMATION DIVISION, USAEC.

INFRARED RADIATION

Electromagnetic radiation from the band of wave lengths lying between about 0.75 micron and 1,000 microns. Infrared region is sometimes subdivided into:

Near infrared—about 0.75 to 3.0 microns
Middle infrared—about 3.0 to 30.0 microns
Far infrared—about 30.0 to 1,000 microns

The strong absorption of infrared by many substances make these waves useful as a means of applying heat energy. Infrared waves are not visible.

INGESTION OF RADIOACTIVE MATERIAL

Ingestion is one of the two most common routes by which radioactive materials enter the body; the other is INHALATION OF RADIOACTIVE MATERIAL. With regard to biospheric contamination, the gastrointestinal tract is the most important portal of entry of strontium-90 and cesium-137, the two radionuclides of major concern from radioactive fallout.

The level of ingestion of radioactive material depends upon dietary habits and upon contamination of the food chain. The ecological cycle is important: If the entry into the food chain is largely due to direct foliate contamination, the levels in humans will depend on the rate of fallout. If contamination of foodstuffs is via soil uptake into the plants, human levels will depend on the integrated soil deposition levels.

Once the radioactive material has been ingested, the level of gastrointestinal absorption is all-important. Table I–3 shows the percentage absorption of 12 intermediate and long-lived radioisotopes formed from thermal neutron fission of uranium-235 and from fast neutron fission of uranium-238. Of the 12 radioisotopes listed, 5 show gastrointestinal absorption values less than 1%, which precludes this portal of entry as an important one.

TABLE I–3.   GASTROINTESTINAL ABSORPTION OF RADIOISOTOPES

RADIOISOTOPE	PHYSICAL HALF-LIFE (days)	EFFECTIVE HALF-LIFE (days)	ABSORBED ON INGESTION (%)
Cesium-137	1.17×10^4	17	100
Iodine-131	8.05	7.7	100
Strontium-90, yttrium-90	10^4	6.4×10^3	30
Strontium-89	50.5	50.4	30
Ruthenium-103	39.8	—	20
Barium-140, lanthanum-140	12.8	—	5
Ruthenium-106, rhodium-106	355	—	3
Promethium-147	920	570	<0.01
Cerium-144	290	243	<0.01
Zirconium-95	63.3	53	<0.01
Niobium-95	35	33.5	<0.01
Cerium-141	33	—	<0.01

A number of other factors are important in gastrointestinal absorption of radionuclides:

1. The water solubility of the material.

2. The chemical and physical states of the material. Elements in acid solutions and in solutions containing citrate are more easily absorbed.

3. Physiological and nutritional state of the subject. For example, the uptake and retention of iron-59 is directly related to the physiological iron demand of the individual.

4. Composition of the diet and intestinal contents. It has been shown that the body burden of potassium-40 and carbon-14 depends upon the metabolic turnover and therefore upon the short-term changes in dietary composition and intake. Lactose enhances the absorption of calcium-45 and strontium-89.

5. Absorption varies with the animal species. Assuming that body retention after 24 to 48 hours represents the amount of the oral dose absorbed, gastrointestinal uptake correlates with body size of the species.

Perhaps the most famous cases of ingestion of radioactive material were the RADIUM DIAL PAINTERS. Ingestion of radium in luminous paints led to death from anemia, destructive lesions of the jawbones and mouth, and sarcoma of the bones in a number of the painters.

It should be remembered that in these cases the normal process of elimination of waste material is at work. For example, cow's milk has only 1/7 the strontium in it per gram of calcium that the cow's food has. Also the calcium-strontium discrimination factor in the transfer from diet to human bone has been calculated to average 4, with a range of from 2 to 8, in favor of calcium over strontium.

See MAXIMUM PERMISSIBLE CONCENTRATIONS for the consumption of drinking water and food.

It must also be remembered that chronic retention may not be related to absorption; e.g., in a mature individual, calcium may be absorbed to the extent of about 25%, but the net retention is zero because the individual excretes just as much as he ingests. This behavior would also be true for strontium at the steady state.

See INTERNAL DECONTAMINATION.

INHALATION OF RADIOACTIVE MATERIAL

Inhalation of radioactive aerosols creates two potential hazards: (1) that of irradiation of the pulmonary tissues themselves from radioactive material retained on the respiratory surfaces and deposited in the bronchial lymph nodes and (2) the hazard of the translocation of radioactive material to a critical organ (e.g., iodine-131 to thyroid or strontium-90 to bone).

In industrial activity, inhalation is considered the most important route of entry of potentially hazardous materials into the body, INGESTION OF RADIOACTIVE MATERIAL being the next most likely. In considering radioactive fallout, ingestion is in most cases the most important portal of entry.

The body has special defense mechanisms to deal with inhaled particulate matter. The nasal passageways have a filtering apparatus, and the airways are long and tortuous and are covered with sticky secretions to catch particles. Ciliary activity of the epithelium of the bronchi move impinged particles up and out of the lung and into the esophagus where they are swallowed. The cough reflex helps to remove larger pieces of material. Phagocytosis of particles by macrophages helps remove particles that actually get into the lung alveoli.

The accumulation of radioactive material in the pulmonary lymph nodes, particularly after prolonged exposure, may greatly exceed that in the lung, and may be the limiting factor on which the MAXIMUM PERMISSIBLE CONCENTRATION is set. For example, from inhalation studies on the toxicity of various uranium compounds, in a variety of animals exposed over periods of time from 1 month to 2 years, it was found that the limiting factor in soluble material was chemical toxicity. But for the insoluble material, the limiting factor was the radiological hazard to the pulmonary lymph nodes. In the case of a plutonium process operator with 6 years' exposure, autopsy showed the concentration of plutonium to be 20 times greater in the lymph nodes than in the lung and 60 times higher than in the bones.

The lung is considered to be a moderately radiosensitive organ with clearly measurable damage resulting from exposure to 1,000 and 2,000 roentgens. Deposition of radioactive material into the lung has been shown to induce cancer.

Particle size is important from the standpoint of LUNG CLEARANCE. Particles 50 microns or larger are effectively trapped in the nasal passageways and the upper bronchi. Deposition of particles within the alveoli is heaviest in the range of 1 to 3 microns, with a second peak for those smaller than 0.1 micron. (See Figure I–2).

In general, the deposition of particulates in the respiratory tract of the standard man is as shown in Table I–4.

Research on the inhalation of radioactive material from the standpoint of quantitative administration is a difficult laboratory procedure. Many different types of "dust" inhalation chambers have

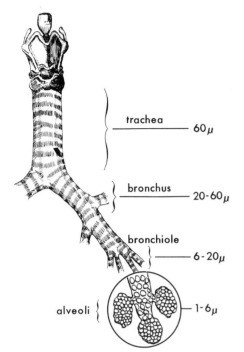

trachea ———— 60μ

bronchus ———— 20-60μ

bronchiole ———— 6-20μ

alveoli ———— 1-6μ

FIGURE I–2. USUAL DISTRIBUTION OF INHALED MATERIALS ACCORDING TO PARTICLE SIZE.

TABLE I–4. FATE OF INHALED PARTICLES

DISTRIBUTION	READILY SOLUBLE COMPOUNDS (%)	OTHER COMPOUNDS (%)
Exhaled	25	25
Deposited in upper respiratory tract and subsequently swallowed	50	50
Deposited in lower respiratory tract	25*	25†

*Absorbed into body.
†Half of this is moved out of the lungs and swallowed in the first 24 hours, making a total of 62.5% swallowed. The remaining 12.5% is retained in the lungs and eliminated with a half-time of 120 days by absorption into the body.

been developed for exposure of animals to air-borne contamination. Techniques have been developed for introduction of the material directly into the trachea, but estimation of the pulmonary toxicity of a compound and the removal rate from the lung are still more qualitative than quantitative.

Prevention of contamination through inhalation relies on careful housekeeping to keep surface contamination down, on the use of air filters and ventilation, and on the use of respirators by all personnel working where the air may be contaminated.

See INTERNAL DECONTAMINATION and LUNG, RADIATION DAMAGE.

INITIAL NUCLEAR RADIATION

Radiation emitted from the fireball of a nuclear device during the first minute after detonation. For a typical air burst (below 100,000 feet) of a fission weapon, the initial nuclear radiation represents 5% of the energy yield. It should be noted that there are no nuclear radiations from a conventional explosion (e.g., TNT), since the nuclei are unaffected in the chemical reactions which take place. The radiation is largely gamma rays and neutrons emitted from the fireball and cloud.

A 1-kiloton nuclear weapon detonated in the air so that the fireball touches the ground would produce over 100,000 roentgens of gamma radiation at ground zero. A number of factors reduce this intensity so that at a slant range of 1 mile, the radiation would only be 2.5 r. Gamma-ray exposure decreases as the distance from the explosion increases owing to the spread of the radiation over larger and larger areas as it travels away from the point of detonation. In addition, the rays are attenuated by absorption and scattering by the intervening atmosphere. Another important factor is the rapid rise of the radioactive cloud to a distance at which it will no longer expose persons or objects on the earth. In general, the cloud from a 1-megaton explosion will have attained a height of 3 miles in 30 seconds and 4.5 miles in about 1 minute, although this varies with the meteorological conditions.

Note that the initial nuclear radiation differs from RESIDUAL RADIATION which continues to emit radiation after the explosion.

INJURIES, RADIATION

An injury due to exposure to ionizing radiation may be exceedingly difficult to diagnose. In fact it may be impossible to establish radiation exposure as the etiological factor in such delayed "injuries" as death from leukemia or cancer, the development of cataracts, or the production of mutations.

However, the acute radiation syndrome associated with radiation illness gives positive evidence of radiation injury, with clinical symptoms and laboratory findings characteristic, in general, with the level of the dose.

Radiation burns, usually due to exposure to heavy beta-ray doses, give positive proof of radiation injury. An example of this type of injury occurred in connection with the removal of filter papers from drone aircraft used to secure samples from the radioactive cloud resulting from the experimental detonation of a nuclear device. Although tongs 2 feet long were supposed to be used, 4 men used their gloved hands to remove the filter papers and received beta-ray burns of the skin of the hands. The amount of beta is not known, but the body gamma doses were 1.7 r, 4.5 r, 5.5 r, and 17.0 r. Hospitalization was required for the treat-

ment of the burns, and in 3 cases skin grafts were necessary. One man had severe residual disability and had additional skin grafts 7 years after the accident.

Lost-time injuries due to radiation accidents are shown in Table I–5. Only 1 lost-time injury in 1960 was caused by radiation.

See CRITICALITY ACCIDENTS, INDUSTRIAL ACCIDENTS, RADIATION ACCIDENTS, SL-1 REACTOR ACCIDENT, and WOUND CONTAMINATION.

TABLE I–5. REPORTED RADIATION ACCIDENTS RESULTING IN LOST-TIME INJURIES

DATE	LOCATION	NUMBER INVOLVED	SOURCE OF INJURY	NATURE OF INJURY	EXPOSURE	DAYS LOST
5/14/48	Eniwetok proving ground	4	Improper handling of fission sample	Beta-ray burns of hand	1.7 r [1] 4.5 r [1] 5.5 r [1] 17 r [1]	36 36 36 36
9/7/48	Los Alamos	1	Unpacking radioactive material	Beta-ray burns of ankle	NA [2]	36
7/9/52	Los Alamos	1	Handling radioactive material with torn glove	Beta-ray burns of hands	NA [3]	3
3/1/55	Nevada Test	1	Entering exlusion area during test	No clinically diagnosed injury	39 r	19
7/27/55	National reactor testing station	1	Radioactive particle entering ear canal	Partial loss of hearing	Not detectable	12
4/30/56	Los Alamos	1	Handling radioactive material with torn gloves	Beta-ray burns of hands	NA [4]	14
6/18/56	Hanford	1	Escape of plutonium solution into control room	Contamination of exposed skin surfaces. No clinically diagnosed injury	In excess of 40,000 d/m/alpha	4
6/14/57	Rocky Flats	1	Explosion in "dry box"	Plutonium lodged in finger necessitating amputation	3.2 m/c Pu	50
11/8/60	Alburquerque, Sandia base	1	Exposure from electronic beam (Not atomic radiation)	Multiple radiation burns of middle section of face, abdomen, and both hands	[5]	10
7/24/62	Puerto Rico Nuclear Center	7	Crane operator moved fuel elements near personnel	Overexposure 80 rem, 55 rem, 20 rem, 15 rem, 7 rem, 3 rem, and 2–3 rem.		7 1 day observation each.

[1] Exposure refers to whole body gamma radiation. Injury caused by beta-ray dose, amount of which exposure not available.

[2] Amount of beta-ray dose not available. Total gamma-ray exposure during week in which accident occurred was 0.27 rem.

[3] Amount of beta-ray dose not available. Total gamma-ray exposure during week in which accident occurred was 1.8 rem.

[4] Amount of beta-ray dose not available. Total gamma-ray exposure during week in which accident occurred was 2.0 rem.

[5] Employee was not wearing his film badge. However, an indirect measurement was made by placing a film badge at 33 cm distance and exposing it under simulated conditions. Calibration was interpreted as 760 rads incident dose to the face at 33 cm.

INSECTICIDE STUDIES. *See* ENTOMOLOGICAL STUDIES.

INSPECTION

In encouraging peaceful uses of atomic energy it is important that its use be carefully controlled in the interest of public safety. The Congress of the United States considered public safety when it gave to the USAEC the statutory responsibility for licensing, regulating, and inspecting activities utilizing atomic energy in the interests of the common defense and security and to protect the public health and safety. In developing the licensing and inspection program the purpose was to limit to acceptable levels any risks involved in working with radiation.

In granting licenses for byproduct material the USAEC retains the right of inspection and performance of such tests as may be deemed appropriate, and accordingly has the right to modify or revoke a special license. The Federal Register* says:

> "Inspection. (a) Each licensee shall afford to the Commission at all reasonable times opportunity to inspect byproduct material and the premises and facilities wherein byproduct material is used or stored. (b) Each licensee shall make available to the Commission for inspection, upon reasonable notice, records kept by him pursuant to the regulations in this chapter.

> Tests. Each licensee shall perform, or permit the Commission to perform, such tests as the Commission deems appropriate or necessary for the administration of the regulations in this part, including tests of: (a) Byproduct material, (b) Facilities wherein byproduct material is utilized or stored, (c) Radiation detection and monitoring instruments, and (d) Other equipment and devices used in connection with the utilization or storage of byproduct material."

In 1961 the USAEC proposed a change in the regulations under which the states, when qualified and requesting it, were to be given the authority and responsibility for licensing and inspection activities involving byproduct material, source material, and special nuclear material in quantities less than a critical mass. The change went into effect and several states have already taken over.

*Federal Register. Title 10—Atomic Energy. Chapter 1—Atomic Energy Commission. Part 30—Licensing of Byproduct Material.

Excluded from such agreements is regulatory authority and responsibility with respect to the construction and operation of any production and utilization facility; any import or export activity; and sea or ocean disposal of radioactive waste.

INSULIN, RADIOACTIVE. *See* HORMONE STUDIES.

INTEGRAL ENERGY SPECTRUM

The energy spectrum of a radioactive nuclide which presents the activity observed as the baseline drive advances the threshold to progressively higher values. This is contrasted with the differential energy spectrum, which shows activity found in a series of energy intervals at increasing levels.

See PULSE HEIGHT ANALYZER.

INTEGRATING CIRCUIT

That part of a rate meter which collects the signal pulses over a specified time interval; its function is characterized by a time constant relating the storage capacity of its condenser C and the delivery or leakage rate of the resistor R, the combination providing an integrated signal to the measuring circuits which follow. The R and C components are adjusted for best compromise of sensitivity and response time, with regard to the rate at which pulses are received and the rapidity with which that rate is changing.

INTEGRATING IONIZATION CHAMBER

An ionization chamber which stores the collected charge in a capacitor for subsequent measurement, as in the thimble chamber of a condenser r-meter.

INTENSITY

Energy or number of photons or particles of any radiation incident upon or flowing through a unit area or unit solid material per unit time. The intensity of a beam of x-rays may be measured by the blackening of a photographic plate, by the rise in temperature of a piece of lead which absorbs the rays, or by the ionization produced in a gas or vapor. An ionization chamber is commonly used. In radiology the term is often used incorrectly in the sense of dose rate.

Of radioactivity, the number of atoms disintegrating per unit time, or derivatively, the number of scintillations or other effects (such as roentgens per hour) observed per unit time. A synonym for activity.

Thermal radiation intensity is expressed as calories per square centimeter per second impinging on a given surface at a specified moment.

INTERAGENCY COMMITTEE ON RADIOLOGICAL ASSISTANCE

In recognition of the possibility that there could be a serious radiation accident as a result of the handling and transportation of radioactive material and nuclear weapons, the Atomic Energy Commission (USAEC) and Department of Defense (DOD) entered into an agreement on February 27, 1958, to provide for the delineation of responsibility between the two agencies and mutual emergency assistance. This agreement was later extended to include mutual assistance in any kind of radiation accident.

After the Windscale reactor accident there was an increased realization of the potential health hazard associated with a radiation accident. Also the increase in the transportation of radioactive materials has increased the possibility of shipping accidents, and expansion of the industrial uses of atomic energy and nuclear research and development programs has increased the probability of radiation accidents. These factors influenced the USAEC decision to bring together on May 28, 1958, a selected group of Federal agencies and to propose that an interagency committee be organized to develop a plan under which their resources could be coordinated. It was evident that there were other Federal agencies that could be involved and could render assistance if serious radiation incidents should occur.

The Interagency Committee on Radiological Assistance was formed and in turn formulated the Interagency Radiological Assistance Plan (IRAP) dated July, 1961, which was approved by 11 Federal agencies signatory to the plan. The plan provides for the integration of Federal capabilities to render advice and assistance in the event of radiation accidents (incidents); for coordination

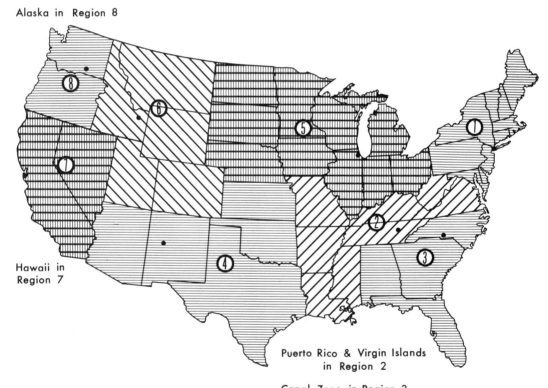

Alaska in Region 8

Hawaii in Region 7

Puerto Rico & Virgin Islands in Region 2

Canal Zone in Region 3

FIGURE I–3.   USAEC REGIONAL AREAS FOR RADIOLOGICAL ASSISTANCE.

1. New York Operations Office
   376 Hudson St., New York, N.Y.

2. Oak Ridge Operations Office
   P.O. Box E, Oak Ridge, Tenn.

3. Savannah River Operations Office
   P.O. Box A, Aiken, S. C.

4. Albuquerque Operations Office,
   P.O. Box 5400, Albuquerque, N. Mex.

5. Chicago Operations Office
   P.O. Box 59, Lemont, Ill.

6. Idaho Operations Office
   P.O. Box 2108, Idaho Falls, Idaho

7. San Francisco Operations Office
   518 17th St., Oakland, Calif.

8. Hanford Operations Office
   P.O. Box 550, Richland, Wash.

with state and local health, police, fire, and civil defense agencies; and for a training program. Administrative responsibility for carrying out the provisions of the plan are assigned to the USAEC.

Although the IRAP will be developed and strengthened in the future, for the present the USAEC and DOD emergency radiological assistance team capabilities should be called upon for assistance in radiological incidents. The accompanying regional map (Fig. I–3) lists the name and regional number of the USAEC Operations Office to which a request should be directed.

Any person, organization, state or local official cognizant of an accident or incident believed to involve radioactive materials or ionizing radiation hazardous to the health and safety of the community or of individuals may request advice and assistance.

Since June 1958 the USAEC has provided radiological monitoring and assistance teams capable of the following: alpha, beta, and gamma radiation monitoring; sampling and radiation monitoring of air, water, or food; radiological decontamination advice and emergency assistance; medical advice on the handling of people who have been exposed to radiation and, in addition, have received internal or external injuries in connection with the accident; radiochemical sample analysis services needed for evaluation of radiation hazards; and specialists in nuclear weapons accident hazards.

In addition, assistance may be provided by the nearest military installation, the local Office of Civil and Defense Mobilization, the U. S. Public Health Service, and the U. S. Coast Guard.

INTER-AMERICAN INSTITUTE OF AGRICULTURAL SCIENCES

The Nuclear Energy Program of the Inter-American Institute of Agricultural Sciences was begun in 1957 in Turrialba, Costa Rica, as a part of the Atoms for Peace effort. The Institute is a graduate agricultural school of the Organization of American States and accepts students from any of the 21 member nations of the OAS.

This program encourages, by way of training and research, the use of radiations and radioisotopes in agriculture. Students from Costa Rica, Venezuela, Bolivia, Peru, Ecuador, Chile, Brazil, Colombia, Argentina, Haiti, and Portugal have been trained.

The staff normally consists of 5 senior and 5 junior scientists as well as the graduate students who are obligated to do research in order to obtain their master's degrees. Courses have been given in advanced laboratory techniques, radioisotope methodology, cytogenetics, plant breeding, and soil chemistry.

The facilities consist of a 1,300-curie cesium-137 irradiator in the largest gamma field installed thus far in Latin America, a water-pool irradiator with 1,850 curies of cobalt-60, and equipment to work with radioisotopes as tracers.

The research program has varied according to the interests of the staff. Radiation work has included a study of the radiosensitivity of tropical plants, including trees. Plant improvement by means of gamma irradiation has been studied with several economic crops, and some mutant rice varieties have been sent to countries in Latin America and to the Rice Institute in the Philippines. Basic radiobiology has been investigated in studies such as the effect of gamma rays on bridge frequency in chromosomes; a comparison of the effect on growth and on nuclear damage of seeds subjected to thermal neutrons, x-rays, and gamma rays; and the effect of oxygen on the radiosensitivity of 2 clones of cacao.

In plant physiology and biochemistry, radioactive substances have been used to study the problems of foliar nutrition. Radioactive zinc has been used to study the location and function of zinc in the cell. Radioactive glutamic acid, an important building block of protein, has been used to study protein formation in rice.

Studies at Turrialba on the binding of radioactive phosphorus by tropical soils could have an important effect on fertilizer practice.

Entomologists are using both gamma rays and isotopes to discover whether the release of irradiated Mediterranean fruit flies can eliminate or control the threat posed by this serious economic pest.

See INTER-AMERICAN NUCLEAR ENERGY COMMISSION.

INTER-AMERICAN NUCLEAR ENERGY COMMISSION

The statute of the Inter-American Nuclear Energy Commission (IANEC) was approved by the Council of the Organization of American States (OAS) on April 22, 1959. According to this statute, it is "a commission of a technical nature within the Organization of American States, established to serve as a center of consultation for the member states and to facilitate cooperation among them in matters relating to the peaceful application of nuclear energy." The Commission is composed of officially designated representatives from each of the 21 nations that make up the OAS.

The Secretariat for the Commission is located in the Pan American Union, Washington, D.C., which serves as the General Secretariat of the OAS. The IANEC Secretariat is in the Department of Scientific Affairs. The Executive Secretary of the Inter-American Nuclear Energy Commission serves also as Director of the Department.

The Commission meets annually. The programs of the IANEC may be divided into 3 general areas: education, training, and research; technical information services; and liason with other organizations of similar interests.

One of the most important programs of the IANEC has been the development of a coordinated and cooperative program for nuclear energy, training, and research in the Americas. It is expected that the completion of this project will permit the most efficient use of limited facilities and personnel.

Recognizing that a desirable nuclear program can be built only upon adequate instruction in the basic sciences and engineering, the OAS Council has approved activities in the Department of Scientific Affairs that are devoted to education and research. Inter-American conferences have been held on the teaching of engineering and the basic sciences. Summer institutes are attended by professors who are interested in improving their teaching methods and in increasing their knowledge. Special courses on technical topics are held from time to time.

An information bulletin, Ciencia Interamericana, is published by the Department. Particular attention is given to the need for texts and scientific journals.

Various general programs of the OAS are used to further the objectives of the IANEC. Among these are the Professorship Program, the Exchange of Scientists, and the Technical Assistance Programs.

See INTER-AMERICAN INSTITUTE OF AGRICULTURAL SCIENCES.

INTERMEDIARY METABOLISM STUDIES

Intermediary metabolism depends upon the controlled operation of a large number of interrelated cycles by means of which energy is made available by degradation, utilized for synthesis, and stored for subsequent use. The radioisotopes of carbon, hydrogen, and phosphorus have made possible the identification of the many steps involved and of the necessary conditions and components for completion of these cycles. In particular, radioisotopes have been used to determine the precursors of important biochemical compounds, the specificity of reaction at molecular sites as determined by spatial considerations, the details of enzyme action, and the various pathways that metabolites can take under different experimental and pathological conditions. For specific examples, *see* AMINO ACID STUDIES; CARBOHYDRATES; PHOTOSYNTHESIS; LACTATION STUDIES; and LIPID STUDIES.

INTERNAL CONVERSION

In emerging from a nucleus, the gamma ray may interact and transfer all its energy to an orbital electron; it is thus internally converted. The electron which interacts with the gamma-ray photon, called a conversion electron, is ejected from the atom and carries with it the kinetic energy that is the difference between the transition energy and the binding energy of that electron. In the transition from the excited state to the ground state, the direct emission of the nuclear excitation energy in the form of a gamma-ray photon is a competing process and occurs frequently. Internal conversion is followed by the emission of characteristic x-rays or Auger electrons.

INTERNAL DECONTAMINATION

Radioactive contamination of personnel may be internal through inhalation, ingestion, or skin penetration (abrasion, cuts, or puncture wounds). First-aid measures for inhalation consist of quickly blowing the nose, coughing, and forceful exhalation. When material has been ingested, wash out the mouth, being careful not to swallow the water, and then induce vomiting mechanically. Wounds should be copiously washed and allowed to bleed freely.

Further internal decontamination measures are considered to be medical treatment and consist of chemical and physicochemical methods of elimination and the use of chelating agents to form a soluble complex with the radionuclide and enhance its elimination.

See INGESTION OF RADIOACTIVE MATERIAL, INHALATION OF RADIOACTIVE MATERIAL, INTERNAL DEPOSITION, INTERNAL EMITTERS, INTERNAL IRRADIATION HAZARD, and PERSONNEL DECONTAMINATION.

INTERNAL DEPOSITION

Deposit of radioactive material or radioisotopes within the body as a result of ingestion of radioactive material; inhalation of radioactive material; injection of radioisotopes for research, diagnosis or treatment; contamination of wounds or abrasions; or absorption through the intact skin.

See INTERNAL DECONTAMINATION and INTERNAL IRRADIATION HAZARD.

INTERNAL EMITTER

Any radioactive isotope deposited within the body.

See INTERNAL IRRADIATION HAZARD.

INTERNAL IRRADIATION HAZARD

The hazard from irradiation of the body by

TABLE I–6. RADIOISOTOPES IN MICROCURIES PER GRAM OF BODY WEIGHT AT WHICH HISTOPATHOLOGY
WAS OBSERVED IN MICE AND RATS

	STRONTIUM-89	RADIUM	BARIUM-140, LANTHANUM-140	SODIUM-24	PHOSPHORUS-32
$LD_{50}/30$	7	1	4	30	4
Bone	0.86	0.02	4.0	—	9.2
Bone marrow	0.5	0.02	1.4	47	2.5
Spleen	0.5	0.06	1.4	47	—
Lymph nodes	2.0	0.06	14	47	—
Testes	2.9	0.02	14	47	9.2

internally deposited radioactive isotopes (*see* INTERNAL DEPOSITION).

Internally deposited radioisotopes have the following unique characteristics: (1) They irradiate the body continuously until they are eliminated. (2) The pattern of behavior in the body is characteristic of each element. (3) Behavior pattern is dependent upon the age or rate of growth and the physiological and nutritional well-being of the individual. (4) The distribution is usually not homogeneous—iodine to the thyroid, strontium to the bone, etc. (5) The radioisotope may become an integral part of an important structure, as carbon-14 in DNA, and thus the radiation may have a greater effect than normally anticipated.

Natural radiation contributes the following radioactive isotopes as internal emitters: potassium-40, radium-226, and carbon-14. Potassium-40, deposited primarily in muscle, adipose tissue, and skeleton, contributes a dose of approximately 19 millirem per year (mrem/yr) to the soft tissues and 11 mrem/yr to the bony tissue. Radium-226 is calculated to contribute a dose of 38 mrem/yr to the bones. (*See* RADIUM DIAL PAINTER CASES). Carbon-14 is a source of radiation to both the bony and soft tissues of the body amounting to about 1.6 mrem/yr. The inhalation of radon, thoron, tritium, and particle-borne radioisotopes in the atmosphere adds to the internal hazard. The aggregate figures for internal irradiation give a dose rate of 20 mrem/yr to the gonads and 50 mrem/yr to the bone.

Inhalation or ingestion of uranium or thorium during the mining, processing, or industrial use of these radioactive materials also contributes to internal irradiation. (*See* INGESTION OF RADIOACTIVE MATERIAL and INHALATION OF RADIOACTIVE MATERIAL.)

Administration of radioactive isotopes for research, diagnosis, or treatments adds slightly to the internal radiation hazard. Each radioisotope has characteristic radiation properties and a specific biological behavior. The observed level at which evidence of histological damage appeared in laboratory animals following parenteral (other than through the alimentary canal) administration for 5 radioisotopes is given in Table I–6.

Radioactive fallout contributes to internal irradiation through contamination of the atmosphere and environment. For short-term fallout, iodine-131 is significant, while for long-term fallout, strontium-90 is considered to be the greatest potential biological hazard.

The relative radiotoxicity of various radioisotopes depends upon the radioactive half-life, biological half-life, type of radiation, energy of radiation, and localization in the body. By use of these criteria internal emitters can be divided according to their internal irradiation hazard into 3 groups.

Group I. Extremely hazardous.
  Calcium-45, iron-55, strontium-90, yttrium-91, zirconium-95, cerium-144, promethium-147, and bismuth-210.

Group II. Moderately hazardous.
  Tritium, carbon-14, phosphorus-32, sodium-22, sulfur-35, chlorine-36, manganese-54, iron-59, cobalt-60, strontium-89, niobium-95, ruthenium-103, ruthenium-106, tellurium-127, tellurium-129, iodine-131, cesium-137, barium-140, lanthanum-140, cerium-141, praseodymium-143, neodymium-147, gold-198, gold-199, mercury-203, and mercury-205.

Group III. Slightly hazardous.
  Sodium-24, potassium-42, copper-64, manganese-52, arsenic-76, arsenic-77, krypton-85, and mercury-197.

See INTERNAL DECONTAMINATION.

INTERNATIONAL ATOMIC ENERGY AGENCY

The International Atomic Energy Agency (IAEA) is an international organization with a relationship agreement with the United Nations, established on October 1, 1957, to "accelerate and enlarge the contribution of atomic energy to peace, health, and prosperity throughout the world."*

---

*IAEA Statute of Establishment.

The IAEA was first proposed on December 8, 1953, by President Eisenhower in his historic "atoms for peace" speech before the United Nations General Assembly, in order to "provide a way to bring the benefits of peaceful uses of atomic energy to all the people of the world despite the deadlock with the Soviet Union over the question of disarmament." Almost 4 years of negotiations were required to bring IAEA into being.

A Director General, appointed for a 4-year term, is responsible to a Board of Governors. The Board consists of 23 members with representatives from the United States, the United Kingdom, and the U.S.S.R. plus representatives from other countries designated by the General Conference for 1-year terms. The General Conference, with each representative of the 78 member countries having one vote, meets annually to approve the program and budget for the forthcoming year, to act on applications for membership, and to consider proposals of various kinds. The permanent staff includes the secretariat of the Director General plus the following program or administrative division directors: Exchange and Training of Scientists and Experts; External Liaison; General Services; Health, Safety, and Waste Disposal; Isotopes; Personnel; Reactors; Research, Research Contract and Laboratories; Scientific and Technical Information; and Technical Supplies.

The 7 functions of the IAEA are: (1) to encourage nuclear-energy research, development, and application; (2) to make provisions for services, equipment, and supplies; (3) to foster exchange of scientific and technical information; (4) to encourage the exchange and training of scientists; (5) to safeguard against use for military purposes of Agency-assisted projects; (6) to establish standards of safety; and (7) to develop facilities for research.

1. Research, Development, and Application. Most of this program is conducted through contracts with existing laboratories in member countries, a limited amount of research being conducted in the Seibersdorf laboratory at the Vienna headquarters. Most of the contracts concern research on problems in the fields of radiobiology, radiation protection, radioactive waste disposal, medicine and agriculture, safeguards and small- and medium-power reactors (ranked by percentage of appropriation spent).

2. Services and Equipment. Some 40 countries have been visited by IAEA assistance missions to assess the possibilities for nuclear energy programs and the means to implement them. Arrangements and supply agreements have been completed with a number of countries for the supply of materials; e.g., 3 tons of natural uranium from Canada were sold to Japan under interim safeguard provisions.

3. Scientific Information. The Agency sponsors 2 or 3 large scientific conferences a year and 10 or more symposia. An extensive publishing program covers proceedings of the scientific meetings, directories and catalogues, safety manuals, training manuals, bibliographies, and technical reports. In addition, documentation service is supplied to requesting members from the Agency's library, which receives about 12,000 research reports from member nations and acquires about 6,000 books and 600 periodicals per year.

4. Exchange and Training. About 500 student fellowships made available by member countries are assigned each year. From 1957 through 1961 over 1,000 fellowships had been received by students in 45 nations; they were trained in centers near Chicago, Moscow, London, and Paris. Instructors were sent to requesting countries, and courses of instruction were organized and staffed, e.g., in 7 countries in 1961. Two mobile isotope laboratories donated by the United States brought training to the doorstep of trainees in the Far East, Latin America, and Europe.

5. Safeguards. Accounting and inspection procedures for source and fissionable materials to prevent diversion to military uses include (a) examination and approval of reactor designs, (b) maintenance by the state concerned of an agreed-upon system of records, (c) submission to the Agency of routine and special reports, and (d) inspections.

6. Safety. A large proportion of the Agency's research contracts have been awarded in radiobiology, health physics, and waste disposal for studies of short- and long-range effects. Radiation safety standards have been established and published. Regulations for transport of nuclear materials have been adopted. Upon request from a member nation the Agency assists in evaluating hazards of operating research reactors. In 1960 a dosimetry project was conducted in connection with a research reactor in Vinca, Yugoslavia, to gain information on the exact doses received in an uncontrolled run of the reactor in 1958 in which 6 scientists were exposed.

7. Facilities. A new laboratory was added in 1960 at Headquarters in Seibersdorf which will supply analytical, standardization, and calibration services and in-service training in standardization techniques.

The IAEA collaborates with various other agencies of the United Nations having special interest in atomic energy activity, and with various regional organizations such as the European Nuclear Energy Agency of the Organization for European Economic Cooperation and the Inter-

American Nuclear Energy Commission of the Organization of American States.

INTERNATIONAL COMMISSION ON RADIOLOGICAL PROTECTION

The International Commission on Radiological Protection (ICRP) has a primary interest in the entire field of radiation protection. It is composed of a chairman and not more than 12 members chosen on the basis of recognized activity in the fields of radiology, radiation protection, physics, radiobiology, genetics, biochemistry, and biophysics. In addition to the main commission there are the following committees on:

I. Permissible dose for external radiation.
II. Permissible dose for internal radiation.
III. Protection against x-rays up to energies of 3 Mev and β and γ rays from sealed sources.
IV. Protection against electromagnetic radiation above 3 Mev and electrons, neutrons, and protons.
V. Handling of radioactive isotopes and disposal of radioactive waste.

The principal function of the ICRP is to analyze and report on the various aspects of the problems of radiation protection. It performs this function by publishing reports, such as "Radiation Protection. Recommendations of the International Commission on Radiological Protection,"* which contains not only a concise history of the Commission but detailed recommendations concerning various aspects of radiation protection.

The ICRP was established in 1928 under the auspices of the Second International Congress of Radiology then meeting in Stockholm, with a membership of 7 scientists from various countries who were working actively in the field of radiation protection. It was then known as the International X-Ray and Radium Protection Commission, since its mission was confined to problems of x-ray and radium protection. Four official meetings were held prior to World War II with discussions on radiation units, shielding, and radiation protection. The third meeting in 1934 was notable because, for the first time, a permissible level of radiation exposure was established. The level was set at 0.2 roentgen per day, or about 64 r/yr—12 times the yearly maximum permissible dose presently allowed a worker. But this was an advance, for at that time "permissible" doses were estimated primarily in terms of x-ray exposures that produced erythema.

Following the war (1950) the committee was

reorganized, given its present name, and enlarged to 12 members (largely from different nations) in order to handle new protection problems more effectively. In 1956, affiliation with the World Health Organization was ratified in order that the Commission might officially give detailed assistance to the WHO, although it still functions under the auspices of the International Congress of Radiology.

Virtually every country in the world follows the recommendations of the ICRP, at least to the extent of adapting its recommendations to local needs. The U.S. NATIONAL COMMITTEE ON RADIATION PROTECTION AND MEASUREMENTS works very closely with the ICRP.

INTERNATIONAL COMMISSION ON RADIOLOGICAL UNITS AND MEASUREMENTS

The International Commission on Radiological Units and Measurements (ICRU) is an international nongovernmental body concerned with developing measurement techniques and standards for radiation dosimetry and for the specification of radiation treatment (see TREATMENT OF RADIATION ILLNESS). The Commission has 4 committees: I. Standards and Measurement of Radioactivity for Radiological Use; II. Standards and Measurement of Radiological Exposure Dose; III. Measurement of Absorbed Dose and Clinical Dosimetry; and IV. Standard Methods of Measurement of Characteristic Data of Radiological Equipment and Materials.

ICRU committees collect and evaluate data and information and prepare reports and recommendations concerning acceptable procedures and units in dosimetry and radiation protection. ICRU works closely with the INTERNATIONAL COMMISSION ON RADIOLOGICAL PROTECTION.

National Bureau of Standards Handbook 62, "Report of the International Commission on Radiological Units and Measurements (ICRU)," is one of the standard references based on deliberations of the Commission.

INTERNATIONAL LABOR ORGANIZATION

The International Labor Organization (ILO) has been a specialized agency of the United Nations since 1946. It was established in 1919 as an autonomous body associated with the League of Nations. ILO has responsibility for protecting the worker's life and health and for raising working and living standards. The Division of Occupational Safety and Health is interested in international standards, model codes, and safety regulations relating to many types of occupational hazards, including radiation protection. As early

*Pergamon Press, Inc., 122 East 55th St., New York 22, N.Y.

as 1934 its publications listed pathological manifestations due to x-rays, radium, and other radioactive substances among the occupational diseases for which compensation might be claimed. ILO continues to issue reports dealing with international standards of radiation protection and health safety.

All the ILO activities encompass only occupational exposures, while the WHO (World Health Organization) is interested particularly in radiation exposure to the general population.

INTERNATIONAL STANDARDS ORGANIZATION

The International Standards Organization (ISO) is a generally recognized but nonofficial international authority on standard nomenclature and measures, on standards for strength and purity, etc., in various fields of science and technology. Most member states have some related formal group; for example, in the United States there are the American Standards Association, which has a Federal charter, and the Bureau of Standards of the U.S. Department of Commerce.

Atomic energy interest centers around the Technical Committee ISO/TC 85 (Nuclear Energy) and its 4 subcommittees: (1) Terms, Signs, and Symbols; (2) Radiation Protection; (3) Reactors; and (4) Radiation Instruments.

ISO works closely with the INTERNATIONAL COMMISSION ON RADIOLOGICAL PROTECTION and other international groups as well as with member state voluntary or governmental standards groups.

INTERSTATE COMMERCE COMMISSION

An agency of the U.S. Government which has among other responsibilities that of regulating the safe transportation of radioactive materials moving in interstate commerce by rail, water, or public highway (except U.S. mail).

INTERSTITIAL IMPLANTS

Used as an effective form of treatment for certain selected cases of cancer. The solid or encapsulated sources are made in the form of seeds, wires, or other conformations and are inserted directly into the tumor tissue (Fig. I–4). An effort is made to distribute them uniformly but there is always unevenness in radiation dose (Fig. I–5). The sources may be removed at the end of treatment, or if an isotope of short half-life is used, it may be left in permanently. Commonly used radioisotopes are cobalt-60, radium-226, radon-222, tantalum-182, and gold-198. The skin-sparing effect is an asset of this form of treatment, which, however, is suitable for only a limited group of accessible tumors (Fig. I–6).

Intracavitary therapy is essentially the same, except that the radioactive sources are inserted into body cavities, such as the bladder, uterine cavity, or paranasal sinuses.

See INTERSTITIAL INJECTION and INTRACAVITY USE OF RADIOACTIVE COLLOIDS.

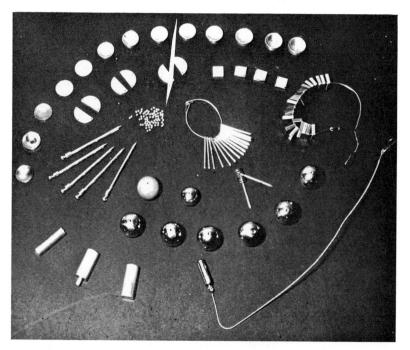

FIGURE I–4. IMPLANTATION OR BRACHYTHERAPY WITH COBALT-60 SOURCES IN VARIOUS SHAPES FOR USE IN INTERSTITIAL IMPLANTS. GOLD-198 CAN BE USED IN A SIMILAR MANNER. (COURTESY MEDICAL DIVISION, OAK RIDGE INSTITUTE OF NUCLEAR STUDIES.)

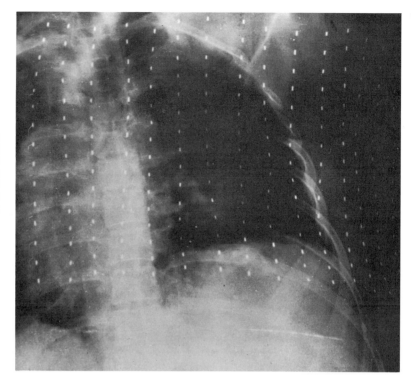

FIGURE I-5. PLANAR NYLON
RIBBON CONTAINING GOLD-198
SEEDS IMPLANTED TO IRRADIATE
A LARGE ULCERATED CANCER
OF THE BREAST. (COURTESY OF
THE MEDICAL DIVISION, OAK
RIDGE INSTITUTE OF NUCLEAR
STUDIES.)

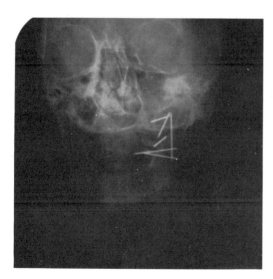

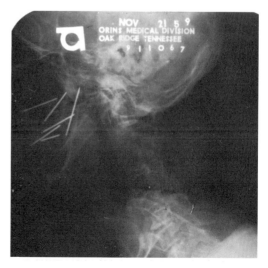

FIGURE I-6. IMPLANTATION OF COBALT-60 NEEDLES IN
A MOUTH LESION. ANTERIOR-POSTERIOR VIEW ABOVE;
LATERAL VIEW ON RIGHT. (COURTESY MEDICAL DIVI-
SION, OAK RIDGE INSTITUTE OF NUCLEAR STUDIES.)

INTERSTITIAL INJECTION

Injection of radioisotopes directly into tumors or adjacent tissues is sometimes used as a form of treatment. Colloidal or particulate suspensions are used. Usually most of the radioisotope remains at the site of injection; under some circumstances a significant part travels to regional lymph nodes. This form of therapy has the advantage of producing intense local radiation, but the placement of the material cannot be accurately controlled and consequently the radiation dose is distributed very unevenly.

INTESTINAL DAMAGE DUE TO RADIATION

The mucosal epithelium of the gastrointestinal tract is highly radiosensitive. The duodenum and small intestine are more vulnerable than the stomach. The large intestine, especially the rectum, is less susceptible. Exposure to whole body irradiation in the dose range below 200 roentgens (r) may produce some slight diminution in the mitotic index (cell-division rate) and loss in weight of the small intestine, both of which return to normal promptly. In the range from 200 to 400 r, the effects are the same but more pronounced, and return to normal takes longer. In the 400 to 600-r group there is an acute nonspecific mucosal and submucosal inflammatory reaction, which is the first gross alteration seen in the intestine and is responsible for many of the symptoms of the acute radiation syndrome. Many bizzare forms of mucosal cell are produced. The mitotic rate decreases, and normally functioning crypt cells are replaced by mucus-secreting cells.

In the dose levels above 600 r (lethal dose range) there may be complete cessation of mitosis with loss of cell production. The adult cells show many bizarre forms. At these levels of exposure there are vascular changes and hyalinization of the collagen throughout the bowel wall. The primary gross lesion in the intestine is ulceration, which leads to severe hemorrhage. Figure I–7 shows an edematous large intestine spotted with hemorrhages and an edematous mesentery containing hemorrhagic lymph nodes, removed from a swine which died 15 days after 400 r in air, total body, 1000 kv x-irradiation delivered bilaterally.

Chronic radiation damage to the intestine consists of multiple poorly healing ulcerations secondarily infected with bacteria and occurring 6 months to years after exposure. Perforation, stenosis, and fistula formation may occur. The delayed type of reaction seen at intermediate levels of exposure is seldom due to radiation alone but often is complicated by secondary infection.

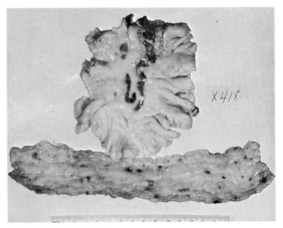

FIGURE I–7. EDEMATOUS LARGE BOWEL SPOTTED WITH HEMORRHAGES AND EDEMATOUS MESENTERY CONTAINING HEMORRHAGIC LYMPH NODES. FROM A SWINE WHICH DIED 15 DAYS AFTER 400 r IN AIR, TOTAL BODY, 1,000 KV X-RAY IRRADIATION, DELIVERED BILATERALLY. (OFFICIAL U.S. NAVY PHOTOGRAPH.)

There also may be fibrosis, arteriosclerosis, atrophy of functional epithelium, and carcinoma.

INTRACAVITARY USE OF RADIOACTIVE COLLOIDS

Radioactive colloids are injected into body cavities (usually pleural or peritoneal) as a means of controlling some of the effects of cancer. Gold-198, yttrium-90, and phosphorus-32 are radioisotopes commonly used in colloidal form. This therapy yields an intense radiation dose to the tissues at the surfaces of the cavity. It is sometimes used prophylactically after operation to prevent spread of cancer cells. More commonly it is used as a rather effective palliative measure for the control of fluid accumulations caused by

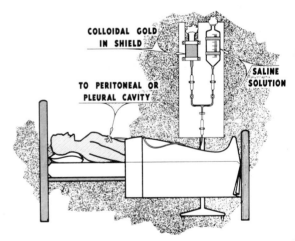

FIGURE I–8. DIAGRAMMATIC REPRESENTATION OF ADMINISTRATION OF GOLD-198 FOR INTRACAVITARY USE IN METASTASIZED CANCER. (USAEC-1D-18A.)

malignancy. Its mechanism of action in relation to fluid accumulations is not well understood. (Figure I–8.)

See COLLOIDS, RADIOACTIVE and COLLOIDAL AND LARGE PARTICLE RADIOISOTOPES FOR MEDICAL USE.

INVERSE SQUARE LAW

When radiation (thermal or nuclear) from a point source is emitted uniformly in all directions, the amount received per unit area at any given distance from the source, assuming no absorption, is inversely proportional to the square of the distance. For example, at 2 miles from a given explosion, the thermal energy received per unit area would be one-fourth of that received at half the distance, i.e., at 1 mile, from the same explosion.

INVERSION

Temperature normally decreases with increase in altitude from the earth's surface up to the stratosphere. However, commonly at night near the ground (a few hundred feet) this is reversed, and temperature increases with altitude. These inversions are usually restricted to shallow layers of air and most frequently occur in the lower 5,000 feet above the earth. Smog is an example of a condition produced by an inversion.

An inversion layer tends to prevent the normal rise of warm radioactive gases; e.g., gases released in stack disposal are held down rather than being allowed to rise.

See METEOROLOGY.

IODINE

Symbol I; atomic number 53; atomic weight 126.91. A halogen, nonmetallic, violet-to-black, lustrous solid, volatilizing at ordinary temperatures into a blue-violet gas with an irritating odor. Discovered by the French chemist Courtois in 1811. Named from Greek *iodes*, violet. Occurs as the iodide in sea water and is concentrated in sea plants, in saltpeter in Chile, and in brines from oil wells. Natural abundance furnished 100% by the stable isotope I^{127}.

Used commercially in the aniline dye industry and in photography. Used in medicine in the manufacture of iodoform and Aristol; the iodide is used as an antiseptic and as a caustic. Essential for man and animals; daily requirement about 2 to 4 micrograms per kilogram body weight ($\mu g/kg$). There is a close correlation between lack of iodine in surface waters and goiter in the United States. The thyroid gland is capable of storing excess iodine (concentration about 10,000 times that of any other organ) so that the requirements need

not be met in the daily diet. Iodized salt is in common usage. The biochemical standard man contains about 0.00004% or 0.028 gram of iodine per 70 kilograms of body weight. The adult man may contain 20 milligrams of iodine—10 mg in the thyroid gland and the other 10 mg in the rest of the body. Blood content ranges from 8 to 16 $\mu g/100$ milliliters (ml). Approximate content level: sea water, 17 to 50 $\mu g/liter$; soils, 600 to 8,000 $\mu g/kg$; crop plants, 2 to 500 $\mu g/kg$ on a dry basis; meat, 30 $\mu g/kg$; milk and eggs, 10 to 400 $\mu g/kg$; and sea fish, 400 to 900 $\mu g/kg$.

Iodine vapor is more irritating and toxic than chlorine or bromine. Iodine compounds are only moderately toxic, even in large doses. The thyroid gland protects itself from overdosage by preventing the addition of more than 0.1 to 0.2 mg iodine per gram of thyroid weight. The weight of the thyroid gland in man is approximately 20 grams.

Twenty radioactive isotopes have been identified, of which 11 may be produced as fission products in nuclear reactors and in the detonation of nuclear devices. These include I^{131} through I^{140}. Several are of grave significance in radioactive fallout: In the time interval from 1 hour to 1 day, I^{135} (half-life 6.68 hours); I^{133} (half-life 20.5 hours), and I^{132} (half-life 2.4 hours) are present and are listed in descending order of availability from the standpoint of yield. From 1 day to 1 week, I^{133}, I^{132}, I^{131} (half-life 8.07 days) and I^{135} are significant; from 1 week to 1 month, I^{131} and I^{132} are still present; and from 1 month to 1 year, I^{131} is the significant radioactive iodine isotope. To put the hazard from iodine in its proper position in relation to other fallout radionuclides, the following are listed in order of decreasing hazard: 1 hour to 1 day (insufficient data for evaluation); 1 day to 1 week, I^{131}, Ba^{140}, La^{140}, and Mo^{99}; 1 week to 1 month, I^{131}, Ba^{140}, La^{140}, Pr^{143}, Y^{91}, Zr^{95}, Sr^{89} and Ce^{144}; 1 month to 1 year, Ce^{144}, Zr^{95}, Y^{91}, I^{131}, Nb^{95}, Ba^{140} and Sr^{89}; 1 year to 70 years, Sr^{90}, Ce^{144}, Cs^{137} and Ru^{106}. It is obvious that for short-term or tropospheric fallout, I^{131} is the most significant of the fission products.

Iodine-131 ($_{53}I^{131}$). Radioactive half-life, 8.07 $\pm$ 0.02 days; biological half-life, 138 days; effective half-life, 7.7 days. It is usually obtained as a fission product. Its decay to stable xenon-131 is complicated by particle radiation of conversion electrons of 7 different energies and 4 different types of beta rays; and by 8 different types of gamma electromagnetic radiation.

I^{131} may be a fallout hazard by direct inhalation by man but is usually important through the food chain: atmosphere ⟶ plants ⟶ animals ⟶ milk ⟶ man. The Windscale incident points up this cycle: reactor fire contamination being released to the atmosphere, I^{131} contamination of the grass which the cows ate in the grazing area around the reactor, and milk sufficiently contaminated that for several days it had to be discarded.

USAEC and USPHS sampling programs always included milk samples, and I^{131} was one of the radionuclides routinely sampled. For the last year of weapons testing, the 12-month average of I^{131} in milk samples from 12 widely separated stations in the United States ranged from 1 micromicrocurie per liter ($\mu\mu c$/liter) in one city to a high average of 27 $\mu\mu c$/liter in another, with individual sample variation from 0 to 181 $\mu\mu c$/liter. The maximum permissible limit for lifetime exposure of population groups is 3,000 $\mu\mu c$/liter.

In 1939 the first use of I^{131} in a metabolic study was reported. To date, over 3,000 reports have appeared in world literature describing the use of I^{131} as a diagnostic, therapeutic, or medical research agent. The principal diagnostic use is in the measurement of the functional state of the thyroid gland, and over 35 different radioiodine tests have been developed, each having its advocates. The measurement of the thyroid uptake of iodine is not simple, as was demonstrated in the early 1950's by sending a manikin with a "standard thyroid" to different hospital laboratories and finding a measurement error that exceeded 100% in many of them. Techniques have been perfected and measurements are now more accurate. Radioactive iodinated human serum albumin (IHSA) is used as the tracer material in measuring blood plasma volume. IHSA is also successfully used in studies of cardiac output and requires no arterial puncture, cardiac catheterization, or gas analysis. Another interesting test uses a scanning technique and IHSA to visualize blood pools within the intact human body. Studies of fat metabolism also use iodinated materials. Liver function tests use I^{131}-tagged rose bengal, a dye which is selectively taken from the blood by the liver and excreted in the bile. Kidney function tests using I^{131}-tagged Diodrast are effective. Pancreatic tests use I^{131}-labeled triolein. I^{131}-labeled diiodofluorescein is used for tumor localization. I^{131} is extensively used for therapy of hyperthyroidism, and in the last 25 years over 15,000 patients have been so treated. Cardiac involvement related to hyperthyroidism is also treated with radioiodine. Certain types of thyroid cancer have responded well to radioiodine treatment. Thus, I^{131} is the most widely used of the radioactive isotopes in medical research, diagnosis, and therapy. One summary lists 85.4% of all isotopes uses as I^{131}, P^{32} coming next with only 4.4%, and Co^{60} third with 3.6%.

All the techniques used in studying human physiology are used in animals—in fact they were worked out on animals first. Studies of metabolism, absorption, kidney function, liver function, utilization of iodine, blood studies, and localization of tumors all make routine use of radioactive iodine compounds.

Since I^{131} taken up by the thyroid will irradiate and kill the cells in the gland, its presence on a continuing basis is undesirable. Thus the maximum permissible concentration is very low. For soluble material on a 168-hour week (continuous exposure) with thyroid as the critical organ, 2×10^{-5} microcurie per cubic centimeter (μc/cc) is allowed in water, and 3×10^{-9} μc/cc in air (0.000000003 of a millionth of a curie).

Iodine-132 ($_{53}I^{132}$).   Radioactive half-life 0.097 days (2.3 hours); with thyroid as the critical organ, biological half-life 138 days and effective half-life 0.097 days; beta (β^-) and gamma emitter. Because of its short half-life, although biologically desirable, it was not available except near a reactor until a new technique was developed for obtaining it as the daughter of the fission product tellurium-132 by repeated extraction.

It can be used for thyroid function tests, in plasma volume determination, for studies of cardiac output, as I^{132}-labeled albumin for the localization of the site of placental attachment instead of sodium-24, and for double-tracer iodine studies with I^{131}. In fact, it can be used for almost all research and medical diagnostic activity for which I^{131} was formerly used, and it is more desirable because of its much shorter half-life.

ION

General name applied to an electrically charged atom or a molecularly bound group of atoms. Occasionally, also a free electron or other charged subatomic particle. The movement of electricity in a gas depends upon ions, those carrying a positive charge traveling in the direction of the current flow, while the negatively charged ions move in the opposite direction. They take their name from the Greek for traveler, because of this action. In their movement through a gas, two things may happen: the ions may collide with gas molecules and lose their energy, or suitable encounters may result in the formation of more ions, called ionization by collision.

Ions are the condensation nuclei formed by the passage of an ionization particle and visualized as a track in the cloud chamber.

The passage of a charged particle through a gas results in the formation of ion pairs. An alpha particle from a radioactive source may produce from 50,000 to 100,000 ion pairs per centimeter of ordinary air (*see* PAIR PRODUCTION). An ion pair consists of a positive ion and a negative ion having charges of the same magnitude and formed from a neutral atom or molecule by the action of radiation.

Ions may be generated in an ion source or ion accelerator.

ION CHAMBER

Chamber with electric field to collect ions liberated by passage of radiation. Usually ION-IZATION CHAMBER.

ION EXCHANGE

Chemical process involving the reversible interchange of ions between a solution and a particular solid material (ion exchanger), such as an ion exchange resin consisting of a matrix of insoluble material interspersed with fixed ions of opposite charge. Ion exchangers are insoluble substances from which ions may be readily and reversibly replaced by others from solutions brought into contact with the exchanger.

Ion exchange between soil particles and soil solution has been recognized for over 100 years. Exchange has been shown to occur with substances such as cellulose, lignin, wool, protein, bone, resins, and inorganic precipitates. The development of synthetic exchange resins with optimum physical and chemical properties for a specific application has greatly extended the use of this technique for biological research.

Examples of applications of this technique are as follows: removal of impurities or interfering substances; concentration of trace constituents; separation of materials; estimation of total salt concentration; determining properties of complex ions; determination of available phosphorus in soils; and removal of potassium from uremic dogs by continuous circulation of blood through a cation exchanger.

ION PAIR

A positive ion and a negative ion (usually an electron), having charges of the same magnitude and formed from a neutral atom or molecule by the action of radiation. A rapidly moving charged particle, such as an alpha or beta particle, creates a strong electric field in its immediate neighborhood and thus has the ability to eject orbital electrons from the atoms or molecules of a gas through which it passes. This results in the creation of positive ions. Some of the expelled electrons attach themselves to other atoms to form negative ions. Thus, the passage of a charged particle through a gas results in the formation of a number of ion pairs. For standard conditions the formation

of a single ion pair requires the expenditure of about 33.5 electron volts.

A primary ion pair is produced directly by the causative radiation. An ion cluster is a group of ion pairs produced at or near the site of primary ionization and includes the primary ion pair and any secondary ion pairs formed.

Ion density is the number of ion pairs per unit volume. Ion-pair yield is the quotient of the number of molecules, M, of a given kind produced or converted, divided by the number, N, of ion pairs resulting from high-energy radiation—the M/N ratio.

Ion pair should not be confused with positron-electron pair. (*See* PAIR PRODUCTION.)

ION TRANSPORT

Ions (mainly Na^+ and K^+) are constantly moving in and out of the normal cell. This dynamic equilibrium of ionic composition of tissue may be affected by ionizing radiations. Increased uptake of sodium-24 has been observed in squid axons after irradiation. Isolated rabbit heart releases potassium into the perfusion fluid after irradiation. Dog heart irradiated in situ loses potassium in the coronary venous blood. Potassium-42 uptake increases in frog erythrocytes immediately after irradiation with 100 roentgens of x-rays, but this is followed by a loss of K^{42} 90 minutes after irradiation. Ion transport is intimately related to water balance. The acute radiation syndrome causes marked changes in the electrolyte balance associated with hemorrhage and damage to the gastrointestinal tract.

IONIZATION

The production of ions in matter by the passage of a radioactive particle, or indirectly by electromagnetic radiation. Any process by which a neutral atom or molecule loses or gains electrons, thereby acquiring a net charge. Although some are presented in detail as separate items, the following 24 closely related ionization items will be summarized here for the sake of completeness.

Alpha particles have a very high level of specific ionization, with the production, for example, of about 230,000 ion pairs by a RaC' (polonium-214) alpha particle in its approximately 5-millimeter ionization path through air. The process of ionization requires the expenditure of about 33.5 electron volts for the production of each ion pair by an alpha particle so that toward the end of its path, its energy and thus its speed are greatly reduced. Specific ionization thus increases until a point is reached at which the particle is converted into a neutral helium atom.

An avalanche results when a single charged

particle, accelerated by a strong electric field, produces additional charged particles through collision with neutral gas molecules. An electron from each original ion pair may lead to the formation of a large number of secondary ion pairs—as many as 10^4 in a region with a high electrical potential gradient. This is sometimes called Townsend ionization, Townsend avalanche, or Townsend cascade in honor of its discoverer, the English scientist J. S. Townsend.

A beta particle also causes ionization as it moves through matter. Such a rapidly moving charged particle causes a strong electric field in its immediate vicinity and thus has the ability to eject orbital electrons from the atoms or molecules of a gas through which it passes, thus converting them into positive ions. The expelled electrons usually remain free for a time, although a few form negative ions by attaching themselves to other atoms or molecules. Thus many ion pairs may be formed by the passage of a charged particle. The beta particle with its higher speed and smaller charge does not produce as many ion pairs per centimeter as do alpha particles, but since the total path is much longer, the total ionization may be about the same.

An ionization chamber is a device used to measure the quantity of ionizing radiation in terms of the electric charge associated with ions produced in the chamber. Five different types are discussed in some detail: AIR WALL IONIZATION CHAMBER, FREE AIR IONIZATION CHAMBER, INTEGRATING IONIZATION CHAMBER, POCKET DOSIMETER, and TISSUE EQUIVALENT IONIZATION CHAMBER.

An ionization counter is an instrument for counting ionizing particles. It has no internal amplification by gas multiplication.

Ionization by collision may result as ions (electrically charged particles) travel through a gas and make suitable encounters with gas molecules. As the pressure of the gas is diminished, the number of ions produced by collisions gradually becomes larger than the number of ions losing their energy by colliding with gas molecules.

Columnar ionization refers to regions of such dense ionization that even a strong external electric field cannot prevent some recombination.

Ionization density refers to the number of ion pairs per unit volume, and is obtained by dividing the LET (linear energy transfer) by W (the energy required to form an ion pair in air), i.e., 34 ev (electron volts).

Ionizing energy is the average amount of energy lost by an ionizing particle in producing an ion pair in gas. For air at standard conditions the figure is 33.5 electron volts.

An ionizing event is any occurrence of a process in which an ion or group of ions is produced.

Fission fragments with their tremendous energy and high velocity produce considerable ionization in their paths.

Gamma rays are also capable of producing ionization indirectly by ejecting electrons with appreciable velocity from atoms present in the substances subject to their radiations. These rapidly moving secondary electrons produce ionization, i.e., produce ion pairs in their paths.

Ion pairs are formed in the process of ionization. The pair is composed of a positive ion and a negative ion that have charges of the same magnitude and that are formed from a neutral atom or molecule by the action of radiation.

Minimum ionization is the smallest possible value of the specific ionization that a charged particle can produce in passing through a particular substance. For an individual, singly charged particle in ordinary air, the minimum ionization is about 50 ion pairs per centimeter of path, and is proportional to the density of the medium and to the square of the charge of the particle.

The ionization path is the trail of ion pairs produced by an ionizing particle as it traverses matter.

The ionization potential for a particular kind of atom is the energy per unit charge, usually expressed in volts, required to remove an electron from the atom to an infinite distance.

Primary ionization is that produced by the original charged particle as contrasted to the total ionization, which includes secondary ionization produced by delta rays. In counter tubes, the total ionization is produced by incident radiation without gas amplification.

Specific ionization is the number of ion pairs formed per unit distance along the track of an ion passing through matter.

Tissue Ionization. When the individual accelerated particles penetrate a biological specimen, inactivation or modification of specific biological functions may occur. These alterations include cell membrane permeability changes and inhibition of cell function such as respiration, glycolysis, synthesis of nucleic acids, and synthesis of new enzymes. This comes about because absorption in matter of ionizing radiation gives rise to a variety of types of electronically excited and ionized molecules. They are usually unstable and initiate the following sequence of events: They dissipate their physical energy either in collisions or spontaneously and are converted to stable molecules, some of which may be chemically different from the surrounding molecules. They also give rise to free radicals, which react with each other and with the general milieu until chemical stability results. Then comes the biological response to the altered physiology of the cells and to the foreign chemical substances. (See BIOLOGICAL EFFECTS OF RADIATION.)

Total ionization may be defined as the total number of ion pairs produced by the ionizing particle along its entire path—or the total electric charge on the ions of one sign when the energetic particle that has produced these ions has lost all its kinetic energy. For a given gas, the total ionization is closely proportional to the initial energy of the radioactive particle and is nearly independent of its type or nature.

The ionization track is the visual manifestation of the path of an ionizing particle in a cloud chamber, bubble chamber, or nuclear emulsion.

X-rays have been known, for many years, for their ability to produce ions, i.e., ionization, in gases. They do this by ejecting electrons with appreciable velocity from atoms or molecules present in the substance subjected to the radiations. These rapidly moving, secondary electrons then produce the ion pairs in their paths. The specific ionization of x-rays thus depends on the energy of the expelled electrons.

IONIZATION CHAMBER

Instrument for radiation measurement based on collecting ions produced by the radiation in a defined volume. Since the roentgen (unit of radiation intensity) is defined in terms of the ionization produced by radiation in air, two of the most important instruments of this kind are the primary standard free-air chamber and the secondary standard air-wall chamber or condenser r-meter, which serve as calibration instruments. Another important type is the rugged pocket dosimeter, which is widely used as a personnel dosimeter. Ionization produced in gases is the chief phenomenon used for precise measurement of radiations. In an ionization chamber the essential parts are the medium that is ionized and the electric field that is maintained between the pair of electrodes. The collecting electrode is often supplemented by a guard ring (see Figure I–9) designed to prevent collection of extraneous ions from outside the defined volume. In operation, the electrodes are supplied with an appropriate voltage; the ions attracted to the collector are measured by a suitably sensitive electrometer. For stable operation, an ionization chamber requires sufficient voltage to insure collection of all the ions initiated by the radiation. The least voltage which will achieve complete collection in a particular cham-

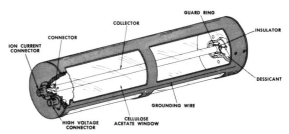

FIGURE I–9.   IONIZATION CHAMBER CONSTRUCTION, SHOWING THIN WINDOW, ELECTRODES, AND GUARD RING. (COURTESY OF TECHNICAL ASSOCIATES.)

ber is its saturation voltage; the current then collected is the saturation current. Figure I–10 shows the relationship between the current collected and the applied voltage in a typical ionization chamber. At low voltages the collection is not entirely efficient, some ions being lost in recombination before they can be swept in by the collector. But after reaching saturation, the current does not increase further as the voltage is raised until it can accelerate the ions to energies at which they cause additional ionization by collision. This effect gives rise to gas amplification, which is made use of in the proportional counter. Still higher voltages lead to the avalanche discharge phenomenon characteristic of the Geiger counter region. Continuous and destructive electrical discharge will take place in the chamber if the voltage is raised to extreme values. The construction of a typical ionization chamber is shown in Figure I–9.

When ionization chambers are designed for standardization measurements, it must be remembered that the roentgen is defined only for electromagnetic radiation and is dependent upon ionization effects in air. However, there are broad fields of use for ionization chambers not limited by this definition. Special materials for the walls, electrodes, and gas are frequently used, as, for example,

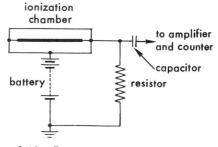

FIGURE I–10.   SIMPLIFIED CIRCUIT FOR IONIZATION CHAMBER WHEN USED AS A PARTICLE COUNTER. THE CENTRAL ELECTRODE IS CONNECTED TO A SUITABLE VACUUM-TUBE (LINEAR) AMPLIFIER SO THAT THE PULSES ARE AMPLIFIED AND MODIFIED BEFORE GOING TO A COUNTING INSTRUMENT.

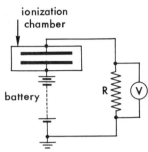

FIGURE I–11. SIMPLIFIED CIRCUIT FOR INTEGRATING (CURRENT MEASURING) TYPE OF IONIZATION CHAMBER. THE STEADY PRODUCTION OF ION-PAIRS IN THE CHAMBER RESULTS IN A VERY WEAK, BUT CONTINUOUS, FLOW OF CURRENT THROUGH THE RESISTANCE R. THE MAGNITUDE OF THIS ION CURRENT CAN BE DETERMINED WITH THE AID OF A VACUUM-TUBE VOLTMETER V CONNECTED ACROSS THE RESISTANCE.

in the tissue equivalent ionization chamber. Substances can be introduced to contribute response to specific radiations, as in the threshold and fission counters. Neutron response can be achieved by using boron-trifluoride gas. Some ionization chambers are capable of responding to individual radiation events and are used as ionization counters, particularly for heavy particles such as alpha rays. These uses are exceptional; ionization chambers are most commonly employed in circuits which determine the integrated effect from the occurrence of many events, continuously or over a period of time. In this type of integrating ionization chamber the circuit (Fig. I–11) is the one generally used. The current strength is directly proportional to the rate at which ionizing (alpha, beta, gamma, etc.) radiation is entering the ionization chamber.

IONIZATION COUNTER

An ionization chamber which is used for counting individual ionizing particles, but without internal amplification. Counters of this type have only limited applicability, their essential utility being confined to the detection and measurement of heavy particles, specifically alpha rays, fission fragments, or energetic heavy ions produced by accelerators. With appropriate chamber design, the charges collected by the counter from individual events can be analyzed to establish the energy or range of the particles.

IONIZATION PATH

The trail of ion pairs produced by the passage of an ionizing particle through matter. This path or track can be seen and photographed by the use of a CLOUD CHAMBER, a BUBBLE CHAMBER, or a NUCLEAR EMULSION.

IONIZING PARTICLE

A particle that directly produces ion pairs in its passage through matter. Commonly, a charged particle such as an alpha particle, a beta particle, a proton, or a meson having considerably greater kinetic energy than the ionizing energy appropriate to the particular medium through which the particle is passing. An ionizing particle leaves a track which can be seen with the aid of a cloud chamber, a bubble chamber, or a nuclear emulsion.

"Directly ionizing particles" are charged particles (electrons, protons, α-particles, etc.) having sufficient kinetic energy to produce ionization by collision.

"Indirectly ionizing particles" are uncharged particles (neutrons, photons, etc.) which can liberate directly ionizing particles or can initiate a nuclear transformation.

See IONIZATION.

IONIZING RADIATION

Any particulate or electromagnetic radiation capable of producing ions, directly or indirectly, in its passage through matter. Alpha and beta particles produce ion pairs directly, while gamma rays and x-rays liberate electrons as they traverse matter, which in turn produce ionization in their paths.

IOWA STATE UNIVERSITY SWINE IRRADIATION PROJECT

A project directed toward an understanding of the genetic effects of radiation in swine, in the hope of gaining a better understanding of radiation effects on human heredity. Conducted by the Animal Science Department at Iowa State University of Science and Technology, Ames, Iowa, with the support of the USAEC.

An equal number of normal males and males whose testicles have been irradiated with 300 roentgens of x-ray are being mated with unirradiated females. The offspring of each are compared by measuring the following: mortality, litter size and sex ratio; weight, feed utilization and morphology; blood antigens; and learning ability. It is planned to have 600 litters farrowed per year in order to have the necessary numbers for study.

IRIDIUM

Symbol Ir; atomic number 77; atomic weight 192.2. A white, very heavy (second to osmium), hard, brittle metal. Occurs naturally with platinum and with osmium. Two stable isotopes furnish the natural abundance: Ir^{191}, 38.5%, and Ir^{193}, 61.5%. Discovered in 1803 by English chemist Tennant.

Named for Latin, *iris*, rainbow. Reflects the colors of its salts—green, red, violet.

Used commercially, alloyed with platinum for standard weights and measures and with osmium in tipping pens. Nontoxic.

There are 12 radioactive isotopes. Iridium-194, available commercially, was early identified as of potential medical interest because it could be reactor produced and had a favorable half-life of 19 hours and an activation index of 8,000. Iridium-192 is also of potential industrial and medical significance.

Iridium-192 ($_{77}Ir^{192}$). Radioactive half-life 74.37 days; with total body as the critical organ, biological half-life 20 days, effective half-life 15.8 days; beta (β^-) and gamma emitter. Formed by the neutron-gamma (n,γ) reaction in iridium-191. Used in industrial radiography and in teletherapy in smaller devices. Also used for interstitial implant therapy.

IRON

Symbol Fe; atomic number 26; atomic weight 55.85. A silver-white metal, ductile, malleable and magnetic. Discovery prehistoric—iron implements used by the Egyptians in 3,000 B.C. Named from Anglo-Saxon, *iron*. Symbol Fe from Latin, *ferrum*. Found widely distributed in the earth's crust as an oxide, sulfide, or as an aluminosilicate. Fourth in abundance of the elements of the earth's crust (5.1% of the solid crust). Native iron is found only in meteorites. Natural abundance furnished by 4 stable isotopes.

Iron is the cheapest metal known and the most abundantly produced—hundreds of millions of tons per year. Used largely in the making of steel. Essential for both animal and plant life. Livestock needs about 9 milligrams per pound (mg/lb). Approximately 0.25 mg/day is adequate for rats. The biochemical standard man contains 0.004% or 3 grams per 70 kilograms, of which 2.4 to 2.7 grams is in the form of hemoglobin. Blood contains about 50 mg/100 milliliters and plasma about 0.5. Crop plants content range from 20 to 5,000 parts per million (ppm) on a dry basis, but the nutrient solution needs are only about 1.2 ppm.

Six radioactive isotopes of iron have been identified. Fe^{55} and Fe^{59} may occur in either soil or sea water as induced radioactivity due to neutron bombardment associated with the detonation of a nuclear device. Both are highly significant as components of residual radiation in the soil at the site of detonation. One year after detonation, Fe^{55} may be found in the amount of 13.8 megacuries per megaton (Mc/MT) of bomb fission or fusion and Fe^{59} in the amount of 0.0091 Mc/MT.

Fe^{55} and Fe^{59} as a mixture are extensively used for tracer and metabolic work in agriculture, because the cost is much less and standard counting techniques will record only the gamma from the Fe^{59}.

Iron-59 ($_{26}Fe^{59}$). Radioactive half-life 45.3 days; with spleen as the critical organ, biological half-life 600 days, effective half-life 41.9 days; beta (β^-) and gamma emitter. Produced in the reactor by neutron bombardment of enriched Fe^{58} by the neutron-gamma (n,γ) reaction. Used extensively in medical diagnosis and research, particularly in relation to red cell life span. Used in biological research for studies of plant metabolism, for example, in the study of the cause of the plant disease, chlorosis. Maximum permissible concentration for 168-hour week (continuous exposure) for soluble material with gastrointestinal tract as the critical organ is 6×10^{-4} microcurie per cubic centimeter ($\mu c/cc$) in water and 10^{-7} $\mu c/cc$ in air.

IRON ABSORPTION STUDIES. *See* ANIMAL NUTRITIONAL STUDIES.

IRRADIATION

Exposure to radiation. One speaks of radiation therapy, but of irradiation of the patient.

The exposure of material to x-ray, gamma ray, or slow neutron radiation.

The exposure of material in a nuclear reactor.

Bombardment of material with particle radiation.

See PARTIAL BODY IRRADIATION and WHOLE BODY IRRADIATION.

IRREPARABLE DAMAGE

Injury or damage to cells, tissues, or organs which is not repaired. The rate and the degree of recovery vary with the criteria used to indicate recovery and with the time of examination after irradiation. Although, soon after irradiation, recovery may appear to be complete by all criteria, irreparable damage must be postulated, or late effects such as LIFE SHORTENING, LEUKEMIA, and cancer due to irradiation would not occur. Thus, although symptomatic and objective recovery may apparently be complete following large doses, late effects may still develop in a small percentage of the population, indicating some irreparable damage.

If experimental animals are exposed to large doses of radiation, and those that recover are later again exposed to radiation, it is found that the $LD_{50}/30$ days is decreased. From work such as this a concept of partial irreversible injury has been developed with a mathematical expression of the irreparable fraction. For example, for x-ray and gamma-ray irradiation the irreparable fraction of the initial damage is of the order of 10%.

Probably RECOVERY FROM IRRADIATION never brings the organism back to the precise state from which it was displaced. In this case, irreparable injury would be the difference between the initial and the final states.

ISOBAR

One of several nuclides having the same number of nucleons but different combinations of protons and neutrons. Nuclides of the same mass number but different atomic numbers. For example, chlorine-36 and argon-36 ($_{17}Cl^{36}$ and $_{18}A^{36}$) have the same mass number A, 36, but a difference of 1 in the atomic number Z, i.e., number of protons, and therefore also a difference of 1 in the number of neutrons N (A = Z + N).

See ISOTOPE and ISOTONE.

ISODOSE CURVES

Curves or lines drawn to connect points of identical calculated or measured amounts of radiant energy reaching a certain depth in tissue. Depth dose of radiation in tissue is in a direct line with the radiant beam and varies with the distance from the direct line beam. Decrease in depth dose results from attenuation by absorption and also from the increase in distance from the radiation source according to the inverse square law. Thus, depth dose varies with the source-to-skin distance as well as with the nature of the tissue being irradiated. The depth of penetration also varies with the type of radiation used, as will be seen in Figure I–12 comparing a cobalt-60 hectocurie unit with a 200 KVP x-ray unit. The depth dose data are recorded as lines of equal dose expressed as percentages of maximum dose at various tissue depths. This study of distribution of radiation was done with an infinite water phantom. The dose depth data are used by the radiologist in calculating the amount of radiant energy a given point in the body or in a cancer will receive, and are carefully plotted for each patient.

The reverse procedure is followed in "looking at" the radiation being given off by the body, e.g., in measuring the thyroid uptake of iodine-131. Measurements here are of the response of a detector to a source of radiation, and since these are responses and not doses, the curves are called isoresponse curves or isoresponse lines and represent what the detecting system "sees."

ISODOSE LINES

Term used both in radiobiology and in the study of radioactive contamination from fallout.

In radiobiology, isodose charts are drawn showing the distribution of radiation in a medium by means of lines or isodose curves drawn through points receiving equal doses. Used in planning treatment with x-rays, cobalt-60 gamma rays, and radium.

In fallout, a term applied to isointensity contours plotted on a radiation field in which the dose rate or the total accumulated dose is the same for all the area included within the isodose lines. (*See* CONTOUR METHODS and FALLOUT PATTERN.)

ISOINTENSITY CONTOURS

Imaginary lines on the surface of ground or water, or lines drawn on a map, joining points in a radiation field which have the same radiation intensity at a given time. The intensity of radiation is measured at various points and at different times, adjustments to a common time reading are made, and lines are drawn to connect all points having the same reading for that time. *See* FALLOUT PATTERN for diagrams and also CONTOUR METHODS and ISODOSE LINES.

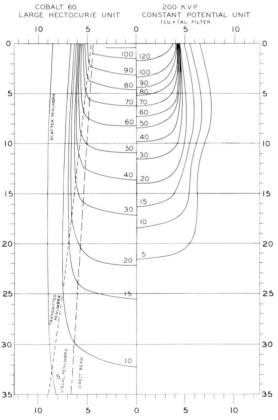

FIGURE I–12. TWO ISODOSE CURVES COMPARING THE DISTRIBUTION OF RADIATION IN A BEAM FROM COBALT-60 AND A 200 KVP X-RAY UNIT. ISODOSE LINES AT 50 CM SOURCE-FOCUS-SKIN-DISTANCE, 6 × 8 CM FIELD. (COURTESY MEDICAL DIVISION, OAK RIDGE INSTITUTE OF NUCLEAR STUDIES.)

ISOLOGOUS TISSUE GRAFTS

Tissue transplants in cases in which the donor and host are of same genetic strain; as human identical twins, or highly inbred strains of mice. *See* BONE MARROW GRAFTS.

ISOMER, NUCLEAR

One of two or more nuclides having the same mass number A and atomic number Z, but existing for measurable times (at least 10^{-9} second) in the excited state with a higher energy and different properties than the ground state isometric pair nuclide. When a nucleus is in an excited state and decays by gamma emission, the transition from the higher to lower energy usually takes less than 10^{-13} second. However, those taking longer are called isomers with metastable energy levels.

The decay process from the metastable state to the ground state is by isomeric transition (I.T.), and the total process is as follows:

Parent metastable state $\xrightarrow{\text{I.T.}}$ parent ground state $\xrightarrow{\beta\ \text{decay}}$ daughter product (ground state may be stable). However in the decay process, nuclear isomers fall into three groups: isomers with independent decay, genetically related isomers, and isomers of stable state nuclei. In the first case, each isomer decays independently of the other, as in the following examples:

Mn^{52m} (β^+, 21.3 minutes) $\longrightarrow Fe^{52}$ (stable)
Mn^{52g} (β^+, 5.55 days) $\longrightarrow Fe^{52}$ (stable)
Cd^{115m} (β^-, 43 days) $\longrightarrow In^{115g}$ (β^-, 6×10^{14} years)
Cd^{115g} (β^-, 53 hours) $\longrightarrow In^{115m}$ (I.T., 4.50 hours)

In the second group of genetically related isomers, the metastable state decays to the ground state by isomeric transition with a definite half-life, emitting a gamma-ray photon; the ground state then decays to form the daughter product with a different half-life. Examples are as follows:

Sc^{44m} (I.T., 2.44 days) $\longrightarrow Sc^{44g}$ (β^+, 3.96 hours) $\longrightarrow Ca^{44}$ (stable)
Co^{60m} (I.T., 10.5 minutes) $\longrightarrow Co^{60g}$ (β^-, 5.27 years) $\longrightarrow Ni^{60}$ (stable)
Br^{80m} (I.T., 4.5 hours) $\longrightarrow Br^{80g}$ (β^-, 18 minutes) $\longrightarrow Kr^{80}$ (stable)

Historically, the Br^{80} reaction was the first, being found in 1935.

The third category, in which the active species are isomers of stable nuclei, decays by isomeric transition from the metastable excited state to the ground state of a stable nuclide with the emission of gamma radiation. More than 30 stable isotopes found in nature are known to form metastable states lasting from a few seconds to several days. Examples are Kr^{83}, Sr^{87}, Rh^{103}, Ag^{107}, and Au^{197}.

Isomers are sometimes formed from stable nuclides in other processes, as $Sr^{86}(n,\gamma)\ Sr^{87m}$.

As seen above, the metastable nuclear isomer is indicated by adding the letter m to the mass number in the symbol for the nuclide, as Br^{80m}, half-life 4.4 hours; Te^{133m}, half-life 63 minutes; and Cs^{133m}, half-life 6.0×10^{-9} second.

ISOMERIC TRANSITION

Radioactive transition from one nuclear isomer to another of lower energy. The decay process from the metastable state to the ground state, with a measureable half-life and the emission of a gamma-ray photon. The de-excitation of the nuclei in the metastable state may occur by gamma emission or by internal conversion followed by the emission of x-rays or Auger electrons.

Figure I–13 indicates the transitions from the parent metastable state through the parent ground state to the daughter decay product.

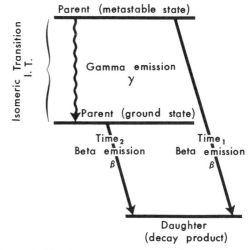

FIGURE I–13. ISOMERIC TRANSITION. TRANSITION FROM THE PARENT METASTABLE STATE THROUGH THE PARENT GROUND STATE TO THE DAUGHTER DECAY PRODUCT.

ISOTONE

One of several nuclides having the same number of neutrons but a different number of protons in their nuclei (the reverse of an ISOTOPE). For example, potassium-39 and calcium-40 ($_{19}K_{20}^{39}$ and $_{20}Ca_{20}^{40}$) are isotones.

See ISOBAR.

ISOTOPE

One of several nuclides belonging to the same element, i.e., having the same atomic number Z (protons) but differing in the number of neutrons N, and hence in mass number A. For example, $_6C_6^{12}$, $_6C_7^{13}$ and $_6C_8^{14}$ ($_{\text{protons}}$ carbon $^{\text{mass number}}_{\text{neutrons}}$) are all isotopes of carbon; the first 2 are stable isotopes and the last one is a radioactive isotope.

Atoms of the same atomic number (same number of protons) occupy the same place in the periodic table but may differ markedly in their radioactive behavior. For example, it was found that although radium C, radium E, thorium C, and actinium C were different in radioactive properties and origins, they were actually all forms of bismuth ($_{83}Bi^{214}$, $_{83}Bi^{210}$, $_{83}Bi^{212}$, and $_{83}Bi^{211}$ respectively) and therefore were identical in chemical properties.

There are over 270 isotopic forms of stable elements and over 40 radioactive isotopes that exist in nature. In addition, more than 900 radioactive isotopes have been produced artificially. Thus there are probably over 1,200 known forms of the elements.

See ISOTONE, ISOBAR, ISOMER, ISOTOPIC COMPOSITION, RADIOACTIVE ISOTOPE, and STABLE ISOTOPE.

ISOTOPE DILUTION

Isotope dilution methods are most valuable procedures in biochemistry and analytical chemistry, making possible volume determinations in medical research—red cell mass or volume, plasma volume, lymph volume, and body water. In addition, the volumes occupied by other ions of biological interest are estimated—chloride space, bromide space, total exchangeable sodium, and total exchangeable potassium.

In principle, the method consists in incorporating uniformly a small amount of a labeled test substance in the material to be analyzed, isolating some of the test substance from the mixture, and determining the isotopic content. For volume determinations it may be assumed that if 1,000 counts/min of radioactivity in a negligible volume is mixed into a volume of water that then measures 10 counts/min/ml, the volume of water was 100 ml. Thus $V = \dfrac{A}{S} - B$, where A is counts/min in B ml solution, which is thoroughly mixed with an unknown volume V ml, and a small sample is taken which measures S counts/min/ml. When B is small compared with V, as is usually the case, then

$$V = \frac{A}{S}.$$

A most important use has been in the determination of the contribution of two sources to a product. For example, it is possible to determine the amount of the phosphorus in a plant that came from soil phosphorus and the amount from fertilizers; how much of the minerals in a newborn came from the mother's diet and how much from the mother's body; how much fecal calcium and phosphorus came from unabsorbed dietary contributions and how much from the body. Considerable advantages are obtained in chemical analysis, since the use of the isotope dilution procedure eliminates the necessity for quantitative separations. This is of particular importance in the systems where purity and high recovery are mutually exclusive, as, for example, in the assays of amino acids in a protein hydrolysate or for individual fatty acids which fall into this category because of the presence of so many chemically similar substances. Various modifications of isotope dilution have been devised, such as the inverse method, in which a known amount of unlabeled substance is added to the labeled material, the latter usually being produced by biosynthesis. In some instances there are advantages from the use of double dilution procedures. Isotope dilution has also been useful in studies involving the separation and isolation of racemic mixtures.

In chemistry, isotope dilution analysis is a method of chemical analysis for a component of a mixture based on the addition to the mixture of a known amount of labeled component of known specific activity, followed by isolation of a quantity of the pure component and measurement of the specific activity of that sample.

ISOTOPE DILUTION ANALYSIS

Isotope dilution methods have been most valuable procedures in biochemistry and analytical chemistry, providing data that are not at all, or only with difficulty, available from other procedures. In principle, the method consists of incorporating uniformly a small amount of the labeled substance in the material to be analyzed, isolating some of the test substance from the mixture, and determining its isotopic content. The amount of dilution that has occurred is a function of the amount of test substance in the original material.

Isotope dilution has been used for estimation of such physiological entities as red blood cell volume, plasma volume, lymph volume, and body water. In addition, the volumes occupied by other ions of biological interest have been estimated, such as chloride space, bromide space, total exchangeable sodium, and total exchangeable potassium.

See LABELING, LABELED COMPOUND, and LABELED MOLECULE.

ISOTOPE EFFECT

The effect of nuclear properties such as mass, size, statistics, spin, parity, magnetic dipole moment, and electric quadrupole moment on the non-nuclear physical and chemical properties of nuclides, leading to differences in the properties of isotopes. Isotope effects are observed in such physicochemical properties as density, rate of diffusion, reaction rate, and equilibrium distribution. In general, isotope effects are relatively small for heavy elements, but may be considerable for light elements. Isotope separation depends upon isotope effect. Differences between isotopes can be demonstrated by the slight difference in wave length for a given spectral line of one isotope as compared with another.

ISOTOPE FARM

Carbon-14 growth chamber, or greenhouse, arranged as a closed system in which plants can be

grown in a carbon-14 dioxide ($C^{14}O_2$) atmosphere and thus labeled with C^{14}. For example, plants produce basic substances called alkaloids (such as atropine, caffeine, coniine, ergotamine, ergotinine, morphine, nicotine, quinine, reserpine, and strychnine) which are physiologically active and useful as drugs. Thus, labeling with C^{14} makes it possible to study their action in the animal body.

This biosynthesis of radioactive compounds has been used in the isotope farms to produce carbon-14-labeled vitamins, starches, fats, oils, sugars, essential oils, rubber, and proteins. (See Figures I–14 and I–15.)

FIGURE I–14. RADIOACTIVE SOYBEAN PLANTS GROWN IN GREENHOUSE OR GROWTH CHAMBER. $C^{14}O_2$ BEING INTRODUCED INTO CHAMBER. THE PURPOSE IS TO OBTAIN TAGGED FORMS OF SOYBEAN OILS FOR USE AS TRACERS IN STUDIES OF FAT METABOLISM IN ANIMALS. (COURTESY ARGONNE NATIONAL LABORATORY.)

FIGURE I–15. MONITORING THE RADIOACTIVITY OF A TOMATO PLANT IN A GROWTH CHAMBER. SCIENTISTS ARE CONDUCTING A RADIOACTIVE TRACER EXPERIMENT TO STUDY THE TRANSLOCATION OF ALKALOIDS. (COURTESY ARGONNE NATIONAL LABORATORY.)

ISOTOPIC COMPOSITION

The number and percentage abundance (used interchangeably with composition) of all the isotopes of an element. This varies widely from element to element: of the naturally occurring stable isotopes, tin has 10 stable isotopes, xenon has 9, and so on, down to a large number of elements with only 1 stable isotope furnishing all the natural abundance. Elements of odd atomic number usually consist of 1 or at the most 2 isotopes, while even atomic number elements rarely have only 1 isotope. Although not fully understood, there is an interesting relationship to the even or odd atomic numbers (protons) Z and neutrons N. As shown below, the even-even nuclides constitute the majority of the stable nuclides found in nature:

Even Z, even N—163
Even Z, odd N—57
Odd Z, even N—50
Odd Z, odd N—5

Experimental data show that the isotopic composition of a given element is relatively nearly the same, no matter where it is found. Meteoric iron has the same isotopic composition as iron taken from the earth.

Radiocarbon dating depends upon the isotopic composition of carbon. In a similar way, measurements of isotopic abundances in lead were used to fix the time of formation of the earth's crust as occurring 3.5 billion years ago.

ISOTOPIC TRACER. *See* TRACER, ISOTOPIC.

JANUS (BIOLOGY RESEARCH REACTOR)

A heterogeneous, light water-moderated tank-type nuclear reactor designed for biological research and suitable for the exposure of a large animal or many small animals simultaneously. Under construction at the Argonne National Laboratory. The reactor is named Janus, after the two-faced Roman god, because it will have 2 radiation faces, the one for use in studies of the biological effects of relatively high dose rates of fission neutrons (2×10^4 to 10^6 rad per week), and the other for low dose rates (0.1 to 50 rad per week).

The core of JANUS will consist of 19 fuel assemblies containing a total of 3 kilograms of uranium-235. The core will be located off-center in an aluminum tank 4 feet in diameter and 7 feet high to provide different neutron intensities at the 2 faces. The reactor will operate at powers of 1 to 200 kilowatts. Figure J–1 shows the proposed arrangement.

JAPANESE FISHERMAN RADIATION ACCIDENT

A thermonuclear device was detonated at the Eniwetok Proving Ground on March 1, 1954. Although a warning area had been set up and searched, a Japanese fishing trawler, the Fukuryu Maru (Lucky Dragon), was caught in the path of the tropospheric fallout. The 23 crew members suffered radiation burns (*see* BURNS, RADIATION) from beta activity of the bomb debris; blood counts were depressed; and 1 death occurred several weeks later, attributed to hepatitis not directly referable to the radiation received. Total radiation dose was probably between 150 and 175 roentgens.

JASPER

Portable ionization chamber type survey meter designed for medium and high levels of radiation.

JOHNSTON ISLAND TESTING AREA. *See* PACIFIC TESTING AREA.

JOINT COMMITTEE ON ATOMIC ENERGY

The Joint Committee on Atomic Energy (JCAE) of the United States Congress was established by the Atomic Energy Act of 1946. It consists of 18 members, 9 from the Senate and 9 from the House of Representatives. The chair-

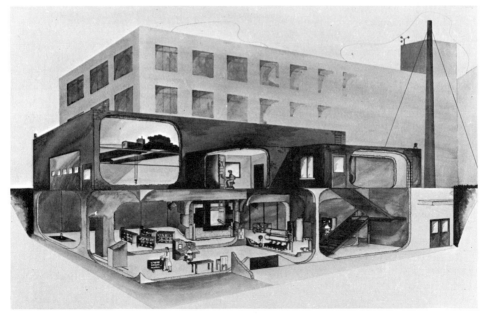

FIGURE J–1. DRAWING SHOWING PROPOSED ARRANGEMENT OF FACILITIES OF THE JANUS BIOLOGICAL RESEARCH REACTOR. IN THE FOREGROUND IS THE BIOLOGY CONTROL ROOM. BEHIND THIS, TO THE LEFT, IS THE LOW-LEVEL EXPOSURE ROOM. THE REACTOR CORE IS IN THE CENTER AND THE HIGH-LEVEL EXPOSURE ROOM IS TO THE RIGHT. THE REACTOR CONTROL ROOM IS SHOWN ON THE SECOND FLOOR. (COURTESY OF ARGONNE NATIONAL LABORATORY.)

manship rotates every 2 years between the House and the Senate and no more than 5 members from either body may be from the same political party. In general, the JCAE engages in 4 types of functions: legislative, investigative, informational and policy-making. The Congress has delegated much of its work in relation to atomic energy research and development to the Joint Committee. It has certain advantages for dealing vigorously with atomic energy problems, including its ability to act for both Houses as a unit, its right to be kept fully informed by the Atomic Energy Commission, and its legislative jurisdiction including annual authorization legislation. The role of the Joint Committee has been evolving from an interest primarily in the weapons program and security to an equal emphasis on peacetime research and development, international cooperation, and declassification. It has stressed the informational function with a series of public hearings; and the policy-making function has been evidenced in atomic power development, basic research facilities, and research in atomic hazards.

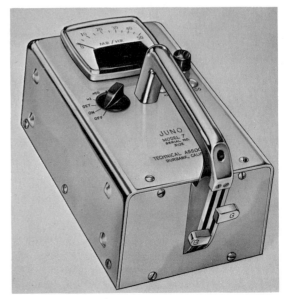

FIGURE J–2. JUNO SURVEY METER. TOP VIEW SHOWING CONTROLS. (COURTESY OF TECHNICAL ASSOCIATES.)

JOINT TASK FORCE

The JTF is a combined force of personnel of the Department of Defense (Army, Navy, Air Force) and the USAEC and their contractors. The JTF has responsibility for all aspects of the testing of nuclear weapons in the Pacific testing areas. The Commander of the JTF is an officer of the general or flag staff designated by the service acting as executive agency of the Joint Chiefs of Staff of the Department of Defense. Joint Task Force 8 came into being with the announcement of the President on April 24, 1962, of the resumption of nuclear weapons tests in the atmosphere over the Pacific.

See ENIWETOK PROVING GROUNDS.

JUNO

Widely used portable survey meter to detect and measure ionizing radiation; uses air ionization chamber as detector and has direct rate meter indication. For the detection of alpha, beta and gamma radiations; capable of discriminating between them through a set of adjustable filter screens which are built into the case. The ordinary ranges provided give readings from 50 mr/hr to 5000 mr/hr. High-range Juno instruments are also available, with ranges which run five times higher. Figure J–2 shows the instrument controls and Figure J–3 its screens for discriminating between radiations.

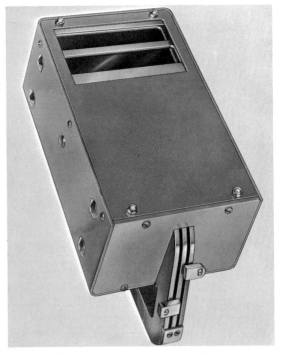

FIGURE J–3. JUNO SURVEY METER. BOTTOM VIEW SHOWING ADJUSTABLE FILTERS AT THE DETECTING CHAMBER. (COURTESY OF TECHNICAL ASSOCIATES.)

K

KERMA

Kerma (K) is an acronym for kinetic energy released in material. The kerma is that quantity which represents the kinetic energy transferred to charged particles by the uncharged particles per unit mass of the irradiated material. The concept is closely related to the energy equivalent of exposure in an x-ray beam. Kerma is the quotient of ΔE_K by Δm, where ΔE_K is the sum of the initial kinetic energies of all the charged particles liberated by indirectly ionizing particles in a volume element of the specified material, Δm is the mass of the matter in that volume element, and Δ represents the appropriate averaging procedure necessary to take into consideration the fact that in general radiation fields are nonuniform in space and also may be variable in time.

$$K = \frac{\Delta E_K}{\Delta m}$$

KEV

The abbreviation, kev, stands for 1 kilo-electron-volt which is 1,000 electron volts (ev).

KICKSORTER

An early type of pulse height analyzer which reports the number of radiation events according to their energy, the energy spectrum being divided into a number of channels covering the selected energy range. The electronic circuitry provides a series of channels having successively higher discriminator values; each pulse, after amplification, passes along the series and falls into the highest channel it can reach. In the process of traveling along the chain from one channel to the next, the pulse automatically cancels its signal from each channel which it has exceeded, giving a differential energy spectrum.

KIDNEY, RADIATION EFFECTS ON

The kidney is relatively radioresistant. Marginal changes in excretory function are observed in dogs and rats only after supralethal whole body radiation doses. The glomerular and tubular epithelia are radioresistant, and few changes are noted during the usual 30-day period of observation. Some hemorrhages may occur in the kidney and urinary tract leading to hematuria as one of the terminal findings in death due to irradiation. Figure K–1 shows petechial hemorrhages in the cortex and medulla and a large blood clot in the pelvis of a kidney from a swine which died 8 days after whole body irradiation during a test detonation of a nuclear device. In animals kept alive by treatment with splenic homogenates or bone marrow injection, failure of kidney function (radiation nephritis) may be a cause of death weeks or months later. In man, postirradiation nephrosclerosis is one of the most debilitating late lesions of radiation damage.

Figure K–1. Kidney from a swine which died 8 days after total body exposure to ionizing radiation from atomic bomb tests at Bikini. Petechial hemorrhages in cortex and medulla and large blood clot in pelvis. (Official U.S. Navy photograph.)

KIDNEY FUNCTION MEASUREMENT

Kidney function is studied effectively by the injection intravenously of labeled compounds that are excreted by the renal route. By means of detectors positioned at appropriate points on the body surface, continuous measurements are made of the amount of radioactivity in each kidney. The plot of counting rates gives an index of the kidney's function. The chemicals most commonly used are Diodrast and Hippuran. Both are labeled with iodine-131.

KILOCURIE

A unit of radioactivity measurement denoting 1,000 curies (kc).

KILO-ELECTRON-VOLT

The kev is 1,000 or 10^3 electron volts (ev). The shortened term kv is used to describe the energy of x-rays.

KILOTON ENERGY

The energy of a nuclear (or atomic) explosion which is equivalent to that produced by the explosion of 1 kiloton (i.e., 1,000 tons) of TNT, which is equal to 10^{12} calories; 4.2×10^{19} ergs; 1.15×10^6 kilowatt-hours; or 1.8×10^9 British thermal units. The energy is produced by complete fission of 0.056 kilograms (56 grams) fissionable material; or the fission of 1.45×10^{23} nuclei.

See MEGATON ENERGY, TNT EQUIVALENT and YIELD.

KINETIC METHOD STUDIES.   *See* COMPARTMENTAL ANALYSIS.

KRYPTON

Symbol Kr; atomic number 36, atomic weight 83.80. A colorless, odorless, chemically almost inert gas existing in air to the extent of 1 volume of krypton to 1,000,000 volumes of air. Discovered by the Scottish scientists Ramsey (Sir William; Nobel prize winner in chemistry in 1904) and Travers in 1898. Named from Greek, *kryptos*, hidden. The natural abundance is furnished by 6 stable isotopes. Stable krypton is used in certain types of electric bulbs.

Twenty radioactive isotopes have been identified, of which 12 may be produced as fission products in nuclear reactor operation or in the detonation of a nuclear device. Kr^{85} has fallout significance with 0.0240 megacurie per megaton of fission remaining at the end of 1 year. Although not quantitatively significant, induced radioactivity may produce 5 radioisotopes of krypton in air.

The maximum permissible concentration for a 168 hour week (continuous exposure) with the total body as the critical organ, is 10^{-6} microcuries per cubic centimeter ($\mu c/cc$) in air for Kr^{85m}; 3×10^{-6} $\mu c/cc$ for Kr^{85}; and 2×10^{-7} $\mu c/cc$ for Kr^{87}. Kr^{85} is used in industrial gages, as a tracer in oil well studies, and to measure ozone in parts per billion; and has potential usefulness in cardiac research. It is found in the effluent from air-cooled nuclear reactors.

A new standard for the meter has been adopted which is defined as 1,650,763.73 wave lengths of the orange-red line of stable krypton-86. This standard replaces the platinum-iridium meter bar which has been kept at Paris as an international standard of length since 1889 under the Treaty of the Meter.

L

LABELED COMPOUND

Also labeled substance. A compound consisting, in part, of radioactive atoms, i.e., atoms that differ in their isotopic composition from the other, chemically identical atoms of which the compound is formed. By observations of radioactivity or isotopic composition a labeled compound can be followed through physical, chemical or biological processes.

Hundreds of labeled compounds are commercially* available, but those containing carbon-14 lead the list with about 350 C^{14}-labeled compounds ready for biological, agricultural and medical research. Compounds may also be labeled with iodine-131, sulfur-35, zinc-65 and other radioactive isotopes. Heavy water (D_2O), added to ordinary water (H_2O) can be used as a tracer when added to a system. Tritium-labeled compounds are also extensively used.

See RADIOACTIVE TRACER and TRACER STUDIES.

LABELED MOLECULE

A molecule containing one or more atoms distinguished by non-natural isotopic composition (with either radioactive or stable isotopes).

See LABELED COMPOUND, RADIOACTIVE TRACER and TRACER STUDIES.

LABELING

The term "labeled" or "tagged" is used to describe an element, compound or organism that contains an altered isotopic content. Usually the asterisk is employed to designate an element labeled with the radioisotope. Loosely, the terms "labeled phosphorus," "radiophosphorus," "P^{32}" and "$P*$" are used interchangeably. An organism may be labeled by physical attachment of a radioactive source such as the insertion of cobalt-60 wire into the body cavities of insects or by painting radium-226 under the wings of insects. In addition, organisms can be labeled by using radioisotopes that become incorporated metabolically in the body. Biochemicals are produced in labeled form by biosynthesis or chemical synthesis.

See ISOTOPE DILUTION ANALYSIS, LABELED COMPOUND and LABELED MOLECULE.

---

*The Isotope Index. Scientific Equipment Co., P.O. Box 19086, Indianapolis 19, Indiana.

LABORATORY ANIMALS. *See* ANIMALS, RADIATION RESEARCH WITH.

LABORATORY DECONTAMINATION

The removal of radioactive contamination from an entire laboratory consists of SURFACE DECONTAMINATION by vacuum cleaning, dusting with a wet cloth and if necessary other wet methods; plus EQUIPMENT DECONTAMINATION, and decontamination of the furniture. Drastic methods such as stripping paint, removal of floor coverings, sandblasting, etc., may be necessary, followed by repainting, reflooring and even refurnishing.

LABORATORY DESIGN

Laboratories for the use of radioactive isotopes require special location, design, construction, and features in order to afford radiation protection for personnel and to provide a radiation-free area to conduct radiation measurements and radioassays.

The radioisotope laboratory should be located in a part of the building frequented by isotope personnel only. In general, high-level activity rooms should be grouped together and require access through a change room complete with showers, monitors, etc. The counting room should be separated from rooms in which radioisotopes are used, whether for chemical or biological work. It should not be near x-ray equipment, cobalt-60 irradiation facilities, or accelerators and should be well shielded from radioisotope storage.

Surfaces should be constructed so as to facilitate laboratory decontamination. Floors, walls and ceilings should be nonporous and washable. Special paints should be used that seal porous material; the final coat should be strippable paint. All dust collectors should be eliminated: cracks, ledges, exposed pipes, loose wiring and sharp corners. Sinks should be stainless steel and desk tops should be heavy plastic.

Shielding should be provided as required by the type of activity: barrier shield, barricade shield, biological shield, close shield and concrete shield.

Hoods and/or glove boxes should be available for radiochemical work involving amounts of radioactive material requiring a specific license. Special ventilation is required for all high-level work and for work in which radioactive dust may be present. The system should be designed to

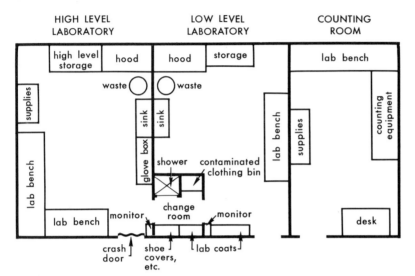

FIGURE L–1. HIGH-LEVEL RA-
DIOCHEMICAL LABORATORY.

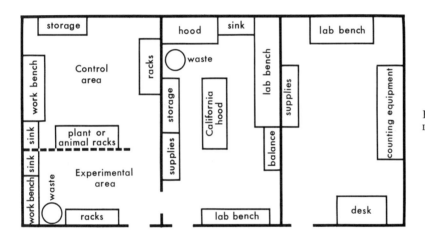

FIGURE L–2. RADIOBIOLOGY
LABORATORY.

prevent cross-contamination within the building and should be properly filtered to prevent contamination of the outside environment. Air conditioning is recommended for the counting room in order to get the best performance from the equipment.

Small amounts of radioactive material can be stored in pigs in the laboratory but for large amounts of material of high activity it is necessary to have well-shielded separate storage vaults.

Arrangements must be made for the disposal of radioactive waste depending upon the level of activity and type: gaseous, liquid or solid wastes.

The layout for the laboratory will depend upon the intended use. The accompanying simple diagrams offer three types of laboratories: Figure L–1, high-level radiochemical laboratory; Figure L–2, radiobiology laboratory; Figure L–3, medical radioisotope laboratory.

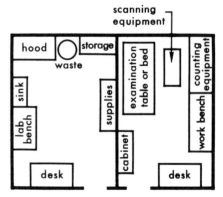

FIGURE L–3. MEDICAL RADIOISOTOPE LABORATORY.

LABORATORIES OF RADIATION BIOLOGY

The following laboratories (discussed separately), supported by the USAEC, have programs in nuclear medicine, radiation biology and/or health physics:

Argonne Cancer Research Hospital
Argonne National Laboratory
Brookhaven National Laboratory
Cancer Research Institute
Davis Radiobiology Project, University of California
Donner Laboratory
Eniwetok Marine Biological Laboratory
Hanford Works
Health and Safety Laboratory
Iowa State University Swine Irradiation Project
Los Alamos Scientific Laboratory
Lovelace Foundation Radiation Biology Research
Oak Ridge Institute of Nuclear Studies
Oak Ridge National Laboratory
Puerto Rico Nuclear Center
Radiological Laboratory, University of California School of Medicine, San Francisco
Rochester Atomic Energy Project
Tennessee-AEC Agricultural Research Laboratory
University of California at Los Angeles Laboratory of Nuclear Medicine and Radiation Biology
Utah University Radiobiology Project
Washington University Laboratory of Radiation Biology
Western Reserve University Project

See ARMY RADIATION BIOLOGY AND ATOMIC MEDICINE PROGRAM; NAVY RADIATION BIOLOGY AND ATOMIC MEDICINE PROGRAM; and PUBLIC HEALTH SERVICE RADIATION BIOLOGY AND ATOMIC MEDICINE PROGRAM.

LACTATION STUDIES

Milk secretion is widely studied because of the nutritional significance of this food, the relationship of lactation to reproduction, the fact that milk is a well-defined external excretion dependent upon a net synthesis of fat, protein and carbohydrate, the sensitivity of lactation to hormonal stimulus, and the readiness with which the responses to stimulus may be evaluated in the intact animal. Radioisotopes have been widely used for investigation of the following general areas: (a) milk fat formation, (b) lactose formation, (c) protein formation, (d) metabolic disturbances such as ketosis, (e) endocrine relationships and (f) mineral secretions.

Carbon-14 and tritium have been used for studies of biochemical synthesis. As an example, experiments indicate the major importance of glucose in lactose synthesis, acetate in fat synthesis, and formate or butyrate-2-C^{14} as precursors of casein. An important technique has been the injection of labeled compounds into the pudic artery that directly feeds the mammary glands. In this way it was possible to use one-half of the udder for control purposes. When acetate-1-C^{14} was injected into the pudic artery, it was found that there was an unequal and unsymmetrical labeling of the glucose and galactose portions of lactose. These and other observations indicated that within the mammary gland glycerol and acetate preferentially label the galactose portion of lactose. From numerous studies of this type, various schemes and models for the carbon cycle in milk production have been proposed.

In another type of study, radioactive molybdenum was used to demonstrate the synthesis of the enzyme xanthine oxidase; this was done by feeding molybdenum-99 to lactating cows and subsequently isolating labeled xanthine oxidase from the milk. It has been shown thereby that molybdenum was an integral part of the xanthine oxidase molecule. Considerable attention has been given to the secretion of various nutritional minerals and fission products into milk. Table L–1 summarizes some typical results.

See FOOD CHAIN.

TABLE L–1. TYPICAL VALUES FOR SECRETION OF VARIOUS RADIONUCLIDES INTO MILK OF DAIRY COW

| | PER CENT OF DOSE IN MILK | | DEGREE OF CONCENTRATION IN SECRETION FROM BLOOD TO MILK† |
	Ingestion	Intravenous Injection	
Ca^{45}	7	32	10–15
P^{32}	10	22	10–20
F^{18}	0.02*	0.2	0.8
Na^{22}	0.2	0.2	—
I^{131}	6	7	1–4
Sr^{90}	1	10	7
Y^{91}	—	1.4	—
Pa^{233}	—	0.3	0.01
Cs^{137}	10	10	3

*Based on short-term study of about 12 hours.

†Expressed as ratio of concentration of radionuclide in milk to that in blood.

LAND DISPOSAL AND BURIAL, RADIOACTIVE WASTE

One method of WASTE DISPOSAL of radioactive material is by releasing it into the soil; another, by burying it underground.

Low-level LIQUID WASTE may be discharged to the ground through trenches, seepage basins, man-made "swamps" or "cribs." Safe disposal into the ground depends upon the geology and hydrology of the site chosen. The greatest hazard associated with ground disposal is the possibility of the radioisotopes entering subterranean water systems. Several factors must be evaluated in selecting a disposal site: the chemical and radio-chemical characteristics of the waste; soil composition and characteristics, including possible ion exchange properties; composition and structure of underlying subsoil and bedrock; location and rate of movement of ground water; the rate of migration of radionuclides; downstream distance from burial site to users of ground water; and proximity of the burial area to the point of waste generation. However, with proper choice and careful monitoring this type of disposal has proved satisfactory.

High-level liquid waste is held in TANK STORAGE buried underground, but research is being conducted investigating the possibility of the direct disposal of these wastes into specific geological formations, such as salt structures, dry oil domes or deep permeable formations.

An AEC licensee may in accordance with the Federal Register (Title 10, Chapter 1, Part 20, Section 20.304) dispose of licensed material by burial in the soil provided: "(a) The total quantity of licensed and other radioactive materials buried at any one location and time does not exceed, at the time of burial, 1,000 times the amount specified in Appendix C (list of radioactive materials a licensee may have) of this part; and (b) burial is at a minimum depth of 4 feet; and (c) successive burials are separated by distances of at least 6 feet and not more than 12 burials are made in any year."

Alpha-contaminated SOLID WASTES are usually buried in holes approximately 15 feet in diameter and 15 feet in depth. The waste material is placed in the hole, covered with a foot of earth and then 8 inches of concrete is poured over the earth; then 2 or more feet of earth are placed on top of the concrete.

Beta-gamma activity solid waste materials are buried by conventional sanitary land-fill methods in trenches about 10 feet wide and 15 feet deep which extend completely across the burial site. Beginning at one end the wastes are dumped into the trench until this portion of the trench is filled. Then the wastes are covered by 3 or more feet of earth; and this dumping and back-filling procedure continues to the other end of the trench.

Burial grounds for solid wastes are available at Oak Ridge National Laboratory in Tennessee; Savannah River Plant in South Carolina; National Reactor Testing Station in Idaho; Los Alamos Scientific Laboratory in New Mexico, and Hanford Works, Washington.

LANTHANIDE SERIES

The remarkable chemically similar group of rare earths: lanthanum, atomic number 57; cerium, 58; praseodymium, 59; neodymium, 60; promethium, 61; samarium, 62; europium, 63; gadolinium, 64; terbium, 65; dysprosium, 66; holmium, 67; erbium, 68; thulium, 69; ytterbium, 70; and lutecium, 71. These rare earths or lanthanide elements are so chemically similar that they must be assigned a single place in the PERIODIC TABLE in order to bring together elements of similar properties into the same vertical column (IIIB). The ACTINIDE SERIES illustrates a similar situation.

LANTHANIDES

Term used to denote elements in the LANTHANIDE SERIES.

LANTHANUM

Symbol La; atomic number 57; atomic weight 138.92. Member of the cerium subgroup of rare earth metals. Discovered by Swedish chemist Mosander in 1837. Named from Latin, *lanthano*, to lie hidden. Found in ores: cerite, orthite, monazite. Natural abundance furnished by the stable isotope La^{139} (99.911%) and by the slightly radioactive (radioactive half-life 1.0×10^{11} years) La^{138} (0.089%).

Lanthanum has few commercial applications and is of very low toxicity and physiological action. It is used for flints in cigarette lighters, in color-free optical glass, and in certain ceramic glazes. No information on naturally occurring levels in biological material is available.

Nineteen radioactive isotopes have been identified. Twelve may be produced as fission products resulting from the detonation of a nuclear device. The parent-daughter combination $Ba^{140} + La^{140}$ is highly radiotoxic and is significant in radioactive fallout. Lanthanum-140 ($_{57}La^{140}$), radioactive half-life 40 hours; effective half-life 1.6 days; beta and gamma emitter is available commercially.

LATENT PERIOD

Interval of seeming inactivity between the time of irradiation and the appearance of the effect in question. The latent period depends upon two general factors: the type, dose rate, and length of exposure to ionizing radiation; and the symptom, physiological response or pathological change being studied. The larger the dose the earlier the appearance of injury, i.e., the shorter the latent period.

Mice exposed to x-ray radiation show the following latent periods for acute symptomatic response: below 100 roentgen (r) no symptoms; between 100 and 700 r, damage to gastrointestinal tract, bone-marrow atrophy, some deaths in 3 to 5 days but some apparently complete recoveries; 1,200 to 15,000 r, all die within 3 1/2 days; 15,000 to 30,000 r, rapid reduction in survival time and death due to lung lesions; 30,000 to 100,000 r, death within an hour associated with convulsions, i.e. central nervous system damage; and over 100,000 r death is instantaneous.

Blood changes in the mid-lethal dose range vary with the type of cell studied: lymphocyte response appears within 24 hours and the degree of decrease is directly related to the total dose of radiation; while the erythrocytes in the exposed animals do not show a definite decrease in the levels of the red cell count until between the tenth and thirtieth days after exposure.

The latent period in the threshold erythema dose is from 7 to 10 days.

Leukemia appeared at an increased level in the Hiroshima and Nagasaki exposed population (50 r whole body or more) in about 5 years, with a maximum fivefold increase in 10 years and then began to recede.

Lung cancer developed in miners working in the pitchblende mines of Joachimstal, Czechoslovakia, with a latent period of about 15 years.

In the radium dial painter cases, osteosarcoma appeared in some individuals from 12 to 30 years after exposure.

Genetic damage from mutations produced by a single radiation exposure would be spread through many generations. In fact half the total damage that would ever be manifested would not be manifested until some 30 to 50 generations had been produced.

See DOSE-EFFECT RELATIONSHIP and THRESHOLD DOSE.

LAWRENCE MEMORIAL AWARD

The Ernest Orlando Lawrence Memorial Award is given to United States citizens under 45 years of age for meritorious contributions to the development, use or control of atomic energy, including medicine and engineering. It was established in 1959 to honor the memory of Dr. E. O. Lawrence, nuclear physicist, University of California, Berkeley, who was the winner of the Nobel prize in 1939 and the Fermi Award in 1957. The award is made by the USAEC, upon recommendation of its General Advisory Committee and with the approval of the President, and consists of a medal, a citation, and up to $25,000, tax exempt. It may be shared by no more than 5 individuals.

In June of 1960 the first awards were given to:

Dr. Harvey Brooks, Harvard University, "For meritorious contributions to fast reactors and fast breeder reactor theory, reactor kinetic theory, and reactor safeguards."

Dr. John S. Foster, Jr., Lawrence Radiation Laboratory, University of California, "For unique contributions, demanding unusual imagination and technical skill, to the development of atomic weapons."

Dr. Isadore Perlman, Lawrence Radiation Laboratory, University of California, "For outstanding contributions to the isolation of plutonium and transplutonic elements, to the study of nuclear energy levels of the actinides and other elements, and to the discovery of spallation."

Dr. Norman F. Ramsey, Jr., Harvard University, "For outstanding contributions to experimental nuclear physics, including the interactions of nuclei, and to studies of atomic and molecular beams."

Dr. Alvin M. Weinberg, Oak Ridge National Laboratory, "For outstanding contributions to nuclear reactor theory, for pioneering work in the design of production, research and power reactors."

The five scientists given the award in 1961 were:

Dr. Leo Brewer, University of California, "For singular contributions and leadership in the development of high-temperature chemistry which have permitted major advances in reactor development."

Dr. Henry Hurwitz, Jr., General Electric Company, "For important contributions requiring unusual analytical skill and physical insight to the theory and design of nuclear reactors."

Dr. Conrad L. Longmire, Los Alamos Scientific Laboratory, "For continued and original theoretical contributions, requiring unusual physical insight, to the development of nuclear weapons and the progress of plasma physics."

Dr. Wolfgang K. H. Panofsky, Stanford University, "For outstanding contributions to nuclear physics and to the international control of nuclear testing."

Dr. Kenneth E. Wilzbach, Argonne National Laboratory, "For his development of methods of tritium labeling of biologically important compounds which have permitted major advances in biology and medicine."

The five scientists given the award in 1962 were:

Dr. Andrew A. Benson, University of California, "For outstanding contributions to elucidation of the carbon reduction cycle in photosynthesis through his development of double labeling techniques employing C^{14}, H^3 and P^{32}."

Dr. Richard P. Feynman, California Institute of Technology, "For important contributions to quantum field theory and particle physics, for invention of Feynman diagrams, and for broad scientific interests and knowledge."

Dr. Herbert Goldstein, Columbia University, "For significant contributions to reactor physics and to nuclear cross sections, and for leadership in establishing a rational scientific basis for nuclear shield design."

Dr. Anthony L. Turkevich, University of Chicago, "For contributions to radiochemistry in activation analysis, to analysis of intranuclear cascades, and to utilization of radiochemical techniques throughout atomic energy."

Dr. Herbert F. York, University of California, "For important contributions to our knowledge of elementary particles, and especially for leadership in applying atomic energy to the national defense."

The five scientists given the award in 1963 were:

Dr. Herbert J. C. Kouts, Brookhaven National Laboratory, "For the development of new experimental techniques in reactor physics and their application to a better understanding of theoretical models of chain-reacting systems."

Dr. L. James Rainwater, Columbia University, "For contributions to nuclear physics including the experimental determination of many important neutron cross-sections and our understanding of complex nuclei."

Dr. Louis Rosen, Los Alamos Scientific Laboratory, "For the development of new experimental techniques and their application to a better understanding of the nucleus as well as to the diagnosis of weapon behavior."

Mr. James M. Taub, Los Alamos Scientific Laboratory, "For contributions to the metallurgy of uranium and other special nuclear materials including the development of ingenious methods for fabricating materials into special shapes with tight dimensional tolerances."

Dr. Cornelius A. Tobias, University of California, Berkeley, "For contributions to the understanding of basic radiobiology of cells including studies of the biological effects of heavy energy particles."

LAWRENCIUM

Symbol Lw; atomic number 103; mass number 257. Last of the actinide series. Discovered in 1961 by the United States scientists Ghiorso, Sikkeland, Larch and Latimer of the Lawrence Radiation Laboratory. First element to be discovered solely by nuclear methods. Experiments were performed with the heavy ion linear accelerator. Named for the late Ernest O. Lawrence. Radioactive half-life 8 seconds. Decays by alpha emission.

LAWS GOVERNING ATOMIC ENERGY

See ATOMIC ENERGY COMMISSION (licensing and regulatory procedure); ATOMIC ENERGY ACTS 1946 AND 1954; and LEGISLATIVE CONTROL OF RADIATION EXPOSURE.

LD$_{50}$

Term for lethal dose for 50% of the population. *See* MEDIAN LETHAL DOSE.

LD$_{50}$ TIME

Time required for death of 50% of the individuals in a large, statistically significant group of animals or organisms, following exposure to a single dose of radiation.

See MEDIAN LETHAL TIME.

LEAD

Symbol Pb; atomic number 82; atomic weight 207.21. A bluish-white, very soft metal. Discovery prehistoric; mentioned in the Book of Exodus. Named from Anglo-Saxon, *lead*. Symbol Pb from Latin, *plumbum*. Lead occurs principally as sulfide ore, galenite; widely dispersed in the crust of the earth. Four stable isotopes furnish the natural abundance. Lead is the end product in the uranium, thorium and actinium radioactive series.

About 1.5 million tons are used industrially in the United States each year. Among its numerous uses are: for storage battery plates, as tetraethyl lead in gasoline; for cable covering, as white lead for paint; and as radiation shielding. Radiation shielding uses include lead bricks for temporary setups, lead containers for shipping radioisotopes, and lead casks or lead-lined tanks for storing radioactive materials. Lead is used because of its high density (11.34) and stopping power, and low cost. Chronic lead poisoning occurs from long-term ingestion or inhalation of lead compounds, fumes or dust.

Fifteen radioactive isotopes have been identified. None have any biological, medical or agricultural uses.

LEAK LOCATION

Gaseous and liquid radioactive isotopes and compounds have been found valuable in locating leaks in various types of closed systems, e.g.: argon-41 to locate underground gas leaks; a radioactive tracer for locating leaks in an air-conditioning system; sodium-24 in buried, earthenware pipe system; and selenium-75 to locate leaks in a gas-

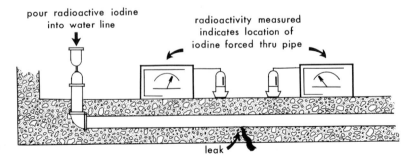

FIGURE L–4. IODINE-131 FOR DETECTING LEAKS IN WATER LINES.

pour radioactive iodine into water line

radioactivity measured indicates location of iodine forced thru pipe

leak

filled, oil-impregnated, underground power cable system. Figure L–4 shows the method by which radioisotopes are used to locate leaks—in this case iodine-131 put in a water main. It will be noted that it is not necessary to remove the floors or to dismantle the system, thus it is less costly and more convenient. With an isotope of short radioactive half-life there is no problem with residual activity.

LEAKAGE RADIATION

In the use of x-ray machines, radiation emitted through all parts of the tube enclosure other than the orifice. For purposes of protection x-rays may also be classified as the useful beam which is emitted through the orifice provided in the x-ray tube enclosure; and any scattered radiation. Good shielding should begin with properly designed enclosure of the x-ray tube so that no appreciable amount of leakage radiation occurs.

Leakage may also refer to escape of radiation or neutrons through a shield, especially by way of holes or cracks in the shield.

In reactor engineering, leakage is the loss of neutrons by outward diffusion from the core of the reactor. When there is a reflector, leakage refers to net loss of neutrons that leave the core and are not reflected back into it.

LEGAL ASPECTS, WASTE DISPOSAL

Radioactive waste disposal is controlled by a number of city, state, national and international rules, regulations and laws.

In the United States the legal responsibility for regulation and control of most pollution problems lies with the State Health Departments. Recognizing this, the Congress in 1959 amended the Atomic Energy Act of 1954 to provide for the delegation of licensing and inspection of uses of radioactive and nuclear materials to any state whose program is in line with AEC standards. Such delegation is under discussion with several states at present, and agreement has been reached with some.

The USAEC licenses and regulates the use of radioactive materials in research, agriculture, medicine and industry. The Commission also has the right of inspection and control. The Commission's regulations establish permissible concentrations of waste effluents and provide for the disposal of minimal quantities of waste by release into sanitary sewer systems, and by burial in soil.

The USAEC issues licenses to commercial firms to collect, package, transport and dispose of radioactive waste generated by licensees. Six of these companies propose to dispose of the waste ultimately at sea. One license has been issued for storage of low-level waste; and one licensee collects, packages and ships waste to the Oak Ridge National Laboratory. All licensees are subject to periodic inspection by the USAEC to insure that the regulations, terms and conditions of licenses are being complied with.

The U.S. Public Health Service has been assigned the primary responsibility for stimulating and strengthening the states to use their powers in the promotion of effective waste disposal administration and of sound technical programs. The USPHS renders assistance to the states through consultation, technical assistance, demonstrations, etc. They also deal with interstate air and water pollution problems, collaborate with other government agencies in solving public health problems, provide information to the public, and assist in the establishment of adequate and reasonable radiation standards.

The National Committee on Radiation Protection and Measurement (NCRP); the International Commission on Radiological Protection (ICRP); the International Commission on Radiological Units and Measurements, and the newly formed Federal Radiation Council have all issued standards, which are utilized as a basis for USAEC radiation protection programs.

During the United Nations Conference on the Law of the Sea held in Geneva in 1958, 2 articles dealing with atomic energy were debated with great heat: "Freedom of the High Seas" was concerned with the movement and docking of atomic powered ships, and "Pollution of the High Seas" dealt with ocean disposal of radioactive wastes. Since 1958 several international meetings have considered the implications of the disposal of radioactive wastes into the sea.

LEGISLATIVE CONTROL OF RADIATION EXPOSURE

The control of exposure to ionizing radiation by legislative means is prescribed for Federal agencies by the radiation protection guides and radioactivity concentration guide of the Federal Radiation Council in 2 reports dealing with radiation protection standards.

The USAEC, under the Atomic Energy Acts of 1946 and of 1954 plus amendments, is officially responsible for control of all types of licenses including licenses for byproduct material, and is also responsible for inspection; prescribes the establishment of radiation areas, the use of caution signs, labels and signals, the radiation warning symbol; makes recommendations concerning radiological safety rules, standards for protection against radiation, and radiation standards; and also sets forth rules for the transportation of radioactive materials.

The National Committee on Radiation Protection and Measurements and the International Commission on Radiological Protection have suggested maximum permissible concentrations, maximum permissible doses and maximum permissible body burdens for a large variety of radiations and radionuclides.

A number of states have established rules, laws and regulations concerning the use of radioactive materials.

The International Commission on Radiological Units and Measurements has established standards for radiation dosimetry and other standard methods of measurement.

In general, the exact levels of exposure are not set by law. Instead general procedures are approved and responsibility is set by law, but operations are governed by somewhat more flexible regulations.

LETHAL DOSE

Shortened to LD. Radiation required to kill within a specified time all the individuals in a large group of animals or organisms. In experimental work the amount of radiation required to kill half the exposed organisms or animals is usually used, i.e., median lethal dose (MLD), or LD_{50}; and usually a time factor is added, as $LD_{50}/30$, or MLD/30, indicating a 30-day period.

In general, the term lethal dose is reserved for use in connection with radiation sterilization of grains and other foods, or commercial products such as surgical and pharmaceutical supplies where radiation is used to kill insect pests and bacteria.

The time factor (*see* MEDIAN LETHAL TIME) is important, for if an immediate kill (24 hours) is desired, much larger doses of radiation are required than for a complete kill in 21 or 30 days following a single exposure.

The stage of development is also important from the standpoint of radiosensitivity, as is illustrated from the results of irradiation of the oriental fruit fly: eggs up to 6 hours old were killed by dosages of about 4,000 r, but eggs 24 hours old were unaffected and hatched after exposure up to 36,000 r, and it took 120,000 r to reduce hatching by 46%.

Sex differences affect the LD. In one study the female German cockroaches were killed by 90,000 r, but it required 98,000 r to kill all the males. Pharaoh ant workers required 210,000 r, but queens were killed by 200,000 r.

The use of irradiation to destroy insects in stored grains, processed and packaged foodstuffs, clothing and wood products is theoretically feasible, and with the use of separated fission products as massive radiation sources (zirconium-95 and cesium-137) may be economically and practically feasible.

LEUKEMIA DUE TO RADIATION

Leukemia has been shown to be one of the chronic effects which may follow whole-body irradiation, or ionizing radiation to large segments of the body containing the blood-forming organs. An increased incidence of leukemia has been reported for the following groups of individuals exposed to external radiation: radiologists; atomic bomb survivors of Hiroshima and Nagasaki; children treated with x-ray in infancy to reduce the size and thus the function of the thymus gland; patients treated with x-ray for arthritis of the spine (spondylitis); and children exposed in utero during x-ray pelvimetry. Other groups, such as the thorium cases (intravenous Thorotrast) and the cases resulting from therapeutic use of iodine-131, add to the list of leukemia cases considered to be due to irradiation, which totals 226 adequately documented cases collected from the world literature from 1911 to 1959. One of the most conclusive DOSE-EFFECT RELATIONSHIPS is found in data on the therapeutic x-ray treatment of spondylitis where out of 13,352 patients treated there were 32 proven and 5 probable leukemia deaths, while the expected number of deaths would have been 2.9 for this group. The annual incidence for the spondylitis patients receiving a mean dose of over 1,750 rad to the spinal bone marrow was found to be between 1,600 to 1,700 per million; and for all patients receiving a mean dose of over 2,250 rad the annual incidence was 7,200 per million; whereas the annual incidence of leukemia in an unirradiated male population is estimated to be 50 per million.

Available data on some of the other groups, such as the radiologists and the 2 groups of children, confirm the fact that radiation is leukemogenic, but add little to the understanding of the dose-effect relationship. However, the effects of acute single doses in the Japanese, and the effects of therapeutic irradiation for spondylitis provide enough quantitative data to estimate the increased risk of leukemia following irradiation at the dose level of 100 rad and above.

Data for leukemia incidence show that about 3 times the normally expected number of cases have occurred among the survivors from Hiroshima and Nagasaki since the bombing, with the increase starting about 1 1/2 years after exposure, reaching a peak in about 6 years, and by 12 years returning almost to a normal incidence. It appears from these data that 90% of all cases of leukemia will occur within about 10 years after an acute radiation exposure. Table L–2, based on cases verified by the Atomic Bomb Casualty Commission, presents facts concerning exposure, incidence and latent period for Hiroshima residents.

TABLE L–2.   LEUKEMIA IN HIROSHIMA SURVIVORS

YEAR OF ONSET	TOTAL	DISTANCE FROM HYPOCENTER (meters)				
		Under 1,000	1,000–1,499	1,500–1,999	2,000–2,999	Over 3,000
1945						
1946						
1947	3		1		2	
1948	7	2	4		1	
1949	5	1	1	1	1	1
1950	9	3	5			1
1951	11	3	7	1		
1952	11	3	5	1		2
1953	12	2	6	2	1	1
1954	6	2	2	1	1	
1955	8	1	4	2		1
1956	6		1	1	1	3
1957	5	1	3			1
TOTAL	83	18	39	9	7	10
Estimated population	95,819	1,241	8,810	20,113	32,692	32,963
Number of cases with onset in 1950–1957	68	15	33	8	3	9
Estimated person-years at risk	766,552	9,928	70,480	160,904	261,536	263,704
Annual incidence of leukemia per 100,000	8.9	151.1	46.8	5.0	1.1	3.4

Based on acute exposure to over 100 rad and a latent period of less than 15 years, the increased leukemia incidence relationship to dose can be expressed as equivalent to 1 case per 10^6 persons at risk per rad per year. The largest exposed group of Japanese available for study are calculated to have received a dose less than 50 to 100 rad. It is interesting to note that with this acute exposure group the incidence of leukemia since 1945 is not significantly greater than for the general Japanese population. The total data on the Japanese do not indicate that there will be a continued constant incidence of leukemia per rad exposure for the duration of life of the group; and neither can the data be interpreted as giving any information on chronic exposure leukemogenesis. Figure L–5 presents hypothetical curves of the interrelation of dose of radiation, incidence and latent period.

So far, study of chronic exposure to external sources of radiation and irradiation from internal deposition of radioactive materials has not provided a basis for predicting the incidence of radiation-induced leukemia. Experimental data in mice suggest that chronic exposure at low dose rate is less efficient than acute exposure for the induction of leukemia. The RADIUM DIAL PAINTERS have shown a significant increase in SARCOMAS but no leukemia. And there is no evidence that will allow a prediction of leukemia based on the absorbed dose of such radioactive isotopes as strontium-89

FIGURE L–5.   LEUKEMIA IN HIROSHIMA ATOMIC BOMB SURVIVORS.

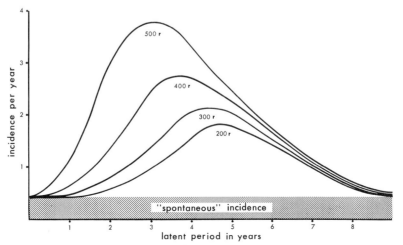

or -90 deposited in the bones. From neither acute nor chronic exposure is it possible to determine whether a threshold dose for leukemia induction does, or does not, exist.

It should be remembered that, although radiation is known to be leukemogenic, there are many toxic substances in the modern environment which are known to be carcinogenic and may also be leukemogenic.

LEUKEMIA TREATMENT

Chronic forms of leukemia respond well to properly administered radiation, internal or external. The radiation suppresses growth of leukemic cells and sometimes results in more adequate formation of normal blood cells. External radiation is given by means of x-ray therapy machines or teletherapy devices using radioisotope sources. The radiation can be directed to specific areas such as the lymph nodes or spleen or to the whole body. Internal treatment is provided by radioisotopes that are taken by injection or, sometimes, by mouth. These produce a rather diffuse type of radiation to the whole body but some degree of enhancement of dose to local areas is provided by the relatively high concentrations of these radioisotopes in blood-forming tissues. Phosphorus-32 is most commonly used; colloidal preparations of gold-198 and other radioisotopes are also occasionally applicable. Internal radioisotopic treatment usually produces less radiation sickness and may be more convenient than external radiation.

In acute and subacute forms of leukemia, radiation is seldom the treatment of choice but may be used in certain situations.

In any case of leukemia the treatment, whether with radiation or with drugs, should be selected for the particular patient; the choice depends upon the type and stage of disease, the response to previous therapy, and other factors.

LEUKOCYTE STUDIES

The leukocytes or white blood cells have been studied extensively with radioisotopic tracers. Most research has been on the most plentiful types of these cells, the neutrophilic granulocytes (polymorphonuclear cells) and lymphocytes; less has been done on the less plentiful forms, the monocytes and eosinophilic and basophilic granulocytes. Informative results have been obtained with tritium (H[3])-labeled thymidine, a substance that is incorporated into the nuclear DNA (deoxyribonucleic acid) of the cell during the time that this material is being synthesized prior to cell division. Thus the label is initially seen in those cells that are still capable of mitosis; later it may

be seen in older cells that have maintained it during maturation. Studies have been done in patients by giving the labeled thymidine intravenously; it is rapidly removed from the blood and is subsequently located in blood-forming cells and in circulating blood cells. The demonstration of the radioactivity is made by means of microscopic autoradiograms prepared from cells of blood, bone marrow, lymph nodes or other tissues. Very early it is seen that primitive precursor cells in the marrow have taken up the radioactivity. Labeling of granulocyte forms begins somewhat later, within an hour, and is maximal in the marrow at the third and fourth days. In circulating blood the labeling of these cells is greatest on the fifth and sixth days. In the lymphocyte series, early labeling is seen chiefly in the large and medium sized cells; this suggests that small lymphocytes may be late stages that do not divide.

Other radioisotopic studies on leukocytes have used labeled amino acids and diisopropylfluorophosphonate containing phosphorus-32. Still other investigations have used P[32] as soluble phosphate, with analyses based upon that portion of the radioisotope bound to DNA.

Studies of this type are beginning to clarify the developmental rates and potential for division of the various blood cells and their precursors. The survival time of leukocytes is not clearly established. Unlike the red blood cells (and probably the platelets) which have a rather definite life span in the circulation, leukocytes may be removed from the blood in random fashion, and may serve a major function in tissues outside the vascular system. Neutrophilic granulocytes are thought to live a few days in the circulation. Lymphocytes may include more than one population, perhaps one type living 3 or 4 days and another living 100 to 200 days. It is likely that in leukemia and other disease states the life span of the cell is altered.

LEUKOCYTIC CHANGES DUE TO RADIATION

Leukocytic changes, such as changes in the total white blood cell count, lymphocyte count and neutrophil count are important in the diagnosis of radiation illness. The lymphocytes show marked radiosensitivity, and a fall in the number of circulating lymphocytes always accompanies whole-body irradiation of 50 roentgens (r) or more (see LYMPHOCYTES, RADIATION DAMAGE). There is usually a mild increase in the total neutrophil count immediately after radiation exposure, but within a day or two it begins a rapid fall to alarmingly low levels and a very slow return to normal (see NEUTROPHIL LEUKOCYTE, RADIATION DAMAGE). After the first few days the total white count invariably decreases (LEUKOPENIA FOLLOWING IRRA-DIATION). This decrease is rapid and alarming for about a week, and then is followed by a period of leveling off and fluctuation, and a very gradual return to normal in the sublethal cases. There is some dose-effect relationship in that for doses of about 100 r the depression of the white cell count is less than for higher doses, and in fatal cases it drops to the vanishing point and does not recover.

LEUKOPENIA FOLLOWING RADIATION

A reduction in the number of circulating leukocytes (white blood cells) to a level less than 5,000 per cubic millimeter of blood (leukopenia) is part of the picture of the acute radiation syndrome following radiation exposure to levels of 100 roentgens or more.

See LEUKOCYTIC CHANGES DUE TO RADIATION.

LIBRARIES

USAEC DEPOSITORY LIBRARIES are maintained in 86 libraries throughout the United States and in 60 foreign countries.

See FILM LIBRARIES.

LICENSES FOR BYPRODUCT MATERIAL

Licenses for use of radioactive isotopes or BY-PRODUCT MATERIAL are of two types. The general license is effective without filing an application with the USAEC or the issuance of any licensing documents. However, only small specified quantities of byproduct material are allowed under the general license. The individual using even these amounts of radioactive material is subject to the same regulations as the person having a specific license.

Specific licenses must be obtained by individual request, and for specific purposes as stated in Part 30:* "human use in institutions . . . use by individual physicians for human use . . . human use of sealed sources . . . multiple quantities or types of byproduct material for use in research and development . . . for multiple quantities and types of byproduct material for use in processing."

LICENSING AND REGULATING, USAEC

Within the Atomic Energy Commission the licensing and regulatory functions are under a Director of Regulation who reports directly to the Commission. This organization consists of the

---

*The regulations are laid down in the Code of Federal Regulations (CFR), Title 10 Atomic Energy, Part 30 Licensing of Byproduct Material, a copy of which may be obtained by writing to the Division of Licensing and Regulation, U.S. Atomic Energy Commission, Washington 25, D.C.

Division of Licensing and Regulation, Division of Compliance and Division of Radiation Protection Standards.

Division of Licensing and Regulation. The Division is organized with a director, assistant director, and additional assistant directors for Reactor Standards, Facilities Licensing, Materials Standards and Materials Licensing. The Division develops policies and procedures concerning facility licenses for commercial facilities, research and development facilities, and medical therapy facilities. It also handles materials licenses in connection with the possession, use or transfer of SOURCE MATERIAL, SPECIAL NUCLEAR MATERIALS or BY-PRODUCT MATERIALS. Matters concerning the health and safety criteria for licensed facilities and operations come under the cognizance of the Division and it is responsible for the issuance, renewal, modification, suspension or revoking of licenses.

Division of Compliance. There is an assistant director for Materials and for Reactors; and there are 5 area offices to assist in the conduct of inspections and for the investigation of nuclear incidents and accidents in licensed facilities or operations. The Division is responsible not only for the conduct of inspections but also for the development of inspection policies, procedures and schedules.

Division of Radiation Protection Standards. This Division has a Radiation Standards branch and a State-AEC Relations branch, and is responsible for the development of basic radiation standards upon which the Division of Licensing and Regulation bases its health and safety criteria. The Division also supplies staff assistance to the Federal Radiation Council, and handles the staff work involved in the transfer of certain regulatory responsibilities to State authorities.

See LEGISLATIVE CONTROL OF RADIATION EX-POSURE; and LICENSES FOR BYPRODUCT MATERIAL.

LIFE SHORTENING DUE TO RADIATION EXPOSURE

Shortening of the life span has been clearly shown in experimental animals to follow single or repeated doses of radiation. Life shortening is a very general, though operationally useful, expression of chronic radiation injury, and is a general manifestation of an almost infinite variety of pathologic changes in the tissues. However, with practically no exception, any changes observed are also found in unirradiated populations, and thus do not specifically identify radiation damage. Longevity averages are obviously reduced in exposed groups of animals as a result of the increased incidence of leukemia and malignancies following heavy dosage radiation. However, aside from these deaths, there

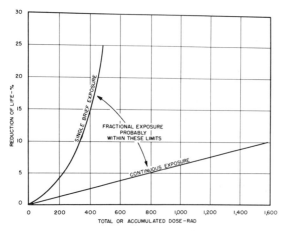

FIGURE L–6. EFFECTS ON LIFE SHORTENING OF BRIEF SINGLE DOSES OF RADIATION COMPARED WITH CONTINUOUS EXPOSURE TO WHOLE-BODY RADIATION. THE EFFECTS OF MULTIPLE BRIEF EXPOSURES, SEPARATED BY DAYS OR WEEKS, WILL PROBABLY HAVE AN EFFECT BETWEEN THE LIMITS FOR SINGLE AND CONTINUOUS EXPOSURE. BASED ON ANIMAL WORK. (NASA LIFE SCIENCES DATA BOOK.)

still appears to be some significant reduction in life span which is probably the result of accelerated aging, due to radiation exposure, and in addition is related to the induction of other diseases. The probability of death from many causes is increased after irradiation, though to a different degree for each cause. Studies with both x-rays and gamma rays on rats and dogs indicate that even though an animal may survive a single acute exposure to radiation, its life span will be reduced in proportion to the amount of radiation received. There is also evidence that ionizing radiation exposure shortens life in proportion to lifetime accumulated dose. This is graphically shown in Figure L–6.

Although the evidence does not suggest the existence of a true threshold dose, the smallest total dose for which a statistically significant life shortening can be demonstrated, is at present of the order of several hundred roentgens. Little effect was manifest in mice under 75 rep; then increasing dosages brought increasing mortality from acute effects, and a reduced life span for survivors. Exposures of 270 r left 34 per cent of the survivors with a life span of 415 days compared to 652 days for controls; while a 640 rep dose caused a 27 per cent reduction in the life span.

Life shortening for a given dose is very much less if divided doses (see FRACTIONATION) are given. For continuous irradiation a significant decrease in life span is shown only with doses that exceed 10 rad of gamma rays per day.

On the other hand, there is positive evidence of extension of the life span in animals by continuous

exposure to low doses of radiation. Careful experiments indicate that, if mice or guinea pigs receive continuously about 1 rad per week, the life span is significantly increased. Another experiment with rats exposed throughout life to 0.8 r per day and kept at 25° C showed a survival time of 600 days for the irradiated rats and only 460 days for the control group. But the most striking extension of life span is shown with work on the flour beetle where 3,000 r given at 10.3 r per minute as well as at 100 r per day prolongs life to an extent well beyond any possible experimental error. The explanation probably is in reducing the infections in the early weeks of life, rather than that radiation is actually beneficial in a somatic sense.

There is very little evidence of human life shortening from radiation exposure. The 1960 report of the National Academy of Sciences (The Biological Effects of Atomic Radiation) concludes that "there are as yet no data for man that provide a satisfactory basis for quantitative estimation of the over-all life-shortening effect. . . ."

LIGHT PIPE
An optical link or pathway connecting a scintillation detector and its associated photo tube; made either of a material similar to the detector itself or of a plastic substance with suitable optical properties, especially transparency and refractive index.

LINEAR ABSORPTION COEFFICIENT. See ABSORPTION COEFFICIENT.

LINEAR ACCELERATOR
A type of high-energy particle accelerator in which the particle path is essentially a straight line. Those used to accelerate positive ions consist of a series of cylinders of increasing lengths arranged in a line and having provision for acceleration by oscillating electrical fields across the gaps between the cylinders. A view of a linear accelerator (Linac) is shown in Figure L–7. In addition to those linear accelerators which are used directly, a number serve as part of the injection mechanism for such machines as the alternating gradient synchrotron.

The most powerful electron linear accelerator yet proposed is the "M" or "SLAC" accelerator being built at Stanford University at an estimated cost of $132,000,000. This machine is to have an over-all length of 10,000 feet and will include 240 klystron-powered accelerator sections. Plans call for initial operation yielding 10–20 Bev electrons at 15 to 30 microamperes beam current, but the design capability provides for a future increase to 40 Bev at 60 microamperes if desired. Table L–3 gives detailed specifications; Figure L–8 shows a sketch of the experimental area and Figure L–9 pictures a klystron tube.

Also located at Stanford is a 6-Mev linear electron accelerator designed and built for medical

applications which was installed in 1956. The accelerating tube, a copper pipe, is 6 feet long. The machine (Fig. L–10) is used primarily to generate 4 Mev supervoltage x-rays by having the accelerated electrons impinge upon a gold target 0.020 inches thick. Alternatively, the electron

FIGURE L–7. OVER-ALL VIEW OF THE LINEAR ACCELERATOR (LINAC) TANK AND AUXILIARY EQUIPMENT, AS SEEN FROM THE LOW-ENERGY END, LOOKING TOWARD THE HIGH-ENERGY END. THE TANK IS 110 FEET LONG AND IS COMPOSED OF ELEVEN 10-FOOT SECTIONS COUPLED TO-GETHER. TO THE RIGHT OF THE TANK AND TOWARD THE REAR ARE 4 "TOWERS," WHICH MAKE UP THE HIGH-POWER RADIOFREQUENCY SYSTEM. THE TOWERS ARE THE FTH TRIODES AND CAVITIES. ON THE LEFT SIDE, AGAINST THE WALL, ARE CABINETS FOR 2 SEPARATE SYSTEMS. THE SMALL UNITS ARE THE CONTROL CENTERS FOR THE LINAC HIGH-VACUUM PUMPS. THE LARGE UNITS HOUSE THE CIRCUITS WHICH PULSE THE QUADRUPOLE MAGNETS, WHICH FOCUS THE PROTON BEAM IN THE LINAC. IN THE BACKGROUND IS A CONCRETE SHIELDING WALL SEPARAT-ING THE LINAC FROM THE MAIN SYNCROTRON MAGNET RING. THE JUNCTION OF THE LINAC WITH THE ALTER-NATING GRADIENT SYNCROTRON IS SHOWN IN THE ARTICLE ON SYNCHROTRONS. (COURTESY BROOKHAVEN NATIONAL LABORATORY.)

FIGURE L–8. EXPERIMENTAL AREA AT END OF PROPOSED "M" ACCELERATOR. THE TARGET BUILDING AT THE LEFT WILL BE 100 FEET × 100 FEET × 70 FEET HIGH. THE DISTANCE FROM THE FIRST DEFLECTION MAGNET TO THE TARGET BUILDINGS IS ROUGHLY 800 FEET. (COURTESY OF STANFORD UNIVERSITY.)

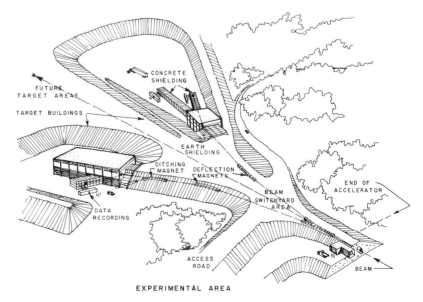

beam can be used directly in the irradiation of superficial tumors. Another linear electron accelerator used clinically is the 8-Mev accelerator at Hammersmith Hospital in England.

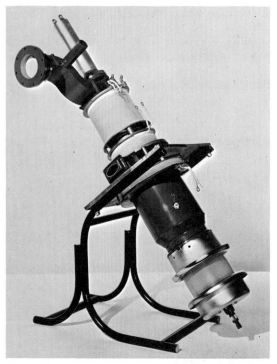

FIGURE L–9. KLYSTRON POWER TUBE, ABOUT 3 FEET LONG, SIMILAR TO THE TYPE TO BE USED IN THE "M" ACCELERATOR. IN STAGE I THE ACCELERATOR WILL REQUIRE 240 KLYSTRON TUBES. (COURTESY STANFORD UNIVERSITY.)

TABLE L–3.   PRINCIPAL "M" ACCELERATOR SPECIFICATIONS, STANFORD UNIVERSITY

Accelerator length	10,000 feet
Length between feeds	10 feet
Number of accelerator sections	960
Number of klystrons	240
Peak power per klystron	6–24 Mw
Beam pulse repetition rate	1–360 pps
RF pulse length	2.5 μsec
Electron energy, unloaded	11.1–22.2 Bev
Electron energy, loaded	10–20 Bev
Peak beam current	25–50 ma
Average beam current	15–30 μa
Average beam power	0.15–0.6 Mw
Filling time	0.83 μsec
Electron beam pulse length	0.01–2.1 μsec
Electron beam energy spread (max)	± 0.5%
Number of electron energy levels	up to 6
Accelerator vacuum	$<10^{-5}$ mm of Hg
Operating frequency	2,856 Mc/sec
Operating schedule	24 hrs/day

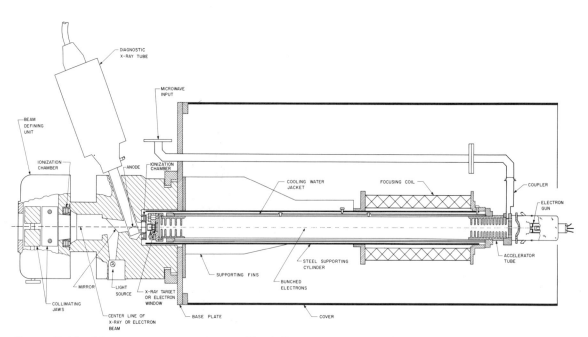

FIGURE L–10.   MEDICAL LINEAR ACCELERATOR NO. 1. THIS ACCELERATOR IS 6 FEET LONG AND IS LOCATED AT THE PALO ALTO-STANFORD HOSPITAL IN PALO ALTO, CALIFORNIA. (COURTESY STANFORD UNIVERSITY.)

LINEAR AMPLIFIER

An amplifier especially designed to increase the strength of signal pulses uniformly and without distorting either the pulse shape or rate in any way; particularly useful in pulse height analyzer procedures.

LINEAR ENERGY TRANSFER

Acronym LET. Energy lost per micron (μ; 10^{-4} centimeter) of track of the primary ionizing particle. The RELATIVE BIOLOGICAL EFFECTIVENESS of physically different ionizing radiations depends solely on their ionization density or LET. LET is a function of the charge and velocity of the ionizing particle. For example, deuterons with an energy of 190 Mev have the same average LET as 200 kev x-rays and are equally effective in killing yeast cells, while less energetic deuterons having a higher LET are more efficient. With a cyclotron it is possible to study a wide range of LETs with the same type of radiation by simply altering the energy of the ionizing particle striking the biological material. Ionization density is directly related to LET and is obtained by dividing the LET by W which is the energy required to form an ion pair in air, i.e., 34 electron volts. What the physicists call "stopping power" is usually referred to as LET by the radiation biologists.

There have been many investigations of the importance of LET in radiobiology. The lethal effect of radiations on the roots of the broad bean showed a systematic increase in efficiency with LET increase. Differences in LET also affect the LD_{50}; for example, for 200-kv x-rays, the LD_{50} for mice is 1.1 Mev which is about 0.8 that for cobalt-60 which is 1.3 Mev, but is about 4 times that for fast neutrons. It is generally believed that LET characterizes the dependence of radiation effects upon the properties of a track segment. For example, many experiments of diverse types give approximately the same result for different particles having equal LET.

LINEARITY

Dose-effect relationship which is a straight line with no threshold dose. In Figure L–11, curve A illustrates the common type of biological response to most physical and chemical agents, in that the effect is not measurable until a certain minimum or threshold dose is exceeded. The majority of radiation-induced somatic effects are considered to be of this type. Curve B represents the nonthreshold case, in which a linear relationship exists between dose and effect. Most geneticists consider genetic damage from radiation to follow this curve.

The implications of a linear response as related to genetic damage from radiation are as follows:

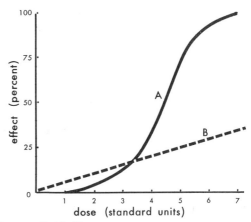

FIGURE L–11. TYPES OF BIOLOGICAL RESPONSE TO RADIATION. CURVE A REPRESENTS THE NON-LINEAR, THRESHOLD RESPONSE, AND CURVE B REPRESENTS THE LINEAR, NON-THRESHOLD RESPONSE.

(1) the effect is proportional to the dose, and frequency increases linearly with increasing dose; (2) the curve extrapolates through zero dose, and there is no threshold (i.e., any dose, no matter how small, will have an effect); (3) the effect is strictly independent of dose rate, i.e., there is no recovery (presumably the effect is described by a single hit target theory, i.e., a single ionizing event is capable of inducing a gene mutation); and (4) the total effect in a population is independent of whether a small number of people receive a large dose of radiation or a large number of people receive a small dose, provided conception perpetuates the mutant genes (in the course of many generations, the induced mutations would distribute themselves and the effect would be the same).

Doubt is cast on the validity of the above statements since it has been shown that under some circumstances the genetic response depends on the dose rate.

LIPID STUDIES

The term lipids refers to a group of naturally occurring substances consisting of the higher fatty acids, their naturally occurring compounds, and substances found naturally in chemical association with them. Examples of important lipids include the phospholipids of phosphatides; the glycolipids; the lipoproteins; the various derived lipids including fatty acids, alcohols and bases such as choline; and the substances associated with lipids in nature, such as the tocopherols and steroids. Early non-radioactive tracer studies employed the characteristic absorption spectra of fatty acids containing conjugated double bonds. Later work was done by using deuterium, which served as a tracer for the carbon atom to which it was attached.

More recent studies have been done with carbon-14, tritium and phosphorus-32, especially for study of phospholipids. Some of the important areas of investigation are concerned with:

    a. mobility of depot fats
    b. absorption of fat from the intestine
    c. role of phospholipids in fat absorption and transport
    d. origin and fate of the plasma phospholipids
    e. turnover rate of liver phospholipids
    f. phospholipid turnover and lipotropic action
    g. mechanism of oxidation of fatty acids
    h. conversion of acetate to acetoacetate
    i. fatty acid oxidation and the tricarboxylic acid cycle
    j. carbon-dioxide incorporation reactions in metabolism of fatty acids
    k. synthesis of higher fatty acids
    l. pyruvate as a precursor of fatty acids
    m. synthesis of steroids, especially of cholesterol
    n. lipid metabolism in diabetes

LIQUID-LEVEL GAGING

Measurement, automatic recording and control of the liquid level in a container by the use of radioactive isotope gages. Operation is based on measuring the change produced by an intervening liquid material in the intensity of a beam of radiation from a fixed source. The simplest arrangement is indicated by the diagram (Figure L–12). This type of gage is particularly advantageous for it does not have to float on the liquid and therefore is not affected by corrosion or temperature; it can also be operated by non-technical personnel. The gage is adaptable to automatic recording and control of the liquid level. Used extensively by the chemical industry.

The pharmaceutical industry also uses liquid-level gaging to determine, record and maintain liquid levels in tanks and other containers; to detect and/or control the liquid-liquid interface between two different dilutions in a closed system, e.g., chloroform solution and water; to determine in a closed system when immiscible solvents have completely separated; to maintain liquid levels in hoppers of liquid fillers; to indicate by an alarm device when a container or pipeline is empty; and most common of all, to determine the height of liquid in a bottle, as illustrated in Figure L–13.

LIQUID SCINTILLATION COUNTER

1. A counting system based on a mixture of the sample and a liquid phosphor, the resultant scintillations being counted by one or more photomultiplier tubes connected into suitable electronic equipment for analyzing the radiations. The prepared sample is held in an assemblage which often consists of a pair of photomultiplier tubes,

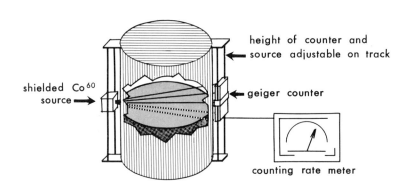

height of counter and source adjustable on track

shielded Co⁶⁰ source →

← geiger counter

counting rate meter

FIGURE L–12.   COBALT-60 FOR INDICATING LIQUID HEIGHT.

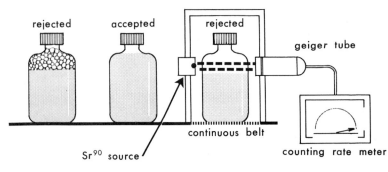

rejected   accepted   rejected

geiger tube

Sr⁹⁰ source

continuous belt

counting rate meter

FIGURE L–13.   STRONTIUM-90 RADIOACTIVE SOURCE FOR GAGING LIQUID HEIGHT.

connected to count only in coincidence and maintained at low temperature to reduce the spurious and background counting rates. The method of mixing samples into the detecting liquid is of particular advantage with radioactive materials of low energy, especially the beta rays from tritium, carbon-14, and sulfur-35. It suffers a disadvantage in that certain kinds of samples and physiological fluids interfere with the scintillation properties and the light transmission of the scintillation detector liquids. However, a broad literature related to the liquid scintillation counting art has quickly grown up, providing many techniques to handle the problems of sample solubilization and scintillator preparation. Determination of the identity and the amount of various radioactivities occurring in mixed samples is readily possible.

2. A counting system in which ionizing radiation emanating from a prepared sample or living subject is detected through scintillations induced in a liquid phospor, usually held in a container which surrounds the sample or subject, coupled with one or more photomultiplier tubes and ancillary electronic apparatus as needed for analyzing and counting the radiation.

See WHOLE-BODY COUNTER.

LIQUID WASTE

High-level radioactive waste in liquid form results from the chemical processing of radioactive spent fuel elements (*see* FISSION PRODUCT WASTE DISPOSAL). Large quantities of low-level liquid waste are produced in the operation of water-cooled nuclear reactors (*see* WASTE DISPOSAL, NUCLEAR-POWERED SHIP). Liquid wastes also result from radioisotope waste disposal, decontamination laundries, water from decontamination scrubbing of tools, equipment, etc., and from many chemical operations.

Low-level liquid wastes are frequently disposed of in the regular sewer system with repeated flushings; or they may be discharged directly into a large stream, or piped out for ocean disposal. They may be disposed of into the ground through seepage areas or "cribs" (*see* WASTE DISPOSAL, RADIOACTIVE) or into ponds or "swamps." Movement of the various isotopes through the soil is not uniform, for in field trials involving mixed wastes the mobility of the different species was found to vary as shown in Figure L–14.

The average speed of movement of radioisotopes in soil depends upon water movement in various strata, and ion-exchange properties of the soil. Movement is much slower than would be thought normal—a study by a French scientist indicates that even in sandy soil water movement is only about 20 to 50 meters per year. Based on a study

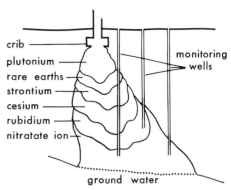

FIGURE L–14. RELATIVE MOVEMENT THROUGH THE SOIL OF DIFFERENT RADIOISOTOPES CONTAINED IN LIQUID WASTE.

of movement of liquid radioactive waste in soil at the Hanford Works it is estimated that it will take 180 years for contaminated ground water to move from the disposal crib areas to the Columbia River 20 miles away.

High-level liquid wastes are usually handled by concentration and storage. Concentration is achieved by evaporation through boiling; by scavenging where fission products are co-precipitated with a suitable carrier; by ion exchange where the radioactive ions are absorbed on an ion exchange resin; and by biological assimilation where microorganisms are used to concentrate specific elements or by a combination of these methods. The concentrated material is then placed in tank storage, or sealed in drums and handled by land burial. Chemical processing, including electrolytic and ion exchange, lime soda softening process, precipitation, co-precipitation, crystallization, flocculation, adsorption, or fixation in a ceramic cake is also used in handling high-level liquid wastes.

LITHIUM

Symbol Li; atomic number 3; atomic weight 6.940. A silver-white light alkali metal. Discovered by Arfvedson in 1817. Named from Greek, *lithos*, stone. Not found free in nature but in traces in nearly all igneous rocks. Natural abundance furnished by 2 stable isotopes: Li[6], 7.52% and Li[7], 92.48%.

Of importance in thermonuclear reactions, in the manufacture of alloys, optical glass and ceramic glazes. Very low-order toxicity. Not an essential element for biological materials and no usefulness in this field has been demonstrated.

Three radioactive isotopes have been identified. Li[8] may be produced in the soil through induced radioactivity as the result of neutron bombardment from the detonation of a nuclear device. It is not significant as a component of residual activity.

None of the radioisotopes has demonstrated biological, medical or agricultural usefulness.

LIVE TIME

The actual time during which a counting system is ready to count; the total counting time minus the dead time. High sensitivity systems working at rapid counting rates, as in whole-body counters, may be controlled to totalize their counts over a specified live time.

LIVER, RADIATION EFFECTS ON

From a functional standpoint the liver is a relatively radiosensitive organ. For example, the rate of incorporation of phosphorus-32 into deoxyribonucleic acid of liver is decreased by 800 roentgens (r) of gamma radiation; and increased incorporation of carbon-labeled phenylalanine into rat liver occurs immediately after irradiation. Also changes in the mitochondria of rat liver have been observed 6 to 8 hours after radiation doses of 500 to 1,200 r whole body. However, significant morphological changes do not occur at doses less than 12,000 r in normal animals, and the liver's ability to regenerate is not impaired by doses of 20,000 r. Hemorrhages, infarcts and focal necroses are sometimes found in the liver of animals dying as a result of radiation damage.

LIVER FUNCTION MEASUREMENT

Certain dyes that are removed from the blood by the liver have been used for many years for testing liver function. Recently, radioisotopically labeled forms of these dyes have greatly improved the tests; greater sensitivity is possible because smaller amounts of the dye can be used, and measurements can be made at several points along the pathway of the dye. Most commonly used is rose bengal labeled with iodine-131. A test dose of less than 1 mg containing 10 to 25 microcuries of the radioisotope is injected intravenously. The level of radioactivity in the blood is then measured continuously or at frequent intervals. Normally, it falls to half its initial level within 6 to 10 minutes, as the dye is removed by the polygonal cells of the liver. A radiation detector placed over the region of the liver shows maximum activity in that organ to be reached at about 30 minutes, normally. Within the liver the dye is excreted into the biliary system; it passes into the gallbladder and eventually reaches the intestinal tract. A detector placed over the mid-abdomen normally shows a rise in counting rate about 30 minutes after the injection; this is when the dye first begins to enter the intestine.

If there is an impaired blood supply to the liver, or defective function of its polygonal cells, the rate of blood clearance will be slowed and the speed and amount of buildup of radioactivity in the liver will be decreased. If there is obstruction of the biliary system the liver radioactivity will fail to decrease normally and there will be a deficiency of the dye in the intestinal tract.

The liver scans shown in Figures L–15 and L–16 were made after intravenous injection of rose

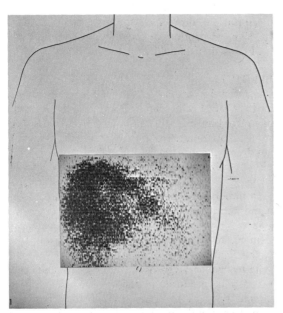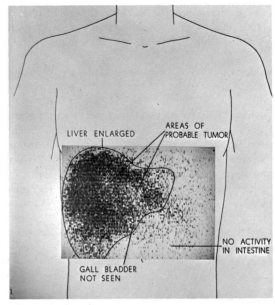

FIGURE L–15. LEFT, LIVER SCAN FOLLOWING INJECTION OF ROSE BENGAL LABELED WITH IODINE-131 IN A PATIENT WITH COMPLETE OBSTRUCTIVE JAUNDICE. RIGHT, THE INTERPRETATION.

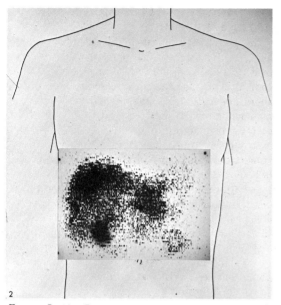 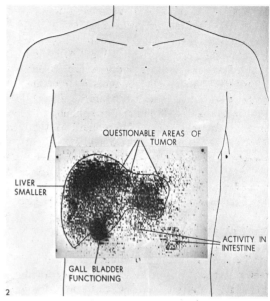

FIGURE L–16.   LEFT, SCAN OF SAME PATIENT FOLLOWING TELETHERAPY TO AREAS OF APPARENT INVOLVEMENT IN THE LIVER. RIGHT, THE INTERPRETATION.

bengal labeled with I[131]. The scans were made at an interval long enough after injection so that gallbladder filling would normally be present. Those on the left are original scans and those on the right are the same scans respectively with sketches to help with interpretation.

The first scan (Fig. L–15) was made when the patient had complete obstructive jaundice due to poorly differentiated neoplasm metastatic to the liver. Following this scan the patient was given teletherapy to the areas of apparent involvement in the liver. The jaundice promptly cleared.

The second scan (Fig. L–16) was made some weeks later. The resumption of biliary flow and gallbladder filling is shown.

LOCAL FALLOUT

Also known as close-in fallout. Fallout which descends, under the influence of gravity, from the atomic cloud to earth in the vicinity of ground zero within the first few hours. A nuclear device, detonated so that the fireball touches the earth, will carry large amounts of surface material up into the fireball where it is vaporized or fused, and becomes intimately mixed with fission products and other "bomb" residues. Upon cooling, all the heavier, now radioactive particles descend from the atomic cloud as local fallout. If the wind is not blowing this material will descend in a circular pattern no more than a mile or 2 in diameter, but with a wind it may be carried for several miles in a roughly cigar-shaped fallout pattern.

The fraction of the total fission product activity which becomes local fallout depends upon the yield of the bomb, the height of burst above ground, and weather conditions, but in general about 50% will have been deposited on the ground by the end of 16 hours.

See TROPOSPHERIC FALLOUT and STRATOSPHERIC FALLOUT.

LOS ALAMOS SCIENTIFIC LABORATORY

LASL is a major USAEC research center at Los Alamos, New Mexico, 35 miles southwest of Santa Fe, operated by the University of California. The Laboratory employs about 1,000 scientists and engineers and over 2,500 supporting personnel. LASL was established in 1942, and, working under the Manhattan Engineer District, did the research, design, construction and successful testing of the first nuclear weapon. The LASL has continued to be active in developing the world's most complete arsenal of atomic weapons of all varieties, but at the same time has conducted basic and applied research in rocket propulsion, power reactor technology, controlled thermonuclear research, and in basic and applied physics in many areas.

Of primary biomedical interest, however, is the Health Division with its 8 groups: Group H-1 (Health Physics) is charged with the responsibility for radiological monitoring and with all monitoring of personnel for radiological exposure. It handles exposure records and is responsible for decontamination. Group H-2 (Industrial Medicine) handles the occupational medicine activity, conducts the first-aid program and has a research section on hematology. Group H-3 (Safety) handles the safety program for LASL and has maintained an excellent safety record. Group H-4 (Biomedical Research) conducts a diversified research program as indicated by its 6 units: Molecular Radiobiology, Cellular Radiobiology, Mammalian Radiobiology, Mammalian Metabolism, Low-Level Counting, and Clinical Investigations. Group H-5 (Industrial Hygiene) must determine in both field and laboratory the existence of all toxic hazards, estimate their magnitude, calculate possible exposures, and devise methods of control. Group H-6 (Radiological Physics) is concerned largely with theoretical considerations such as weather prediction, shielding calculations, theoretical evaluation of radiological hazards from new and unusual sources, and a certain amount of effort involving the radiological hazard of weapon tests. Group H-7 (Industrial Waste) does research and handles the problems of radioactive waste disposal. Group H-8 (Field Studies) has a largely applied function devoted mainly to conducting experiments and measurements in the field (Nevada Test Site; Pacific testing areas) at weapons tests and tests of prototype nuclear propulsion systems for rockets (Rover project).

This complex laboratory program and organization developed from the appointment of a medical officer to handle physical examinations of employees, records of radiation exposure, and the usual industrial medical control measures. This early work provided an understanding of methods for diagnosis and control of plutonium exposure, but perhaps the outstanding accomplishment is the maintenance of an active and effective industrial medical and radiological safety program for a period of 19 years. In addition, the Health Division has: contributed to the understanding of acute and chronic effects of all types of radiations of interest to the atomic energy program; added to the understanding of the relative biological effects of radiations of different types and different energies; elucidated the incapacitating effects of massive doses of radiation and defined the acute radiation syndrome in man as a result of studying 3 fatal accidents at LASL involving critical assemblies; contributed to the understanding of the prompt radiation effects of nuclear weapons; developed a well-known type of whole-body counter for diagnosis of exposure of personnel and for the study of world-wide fallout; contributed to an understanding of the distribution and uptake of cesium-137 from fallout; and conducted basic research in many aspects of radiation biology.

LOVELACE FOUNDATION RADIATION BIOLOGY RESEARCH

The Lovelace Foundation for Medical Education and Research, Albuquerque, New Mexico since 1952 has been participating in studies of the biomedical effects of nuclear weapons, both in the laboratory and during test detonations of nuclear weapons at the Nevada Test Site. Their primary interests have been in blast biological damage and blast physical phenomena responsible for blast-induced environmental variations that are potentially hazardous to animals and man; i.e., pressure-time variations, penetrating and non-penetrating missiles (debris) and the gross displacement of biological media. Working as a part of the Civil Effects Test Operation, the Lovelace group studied other aspects of biomedical interest such as non-line-of-sight thermal damage seen in open underground shelters, and dust occurring in open and closed underground structures; they also have assisted in analyzing available data bearing upon the changes nuclear explosions induce in the environment and have helped present relevant information in simplified form.

In 1959 the Lovelace Foundation began planning a long-term study concerning "The Biological Effects of Exposure to Fission Products" for the Division of Biology and Medicine of the Atomic Energy Commission. Individual radionuclides have been studied biologically, but mixed fission products likely to be present following the detonation of a nuclear weapon or a catastrophic incident with a nuclear reactor have not been investigated systematically in test animals exposed via the inhalation route. The program underway will initially expose, by inhalation, various animal species to individual, and then mixtures of the following radioisotopes: iodine-131, strontium-90, barium-140, yttrium-91, tellurium-132, cesium-137 and ruthenium-106; exposures to the effluent from heated irradiated fuel elements are also visualized.

Various exposure levels are likewise planned and many of the animals will be observed over their life span. Interim facilities are currently being utilized and permanent construction, now underway to be completed in the 1963–1964 time period, will house about 1,500 rats, 4,000 mice, 300 guinea pigs and 1,000 Beagle dogs. This study should add valuable information concerning the possible deleterious effects of radioactive fallout.

LOW BACKGROUND SHIELD

Massive radiation protective structure surrounding a detector for low-level measurements to minimize the background count; sometimes employed in conjunction with a cosmic-ray guard. *See* SHIELD.

LOW-LEVEL COUNTING

Procedures devised to evaluate the radioactive content of sample materials at minimal levels. The detectors employed in this work are of high sensitivity and have excellent discrimination in favor of the desired activity; the installation is characterized by good shielding and anti-coincidence (cosmic-ray guard) circuits. The total arrangements thus provide an exceptionally low background counting rate, so that statistically adequate counts can be obtained in spite of the lengthy counting times required for specimens of extremely low activity.

See COSMIC-RAY GUARD.

LUMINESCENCE

Emission of light due to any cause other than high temperature.

Bioluminescence is illustrated by the firefly.

Chemiluminescence is produced by certain chemical reactions.

Vigorously grinding ordinary sugar produces light called *triboluminescence*.

Photoluminescence is the emission of light as a result of nonluminous radiations.

A large number of substances become luminescent when stimulated or excited by suitable radiation.

See FLUORESCENCE and PHOSPHORESCENCE.

LUNG, RADIATION EFFECTS ON

The lungs and bronchial tree are fairly radioresistant. Damage to the lungs from external radiation requires heavy doses in the range of 1,000 to 2,000 roentgens. When thus heavily irradiated the lungs show slowly developing progressive changes called radiation pneumonitis. Following death from whole-body irradiation autopsies show a good deal of fluid in the lungs (edema) and there are many hemorrhages. Proof of the production of cancer by external radiation has not been obtained.

There is ample proof from experimental animals and from human case histories for the development of cancer as the result of internal deposition of radioactive materials. Fibrosis and cancer of the lung have been described in miners of pitchblende and other radioactive ores. Retention time of inhaled radioactive material is variable and depends upon lung clearance, but there is evidence that lung cancer can be produced by inhalation of radioactive material as well as by intratracheal administration, and by radioactive beads im-

planted in the bronchi. The radioactive isotopes used in these inhalation and implantation experiments were polonium-210 aerosol, plutonium-239 aerosol, cerium-144-praseodymium-144 dust, ruthenium-106 oxide and strontium-90 beads. The calculated dose in these experiments ranged from a low of about 1,885 rad (intratracheal implantation) to produce a squamous cell carcinoma (cancer) in a mouse in 500 days, to 200,000 rad to produce bronchogenic carcinoma in a rat by an implanted source.

See INHALATION OF RADIOACTIVE MATERIAL and LUNG CLEARANCE.

LUNG CLEARANCE

Transport of materials from the lung. This removal of particulate material from the respiratory tract is considered to involve at least 4 physiological mechanisms. The mechanism which accounts for the removal of the most material is the action of the ciliated epithelium in combination with the mucus secretion which moves the impinged material up and out of the respiratory tract and into the esophagus where it is swallowed. The second mechanism is the transfer of the soluble material across the alveolar membrane into the blood stream. The third mechanism is the engulfing of the particles by large white blood cells (macrophages) which is called phagocytosis. The phagocytized particle may be moved up and out, or the phagocyte may enter the lymphatics and be deposited in the lymph nodes. The fourth clearance mechanism may be the movement of particles through the respiratory membrane without the mediation of phagocyte cells.

Retention is the amount or fraction of material deposited in the respiratory tract which remains and is not translocated from the respiratory tract to other tissues or organs. Retention is important because the rate of clearance of radioactive particles determines the radiation dose, and therefore the degree of hazard to the lung.

See INHALATION OF RADIOACTIVE MATERIAL; LUNG, RADIATION EFFECTS ON; and RESPIRATORS.

LUNG STUDIES. *See* RESPIRATION STUDIES.

LUTECIUM

Symbol Lu; atomic number 71; atomic weight 174.99. A member of the yttrium subgroup of the lanthanide series of rare earths. Discovered in 1907 by Urbain and von Welsbach and named after Lutetia, the ancient name of Paris. Found naturally in certain types of earth and rock formations, but not in living material. The stable isotope

Lu[175] accounts for 97.40% of the abundance; the very slightly radioactive Lu[176] for the remaining 2.60%.

There are 12 radioactive isotopes of lutecium of which only Lu[177] has any biological, medical or agricultural significance.

Lutecium-177 ($_{71}$Lu[177]). A rare earth radio-isotope with a half-life of 6.8 days; with bone as the critical organ, biological half-life 1,000 days, effective half-life 6.75 days; decays by beta (β^-) emission. Among 25 radioisotopes selected for medical study on the basis of producibility in a nuclear reactor and an acceptable half-life, it ranked second because of its high activation index of 9,500. It is of particular medical interest in that it can be used in the same way as colloidal gold-198 for the treatment of malignancy. Increased future use is predicted because it has a longer half-life than gold-198 (an advantage when shipping long distances) and it is less expensive to administer.

LYMPH NODES, RADIATION EFFECTS ON

Lymph nodes and other lymphoid tissues are highly radiosensitive, with changes being evident following a single dose of external radiation of 50 to 100 roentgens. Immediately after such an exposure the lymph nodes usually decrease in size, but within a week following these low doses the cellular debris has been phagocytosed and the lymph nodes reconstituted. With higher doses the lymph nodes may shrink below normal size immediately after irradiation but by the end of a week they are swollen, edematous and contain gross hemorrhages. Figure L–17 shows the lymph nodes from a swine which died 8 days after whole-body irradiation (400 roentgens) by ionizing radiation during a test detonation of a nuclear device. Even with this damage the debris is cleared up and in most cases mitosis begins and some repopulation of the lymph nodes occurs.

Lymph nodes in the pulmonary region may become critical organs following inhalation of radioactive material.

See SPLEEN, RADIATION EFFECTS ON.

LYMPH NODE STUDIES

When colloidal preparations of radioisotopes such as gold-198 are injected into soft tissues, a portion of the material enters lymphatic channels and is collected by the reticuloendothelial tissue of lymph nodes draining the area. The distribution is very uneven, however, some nodes of the group receiving much more than others. Such a radioisotopic distribution is of interest in view of the lymphatic spread of cancer. Diagnostic doses of colloidal radioisotopes when used in connection with probe counters or scanners may help to locate lymph nodes for surgical removal. With much larger, therapeutic doses, lymph nodes may be effectively irradiated. Those nodes that are completely replaced by cancer lose their ability to concentrate the radioisotope in this manner, but when only a small focus of malignant cells is present, the radioisotope in the rest of the node may irradiate it effectively.

Radiophosphorus given orally or intravenously

FIGURE L–17. ENLARGED, EDEMATOUS, HEMORRHAGIC LYMPH NODES FROM A SWINE WHICH DIED 8 DAYS AFTER TOTAL BODY EXPOSURE TO IONIZING RADIATION FROM THE ATOMIC BOMB TESTS AT BIKINI. (OFFICIAL U.S. NAVY PHOTOGRAPH.)

concentrates somewhat in lymph nodes by being incorporated in the lymphatic cells. The concentration tends to be higher than normal in nodes involved with leukemia or lymphosarcoma and this may contribute to therapeutic usefulness.

Radioisotopes have been used to study the metabolism, life span and behavior of lymphocytes.

See LEUKOCYTE STUDIES.

LYMPHOCYTES, RADIATION DAMAGE

The lymphocyte count followed over a period of 24 to 48 hours is a most sensitive indicator of radiation damage to components of the hematopoietic system. A total dose of only 40 roentgens given in 2 divided doses causes a measurable depression of the peripheral blood lymphocyte level in man. A lymphocyte count that decreases to a level of 100 to 200 per mm^3 within 12 to 24 hours probably indicates a dose in the lethal range; and a decrease to 500 per mm^3 in the first 24 to 48 hours indicates a heavy dose and a grave prognosis for recovery. However, even in the sublethal range the decrease in the lymphocyte count is likely to occur early and be marked, so it is not always a good indicator of the severity of the exposure, at least in the first few hours. After the first 2 or 3 days the lymphocyte count levels off and shows dose-effect relationship—with high doses there is a marked depression and with low doses the depression is moderate. If the count remains above 1,000 mm^3 the prognosis is good, and an increasing count after the first week is a good prognostic sign. Complete return to a normal level usually takes weeks or months, and may be delayed for a year or more.

M

MAGNESIUM

Symbol Mg; atomic number 12; atomic weight 24.32. A silver-white, light and fairly tough metal. Recognized by English chemist, physicist and physician Black in 1755, isolated by English chemist Davy in 1808, and prepared in coherent form by Bussy in 1831. Named for Magnesia, district in Thessaly, Greece. One of the most abundant metals and the eighth element in estimated amount in the earth's crust. Many carbonates and silicates contain considerable amounts, and soluble sulfate and chloride are found in mineral springs and in the ocean. Its natural abundance is furnished by 3 stable isotopes.

Used industrially in photographic flashlight powders, incendiary bombs and signal flares; as an alloy with other metals such as aluminum for light, strong construction; in the chemical industry; and in the nuclear field. Fire and explosion are hazards; magnesium in the tissues from cutting or puncture wounds leads to tissue necrosis, but otherwise toxicity is very low. An essential mineral constituent of chlorophyll.

Three radioactive isotopes have been identified. Mg^{27} may be one of the radionuclides induced in either soil or sea water by neutron bombardment associated with the detonation of a nuclear device. Is not an important residual contaminant. Mg^{28} is coming into use in biomedical activity, in studying plant pigments and in animal metabolism of magnesium.

MALIGNANT LYMPHOMAS, TREATMENT

Internally administered radioisotopes play a relatively small role in the treatment of lymphomas. They are of value in some cases of lymphosarcoma but are usually not useful in Hodgkin's disease. This group of diseases is usually treated by external radiation delivered by x-ray machines or teletherapy devices.

MALIGNANT TUMORS, DIAGNOSIS

Radiophosphorus concentrates in cancer tissue more than it does in most types of normal tissue. This concentration is the basis for several types of diagnostic tests for malignancy. The fact that phosphorus-32 has no gamma emission makes the tests useless if any large thickness of tissue separates the suspected cancer from the detector. Fortunately the beta emission is a fairly energetic one. In each procedure the significant measurements are made after an oral or intravenous tracer dose of P^{32}. A high level of activity in the area under suspicion suggests malignancy. Comparison with normal control sites is always important.

Tumors of the breast and testis, and melanomas, have been studied with detectors placed on the skin; lesions of the eye, with detectors inserted at the edge of the eyeball; stomach disease, by means of a detector that is swallowed; tumors of the prostate and brain, by detectors inserted into the tissues. With brain tumors the objective is usually to determine the extent of the lesion rather than the existence of malignancy.

Most of these diagnostic procedures are still somewhat experimental and are not widely accepted as standard practice.

MANGANESE

Symbol Mn; atomic number 25; atomic weight 54.94. A silver-white metal, brittle, harder than iron. Recognized by Bergman, Scheele and others; discovered by Gahn in 1774. Named for Latin *magnes*, magnet. Occurs chiefly as pyrolusite (MnO_2). Natural abundance 100% Mn^{55}.

Several million tons are used each year in the United States, the bulk being consumed in the manufacture of iron and steel. Also used in manufacture of dry cells, photographic supplies, chemicals, fertilizers, coloring agents for paints and ceramics and for bleaching glass. Manganese is present in all living matter. Animal tissues contain 0.2 to 4 parts per million (ppm) and plants have been found to have from 25 to 1000 ppm. The biochemical standard man contains .0003% or 0.210 gram per 70 kilograms body weight. Normal intake for man is about 4 milligrams per day. Dietary levels on a dry-matter basis are about 50 ppm for sheep and cattle, 7 to 50 ppm for swine and 50 ppm for poultry. Nontoxic for ingested material but toxic for inhalation of dust or fumes. Adequate ventilation is required in industrial activity involving dust or fumes of manganese.

Eight radioactive isotopes have been identified. Mn^{56} (half-life 2.58 hours) may be produced as induced radioactivity by neutron bombardment associated with the detonation of a nuclear device.

Mn^{52} (half-life 6.0 days) and Mn^{54} (half-life 300 days) are used along with Mn^{56} for biological research in metabolism and distribution of manganese in animal and plant tissues.

MANHATTAN ENGINEER DISTRICT

In June 1942 the President gave the Army the responsibility of directing all activities concerned with the research and development of an atomic bomb. The S-1 activities (Uranium Section) of the OSRD committee supervised the pilot-plant studies of centrifuge, gaseous-diffusion and electromagnetic methods as well as the construction of the heavy-water plant at Trail. Colonel James Marshall, having been assigned to the project, established his headquarters in New York with the appropriate title: Manhattan Engineer District.

Gen. Leslie R. Groves, deputy chief of construction in the Corps of Engineers took complete charge of the entire project and directed it throughout the war. Representatives from Army, Navy and OSRD formed a military policy committee with Vannevar Bush as chairman and James B. Conant as his alternate. Admiral William R. Purnell served for the Navy, and Brig. General Wilhelm D. Styer as the Army member. Emphasis shifted rapidly from exploratory research to the development of a production enterprise. Every feasible method was intensively studied and minerals were purchased. Intensified physical and chemical research was continued at laboratories where top scientists were already working; e.g., Columbia University, the University of Chicago, and the University of California. Large commercial firms such as Du Pont, Union Carbide, Westinghouse and General Electric, with competent scientists were put to work setting up new facilities at Hanford, Wash.; Oak Ridge, Tenn.; and Los Alamos, N.M.

It was early recognized that a health division was needed at the laboratories and one was established at the Metallurgical Laboratory (predecessor to the Argonne National Laboratory). Dr. Simeon Cantril was put in charge of the medical section, which collected radiation exposure data on all laboratory employees. Pocket ionization chambers and film badges were required in high-radiation areas. Maximum permissible exposures were placed at 0.1 r/day for gamma radiation and 0.01 r for fast neutrons. Toxicology of radioactive substances was intensively investigated in a program conducted at the University of Rochester under Dr. Stafford Warren. Another laboratory aiding the health aspects of the Manhattan District was at Western Reserve University under Dr. Hymer Friedell.

When Congress passed the Atomic Energy Act of 1946, control of atomic energy matters was transferred to the civilian agency, the Atomic Energy Commission, on 1 January, 1947.

MANIKIN, RADIATION EQUIVALENT. *See* STANDARD MAN.

MARINE ORGANISMS. *See* AQUATIC ORGANISMS, UPTAKE OF RADIONUCLIDES.

MARSHALL ISLANDERS, RADIATION EXPOSURE

Following a thermonuclear explosion during testing operations at the Eniwetok Proving Ground on March 1, 1954, a shift in winds carried the cloud (CLOUD, RADIOACTIVE) over the Marshall Islands, where fallout occurred. Radioactivity levels became sufficiently high to warrant evacuation of inhabitants from some of these islands to Kwajalein, where decontamination procedures were conducted.

Sixty-four Marshallese on Rongelap received approximately 175 roentgens (r); 18 on Alinginae received an average of 69 r; 157 on Utirik received an estimated dose of 14 r; and some U.S. servicemen on Rongerik were exposed to about 78 r. They were under close medical observation until June 29, 1957, when the USAEC determined that contamination was negligible and the islanders were returned to their newly built homes.

Earliest symptoms were gastrointestinal— nausea, vomiting and diarrhea, which were mild and transitory. Examination of blood revealed depression in blood platelet and leukocytes. Itching and burning of the skin occurred in the most heavily exposed groups, followed by epilation, and later frank breakdown of tissue, especially between the toes, where beta radioactive material had remained in contact with the skin. These lesions healed, leaving slight scars and skin color changes.

Medical teams occasionally visit the islands to ascertain additional or belated effects. In 1959 no apparent effects related to their fallout exposure were found with the possible exception of a lag in complete recovery of the blood platelet level. The leukocytes had recovered to levels comparable with those of control groups. Twelve cases showed limited residual effects from beta irradiation of the skin consisting of scarring and pigment aberration. Measurement in a whole body counter indicated low levels of internally deposited cesium-137 and zinc-65.

MASS ABSORPTION COEFFICIENT. *See* ABSORPTION COEFFICIENT.

MASS EFFECTS

The mass of the principal element in a radio-isotope preparation used in biological research may be an important consideration. The mass that is employed depends upon the specific activity of the preparation available, the degree of accumulation in the samples to be measured, and the sensitivity of the measurement. The following terminology is often used:

Tracer dose: The amount of the administered element is small compared with the normal intake or that normally present in the system.

Physiological dose: The amount of the administered element is of the same order of magnitude as the normal intake.

Massive dose: The amount of the administered element far exceeds the normal intake.

The tracer and physiological doses usually follow the normal path, since the amount of the element introduced into the system is not large enough to disturb equilibrium or steady-state conditions. The massive dose, however, may flood the tissues and present an abnormal picture.

The classic example of flooding is the effect of massive iodine administration upon the percentage uptake by the thyroid gland. The percentage of accumulation of iodine in the thyroid gland is decreased as the radioisotope preparation given contains increased amounts of iodine. For example, in mammals, when iodine is administered at the rate of 0.00001 mg per kg of body weight, the percentage uptake by the thyroid may be about 60. When the iodine is administered at about 1 mg per kg of body weight, the percentage uptake by the thyroid is less than 1.

MASS NUMBER

Symbol A. Total number of nucleons, i.e., protons and neutrons in the nucleus of an atom or nuclide. The atomic number represents the number of protons in the nucleus, the neutron number represents the number of neutrons in the nucleus; therefore the mass number is the sum of the two. Mass number is the whole number or integer nearest in value to the atomic mass when the latter is expressed in atomic mass units. The mass number is commonly written after the name of the element (potassium-40), as a superscript after the symbol (K^{40}), and less commonly as a superscript before the symbol (^{40}K). The tables associated with the stable isotope and radioactive isotope entries give the mass numbers of the known nuclides of the elements.

MASS SPECTROMETER

Apparatus designed to measure the mass of ions, for determining masses or mass differences of iso-topes or compounds. An ion source chamber is provided in which the substance to be analyzed is first ionized and then accelerated into the analyzer section, where carefully controlled electric and/or magnetic fields are used to separate the ions of different masses. Measurement is achieved either by direct electrical collection of the ions or by photographic registration. This device was extensively used to establish molecular and atomic weights and has also been used in tracer studies. The same principles are applied on a much grander scale in the isotope separation process for production of fissionable materials or nuclear fuels.

MAXIMUM PERMISSIBLE BODY BURDEN

Symbol q. A value, usually expressed in microcuries (μc), based on that amount of an internally deposited radionuclide in the total body which produces the maximum permissible relative biological effectiveness dose rate to a given organ of the body. A q figure does not exist except in relation to an organ of reference, which may or may not be the critical organ. In most cases, significantly different values of body burden result for a given radionuclide when effects on different organs are considered. Calculations for 4 different radio-nuclides (Table M–1) taken from the table in NBS Handbook 69* illustrate this point clearly.

MAXIMUM PERMISSIBLE CONCENTRATION*

The MPC is a numerical figure indicating the amount of a radionuclide allowable in air $(MPC)_a$ and in water $(MPC)_w$ for radiation workers. Calculation of such exposure maximum limits is an attempt to furnish guide lines for industrial activity within safety limits for the worker. The exposure should, of course, be held to the lowest possible level; the MPC is the maximum and not the recommended operating level.

The MPC for an individual will depend upon many factors such as his age, physical condition, eating habits, and hygienic standards. It will depend also upon the physical and chemical properties of the radioactive material and upon the method of intake—by ingestion, by inhalation, through wounds, or by absorption through the skin. The radioactive half-life and biological half-life are considered. However, the data concerning the effect of most of these factors do not warrant

---

*National Bureau of Standards Handbook 69, "Maximum Permissible Body Burdens and Maximum Permissible Concentrations of Radionuclides in Air and in Water for Occupational Exposure." U. S. Department of Commerce.

TABLE M–1.   MAXIMUM PERMISSIBLE BODY BURDENS FOR TOTAL BODY FOR FOUR RADIONUCLIDES

RADIONUCLIDE AND TYPE OF DECAY		ORGAN OF REFERENCE	MAXIMUM PERMISSIBLE BURDEN IN TOTAL BODY q (μc)
Zinc ($_{30}Zn^{65}$) (β^+, EC, γ)	Soluble	**Total body***	60
		Prostate	70
		Liver	80
		Kidney	100
		GI (LLI)†	—
		Pancreas	200
		Muscle	200
		Ovary	300
		Testes	400
		Bone	700
	Insoluble	**Lung**	—
		GI (LLI)	—
Strontium ($_{38}Sr^{90}$) (β^-)	Soluble	**Bone**	2
		Total body	20
		GI (LLI)	—
	Insoluble	**Lung**	—
		GI (LLI)	—
Antimony ($_{51}Sb^{125}$) (β^-, γ)	Soluble	GI (LLI)	—
		Lung	40
		Total body	60
		Bone	70
		Liver	3×10^3
		Thyroid	7×10^4
	Insoluble	**Lung**	—
		GI (LLI)	—
Uranium ($_{92}U^{238}$) (α, γ)	Soluble	GI (LLI)	—
		Kidney	5×10^{-3}
		Bone	0.06
		Total body	0.5
	Insoluble	**Lung**	—
		GI (LLI)	—

*Boldface type represents critical organs.
†GI refers to the gastrointestinal tract and LLI to the lower large intestine. No q value is given for either GI or for lung, for material is not considered to be deposited in these organs for any extended period.

such detailed treatment. All calculations are based on the standard man, ingestion and inhalation being the routes of intake in most cases. Also the most restrictive case for the maximum permissible dose is used, i.e., the age 18 applied to the formula $5(N - 18)$, where N is the age of the worker and the resulting number is the average yearly dose of radiation in rems. Only the more important compounds have been calculated.

The MPC's are calculated on the basis of both a 40-hour work week and an 168-hour week or continuous exposure. If work assignments are such that only 8 hours are spent each week in an exposure area and there is no exposure for the remainder of the week, then the applicable MPC values are 5 times those listed for a 40-hour week; and if the worker spends 48 hours each week in the exposure area, the applicable MPC values are five-sixths of those listed for the 40-hour week. The rules say that "the dose in any 13 consecutive weeks shall not exceed 3 rems," but they permit this exposure during any time interval, e.g., 1 minute, 1 day, 1 week, etc., provided the limit is not exceeded. This is a combined external and internal dose. An older person may receive up to 12 rem exposure in a single year provided the dose does not exceed the limits of the formula $5(N - 18)$. This flexibility as to dose and time may be allowed for accurately measured external exposure, but it is too risky for internal exposures. The permissible levels take into account the exposure period, as the following example indicates. Assuming no exposure for the previous 13-week period, assuming sufficiently accurate monitoring, and assuming the restrictions implied by the formula $5(N - 18)$ are met, it is possible for a person to work for 1 hour where the air concentration of a radionuclide with the total body as the critical organ is roughly 1,200 times the MPC (air) for a 40-hour week. In such a case no further exposure would be permitted in the succeeding 13 weeks.

TABLE M-2. MAXIMUM PERMISSIBLE CONCENTRATIONS OF RADIONUCLIDES IN AIR AND IN WATER FOR OCCUPATIONAL EXPOSURE TO CESIUM-137

ORGAN OF REFERENCE	MAXIMUM PERMISSIBLE CONCENTRATIONS			
	For 40-hour week		For 168-hour week	
Soluble material	$(MPC)_w$	$(MPC)_a$	$(MPC)_w$	$(MPC)_a$
Total body*	4×10^{-4}	6×10^{-8}	2×10^{-4}	2×10^{-8}
Liver	5×10^{-4}	8×10^{-8}	2×10^{-4}	3×10^{-8}
Spleen	6×10^{-4}	9×10^{-8}	2×10^{-4}	3×10^{-8}
Muscle	7×10^{-4}	10^{-7}	2×10^{-4}	4×10^{-8}
Bone	10^{-3}	2×10^{-7}	5×10^{-4}	7×10^{-8}
Kidney	10^{-3}	2×10^{-7}	5×10^{-4}	8×10^{-8}
Lung	5×10^{-3}	6×10^{-7}	2×10^{-3}	2×10^{-7}
GI (Small intestine)	0.02	5×10^{-6}	8×10^{-3}	2×10^{-6}
Insoluble material				
Lung		10^{-8}		5×10^{-9}
GI (Lower large intestine)	10^{-3}	2×10^{-7}	4×10^{-4}	8×10^{-8}

*Boldface type represents critical organs.

The National Committee on Radiation Protection and Measurements has set numerical standards for the maximum permissible concentrations for air, water, milk and various foods which are to be consumed by man. For example, the MPC for strontium-90 in water is 800 micromicrocuries per kilogram of water as the occupational exposure for continuous intake over a lifetime. One-tenth of this amount is the MPC for the general public. Handbook 69 presents recommended values of maximum permissible concentration in air and in water for about 240 radionuclides. Both soluble and insoluble compounds are considered. In all cases the calculated dose rate which determines the MPC takes into account the actual amounts of the radionuclide in the body or critical organ rather than assuming a state of equilibrium, and is set by the requirement that the dose rate (rems per week) after 50 years of occupational exposure shall not exceed the basic standards set forth for the maximum permissible dose.

The MPC for various important radionuclides may be found under the description of the elements. The maximum permissible concentrations for all organs for a single radionuclide, cesium-137, is given in Table M-2 as an example of the coverage of NBS Handbook 69.*

See RADIOACTIVITY CONCENTRATION GUIDE

*National Bureau of Standards Handbook 69, "Maximum Permissible Body Burdens and Maximum Permissible Concentrations of Radionuclides in Air and in Water for Occupational Exposure." U. S. Department of Commerce.

MAXIMUM PERMISSIBLE DOSE†

In principle there is a maximum DOSE that just fulfills the requirements set forth in the definition of PERMISSIBLE DOSE. Obviously, any lesser dose would also meet the requirements. In protection rules or recommendations the values are the highest ones permissible under the stipulated conditions of exposure. In order to bring this out explicitly they were called maximum permissible doses.

Several subcommittees of the National Committee on Radiation Protection and Measurements (NCRP) carefully studied all the new biological information bearing on the problem of maximum permissible radiation exposure to man and on April 18, 1958, issued the following:

Basic Rules
1. Accumulated Dose (Radiation Workers).
A. External exposure to critical organs.
Whole body, head and trunk, active blood-forming organs, or gonads: The maximum permissible dose (MPD), to the most critical organs, accumulated at any age, shall not exceed 5 rem multiplied by the number of years beyond age 18, and the dose in any 13 consecutive weeks shall not exceed 3 rem.

Thus the accumulated $MPD = (N - 18) \times 5$ rem, where N is the age in years and is greater than 18.

†Taken in part from the National Bureau of Standards Handbook 59, "Permissible Dose from External Sources of Ionizing Radiation." U. S. Department of Commerce.

Comment: This applies to radiation of sufficient penetrating power to affect a significant fraction of the critical tissue. (This will be enlarged upon in the revision of H59.)

B. External exposure to other organs.

Skin of whole body: MPD = 10(N − 18) rem, and the dose in any 13 consecutive weeks shall not exceed 6 rem.

Comment: This rule applies to radiation of low penetrating power. See figure 2, H59.

Lens of the eyes: The dose to the lens of the eyes shall be limited by the dose to the head and trunk (A, above).

Hands and forearms, feet and ankles: MPD = 75 rem/year, and the dose in any 13 consecutive weeks shall not exceed 25 rem.

C. Internal exposure.

The permissible levels from internal emitters will be consistent as far as possible with the age-proration principles above. Control of the internal dose will be achieved by limiting the body burden of radioisotopes. This will generally be accomplished by control of the average concentration of radioactive materials in the air, water, or food taken into the body.

2. Emergency Dose (Radiation Workers).

An accidental or emergency dose of 25 rem to the whole body or a major portion thereof, occurring only once in the lifetime of the person, need not be included in the determination of the radiation exposure status of that person (see p. 69, H59).

3. Medical Dose (Radiation Workers).

Radiation exposures resulting from necessary medical and dental procedures need not be included in the determination of the radiation exposure status of the person concerned.

4. Dose to Persons Outside of Controlled Areas.

The radiation or radioactive material outside a controlled area, attributable to normal operations within the controlled area, shall be such that it is improbable that any individual will receive a dose of more than 0.5 rem in any 1 year from external radiation.

In order to give guidance to Federal agencies in the formulation of radiation standards, the Federal Radiation Council was formed in 1959. The Council has said that the term "maximum permissible dose" has unfortunate connotations, in that there can be no single permissible or acceptable level of exposure, and they have promulgated the radiation protection guides which now are binding for Federal agencies. However, since all the current literature and standards refer to the maximum permissible dose, this term is used throughout this book.

MEAN FREE PATH

The average distance that a particle travels between successive collisions with other particles in the matter being traversed. One may speak of the mean free path for absorption, mean free path for inelastic collisions, or the mean free path for any other kind of particle encounter. The mean free path for ionization is the average distance an ionizing particle travels in a given medium between successive ionizing collisions.

MEAN LIFE

Symbol τ. The average time during which an atom or other system exists in a particular form. The mean time between the birth and death of a particle. Examples are the mean life of: atoms of a radionuclide before undergoing radioactive transformation; of mesons before undergoing transformation; of excited nuclei or atoms before losing their energy of excitation; and of diffusing neutrons before being captured. For a radionuclide the mean life is the reciprocal of the decay constant λ. For branching decay, mean life is given by

$$\tau = \frac{1}{\lambda} = \frac{1}{\lambda_1 + \lambda_2 + \lambda_3 + \ldots \ldots},$$

where λ_1, λ_2, λ_3, . . . are the partial disintegration constants for the various modes involved.

See AVERAGE LIFE.

MEDIAN LETHAL DOSE (MLD)

Dose of radiation that will kill, within a specified period, 50 per cent of the individuals in a large group of organisms or animals. It may also be referred to as the LD_{50}, the lethal dose for 50 per cent of those exposed. $LD_{50}/30$ brings the time factor of 30 days into consideration. Time is also considered in MEDIAN LETHAL TIME (MLT).

The MLD does not give information about the amount of radiation which will cause death of the individual animal, for as will be seen by reference to the dose response curve, some of those exposed to ionizing radiation will die following relatively light dosage, whereas others will live even following much higher dosage. MLD indicates only that in a large, statistically significant population one can expect half of those exposed to die within a stated time interval.

Marked differences are found in sensitivity of various plant and animal cells to ionizing radiation; in fact lethal doses for the extremes in sensitivity of living organisms differ by a factor of 10,000 or more. Even in mammals and larger organisms, as will be seen by the following partial listing of MLD's, there is a wide species-variation in radiosensitivity:

Guinea pig . . . . 200 r (roentgen)
Dog . . . . 300–430 r

Man...................... 400 ± 100 r
Swine.................... 420 r
Monkey.................. 500 r
Rat (laboratory)........... 590 r
Mouse (laboratory)......... 650 r
Rabbit................... 790 r
Chicken.................. 1,000 r
Turtle................... 1,500 r
Bat...................... 15,000 to 16,000 r

Figures in this list are based on a single, non-fractionated dose of ionizing radiation.

MEDIAN LETHAL TIME (MLT)

Also called LD_{50} time. Time required, following administration of a specified single dose of radiation, for death of 50 per cent of the individuals in a large group of animals or organisms.

The time factor must always be taken into account in considering either the lethal dose or the median lethal dose. For example, it required a single exposure of 193,000 roentgens (r) to kill all the experimental Drosophilae (fruit flies) within 2 days; but a single dose of 64,400 r, or one third as much, was sufficient to cause a complete kill when the time of observation was extended to 21 days.

Time is a factor in the expression $LD_{50}/30$, where the dose required to cause death of half the exposed animals within 30 days is indicated.

See DOSE RATE.

MEDICAL APPLICATIONS OF ATOMIC ENERGY

The use of radioisotopes in medicine is covered under MEDICAL RESEARCH, MEDICAL DIAGNOSIS and MEDICAL TREATMENT. See also specific radioisotopes and organ systems.

In addition, some of the newer instruments developed in the atomic energy program have been applied medically. Radiotherapy with some of these instruments has certain potential advantages. Its development is as yet limited to research institutions and it is quite expensive, particularly because of the difficulties of maintaining the instruments in operating condition. Cyclotrons accelerate positively charged particles —protons, alpha particles, and deuterons—and beams of some of these have been used in treatment aimed at destruction of the pituitary gland and in therapy of deep tumors. The Van de Graaff accelerator is used in medicine to produce beams of electrons of energy less than 2 Mev. These electrons can be used as such for the treatment of superficial malignancies, as in the skin, or can be directed at targets that yield x-rays, which in turn are used in therapy. Betatrons and linear accelerators can accelerate electrons to exceedingly high energies which may be used directly for treatment, including deep tumors, or which may be used to produce x-rays of very high energy.

See NEUTRON CAPTURE THERAPY and NEUTRON THERAPY.

MEDICAL DIAGNOSIS

Since 1946, when clinically useful amounts of radioactive isotopes became available, there has been a continuous increase in their use in medical diagnosis. Well over a half million doses of radiopharmaceuticals are administered to humans annually (1962), more than 85 per cent of all administrations being for diagnostic purposes and the balance for treatment of disease. Although more than 25 different nuclides are in relatively routine use for different procedures, almost four fifths of the diagnostic procedures use radioactive iodine, largely I^{131}. Phosphorus-32, cobalt-60, and chromium-51 each account for approximately 1 out of every 25 to 30 administrations; the remaining radiopharmaceuticals used are in total administered in 1 out of every 30 cases.

In medical diagnosis, radioisotopes are used in 4 different approaches: dilution techniques, flow or diffusion measurements, biochemical concentration, and radiography. A typical dilution technique is used to determine the need for blood transfusion. Human serum albumin labeled with iodine-131 is injected into the blood stream of the patient, and after allowing time for mixing, a sample of blood is measured for radioactivity. The degree to which the label has become diluted gives a measure of the blood volume. Cardiac output is measured by a flow technique using the same material (radioiodinated human serum). Biochemical placement is illustrated by the selective absorption of iodine by the thyroid gland; radioactive iodine (I^{131}) is taken up by the thyroid tissue and screening tests can then be used to determine the activity of the thyroid. Radiography is commonly considered as "x-ray pictures" but satisfactory pictures can be taken using radioisotopes as the source.

Clinical diagnostic procedures using radioisotopes involve: thyroid uptake and excretion studies; protein-bound iodine and conversion ratios; thyroid scanning and mapping; total blood volumes; plasma volumes; red cell mass; red cell survival times; blood loss by bleeding; liver function; pernicious anemia; iron turnover rates; total body water; extracellular space; circulation times; cardiac output; liver circulation; presence and location of brain tumors; eye and skin tumor diagnosis; and kidney function.

Table M–3 gives more detail of some of the most frequently used diagnostic procedures.

TABLE M–3

TEST	PROCEDURE	USEFULNESS
Radioactive *iodine* in thyroid disease	I^{131} usually given by mouth. Measurement of percentage in thyroid gland, percentage in urine, amount of free and protein-bound in the blood. Scanning of thyroid tissue.	Valuable in diagnosis of overactive or underactive thyroid gland. (May be interfered with by medications.) May show local disease in the thyroid (scanning) or tumors of thyroid origin.
Radioactive *iron* for blood diseases	Fe^{59} given intravenously for most purposes, by mouth for study of absorption. After intravenous dose, plasma radioactivity is studied for a few hours; red cell radioactivity for about 10 days. After oral dose blood levels and fecal excretions are measured.	The intravenous test helps explain some anemias, especially those in which there is a failure to use iron for red cell formation in bone marrow. It may also reveal a very active marrow as in polycythemia or anemias caused by red cell destruction. Oral doses may reveal defects in iron absorption.
Radioactive *chromium* in blood diseases	Red cells are labeled in vitro with Cr^{51} and reinjected intravenously. Blood radioactivity is measured usually for 2 to 3 weeks.	Rate of reduction in label in blood is index of blood cell destruction or hemorrhage.
Radioactive *cobalt* in blood disease	Vitamin B_{12} labeled with a radioisotope of cobalt is given by mouth along with an injected dose of stable B_{12}. Radioactivity is measured in urine and sometimes in feces.	This test shows the basic defect in pernicious anemia and may be of value in some other related disorders.
Radioactive dyes in liver disease	A labeled dye such as I^{131}-tagged rose bengal is given intravenously. Serial measurements are made of radioactivity in blood and over liver. Liver may be scanned.	Failure to excrete the dye efficiently is evidence of liver disease. Scanning may show abnormal areas in liver.
Radioactive fats for diseases of digestive tract	Radioactive (I^{131}) neutral fat or fatty acid given orally. Blood levels and fecal excretion measured.	Impaired absorption evidence of disease of pancreas or gastrointestinal tract.
Measurement of kidney function	Intravenous injection of labeled (usually I^{131}) substances excreted by the kidney—Diodrast or Hippuran. Measurement of radioactivity over each kidney, in bladder, and in urine.	These tests give quantitative measurement of the efficiency of function of each kidney.
Diagnosis of brain tumors	Intravenous injection of radioactive test materials such as I^{131}-labeled human serum albumin or mercury-203-labeled Neohydrin. Subsequent scans of brain may show increased amounts of radioactivity at sites of tumors as compared with normal brain.	Valuable test in conjunction with other diagnostic procedures for brain tumors.

MEDICAL DIAGNOSTIC RADIATION

The use of x-ray and the fluoroscope in medical diagnosis is a radiation source which adds from 40 to 240 millirem to the gonadal or genetically significant dose of the average resident of the United States, some individuals receiving none and others a great deal more than this amount. The per capita annual mean bone marrow dose is estimated at 50 to 100 millirem. Another estimate indicates that the annual gonadal dose from medical and dental diagnostic radiation is 100,000 to 300,000 rem per million persons. In the same manner the dose per million persons from weapons testing fallout is calculated as 7,000 to 15,000 rem (1960). The NAS-NRC report* states, "According to present estimates, each person in the United States receives, on the average, a total accumulated dose to the gonads which is about 3 roentgens of x-radiation during a 30-year period."

Continued use of radiation for diagnosis and treatment is essential in modern medicine and dentistry, but the amount of radiation exposure can be reduced and in good practice is being reduced by practical measures and by careful handling of equipment. "It is folly to incur an x-ray exposure to the gonads which can be avoided without impairing medical service or progress."*

See ENVIRONMENTAL RADIATION.

MEDICAL RESEARCH

Radioisotopes are uniquely suited for biological and medical research. Radioactive atoms correspond in size and kind to the materials they trace; they are not foreign or chemically different; they are not added to the material; they are the material or a true part of it. A molecule of vitamin B_{12} is exactly that compound whether its cobalt atom is in a stable or in a radioactive form, and the body does not know the difference. Thus, radioisotopes are a most valuable tool for general medical research. In an analysis of over 2,500 research studies in the life sciences using radioisotopes it was found that less than 9 per cent of the projects dealt with radiation injury, 18 per cent were used in the study of cancer, 12 per cent of the research in human subjects dealt with thyroid function, and the rest were used in general medical research projects. Medical research preceded and formed the basis for most of the clinical use of radioisotopes (*see* MEDICAL DIAGNOSIS and MEDICAL TREATMENT).

About 120 different radioisotopes are used in medical research, carbon-14 leading the list for general medical research and iodine-131 being most commonly used for human administration (see Table M-4).

TABLE M-4

	NUMBER OF STUDIES	
	Total	Involving Human Administration
Carbon-14	669	85
Iodine-131	337	169
Phosphorus-32	236	58
Sulfur-35	118	25
Chromium-51	110	71
Potassium-42	94	33
Cobalt-60	91	32
Sodium-24	91	34
Iron-59	80	35
Calcium-45	59	20
Tritium	55	13
Gold-198	33	12
100 others	626	189
Total	2,599	776

Radioisotopes have been found to be of great value in research in biochemistry, biophysics and biology and in studies at the cellular and molecular level where tritium labeling has permitted investigation of cell division and chromosomal activity. Tritium-labeled compounds have been used to study the biosynthesis of protein, deoxyribose nucleic acid (DNA) and ribose nucleic acid (RNA). Localization of radioactive materials in cells and tissues can be observed by means of autoradiography. Tracer methods permit sensitive measurements of the effect of radiation on individual cell components. The art of labeling has progressed so that almost any desired compound can be labeled for a particular research use at reasonable cost.

There is no question that the most important contributions of isotopes to medicine have been in research.

MEDICAL RESEARCH REACTOR

The Medical Research Reactor (MRR) is the first nuclear reactor designed solely for medical use. It was constructed as an adjunct to the research wing of the Brookhaven Medical Research Center. NEUTRON CAPTURE THERAPY and other medical applications require a highly thermalized, relatively gamma-free, high-flux external neutron beam; the MRR was designed to meet this need.

The core of the MRR includes 17 plate-type fuel elements, each of which contains about 140 grams

---

*National Academy of Sciences–National Research Council. The Biological Effects of Atomic Radiation. Summary Reports. 1956.

of fully enriched uranium-235 as the fissionable material. The active portion of the fuel elements is 23 5/8 inches long. The core is contained in an aluminum tank and is light water-cooled. The cooling water, which is recirculated via a heat exchanger, also serves as a moderator. One regulating rod and 3 safety rods enter the core from above. A magnetic coupling between the rods and the rod drives provides a "fail-safe" mechanism which shuts down the reactor in the event of a power failure. Immediately outside the core tank is a graphite reflector consisting of 724 blocks of graphite having cross sections varying from 4 × 4 inches to 4 × 12 inches, and arranged in a 17-layer array. The over-all dimensions of the assembly are 68 inches high by 101 1/4 inches by 63 1/4 inches. The reflector is air-cooled, the air being exhausted through a 150-foot-high stack. The core and reflector are enclosed by a dense concrete shield which is lined with boral and boron carbide. Openings through the shield provide access to the reflector and channels for the neutron beams. The 2 principal channels are controlled by vertically-moving shutters, which, when in the open position, provide a truncated pyramid-shaped channel between the reflector and the treatment ports. Each of the 2 treatment ports opens into an 11 × 21-foot shielded room, the treatment ports being 36 inches above the floor. (See Figures M–1 and M–2.)

Neutron capture therapy is an experimental therapeutic modality in which selectively localized

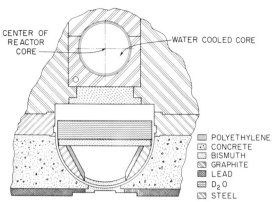

FIGURE M–2. MEDICAL RESEARCH REACTOR. DETAIL OF CROSS-SECTION THROUGH MRR SHUTTER AT TREATMENT PORT LEVEL. PRINCIPAL GAMMA SHIELDING MATERIAL IN THE NEUTRON CHANNEL IS BISMUTH. GRAPHITE AND HEAVY WATER SERVE AS NEUTRON MODERATORS. THE POLYETHYLENE LINING REFLECTS SOME NEUTRONS BACK INTO THE CHANNEL AND IS BACKED UP BY A LAYER OF BORAL TO PREVENT NEUTRONS FROM ESCAPING INTO THE CONCRETE SHIELD AND GIVING RISE TO (n, γ) REACTIONS. (COURTESY OF BROOKHAVEN NATIONAL LABORATORY.)

radiation is produced "in vivo" through energetic heavy particles from the reaction following the capture of a thermal neutron by a suitable nuclide. With the MRR, neutron capture therapy has been studied in experimental animals and in patients with neoplasms of the brain (principally glioblastoma multiforme), using boron-10 as the capturing nuclide. Palliative but not curative results have been attained, the major difficulty being attainment of adequate depth doses for therapeutic results without inducing unwanted complications.

MEDICAL TREATMENT

More than 25 years have passed since a man-made radioisotope was first used to treat a disease of man—phosphorus-32 for leukemia and polycythemia vera. Certain types of leukemia are still treated with radioisotopes, as is polycythemia, and in addition radioisotopes are used to treat hyperthyroidism, cardiac dysfunction, and many different types of cancer.

The use of radioisotopes in the treatment of disease may conveniently be considered under 3 modes of application: BIOCHEMICAL PLACEMENT; BRACHYTHERAPY, or physical placement in the tissue; and TELETHERAPY, or treatment at a distance.

For details of their use see INTERSTITIAL IMPLANTS, INTERSTITIAL INJECTION and RADIOTHERAPY.

Table M–5 outlines the usefulness of the more common types of treatment.

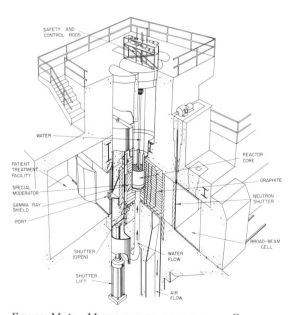

FIGURE M–1. MEDICAL RESEARCH REACTOR. CUTAWAY DRAWING SHOWING ARRANGEMENT OF CORE, SHUTTER, TREATMENT ROOMS AND CONTROL MECHANISM. (COURTESY OF BROOKHAVEN NATIONAL LABORATORY.)

TABLE M–5. EXAMPLES OF USEFULNESS OF RADIOISOTOPES IN TREATMENT OF DISEASE

AGENT	DISEASE	USEFULNESS
Iodine-131 as sodium iodide	Hyperthyroidism, diffuse toxic goiter	The ideal form of treatment for all patients over 40 years of age, for those previously operated upon for goiter, and for those who are poor surgical risks.
Iodine-131 as sodium iodide	Toxic nodular goiter	Not suitable for all patients with this disease. Good results in some cases. May be followed by surgery.
Iodine-131 as sodium iodide	Angina pectoris and congestive heart failure	Clinical improvement in the majority of carefully selected patients treated.
Phosphorus-32 as sodium phosphate	Chronic granulocytic leukemia	One of several good forms of treatment for this disease.
Phosphorus-32 as sodium phosphate	Chronic lymphocytic leukemia	Good results in many patients; may need to be supplemented with other forms of treatment.
Phosphorus-32 as sodium phosphate	Polycythemia vera	A widely used form of treatment generally producing a good response. There are possible disadvantages from radiation, especially in young patients.
Gold-198, phosphorus-32, yttrium-90 in colloidal preparations	Fluid accumulations in body cavities, caused by cancer	Radioisotope injected directly into body cavities gives symptomatic relief in many cases.
Gold-198, phosphorus-32, yttrium-90 in colloidal preparations	Chronic granulocytic leukemia, diffuse lymphoma of the liver	Intravenous injection of the radioisotope may have good effect.
Gold-198, phosphorus-32, yttrium-90 in colloidal preparations	Selected types of local cancer	Injection of isotope directly into tumor (as in cancer of prostate) or into adjoining tissues (as in cancer of the uterine cervix) may be beneficial in selected cases.
Cobalt-60, cesium-137, radium-226, radon-222, strontium-90, gold-198 in form of seeds, wires, pellets, etc.	Certain accessible local tumors	Used for brachytherapy and implantation. Skilled application required. Limited but definite usefulness.
Cobalt-60, cesium-137 in teletherapy machines	Many types of cancer suitable for treatment with penetrating external radiation beam	Highly useful and practical. Is replacing x-ray therapy in many situations.

MEGACURIE

Symbol Mc. A unit of radioactivity measurement denoting 1 million curies.

MEGATON ENERGY

The energy of a nuclear (or atomic) explosion which is equivalent to 1,000,000 tons (or 1,000 kilotons) of TNT, i.e., 10^{15} calories or 4.2×10^{22} ergs.

See TNT EQUIVALENT and YIELD.

MEIOSIS, RADIATION EFFECTS. See CELL DIVISION, RADIATION EFFECTS ON.

MEMBRANE PERMEABILITY STUDIES

An important biological problem is the permeability of cells to substances in their surrounding medium, since nearly every living organism has the ability to maintain a constant cellular composition of a series of inorganic ions at concentrations that differ greatly from those in the surrounding

TABLE M–6. TRANSPORT INTO AND OUT OF CELLS

MATERIAL	Na	K	H	Cl	I	PHOSPHATE
Red cells						
Human	X	X				
Chicken	X	X				
Leukocytes	X	X				
Ehrlich ascites cells	X	X				
Giant nerve axon	X	X				
Muscle fiber	X	X				
Yeast	X	X	X			
Algae						
Ulva lactuca	X	X				
Halicystis ovalis	X			X		
Nitellopsis	X			X		
Staphylococcus aureus						X

TABLE M–7. TRANSPORT ACROSS CELLS

MATERIAL	Na	K	H	Cl	I	PHOSPHATE
Stomach (frog)				X		
Rumen (sheep)	X					
Ileum (rat)	X			X		
Colon (toad)	X					
Cecum (guinea pig)	X					
Kidney	X	X	X			X
Urinary bladder (toad)	X					
Seminal vesicle mucosa	X	X				
Thyroid gland					X	
Salivary gland				X		
Skin (frog)	X					
Skin after adrenaline				X		
Gill (eel)				X		
Gill (Eriocheir sinensis)	X	X				
Malpighian tubule of insects		X				
Plants						
Roots of cereals				X		
Disks of storage organs				X		

medium. The outstanding example is the fact that most animal and plant cells can accumulate potassium and at the same time exclude sodium. The availability of radionuclides of inorganic ions has permitted some understanding and clarification of transfer processes. Particular attention has been given to "active transport processes," in which energy from cell metabolism is required to move the ion. The nature of these processes is still unexplained, but it is generally considered that chemical reactions with membrane constituents are involved. Table M–6 presents some established instances of active transport into and out of different cell types, and Table M–7 indicates some examples of transport across cells.

Some of the present theories, none of which is generally acceptable, are as follows: (a) carrier hypothesis, based on the assumption that a substance in the membrane forms a specific complex with the ion at one border of the membrane, which can then diffuse through the membrane; (b) fluid circuit hypothesis, based on the existence in the membrane of structures with different permeabilities toward water, monovalent salts and divalent salts; (c) electron-linked transport hypothesis, based on the concept that the energy of the electron-transferring reactions of respiration can be used directly for ion transport; (d) interaction with enzymes; (e) concept of contractile-protein as a propelled carrier.

MENDELEVIUM

Symbol Mv (Md has been suggested); atomic number 101; atomic weight 256; a radioactive transuranic element of the actinide series. Discovered in 1955 by A. Ghiorso, B. G. Harvey, G. R. Choppin, S. G. Thompson and G. T. Seaborg as a result of bombardment of einsteinium-

253 with a beam of 41 Mev alpha particles in the cyclotron at the Radiation Laboratory, University of California, Berkeley. Named in honor of Russian D. I. Mendelyeev (noted for explanation of periodic table). The nuclide first produced was Mv^{256}, half-life about 30 minutes, decaying by electron capture. Another nuclide has been reported with mass number 255. Neither occurs in nature nor has either any known biological, medical or agricultural significance.

MERCURY

Symbol Hg; atomic number 80; atomic weight 200.61. A silver-white liquid metal frequently called quicksilver. Known to ancient Chinese and Hindus; found in Egyptian tombs of 1500 B.C. Named for the planet Mercury. Symbol Hg from hydrargyrum, liquid silver; formerly named hydrargium. Occasionally occurs as the free metal but chiefly as the sulfide. Its natural abundance is furnished by 7 stable isotopes.

Eighty different industrial processes utilize mercury in some form for: electrical apparatus; industrial and control instruments; thermometers; antifouling paint; disinfectants; pharmaceuticals; dental amalgam; munitions; a coolant in nuclear reactors.

Organic mercurial drugs have been used for many years in medicine, particularly as diuretics and in treating syphilis. Mercury bichloride is used as an antiseptic. Found in nearly all foods in amounts of 0.005 to 0.05 parts per million (ppm). Mercury in fresh human glandular tissues ranges from 0.01 to 0.13 ppm. However, it is not considered an essential element. Both acute and chronic mercury poisoning have been known for years. Soluble mercurial salts are violent corrosive poisons and have been taken with suicidal intent. Particular care must be taken to control mercury vapor in mining operations.

Fifteen radioactive isotopes have been identified. Hg^{197} and Hg^{203} may be induced in sea water by the neutron bombardment associated with the detonation of a nuclear device. Not important in residual contamination. Hg^{203}, half-life 47.9 days, beta and gamma emitter, has found medical usefulness primarily in tracer and chemotherapeutic studies.

MESON

Any elementary particle having a rest mass intermediate between the mass of the electron (m_e) and the mass of the proton (m_p). Named from the Greek prefix, *meso*, meaning intermediate. The two first identified are the pi (π)-meson, or pion, which has a mass 273 times that of the electron (or positron); and the mu (μ)-meson, or muon, which

is 207 times as heavy as an electron. In the free state the pi-meson changes within a few hundred-millionths of a second into the mu-meson of the same sign. Both negative and positive electrically charged pi-mesons and mu-mesons have been found in cosmic rays and have been produced in the laboratory. The sequence of events may be represented as follows:

$$\text{pi-meson} \longrightarrow \underset{(+\text{ energy})}{\text{mu-meson}} \longrightarrow \underset{(+\text{ energy})}{\text{electron or positron}}$$

A number of unstable heavier particles have been found but their weight, 966 times the electron mass, is roughly halfway between the mass of the electron and the proton so they are also mesons, called K-mesons. They have both those with a negative charge and those with a positive charge and their average life is about a hundred-millionth (10^{-8}) of a second.

The next of the strange particles to be found has a mass of about 2,000 m_e, and is called a hyperon. Various other particles have been found but at present 3 mass categories are recognized:

L (light mesons): mass between electron and pi-meson (1 to 283 m_e);

K (heavy mesons): mass between pi-meson and proton (283 to 1,836 m_e);

Y (hyperons): mass between proton and deuteron (1,836 to 3,070 m_e).

A specific particle is represented by a Greek lower case letter if it falls in the L or K group and by a capital letter if in the hyperon or Y group.

Additional particles are being produced and studied in particle accelerators and are being found in cosmic-ray studies.

MESOTHORIUM I and II

Nuclides appearing in the THORIUM RADIO-ACTIVE SERIES:

$$\text{Thorium } (_{90}\text{Th}^{232}) \xrightarrow[\alpha]{1.39 \times 10^{10} \text{ yr}}$$
$$\downarrow$$
$$\text{Mesothorium I } (_{88}\text{Ra}^{228}) \xrightarrow[\beta]{6.7 \text{ yr}}$$
$$\downarrow$$
$$\text{Mesothorium II } (_{89}\text{Ac}^{228}) \xrightarrow[\beta]{6.13 \text{ hr}}$$
$$\downarrow$$
$$\text{Radiothorium } (_{90}\text{Th}^{228}) \xrightarrow[\alpha]{1.91 \text{ yr}}$$

These nuclides were discovered in 1907 by O'Hahn in monazite residues from isolating thorium.

Mesothorium I is a radioactive isotope of radium. Mixed with phosphorescent zinc sulfide it is used in luminous pigments to paint watches, clocks, gages, and other indicating dials. It is itself highly radiotoxic and contributes to the radiotoxicity of radium.

METABOLISM STUDIES. *See* ANIMAL METAB-
OLISM STUDIES, CARBOHYDRATE STUDIES, IN-
TERMEDIARY METABOLISM STUDIES, PHOTOSYN-
THESIS, LIPID STUDIES, and AMINO ACID STUDIES.

METAL DISPLACEMENT THERAPY. *See*
CHEMICAL TREATMENT TO REDUCE RADIOISOTOPE
RETENTION.

METASTABLE STATE

An excited system capable of undergoing a
quantum transition to a state of lower energy.
Applied only to those excited nuclear states with
lifetimes that are measurable, i.e., exceeding 10^{-20}
to 10^{-9} seconds. The decay process from the
metastable state to the ground state is by isomeric
transition. The metastable nuclear isomer (*see*
ISOMER, NUCLEAR) is indicated by adding the letter
m to the mass number in the symbol for the
nuclide: Ag^{107m}, Cd^{115m}, In^{113m}, etc.

In radiobiology metastable states of molecules
rather than nuclei are most frequently encountered.

METEOROLOGY

The science of weather, or the science of all
aspects of the ATMOSPHERE. Meteorological conditions, such as temperature, humidity, wind, local
turbulence, precipitation (rain, snow, dew), atmospheric pressure, inversions, and other climatic
factors have a direct bearing on "close-in" FALL-
OUT and tropospheric fallout, both as to spread and
residence time in the atmosphere.

Meteorological surveys and area radiation
monitoring are conducted at all USAEC plants and
laboratories as a check on the possibility of atmospheric pollution from air-cooled reactors or
other operations utilizing radioactive materials.
For example, the meteorological survey at the
Oak Ridge National Laboratory includes determining the effect of upper atmosphere conditions
on detailed wind flow and temperature in the
surrounding broken-ridge country. Turbulence or
gustiness, the primary atmospheric factor in dis-
persing stack gases, is measured by special techniques employing highly sensitive wind instruments, small free balloons, and chemical smoke
pots.

The HIGH-ALTITUDE SAMPLING PROGRAM (HASP)
has involved meteorological research and extensive
operational activity.

MEV

Abbreviation for one million or 10^6 electron
volts (ev). A common unit of energy in nuclear
science. For example the particle radiation of
cobalt-60 for one type of beta is expressed as
0.314 Mev.

MICROCURIE

Symbol μc. A unit of radioactivity measurement
denoting one millionth of a CURIE.

MICROMICROCURIE

Symbol μμc. Sometimes called a picocurie. A
unit of radioactivity measurement denoting one
millionth of a millionth of a curie. Used particularly in reporting the deposition of strontium-90
in the bone as a result of fallout contamination;
e.g., 0.20 μμc of Sr^{90} per gram of calcium. *See*
STRONTIUM UNIT.

MICRONUTRIENT STUDIES

Micronutrient elements are those which are required in small quantity for normal growth and
reproduction of plants and animals. Radioisotopes
have been especially important because without
them it would have been most difficult to study
micronutrient metabolism in living systems without using high nonphysiological levels of the
element. In studies with plants, radioisotopes of
the following micronutrients have been successfully used: iron, zinc, manganese, copper, molybdenum, chlorine and cobalt. The radioisotopes of
greatest importance in studies of animal metabolism include those of cobalt, copper, iron, iodine,
manganese, zinc and sulfur. Some of the more
recent work has suggested that under certain
conditions arsenic, selenium and chromium may
be essential elements for mammals, and radioisotopes of these elements have been used. *See* ANIMAL
METABOLISM STUDIES.

MICRO-ORGANISM STUDIES

Interest in the bacteria, yeasts and molds generally stems from (a) exploitation of these organisms for the benefit of man, such as in industrial
fermentations or preservation of certain foods;
(b) elimination to avoid certain diseases of man,
animals and plants, and to preserve foods; (c) the
use of bacteria as an essential tool for development
of modern scientific knowledge, particularly along
the lines of biochemistry and genetics.

In general, the same radioisotopes and the same
approach and procedures are used as have been
discussed under other topics such as TRACER
STUDIES, ANIMAL METABOLISM STUDIES, ANIMAL
NUTRITIONAL STUDIES, ANIMAL PHYSIOLOGY STUD-
IES, CELLULAR STUDIES, etc.

Some of the general fields of recent interest are:

a. bacterial nutrition and physiology, including
bacterial photosynthesis, aerobic respiration,
anaerobic respiration and fermentation;

b. bacterial growth and reproduction, including
cell multiplication, gene transfer, bacterial variation;

c. bacterial ecology, including studies of soil bacteria, symbiosis and parasitism;

d. detailed studies of the bacterial cell regarding surface appendages, surface adherence, surface layers and internal structures, such as the cytoplasm, intracellular organelles, particles and granules;

e. bacterial genetics, including transformation, mutation, genetic markers, genetic fine structure, infectious heredity and conjugation;

f. bacterial nutrition, including carbon sources, nitrogen supply, mineral supply, growth factors, energy supply, and other factors such as osmotic pressure and pH of the medium.

As a simple example of tracer studies with bacteria, Escherichia coli have been labeled with phosphorus-32 (P^{32}) and fed to houseflies to obtain information on the persistence, multiplication and distribution of this bacterium in the insect. As another instance, bacteria have been labeled with P^{32} in order to study the role played by air-borne infection in the spread of tuberculosis.

MICROWAVE RADIATION

Electromagnetic radiation emanating from the region lying between the far infrared and the conventional radiofrequency portion. Commonly regarded as extending from 300,000 megacycles to 1,000 megacycles (1 millimeter to 30 centimeters in wave length).

MILK FORMATION STUDIES. *See* LACTATION STUDIES.

MILK SAMPLING

The most important feature of the total SAMPLING PROGRAM FOR RADIOACTIVE FALLOUT conducted by the USPHS and other Federal agencies. The importance of the milk sampling program lies in the facts that strontium-90: (1) is produced in the detonation of a nuclear device; (2) is a constituent of stratospheric fallout; (3) is a contaminant in the food chain, being found in cow's milk, which is the most important item in the diet of growing children; (4) is metabolized like calcium into bone; (5) has an effective half-life of 17.4 years; and (6) as a long-term source of irradiation may have deleterious effects.

The USAEC through its Health and Safety Laboratory has been operating a milk sampling program since 1954. The USPHS has more recently started an extensive program. Typical findings are shown in Table M–8.

TABLE M–8. CONCENTRATION OF Sr^{90} IN COW'S MILK DURING FINAL THREE MONTHS OF 1958

PLACE	TYPE OF MILK	μμc/gm Ca*
New York City	Liquid	9.8
Perry, New York	Dry	8.2
Mandan, North Dakota	Dry	20.0
Sacramento, Calif.	Liquid	4.2
Salt Lake City, Utah	Liquid	4.8
St. Louis, Missouri	Liquid	16.0
Cincinnati, Ohio	Liquid	10.0
Atlanta, Georgia	Liquid	8.8
Austin, Texas	Liquid	3.8
Chicago, Illinois	Liquid	7.4

*Micromicrocuries per gram of calcium.

In 1958, the powdered milk in the New York area showed 5.9 μμc Sr^{90}/gm Ca in comparison to the 3.9 average for 1957. In considering the maximum level of fallout from all tests prior to the end of 1958, it was estimated that the maximum foreseeable sustained level of milk contamination in the New York area would be 11 μμc Sr^{90}/gm Ca. A child deriving its calcium from dairy sources would from this develop a skeleton having 5.5 μμc Sr^{90}/gm Ca, which would deliver a dose of about 5.5 millirem per year to the bone marrow.

MILLICURIE

Symbol mc. A unit of radioactivity measurement denoting one one-thousandth of a CURIE.

MILLION ELECTRON VOLT

Abbreviation Mev. Common unit of energy in nuclear science, equivalent to 10^6 ELECTRON VOLTS (ev).

MILLIREM

One one-thousandth of a ROENTGEN EQUIVALENT, MAN.

MILLIROENTGEN

One one-thousandth of a ROENTGEN.

MINING RADIATION HAZARDS

In mining and processing ore containing uranium, radium or thorium, radioactive dusts are produced which have been shown to be carcinogenic. Lung cancer incidence has been reported to be significantly increased among miners in European mines, and is usually attributed to the radioactive dusts and/or gases inhaled. Although these observations extend over many generations, clear proof of this as a cause and effect relationship is still lacking. An extensive study is now being made of miners in the Colorado plateau region of the United States to check these findings.

MITOSIS, RADIATION EFFECTS ON. *See* CELL DIVISION, RADIATION EFFECTS ON.

MLD. *See* MEDIAN LETHAL DOSE.

MOISTURE STUDIES. *See* SOIL STUDIES.

MOLE

Mass numerically equal to the molecular weight. It is most frequently expressed as the gram molecular weight, i.e., as the weight of one mole expressed in grams. The gram mole is the mass in grams numerically equal to the molecular weight. The molecular volume is that occupied by one mole, which is numerically equal to the molecular weight divided by the density. The mole fraction is the number of atoms of a certain isotope of an element expressed as a fraction of the total number of atoms of that element present in the isotopic mixture.

MOLECULAR BIOLOGY

Studies of biological systems at the cellular, subcellular and molecular levels. Studies of radiation effects at the levels being considered are crucial toward an understanding of the complex mechanisms leading to radiation damage, especially that occurring during the first few minutes after exposure. Various cellular and subcellular changes must occur before they become manifest as acute effects (radiation illness) or chronic effects (tumors, cataracts, etc.), or as mutation, leading to genetic damage.

Studies in molecular biology concern themselves with: energy absorption and stability; energy movement; effects of radiation on molecules and molecular structure; molecular biosynthesis; cell metabolism, cell permeability and electrolyte behavior; and biochemical genetics.

MOLECULAR WEIGHT

The sum of the atomic weights of all the atoms in a molecule.

MOLECULE

The smallest unit or particle of any substance or compound which can exist free and still retain all the chemical properties of the original substance. Molecules of some of the rare gases such as helium, neon, argon, krypton and xenon consist of a single atom and are therefore identical with the atom itself. The number of atoms in a molecule may range from 2 in oxygen, nitrogen and hydrogen up to many thousands. A molecule of insulin used in the treatment of diabetes has a molecular weight (sum of the atomic weights of all the atoms in the molecule) of not less than 6,000; many of the complex proteins have molecular weights in tens of thousands.

MOLYBDENUM

Symbol Mo; atomic number 42; atomic weight 95.95. A silver-white, malleable metal obtained from molybdenite and wulfenite. Discovered by Swedish chemist Scheele in 1778. (Also credited to Hjelm in 1782.) Named from Greek *molybdos*, lead. Natural abundance furnished by 7 stable isotopes.

Used principally as an alloying element in iron and steel; also in printers' inks, pigments and colors.

Almost universally found in plant and animal materials. Essential for plant growth and probably essential in trace amounts for animal growth. Mildly toxic in heavy doses. Chronic toxicity depends upon the level of copper in the diet; with low copper levels as little as 80 parts per million caused toxic symptoms in rats, whereas with normal copper levels rats could tolerate as much as 80 milligrams per kilogram of body weight.

There are 14 radioactive isotopes, of which Mo^{99} and Mo^{101} through Mo^{110} are fission products.

Molybdenum-99 $(_{42}Mo^{99})$. Radioactive half-life 2.85 days; with kidney as the critical organ, biological half-life 3 days; effective half-life 1.5 days; beta (β^-) and gamma emitter. Mo^{99} is the parent of technetium-99. Available commercially. Used in plant and animal uptake, distribution and metabolism studies of molybdenum. Significant as a component in radioactive fallout, for there is a measurable amount left at the end of 1 year. Maximum permissible concentration for soluble material, kidney as the critical organ, 168-hour week (continuous exposure) 2×10^{-3} microcuries per cubic centimeter ($\mu c/cc$) in water and 3×10^{-7} $\mu c/cc$ in air.

MONAZITE

A mineral, essentially a phosphate of the rare earth metal cerium ($CePO_4$), but also containing cobalt, lanthanum, neodymium, praseodymium, and thorium, the latter in sufficient quantity to be its chief source. Named for Greek *monas*, solitary, because of its relative rarity. Commercial deposits are usually residual sands. One of the most extensive deposits is in the Kerala-Madras area of India, where it has been estimated that the thorium metal alone amounts to a million tons or more. Another extensive deposit is in the coastal region of Espirito Santo, Brazil.

Most of the radioactivity, perhaps 95%, arises from the thorium and its decay products. As will be seen in the thorium radioactive series, most of the total energy released in the decay of thorium-232 to stable lead-208 is in the form of alpha particles, but some beta particles and moderately hard gamma rays are also emitted. The range for gamma activity in the various villages in the Indian region may be from a high of 3.95 roentgens per year (r/yr) to a low of 0.14 r/yr. This is to be compared with 0.045 to 0.090 r/yr for the lowlands of most of the rest of the surface of the earth. An average figure including 0.2 for beta rays may be 1.5 r/yr. Expressed another way, there is an aggregate mean external exposure dose of 830 millirem per year (mrem/yr) to the gonads, using a body shielding factor of 0.63 for gamma rays. This is comparable to an exposure of 75 mrem/yr for normal regions. The 30-year cumulative dose comes to some 25 r, which is near the upper range of the amount of radiation to the gonads which the geneticists have calculated ought to double the frequency of mutations in the population at risk. About 100,000 live in this region of India in almost continuous contact with the radioactive sand.

In Brazil less than half the number of people live in the monazite sand region, and the aggregate mean radiation dose is only 315 mrem/yr.

MONITORING

Periodic or continuous determination of the amount of ionizing radiation or of radioactive contamination present in an occupied region, or in or on a person, as a safety measure for purposes of health protection. Several types of monitoring are conducted as part of the nuclear energy activity. In the MONITORING PROGRAM FOR RADIOACTIVE FALLOUT, the detonation of every nuclear device is extensively monitored from the time of detonation until local fallout has ceased.

AERIAL MONITORING is used as a method of making a quick survey of the gamma radiation in an area.

Industrial monitoring is an essential part of any industry working with radioactive materials.

PERSONNEL MONITORING is required where exposure to ionizing radiation may occur.

MONITORING DEVICES are an essential part of any program using radioactive material in any form.

See AREA MONITORING and RADIATION MONITORING.

MONITORING DEVICES

Specialized instruments or other devices for periodic or continuous evaluation of the amount of ionizing radiation or radioactive contamination present in an occupied environment or sustained by an individual. Monitoring devices have been developed for many particular applications, including: (1) air monitoring, utilizing detectors sensitive to gaseous or particulate radioactive materials placed in working areas or in exhaust gases, as from reactor cooling stacks; (2) aerial monitoring, based on scintillation counters transported above the terrain within or trailing from an aircraft; (3) area monitoring, where a variety of instruments can be installed for constant surveillance of working areas where radiation hazards are present or suspected; (4) monitoring program for radioactive fallout, which relies on a worldwide network of stations collecting particulate matter and precipitation samples for evaluation by low-level procedures in a central laboratory; also studies on autopsy material from all regions of the world; (5) PERSONNEL MONITORING, with FILM BADGES, POCKET DOSIMETERS, glass dosimeters, or other small monitoring devices worn on the person; to detect contamination on personnel, HAND AND FOOT COUNTERS are installed at exits from working areas where contamination is possible.

MONITORING PROGRAM FOR RADIOACTIVE FALLOUT

The extensive organization established to continuously determine the amount of radiation resulting from fallout during the test detonation of nuclear devices is best illustrated by outlining the actual organization set up for the Plumbbob test series, conducted at the Nevada Test Site in the spring of 1957.

An advisory panel of experts in the fields of biology, medicine, blast, fallout prediction and meteorology was established. In addition, a complete weather unit was in operation at the site with 6 additional weather stations around the test site. No "shot" was fired unless all conditions were considered right by these experts.

Within the test site area (radius of 200 miles) 17 monitoring teams were stationed, one to each community. In addition, 8 two-man mobile monitoring teams were used to monitor downwind after each detonation and to assist the community teams. Aircraft were used to track and sample the radioactive cloud for about 600 miles or until it was dispersed. At least 1,000 film badge stations were established, and all community residents, except small children, wore badges throughout the series.

Outside the 200 mile area, the Weather Bureau collected fallout samples on a 24-hour basis in 93 stations located throughout the United States. The Public Health Service operated a network of 38 monitoring stations for immediately reporting the level of radioactivity; and 11 USAEC installations throughout the country also maintained continuous monitoring. In addition, dust samples were collected at 73 stations outside the continental United States. Soil samples, as well as food samples were collected on a world-wide basis and analyzed for their radionuclide content. A human bone sampling program was conducted on a world-wide basis and the bones were analyzed for their strontium-90 content.

In a unique system of telemetering, instruments were connected with the telephone system so that all USAEC in Washington had to do was to dial a number to receive signals which were translated in a matter of seconds into gamma radiation dose rates. In addition there were 20 instruments located in communities surrounding the test area that continuously and permanently recorded the gamma dose rates throughout the test series.

MORTALITY FROM RADIATION

The effects leading to death following acute whole-body irradiation may be divided into 3 categories:

1. Cerebral, characterized by weakness, listlessness, convulsive seizures and intermittent stupor, ending in death within the first few hours or within the first week, as the result of exposure to over 1,500 roentgens (r).

2. Gastrointestinal, characterized by nausea, vomiting, diarrhea, loss of appetite, extreme weakness, prostration and death within the first 2 weeks as the result of an exposure to from 700 to 1,000 r.

3. Hematopoietic, with early nausea and vomiting followed by a symptomless latent period of 2 to 3 weeks and then general malaise, fever, hemorrhages, purpura, petechiae, nosebleed, pallor, diarrhea, emaciation and death within the first month and a half from whole-body irradiation in the range of 400 to 700 r.

This division is not often clear-cut; frequently it is quite impossible to determine the actual immediate cause of death. The case of the scientist who died 32 days after irradiation in the reactor accident in Yugoslavia illustrates the difficulty: Pulmonary hemorrhage was fatal at a time when surgical intervention was planned for intestinal occlusion, which was part of the gastrointestinal syndrome.

The delayed effects leading to mortality from radiation are leukemia, cancer and general non-specific shortening of the life-span. Although such responses may be statistically significant, in a single individual it is impossible to assign irradiation as the definite cause of death.

Mortality from radiation is usually spoken of in terms of the lethal dose, median lethal dose, MLD or LD_{50}.

MOTION PICTURES, USAEC EDUCATIONAL. *See* FILM LIBRARIES.

MPC. *See* MAXIMUM PERMISSIBLE CONCENTRATION.

MPD. *See* MAXIMUM PERMISSIBLE DOSE.

MULTICHANNEL ANALYZER

A circuit combining 2 or more single channel analyzers to provide simultaneous or sequential counting of radioactivity in more than one energy range. Such analyzers may be used to give background or other correction factors in an experiment, or to develop energy spectrum information. *See* KICKSORTER and PULSE HEIGHT ANALYZER.

MULTICHANNEL SCALER. *See* MULTICHANNEL ANALYZER.

MULTIPLE LABELING

The simultaneous use of two or more radioisotopes in an experiment is very often feasible because measurements of each in the same sample are possible. This procedure, which allows two or more sets of data to be obtained from the same study, may save considerable time and expense, especially when the investigation involves systems that are difficult to prepare. For example, pairs of elements such as phosphorus-32 and carbon-14, phosphorus-32 and potassium-42, phosphorus-32 and cesium-137 have been simultaneously traced in a plant to give information on translocation. In animal nutrition and physiology, the close relationships of calcium and phosphorus have made the use of this pair of elements very fruitful.

A very powerful method is available in those instances in which it is possible to use two different radioisotopes of the same element—for example, calcium-45 and calcium-47; sodium-22 and sodium-24; iron-55 and iron-59; strontium-85, strontium-89 and strontium-90; yttrium-90 and yttrium-91; silver-110 and silver-111. A considerable advantage lies in the ability to correct for secondary losses. For example, if a substance is to be analyzed for strontium-90, it is possible to add a known amount of strontium-85 to the sample and then to correct the final results for strontium-90 by values obtained for the percentage recovery of the strontium-85. Multiple labeling is of particular importance in the survey of body electrolytes in animals and man for medical purposes. Routine procedures have been developed for the simultaneous use of sodium-24, potassium-42, bromine-82 and tritium.

Simultaneous measurement can be accomplished because (a) the radioisotopes may have different half-lives, (b) they may have different beta particle energies and therefore exhibit differential absorption, (c) they may have different types or energies of radiation, or (d) chemical separation can be done. The development of gamma spectrometers for routine laboratory use has greatly increased the feasibility of making differential measurements by choice of different gamma energies when the radionuclides have sufficiently different gamma energy peaks; the procedure is analagous to differential measurement of substances that have different light absorption by using a spectrophotometer.

MULTIPLE MYELOMA, TREATMENT

This is a form of cancer characterized by painful tumors of bones. Repeated efforts have been made to treat it with internally administered radioisotopes including phosphorus-32 as phosphate ion and iodine-131 as iodide and attached to serum albumin. Occasionally some improvement is noted following treatment with one of these agents but more commonly there is no benefit and drug therapy is usually considered preferable. External radiation therapy directed to local areas of bone involvement often produces relief of symptoms.

MULTIPLE SCATTERING

SCATTERING in which the final displacement is the vector sum of many, usually small, displacements.

MUTATION, RADIATION INDUCED

A mutation is, in general, a permanent transmissible change in the characteristics of an offspring from those of its parents. Ionizing radiation has been shown to be a mutagenic agent. H. J. Müller was awarded the Nobel prize in 1946 for his pioneering work in detecting sex-linked lethal mutations in Drosophila induced by x-ray exposure. Radiation thus became known as the first effective agent in producing large quantities of mutants.

Radiation-induced mutations are the same as those which appear naturally. Whether the natural and induced mutations occur with the same probability remains an open question until more data are available on a wider variety of plants and animals.

Mutations are almost never beneficial to their recipients. However, in plants and to a lesser extent in animals, "mutation breeding" has led to commercially successful species (*see* CROP IMPROVEMENT, USING RADIATION). Figure M–3 shows a radiation-induced mutant petunia to illustrate this point.

FIGURE M–3. RADIATION-INDUCED MUTANT PETUNIA, LEFT. CONTROL ON THE RIGHT. (COURTESY A. H. SPARROW, BROOKHAVEN NATIONAL LABORATORY.)

N

NAGASAKI

At 1102 on the morning of 9 August, 1954, the second atomic bomb to be used in combat was dropped, as an air burst, detonated at about 1,850 feet, over the Japanese city of Nagasaki. The bomb's fissionable material was plutonium and had a yield of approximately 20 kilotons (TNT equivalent).

Nagasaki was an important industrial center on the western coast of Kyushu. The terrain is hilly, with the city spread out along the shore and up 2 valleys. The houses were predominantly of wood-frame construction, but there were more reinforced-concrete buildings which afforded shielding than in HIROSHIMA. The civilian population of 174,000 was completely surprised by the attack.

The bomb fell short of the target and burst above the northern section, over one of the valleys, where its effects were limited by the confining hills to this quarter of the city.

About 30% of the population was within 1.2 miles (2,000 meters) of ground zero. The casualties within this "proximal zone" are shown in Table N–1. Few deaths occurred outside this zone, and those were due to injuries and burns and not to direct thermal radiation or ionizing radiation. The casualty-distance curves indicate that the point at which the chance of death was 50% was 0.80 mile. By the middle of November the number of deaths was approximately 39,000, or about 22.4% of the total population.

Blast and thermal radiation were directly or indirectly responsible for almost all first-day deaths, and for most of the injuries to first-day survivors. The 50% point for injury or death was 1.24 miles.

The burns of the survivors were largely flash burns, occurring out to a distance of 2.48 miles, but blistering beyond 2 miles was rare.

The mortality rate and the casualty rate of persons in deep air-raid shelters, caves and tunnels were the lowest reported for any group; e.g., persons survived uninjured who were in caves directly beneath the exploding bomb.

The ionizing radiation effects were similar to those experienced at Hiroshima, and the delayed effects are being studied on the combined populations.

See HIROSHIMA.

NATIONAL ACADEMY OF SCIENCES-NATIONAL RESEARCH COUNCIL

A quasi-official agency which has recently taken an active interest in studying the biological effects of radiation. In 1955 six committees were appointed as follows: Genetic Effects of Atomic Radiation; Pathologic Effects of Radiation; Effects of Atomic Radiation on Agriculture and Food Supplies; Meteorologic Aspects of Effects of Atomic Radiation; Effects of Atomic Radiation on Oceanography and Fisheries; and Disposal and Dispersal of Radioactive Wastes. The Committee on Pathologic Effects of Atomic Radiation had 5 subcommittees: Hematologic Effects; Inhalation Hazards; Internal Emitters; Long-Term Effects of Ionizing Radiations from External Sources; and Neuropathologic Aspects. Each of these committees and subcommittees has issued authoritative reports on research and activity in its area of interest.

The Division of Medical Sciences of the National Research Council has the administrative responsibility for the ATOMIC BOMB CASUALTY COMMISSION.

NATIONAL BUREAU OF STANDARDS

The NBS, a bureau of the Department of Commerce, is active in research on radiation dosimetry

TABLE N–1. ESTIMATED CIVILIAN CASUALTIES WITHIN 2,000 METERS OF GROUND ZERO

DISTANCE FROM GROUND ZERO (METERS)	EXPOSED POPULATION (NUMBER)	SURVIVORS (NUMBER) (20 DAYS)	SURVIVORS (PER CENT OF THOSE EXPOSED)
0–499	30,900	3,580	11.6
1,000–1,499	14,320	6,950	48.5
1,500–1,999	6,550	4,690	71.6
Total	51,770	15,220	29.4

and techniques for measurement of radiation, and in the development of radiation instruments. Maintains the secretariat for and publishes the recommendations of the National Committee on Radiation Protection and Measurements through the NATIONAL BUREAU OF STANDARDS HANDBOOKS. In cooperation with USAEC develops nuclear materials measurement standards.

NATIONAL BUREAU OF STANDARDS HANDBOOKS

The NATIONAL BUREAU OF STANDARDS, U.S. Department of Commerce, is the headquarters for the National Committee on Radiation Protection and Measurements (NCRP), and publishes the committee's recommendations as part of the series of Bureau of Standards handbooks. They are referred to as NBS Handbook 41, 42, etc., and may be purchased from the Superintendent of Documents, Government Printing Office, Washington 25, D.C.

H41—Medical X-Ray Protection up to Two Million Volts (1949). Superseded H15 and H20, and was superseded by H60, which was, in turn, superseded by H76

H42—Safe Handling of Radioactive Isotopes (1949)

H48—Control and Removal of Radioactive Contamination in Laboratories (1951)

H49—Recommendations for Waste Disposal of Phosphorus-32 and Iodine-131 for Medical Users (1951). 15 cents

H50—X-Ray Protection Design (1952). 20 cents

H51—Radiological Monitoring Methods and Instruments (1952). 20 cents

H52—Maximum Permissible Amounts of Radioisotopes in the Human Body and Maximum Permissible Concentrations in Air and Water (1953). Superseded by H69

H53—Recommendations for the Disposal of Carbon-14 Wastes (1953). 15 cents

H54—Protection Against Radiation from Radium, Cobalt-60, and Cesium-137 (1954). Superseded by H73

H55—Protection Against Betatron-Synchrotron Radiations up to 100 Million Electron Volts (1954). 25 cents

H56—Safe Handling of Cadavers Containing Radioactive Isotopes (1953). Superseded by H65

H57—Photographic Dosimetry of X- and Gamma Rays (1954). 15 cents

H58—Radioactive-Waste Disposal in the Ocean (1954). 20 cents

H59—Permissible Dose from External Sources of Ionizing Radiation (1954). An addendum, Maximum Permissible Radiation Exposures to Man, was issued 1957. 35 cents

H60—X-Ray Protection (1955). Superseded by H76

H61—Regulation of Radiation Exposure by Legislative Means (1955). 25 cents

H62—Report of the International Commission on Radiological Units and Measurements (ICRU) (1956). 40 cents

H63—Protection Against Neutron Radiation up to 30 Million Electron Volts (1957)

H64—Design of Free-Air Ionization Chambers (1957). 20 cents

H65—Safe Handling of Bodies Containing Radioactive Isotopes (1958). 15 cents

H66—Safe Design and Use of Industrial Beta-Ray Sources (1958). 20 cents

H69—Maximum Permissible Body Burdens and Maximum Permissible Concentrations of Radionuclides in Air and in Water for Occupational Exposure (1959). 35 cents

H72—Measurement of Neutron Flux and Spectra for Physical and Biological Applications (1960). 35 cents

H73—Protection Against Radiations from Sealed Gamma Sources (1960). 30 cents

H75—Measurement of Absorbed Dose of Neutrons and of Mixtures of Neutrons and Gamma Rays (1961). 35 cents.

H76—Medical X-Ray Protection up to Three Million Volts (1961). 25 cents

H80—A Manual of Radioactivity Procedures (1962)

H84—Radiation Quantities and Units (ICRU Report 10a) (1962)

H85—Physical Aspects of Irradiation (ICRU Report 10b) (1962)

H86—Radioactivity (ICRU Report 10c) (1962)

H87—Clinical Dosimetry (ICRU Report 10d) (1962)

H88—Radiobiological Dosimetry (ICRU Report 10e) (1962)

H89—Methods of Evaluating Radiological Equipment and Materials (ICRU Report 10f) (1962)

Note: H83 and H85 through H89 are "in preparation."

NATIONAL COMMITTEE ON RADIATION PROTECTION AND MEASUREMENTS

The NCRP is a nongovernmental, voluntary body of individuals with primary interest in radiation protection and radiation safety. The committee is composed of 41 members from 17 different scientific societies, industrial associations and federal agencies, plus subcommittee chairmen and members-at-large. These individuals are to be "technically qualified representatives" appointed by their organizations, and the representatives-at-large are chosen for their scientific competence. There is an executive committee of 8 members in addition to chairmen of the main committee, and there are 18 different subcommittees with 9 task groups.

The NCRP came into being as the result of the need for a single voice to represent the United States in the INTERNATIONAL COMMISSION ON RADIOLOGICAL PROTECTION, and was originally organized under the name, "Advisory Committee on X-ray and Radium Protection." With Lauriston

S. Taylor as Chairman this group met regularly and productively on such problems as x-ray protection and radium protection from the date of its first official meeting in 1929 until World War II. During the war there were no official meetings, but most of the members were active in the Manhattan Engineer District (the forerunner of the U.S. Atomic Energy Commission) and thus gave continuity to radiation protection activities.

The first formal postwar meeting was held on 4 December, 1946, at which time, in response to evident need, the committee was completely reorganized along the lines of its present structure. The NCRP has been very productive of valuable information which has been used by all agencies working with radioactive isotopes, radioactive materials, or radiation in any form. All its recommendations, published by the U.S. Department of Commerce as NATIONAL BUREAU OF STANDARDS HANDBOOKS, are particularly used in the United States and have influenced international bodies. The area of responsibility of each of the subcommittees identifies the activities of the NCRP:

1. Permissible dose from external sources
2. Permissible internal dose
3. X-rays up to 2,000,000 volts
4. Heavy particles (neutrons, protons and heavier)
5. Electrons, gamma rays and x-rays above 2,000,000 volts
6. Handling of radioactive isotopes and fission products
7. Monitoring methods and instruments
8. Waste disposal and decontamination
9. Protection against radiations from Ra, Co^{60}, and Cs^{137} encapsulated
10. Regulation of radiation exposure dose
11. Incineration of radioactive waste
12. Electron protection
13. Safe handling of bodies containing radioactive isotopes
14. Permissible exposure doses under emergency conditions

M-1 Standards and measurement of radioactivity for radiological use
    Task groups:
      (1) Preparation of standards and procedures for their measurements
      (2) Preparation and measurement of radionuclides for clinical and biological application

M-2 Standards and measurement of radiological exposure dose
    Task groups:
      (1) Instruments for measurement in roentgens
      (2) Measurement of radiation output of protons and electrons
      (3) Measurement of neutron flux and spectrums
      (4) Clinical measurement of exposure dose and depth dose

M-3 Standards and measurement of absorbed radiation dose

Task groups:
      (1) Measurement of absorbed dose of neutrons, and of mixed neutrons and gamma rays
      (2) Measurement of and data on spectrums of x-rays and electrons
      (3) Measurement of stopping power ratios and analysis of present data

M-4 Relative biological effectiveness

NATIONAL RESEARCH COUNCIL. *See* NATIONAL ACADEMY OF SCIENCES–NATIONAL RESEARCH COUNCIL.

NATIONAL SCIENCE FOUNDATION

An agency of the U.S. Government whose mission is to support research, education and training, and communication in science. The NSF atomic energy interests include a program of grants to United States educational institutions for the purchase of research reactors. They also have a joint program with the USAEC in support of radiation biology institutes for both high school and college science teachers.

NATURAL RADIATION

Irradiation from natural sources affects the entire population of the world; it remains relatively constant in time, but varies from place to place with local geological conditions. Natural sources include external radiation sources of extraterrestrial origin, i.e., cosmic rays, and external sources of terrestrial radiation, i.e., the radioactive isotopes present in the earth's crust and in air. Internal radiation from ingestion and inhalation of naturally occurring radioisotopes, potassium-40, carbon-14, radium-226 and its decay products (particularly the gas radon), and thorium-232 and its decay products (also note thoron) add their part to the total of natural radiation.

After an exhaustive study of available information the U.S. National Academy of Sciences–National Research Council reported that the average person in the United States receives a total accumulated gonadal dose of about 4.3 roentgens over a 30-year period from radiation from natural sources.

In this book the term ENVIRONMENTAL RADIATION is reserved for man-made radiation from industrial use of radioisotopes, from contamination of the environment, from building materials and from research and medical use of radioactive material.

See RADIATION SOURCES.

NATURAL SELECTION AND RADIATION. *See* POPULATIONS, RADIATION EFFECTS ON.

NAVY RADIATION BIOLOGY AND ATOMIC MEDICINE PROGRAMS

Within the Department of the Navy the responsibilities for the program for defense against the effects of nuclear weapons, the nuclear propulsion program, and the nuclear medicine program have been distributed among several of the Bureaus. The Chief of Naval Operations exercises policy control in the fields of organization, equipment, and personnel qualifications, assignments and training in the program for defense against nuclear weapons and the nuclear propulsion program.

The Bureau of Ships is responsible for the following:

a. The development of equipment for individual and collective protection of personnel from the effects of nuclear explosions
b. The development of equipment and shielding for the protection of personnel from radiation emanating from nuclear reactors
c. The development of radiac instruments
d. The investigation of radiological contamination and the development of methods for decontamination
e. The development of reactor safety programs
f. The development of procedures for the disposal of radioactive waste materials

The Bureau of Medicine and Surgery is responsible for the following:

a. The establishment of radiation tolerances for exposure to nuclear detonations
b. The investigation of the physiological effects of exceeding those tolerances (*see* SOMATIC EFFECTS, RADIATION-INDUCED)
c. The development of procedures for the treatment of mass casualties resulting from exposure to nuclear detonations
d. The establishment of radiation tolerances for occupational exposures to nuclear reactors, radiation-generating equipment and radioactive materials (*see* MAXIMUM PERMISSIBLE CONCENTRATION)
e. The investigation of the physiological effects of exceeding the tolerances for occupational exposures to radiation
f. The development of procedures for the treatment of occupational overexposures to radiation (*see* TREATMENT OF RADIATION ILLNESS)
g. The clinical use of radiation-generating equipment and radioisotopes for diagnostic and therapeutic procedures for military personnel and their dependents, in accordance with the highest standards of practice in the medical profession (*see* MEDICAL APPLICATIONS OF ATOMIC ENERGY)

h. The investigation of physiologic functions in health and in disease states, utilizing radioactive trace elements

To fulfill its responsibilities, the Bureau of Medicine and Surgery exercises management control over a number of research institutes and laboratories as described below, and supervises the operation of isotope clinics in all its major hospitals. In addition, the Bureau supplies technical assistance in this field to activities which are under the management control of other naval bureaus.

National Naval Medical Center. The various components of the Center at Bethesda, Md., have a large variety of x-ray equipment ranging in size up to and including a 200-kv x-ray therapy unit. These activities also hold USAEC licenses to operate a pulsed nuclear reactor, a 5-watt nuclear reactor, a linear accelerator, a positive ion accelerator, a 2,500-curie cobalt-60 whole-body irradiator, a 1,000-c cobalt-60 teletherapy unit and AEC byproduct licenses (*see* LICENSES FOR BYPRODUCT MATERIAL) to use radioactive sources with specific activities up to 10 c for any and all isotopes with atomic numbers from 3 to 37, for radioactive sources with specific activities up to 0.5 c for any and all isotopes with atomic numbers from 39 to 83, and for tritium, strontium-90, iodine-131, cesium-137, irridium-192, polonium-210 and radium-226 sources ranging in specific activity from 0.5 to 20.0 c.

Naval Medical Research Institute (NMRI), an integral part of the National Naval Medical Center, maintains an active and continuing research program in the fields of stress physiology, regulatory physiology, biochemistry, biophysics, preventive medicine, occupational medicine, aviation medicine and toxicology.

The studies in stress physiology include basic research into the physiological mechanisms which are affected by exposure to extremes of climate, methods for the prevention of heat casualties, including the mechanisms involved in acclimatization, and methods for the treatment of heat casualties. The results of these studies are essential to the design of adequate blast shelters for protection from the effects of a nuclear attack.

In the fields of biochemistry and toxicology as they are related to radiation biology, many studies of enzymatic activity are being conducted, utilizing radioactive trace elements.

The biophysics research at NMRI is directed toward the biological effects of radiation, the medical problems related to injury produced by ionizing radiation, the treatment of injuries resulting from exposure to ionizing radiation, the development of a chemical dosimeter, flash burns of the retina, and the effects of blast and the tolerance levels for blast in animals and man. The studies of biological effects are concerned primarily with the mechanisms of both acute and late deaths due to irradiation, and the determination of the dose of whole-body irradiation necessary to produce death in various animals in an attempt to determine the minimum lethal dose for man. Various cell-free splenic extracts which effectively reduce mortality are also being studied in an effort to determine the best form of treatment for radiation injuries.

The Naval Medical School, a component of the National Naval Medical Center, maintains an active research program in the storage and use of preserved tissues. A large part of this program involves the study of the in-vivo metabolism of the collagen components of transplanted, freeze-dried homografts using tissues which have been tagged with carbon-14 and/or tritium. Another part of this program encompasses the study of the in-vitro metabolism of various tissues during storage in the tissue bank. This part of the program is accomplished by utilizing a variety of radioisotopes.

The Naval Medical School also conducts a number of courses each year dealing with various aspects of nuclear medicine, radiation safety and the use of radioactive isotopes. An extensive correspondence course for Navy Medical personnel covers the possible effects of nuclear weapons from all aspects.

Although the Radiation Exposure Evaluation Laboratory (REEL) forms a small part of the National Naval Medical Center, it has an extensive research program in radiation biology and nuclear medicine.

The Naval Medical Field Research Laboratory (NMFRL), located at Camp Lejeune, N.C., is under the management control of the Bureau of Medicine and Surgery and is partially funded by the Defense Atomic Support Agency (DASA) of the Department of Defense.

In the field of radiation biology, the laboratory has a small but continuing research program directed toward the radiation effects resulting from exposure to the detonation of nuclear weapons and toward the development of equipment for use by personnel in the field for protection against the ionizing radiation produced by a nuclear detonation. To accomplish its mission, the scientific staff at NMFRL has the cooperation and support of Marine Corps personnel stationed at Camp Lejeune for field studies.

The U.S. Naval Radiological Defense Laboratory (USNRDL), San Francisco, is under the management control of the Bureau of Ships and obtains financial assistance from the DASA and

technical assistance from the Bureau of Medicine and Surgery. In addition to its research and development programs in the field of radiation detection instruments and equipment protection, NRDL has a variety of research studies in the field of radiobiology, including (a) recovery and residual damage from exposure to repeated doses of x-irradiation in 11 mammalian species; (b) effects of irradiation on performance and behavior; (c) effects of radiation on gastrointestinal tissues; (d) radioprotective effects of drugs given before exposure; and (e) the effects of radiation on subcellular and immunological systems.

NCRP. *See* NATIONAL COMMITTEE ON RADIATION PROTECTION AND MEASUREMENTS.

NECROSIS DUE TO RADIATION
Irradiation of cells may cause their death and subsequent necrosis, i.e., disintegration of the cellular structure with destruction of the nucleus and coagulation or liquefaction of the cytoplasm. Such cell and tissue death is known as radiation necrosis. It may occur in any tissue, e.g., skin heavily irradiated (15,000 to 20,000 beta, or 1,500 to 2,000 gamma) or in bone (*see* BONE DISEASES DUE TO RADIATION) irradiated either externally with heavy localized x-ray treatment, or internally from severe radium poisoning causing necrosis of bones with subsequent spontaneous fracture.

NEGATRON
Symbol β^-. An elementary charged particle; a negative electron. Term used only when it is necessary to distinguish between positive and negative electrons (positrons and negatrons), and not generally adopted in the United States.

NEODYMIUM
Symbol Nd; atomic number 60; atomic weight 144.27. A member of the cerium subgroup of rare earth metals. Discovered by Austrian chemist Karl Welsbach in 1885 and named from Greek *neos*, new, and *didymos*, twin. Natural abundance is furnished by 5 stable isotopes and 2 very long-lived radioactive isotopes, Nd^{144} (23.87%) and Nd^{150} (5.60%).

There are 15 radioactive isotopes, 12 of which are produced in the fission process, with Nd^{147} (11.3 days half-life; β^- and γ emitter) produced in relatively small yields, having a significant count at the end of 1 month. Nd^{147}, together with its daughter, promethium (Pm^{147}), is a potential bone-seeking nuclide from tropospheric fallout.

Not of general biological, medical or agricultural interest.

TABLE N–2. THE NEPTUNIUM RADIOACTIVE SERIES

Plutonium ($_{94}Pu^{241}$)	$\xrightarrow[\beta]{10\ yr}$		Americium ($_{95}Am^{241}$)	$\xrightarrow[\alpha]{500\ yr}$
Neptunium ($_{93}Np^{237}$)	$\xrightarrow[\alpha]{2.20\ \times\ 10^6\ yr}$		Protactinium ($_{91}Pa^{233}$)	$\xrightarrow[\beta]{27.4\ days}$
Uranium ($_{92}U^{233}$)	$\xrightarrow[\alpha]{1.62\ \times\ 10^5\ yr}$		Thorium ($_{90}Th^{229}$)	$\xrightarrow[\alpha]{7.0\ \times\ 10^3\ yr}$
Radium ($_{88}Ra^{225}$)	$\xrightarrow[\beta]{14.8\ days}$		Actinium ($_{89}Ac^{225}$)	$\xrightarrow[\alpha]{10.0\ days}$
Francium ($_{87}Fr^{221}$)	$\xrightarrow[\alpha]{4.8\ min}$		Astatine ($_{85}At^{217}$)	$\xrightarrow[\alpha]{1.8\ \times\ 10^{-2}\ sec}$
Bismuth ($_{83}Bi^{213}$)	$\xrightarrow[\alpha\ 2\%]{47\ min}$		Thalium ($_{81}Tl^{209}$)	

Bismuth ($_{83}Bi^{213}$) — 47 min, β 98% ↓ — Polonium ($_{84}Po^{213}$)

Thalium ($_{81}Tl^{209}$) — 22 min, β ↓ — Lead ($_{82}Pb^{209}$)

Polonium ($_{84}Po^{213}$)	$\xrightarrow[\alpha]{4.2\ \times\ 10^{-6}\ sec}$		Lead ($_{82}Pb^{209}$)	$\xrightarrow[\beta]{3.3\ hr}$
Bismuth ($_{83}Bi^{209}$)	Stable-end product			

The Collateral Neptunium Radioactive Series

Uranium ($_{92}U^{229}$)	$\xrightarrow[\alpha]{58\ min}$		Thorium ($_{90}Th^{225}$)	$\xrightarrow[\alpha]{8.0\ min}$
Radium ($_{88}Ra^{221}$)	$\xrightarrow[\alpha]{30\ sec}$		Radon ($_{86}Rn^{217}$)	$\xrightarrow[\alpha]{\sim\ 10^{-3}\ sec}$
Polonium ($_{84}Po^{213}$)	$\xrightarrow{}$		Neptunium decay series	

NEON

Symbol Ne; atomic number 10; atomic weight 20.183. Colorless, odorless gas found in ordinary air (1 part neon in about 65,000 parts air). Discovered by the Scottish chemists Ramsey and Travers in 1898. Named from the Greek *neos*, new. Natural abundance from 3 stable isotopes: Ne^{20}, 90.92%; Ne^{21}, 0.26%; and Ne^{22}, 8.82%.

Used extensively in illuminated advertising because in a vacuum electric discharge tube neon shows a crimson glow. Also used in high-voltage indicators for high-tension electric lines, lightning arrestors and television tubes. No known biological, medical or agricultural significance.

Two radioactive isotopes are known: Ne^{19} (half-life 18.2 seconds, β^+ emitter) and Ne^{23} (half-life 40.2 seconds, β^- emitter). Ne^{23} may be produced in air by induced activity from neutrons released in the detonation of a nuclear device.

NEPTUNIUM

Symbol Np; atomic number 93; atomic weight 237; a radioactive transuranic element of the actinide series. Discovered in 1940 by E. M. McMillan and P. H. Abelson working in the Radiation Laboratory, Berkeley, California. Named after the planet Neptune, lying beyond Uranus in the solar system. Neptunium radio-active isotopes of mass numbers 231 through 241 have been reported. Neptunium-237 ($_{93}Np^{327}$, α emitter, half-life 2.20×10^6 years) is the longest-lived radioisotope of the neptunium decay series and exists in trace quantities in nature associated with uranium minerals, and probably arises from interaction of U^{238} with high-energy neutrons. Neptunium-239 ($_{93}Np^{239}$, β emitter, half-life 2.3 days) is of interest as an intermediate product in the transmutation of fertile* uranium-238 into fissionable plutonium-239. For all practical purposes none of the isotopes of neptunium exist in nature, and none have any known significance in biological, medical or agricultural activity.

NEPTUNIUM RADIOACTIVE SERIES

The neptunium series shown in the accompanying table depicts the decay disintegration chain, and parent-daughter transmutation from radioactive plutonium ($_{94}Pu^{241}$) to stable bismuth ($_{83}Bi^{209}$). This series does not occur in nature, for since the earth was formed about 4.5×10^9 years ago, the longest-lived member of the series, Np^{237} with a half-life of 2.20×10^6 years, long ago ceased to exist. The series has been obtained artificially in the laboratory.

*Capable of being transformed into a fissionable substance by capture of a neutron.

Table N–2 shows that in disintegrations in which an alpha (α) particle is emitted, the atomic weight of the daughter element is 4 units less than that of the parent. This is because an alpha particle, on the atomic weight scale, has a mass of 4, and thus the loss of 1 alpha particle would reduce the weight by 4. On the other hand, since a beta (β) particle is an electron with a negligible mass, the daughter element will have the same weight as the parent. It was found in the THORIUM DECAY SERIES that the atomic weights of all members of the series could be represented by 4n, where *n* is an integer varying from 58 for thorium ($4 \times 58 = 232$, the atomic weight of thorium) to 52 for lead ($4 \times 52 = 208$). In a similar way it was shown that $4n + 2$ would give all the atomic weights in the URANIUM RADIOACTIVE SERIES, and $4n + 3$ would be the formula for the ACTINIUM RADIOACTIVE SERIES. It was predicted that logically there should be a $4n + 1$ series, and although none was found in nature, the artificially produced neptunium series is described by $4n + 1$. For example, the integer for plutonium would be 60 ($4 \times 60 = 240$), and $240 + 1 = 241$; and the integer for the end-product bismuth would be 52 ($4 \times 52 = 208$), and $208 + 1 = 209$.

There is a branched disintegration, 98% of bismuth-213 going by way of polonium-213 to lead-209, and the other 2% going by way of thallium-209 to lead-209. The significance of this branching, which also occurs in the other series, is not known.

A so-called collateral $4n + 1$ series has been demonstrated (see accompanying table) which has the element radon ($_{86}Rn^{217}$), not occurring in the main series.

NERVOUS SYSTEM, RADIATION EFFECTS ON

There is general agreement that peripheral nerve fibers are more radioresistant than components of the central nervous system. Exposure doses of many thousands of roentgens (r) are required to produce detectable structural changes in peripheral nerve fibers. Functional changes also require large doses: 10,000 r of x-ray have no effect on the conduction of nerve impulses in a frog nerve-muscle preparation, while 20,000 r are needed to decrease the amplitude of muscular contraction. In experimental studies excised peripheral nerve has been exposed to as much as 180,000 r before the action potential begins to fall, and even after a 360,000-r dose 15% of the action potential remains. Conduction of impulses in the isolated sciatic nerve, however, was altered by doses of about 20,000 r.

NEUTRINO

An electrically neutral particle with a rest mass less than 0.01 of the rest mass of an electron (m_e). An Italian word meaning a small neutral one. In negative beta disintegration, a neutron divides into a proton, a negatron and an antineutrino, the latter 2 being emitted, carrying off the excess energy. In positive beta disintegration a proton is converted into a neutron, a positron and a neutrino, the latter 2 being emitted. The neutrino has been postulated as one of the particles in pi-meson decay and as one or two of the particles in mu-meson decay. The energy of a neutrino or an antineutrino, emitted in a beta disintegration, is assumed to be equal to the difference between the energy of the beta particle (β⁻ or β⁺) and the energy corresponding to the upper limit of the continuous spectrum for that beta transition. Experimental evidence has established both the neutrino and the antineutrino as part of the beta decay process.

NEUTRON

Symbol n. An elementary particle of neutral or zero electrical charge, and of mass number 1. Considered to be a constituent particle of all nuclei of mass number greater than 1. Unstable with respect to beta decay (β⁻) to give hydrogen ($_1H^1$), with a radioactive half-life of about 12 minutes. The neutron produces no detectable primary ionization as it traverses matter, but interacts by collisions where NEUTRON CAPTURE occurs, or less frequently it interacts magnetically. Collisions may also result in elastic scattering, inelastic scattering and other nuclear reactions. Neutrons undergo capture by all nuclides except He^4. Ionization is produced by the products of these collisions and interactions. Some properties of neutron are rest mass, 1.00894 atomic mass units; charge, 0; spin quantum number, 1/2; magnetic moment, −1.9125 nuclear Bohr magnetons.

Neutrons are produced in enormous quantities in the fission process, either controlled in a nuclear reactor or in the detonation of a nuclear device. (*See* NEUTRON SOURCE.)

Neutrons are designated according to their energies:

THERMAL NEUTRONS, i.e., in thermal equilibrium with the substance in which they exist. Commonly of kinetic energy of about 0.025 electron volt (ev).

Epithermal neutrons have energies from a few hundredths ev up to 100 ev.

Slow neutrons is a term used for thermal neutrons or for a less general class up to 100 ev.

Intermediate neutrons have energies that extend roughly from 100 to 100,000 ev.

FAST NEUTRONS have energies exceeding 10^5 ev.

Resonance neutrons, for a specified nuclide or element, have energies in the region where the cross section of the nuclide or element is particularly large; i.e., a resonance peak for neutrons of certain energies where the absorption rises sharply to a high value.

Neutrons may be classified as to time of emission as prompt neutrons, or those released coincident with the fission process; or delayed neutrons, i.e., released subsequent to the fission process, or more commonly those emitted by excited nuclei formed in any radioactive process.

Activation analysis is based on making an isotope of an element radioactive by exposing the sample to a neutron flux in a reactor and then detecting the radioactive isotope by its radiation characteristics.

Neutron activation occurs when an element is placed in a nuclear reactor or is exposed to intense neutron bombardment associated with the detonation of a nuclear device. A number of neutron-induced nuclear reactions may occur which will render the element radioactive.

Neutron balance, in reactor theory, is the time rate of change of neutron density which is equal to the rate of production minus the rate of leakage and the rate of absorption.

NEUTRON BIOLOGICAL RESEARCH is being conducted, using various neutron sources, including accelerators, cyclotrons and reactors.

Neutron-induced cataracts are some of the most unusual of the biological effects of radiation.

Neutron cycle in reactor theory is the life history of the neutrons in a reactor, starting with the fission process and continuing until all the neutrons have been absorbed or have leaked out.

Neutron density refers to the number of neutrons per unit volume. Related to neutron flux.

Neutron detection by any direct method has proved impossible, but neutrons may be detected by observing charged particles produced by the interaction of neutrons with atomic nuclei, or by observing charged particle recoils resulting from the collision of neutrons with protons.

Neutron economy in reactor engineering refers to the degree to which neutrons are used in desired ways instead of being lost. Desired uses may be the production of radioactive isotopes; boron neutron capture in the treatment of brain tumor; converting fertile to fissile material; or maintaining the chain reaction.

Neutron excess is the difference between the number of neutrons and the number of protons in the nucleus. Determined by subtracting the atomic number of a given nuclide from the NEUTRON NUMBER, or by subtracting twice the atomic number from the mass number.

NEUTRON FLUX is a term used to express the intensity of neutron radiation.

Neutron hardening is the effect caused by the diffusion of thermal neutrons through a medium having an absorption cross section decreasing with energy. Because the slower neutrons are preferentially absorbed, the average energy of the diffusing neutrons becomes greater.

Neutron instruments will be discussed under the following items: NEUTRON CHOPPER, NEUTRON COUNTERS, NEUTRON SPECTROMETER and NEUTRON VELOCITY SELECTOR.

Neutron inventory is the total number of neutrons present in a reactor at a given instant of time.

Neutron leakage refers to the loss, due to their motion, of neutrons of a given energy range from a specified region of a nuclear reactor.

The neutron magnetic moment is equal in magnitude to 1.913 Bohr nuclear magnetons. The direction of the moment is opposite to that of the angular momentum (spin).

The NEUTRON NUMBER is the number of neutrons in a nucleus, and is equal to the difference between the mass number and the atomic number.

Neutron reflection may be caused by crystalline materials as a result of their wave-mechanical properties, or they may be totally reflected by highly polished surfaces of selected materials. Neutron loss can be minimized and thus the critical size of a system reduced by surrounding it with a neutron reflector.

In reactor engineering a neutron reflector is a layer or structure of material surrounding the core of a reactor to reduce the escape of neutrons. The reflector is made of material having a high scattering cross section and a low absorption cross section. By proper design 90% of the neutrons that would be lost may be returned to the core.

Neutron shielding requires different techniques than shielding against gamma rays, but can be accomplished by using a suitable inelastic scattering material, then a material to cause deceleration and finally a material to absorb the thermal neutrons. (*See* NEUTRON SHIELD.)

Any material that emits neutrons is a NEUTRON SOURCE, and of course neutrons are produced in the fission process in enormous numbers.

NEUTRON THERAPY and NEUTRON CAPTURE THERAPY have become feasible with the development of the medical research reactor.

NEUTRON BIOLOGICAL RESEARCH

An extensive amount of biological research has been done using neutrons as the radiation source. The following review gives an indication of the variety and extent of such work:

1. An early experiment (1936) demonstrated that the effects of neutrons on animals were greater than those produced by x-rays of the same dose.

2. The various physiological responses and pathological effects of neutron exposure have been studied in comparison with other types of radiation.

3. Life-shortening effects on male mice have been shown to be greater after exposure to neutrons than for similar exposure using x- and gamma-ray irradiation.

4. Dose-effect relationship studies have been conducted using neutrons in comparison with other types of radiation.

5. Extensive work has been done on the relative biological effectiveness (RBE) of neutrons and other types of radiation; and the dependence of RBE on ionization density, measured in terms of linear energy transfer (LET). For example, the RBE for 14-Mev neutrons is 1.5 for splenic atrophy, 1.7 for thymic atrophy, 0.84 for iron-59 uptake in red blood corpuscles in rats, 2.3 for gut weight loss in CF1 mice, and 1.6 for 30-day mortality in mice.

6. Neutrons are very effective in the production of cataracts, with an RBE for fast neutrons of 2- to 3-Mev mean energy of 9 for induction of mild opacities in mice, and greater than 9 for induction of threshold lens damage.

7. Bone marrow therapy is less effective against fast neutron damage than against x-ray damage.

8. Activation analysis using neutrons in a nuclear reactor to activate a small quantity of an element in a specimen for further study is a common type of research using neutrons.

9. Boron neutron capture therapy has been used in treatment of brain tumor (neuroglioblastoma). A boron compound is injected which is absorbed by the tumor cells, and then at the proper time the tumor area is exposed to a flux of neutrons which activate the boron into a very effective alpha emitter.

10. A focused beam of neutrons has been used to destroy the hypophysis, thus avoiding the necessity for surgical removal.

11. Induced radioactivity due to heavy accidental exposure to neutrons occurs within the human body, and has been used as a method of estimating the level of exposure. Analysis is usually for sodium-24 formed by neutron bombardment of the serum sodium.

Most of the biological work with neutrons is carried out with Cockcroft-Walton machines, Van de Graaf accelerators, linear accelerators and cyclotrons, and with reactors using thermal neutrons and uranium conversion plates. The most frequent neutron-producing nuclear reactions giving monoenergetic neutrons are the following: $H^2(d,n)He^3$, $H^3(d,n)He^4$, $C^{12}(d,n)N^{13}$, $N^{14}(d,n)O^{15}$ and $H^3(p,n)He^3$. Other important nuclear reactions producing neutrons are $Li^7(d,n)Be^8$, $Be^9(d,n)$-B^{10} and $Be^9(\alpha,n)C^{12}$.

NEUTRON CAPTURE

Any process by which a neutron, on colliding with an atomic nucleus, sticks to it or is absorbed into it, or from which fission results, i.e., capture of a neutron by an atomic nucleus. Neutron radiative capture is responsible for two frequently observed types of nuclear reaction: transmutation and activation. Neutrons of relative low energy, called slow or thermal neutrons, usually produce activation by the (n,γ) nuclear reaction, in which a neutron is captured by a target nucleus and the resulting compound nucleus then emits its excess energy as gamma radiation. A typical example is as follows:

$$\text{Cobalt-59} + \text{neutron} \longrightarrow \text{cobalt-60} + \text{gamma rays}$$

or,

$$_{27}Co^{59} + {_0}n^1 \longrightarrow {_{27}}Co^{60} + \gamma$$

or,

$$Co^{59}(n,\gamma)Co^{60}$$

The product is always isotopic with the target element, but its mass number is 1 unit higher.

With fast neutrons, above 10^2 electron volts, the transmutation (n,p) type of reaction is fairly common. Here a neutron is captured and a proton escapes from the resulting compound nucleus. Reactions of this type are $N^{14}(n,p)C^{14}$ and $Cl^{35}(n,p)S^{35}$. The product nucleus has the same mass, but its atomic number is 1 unit less than that of the target. A number of other neutron capture reactions are also possible.

Since virtually all elements, except some of the very lightest, exhibit radiative capture of slow neutrons, and many others react with the faster neutrons, it is obvious that this is a useful method for the production of radioactive isotopes. Most commercially available radioactive isotopes are produced by neutron bombardment of selected target materials in nuclear reactors.

Enormous numbers of neutrons are released in the detonation of a nuclear weapon. Some of these neutrons liberated in the fission process are immediately captured by various nuclei present in the bomb, others by the bomb casing, the tower material, etc. Still others are captured by nitrogen nuclei to form carbon-14. Those coming in contact with the earth or sea produce induced activity in air, water and soil constituent elements. Neutrons are the only significant nuclear particles produced in fusion or thermonuclear reactions—the same capture process will occur for weapons of this type as for fission weapons.

NEUTRON CAPTURE THERAPY

In brain tumors there is a tendency for local concentration of a variety of compounds, presumably on the basis of vascular disturbances in the tumor. Among elements that can be so localized is boron-10. This element has the property that when it is subjected to a field of slow neutrons, some of these are captured by the boron, with the formation of lithium-7 and the release of alpha radiation. This phenomenon offers the intriguing possibility of the internal release of radiation well localized to the region of the tumor. The period of optimal concentration of the boron in the tumor is brief, however, and the neutron irradiation must be timed to coincide with it. Furthermore, the boron compounds are somewhat toxic, and the field of neutrons falls off significantly with depth. With these various limitations, neutron capture therapy of brain tumors in patients has, as yet, had only restricted clinical usefulness.

NEUTRON CHOPPER

Mechanical velocity selector which allows neutrons to pass only when they can travel through slots in successive rotating selector discs. The initial collimated neutron stream passes parallel to the axis of the discs; a slot in the first disc permits a pulse of neutrons to go through, but the second disc transmits just those which arrive in the interval when its open slot is crossing the path of the stream. Adjustment of the angular separation of the slots in the spinning discs accomplishes selection of an intermittent but monoenergetic group of neutrons on each rotation.

NEUTRON COUNTERS

Geiger and proportional counters are made especially sensitive to neutrons by using materials of construction which exhibit specific and high response in reaction with the neutrons. Important examples of this approach are the use of boron-trifluoride in gas-filled counters or the coating of proportional counter electrodes with fissionable materials.

Scintillation crystal or solid state (semiconductor) detectors are adaptable for neutron studies in a similar manner, by including neutron-sensitive materials in their structure or by providing them with a sensitive foil facing.

See GAS COUNTER.

NEUTRON FLUX

Number of neutrons passing through a unit area in unit time. Term expressing the intensity of neutron radiation. If a neutron source produces a neutron density of n neutrons per cubic centimeter and moving in a given direction with a velocity (v) expressed in centimeters per second, then the product nv, in neutrons per square centimeter per second, is called the neutron flux.

For example, the Brookhaven Medical Research Reactor (MRR), a light-water-moderated research reactor in the medical department at the Brookhaven National Laboratory, designed and used for medical research, neutron capture therapy and related biological research, has a maximum thermal-neutron flux of 3×10^{13} neutrons per square centimeter per second ($n/cm^2/sec$), with the beam for patient irradiation having a neutron flux of 1×10^{11} $n/cm^2/sec$. The Materials Testing Reactor (MTR) at the National Reactor Testing Station has a maximum thermal-neutron flux of 9×10^{14} $n/cm^2/sec$. The Oak Ridge X-10 area graphite reactor (X-10), used extensively to produce radioactive isotopes by activation of stable isotopes, has a maximum thermal-neutron flux of 1.1×10^{12} $n/cm^2/sec$, and a maximum fast-neutron flux of 1×10^{12} $n/cm^2/sec$.

See FLUX.

NEUTRON MODERATOR

Substance of low atomic number and small neutron capture cross section, used to reduce the speed or moderate the energy of neutrons. Used in nuclear reactors to provide thermalization necessary to sustain the nuclear chain reaction; certain instruments use moderators to bring neutron energies down into their sensitive range. Graphite, water and heavy water are commonly used in reactors, sometimes also beryllium; when solid hydrogenous substances are desired, paraffin and plastics are frequently used.

NEUTRON NUMBER

Symbol N. Number of neutrons in a nucleus. For a given nuclide the neutron number is equal to the difference between the mass number for that nuclide and the atomic number ($A - Z = N$). If written, it is added as a subscript following the symbol, as $_{26}Fe^{59}_{33}$ where N is 33, A is 59, and Z is 26, Fe being the symbol for iron.

NEUTRON SHIELD

SHIELD constructed so as to absorb neutrons; e.g., the shield of a nuclear reactor is a body of material (usually a concrete shield) surrounding the reactor to prevent the escape of neutrons and radiation into a protected area (usually the entire space external to the reactor).

NEUTRON SOURCE

Any material that emits neutrons. In a general sense a machine such as a nuclear reactor that produces large numbers of neutrons, or the fission or fusion process in the detonation of a nuclear device.

The first laboratory production of neutrons was with the (α,n) type of nuclear reaction. A polonium source produced alpha particles which bombarded beryllium with the production of neutrons of about 5-Mev energy. An intimate mixture of radium (α emitter) and finely divided beryllium powder is used for the production of neutrons. They emit in the order of 10^7 neutrons per second; i.e., neutrons can be obtained by the $Be^9(\alpha,n)C^{12}$ process.

A number of reactions of the (d,n) type have been used, with deuterons produced by means of a cyclotron. For example, the University of Chicago 37-inch cyclotron utilizes the $Be^9(d,n)B^{10}$ reaction on a thick beryllium target to produce 9.5 maximum Mev neutrons. Perhaps the most convenient source of fast neutrons is the Cockcroft-Walton machine, which, using a deuteron beam and a thin zirconium target, produces neutrons of 14.1-Mev energy by the reaction $H^3(d,n)He^4$ The neutrons in this case are monoenergetic.

Reactions of the (γ,n) or photonuclear type produce monoenergetic, i.e., homogeneous neutron beams. Two photonuclear reactions have been extensively used as neutron sources: $H^2(\gamma,n)H^1$, 2.225 Mev, and $Be^9(\gamma,n)Be^8$, 1.66 Mev. A convenient research source of neutrons consists of a rod of antimony containing the Sb^{124} radioactive isotope (radioactive half-life 60 days), surrounded by a beryllium metal cup. Energy release about 0.03 Mev at the rate of 8 million neutrons per second. The Sb^{124} can easily be regenerated in a nuclear reactor.

A (p,n) reaction has been used. For example, the Oak Ridge National Laboratory 86-inch cyclotron utilizes 22-Mev protons in the $Be^9(p,n)B^9$ reaction to obtain about 1-Mev neutrons.

But for enormous quantities of fast neutrons the nuclear reactor is the ideal source. Uranium undergoing fission emits neutrons with average energies of the order of 1 to 2 Mev. The fission can be controlled so as to have a continuous, uniform stream of neutrons (see NEUTRON FLUX).

In the detonation of a nuclear device the neutron yield and the neutron energy depend upon the size and type of device, but they are virtually all fast neutrons, and 99+% are released in less than a millionth of a second.

Neutrons cause ionization indirectly and have biological effects with a relative biological effectiveness (RBE) of 1.7 for acute radiation injury and a greater RBE for the production of cataracts.

NEUTRON SPECTROMETER

Apparatus for determining the energy spectrum

of a stream of neutrons, or to provide information related to their energy. Since the energy of individual neutrons can be as readily characterized in terms of wave length or velocity, the selection of neutrons for counting is ordinarily effected on the basis of one of these parameters. Crystal diffraction can be used for the former principle; the latter can be done with neutron velocity selectors or neutron choppers. Neutron spectrometers are also used for analysis of crystal structures, similar to the well-known use of x-ray diffraction units. In this field, neutrons display a unique advantage over x-rays in their ability to detect the crystal lattice positions of hydrogen atoms and certain other light elements of special interest in biological materials.

NEUTRON THERAPY

A beam of fast neutrons has been used experimentally in the treatment of cancer in human beings. The results in one carefully performed study were not encouraging. In this experiment the neutrons were produced from a cyclotron that gave multimillion volt deuterons; these deuterons were directed onto a beryllium target to yield the neutrons used for therapy. Neutrons produce more effect on tissues per given amount of energy absorbed than do x-rays and gamma rays; i.e., neutrons have a greater RBE (RELATIVE BIO-LOGICAL EFFECTIVENESS). The extent of this difference is poorly understood, and thus it was difficult to select a suitable dose of neutrons on the basis of experience with conventional radiation therapy. Furthermore, it appeared that the neutron beam produced disproportionately severe delayed undesirable effects on normal tissues. It was demonstrated that neutron therapy could be effective in killing cancer cells, and that some patients could be cured, but the over-all results compared unfavorably with those of conventional radiation therapy.

NEUTRON VELOCITY SELECTOR

Device for selecting and transmitting neutrons, especially when the energy is of a specific energy; characterized by the associated velocity. Since cadmium and other materials absorb and filter out very slow neutrons, simple shields are crude but effective velocity selectors. Time-of-flight selectors accept only those neutrons which travel a fixed distance in a required time interval; this principle is embodied in the neutron chopper and other similar apparatus. Diffraction in crystals provides another highly selective method.

NEUTROPHIL LEUKOCYTE, RADIATION DAMAGE

The total neutrophil count usually shows an

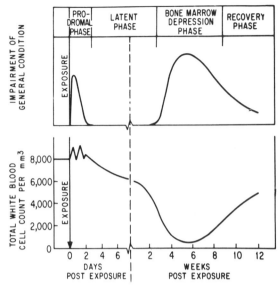

FIGURE N–1. TYPICAL WHITE BLOOD CELL RESPONSE TO TOTAL BODY RADIATION, HEMATOLOGIC TYPE SYNDROME. (COURTESY OF MEDICAL DIVISION, OAK RIDGE INSTITUTE OF NUCLEAR STUDIES.)

initial rise in the first 12 to 48 hours after both high- and low-level doses of radiation. This rise is followed by a fall during the first week to below pre-exposure level, where it fluctuates until about the third or fourth week, when there is a deeper depression lasting 2 or 3 weeks. A gradual return to pre-exposure levels may then occur in patients exposed in sublethal ranges. Figure N–1 shows a typical response.

In the lethal range of exposure (400 to 600 roentgens of whole-body irradiation) the neutrophil count may still rise during the first 2 days, but then falls, by the fifth to the tenth postexposure day, to values below 1,000 cells per cubic millimeter of blood. In survivors, recovery begins about the fifth week, taking several months to return to normal. In one fatal case of accidental exposure (see ACCIDENTS) there was an immediate rise in the neutrophil count from a normal for this patient of about 7,000 to about 23,000 per mm³ by the third day and then a precipitous fall to about 200 per mm³ by the sixth day, with a continuation at that level until death.

NEVADA TEST SITE

Formerly called Nevada Proving Ground; only area within the continental United States used for nuclear weapons testing. The site covers about 640 square miles of desert country in southeastern Nevada, about 65 miles northwest of Las Vegas. This large controlled area is within the boundaries of the Las Vegas Bombing and Gunnery Range

(USAF), affording excellent conditions for maximum safety.

It was first used for nuclear test detonations in the January–February series of 1951. Only relatively small nuclear devices which have been carefully screened for their anticipated yield are detonated here. Elaborate safety precautions are taken before detonation: aerial and ground surveys are conducted to make certain that no persons or domestic animals have entered the testing area; announcements of shot time are made before tests; and weather conditions are carefully studied for conditions likely to minimize fallout effects on off-site populated areas.

The Nevada test site has been extensively used for deep underground or contained bursts (see UNDERGROUND BURST).

See PACIFIC TESTING AREA.

NICKEL

Symbol Ni; atomic number 28; atomic weight 58.71. Silver-white metal, harder than iron, malleable, ductile and somewhat magnetic. Discovered by Swedish mineralogist A. F. Cronstedt in 1751. Named from Swedish abbreviation of kopparnickel, false copper. Obtained chiefly from pyrrhotite and garnierite. Natural abundance furnished by 5 stable isotopes.

About 200,000 tons of nickel is consumed per year in the United States, largely in the composition of nickel steel and in other alloys. Very mildly toxic except for nickel carbonyl, which is from 5 to 10 times as toxic as carbon monoxide. One hundred and eighty parts per million in the air will kill animals after 1 hour of exposure. Dermatitis may result, especially in an allergic person. Found in almost all biological materials, although not considered an essential element. Some typical values for fresh tissues are as follows: human liver, 0.09 part per million (ppm); ox liver, 0.125 ppm; cow's milk, 0.004 ppm; egg yolk, 0.02 ppm; and fish, 0.015 ppm. Crop plants average about 0.9 ppm on a dry basis.

Nine radioactive isotopes have been identified. Three are likely to occur as fission products from the detonation of a nuclear device. None has radioactive fallout significance. Ni⁵⁷, Ni⁵⁹, Ni⁶³ and Ni⁶⁵ may be formed in the soil or sea water as a result of induced radioactivity from neutron bombardment associated with the detonation of a nuclear device coming in contact with either the earth's land or water surface. Although the half-life of Ni⁵⁹ is 8×10^4 years, the amount formed is not sufficient to make any of the induced nickel radioactivity significant in residual nuclear radiation. Nickel-63, half-life 85 years, a beta emitter, is available for biological research, and studies have been made on distribution, movement and metabolism of nickel in plants and animals.

NIOBIUM

Symbol Nb; atomic number 41; atomic weight 92.91. Formerly columbium (Cb) (in the United States, and still used by metallurgists). Rare metallic element, found as columbite (hence the earlier name) in pegmatite veins, volcanic intrusions through the crust of the earth. Discovered by Hatchett in 1801 in an ore sent to England more than a hundred years before by John Winthrop, first governor of Connecticut. Named for Niobe, daughter of Tantalus, for it usually occurs in nature with tantalum. One hundred per cent abundance as stable isotope Nb^{93}.

Added to stainless steel to increase corrosion resistance. Not an important naturally occurring constituent of living materials. Toxicity of a low order.

Twenty-four radioactive isotopes have been identified. Fifteen occur as fission products produced by the detonation of a nuclear device; or in the operation of a reactor.

Niobium-95 ($_{41}Nb^{95}$). Radioactive half-life 35 days; with total body as the critical organ, biological half-life 760 days; effective half-life 33.5 days; beta and gamma emission. Of importance primarily in radioactive fallout, where at the end of 1 month it is found as 7.84 megacuries per megaton (Mc/MT) of fission, and at the end of 1 year still measures 0.892 Mc/MT of fission. In measurements taken at the site of a nuclear detonation, Zr^{95}-Nb^{95} is one combination among 5 radioisotopes that constitute most of the gamma radiation from the residual material. In fact, 2 months after detonation the 750-kev gamma radiations from Zr^{95}-Nb^{95} dominate the spectrums. Niobium-95 is formed in the uranium fission process as indicated below.

NITROGEN

Symbol N; atomic number 7; atomic weight 14.008. A colorless, odorless, tasteless, nontoxic inert gas. Discovered by Daniel Rutherford in 1772. Named from Latin, niter-forming. Found in great abundance in our atmosphere (78.03% nitrogen by weight), estimated amount more than 4,000 billion tons. Natural abundance furnished by 2 stable isotopes: N^{14}, 99.635%, and N^{15}, 0.365%.

The element is so inert that Lavoisier in 1776 named it azote, without life. Yet its compounds are so active as to be exceedingly important: the nitrates in fertilizers as plant nutrition; nitroglycerine as an explosive; nitrous oxide as an anesthetic "laughing gas"; as a food for man and animals in the form of protein; other compounds in dyes, drugs and poisons. The chemical standard man contains 3.0%, or 2,100 g of nitrogen per 70 kg of adult human body weight.

Atmospheric nitrogen is of critical importance in radioactive fallout because of the production of carbon-14 by bombardment of nitrogen-14 by neutrons released by the detonation of a nuclear device. The reaction is the result of the capture of a slow neutron and the emission of a proton, $N^{14}(n,p)C^{14}$, as in the following reaction:

$$_7N^{14} + {}_0n^1 \longrightarrow (_7N^{15}) \longrightarrow {}_6C^{14} + {}_1H^1,$$

followed by

$$_6C^{14} \longrightarrow {}_7N^{14} + \beta^- \quad (C^{14} \text{ half-life } 5,760 \text{ years})$$

Obviously the same reaction occurs from bombardment from cosmic rays. The normal atmospheric content of C^{14} from this cause is estimated to be about 9×10^{27} atoms. As of the date of cessation of United States weapons testing it was estimated that man-made C^{14} amounted to about 10^{28} atoms, resulting in a doubling of the atmospheric content of C^{14}.

There are 4 radioactive isotopes, N^{16} and N^{17}

Rubidium ($_{37}Rb^{95}$) $\xrightarrow[\beta^-]{2 \text{ sec}}$ Strontium ($_{38}Sr^{95}$) $\xrightarrow[\beta^-]{6 \text{ sec}}$

Yttrium ($_{39}Y^{95}$) $\xrightarrow[\beta^-]{10.5 \text{ min}}$ Zirconium ($_{40}Zr^{95}$)

2% / 65 days β⁻ & γ   98% / 65 days β⁻ & γ

Niobium ($_{41}Nb^{95m}$) $\xrightarrow[\text{IT}]{90 \text{ hrs}}$ Niobium ($_{41}Nb^{95}$) $\xrightarrow[\beta^- \& \gamma]{35 \text{ days}}$

Molybdenum ($_{42}Mo^{95}$) (stable)

being possible nuclides produced in air as a result of the detonation of a nuclear device. Although the radioactive isotopes have not been found useful in biological research, separated stable N^{15} has been used in biological and medical research. For example, N^{15}-labeled glycine has been administered to human subjects, and the N^{15} concentration followed in the various nitrogenous metabolic constituents as a function of time.

NITROGEN FIXATION STUDIES

The important ability of plants and/or microorganisms to fix nitrogen has been studied intensively by use of the stable isotope nitrogen-15, since there is no satisfactory radioisotope of nitrogen. This technique was especially valuable when the organism being studied fixed very little nitrogen under such conditions that common analytical procedures were not satisfactory. It has been shown, for example, that practically all photosynthetic bacteria fix nitrogen. Previous claims of fixation by barley, uninoculated legumes, germinating peas, pure cultures of rhizobia and other organisms have been shown most probably to be incorrect. This technique has also been used to study the mechanism of biological fixation as well as the gaseous losses of nitrogen from soils.

NOBELIUM

Name proposed for transuranic element with atomic number 102; atomic weight 254. Discovered in 1957 by a team of United States, British and Swedish scientists at Nobel Institute of Physics in Stockholm as a result of bombarding curium-244 with nuclei of carbon-13 accelerated to high energies (110–120 Mev) in a cyclotron. Named for chemist A. B. Nobel, whose fortune provides the Nobel prizes.

NOBLE GASES

Also called inert gases and rare gases. Elements helium, neon, argon, krypton, xenon and radon. Named because of their chemical inactivity. Characterized by closed shells or subshells of electrons.

NOMINAL YIELD WEAPON

Also nominal atomic bomb. A term, now becoming obsolete, formerly used to describe a nuclear weapon with a 20-kiloton energy release (TNT equivalent). This is approximately the energy yield of the bombs dropped over Hiroshima and Nagasaki, Japan, during World War II.

NUCLEAR BOMB. *See* NUCLEAR WEAPONS.

NUCLEAR BOMB EFFECTS COMPUTER

A pocket calculator* designed to provide quick estimates of such effects of nuclear weapons as blast parameters, reflected overpressure, translated velocities for man and window glass, thermal radiation, initial nuclear radiation, early fallout dose rate, crater dimensions and maximum fireball radius and minimum height of burst for negligible early fallout. Based on data from "The Effects of Nuclear Weapons," Revised Edition, 1962; developed by the Lovelace Foundation, Albuquerque, New Mexico.

NUCLEAR DEVICE

An explosive device which derives its energy from nuclear fission or a combination of nuclear fission and nuclear fusion. A nuclear device may be used for peaceful purposes (*see* NUCLEAR EXPLOSIONS, PEACEFUL USES OF, and PLOWSHARE PROGRAM) or for military purposes (*see* NUCLEAR WEAPONS). The nuclear weapons may be further subdivided into atomic weapons, in which the energy arises from fission, or thermonuclear weapons, involving fusion. In this book the term "nuclear device" has been used almost exclusively, even when referring to nuclear weapons. For details of phenomenology *see* NUCLEAR EXPLOSION.

NUCLEAR EMULSION

A photographic emulsion especially designed to register the track of a charged particle as a series of dark grains. French physicist Becquerel was working with sensitized photographic plates when he discovered the phenomenon of radioactivity. Throughout the years plates and films have been used extensively for the study of radioactivity. Information on the distribution of radioactive elements in plants and animals is obtained by autoradiography, and x-ray film is widely used industrially and in the practice of medicine.

The nuclear physicist sporadically used sensitized plates and film to study tracks produced by ionizing radiation during the 1920s and 1930s, but there has been an increase in their use due to the development of special nuclear track emulsions and to new techniques. Modern emulsions contain large-grain silver bromide in about 10 times the quantity of ordinary photographic plates (80% by dry weight), which are thus more sensitive to ionizing radiations. The emulsions may be deposited on glass plates, or are available as stripped emulsions (pellicles) without backing. They can be

*Available from Superintendent of Documents, U.S. Government Printing Office, Washington 25, D.C. $1.00.

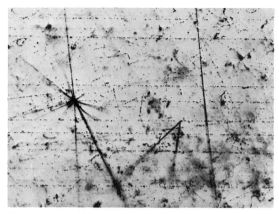

FIGURE N–2. PHOTOGRAPHIC PLATE, OR EMULSION, EXPOSED TO BILLION-VOLT PROTONS PRODUCED BY THE COSMOTRON AT BROOKHAVEN NATIONAL LABORATORY. THE DOTTED LINES MOVING IN A PARALLEL COURSE, LEFT TO RIGHT, WERE MADE BY PROTONS. THE STAR, LEFT, REPRESENTS THE DISINTEGRATION OF AN ATOM (SUCH AS BROMINE OR SILVER) IN THE EMULSION, WHERE AN INCOMING PROTON CAUSED 10 OR MORE PARTICLES TO FLY OUT OF THE NUCLEUS OF THE ATOM.

stacked one on top of another, in order to record continuous tracks in various directions. The tracks produced are usually very short, e.g., a few thousandths of an inch for alpha particles from radioactive sources, but they can be magnified and photographed or studied with a special binocular microscope. See Figure N–2.

Like the Wilson cloud chamber, other CLOUD CHAMBERS, and the BUBBLE CHAMBER, the photographic emulsion can record individual events involving atomic nuclei and other charged particles. But in comparison with the chambers the emulsion has the drawback that the bending of the particle in a magnetic field is impossible with short tracks and most difficult even with long tracks and strong magnetic fields. It has the advantage, however, of being continuously sensitive and having high stopping power.

NUCLEAR ENERGY

Energy released in nuclear reactions, especially in quantities sufficient to be of interest to engineering. Frequently used synonymously with nuclear power, ATOMIC POWER or ATOMIC ENERGY.

NUCLEAR EXPLOSION

Also nuclear shot, atomic shot, or shot; the detonation of a nuclear device. An explosion results from the rapid release of a large amount of energy within a limited space. This is true for a conventional explosive such as TNT as well as for a nuclear device. The sudden release of energy causes an increase in temperature and pressure, convert-

ing bomb materials into gases. These hot gases expand rapidly upon release, initiating a blast wave in the air or a shock wave in water or earth.

So far as blast and shock are concerned, nuclear weapons, although many thousands (or millions) of times more powerful than conventional explosives, produce their destructive action in a similar way. In addition to being much more powerful, nuclear devices have a number of other differences from conventional explosives. About 35% of the energy is released as thermal radiation which is capable of producing skin burns (flash burns can theoretically be caused 15 miles away from a 1-megaton burst) and of starting fires at distances of several miles. Also, a nuclear fission explosion is accompanied by initial nuclear radiation (5% of the energy) which is highly penetrating and hazardous. Even the substances remaining after a nuclear explosion are radioactive, emitting radiations over an extended period of time—residual nuclear radiation (10% of the energy). In addition, a nuclear device detonated on the surface produces radioactive fallout.

Energy yield of a nuclear explosion is expressed in terms of TNT equivalent; e.g., a 1-kiloton nuclear device is one which produces the same amount of energy in an explosion as does 1 kiloton (1,000 tons) of TNT.

The following terms are related to nuclear explosion:

Effect equivalence. The effect of a particular phenomenon of a nuclear detonation expressed in terms of the amount of TNT which would produce the same effect.

Nuclear efficiency. The ratio (expressed as percentage) between the number of atoms that fission and the total number of fissionable atoms available, in a specific atomic device.

See AIR BURST, SURFACE BURST, UNDERGROUND BURST and UNDERWATER BURST.

NUCLEAR EXPLOSIONS, PEACEFUL USES OF

The peaceful uses of nuclear explosions include several possible industrial and scientific applications. The principal objection to such applications is the potential release of radioactive products into the biosphere. This hazard may be minimized by using fusion devices of low fission yield, and in many situations the release of radioactivity can be adequately controlled even for purely fission explosions.

In the Ranier underground shot (September, 1957), 30% of the total energy released was initially deposited in hot (more than 1,200° C) debris in the cavity formed by the explosion. The rapid fall-off of the temperature was attributed to the presence of a large quantity of water, and this concept led to the idea that an explosion in a dry medium might provide a longer-lasting source of heat which could be used to generate steam and produce electrical power. Project Gnome was designed to test the feasibility of this idea, and in December, 1961, a 3 ± 1 KT fission explosion was achieved 1,200 feet below the earth's surface in a salt bed near Carlsbad, New Mexico. Neutron cross-section measurements and earth motion measurements were included in the associated studies. Methods used in the assessment program which extended from 90 days before through 14 days after the event included visual and photographic inspection, surface and underground profile surveys, underground and surface seismic recordings, radiation surveys, microseismic surveys, and water level surveys.

In Project Oil Sand it is proposed to use a nuclear detonation to make available oil deposits in the Athabaska tar sands deposit in Alberta, Canada. At present, extraction of the oil in this deposit is not economically feasible because of the high viscosity of the oil and the approximately 1,000 feet of overburden. It has been estimated that a 9-KT explosion would make 100,000 barrels of oil recoverable.

In Project Chariot, the excavation of a harbor near Cape Thompson, Alaska, is proposed. Several devices would be detonated simultaneously to produce a single crater. If Project Chariot can be achieved with sufficiently low release of radioactivity into the environment, the use of similar detonations for excavations for harbors, canals, strip mining or flood control reservoirs is foreseen.

The first detonation of Project Sedan, designed to obtain knowledge about nuclear explosive earth-moving technology, was fired at the Nevada test site on 6 July, 1962. It was an underground burst (650 feet below the surface), with a yield of about 100 kilotons, and formed a large crater which will provide excavation information.

Other suggested scientific applications of nuclear explosions include associated seismological studies to give data on the earth's structure, studies of neutron cross sections, production of transuranic isotopes, and high-altitude nuclear explosions to provide data on the conductive properties of space, to excite the auroras and to investigate the trapping and injection of particles in the magnetospheric radiation belts.

See PLOWSHARE PROGRAM.

NUCLEAR FISSION

Division of a heavy nucleus into 2 approximately equal parts. A well known example is the FISSION of the compound nucleus formed when uranium-235 captures a slow neutron; another is the fission of plutonium-239 by the capture of slow (thermal) neutrons.

A nuclide is said to be fissionable when it has the property, such as some isotopes of uranium and plutonium have, of capturing neutrons and then splitting into 2 particles with the release of large amounts of kinetic energy. Fission has been induced by neutrons, charged particles and gammaray photons. When induced by photons, it is called photofission. Spontaneous fission occurs rarely and only in the heaviest elements.

Fission neutrons are emitted as a result of nuclear fission. Those emitted during the fissions are called prompt fission neutrons; those emitted by the fission products are called delayed fission neutrons. The nuclear species when an atom such as plutonium-239 undergoes fission are referred to as fission fragments. At the instant of separation they are called fission recoils. Fission products are the nuclides produced by the fission of a heavy element such as uranium-235. Thirty-five fission product elements from zinc through gadolinium have been identified as produced by slow neutron fission. Fission fragments which have an appreciable cross section for the capture of neutrons are known as fission poisons.

The energy released in the fission process is enormous, about 170 Mev per fission. Calculated out, this results in the power production corresponding to the fission of 1 g of uranium per day of 1 million watts. To obtain the same amount of heat by combustion would require over 3 tons of coal or nearly 700 gallons of fuel oil.

Since neutrons are emitted in the fission process, and since a single neutron can cause the fission of a nucleus, it follows that a chain reaction can be started. With each fission of a compound nucleus about 2 neutrons are produced, and if we assume, for simplicity, that each initiates another fission, we have, thus, 1, 2, 4, 8, 16, 32, 64 .... In less than 90 generations the neutron yield would be sufficient to cause the fission of every nucleus in 50 kg (110 pounds) of uranium. This would result in the liberation of the same amount of energy as in the explosion of a million tons of TNT. If the process is allowed to go uncontrolled, the ninetieth generation will be attained in less than a millionth of a second and a nuclear explosion, i.e., an atomic bomb explosion, will result.

Fortunately this nuclear fission reaction can be controlled in a nuclear reactor for the production of heat and thus power; and for the production of radioactive isotopes through neutron bombardment.

NUCLEAR ISOMER. *See* ISOMER, NUCLEAR.

NUCLEAR MEDICINE

That field of medicine which seeks to obtain diagnostic or therapeutic advantage through the utilization of the properties of particles resulting from nuclear transformation and from atomic transpositions resulting from nuclear changes. It is thus concerned with the fundamental particles: the nucleus, the alpha particle, the neutron, the neutrino, the meson, the pion, and other high-energy particles, produced in synchrocyclotrons, linear accelerators and nuclear reactors. Beta and gamma emissions as manifestations of nuclear changes (radioactive isotopes) may be utilized. Nuclear medicine differs from radiology, which is concerned with electromagnetic and particle bombardment, and from tracer techniques (*see* TRACER STUDIES), which are applications or extensions of biochemistry and physiology.

NUCLEAR PHYSICS

The branch of physics that deals with the atomic nucleus. The development of the atomic bomb, the development of controlled fission in the nuclear reactor and the development of fusion all come within the field of nuclear physics. Scientists working in these areas are known as nuclear physicists.

NUCLEAR POWER. *See* ATOMIC POWER.

NUCLEAR-POWERED SHIPS. *See* POWER REACTORS.

NUCLEAR RADIATION

An inexact term used to indicate radiation consisting of alpha and beta particles and gamma rays. *See* RADIATION.

NUCLEAR REACTION

Broadly, any process in which the nucleus in an atom undergoes a change in its atomic number, mass number, radioactive behavior, or in more than one of these properties. This definition includes the changes in nuclei produced by interaction with elementary particles, other nuclei, and radiations; the disintegration of naturally occurring radioactive isotopes and of artificially produced radioactive isotopes. There are 2 types of nuclear reactions: activation and transmutation.

The first controlled nuclear reaction was reported in 1919 by the English physicist Rutherford. He directed a stream of alpha (α) particles through a chamber, containing gas at low pressure, then through a metal disc and onto a fluorescent screen. He noted that when dry air containing nitrogen as well as oxygen was used as the gas, the number of scintillations was increased. He concluded, and it was later proved, that charged hydrogen atoms had been formed as the result of the interaction of the α particles with the nitrogen. Knowing this much, and knowing that although there will be rearrangement there is no change in the total numbers of neutrons and protons, and also knowing that the 2 sides of the equation must balance, we may proceed as shown at the bottom of this page:

Thus the residual nucleus has a mass of 17 ($14 + 4 - 1$) and an atomic number of 8 ($7 + 2 - 1$). Since 8 is the atomic number of oxygen, the residual element must be oxygen-17. It can be conveniently represented by the equation

$$_7N^{14} + _2He^4 \longrightarrow _1H^1 + _8O^{17},$$

and again the mass numbers and the atomic numbers are properly balanced. The reaction can also be formulated as

$$N^{14}(\alpha,p)O^{17}$$

with the following interpretation: a nitrogen (N^{14}) nucleus interacts with, and engulfs, an alpha (α) particle, a proton (p) is ejected, and a nucleus of an oxygen (O^{17}) isotope remains. By 1924 it was established that nearly all the lighter elements up to and including potassium emitted protons when subjected to the action of alpha particles and are therefore of the (α,p) type.

The proton (hydrogen nucleus), symbol $_1H^1$, also produces a nuclear reaction in which the products are a new nucleus that is equivalent to the old nucleus, plus the charge and the essential mass of the proton, and also produces a gamma ray emitted in the process. An example is:

$$_{24}Cr^{50} + _1H^1 \longrightarrow _{25}Mn^{51} + \gamma,$$

in which a proton reacts with a chromium atom, resulting in the formation of manganese atom and the emission of a gamma ray. There are several other types of proton-initiated nuclear reactions: the (p,n) resulting in the production of a neutron, the (p,α) with the production of an alpha particle, the

	NITROGEN NUCLEUS	+	ALPHA PARTICLE	→	COMPOUND NUCLEUS	→PROTON	+	RECOIL NUCLEUS
Mass number	14		4		(18)	1		17
Atomic number	7		2		(9)	1		8

(p,d) reaction with the production of a deuteron, and the (p,p) with a lower energy proton resulting.

Deuteron-induced nuclear reactions of the (d,p) type are the most common.

$$_1H^2 + {}_{83}Bi^{209} \longrightarrow {}_{83}Bi^{210} + {}_1H^1$$

is an example in which the deuteron reacts with a heavy atom of bismuth to produce a bismuth atom 1 unit greater in mass number and a proton. In other reactions with deuterons, neutrons are emitted: (d,n), (d,2n) and (d,3n).

Nuclear reactions with alpha particles are of interest, for, as mentioned earlier, this was the first nuclear reaction to be observed, i.e., the (α,p) reaction. There are other reactions with an alpha particle in which protons or neutrons are emitted: (α,2n), (α,3n), (α,4n), (α,np) and (α,3np).

Highly energetic x-rays and gamma rays produced by particle accelerators have brought about nuclear reactions of the following types: (γ,n), (γ,p), (γ,np), (γ,2n), (γ,n2p), (γ,α) and others.

Neutrons of relatively low energy, called thermal neutrons, react with virtually all the elements to give a nuclear reaction of the (n,γ) type:

$$_{30}Zn^{64} + {}_0n^1 \rightarrow {}_{30}(\text{compound nucleus})^{65} \rightarrow {}_{30}Zn^{65} + \gamma,$$

in which the neutron is readily captured by the zinc atom to form a compound nucleus, which immediately decays to yield the gamma radiation. Fast neutrons cause more drastic reactions: (n,p), (n,α) and (n,2n) types.

FISSION and FUSION nuclear reactions are discussed separately.

See NUCLEAR REACTOR, CHAIN REACTION and NUCLEAR DEVICE.

NUCLEAR REACTOR

A nuclear reactor is a device in which the chain reaction of neutron-induced fission is sustained and controlled. Atomic bombs have been called reactors, but common usage usually restricts the term "reactor" to devices in which the chain-reaction intensity is maintained at a desired level, either through control or by use of inherently self-limiting reactions.

A fission chain reaction is possible when, as in the fission of uranium-233, uranium-235 or plutonium-239, several neutrons are liberated for each one absorbed in fission, each of which is then potentially capable of producing another fission event. Over 99 per cent of the neutrons are prompt neutrons, i.e., are liberated within a period of 10^{-14} second or less after the instant of fission. The remainder, or delayed neutrons, which are emitted over a period of several hours, are extremely important in determining the time-dependent characteristics of behavior of a reactor and thereby reducing the difficulty of its control.

Several other conditions in addition to the presence of fissionable material and the effective multiplication of neutrons must be met for actual maintenance of a chain reaction: The neutrons must have the proper energy for initiating fission; neutron losses through capture in non-fission reactions, and neutron leakage from the system must not be excessive. If the effective multiplication factor is just equal to 1, the chain reaction is self-sustaining, or critical; if less than 1, the system is subcritical; and if greater than 1, the chain is divergent and the system is supercritical. The leakage, a surface effect, depends primarily upon the surface area-volume ratio of the reactor. The size for which the neutron production by fission is just balanced by neutron leakage, and absorption is called the critical size. Use of a reflector, which scatters neutrons back into the reactor, decreases the critical size of the core containing the fissionable material.

Reactors may be classified according to (1) the purpose of the reactor, (2) the energy of the neutrons sustaining the reaction, and (3) the type and arrangement of the reactor components.

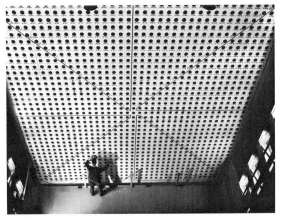

FIGURE N–3. SOUTH FACE OF THE BROOKHAVEN NATIONAL LABORATORY REACTOR. TONS OF PURE URANIUM METAL IN THE FORM OF ALUMINUM-CLAD FUEL ELEMENTS MUST BE LOADED THROUGH THE HOLES IN THIS SHIELDING WALL INTO THE GRAPHITE MODERATOR BEFORE URANIUM ATOMS CAN FISSION IN A CHAIN REACTION. NEUTRONS ARE PRODUCED AND USED EXPERIMENTALLY AND FOR THE PRODUCTION OF RADIOISOTOPES.

THE ROWS OF HOLES ARE 8 INCHES APART AND REPRESENT THE ARRANGEMENT OF THE URANIUM FUEL ELEMENTS IN THE GRAPHITE MODERATOR. THE HOLES CAN ALSO BE USED TO INSERT CERTAIN TYPES OF METALS AND OTHER SUBSTANCES TO BE IRRADIATED BY THE NEUTRONS. WHEN REMOVED, THEY MAY BE HIGHLY RADIOACTIVE—THOUSANDS OF CURIES.

THE TECHNICIAN IN THIS PHOTOGRAPH IS STANDING ON AN ELEVATOR WHICH ENABLES HIM TO MOVE TO ANY LEVEL OF CHARGING HOLES. HE IS USING A PERISCOPE TO VIEW THE HANDLING OF THESE HIGHLY RADIOACTIVE SOURCES BY REMOTE CONTROL. A WALL OF CONCRETE 5 FEET THICK PROTECTS HIM FROM RADIATION.

FIGURE N–4. THE MAIN EXPERIMENTAL FACE (WEST FACE) OF THE BROOKHAVEN NATIONAL LABORATORY REACTOR, SHOWING SOME OF THE MANY EXPERIMENTAL INSTALLATIONS THAT UTILIZE THE NEUTRONS PRODUCED BY THE CHAIN REACTION IN THE REACTOR. AT THIS FACE THERE ARE 30 EXPERIMENTAL HOLES THROUGH THE 5-FOOT-THICK HEAVY CONCRETE SHIELDING WALL.

Among the purposes for which reactors may be built are research (see MEDICAL RESEARCH REACTOR), production (of fissile materials) and power (see POWER REACTORS). The medical and biological uses of reactors usually involve research reactors. In all reactors the biological hazards of radiation impose strong influences on the design and operation.

The neutrons sustaining the chain reaction may be of fast, thermal or intermediate energies. Fast reactors permit a broader choice of component materials, since the parasitic losses due to neutron capture are lower for fast than for thermal neutrons. Thermal reactors have the advantages of being simpler to control, easier to cool, and less restricted as to size.

The third basis of classification of reactors is based upon the relative distribution of fuel and moderator. In a heterogeneous reactor, the fuel is concentrated in fuel elements and is distributed within the moderator in fairly definite geometrical patterns. In a homogeneous reactor, the fuel is dissolved, or at least reasonably evenly dispersed, throughout the moderator.

The first self-sustaining nuclear chain reaction was achieved with the first nuclear reactor, designated CP-1, on December 2, 1942, at the University of Chicago. The original reactor was later disassembled and then reassembled at the Argonne National Laboratory as CP-2. The original reactor consisted of some 40 tons of natural uranium, mostly as uranium oxides, distributed as lumps in 385 tons of graphite which served as the moderator and reflector. A typical reactor is shown in Figures N–3 and N–4.

NUCLEAR REACTOR OPERATIONS— RADIATION SOURCE

About 8 per cent of the 200 Mev of fission energy appears as penetrating ionizing radiation. Typically, about 5 Mev appears as instantaneous gamma-ray energy, 5 Mev as kinetic energy of fission neutrons and another 6 Mev as the gamma rays from radioactive decay of fission products. Although most of the 200 Mev is absorbed within the reactor (170 Mev appears as the kinetic energy of fission products and as beta particles and is absorbed; another 10 Mev escapes as the kinetic energy of neutrinos), it is obvious that a reactor is an intense source of ionizing radiation. Thermal neutron fluxes of over 10^{14} n/cm^2/sec are available within the core of some reactors. The Medical Research Reactor at Brookhaven delivers an external beam having a thermal neutron flux of 10^{11} n/cm^2/sec at the treatment port (120 cm from the core) when the reactor is operating at 5 megawatts. In most biological and medical applications the presence of fast neutrons and gamma rays is regarded as an undesirable hazard, but there have been occasional proposals to use a reactor as a source of gamma rays. The gamma-ray intensity is a complicated function of the size of the reactor, its power level and the distribution of fission reactions within the reactor. Gamma dose rates measured in hundreds of roentgens per second are generated within reactors operating at a few megawatts; several feet of concrete are required to provide an adequate biological shield against the intense radiation reaching the surface of a reactor core. The intensity both of neutrons and of gamma rays available in an external beam is diminished by the operating distance from the core surface, so that small reactors with low fission-product inventories and with thinner biological shields to be penetrated are more efficient in providing external beams of a given intensity than are larger reactors which require thicker shields.

NUCLEAR SAFETY

Term applied to study of specifications necessary to prevent the development of a critical condition in process operations, transportation or storage of fissionable material. One part of the problem is the scientific measurement of basic nuclear properties and their use in calculating critical parameters.

The engineering aspects of nuclear safety deal with critical mass and critical size, the location, and the physical configuration of the fissionable material. This involves selecting limiting geometry as the control factor; e.g., a 5-inch diameter cylinder is safe storage no matter what its length, and a 5-inch bottle is safe for transfer, provided both the cylinder and the bottles are handled and stored in a rack which separates them to a safe distance. Safe volumes, use of reflectors and the use of poisons are also factors used to ensure nuclear safety.

The third aspect is administrative and involves considering and setting up safety regulations to prevent any possible events which could lead to a dangerous configuration of fissionable material.

In spite of these precautions fatal CRITICALITY ACCIDENTS have occurred, although they are extremely unusual.

NUCLEAR WEAPONS

Explosive nuclear devices designed for military use, i.e., one with energy derived from the process of nuclear fission (*see* ATOMIC WEAPONS), or a combination of nuclear fission and nuclear fusion (*see* THERMONUCLEAR WEAPON).

The basic design principles and 2 mechanisms (gun-type weapon and implosion weapon) for producing the desired supercritical state are described under the heading CRITICAL MASS. Nuclear weapons have been designed as bombs to be dropped from planes, projectiles fired from a cannon, and as warheads for missiles. Polaris missiles (without the nuclear warhead) have been successfully fired from a submerged nuclear-powered submarine.

Nuclear weapons may be classed as clean weapons or "dirty" weapons, depending upon the amount of radioactivity released per unit of energy released.

NUCLEAR WEAPONS TESTING

Trial or test of new or untried nuclear weapons by detonation under experimental conditions, where recordings and measurements are made to obtain information on the phenomena and effects of nuclear explosions. As in any type of weapons arsenal, nuclear weapons must be tested to assure that new developments are, in fact, advances in the state of the science.

Weapons have been tested with yields varying from 0.1 kiloton energy to 15 or more megatons energy (as of 1962 the USSR has tested to 56–58 megatons); with different proportions of fission and fusion material (ATOMIC WEAPONS and THERMONUCLEAR WEAPONS); and of many different types of construction. Tests have been made of

nuclear weapons detonated on the earth's surface, underground, underwater, on towers, suspended from balloons, dropped from aircraft, shot from cannon, and as warheads on rockets and missiles (*see* AIR BURST, SURFACE BURST, UNDERGROUND BURST and UNDERWATER BURST).

The first nuclear weapon test was the Alamagordo, N.M., tower shot (19 kilotons) on 16 July, 1945. First United States testing in the Pacific was at the ENIWETOK PROVING GROUND in the spring of 1946; and the first tests at the NEVADA TEST SITE were the January–February series in 1951. Testing was conducted by the United States each year thereafter at both the latter areas, except for 1947, 1949 and 1950, until the moratorium, which was suggested by the United States in 1958, and which became officially effective on October 31, 1959, when the United States, the United Kingdom and the USSR met in Geneva, Switzerland, in a tripartite "Conference on the Discontinuance of Nuclear Weapons Tests." The United States suspended testing as of 31 October, 1958. The USSR broke the test moratorium September, 1961, with a large series of atmospheric shots, after which the United States started testing with completely contained underground shots. On 24 April, 1962, Operation DOMINIC got under way in the PACIFIC TESTING AREAS with a nuclear device dropped from an airplane in the vicinity of Christmas Island.

Before the moratorium the United States tests of low yield were conducted at the Nevada test site, while those of higher yield were conducted at the Eniwetok Proving Ground (formerly Pacific Proving Ground). With the breaking of the moratorium underground tests as well as tests of low yield were conducted at the Nevada test site; and the atmospheric shots of higher yield were conducted in the Pacific testing areas. With the United States signing of the limited nuclear test ban treaty, only underground testing is permitted.

In addition to information about yield and physical performance of the devices, a great deal of information of biomedical interest is obtained from nuclear weapons tests. Blast, thermal and radiation effects have been studied on many living forms, yielding information ranging from the median lethal dose for various species of animals to long-range genetic damage from radiation. Information has been obtained through these animal studies on the possible acute and chronic somatic effects, radiation-induced, and on possible genetic effects on human beings. Through the Civil Effects Test Operations the effectiveness of both blast shelters and fallout shelters has been determined. Buildings of various types have been studied to determine their ability to offer protection from radiation and blast; and data have been obtained on the effects on equipment.

The testing program has been carefully conducted so as to furnish the maximum of useful information for all interested groups. Preparations for a nuclear weapons test are time-consuming, detailed, technically complicated and expensive.

Erection of structures, placing of equipment, assembling of experimental apparatus and installation and checkout of instrumentation are all essential in obtaining information on yield, blast and shock, thermal radiation, initial nuclear radiation and residual ionizing radiation. Logistic support for the nuclear weapons testing program is provided by the JOINT TASK FORCE.

Safety Precautions for Weapons Testing. As a safety precaution, worldwide announcement is made of the establishment of the testing areas, and the "danger area" or exclusion area of each. No citizen or persons subject to the jurisdiction of the United States, its territories and possessions (other than test personnel) "shall enter, attempt to enter, conspire to enter or remain in any of the defined danger areas" (Paragraph 112.3, Title 10—Atomic Energy, Chapter 1—Atomic Energy Commission, Part 112—DOMINIC nuclear Test Series, 1962, of the Congressional Register).

As an additional safety precaution, before any nuclear detonation at the Nevada test site, aerial and ground surveys are made to ensure that no persons or domestic animals have entered the danger area. In a similar way planes and ships search the ocean for ships that may have strayed into the Pacific danger areas.

All commercial air lines are notified of the exclusion areas, and are additionally notified of the time of detonation of nuclear weapons. For continental shots the Federal Aeronautics Administration establishes an "air space closure" to assure that commercial or private aircraft do not fly into the predicted path of the radioactive cloud (see CLOUD, RADIOACTIVE). This warning system extends out to several hundred miles from the detonation point if predicted or actual radioactivity makes it necessary for aircraft to avoid certain sectors. Monitoring radiological safety aircraft follow the cloud until it disperses; they also track fallout on the ground, charting surface residual radioactivity.

As part of the Joint Task Force, there is an advisory panel of experts on meteorology, fallout, blast and biological and medical effects. This panel studies weather conditions and advises postponement if conditions are adverse. Weather conditions are of great importance, since they directly affect the fallout pattern, severity of the blast wave reaching outlying areas, and flying conditions having a bearing on tracking flights. Weather stations are maintained in connection with the test sites. At the Pacific testing areas similar precautions are taken, with weather and fallout prediction units as a functioning part of the test organization.

Despite these elaborate precautions an unfortunate exposure to fallout occurred in the Pacific after the Bravo shot (experimental thermonuclear weapon) of Operation Castle in 1954, when JAPANESE FISHERMEN and natives of the MARSHALL ISLANDS, particularly those of Rongelap Atoll, were exposed to fallout.

NUCLEIC ACID STUDIES

The nucleic acids are comprised of long chains of repeating units called nucleotides. A nucleotide consists of a sugar phosphate joined to a nitrogenous base. There are two kinds of nucleic acid, and these are distinguished by the sugar component of their respective nucleotides. Nucleic acids which contain D-ribose are known as ribonucleic acid (RNA), while those which contain deoxy-D-ribose are known as deoxyribonucleic acid (DNA). The nucleic acids are of biological interest because they are now known to be the carriers and mediators of genetic information. For this reason considerable scientific effort is now being applied to studies of these compounds. Radioisotopes have played a most important role in this work with techniques based on the use of phosphorus-32 to label the sugar phosphate, and carbon-14 or tritium to label the carbon chain of the nitrogen bases. Especially valuable has been the use of tritiated precursors, such as tritiated thymidine, tritiated cytidine and tritiated uridine, to permit incorporation of the label into the nucleic acid of an organism growing on the labeled substrate. Autoradiograms have been used to show the appearance of a labeled nucleic acid within the cell and even within the chromosome. As an example, the following conclusions were drawn from a recent study:

(a) The nucleus is the sole site of RNA synthesis in the cell, and RNA is transferred continuously from the nucleus to cytoplasm.

(b) DNA cannot simultaneously support its own replication and reproduction of RNA, and therefore during DNA synthesis dissemination of genetic information through RNA carriers is suspended.

(c) DNA condensed into a mitotic chromosome is unable to support RNA synthesis.

It appears that this type of investigation, whereby labeled molecules of DNA can be followed through various cell divisions, will lead to a clear understanding of a most basic problem of life;

namely, how the basic hereditary information is transmitted.

NUCLEOGENESIS

Large-scale formation of nuclei in nature. Probably occurred when the primordial substance, ylem, was forming the chemical elements from which the world developed.

NUCLEON

Constituent particle of the atomic nucleus. The total number of nucleons in a nucleus is equal to the mass number A of the particular isotope of the element. A nucleon thus has a mass number of 1; at present 2 particles of nuclear size and of mass nearly unity are known, the proton with a mass of 1.007595 atomic mass units (amu) and the neutron with a mass of 1.008987 amu. Thus according to present theory, nucleons may be either protons or neutrons. For example, carbon-12 has an atomic weight ($A = 12$) and an atomic number ($Z = 6$) and is made up of 6 protons and 6 neutrons, or 12 nucleons.

NUCLEONICS

Word used in nuclear technology to indicate the application of nuclear science and the associated techniques in armaments, astronomy, biology, chemistry, geology, industry and physics.

NUCLEUS

In biology, a definitely delineated complex spheroidal mass containing the chromosomes, and essential to the life of the cell.

In nuclear technology, that part of an atom in which the total positive electric charge resides, and which contains almost the entire mass of the atom, but only a minute fraction of the volume. *See* ATOMIC NUCLEUS.

NUCLIDE

Any atomic configuration capable of more than a transient existence, i.e., for a measureable lifetime, usually considered to be greater than 10^{-9} seconds. Thus promptly decaying states and unstable intermediates in nuclear reactions are not considered to be nuclides, while nuclear isomers are. The term "nuclide" was proposed by United States scientist Kohman as a more precise term than isotope for species of atom characterized by the constitution of its nucleus, i.e., by the numbers of neutrons and protons that it contains. Thus the species whose masses are given in the table of STABLE ISOTOPES may be called naturally occurring stable nuclides. In a similar way every radioelement listed in the table of RADIOACTIVE ISOTOPES is a radioactive nuclide or radionuclide.

Accordingly, an isotope would be one of a group of 2 or more nuclides having the same atomic number, i.e., the same number of protons. For an element such as fluorine, of which only one species exists in nature, it is more meaningful to say that it forms a single stable nuclide, rather than a single stable isotope.

NUTRITION IN TREATMENT OF RADIATION ILLNESS. *See* TREATMENT OF RADIATION ILLNESS.

O

OAK RIDGE INSTITUTE OF NUCLEAR STUDIES (ORINS)

ORINS, a nonprofit educational corporation located at Oak Ridge, Tennessee, was formed in October, 1946, by 14 southeastern universities. Its purpose is to advise and assist in education and research, and in developing programs relating to nuclear sciences; to assist in developing improved methods of education and training in nuclear science in universities and colleges of the Southeast; and to encourage advancement of knowledge about nuclear science.

Representatives from each of the universities (now 39) comprise the Institute Council, which elects a Board of Directors which acts as the governing body of the Institute, approving new programs, establishing broad policy and giving general direction to Institute activities. The Council appoints an Executive Director as chief resident official of the Institute.

Under contract with the USAEC a number of programs are conducted by its 4 divisions: Medical Division; Information and Exhibits Division; Special Training Division; and University Relations Division.

The Medical Division of ORINS was established in 1949. Its program is chiefly one of clinical research, with emphasis upon the use of radioisotopes and application of other special facilities available in Oak Ridge to problems of human disease, especially cancer. The activities are supported by the Division of Biology and Medicine of the AEC and administered through ORINS.

The Medical Division includes a 34-bed research hospital with extensive adjoining laboratories and, at a nearby separate site, an additional set of laboratories for work in experimental animals. The staff includes 14 senior scientists and a larger number of supporting personnel for a total of 80 employees. The patients admitted to the hospital are selected for their suitability for the clinical research activities.

An early area of research was in the development of cobalt-60 and cesium-137 teletherapy devices, and many of the standard design features of teletherapy machines were worked out in this Oak Ridge program. Another early area of endeavor was in the use of gallium-72 in the treatment of bone tumors. This radioisotope proved ineffectual in extensive clinical trials.

More recently the principal subject of study has been the effects of total-body irradiation and the potential clinical usefulness of marrow grafts. As a part of this effort, studies in patients with acute leukemia showed that total-body irradiation alone could sometimes induce remissions in acute leukemia and that when such remissions occurred after bone marrow therapy had been given, they were not necessarily evidence that a successful graft had been achieved. Biochemical studies are being done on the effects of irradiation on protein and fat metabolism. An immunologic program is directed toward problems of tissue compatibility and effects of irradiation on antibody responses.

The staff has investigated a group of rare-earth elements of importance in connection with fallout and industrial uses of atomic energy. An unusual type of temporary liver disorder (fatty liver) was produced in experimental animals when certain of these elements were injected in stable form.

Other research areas have emphasized clinical scanning, treatment of cancer of the thyroid, clinical uses of radioactive colloids, and study of effects of local irradiation on bone marrow.

Information and Exhibits Division. The activities of the Information and Exhibits Division of ORINS constitute a main national instrument in public information in the atomic energy field. These activities are presented to the general public through a nationwide exhibits program which is developed and operated by the Division under USAEC sponsorship. The technical library in the Division makes its facilities available to institutions and the general public interested in unclassified AEC reports and other nuclear science references.

The exhibits program headquarters is the American Museum of Atomic Energy at Oak Ridge, which houses the local museum and the facilities for design, fabrication and operation of a large traveling exhibits program. Since its opening in 1949, more than a million people have visited the Museum in Oak Ridge.

Several types of traveling exhibits have been developed and operated at fairs, expositions, special events and educational institutions. Exhibits are provided to qualified sponsors at no charge. These include various-sized, temporary, installation-type exhibits which are transported, set up and manned by trained ORINS personnel.

Other manned exhibits, the high school demonstration units, are used at secondary schools to present at assembly programs and classroom sessions. There are also package exhibits with panels and models that operate without accompanying personnel. Since initiation of the traveling exhibits program in 1949, they have been visited by more than 50 million people throughout the United States.

Special Training Division. A great many training courses and special training devices have been developed by this division since its organization in 1948. Perhaps the 2 best-known are the Radioisotopes Training School and the Mobile Radioisotope Laboratory.

Radioisotopes Training School. In general, the instruction covers the principles and use of radiation instruments and the safe handling and use of radioisotopes, and is for physicians, engineers and research scientists who wish to use radioisotopes in their activities. For details, *see* TRAINING, RADIOISOTOPES. Foreign students are accepted in all courses. Several thousand students from all over the United States and from 37 foreign nations have completed the course.

Mobile Radioisotope Laboratory. This ORINS training laboratory is designed to provide faculty members and advanced science majors at undergraduate institutions the opportunity for specialized training in techniques and applications of radioisotopes. (*See* TRAINING, RADIOISOTOPES.)

University Relations Division. This division handles most of the fellowship programs for the USAEC (*see* EDUCATION AND TRAINING, USAEC), and the university faculty and student participation in research activity at the Oak Ridge National Laboratory and in the ORINS Medical Division. Programs are conducted for the National Science Foundation, the Armed Forces and other federal agencies.

OAK RIDGE NATIONAL LABORATORY (ORNL)

ORNL, located in Oak Ridge, Tennessee, is operated by the Union Carbide Nuclear Co. for the USAEC. ORNL is the largest of the USAEC's nuclear research centers. The laboratory is an outgrowth of the wartime Clinton Engineer Works (a branch of the Manhattan Project's Metallurgical Laboratory) and has had a role in virtually every principal scientific operation and activity of the atomic energy program. Its research projects range from basic studies in physics, chemistry, metallurgy and biology to reactor technology, isotope production, health protection, and education. The 2 principal production facilities are the K-25 Gaseous Diffusion Plant, designed for large-scale separation of the isotope uranium-235, and the

Y-12 Plant for the production of stable isotopes and research on process improvements.

The 3 principal activities of biomedical interest are the Biology Division, the Health Physics Division, and the radioisotope production facility. The Biology Division was established in 1946 to explore the hazards associated with plutonium and uranium and with radiation. It has continued to concentrate on fundamental biochemical, biophysical, physiological and pathological changes produced by radiation. The Biology Division is perhaps best known for its mammalian genetics study with its enormous mouse colony, for the early excellent work on chemical protection against radiation injury, and for comprehensive fundamental work on the possibility of using bone marrow grafts in the treatment of radiation illness. The following brief listing of various sections and groups gives a more complete idea of the extensive coverage of the entire field of radiation biology: cytology and genetics section with cell growth and reproduction, and Drosophila groups; mammalian genetics with genetic effects of radiation in mice, effects of radiation on mammalian gametogenesis, and mammalian cytogenetics; mammalian recovery with hematopoietic recovery, bone marrow physiology and mammalian cytology and genetics in vitro; radiation immunology; radiation microbiology with mutagen mechanisms, and bacterial genetics; pathology and physiology with pathological effects of radiation, physiological and chemical effects, experimental embryology, virology, histology and autoradiography; cell physiology; nucleic acid chemistry; nucleic acid enzymology; chemical protection and enzyme catalysis; enzymology; microbiology; plant physiology and photosynthesis; biophysics; and biometrics.

The Biology Division personnel numbers approximately 200 persons, 75 of whom are at the Ph.D. or M.D. level. The buildings which house the Division provide ample laboratory space with room for expansion; there are machine, carpentry and glass-blowing shops, a facility for electronic instrument construction and repair, and ample radiation sources and facilities. There is a well equipped library. Productivity is indicated by over 200 scientific papers appearing annually, by the internationally known symposium held each spring, by the staff activity in national and international conferences, and particularly by the extensive activity in the educational problems of the colleges and universities of the Southeast.

The Health Physics Division of ORNL is well known for its radioactive waste disposal research, for its pioneering work in radiation dosimetry and for its activity in health physics education. The radioactive waste disposal section includes the following projects: studies of disposal in salt, studies of disposal in deep wells, studies of sorption and retention by minerals, White Oak Creek basin study, Clinch River study, long-range evaluation studies, and geologic and hydrologic explorations. The activity of the radiation physics and dosimetry section is indicated by the following groups: theoretical physics, experimental physics, dosimetry methods, dosimetry applications, and physics of tissue damage. In addition, there is an active section in ecology, and others in internal dose estimation, health physics technology, education and training, and applied health physics. The educational activity includes practical training for the Health Physics Fellowship Program, special courses in health physics, and training assistance for the colleges and universities of the Southeast in the form of lectures and seminars and in research opportunities in the Health Physics Division laboratories.

ORNL is the center for the production and distribution for both stable and radioactive isotopes in the United States. When the program started, 3 major radioisotopes were available in purified form; now well over 100 are in routine production. In a similar way the number of stable isotopes available has increased from 10 to almost 200.

OCCUPATIONAL MEDICINE

The prevention and treatment of injury or disease related to or resulting from a particular occupation, i.e., occupational diseases.

See INDUSTRIAL MEDICINE.

OCEAN DISPOSAL, RADIOACTIVE WASTE

Disposal of RADIOACTIVE WASTE in the ocean is attractive because of the great volume and expanse of the oceans and the ease with which disposal can be accomplished. There are many unknowns and uncertainties, however, and the international implications are so important that this method of disposal seems less favorable than permanent land disposal.

Nevertheless direct and indirect discharge of low-level liquid waste into the oceans is practiced by a few nations at present, and careful monitoring indicates no undue contamination of the water or fish, i.e., no increase of radioactivity over the maximum permissible concentration allowed. Such a concentration might occur, however.

Research is in progress on a number of aspects of disposal of low-level liquid waste into coastal waters and tidal estuaries. The fate of radioactive material introduced into the marine environment depends upon the following considerations: (1) the physical or chemical form in which the material occurs, (2) initial mechanical dilution of the waste by the receiving water, (3) advection of the wastes away from the source region by currents and simul-

taneous turbulent diffusion, (4) uptake of the activity by suspended silt and bottom sediments which removes some of the material from the water and restricts further dispersion, (5) concentration of activity by various parts of the biota, including shellfish and finfish important to man as a source of food. Some important fission products may be concentrated by certain marine organisms by factors of 100 to 1,000,000.

Further information about some of these factors may clear the way for more active use of the oceans for waste disposal, at least of low-level liquid waste, and of solid or packaged waste.

Disposal of solid waste and sealed containers of liquid waste into the ocean is a method of burial commonly used. Eight governmental organizations are licensed by the USAEC to dispose of waste generated in their own laboratories; and 9 commercial firms are licensed to dispose of at sea, in at least 1,000 fathoms, solid or packaged low-level radioactive waste. In addition to the ocean depth requirement, the waste material must be packaged with shielding and in such a manner that it will not be easily damaged or broken; the containers must be of sufficient density (10 pounds per gallon) to carry the material to the ocean bottom; the package must be appropriately labeled; and the containers must conform to shipping regulations. By 1960, licensed users had disposed of about 2,600 curies (c) of radioactive material into the Atlantic Ocean, approximately 14,050 c into the Pacific Ocean and about 10 c into the Gulf of Mexico. A recent survey (1960) of the Pacific disposal sites revealed no detectable radioactivity attributable to waste disposal operations.

Waste disposal of the coolant water from nuclear-powered submarines is directly to the sea. (*See* WASTE DISPOSAL, NUCLEAR-POWERED SHIP.)

Disposal of high-level radioactive material to the open sea will probably never be common practice.

OCEANOGRAPHIC STUDIES

Radioisotope tracer techniques are used to measure the mixing phenomena in the ocean and in the atmosphere and between the atmosphere and the ocean. As the atmosphere is divided by the tropopause into an upper stratosphere and the lower troposphere, so the ocean is divided at about 100 meters into an upper layer and lower layer. The problem of mixing is particularly important in relation to ocean disposal of radioactive waste, and fallout from testing nuclear weapons. Three radioisotopes, rubidium-86, iodine-131 and barium-140, have been found most suitable for studies of the mixing rates in the ocean.

Most of the carbon-14 formed in the atmosphere finds its way into the ocean. Tritium, also made in the upper atmosphere, finds its way into natural waters and finally into the sea. Much of the present understanding of natural transfer phenomena has been obtained by studying these naturally occurring radioisotopes in their steady state biogeochemical cycles.

Physical processes in the oceans have been studied by following large masses of water contaminated with radioactive fission products from the test detonation of a nuclear device. Ships can follow movements of water masses, and it is even possible to spot and follow them by airplane with the use of reliable radiation detection instruments.

OCULAR TUMORS, DIAGNOSIS

Sometimes it is exceedingly difficult to distinguish between benign and malignant lesions of

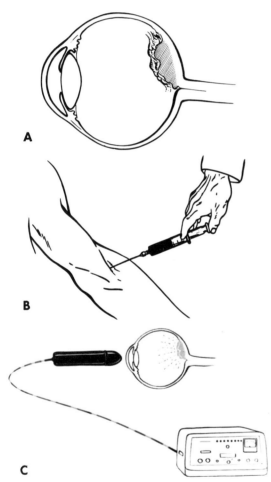

FIGURE O–1. DIAGNOSIS OF OCULAR TUMOR (MALIGNANT MELANOMA) BY USE OF RADIOPHOSPHORUS. A, A 61-YEAR-OLD MAN HAD REDUCTION OF VISION IN HIS RIGHT EYE FOR 2 WEEKS. A PHYSICIAN SUGGESTED A STUDY WITH RADIOACTIVE PHOSPHORUS (P^{32}). B, P^{32} IS INJECTED INTO A VEIN OF THE LEFT ARM. C, THE TUMOR TAKES UP P^{32}, AND THE DETECTOR SHOWS ITS PRESENCE IN THE TUMOR.

the eye, particularly of its deeper parts, and it may be impossible to take a tissue specimen for microscopic study without sacrificing the eye. Diagnostic methods using radiophosphorus have been found useful. A test dose sometimes as large as 0.5 to 1.0 millicurie may be required (this is a rather high dose for a diagnostic test, but is considered justifiable in the presence of suspected serious disease). After the dose has been given, a special detector is inserted at the edge of the eye in order to measure the radiations coming from the tumor. A high counting rate is evidence of malignancy; the counting rate is evaluated by comparing the region of the tumor with the other, normal eye or an uninvolved area of the same eye. Figure O–1 presents the sequence of events.

OFFICE OF CIVIL AND DEFENSE MOBILIZATION

OCDM has been reconstituted as a small staff agency, called the Office of Emergency Planning, to assist the President in coordinating the functions now assigned to various other Government agencies (for further details see CIVIL DEFENSE).

OFFICE OF TECHNICAL SERVICES

The OTS is a unit of the U.S. Department of Commerce which acts as the sales agency for many of the reports produced by the USAEC and its contractors. In addition to handling the printing and distribution, the OTS regularly publishes lists of available documents (Washington 25, D.C.).

ORBITAL-ELECTRON CAPTURE. See ELECTRON CAPTURE.

ORGANIZATION FOR EUROPEAN ECONOMIC COOPERATION (OEEC)

OEEC, an organization of 18 Western European nations with Canada and the United States as associates, was formed in 1948 to promote economic growth through cooperative action. The European Nuclear Energy Agency is the unit of the OEEC which implements the atomic energy program.

ORGANIZATION OF AMERICAN STATES (OAS)

OAS, an organization for the collective security of the American states, was formed under the Rio Treaty and signed by 20 North, Central and South American countries. OAS activity in the atomic energy field is handled by the Inter-American Nuclear Energy Commission.

See INTER-AMERICAN INSTITUTE OF AGRICULTURAL SCIENCES.

ORGANS, RADIATION EFFECTS ON

Cell damage due to radiation exposure may lead to demonstrable radiation effects on the organs of the body. Organs containing rapidly proliferating cells and with a high mitotic index (rapid cell division) have greater radiosensitivity than those with little proliferative activity. Therefore such organs as bone marrow, gonads (ovaries, testicles) or gastrointestinal tract are more easily damaged than the brain or the kidney. A variable latent period may be interposed between exposure of organs and their alteration or death. A more detailed presentation of the radiation effects for individual organs will be found under each organ, as ADRENAL GLANDS, RADIATION EFFECTS ON; BLOOD CELLS, RADIATION EFFECTS ON, etc.

ORINS

Acronym for OAK RIDGE INSTITUTE OF NUCLEAR STUDIES.

OSCILLOSCOPE

Device for displaying the shape or wave form of transient or recurrent electrical signals through controlling the play of an electron beam on the fluorescent screen face of a cathode ray tube. Widely useful in studying performance of electronic circuits and in analyzing behavior from related experimental situations; often used as the output or display device in analogue computers.

OSMIUM

Symbol Os; atomic number 76; atomic weight 190.2. The densest known form of matter; a metal occurring naturally in iridosmine- and platinum-bearing sands. Discovered in 1804 by English chemist Tennant. Named for the Greek *osme*, odor. Six stable isotopes furnish the natural abundance.

Industrial uses: as a catalytic agent, as an alloy for tipping fountain-pen nibs, and for electrical contacts.

Metallic osmium is nontoxic. Osmium tetroxide is toxic, causing dermatitis and ulceration on contact with the skin, asthmatic condition on inhalation, and central nervous system irritation with headaches and ocular disturbance.

There are 9 radioactive isotopes, with OS^{191} (half-life 16.0 days, β^- and γ emitter) available commercially. No biological, medical or agricultural uses.

OSMOSIS STUDIES

Osmosis is the spontaneous flow of fluid through a semipermeable membrane. The direction of flow is determined by the composition of fluids separated by the membrane; the fluid tends to move to the side of higher concentration, leading to an equalization of ionic concentrations. Such membrane phenomena are advantageously studied with radioisotopic tracers.

See MEMBRANE PERMEABILITY STUDIES.

OVARIES, RADIATION EFFECTS ON.   *See* GONADS, RADIATION EFFECTS ON.

OXYGEN

Symbol O; atomic number 8; atomic weight 16.0000, used as the standard of comparison for the atomic weight of each of the other elements. A colorless, odorless, tasteless, nontoxic gas. Discovered by Priestley in 1774, and independently by Scheele the same year. Named from Greek *oxys*, acid, and *genes*, forming, acid-forming. Found free in the atmosphere, 23.15% by weight in dry air and 20.98% by volume. The most abundant element in the ocean (85.8% oxygen). Occurs combined with silicon, aluminum, iron and other metals in all rocks; in fact, the solid crust of the earth averages 46.7% oxygen. A constituent of practically all plant and animal substances, except hydrocarbons. The biochemical standard man contains 65% oxygen, or 45,500 g per 70 kg of body weight. Natural abundance furnished by 3 stable isotopes.

Oxygen is essential in the process of respiration of all animals. The burning of fuels is a process of combination with free oxygen. Capable of reacting chemically with all other elements except the inert gases and fluorine. Used as a propellant for rockets.

Three radioactive isotopes have been identified. O^{19} with a radioactive half-life of 29.4 seconds is one of the possible radionuclides produced in air, soil and water as the result of neutron bombardment associated with the detonation of a nuclear device. Not considered a significant hazard. O^{14}, half-life 76.5 seconds, and O^{15}, half-life 118.0 seconds, have been used in physical oceanography research and in medical research. For example, the absorption of water vapor was studied by inhaling 2% water vapor labeled with O^{15}.

OXYGEN, RADIATION SENSITIVITY

High oxygen tension in the cells and tissues increases the sensitivity to radiation, and low oxygen tension decreases RADIOSENSITIVITY in all living organisms studied. In general, increasing the oxygen tension above normal (atmospheric air) causes a slight increase in the degree of radiation effect; but decreasing the oxygen tension below normal causes a decrease in the degree of biological effect (lowered radiosensitivity).

It has been conclusively demonstrated that the oxygen tension (up to 21%) in the cell at the time of radiation exposure is a determining factor in governing the degree of indirect action of x-rays, less a factor with neutrons, and of little importance with alpha particles. There is, thus, a correlation (inverse relation) between the density of ion pair production and the magnitude of the oxygen effect. In mammals the living material experimentally shown to be most sensitive to oxygen effect is isolated lymph gland of the rat cultivated in vitro. The radiation dose needed to produce degeneration of the small lymphocytes in pure oxygen was found to be 275 roentgens (r) in vitro (150 r in vivo); but to produce the same effect in an atmosphere of pure nitrogen a dose 12 times as great (3,300 r) was required. The lymphocyte radiosensitivity shows a linear increase with oxygen pressure over the entire range of 0 to 760 mm of oxygen tension. Much more difficulty is encountered in interpreting the oxygen effect on the intact mammal, for the partial pressure of oxygen in the tissues and cells is difficult to determine accurately; in addition, deprivation of oxygen sets in action an entire complex of reflex actions which alter the internal body environment.

Anoxia (or hypoxia) is one of the most effective ways of reducing the degree of radiation damage in lower organisms or mammals. It is effective for a wide variety of criteria, including severity of skin lesions, regression of tumors (cancer), genetic effects, and even death. The protective effect of anoxia against radiation injury shows a typical maximum dose reduction of 3, with maximum sensitivity reached when the oxygen tension is the same as in air; with oxygen enrichment not increasing the sensitivity, but any decrease (anoxia)

leading to a decrease in radiosensitivity. The effect of anoxia in decreasing radiation mortality was clearly demonstrated by the experimental finding of 100% survival at 30 days in rats irradiated in 5% oxygen versus 100% mortality for the irradiated controls. The LD_{50}/30 days for this experiment was 1,200 to 1,400 roentgens (r). With mice in 7% oxygen, 80% survived 800-r exposure, while all controls irradiated in normal air died.

A large fraction of the biological damage resulting from irradiation is attributable to oxidizing agents produced by energy absorption in water. Thus the degree of protection is clearly dependent on the amount of dissolved oxygen in the body fluids, for the number of damaging chemical intermediates normally produced along the track of ionizing particles is greatly reduced with reduction of the oxygen tension. The anoxia theory is one of 3 developed to explain the protective action of cysteamine and —SH protectors, but experimental evidence indicates that anoxia is but one contributing factor when the whole mammalian organism is under the influence of these substances. The following weak protectors are believed to act by reducing the oxygen transportation to the tissues of mammals through their action on hemoglobin: nitrate, p-aminopropiophenone and carbon monoxide.

The oxygen radiosensitivity effect is utilized in radiotherapy of cancer, by using various methods to increase the oxygen tension of tumor cells in relation to normal tissue cells (many tumor cells are anoxic), during the time of irradiation.

P

PACIFIC TESTING AREAS

Exclusion or danger areas in the Pacific Ocean set aside by Joint Task Force 8 for testing nuclear weapons. These areas were established in connection with the DOMINIC series of nuclear weapons testing to be conducted in 1962. On April 4, 1962, the Christmas Island testing area was established effective April 15; and on April 9, 1962, two additional danger areas were established effective April 30, as follows:

(1) An area bounded by a line joining the following coordinates:

06° 50′N, 147° 20′W
02° 50′N, 147° 20′W
02° 50′N, 149° 20′W
06° 50′N, 149° 20′W

(2) An area, encompassing Johnston Island, which is a circle of 470 nautical miles radius at the surface gradually extending to a circle of 700 nautical miles radius at an altitude of 30,000 feet and above, centered at the following geographic coordinates:

16° 45′N, and 169° 31′W*

The purpose of establishing and public announcement of testing exclusion areas is to prevent entrance of ships and planes thus permitting the USAEC to conduct testing "efficiently and expeditiously as possible with a minimum hazard to the health and safety of the public."

The United Kingdom also has used the Christmas Island area.

See ENIWETOK PROVING GROUND.

PAIR PRODUCTION

An absorption process in which the incident photon of high-energy x or gamma radiation is annihilated in the vicinity of the strong electrical field of the nucleus of the absorbing atom, with the production of a pair of electrons, one positive (e+, POSITRON) and the other negative (e−, NEGATRON, usually called electron). The electric charge is

---

*Extended June 12, 1962, to 530 nautical miles at the surface and to 1050 nautical miles at 40,000 feet elevation.

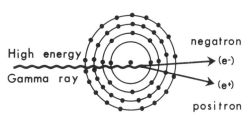

FIGURE P–1. PAIR PRODUCTION. ANNIHILATION OF THE INCIDENT PHOTON AND THE CREATION OF A PAIR OF ELECTRONS.

conserved in that it is transferred entirely to the positron and negatron which have exactly the same masses and magnitude of electrical charges, but of opposite sign. Pair production accounts for most of the photon absorption of high-energy gamma rays, especially in elements of high atomic number. A minimum energy of 1.02 Mev is required, and the probability for pair production increases almost linearly as the energy increases. This rather remarkable phenomenon of the complete disappearance of the incident photon and the creation of a pair of electrons is illustrated in Figure P–1.

PALLADIUM

Symbol Pd; atomic number 46; atomic weight 106.4. A steel-white metal of the platinum family. Discovered by English scientist W. H. Wollaston in 1803. Named for the planetoid, Pallas. Occurs native in platinum ores (2%) and in nickel ores. Natural abundance furnished by 6 stable isotopes.

Used in alloys for electrical contacts, in jewelry and dental fillings. Very low toxicity.

Twenty-two radioactive isotopes have been identified. Fourteen of these may be formed as fission products in a nuclear reactor or associated with the detonation of a nuclear device. None are significant in radioactive fallout. Palladium-109, half-life 13.6 hours, beta emitter, is available commercially.

PANCREAS, RADIATION EFFECTS ON

This organ rarely shows any anatomic effects of radiation other than an occasional small hemorrhage. It is considered relatively radioresistant.

PAPER CHROMATOGRAPHY

The separation of a mixture of components in a solution by permitting the mixture to diffuse

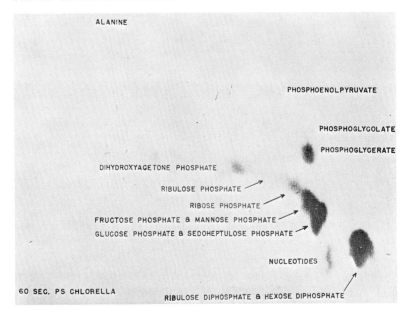

ALANINE

PHOSPHOENOLPYRUVATE

PHOSPHOGLYCOLATE

PHOSPHOGLYCERATE

DIHYDROXYACETONE PHOSPHATE

RIBULOSE PHOSPHATE

RIBOSE PHOSPHATE

FRUCTOSE PHOSPHATE & MANNOSE PHOSPHATE

GLUCOSE PHOSPHATE & SEDOHEPTULOSE PHOSPHATE

NUCLEOTIDES

60 SEC. PS CHLORELLA

RIBULOSE DIPHOSPHATE & HEXOSE DIPHOSPHATE

FIGURE P–2. AUTORADIOGRAM OF TWO-DIMENSIONAL CHROMAT-OGRAM SHOWING INCORPORATION OF RADIOACTIVITY IN VARIOUS SUBSTANCES BY CHLORELLA DURING 60 SECONDS OF PHOTOSYNTHESIS WHILE EXPOSED TO C^{14}. (UNIVERSITY OF CALIFORNIA RADIATION LABORATORY.)

through the matrix of various forms of paper such as strips, discs, sheets, and fibers. Briefly, the procedure is as follows: a drop of the solution to be tested is applied near one end of a strip of paper and allowed to dry. Then this end is placed in an appropriate solvent, so that the latter moves past the spot and along the paper by capillary action, which results in differential movement of the components of the test solution along the paper. After separation is complete, individual spots on the paper may be identified by color reaction, radioactivity, or other methods.

Paper chromatography is useful in: separation of mixtures into their constituents; demonstration of homogeneity of chemical substances; demonstration of identity of substances; and qualitative (and quantitative) estimation of one or more substances present in the mixture. With the use of radioisotopes the usefulness of this technique is vastly extended. If radioactive labeled compounds are being studied the spots can be detected by counting procedures, or by autoradiograms.

A classic illustration of the use of chromatography combined with autoradiography is shown in the accompanying autoradiogram (Fig. P–2). In photosynthesis studies Chlorella were exposed to carbon-14 carbon dioxide for a 60-second period of photosynthesis and then killed and extracted with alcohol. The extract was concentrated and a drop was placed on the corner of a square sheet of filter paper and dried. A two-dimensional chromatogram was prepared and then exposed on x-ray film with the results shown.

There are 3 principal methods of utilizing radioactivity in studies with paper chromatography: labeling the original material by growing plants with radioactive material (carbon-14, sulfur-35), or by injecting animals with radioactive material (iodine-131); labeling the chromatogram by applying labeled reagents; or neutron activation through irradiation in a nuclear reactor. Labeling the original mixture is used most extensively.

See CHROMATOGRAPHY and ELECTROPHORESIS.

PARASITE STUDIES

It has been estimated that various internal parasites cause losses of about 40 million dollars annually to the animal industry; the more important parasites include coccidia in poultry, roundworms, flukes and tapeworms. Parasites can be labeled to study their physiology, nutrition and life cycle; also the various compounds that may be developed to treat parasites can be labeled to study their distribution in the parasite and in the host. Within recent years studies have been done in which parasites have been irradiated to an extent that they cannot follow through their life cycle, and then administered to animals in order to produce an immunological response that would thereafter protect the animal against the particular parasite. This approach may have important practical application after sufficient research has been done to develop procedural details.

PARENT

A radionuclide that upon radioactive decay or disintegration yields a specified nuclide, the DAUGHTER, either directly or as the radioactive precursor of a radioactive series. For example zinc-69m is the parent of zinc-69; zinc-72 is the parent of gallium-72 which in turn is the parent of germanium-72. In the same way thorium-232 is the parent or precursor for the entire thorium radioactive series.

PARTIAL BODY IRRADIATION

Irradiation of part of the body in contrast to WHOLE BODY IRRADIATION. Partial body irradiation is the basis of x-ray therapy. One of the earliest experimental attempts at partial body irradiation was reported in 1920 when it was shown that shielding the lower legs of a guinea pig prevented the hemorrhagic aspects of radiation illness. Numerous studies in radioprotection by exposing only part of the body have demonstrated that protection of certain organs effectively protects against development of leukemia, lymphoid tumors, and radiation illness (particularly hematopoietic damage), and partially protects against life shortening. The spleen appears to be a most important organ to shield, as shown when mice were exposed to 1,025 roentgens of x-ray. 77.7% of 135 mice survived and had complete regeneration of the hematopoietic tissue when the exteriorized spleen was protected by a lead shield, while all 143 unprotected irradiated controls died. Protection of bone marrow particularly in the long bones is also effective.

Partial body exposure is also considered in the maximum permissible dose (MPD) regulations where the "whole body occupational exposure accumulated at any age was limited to: MPD = (N — 18) × 5 rem (per year), where N is age in years and is greater than 18; whereas for partial body exposure of the hands and forearms, feet and ankles the MPD = 75 rem per year and the dose in any 13 consecutive weeks shall not exceed 25 rem."

The NAS–NRC report* says, "The lethal dose for partial body irradiation exceeds, in general, that for the whole body. A small volume of tissue may receive many thousand roentgens without death resulting. This permits doses much greater than the lethal level for total body radiation to be employed in radiation therapy."

PARTICLES, RADIOACTIVE

The primary radioactive particles are the alpha particle, the beta particle, the neutron, and the proton. Fission fragments (see FISSION PRODUCTS) also contain many radioactive particles. Secondary particles, from cosmic rays, consist of mesons, protons, electrons, and neutrons. A new particle, $f°$, was discovered in 1962.

The International Commission on Radiological

---

*National Academy of Sciences–National Research Council. The Biological Effects of Atomic Radiation. Summary Reports. 1960.

Units and Measurements (ICRU) suggested (†) the following definitions relating to radioactive particles:

The particle fluence or fluence (Φ) of particles is the quotient of ΔN by Δa, where ΔN is the number of particles that enter a sphere of cross-sectional area Δa and Δ represents the appropriate averaging procedure necessary to take into consideration the fact that in general radiation fields are nonuniform in space and also may be variable in time.

$$\Phi = \frac{\Delta N}{\Delta a}$$

The particle flux density or flux density of particles (φ) is the quotient of $\Delta\Phi$ by Δt where $\Delta\Phi$ is the particle fluence in time Δt and Δ has the meaning indicated above.

$$\varphi = \frac{\Delta\Phi}{\Delta t}$$

This quantity may also be referred to as particle fluence rate.

The energy fluence (F) of particles is the quotient ΔE_F by Δa, where ΔE_F is the sum of the energies, exclusive of rest energies, of all the particles that enter a sphere of cross-sectional area Δa and Δ has the meaning indicated above.

$$F = \frac{\Delta E_F}{\Delta a}$$

The energy flux or intensity (I) (may also be referred to as energy fluence rate) is the quotient of ΔF by Δt where ΔF is the energy fluence in the time Δt and Δ has the meaning indicated above.

$$I = \frac{\Delta F}{\Delta t}$$

PEACEFUL USES OF ATOMIC ENERGY

The use of atomic energy for peaceful purposes is a basic element in United States policy, as well as an international objective. On December 4, 1954, at the suggestion of President Eisenhower, the United Nations voted unanimously to establish the International Atomic Energy Agency. The Atomic Energy Act of 1954 established the policy of the Atomic Energy Commission to be "the development, use and control of atomic energy shall be directed so as to promote world peace...."

The ATOMS FOR PEACE AWARDS were a response to the challenge of Dwight D. Eisenhower, when he remarked in his address to the United Nations at Geneva, Switzerland, July 20, 1955, that "I hope that private business and professional men

---

†National Bureau of Standards Handbook H62.

throughout the world will take an interest and provide an incentive in finding new ways that this new science can be used for the benefit of mankind and not destruction." Throughout the world discoveries are showing that nuclear energy has many peaceful uses in medicine and biology, in agriculture, in the processing of food and other products, and in the field of energy production.

See NUCLEAR EXPLOSION, PEACEFUL USES OF, and PLOWSHARE PROGRAM.

PENETROMETER

A simple device used for evaluating the penetrating power of a beam of x-rays or other radiation, by means of a direct comparison of the transmission through a series of absorbers arranged in graded thicknesses or steps and permanently fastened together. Common uses of the device are to establish best exposure conditions for a given photographic film or experimental arrangement or to indicate the quality of radiation.

PERIODIC TABLE

A table listing all the known elements, arranged in the order of increasing atomic numbers and with consideration of the physical and chemical properties. The table shown below is seen to consist of 7 horizontal lines, called periods, containing 2, 8, 8, 18, 18, 32, and 17 elements respectively. In each period there is definite and characteristic graduation of chemical and physical properties, from one element to the next. The vertical columns contain the elements in subgroups having analogous physical and chemical properties, but gradual variation with increasing atomic weight. It is this repetition of physical and chemical characteristics, occurring at regular intervals, that represents the periodicity to which the discoverer, the Russian chemist Mendelyeev, called attention.

The O group, discovered after the table had been numbered from I to VIII, are of interest in that they are highly chemically inert gases. In Period 6, Group IIIB, in place of a single element a

PERIOD TABLE OF THE ELEMENTS

Groups ⟶

Periods	IA	IIA	IIIB	IVB	VB	VIB	VIIB	VIII			IB	IIB	IIIA	IVA	VA	VIA	VIIA	O
1	1 H																	2 He
2	3 Li	4 Be											5 B	6 C	7 N	8 O	9 F	10 Ne
3	11 Na	12 Mg											13 Al	14 Si	15 P	16 S	17 Cl	18 Ar
4	19 K	20 Ca	21 Sc	22 Ti	23 V	24 Cr	25 Mn	26 Fe	27 Co	28 Ni	29 Cu	30 Zn	31 Ga	32 Ge	33 As	34 Se	35 Br	36 Kr
5	37 Rb	38 Sr	39 Y	40 Zr	41 Nb	42 Mo	43 (Tc)	44 Ru	45 Rh	46 Pd	47 Ag	48 Cd	49 In	50 Sn	51 Sb	52 Te	53 I	54 Xe
6	55 Cs	56 Ba	57–71 Lanthanides	72 Hf	73 Ta	74 W	75 Re	76 Os	77 Ir	78 Pt	79 Au	80 Hg	81 Tl	82 Pb	83 Bi	84 Po	85 At	86 Rn
7	87 Fr	88 Ra	89–103 Actinides															

Lanthanide Series	57 La	58 Ce	59 Pr	60 Nd	61 (Pm)	62 Sm	63 Eu	64 Gd	65 Tb	66 Dy	67 Ho	68 Er	69 Tm	70 Yb	71 Lu

Actinide Series	89 Ac	90 Th	91 Pa	92 U	93 (Np)	94 (Pu)	95 (Am)	96 (Cm)	97 (Bk)	98 (Cf)	99 (Es)	100 (Fm)	101 (Md)	102 (No)	103 (Lw)

series of 15 elements appear, known as the lanthanide series or the rare-earth series. They are very closely related chemically. In Period 7, Group IIIB, appears the actinide series, also chemically very much alike, and in addition the series is composed of many artificially produced elements too unstable to exist in nature, marked by parentheses. The ordinal· or atomic number is given in each case.

PERIPHERAL CIRCULATION, MEASUREMENT

Sodium is a substance freely diffusible between the blood vessels and the extracellular fluid. The rate of removal (or clearance) of a small test dose injected subcutaneously has been shown to be a valuable measure of the adequacy of the circulation, especially in the lower extremities and in pedicle grafts. A volume of 0.1 milliliter or less containing about 2 microcuries of the radioisotope is injected subcutaneously. A gamma detector is placed over the site of injection and the changing level of radioactivity is recorded over a period of several minutes. The radioactivity decreases exponentially. Normally there is loss of from 5 to 15% of remaining activity each minute. Slow removal indicates impaired circulation. Differences between 2 separate areas in the same patient, and changes over a period of time with repeated tests in the same patient, are more significant than absolute values.

See CIRCULATION TIME, MEASUREMENT.

PERMEABILITY OF INTESTINAL MUCOSA, MEASUREMENT

Polyvinylpyrrolidone (PVP) is a high molecular weight material sometimes used as a plasma expander. The labeled form has been given intravenously to show abnormal permeability of the intestinal tract. Normally less than 2% of an administered dose can be recovered in the feces, but in certain patients believed to be "leaking" serum proteins into the intestinal tract, from 3 to 20% of the PVP-I will be recovered in the feces. Thus it is believed that intestinal loss may account for low serum protein values that were formerly erroneously attributed to excessive catabolic activity.

See MEMBRANE PERMEABILITY STUDIES and OSMOSIS STUDIES.

PERMISSIBLE DOSE*

That dose of ionizing radiation which, in the

*Taken in part from the National Bureau of Standards Handbook 59, "Permissible Dose from External Sources of Ionizing Radiation," U.S. Department of Commerce.

light of present knowledge, is not expected to cause appreciable bodily injury to a person at any time during his lifetime. Appreciable bodily injury means any injury or effect that the average person would regard as being objectionable and/or competent medical authorities would regard as being deleterious to the health of the individual. Dose is used in its radiological sense and particularly as tissue dose in the irradiated tissue, organ or region of interest.

The concept of a permissible dose involves the concept of an acceptable risk in that there is the possibility of radiation injury manifesting itself during the lifetime of the exposed person or in subsequent generations; however, the probability of such an injury is so low that the risk would be readily acceptable to the average individual.

The ideal would be no radiation exposure at all, but this is both impossible and undesirable: impossible, for natural radiation cannot be eliminated by setting up regulations; and undesirable, for this would mean not taking advantage of the many beneficial uses of x-ray, radium, radioisotopes, and the other forms of atomic energy. Thus a compromise must be made which holds the probability of risk low enough to be acceptable in accordance with the usefulness of radiation in research, medicine, agriculture, and industry.

PERNICIOUS ANEMIA, DIAGNOSIS

Vitamin B_{12} (cyanocobalamin) is essential for normal red blood cell formation. It is normally taken in with the diet and is absorbed with the assistance of Castle's intrinsic factor produced by the stomach. In pernicious anemia, lack of intrinsic factor leads to impaired absorption of the vitamin. In some other disorders of the gastrointestinal tract, intrinsic factor may be present but absorption is nevertheless impaired and a blood picture resembling pernicious anemia may be produced.

Cyanocobalamin can be labeled with cobalt-57, -58, or -60; for most purposes Co^{57} appears to be the best label. The most common clinical diagnostic procedure is the Schilling test. For this, the patient is given an oral dose of about 1 microgram of the vitamin containing about 0.5 microcurie of radiocobalt. One or two hours later the patient is given an injection of a large amount (1 milligram) of the vitamin (nonlabeled). Urine is collected for 24 hours and the per cent of administered radioactivity in the urine is determined. In normal persons the urine will always contain more than 7% and usually more than 15% of the amount given. In pernicious anemia and severe gastrointestinal disorders, the amount recovered is usually less than 4%. When a low excretion is

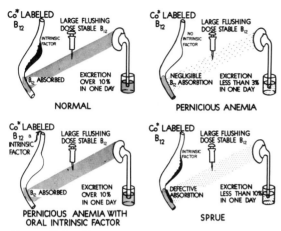

FIGURE P–3. GRAPHIC PRESENTATION OF THE TEST FOR DIAGNOSING PERNICIOUS ANEMIA USING RADIOCOBALT-LABELED CYANOCOBALAMIN.

obtained the test is repeated with the addition of intrinsic factor to the oral dose of labeled vitamin. If this procedure causes a return to normal excretion levels, the diagnosis of pernicious anemia is confirmed. If low excretion levels persist, a diagnosis of sprue or some other intestinal disorder is suggested. (See Fig. P–3.)

The essential aspect of the test is the amount of labeled vitamin absorbed from the gastrointestinal tract. The large dose of nonlabeled vitamin is injected to produce a flushing effect and thus to allow urinary excretion to become an index of absorption.

In variations of this procedure, the flushing dose is omitted and absorption is assessed by measuring fecal excretion or by estimating radioactivity in the liver on the basis of external counting procedures.

PERSONNEL DECONTAMINATION

Removal of external contamination from the body. Decontamination is essential for 4 reasons: radioactive material may be transferred into the body by inhalation or ingestion; it may cause direct radiation damage to the skin; contamination may enter through skin breaks; and, particularly when present with certain organic solvents, the radioactive material may penetrate the intact skin.

If contamination is suspected, personnel should leave the contaminated area at once, remove contaminated clothing and immediately wash in tepid water (not too hot) with a nonabrasive soap. Shower facilities are required to be adjacent to areas where high-level radioactivity is being used. A soft brush may be used on contaminated parts, taking care not to abrade the skin. Contaminated hair should be washed several times with an efficient shampoo and large amounts of water, so that ears and face are not contaminated. For the face use copious amounts of water and soap with the hands alone making the lather. For the hands (the part of the body most likely to be involved) use a soft-bristle nail-brush with soap and water and repeated washings. After each few minutes of washing, the skin should be dried without rubbing, towels discarded, and skin surface radioactivity determined. Repeat washing as necessary using care not to abrade the skin. Irrigation of the eyes with large amounts of water or normal saline should be undertaken immediately. Mild acids, such as equal parts of tartaric and citric acid, and citric acid paste may be used on the skin. The most commonly used decontaminating agent, however, is potassium permanganate followed by sodium sulfite solution.

See INTERNAL DECONTAMINATION.

PERSONNEL MONITORING

The wearing of some type of personnel monitoring device such as a FILM BADGE or POCKET DOSIMETER for determination of the amount of radiation to which an individual has been exposed; or monitoring any part of an individual, his

FIGURE P–4. PERSONNEL MONITORING DEVICES. ION CHAMBERS IN BREAST POCKET, FILM BADGE ON LAPEL OF COAT, SMALL METER ON TIE, AND METERS ON FINGER AND WRIST (PARTS OF BODY SPECIFICALLY SUBJECTED TO EXPOSURE.) (COURTESY OF OAK RIDGE NATIONAL LABORATORY.)

breath (RADON BREATH ANALYSIS), or excretions (URINALYSIS FOR RADIOACTIVITY), or any part of his clothing—thus monitoring of personnel is both physical and biological. Personnel monitoring provides the best means for determining the actual dose of radiation accumulated by the worker. If the dose is low it gives the radiation worker a sense of security and provides some degree of legal protection for management. Regulations vary, but, in general, personnel monitoring is required whenever an individual is working in a situation where exposure to ionizing radiation is likely to occur.

Personnel monitoring devices are shown in Figure P–4.

See WHOLE BODY COUNTERS.

PESTICIDE STUDIES. *See* INSECTICIDE STUDIES.

P–GAS

Also known as PR gas or P-10 gas. A mixture of 90% argon and 10% methane used in filling proportional counter tubes or in flow counters operating in the proportional region.

PHANTOM

A volume of material approximating as closely as possible the density and effective atomic number of tissue. With respect to radiation it should ideally behave with respect to absorption in the same manner as tissue. The phantom may represent the entire human body as in the plastic or standard man, a single organ or a type of tissue, but is most frequently used to simulate a portion of the human body. Ionization chambers may be placed on or in the phantom and measurements thus permit the determination of the radiation dose which would be delivered to the skin or points within the body.

A phantom may be a plastic mold the size of the organ to be studied, filled with water or tissue equivalent fluid, or may be a tissue equivalent plastic solid. For phantoms to be used with condenser ionization chambers it is important that they be dry, and thus for the construction of heterogeneous phantoms a number of dry materials have been developed. For example, for simulating soft tissue a Mix D has been developed which can be cast, machined, and drilled. It consists of paraffin wax 60.8 wt. %, polyethylene, 30.4 wt. %, magnesium oxide, 6.4 wt. %, and titanium oxide, 2.4 wt. %; and has proved satisfactory in all electron density and absorption tests. Lincolnshire bolus (sucrose, 87 wt. %, and magnesium carbonate, 13 wt. %) is made up in small hard spheres 2 mm in diameter, which can be readily poured into interstices and holes which have been drilled in the Mix D to position the condenser ionization chambers. It also has radiation absorbing properties similar to soft tissue.

For a lung phantom with an assumed density of 0.3 g/cm³, a mixture of granulated cork, bulk density 0.1, and Grape Nuts cereal, bulk density 0.46, works very well. To prepare a bone phantom it is well to take a processed skeleton from an anatomical dealer and then plasticize it using melted Mix D under reduced pressure. Phantoms may be prepared using a heterogeneous tissue equivalent and containing a plasticized skeleton, but as Figure P–5 shows, a successful phantom does not need to look like the human body but can consist of a series of boxes offering equivalent absorption.

Phantoms are used for the development of iso-

FIGURE P–5. A PHANTOM CONSISTING OF PLASTIC BOXES OFFERING ABSORPTION EQUIVALENT TO THAT IN VARIOUS PARTS OF THE HUMAN BODY. (COURTESY MEDICAL DIVISION, OAK RIDGE INSTITUTE OF NUCLEAR STUDIES.)

dose curves to be used in determining the various parameters for the treatment of a malignant tumor by the use of teletherapy with either x-ray, cobalt-60 or cesium-137.

An infinite water phantom can be used to determine the relative penetration and dosage received from a 250 kvp x-ray unit and a cobalt-60 teletherapy unit.

PHARMACOLOGICAL STUDIES

To understand drug action, it is necessary to know what happens to drugs in the body; they are frequently so altered in structure and physical property in the course of metabolism that their degradation products may be recognized only by means of isotopic labeling. The synthesis of labeled drugs provides a powerful tool for investigating the degradation in the animal body and offers particular promise for identification of metabolites of the more potent pharmacological agents which can be administered only in minute amounts. Studies generally include investigation of drug action, release, absorption, stability, excretion, retention, penetration, and fundamental biochemistry. Drugs are usually labeled by biosynthesis or chemical synthesis with carbon-14, sulfur-35, or tritium. Typical drugs that have been studied in this way are phenolphthalein, salicylates, and pentobarbital. In addition, drugs that are to be used in domestic animals can be tested by very sensitive isotopic methods to determine whether there will be any residues harmful to the consumer of animal products.

PHOSPHOLIPID STUDIES. *See* LIPID STUDIES.

PHOSPHOR

A luminescent substance; i.e., a material that has the capability of emitting light when stimulated by a physical event such as the passage of ionizing radiation. Specifically, LUMINESCENCE is the emission of light due to causes other than incandescence at high temperature. Many such substances, both organic and inorganic, show good selective response to specific kinds of ionizing radiation and are used as the scintillation component in radiation detectors. The most widely useful are sodium iodide crystals which are produced with a small addition of thallium to provide impurity centers in the crystalline structure. Historically, zinc sulfide was of early importance in atomic energy studies, and continues in wide use in certain types of x-ray intensifiers. Anthracene and stilbene have special value because of their high sensitivity to beta particles. Liquid phosphors are of special utility in the detection of weak radiations as noted under liquid scintillation

counters. Plastic phosphors likewise have particularly valuable applications where large volume detectors are needed.

The ionizing radiation-to-light conversion process in luminescent phosphors may take place through either PHOSPHORESCENCE or FLUORESCENCE phenomena. The distinction between these is made essentially on the basis of the time interval between stimulation and emission, the fluorescent type of event taking place almost instantaneously while the phosphorescent type has an interval of persistence. The delay or protraction of emission can become a detriment in the counting procedure if the counting rate is extremely rapid.

PHOSPHORESCENCE

Emission of electromagnetic radiation by a substance as a result of previous absorption of radiation, generally of shorter wave length. Luminescence, in contrast to fluorescence, is delayed or continues for more than 10^{-8} seconds after excitation.

The phenomenon is used industrially for radioisotope activated markers visible in the dark. For example, strontium-90 is mixed with zinc sulfide, the beta particle activates the zinc sulfide, and a light ray is produced.

PHOSPHORUS

Symbol P; atomic number 15; atomic weight 30.975. Ordinary phosphorus is a waxy solid, colorless when very pure and insoluble in water. The chemical element is known in 5 forms: yellow phosphorus (alpha form); yellow phosphorus (beta form); violet phosphorus; black phosphorus; and red phosphorus. Discovered in 1669 by Brandt, who prepared it from urine. Named from Greek, *phosphoros*, light-bearing. Never found free in nature, but widely distributed in combination in minerals. Commercial phosphates are found in South Carolina, Florida, Canada, and Spain. Natural abundance furnished 100% by the stable isotope P[31].

The most extensive use of phosphorus is as phosphate fertilizer (millions of tons of phosphate rock are made into superphosphate by the action of sulfuric or phosphoric acid on pulverized rock phosphate). It is also used for match heads, in detergents, for prevention of boiler scale, and for production of toxic smoke. It is an essential element for plants, animals, and man. Approximate daily intake: man 1.5 gram (g); rat 45 milligrams (mg); laying hen 1 g; sheep 2.5 g; 100-lb pig 8 g; and cow 15 g. Whole blood of most species contains 35 to 45 mg/100 ml and the inorganic phosphorus of the plasma ranges from 4 to 9 mg/100 ml. Soft tissues of animals contain 2 to 3 mg per gram fresh weight, and bones range from 40 to 130 mg/g. The biochemical standard man contains 0.8 to 1.2% or 700 g per 70 kilograms of body weight. A recommended nutrient solution for plants is about 32 parts per million.

Toxicity depends upon the type of material. For example, 1 mg of yellow phosphorus per kilogram of body weight is usually fatal, while red phosphorus is relatively nontoxic even in comparatively large amounts. Fumes are known to be toxic and phosphorus skin burns are relatively common.

Five radioactive isotopes have been identified. Of these P^{32} may be formed in soil or sea water by induced radioactivity from neutron bombardment associated with the detonation of a nuclear device. Residual contamination is significant at 1 month with 43.8 megacuries per megaton of fission remaining in the soil.

Phosphorus-32 $(_{15}P^{32})$. Radioactive half-life 14.22 days; with bone as the critical organ, biological half-life 1155 days, effective half-life 14.1 days; pure beta (β^-) emitter. Beta particle maximum energy 1.710 Mev, range in water 0.79 centimeter. Usually produced in a nuclear reactor by neutron bombardment of P^{31} with the following reaction: $P^{31}(n,\gamma)P^{32}$. Decays to stable sulfur-32.

P^{32} is the most extensively used of all radioisotopes in agricultural research. Its uses in animal sciences and veterinary medicine cover such activities as the following: mechanism of absorption of phosphorus; kidney function and excretory mechanisms; body utilization of phosphorus; bone accretion and resorption; tooth formation; milk formation; egg formation; nutritional requirement availability of phosphorus in foodstuffs; studies in placental transfer related to selective breeding; studies of the cause and treatment of disease; diagnosis of blood supply to bone fractures; studies of blood; and localization of tumors.

Used in soil and plant studies: fixation of phosphorus by soil; phosphorus uptake from soil by plant; uptake by foliage, uptake by roots; efficiency of fertilizer; and uptake from green manures.

Used extensively in medical research, diagnosis and treatment: treatment of polycythemia, leukemia, bone metastases; interstitial use in therapy of cancer; intercavity use in palliation of cancer; diagnosis of intraocular tumors; localization of brain tumors; and research on bone and blood system. Used in plaques to beta-irradiate animal skin experimentally.

Maximum permissible concentration for 168-hour week (continuous exposure), soluble material, bone as critical organ, 2×10^{-4} microcuries per cubic centimeter ($\mu c/cc$) in water and 2×10^{-8} $\mu c/cc$ in air.

PHOTOCATHODE

Electrode formed of or treated with a material that responds to electromagnetic radiation by emitting electrons through the photoelectric effect. In a phototube or photomultiplier tube, these photoelectrons are accelerated by suitable voltages and collected on an anode or dynode.

PHOTOCHEMISTRY

The study of the chemical change in a substance due to the absorption of light. The reaction is generally proportional to the length of exposure and to the intensity of light. Photosynthesis is the classic example of the photochemical reaction where light supplies the energy necessary for the activation of the reacting molecules. Perhaps the most familiar example of a chemical change in response to light is the production of an image in the photographic plate.

There is a converse type of reaction in which light is produced from the heat developed in a chemical reaction. The burning of magnesium metal in air produces not only high temperature but light of high actinic value. FLUORESCENCE is an example of the emission of light by a material as a result of the absorption of energy from radiation. LUMINESCENCE is another example of the production of light by causes other than high temperature.

Each molecule taking part in a chemical reaction induced by exposure to light absorbs but one quantum of radiation. This may cause a disruption of the molecule into fragments, or an electron may simply be excited from a lower orbit to a higher one. The molecular fragments may either recombine to give the original reactant or cause further chemical reactions. The excited molecule may emit its extra energy as light, causing fluorescence, it may transfer its energy to another molecule as thermal energy, or it too may cause a chemical reaction. The energy of light is measured in quanta. If the quantum yield is one, every photon absorbed decomposes one molecule. If the quantum yield is less than one, fluorescence, deactivation, or recombination of fragments must take place. If the quantum yield is greater than unity, and it may be as much as a million, chain reactions take place. The classic example is the combination of hydrogen and chlorine, where one quantum of light can bring about a combination of a million molecules of hydrogen and chlorine.

PHOTOELECTRIC EFFECT

The ejection of a bound electron from a system when an x-ray quantum or a gamma-ray photon collides with an atom. The photoelectron thus ejected absorbs the entire energy of the incident

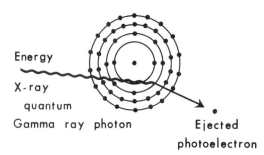

Energy

X-ray quantum

Gamma ray photon

Ejected photoelectron

FIGURE P–6. EJECTION OF A PHOTOELECTRON AS A RESULT OF AN X-RAY QUANTUM OR A GAMMA-RAY PHOTON COLLISION WITH AN ATOM.

radiation, or carries any excess with it as kinetic energy. Figure P–6 graphically illustrates this effect.

Ultraviolet radiation falling on certain metals such as zinc causes the emission of negatively charged particles—the photoelectric effect also.

PHOTOGRAPHIC FILM DETECTORS

These indicate the presence of ionizing radiation by alteration of the chemical structure of the film emulsion. Emulsions are available with sensitivities specific for the several types of radiation. They are variously employed (a) through the pattern of exposure as in a medical x-ray, (b) by measurement of their developed density as in FILM BADGE DOSIMETRY, or (c) as nuclear track emulsions in which information is taken from the geometric pattern caused by passage of particles.

See RADIATION DETECTOR.

PHOTOMULTIPLIER TUBE

A detector for electromagnetic radiation incorporating a PHOTOCATHODE and a series of accelerating DYNODES which operate in cascade at successively higher voltages. When exposed to radiation, the photocathode releases photoelectrons which are attracted toward and impinge upon the first dynode, each electron causing ejection of a quantity of secondary electrons; subsequent dynodes provide further multiplication of the electron stream so that the current finally collected at the anode can be as much as a million times greater than that originating at the photocathode. Since photocathode surfaces are principally responsive to visible or ultraviolet light, photomultiplier tubes are generally used in conjunction with crystal, liquid, or plastic scintillators, selected to achieve optimum response to particular kinds of radiation. Phototube and scintillator are sometimes coupled optically through a light-pipe.

PHOTON

Quantity or quantum of radiation associated with a single quantum of energy. From the Greek *photos*, meaning light. In 1905 Albert Einstein suggested that radiation was emitted and absorbed in whole numbers of energy quanta and that it was propagated through space in definite quanta or individual photons. The term was introduced in 1923 by the United States physicist A. H. Compton who used it in the sense of particles of energy or radiation.

The energy of a photon is $h\nu$, where h is the Planck constant, and ν is the frequency associated with the photon. The term photon usually refers to a planewave quantum of electromagnetic energy, for which the momentum is $h\nu/c$, and the component of angular momentum in the direction of the momentum is $\pm\hbar$ where c is the velocity of light and $\hbar$ is $h/2\pi$.

PHOTONUCLEAR REACTION

Also known as photodisintegration, and nuclear photo-effect. A nuclear reaction of the (γ,n) type produced by a gamma-ray photon. The photonuclear reactions $H^2(\gamma,n)H^1$ and $Be^9(\gamma,n)Be^8$ are used to produce neutrons. Neutrons thus produced are called photoneutrons. A photoproton may also be released in the photonuclear reaction.

PHOTOREACTIVATION

Also photorestoration. Restoration of normal metabolic function by the use of light. The phenomenon usually referred to is the use of visible and infrared light-photoreactivation after damage by ultraviolet irradiation. Such restoration of function has been observed with microorganisms and with ova or spermatozoa of echinoderms, and with habrobracon eggs. This type of treatment was tried extensively in an attempt to accelerate the processes of restoration and repair after ionizing irradiation, but the results have generally been negative.

PHOTOSCAN

The picture derived from recording photographically the pattern of radioactivity residing throughout the body of a subject. Produced by use of an automatically moving radiation detector, usually a scintillation detector, and an associated print-out device consisting of a film cassette with a light source controlled by the radiation intensity as a function of position.

See SCINTILLATION SCANNER.

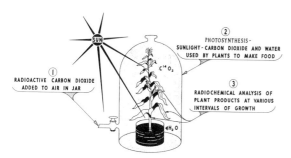

FIGURE P–7. STUDY OF PHOTOSYNTHESIS USING RA-
DIOACTIVE CARBON (C¹⁴) AS A TRACER. (USAEC-1D-190.)

PHOTOSYNTHESIS STUDIES

Photosynthesis is the utilization of light by plants for conversion of carbon dioxide into organic matter, and is perhaps the most important process by which living organisms acquire the necessary energy for the performance of synthetic reactions. It is necessary to understand the various pathways and mechanisms by means of which carbon dioxide is converted to carbohydrate or other organic end products. Early work was done with short-lived carbon-11, but in more recent years the availability of carbon-14 has allowed detailed experimentation. In 1961 Dr. Melvin Calvin received the Nobel Prize for studies on the mechanisms of photosynthesis based on the use of radioactive tracers.

The usual procedure is to expose the experimental material to $C^{14}O_2$ under given conditions and then to determine into what organic fraction the labeled carbon has been incorporated (see Fig. P–7). Some of the important areas of investigation have been:

a. the relationship of photosynthesis to respiration;
b. the significance of fixation of CO_2 in the dark;
c. the nature of the first product formed in photosynthesis;
d. the sequence of formation of the hexose units;
e. the formation of ribulose and sedoheptulose phosphates;
f. the source of photosynthetic oxygen;
g. the precursors of chlorophyll.

On the basis of this type of study, detailed metabolic schemes have been developed; a recent one is shown on page 312.

PIGS

Containers in the form of cylinders, with or without a cover, of lead, concrete, or steel, into which bottles or other containers of radioactive

material fit. Pigs provide shielding for storage or transportation and also provide stability. Soft rubber is often placed in the pig to grip the bottle. A series of holes in a lead brick can accommodate several small bottles, but the usual pig resembles that shown in Figure P–8.

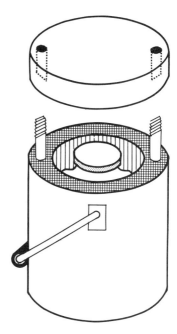

FIGURE P–8. LEAD CARRYING CONTAINER (PIG) FOR SAFE TRANSPORTATION OF RADIOACTIVE MATERIAL.

PILE

The moderator of the first nuclear reactor consisted of graphite blocks stacked or piled in multiple layers. Thus the term, pile, early became jargon for a graphite-moderated nuclear reactor and, by extension, for any reactor.

PITCHBLENDE

A uranate of uranyl and lead, with oxides of thorium and varying amounts of the rare earths, plus gaseous nitrogen, helium and argon. It occurs occasionally in crystals, but more commonly in masses of pitchy to submetallic luster and greenish, brownish, or black color. All pitchblende and uraninites contain minute amounts of radium. Madame Curie discovered radium in pitchblende from Joachimsthal, Czechoslovakia. Pitchblende occurs in several parts of the world but the most important deposit is at Great Bear Lake, Northwest Territories, Canada.

Carcinoma of the lung may result from continuous exposure.

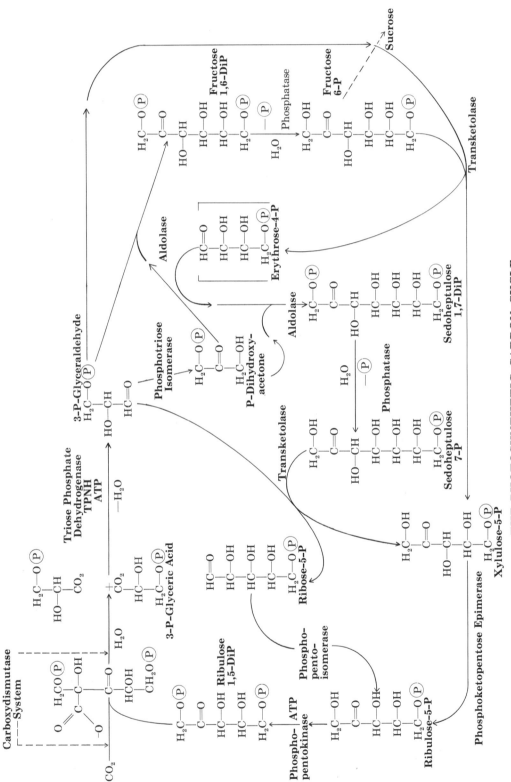

THE PHOTOSYNTHETIC CARBON CYCLE

The energy required to cause synthesis from CO_2 to carbohydrate is delivered to the cycle in the form of compounds of high chemical potential of which triphosphopyridine nucleotide and adenosine triphosphate can drive the cycle in the absence of light. The light absorbed by chlorophyll gives rise to such compounds as these. Little is yet known as to what actually happens after chlorophyll has absorbed light and has become an excreted molecule.

PITUITARY GLAND IRRADIATION

The pituitary gland, which normally serves an important function in stimulating and regulating the function of other endocrine organs, is sometimes subjected to intensive radiation treatment. The fact that it can be located precisely by roentgenograms makes the gland suitable for highly controlled external beam treatment; for example, with high energy alpha particles. The pituitary is also irradiated by direct insertion into its substance of beads containing yttrium-90. This radioisotope yields high-energy beta particles that produce intense, highly localized radiation. Although irradiation is sometimes used for tumors of the pituitary, in recent years the majority of patients have been so treated because of cancer of the breast. In these patients the normal pituitary may give rise, either directly or through its effect on the adrenals and ovaries, to hormonal substances that stimulate the growth of some tumors. Thus destruction of the pituitary may give benefit to such patients. Very high doses of radiation are required. After-treatment hormone medications are given to reduce the undesirable effects of destruction of the pituitary gland.

PLACENTAL TRANSFER STUDIES

The nutrition of the developing fetus has been widely studied in experimental animals, using various available radioisotopes. The type of information available is:

    a. the rate of transfer of a given element or substance from the circulation of the mother to the developing fetus;

    b. the rate of transfer from the fetus to the circulation of the mother;

    c. the relative contribution of substances to the fetus from the diet and from the body of the mother;

    d. by use of autoradiograms, the visualization of locations of nutrients in the various tissues of the fetus.

See EMBRYONIC DEVELOPMENT STUDIES.

PLANCHET

Dish-shaped pan of metal or glass (usually 1 to 2 inches in diameter) in which radioactive samples are prepared and mounted for counting; used to improve uniformity of sample preparation and counting geometry.

PLANT BREEDING AND RADIATION

Selective breeding of livestock and crop plants is a means to increase productivity. The use of irradiation to induce mutations allows a breeder to study more variations than would otherwise be possible. This technique can be and has been used successfully with crop plants, but not with animals.

Irradiation of a crop plant produces variants whose characteristics are different from their antecedents. By selection of varieties with good production characteristics, breeders have been able to develop plants that are more resistant to disease, are more amenable to mechanical harvesting, and have a better food value and a higher yield per acre. As an illustration of commercial application, the Sanilac bean produced by irradiation with x-rays possesses dwarf plant characters adapted to easier mechanical harvesting. This bean is now the dominant variety of white pea bean in the United States used in canning, amounting to over 2 million bushels a year.

Mutation studies using radiation have been done on over 60 different crop plants. Table P–1 indicates an example of useful or potentially useful mutations or sports obtained in plants by irradiation (page 314).

See CROP IMPROVEMENT and PLANT GENETICS AND RADIATION.

PLANT CELL METABOLISM STUDIES. *See* CELLULAR STUDIES.

PLANT CELL RADIOSENSITIVITY

RADIOSENSITIVITY is the relative susceptibility of cells, tissues, plants, or any substance to the injurious action of radiation. It is the opposite of RADIORESISTANCE. Wide differences in radiosensitivity are noted among plants; e.g., severe defects were noted in tradescantia at a dose rate of 40 roentgens (r) per day for a number of weeks, while in a hybrid gladiolus, 6,000 r per day were required to produce the same effect.

Plants are generally less sensitive to radiation damage than are animals. However, when they do reproduce, their gametic products, e.g., pollen, may be even more exposed than those of many animals whose gametes are transferred by coitus. In the dormant stage radioresistance is very high, and in the early developing and growing stage radioresistance is low; thus an ecosystem might survive massive radiation in the winter, but suffer enormously if it is received in the spring. Mature barley can absorb heavy radiation without showing obvious somatic effects, while the early developing stage is sensitive to a few hundred roentgens.

Plant radiosensitivity has been extensively studied by the use of the gamma field where somatic changes are produced and studied. Seed

TABLE P–1. MUTATIONS INDUCED: SOME EXAMPLES OF USEFUL OR POTENTIALLY USEFUL MUTATIONS
OR SPORTS OBTAINED IN PLANTS BY IRRADIATION

CHARACTER IMPROVED OR MODIFIED	CHARACTER OR DIRECTION OF CHANGE	PLANTS
In Crop Plants		
Disease resistance	To stem rust	Barley, oats, wheat
	To stripe rust	Wheat
	To Victoria blight	Oats
	Leafspot	Peanut
Insect resistance	To gall fly	Sesame
Growth habit	Shorter	Barley, flax, oats, rice, wheat
	Taller	Flax, jute
	Dwarf	Sorghum, bean
	Giant	Pea, peanut, red clover
Maturity	Earliness	Barley, oats, soybean
	Lateness	Barley, oats, wheat
Self-incompatibility	To self-fertility	Red and white clovers
Quality	Improved	Tobacco, wheat
Yield	Increased	Oil mustard, peanut, peas, sesame, barley, oats, wheat
Hardiness	Increased	Oats, wheat
In Horticultural Plants		
Disease resistance	To rust	Black currant
Flower color, shape, size	Various	African violet, carnation, cyclamen, petunia, phlox, snapdragon, tulip
Self-incompatibility	Self-fertility	Sweet cherry
Growth habit	Varied	Black currant
Leaf shape and color	Various	African violet, apple, phlox
Quality	Varied improvement	Black currant
Fruit size	Increased	Black currant
Fruit color	Improved	Apple, pear
Time of ripening	Earlier and later	Peach

irradiation in genetic and plant breeding studies has shown wide variation in plant seed radio-sensitivity. Lily seeds (embryos) show practically no growth after 2,000 r whereas seeds of cabbage and radish are practically unaffected by 64,000 r. Algae are certainly radioresistant, for the entire algal flora were abundant and in good anatomical and physiological condition on the most radio-active reefs at Bikini.

In radioecology studies it appears that certain species of plants, now somewhat depressed by other more vigorous forms, may become successful because of the destruction of their more highly radiosensitive competitors. This would lead to the possible evolution of more radioresistant types.

PLANT GENETICS AND RADIATION

In addition to the obvious economic value of radiation-induced useful mutations in cultivated plants, basic genetic studies have been given a very significant boost by the appropriate use of ionizing radiation. First, the large number of radiation-induced mutations has greatly extended our ability to perform genetic research and hence our basic understanding of genetic processes. Likewise, our comprehension of the mechanisms of chromosome breakage and rejoining and the relationship of these events to mutation, crossing-over, position effect, and sterility has been greatly enriched by the use of mutagenic radiation. Such studies have also led to more advanced methods of utilization of radiation in plant breeding by what might be called "chromosome engineering." An example of this was the combined use of colchicine and radiation to produce polyploidy and the more recent and more elegant technique to transfer leaf-rust resistance from the wild grass Aegilops umbellata to common wheat Triticum aestivum.

Probably the use of induced mutations in microbial genetics has advanced the science of genetics more than is generally realized since the extensive use of Neurospora mutations led the way into biochemical genetics. This in turn has contributed very significantly to the happy prospect

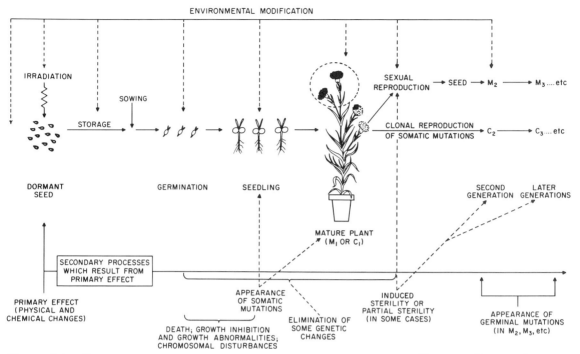

FIGURE P–9. POSSIBLE SEQUENCE OF EVENTS FOLLOWING IRRADIATION OF A SEED. (COURTESY BIOLOGY DIVISION, BROOKHAVEN NATIONAL LABORATORY.)

of breaking the DNA "code" in the very near future.

Figure P–9 demonstrates the possible sequence of events following the irradiation of a seed. The majority of mutations will not appear until later generations, but some may be detected in the irradiated plant (M_1) when it has matured. The changes resulting from irradiation of the developing plant are somatic mutations and can be propagated asexually in many plant species.

PLANT NUTRITIONAL STUDIES. *See* FERTILIZER STUDIES.

PLANT PHYSIOLOGICAL STUDIES

Many phases of plant physiology are being studied with radioisotopes. For example, the site and nature of synthesis of alkaloids and other organic compounds in plants have been determined. A portable photosynthetic chamber of 60 cubic meter capacity is placed over a 30-year-old pine tree and radioactive carbon dioxide introduced into the chamber. Thus the optimal time for tapping for turpines or tannins has been determined. It has been shown that the roots of plants are organs not only for the uptake of water and nutrients, but also for the synthesis of a number of compounds present in the plant. Using $C^{14}O_2$ it was shown that approximately 50% of the material derived from photosynthesis in the leaves moves downward as sucrose to the roots. There the

material is converted into various organic compounds, such as amino acids. Studies of translocation of minerals and organic substances in the plant, and of the factors that affect the translocation, have been greatly facilitated by use of radioisotopes. It was shown, for example, with sugar cane that sucrose may move at the rate of 60 to 70 cm per hour in the plant.

The relationships between the growth of a plant and availability of water, especially in arid regions where water is limited, have been studied. These data provide a new approach to understanding the water requirements of plants, especially as regards irrigation. Other areas of study include the availability of the decomposition products of green manure crops to plants, the factors affecting root efficiency and root distribution, and the loss of nutrients from leaves by leaching.

See PLANT BREEDING AND RADIATION; PHOTOSYNTHESIS STUDIES; FERTILIZER STUDIES.

PLANT REGULATOR STUDIES

Weed control through use of chemical plant regulators is a recent important discovery in agriculture, and radioisotopes have led to an understanding of how these materials enter and move within the plant, and their mechanism of action. Tracer studies with the well-known selective herbicide 2-4-D (which is much more toxic to broad-leaved plants than to narrow-leaved plants) show that the chemical is distributed throughout the plant in the course of 24 hours, thus helping to explain its effectiveness and mode of action. Such tests have shown why high rates of application of the herbicide sometimes resulted in less efficiency in weed control than did moderate rates of application, and have demonstrated that the absorption of the herbicide by the leaves became somewhat less as the plant grew older and the leaves matured. This explains why older plants may be more tolerant to the herbicide than are younger plants.

The entry, distribution, and mode of action of plant regulators, used in preventing preharvest drop of fruit and in chemical thinning of blossoms from fruit trees, have been studied with various radioisotopes to lead to practices that have helped make such treatments commercially effective.

PLASMA VOLUME MEASUREMENT

For this determination the patient is given an intravenous injection of serum albumin labeled with iodine-131. A dose of 4 to 10 microcuries is adequate if a sensitive well scintillation counter is available. After a period of 10 minutes has been allowed for mixing in the vascular system, a blood sample is withdrawn, red cells are separated by centrifugation, and a measured volume of the supernatant plasma is assayed for radioactivity. A calculation is made based on this relationship: total plasma volume equals the total amount of radioactivity injected divided by the final radioactivity per unit volume of plasma. (See Fig. P–10.)

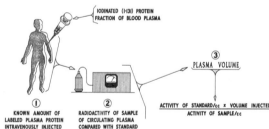

FIGURE P–10. METHOD OF DETERMINING PLASMA VOLUME USING IODINE-131. (USAEC-1D-303.)

To correct for slight diffusion of the labeled material from the vascular system, additional blood samples may be obtained at intervals up to 40 minutes and a plot of plasma radioactivity constructed which can be extrapolated back to zero time for a more accurate calculation.

See BLOOD VOLUME MEASUREMENT.

PLASTIC FILM DETECTORS

Thin film or plastic sheet containing materials that respond to ionizing radiation. Common types include (1) film which incorporates the constitu-

ents of a chemical dosimeter system and (2) plastic sheet made of scintillator materials, either organic or inorganic. Finely ground crystalline substances have also been used in such detectors. For certain purposes, the plastic serves also as a vehicle for a converter which is sensitive to one specific type of radiation and re-emits another type to which the chemical dosimeter system can respond. An example of this is the use of lithium-6 which captures slow neutrons and gives off alpha particles capable of changing the color of a chemical system with which it is intimately mixed.

See RADIATION DETECTORS.

PLASTIC MAN. *See* STANDARD MAN.

PLATEAU, COUNTING

The practical operating voltage range for a Geiger-Mueller counter or other gas pulse type of detector for ionizing radiation. The plateau is a region of nearly uniform sensitivity or response, a relatively flat section of the characteristic curve which relates counting performance to the voltage applied on the accelerating or collecting electrode. It is broadly defined as the range over which the Geiger region extends, throughout which reproducible counting rates can be established, utilizing the phenomenon of avalanche formation in the counting gas. It is that part of the voltage characteristic curve over which the counting rate, taken with a given source, varies only slightly with voltage. Referring to Figure P–11 under PLATEAU SLOPE, the plateau begins just above the threshold voltage and extends to just below the point where the counting rate starts to increase rapidly.

The Geiger point counter and Geiger-Mueller counter are normally operated in this region. As the voltage is brought up from zero, the first avalanche pulses are observed at a value called the starting potential; but the plateau begins after reaching a higher value called the Geiger threshold, where the pulse formation process becomes completely established. However, the counting rate found with a given source is not strictly uniform over the plateau but rises gradually with increasing voltage at a rate called the plateau slope. The upper or high voltage end of the plateau is marked by a sharply increased rate of counting, indicating the approach of incipient destructive continuous discharge which can lead to destruction of the sensitive electrode surfaces as well as depletion of the counting qualities of the gas itself. The working voltage is ordinarily set at an operating point at or below the mid-point of the plateau, most commonly about one third of the plateau length above the threshold. The special advantage of this plateau characteristic of counting tube be-

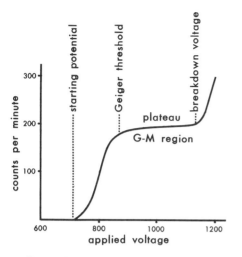

FIGURE P–11. PLATEAU SLOPE CHARACTERISTIC OF A GEIGER-MUELLER TUBE.

havior is that it keeps to a minimum the fluctuation of counting response which might arise from small incidental variations of the electrical power supply to the collecting electrode.

PLATEAU SLOPE

The increase of the counting rate of a radiation detector as its voltage is raised along the counting plateau; expressed as the per cent change in the counting rate per 100-volt change in the applied voltage. Consider an instrument similar to a proportional counter connected with a device capable of indicating only relatively large pulses. As the potential applied between the electrodes is increased the number of pulses recorded per minute will change as shown in Figure P–11. Until the voltage reaches the value indicated as the starting potential the pulses are too small to be detected. As the potential rises the gas amplification increases, and pulses are recorded in increasing numbers until the Geiger threshold is reached where the number of pulses per minute becomes essentially constant. The plateau slope for a good organic quenched counter can be less than 3% per hundred volts, while halogen-filled counters are rarely better than 10%. Beyond this Geiger plateau and starting with the breakdown voltage, continuous discharge takes place and counting is not possible.

PLATELET SURVIVAL, MEASUREMENT

The blood platelets, or thrombocytes, which play an important role in blood clotting and in the reaction of small blood vessels to damage have been studied advantageously with radioisotopic tracers. Radiosulfur (sulfur-35) as sulfate and radiophosphorus (phosphorus-32) as phosphate

are incorporated into platelets as they are formed in the bone marrow. DFP (diisopropylfluorophosphonate) tagged with phosphorus-32 combines with the cholinesterase of red cells, leukocytes, and platelets. It is usually used in vitro to provide a label for cells and platelets to be reinjected. To determine life span, platelets are labeled by one of these methods and blood samples are drawn at intervals for several days. Platelets are separated from other elements (since none of these isotopic preparations label platelets exclusively) and are assayed for radioactivity. The results obtained are plotted. With in vitro labeling the levels fall with time as the platelets are removed. With in vivo labeling, a single dose of radioisotope yields a bell-shaped curve; a series of daily uniform doses yield a curve that rises for several days and then forms a plateau. Interpretation of these curves indicates that in the normal person platelets have a life span of about 8 to 10 days. The fact that there is a linear fall in radioactivity with platelet death suggests that they have a definite life span and are not simply subject to random removal.

PLATELETS, RADIATION EFFECTS ON

Following exposure to radiation of 200 or more rad there usually is a temporary increase amounting to as much as 50% in the number of circulating platelets. About the 4th or 5th day after irradiation the count commences to decrease in a linear fashion with time, and reaches a low point about

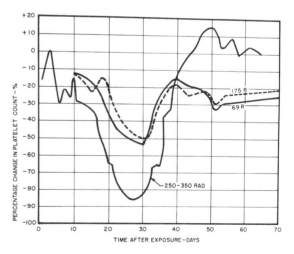

FIGURE P–12. OBSERVED COURSE OF PLATELET COUNTS IN ADULTS FOLLOWING ACCIDENTAL EXPOSURE TO 69 R AND 175 R FROM GAMMA RADIATION IN FALLOUT (MARSHALL ISLANDERS), AND TO 250 TO 350 RAD FROM A MIXTURE OF FAST NEUTRONS AND GAMMA RAYS (Y-12 CASES AT OAK RIDGE). THE DATA HAVE BEEN REPLOTTED INTO PERCENTAGE CHANGE FROM AN ESTIMATED NORMAL COUNT, TO MAKE THE CURVES COMPARABLE. (FROM NASA LIVE SCIENCES DATA BOOK.)

the 28th to the 32nd day. This level which apparently follows a dose-effect relationship is normally maintained for 2 to 3 weeks and then very slowly recovers, taking in some cases 2 to 3 years. In the case of the Marshall Islanders recovery required 2 years. Figure P–12 graphically presents actual figures.

HEMORRHAGE is directly related to the circulating blood platelet level. In man, bleeding (even petechiae in the skin) seldom occurs unless the count falls below 20,000 per cubic millimeter. In a hypothetical case receiving a whole body irradiation dose of 182 rad fast neutrons and 536 rad of prompt gamma the platelet count would be 320,000 for the first 5 days; 300,000 on day 6; 90,000 on day 9; 60,000 on day 12; 50,000 on day 15; and so on down in a linear fashion with time to 10,000 on day 27; with death on day 29. In one case terminating in death the platelet count fell to almost zero on the 10th postexposure day.

PLATINUM

Symbol Pt; atomic number 78; atomic weight 195.09. A grayish-white metal, tenacious, malleable (softer than silver), and ductile. Its discovery is credited to 3 men: to Ulloa in South America in 1735, to Wood in 1744, and to Scaliger "in the 16th century." Named from the Spanish, *platina*, little silver. Platinum occurs native, usually accompanied by small quantities of iridium, osmium, ruthenium, rhodium, and palladium, all belonging to the same group of metals. Natural abundance furnished by 5 stable isotopes.

Used as an alloy in jewelry, pen points, scientific apparatus, surgical tools, standard weights, and containers for scientific work such as crucibles and dishes. Platinum salts are an industrial toxic hazard, causing respiratory symptoms; dermatitis has resulted from contact with skin.

Seven radioactive isotopes have been identified.

PLOWSHARE PROGRAM

An organized series of projects directed to the development of the use of nuclear detonations to achieve peace-time goals such as generating steam from heat stored in rocks at high temperature, digging canals, and creating harbors. The project derives its name from the Biblical quotation: Isaiah 2:4, "They shall beat their swords into plowshares. . . ."

See NUCLEAR EXPLOSIONS, PEACEFUL USES OF.

PLUTO PROJECT

Nuclear ramjet propulsion for unmanned vehicles, such as missiles. A joint USAEC and U.S. Air Force program to demonstrate the feasibility of a high-temperature air-cooled reactor for ramjets. A nuclear ramjet could propel missiles with essentially unlimited range within the earth's atmosphere.

PLUTONIUM

Symbol Pu; atomic number 94; atomic weight 242; a radioactive transuranic element of the actinide series. Discovered in controlled transmutation experiments in 1940 by G. T. Seaborg, E. M. McMillan, J. W. Kennedy, and A. C. Wahl working in the Radiation Laboratory, Berkeley, California. Named after Pluto, the planet beyond Neptune, for plutonium-238 is formed in the beta decay of neptunium-238. Plutonium was the second transuranic element discovered and has become the most important because of its successful use in the nuclear device and in nuclear power production.

Because of its importance and also because large-scale production was successful, extensive studies have been made of the toxicity of plutonium. Plutonium (Pu^{239}) when injected intravenously becomes most concentrated first in the liver and spleen and then is gradually translocated to the bone where it localizes in and adjacent to the osteoid matrix and not in the mineral structure as strontium does. Acute plutonism, in addition to gross liver damage and splenic atrophy, shows the symptomatology of acute radiation illness. Chronic effects of exposure to plutonium involve local graying of hair, progressive liver damage, and bone sarcoma. Subcutaneous injection of 1 microgram of Pu^{239} (in animal experimentation) caused ulceration, keratoses, muscle destruction, and local fibrosarcomas within 1 year. Lethal-dosage studies of plutonium indicated that the LD_{50} at 20 days was 83 microcuries per kilogram ($\mu c/kg$) which compares to 43 $\mu c/kg$ for polonium and 2,100 for radium. The LD_{50} at 60 days was 46 $\mu c/kg$ and at 100 days was 37 $\mu c/kg$. It has been concluded that plutonium alpha particles are more dangerous to blood-forming tissues than those of radium not only because of toxicity but because of its location in the bone in such a way that it can readily irradiate the marrow cavity.

Metal displacement treatment with nontoxic doses of zirconium dissolved in sodium citrate markedly increases the urinary excretion of plutonium. The plutonium is first displaced from the liver and later from bones. EDTA is also used in the treatment of plutonium poisoning.

Plutonium has been found to exist in pitchblende and in carnotite in the minute amount of about 1 part in 10^{14}; obviously, for all practical purposes it is man-made.

Plutonium radioactive isotopes have been reported with mass numbers 232 through 246, but plutonium-239 is of greatest importance.

TABLE P–2

RADIONUCLIDE	RADIOACTIVE HALF-LIFE (years)	BIOLOGICAL HALF-LIFE (years)	EFFECTIVE HALF-LIFE (years)	% EQUILIBRIUM REACHED IN 50 YEARS
Pu²³⁸	89.6	200	62	43
Pu²³⁹	2.44×10^4	200	200	16
Pu²⁴⁰	6.6×10^3	200	190	16
Pu²⁴¹	13.2	200	12	94
Pu²⁴²	3.8×10^5	200	200	16

Plutonium-239 ($_{94}Pu^{239}$). An alpha-emitter with a half-life of about 24,000 years. Has a relatively high specific alpha-radioactivity of about 140,000,000 alpha disintegrations per minute per milligram. One microgram of plutonium equals approximately 1/16 microcurie.

The fissionable isotope Pu²³⁹ was isolated and characterized in 1941 by J. W. Kennedy, G. T. Seaborg, E. Segrè, and A. C. Wahl. It is now produced on a large scale in reactors by irradiation of normal uranium-238 which absorbs slow neutrons with the formation of the short-lived uranium-239, which is ultimately transformed into plutonium-239.

Plutonium-239 is one of the 3 (with uranium and thorium) fissionable materials used in the atomic bomb, and is thus a source of energy of explosive violence, but it can be controlled and used in a reactor so as to release energy more slowly for the production of power. In addition, it is possible for plutonium-239 to regenerate, by breeding, more than is consumed, through utilizing material, such as fertile uranium-238, that would not be fully utilized otherwise.

Five radionuclides of plutonium do not reach equilibrium in the body within 50 years (critical organ, bone). (See Table P-2.)

POCKET DOSIMETER

Small ionization chamber, approximately the size and shape of a fountain pen, worn by radiation workers to monitor the quantity of radiation exposure. The ordinary variety requires an external battery for charging; its exposure is read by connecting into an electrometer-reader circuit. Direct self-reading types incorporate minute fiber electrometers within their structure, as in Figure P–13, designed and calibrated in roentgens or rem for the particular types of radiation anticipated.

POCKET IONIZATION CHAMBER.   *See*
POCKET DOSIMETER.

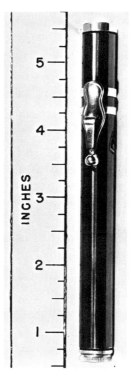

FIGURE P–13.   POCKET DOSIMETER OF "FOUNTAIN PEN" TYPE. (COURTESY U.S. ATOMIC ENERGY COMMISSION.)

POISON

Material of high-absorption cross section that absorbs neutrons unproductively (i.e., without producing subsequent fission events) and reduces the reactivity of a reactor, or of stored fissionable material (boron and cadmium are examples of such materials).

POLLEN STUDIES

Pollen has been labeled with radioactive phosphorus and radioactive sulfur to study the relationships between the contents of the pollen tube and the metabolism of the mother plant. For example, the degree of dispersion of pollen in alfalfa was found to be about 9 to 10 meters. Furthermore, only about one-fifth of the pollen observed on the stigmatic surface of a flower was found to be from the plant itself; a pollen tube from a foreign alfalfa plant is about 40 times more likely to fertilize an ovule than a pollen tube from the mother plant.

POLONIUM

Symbol Po; atomic number 84; atomic weight 210. Discovered in 1898 by Pierre and Marie Curie in seeking the cause of the radioactivity of pitchblende from Joachimsthal, Bohemia. Named for Poland, the native country of Marie Curie.

Twenty radioactive isotopes have been identified. Eight of them appear in the radioactive series of uranium, thorium, actinium, and neptunium:

Radium A (Po^{218}), α and β emitter, half-life 3.05 min.

Radium C′ (Po^{214}), α emitter, half-life 1.6×10^{-4} sec.

Radium F (Po^{210}), α emitter, half-life 138.4 days.

Thorium A (Po^{216}), α emitter, half-life 0.16 sec.

Thorium C′ (Po^{212}), α emitter, half-life 3×10^{-7} sec.

Actinium A (Po^{215}), α and β emitter, half-life 1.83×10^{-3} sec.

Actinium C′ (Po^{211}), α emitter, half-life 0.52 sec.

Polonium (Po^{213}), α emitter, half-life 4.2×10^{-6} sec.

Polonium offers a strong alpha source for experimental work. It is used in nuclear-powered batteries and in static eliminators, and in biology in studying the effects of an alpha emitter which does not deposit in bone. Polonium metabolism and toxicity have been studied in detail in both animals and in man. Polonium inhaled, ingested, or given intravenously is eliminated rather rapidly in the feces and urine: 26% by the end of 10 days; 56% by the end of 50 days; 73% by the end of 100 days; 88% by the end of 200 days; and 96% by the end of 300 days. Since the radioactive half-life of most of the isotopes of polonium is short there is an added elimination factor making the effective half-life somewhat shorter than 30 days.

The maximum permissible concentration for soluble Po^{210} material with spleen as the critical organ for a 168-hour week (continuous exposure), is 7×10^{-6} microcuries per cubic centimeter (μc/cc) in water and 2×10^{-10} μc/cc in air.

POLYCYTHEMIA VERA, TREATMENT

This chronic disease, characterized by the overproduction of red cells, is often treated with radioactive phosphorus. The isotope is given orally or intravenously, usually in doses of from 2 to 6

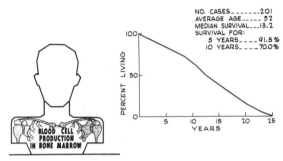

FIGURE P–14. DIAGRAMMATIC PRESENTATION OF THE EFFECT OF TREATMENT WITH RADIOACTIVE PHOSPHORUS ON THE LIFE EXPECTANCY OF POLYCYTHEMIA VERA PATIENTS. IT APPEARS THAT THE USE OF RADIOACTIVE PHOSPHORUS IN POLYCYTHEMIA VERA PRODUCES A LIFE EXPECTANCY AS GOOD AS OR BETTER THAN THAT RESULTING FROM THE USE OF LIVER EXTRACT IN PERNICIOUS ANEMIA OR INSULIN IN DIABETES. (USAEC-1D-279A.)

millicuries. Treatment is repeated at intervals of from a few weeks to many months, depending upon clinical and laboratory changes. A favorable response to treatment is manifested by a gradual reduction in the number of red cells, improvement in other aspects of the blood picture, reduction in size of the spleen, and relief of symptoms such as headache and itching. The treatment is not curative but may control the disease for a number of years (Fig. P–14). Some patients with polycythemia vera eventually develop serious complications and it has been claimed that radiophosphorus treatment may increase their incidence, but this has not been clearly established. Other forms of treatment include the repeated withdrawal of blood, the use of drugs that depress blood formation in the bone marrow, and external radiation treatment.

POPULATIONS, RADIATION EFFECTS ON

Damage to the fitness of a population exposed to increased level of radiation is expected to be proportional to the increased mutation rate. By using this expected proportionality, one may estimate the increased rate of defective births in a human population exposed, for example, to 5 roentgens in 30 years. Some assumptions are necessary, particularly because of the lack of reliable statistical evidence as to the rate of occurrence of mutations uninfluenced by radiation. First, the fraction of human births defective for genetic reasons has been variously estimated to be as high as 4% or as low as 0.5%. This genetic burden may be equivalent to that produced by as little as 3 r or to as much as 80 r of radiation. Taking any admissible values, one may compute many different estimates of the effect of increased radiation. For example, if 2% of present human births are defective for genetic reasons, and if this genetic burden is equivalent to the burden produced by 50 r, then a 5 r exposure should add 1/10 to the burden. That is, with these assumptions the percentage of defective births should increase from 2% to 2.2%. In a population with 4,000,000 births per year, the increase in genetically caused defective births would with these assumptions be from about 80,000 to 88,000, or an increment of about 8,000.

Studies of human populations exposed to radiation do not provide unequivocal evidence of the effects of radiation on the genetic constitution. Conversely, studies with nonsignificant findings cannot be used as proof that radiation has no effects on the genetic makeup of human populations.

Natural selection must be considered in studying the response of populations to the effects of radiation. Natural selection may be defined as that natural process whose action results in the survival of certain members of a species, or certain types of organisms, rather than others. The best working hypothesis of modern evolutionists is based on the general conclusion that those who survive are more adapted, or more fit (on the average at least), than those who do not.

To survive in a population, whether in laboratory, greenhouse, field plot, or in nature, a new gene mutation must provide sufficient fitness, along with all other genes, to allow the organism to develop, mature, and reproduce. Genes and genotypes that do not do so are said to have low adaptive value and are selected against. In the extreme a gene or genotype may be lethal to the recipient. A lethal mutation has no adaptive value and is promptly selected against. In less extreme cases, the gene or genotype may merely depress the viability, fertility, or fecundity of the bearers. These genes or genotypes are also selected against but at less severe rates.

Mutations induced by high-energy radiation, like those that occur naturally, almost always have less adaptive value than the preexisting genes. This means that radiation-induced mutations cannot generally be considered a source of improving natural plant and animal species. Under experimental, in contrast to natural, conditions one may be able to select the rare beneficial mutations and hence establish improved domesticated lines.

In an ecosystem being constantly irradiated, one can predict that over a long period of time the species with high radioresistance will increase in number, while those that are radiosensitive will decrease and tend to die out. The composition of such a replacement ecosystem might be quite different but would be governed by the same ecological principles and have the same niches as the original ecosystem.

The persistence of a mutation with a deleterious effect in a population is inversely proportional to its selective disadvantage. For example, a gene that depresses fitness by 20% is expected to persist for 5 generations on the average.

See DEMOGRAPHY, USE IN STUDY OF RADIATION EFFECTS; and GENETIC DOSE.

POSITRON

Symbol β^+. An elementary charged particle; a positive electron. First observed in a cloud chamber by means of ionization tracks due to the impacts upon atoms of high-energy cosmic rays. Also formed in beta decay, in pair production, and in other processes. The average life of a positron is of the order of 10^{-9} of a second, for it immediately combines with an electron, many of which are always available. When a positron and an electron unite, their positive and negative charges neutralize each other and both particles are annihilated, leaving only energy in the form of radiation, often called annihilation radiation, with properties identical with those of gamma rays.

POTASSIUM

Symbol K; atomic number 19; atomic weight 39.100. A silver-white metal, readily molded, can be cut by a knife, reacts violently with water, oxidizes instantly on exposure to air. Discovered by English chemist Davy in 1807. Named from English potash in which it was found (K_2CO_3). Symbol K from Latin, *kalium.* Found naturally as the chloride or sulfate in certain salt deposits, in common rocks, and in various mineral deposits. Eighth element in abundance in the solid crust of the earth (2.6%). Natural abundance furnished by two stable isotopes: K^{39}, 93.08%; and K^{41}, 6.91%; and also by one naturally occurring radioactive isotope, K^{40}, 0.0119%.

Potassium forms an essential constituent of fertilizers and is used in huge quantities, principally as the chloride. Examples of uses of other salts: potassium bromide in photography, engraving, lithography and as a sedative in medical therapy; potassium carbonate in special glass, soft soap, and various chemicals; potassium chlorate in matches, pyrotechnics, and disinfectants; potassium chromate in leather tanning, textile dyeing and inks; potassium ferrocyanide in blueprint paper, in tanning and in tempering steel; potassium permanganate in disinfectants and bactericides, and as an oxidizing agent in many chemical reactions; potassium persulfate as an antiseptic; and potassium tartrates in medicines, in baking powder and as a source of tartrate.

Human adult daily intake averages 2 to 3 grams (g). Animal tissues have about 3 milligrams (mg) K per gram fresh weight; plasma, about 0.2 mg/ml and urine about 2 mg/ml. Crop plants may have 1 to 5% K on a dry-weight basis. The biochemical standard man contains 0.35% or 245 grams per 70 kilogram adult body weight.

In addition to K^{40} there are 6 other radioactive isotopes. K^{40} and K^{42} may be produced by induced radiation as a result of neutron bombardment associated with the detonation of a nuclear device in contact with the soil or water on the earth's surface. Not significant as residual nuclear radiation.

Potassium-40 $({}_{19}K^{40})$. Half-life 1.3×10^9 years, beta (β^-) and gamma emitter. Is feebly radioactive, being one of the few naturally occurring radionuclides of low mass number. It is one of 4 naturally occurring elements (Ra^{226}, U^{238}, Th^{232}, and K^{40}) which contribute to natural background radiation.

K^{40} is ingested in solid food, and since potassium is widely distributed throughout the body there is constant irradiation of the tissues. Naturally occurring K^{40} is normally the most abundant gamma emitting radioisotope in the human body, and always shows up as a distinct peak in a whole body counter. However, the gamma radiation is of negligible importance compared with its beta radiation in the case of K^{40} deposited in the skeleton. The dose rate from internal radiation in millirem per year from K^{40} is 19 for the gonads (ovaries and testicles), 11 for bone structure, and 11 for bone marrow.

Potassium-42 $({}_{19}K^{42})$. Radioactive half-life 12.42 hours; with muscle as the critical organ, biological half-life 58 days, effective half-life 12.24 hours; beta and gamma emitter. Normally made by the reaction $K^{41}(n,\gamma)K^{42}$ in a nuclear reactor. Used extensively in animal research for: study of factors controlling the preferential sequestering of potassium by the cells; study of the function of potassium in acid-base balance; determination of the mechanism of potassium excretion by the kidney; and estimation of the requirement for potassium by animals. Used extensively in medical research for metabolic studies, plasma volume level studies in muscular activity, measurement of total muscle mass, studies in muscular dystrophy and in potassium distribution. Used in diagnostic studies for the localization of tumors. Radiopotassium (K^{42}) chloride sterile solution available for medical use. Maximum permissible concentration for a 168-hour week (continuous exposure) for soluble material with gastrointestinal tract as the critical organ is 3×10^{-3} microcuries per cubic centimeter ($\mu c/cc$) in water and 7×10^{-7} $\mu c/cc$ in air.

POTATOES, IRRADIATION OF. *See* FOOD PRESERVATION.

POTENCY, RADIATION EFFECTS ON

Radiation exposure, except in lethal doses, does not seem to affect human potency. Potency may be affected by fatigue accompanying radiation illness, and by psychological factors. The difference in amount of radiation required to cause STERILITY without causing impotency is demonstrated experimentally by the SCREW WORM FLY ERADICATION PROGRAM, where male flies were made sterile but not impotent by exposure to about 7,500 roentgens ionizing radiation.

Radiation to the testes depresses or prevents spermatogenesis but not hormonal secretion, and thus potency is not affected.

See SPERMATOGENESIS, RADIATION EFFECTS ON; and GONADS, RADIATION EFFECTS ON.

POTENTIOMETER

1. Instrument for accurate comparison or measurement of small voltages and differences of electrical potential, based on the principle of balancing the potential drop in parallel arms of a bridge circuit tied respectively to the unknown source and a standard source.

2. General term for a variable resistor.

POWER, ATOMIC. *See* ATOMIC POWER.

POWER REACTORS

Those NUCLEAR REACTORS that are used primarily as sources of energy are called power reactors. Reactors used in the generation of electrical power and those used in nuclear-propelled ships and submarines are included in this category.

Although more direct and more efficient methods of conversion of fission energy to electrical power may eventually be developed, the present methods of using power reactors all depend upon the generation of heat. As in conventional power plants, the heat is used to produce steam which in turn drives a turbogenerator for the production of electrical power. Power reactor installations generate 1 kilowatt of electrical power for each 4 to 5 kilowatts of thermal power produced. The over-all efficiency at present is somewhat lower than that of the best conventional plants. The power reactors are subject to further improvement as the techniques of working with the low temperatures and steam pressures are adapted for their use.

The Shippingport, Pa., power reactor, the United States' first full-scale central-station atomic power plant built for civilian needs, went "on the line" December 23, 1957, and within a few days was operating at full power, delivering 60,000 kilowatts (electrical) to the Duquesne power grid. The power was subsequently raised to 100,000 kilowatts (electrical) when a second core was installed. The Yankee reactor, jointly owned by 10 New England utilities, became operational at 110,000 kilowatts (electrical) in 1961. Each of these installations has subsequently delivered over a billion (10^9) kilowatt hours.

England has a 5.8 million kilowatt civilian nuclear-power program under way, with eight 800–1000 megawatt (thermal) reactors being built at 4 sites in addition to those already in operation at Berkeley and at Calder Hall. Canada, France, Italy, Belgium, Russia and several other countries also have active nuclear-power programs. With the increasing rate of demand for electrical power and the probable increasing costs of fossil fuels (coal, oil, etc.), reactors may be expected to become progressively more important sources of electrical energy and eventually may become the dominant source.

Another significant application of power reactors has been in the propulsion of ships. As of September 1963, the United States Navy had 31 nuclear-powered submarines in operation, with another 55 in various stages of completion. Figure P–15 illustrates the arrangement. A cruiser (the Long Beach), an aircraft carrier (the Enterprise) and a destroyer-leader (the Bainbridge) are at sea, and another destroyer-leader (or guided-missile frigate)* is under construction. These surface ships also have nuclear power plants. The N.S. Savannah, the world's first nuclear-powered passenger and cargo ship, has a length of 588 feet and displaces 21,840 tons. Its reactor has an inventory of 330 kg of uranium-235, operates at 70 MW, and delivers 21,000 shaft horsepower. The ship cruises at 21 knots and is expected to operate for

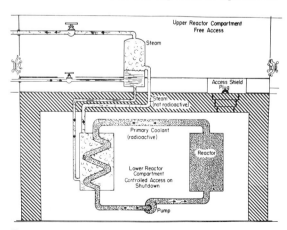

FIGURE P–15. SCHEMATIC DRAWING OF NUCLEAR POWER PLANT FOR A UNITED STATES SUBMARINE.

*The U.S.S. Truxton, DLC, N-35.

3 years (350,000 miles) without refueling. While in restricted waters the Savannah can store liquid and gaseous waste aboard, thus avoiding their dissemination in areas where they would constitute a public health hazard.

The Russian ice breaker, the Lenin, is also nuclear-powered.

PRASEODYMIUM

Symbol Pr; atomic number 59; atomic weight 140.92. A member of the cerium subgroup of the rare earth metals. Discovered by Austrian chemist Karl Welsbach in 1885. Named from Greek *praseos* (green) and *didymos* (twin) because it forms green salts. Occurs in cerite and other rare minerals with 100% of the abundance stable isotope Pr^{141}.

There are 20 radioactive isotopes with 14 (Pr^{143} through Pr^{156}) produced as fission products from the detonation of a nuclear device. Pr^{142} and Pr^{143} are available commercially and their metabolism has been studied. Considered to be highly radiotoxic, but of no other biological, medical, or agricultural interest.

Praseodymium-143 ($_{59}Pr^{143}$). Radioactive half-life 13.7 days; with bone as the critical organ, biological half-life 1,500 days; effective half-life 13.6 days, pure beta (β^-) emitter. A biologically important fission product because of its bone-seeking quality and its abundance at 1 month (21.85 megacuries per megaton (Mc/MT) of fission). Maximum permissible concentration for soluble material with bone as the critical organ is 4 microcuries per cubic centimeter ($\mu c/cc$) in water and 2×10^{-7} $\mu c/cc$ in air.

Praseodymium-144 ($_{59}Pr^{144}$). Half-life 17.5 minutes, intensive beta (β^-) and gamma emitter. One of the biologically most important radionuclides in fallout because it is found at one year to measure 1.291 Mc/MT. Also important because, together with its parent cerium-144, it accounts for about three-fourths the beta activity and one-third the gamma activity given off the first year by fission product wastes.

PREAMPLIFIER

Electronic circuit for coupling a detector to its main amplifier. Usually situated close to the radiation detector in order to minimize loss of signal and to avoid stray effects. Preamplifiers may also be employed to improve performance of counting systems through additional functions such as pulse shaping or improving signal to noise ratio. They are widely used in scintillation and proportional systems where best reliability and precision are needed.

PRECURSOR IDENTIFICATION

In biological systems it is often important to know whether a given biochemical compound is acting as the direct precursor from which another biochemical compound is being synthesized. Assume that compound B is being synthesized in the body, with compound A as one of the starting materials. To study this system, the radioactive isotope is incorporated into compound A and introduced into the biological system; the amount of the radioisotope can then be determined in both compounds A and B as a function of time. If the specific activity of both compounds is not equal when the specific activity of B reaches a maximum, it may be assumed that compound A is not a precursor of compound B (see Fig. P–16). This general precursor relationship was originally demonstrated in terms of the incorporation of a phosphate label into phospholipid.

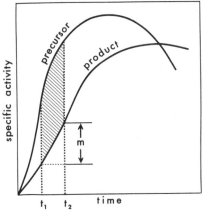

FIGURE P–16. SPECIFIC ACTIVITY-TIME RELATIONS BETWEEN PRODUCT AND PRECURSOR.

PREFLUSH FLOW COUNTER

Windowless flow counter in which samples and associated volume are continuously flushed with counting gas prior to actual counting interval; usually in an antechamber.

PREGNANCY, RADIATION EFFECTS ON

In laboratory mammals doses of 100 to 300 roentgens (r) to the embryo or fetus cause a predictable spectrum of malformations depending on the stage of development when exposed. In certain laboratory mammals as little as 20 r may alter development. High doses are usually lethal to embryos and lead to spontaneous abortion.

Little is known about the effects of radiation on man during early development except that malformation or death follows irradiation of embryos in a dose range comparable to that known to harm other mammals. Virtually nothing is known about the effects on late fetuses, except possible development of leukemia.

Of 4,400 pregnant women exposed to radiation from the atomic bombs detonated over Hiroshima and Nagasaki, 33 were delivered of children with microcephaly, a type of deformity in which the skull is unusually small and associated in many cases with mental retardation. It is known that this deformity can occur following relatively small amounts of radiation to the fetus during the second trimester. Spontaneous abortion and stillbirths were also reported as the result of the bombings in Japan. Among 30 Japanese women pregnant at the time and exposed within 2,000 meters of hypocenter, and developing signs of acute radiation illness, there were 7 fetal deaths, 6 neonatal and infant deaths, and 4 instances of mental retardation among 16 surviving children. The morbidity and mortality in this group was 60% compared to a control group with 6%.

Among the Rongelap group of Marshall Islanders there were 4 women who were pregnant at the time of exposure to fallout from the test detonation of a nuclear device. For their exposure it is calculated that a "point source" beam air dose with comparable biological effect would be 260 r; and yet none of these women had abnormal symptoms referable to their pregnancy.

See FETUS, EFFECTS OF RADIATION ON.

PRESET COUNT

Method of counting wherein the COUNTING RATE is measured by determining the time required to accumulate a fixed total number of counts.

PRESET TIME

Procedure in which the COUNTING RATE is determined from counts accumulated during a uniform and automatically controlled time interval.

PROBE, DETECTOR.   See DETECTOR PROBE.

PROMETHIUM

Symbol Pm; atomic number 61; atomic weight 147; member of the lanthanide series of rare earths. Long searched for but not yet found in nature. Was discovered during studies of uranium fission products, by J. A. Marinsky and L. E. Glendenin working in C. D. Coryell's group in connection with the U.S. Manhattan Project's wartime fission project identification program. Named for the Greek god Prometheus who brought fire from heaven for the use of man, just as fission has made available the energy of the nucleus.

Radioactive isotopes of promethium with mass numbers 141 through 161 have been reported.

Pm¹⁴⁷ through Pm¹⁶¹ have been identified as fission products from the detonation of a nuclear device. Pm¹⁴⁷ is important in radioactive fallout since 0.386 megacurie per megaton of fission remains at the end of 1 year.

Promethium–147 ($_{61}$Pm¹⁴⁷).   Radioactive half-life 920 days; with bone as the critical organ, biological half-life 1,500 days; effective half-life 570 days, pure beta (β⁻) emitter. Now available in kilocurie quantities recovered from fission product wastes from operation of nuclear reactors. Of interest industrially as a possible source of long-lived beta radiation for use in nuclear batteries.

Used biologically in studying its behavior in animals, particularly its property of accumulation in liver and bone. Maximum permissible concentration for a 168-hour week (continuous exposure) for soluble material, with critical organ bone, 0.5 microcurie per cubic centimeter (μc/cc) in water and 2 × 10⁻⁸ μc/cc in air.

PROMPT RADIATION

Radiation produced by the primary fission or fusion process, as distinguished from the radiation of fission products, their decay chain and other later reactions, such as RESIDUAL NUCLEAR RADIATION. The first part (in point of time) of INITIAL NUCLEAR RADIATION.

PROPORTIONAL COUNTER

A gas pulse-type detector for ionizing radiation which is operated with the voltage on its collector electrode in the range where the size of the pulse is proportional to the energy of the incident radiation. Figure P–17 shows the characteristic relationship between collecting voltage and the quantity of electrical charge collected from a single ionizing radiation event, comparing the proportional region with the ionizing chamber region, which uses lower voltages.

Proportional counters are similar to ionization chambers in that the amount of electrical charge collected is directly related to the amount of ionization actually caused by the incident radiation. Whereas in the ionization chamber the liberated charge is collected and integrated into the current or quantity of electricity to be measured, in the proportional counter the measure is made by counting pulses that are of a specified size, uniformly enlarged through controlled gas amplification. When the counter voltage is raised still further, into the Geiger region, the pulses lose all relationship to the size of the initiating event, much stronger signal pulses being developed but the proportionality feature being lost.

Although the pulses produced by a counter operating at the voltages of the proportional region

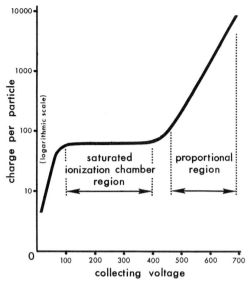

FIGURE P–17.   CHARACTERISTIC ION COLLECTION CURVE SHOWING SATURATION AND PROPORTIONAL REGION FOR A PROPORTIONAL COUNTER.

are smaller and require additional amplification in the associated circuitry, they do have distinct advantages of great merit, in that the limited nature of their pulses makes them capable of faster counting rates and their proportionality of response provides for discrimination or identification of radiations of different energies or of different types. An additional advantage of the proportionality feature is the possibility of reducing background or other interfering radiation counts by use of amplifier discriminator circuits which reject all pulses except those of the selected size.

In their construction, proportional counters may be similar to Geiger-Mueller counters, and in fact certain types can be operated in either region, especially those with continuous gas flow or those that require gas filling with each new sample.

PROTACTINIUM

Symbol Pa; atomic number 91; atomic weight 231. Takes its name from Greek *protos*, first, as it is the first element of the actinium series of radioactive elements. Pa²³¹ is found in all uranium ores to the extent of 1/4 part per million parts of uranium.

Pa²³¹ was found by L. Meitner, F. Strassmann, and O. Hahn in Germany in 1917 and independently by Soddy and Cranston. Eleven other radioisotopes have been identified with mass numbers 225 through 235. Pa²³⁴ occurs in the uranium decay series; and Pa²³⁰ is the parent for one collateral radioactive series of the uranium series; Pa²²⁶ is the parent for another. Protactinium occurs in the actinium decay series as Pa^{231}; and Pa^{227} is the parent of a collateral radioactive series leading into the actinium series. Although protactinium does not appear in the regular thorium decay series, Pa^{228} is the progenitor for a collateral radioactive series leading into the thorium series.

None of the radioisotopes have any known value in biological, medical, or agricultural activity.

Pa^{231} has a radioactive half-life of 3.4×10^4 years, biological half-life 200 years, effective half-life 200 years, and is one of the 9 radionuclides that do not reach equilibrium in the body within 50 years (16% of equilibrium).

PROTECTION. *See* RADIATION PROTECTION.

PROTECTION STANDARDS. *See* RADIATION PROTECTION STANDARDS and STANDARDS FOR PROTECTION AGAINST RADIATION.

PROTECTIVE CLOTHING

Clothing worn by the radiation worker to prevent contamination of the body or personal clothing. From the standpoint of shielding the body against radiation it is not protective except that such clothing offers: complete protection of the skin from alpha particle radiation and partial protection against beta particle radiation; and protection of the skin from direct contact with radioactive materials.

Protective or anticontamination clothing may consist of: laboratory coats; coveralls; shirts; trousers; underwear; socks; shoe covers (booties); rubbers; boots; gloves (surgical, canvas, lead-impregnated); head coverings (surgeons' caps, safety helmets); face protectors (goggles, safety glasses, face shields); rubber aprons; and sometimes complete polyethylene suits. Respirators may also be considered as protective clothing.

All persons working in a radiation area must wear the prescribed protective clothing, depending upon the type of operation, the activity level, and the degree of hazard. Not only should the clothing be furnished by the plant but provision must be made for associated activities: a nonradioactive or "cold" room for changing and lockers for street clothes; a protective clothing-issue room; facilities for monitoring clothing and the body of the worker upon leaving the radiation area; a "hot" laundry for clothing decontamination; and a place to dispose of clothing too radioactive to launder and reuse.

The properly clothed emergency crew in Figure P–18 are wearing protective clothing, respirator, pocket dosimeter, and using a cutie pie counter.

FIGURE P–18. MEASURING LEVELS OF RADIOACTIVITY AND RECORDING READINGS. (RADIOLOGICAL HEALTH PROGRAM, DEPARTMENT OF HEALTH, EDUCATION, AND WELFARE.)

PROTECTIVE EQUIPMENT

Any type of PROTECTIVE CLOTHING or RESPIRATOR worn by the radiation worker to prevent contamination from radioactive material. Frequently used to mean only respiratory equipment.

PROTEIN STUDIES

Tracer studies with radioisotopes have played a major role in acquisition of modern knowledge of proteins, particularly of the dynamics of their formation and breakdown.

Proteins are made up of large numbers of simpler compounds—amino acids—and the backbone of the protein molecule is the peptide bond which holds the amino acids together. The modern concept of the formation of proteins involves the method by which sufficient energy is made available to form the peptide bond. Adenosine triphosphate (ATP), a cofactor in many enzyme systems, provides the energy for the transfer. This knowledge was obtained in experiments that used carbon-14 as a label for amino acids and phosphorus-32 as a label for the phosphorus of adenosine triphosphate.

Another area of study has been the rate of formation of specific proteins in the body. This is determined by measuring the rate of incorporation of a C^{14}-labeled amino acid from the amino acid pool into the protein. Similarly, the breakdown of a labeled protein can be measured on the basis of the rate of appearance of its labeled component in the amino acid pool.

On a still broader level, the over-all fate of a protein may be investigated. For this one may even use a tacked-on label of radioiodine, which is not a normal component of the molecule. Such labels are not ordinarily desirable, since they may alter the chemical behavior of the compound, but in studies of serum albumin they have been found useful. The radioiodine provides a suitable gamma emission, something that is not available from any of the radioisotopes of the elements usually present in proteins.

In a still different type of study, in vitro tests with the isotope dilution technique have served to show the per cent of the total protein that certain amino acids comprise.

PROTEOLYTIC ENZYMES, ESTIMATION

In studies of gastrointestinal absorption a protein such as albumin is labeled with iodine-131 and given by mouth; subsequent studies of blood, urinary, and fecal radioactivity are indicative of the degree of absorption. Poor absorption suggests a deficiency of the proteolytic enzyme from the pancreas, trypsin. However, this test has not proved a very reliable measure of pancreatic function; considerable absorption of the radioisotope may occur even in the presence of severe pancreatic disease. Labeled fat studies (see FAT DIGESTION AND ABSORPTION) are of greater usefulness.

PROTIUM

Lightest of the 3 isotopes of hydrogen; atomic number 1; mass number 1 ($_1H^1$); constitutes $99.98 + \%$ of the natural abundance. Nontoxic. *See* DEUTERIUM and TRITIUM.

PROTON

An elementary particle of mass number 1, and with a positive charge equal in magnitude to the negative charge of the electron. Named from Greek, *protos*, first. The proton is in effect the positive nucleus of the hydrogen atom. However, it is also one of the constituents of every nucleus. The atomic number (Z) indicates the number of protons in the nucleus of each atom of an element. $_2He^4$ indicates that helium has 2 protons + 2 neutrons = an atomic weight of 4. The number at the lower left of the element symbol always indicates the number of protons in the nucleus. For example, $_{92}U^{238}$ means that uranium has 92 protons in the nucleus, and 146 neutrons for an atomic weight of 238. The rest mass of a proton is 1.67×10^{-24} gram, or 1.0075 atomic mass units (amu).

PROTON RECOIL COUNTER

Neutron detector of proportional counter type; detects neutrons and determines their energies through the recoil of protons resulting from the interaction of energetic neutrons with nuclei of hydrogenous material.

PUBLIC HEALTH SERVICE RADIATION BIOLOGY AND ATOMIC MEDICINE PROGRAM

The expansion of industrial applications of atomic energy along with an increasing number of other radiation sources has brought about a corresponding rise in radiological health problems. From the very first the public health aspects of these problems in the United States have been, in large part, logically the responsibility of the U.S. Public Health Service.

As early as 1947, the Service began to increase its effort in radiological health when it established a Radiation Energy Unit, later called the Radiological Health Unit, in the Division of Industrial Hygiene. The Service's radiological health activities were accelerated when the Unit became the Radiological Health Branch in the Bureau of State Services in 1949. These activities received their greatest impetus, however, with the establishment of the Division of Radiological Health by the Surgeon General in July 1958.

The new Division was assigned 6 major responsibilities: (1) Research on the effects of radiation on living matter, including man; (2) establishing environmental surveillance; (3) training of the scientific, professional, and technical workers needed in the rapidly expanding radiological health programs of Federal, state, and local agencies; (4) technical assistance to Federal, state, and local agencies as needed; (5) development of recommendations for acceptable levels of radiation exposure from air, water, milk, medical procedures, and the general environment; (6) public information and health education activities related to radiological health.

In carrying out these responsibilities, certain duties were assigned to various organizational units within the Division. Administratively, the Division consists of an Office of the Chief and 4 branches:

A State Assistance Branch, which is a technical services unit working with the states through Regional Offices of the Department of Health, Education, and Welfare on their radiological health concerns.

A Technical Operations Branch responsible for interagency operating relationships, mainly at the Federal level and involving work with the Atomic Energy Commission, Department of Defense, Maritime Administration, Coast Guard, and other agencies.

A Research Branch for both fundamental and developmental research and for epidemiological studies which are demanding increasing attention.

A Training Branch which has the responsibility for directing Divisional efforts toward the training of personnel, for which there is a critical need in state and local health departments, research institutions, and elsewhere.

Environmental Surveillance. A major responsibility of the DRH is the development of methods and facilities, and the conduct of programs for collecting, collating, analyzing, and interpreting data on all forms of radiation exposure throughout the United States. This responsibility requires that surveillance activities receive major emphasis by the Division. A nationwide environmental network system has been developed to include an early "alert" atmospheric Radiation Surveillance Network of 67 stations, a 60-station pasteurized Milk Monitoring Network operated in cooperation with state and local health departments and milk sanitation agencies, a National Air Sampling Network operated by the Division of Air Pollution, and a National Water Quality Network operated by the Division of Water Supply and Pollution Control.

Another important part of the surveillance program is the measurement of radioactivity levels in the total diet. An Institutional Diet Sampling Program was initiated to secure an estimate of the total dietary intake of radionuclides by children aged 5 to 18 years; 20 boarding schools and institutions are currently providing diet samples for radioanalysis. In conjunction with this program, a contract was negotiated with Consumers Union of U.S.A., Inc., early in 1962 to sample teenage and infant diets in 30 cities for the presence of strontium-90 and other radionuclides.

To supplement the environmental network, a Radiation Intelligence System is being organized which will ultimately provide, on a continuing basis, data on exposure from all sources of ionizing radiation for various population groups in the United States. In accordance with the objectives of the system, a pilot project was conducted in the summer of 1961 in Montgomery Co., Md., to evaluate the effectiveness of household interviewing techniques in assessing radiation exposure to the population. The findings were sufficiently encouraging to warrant extension of the methodology on a national scale, utilizing the interview system of the Bureau of the Census.

Surveillance activities of the DRH are largely dependent upon specialized laboratory support. In the past 3 years, regional radiological health laboratories were established at Montgomery, Alabama, Las Vegas, Nevada, and Winchester,

Mass., to extend the work being carried out at the Robert A. Taft Sanitary Engineering Center in Cincinnati, Ohio, in (1) environmental sample analysis, (2) technical training, and (3) research in radiochemistry, radiophysics, and radiobiology. In addition, a special laboratory was opened at Rockville, Md., to develop methods for the effective control of radiation hazards from medical, dental, and industrial x-ray units.

At first, data from all these sources were not readily available for emergency use. Thus it was soon realized that a system for rapid collection, coordination, and evaluation of all available data was needed. Therefore, upon the resumption of Soviet nuclear testing in the fall of 1961, a Radiation Surveillance Center was established on an emergency basis in the Division to provide a continuous assessment of environmental radiation levels. The Center provides immediate assessment of significant changes and trends in environmental radiation so that monitoring schedules can be adjusted to needs and possible countermeasures to reduce radionuclide intake initiated, if necessary, by authorities in the areas affected.

In addition to the Radiation Surveillance Center, which provides immediate assessment of current environmental levels and continuing trends, the Division's Radiological Health Data and Reports Section, established in 1960, collects and maintains a permanent official record for the Federal government of information on the sources and levels of radioactivity in the environment, through publication of a technical monthly, Radiological Health Data. This publication is distributed to health authorities and investigators in the United States and throughout the world.

In addition to the operation of nation-wide environmental monitoring networks, the Division is participating in a number of long-term special radiation safety projects such as the investigation of river and port environments associated with AEC nuclear reactor operations and the construction and support of maritime and naval nuclear vessels; special survey of environmental radioactivity in Antarctica; and support of off-site monitoring in areas adjacent to United States nuclear weapons testing.

Research. In view of the pressing need for greater knowledge of the sources and biological effects of ionizing radiation, particularly at sustained low levels, the Division's research effort has been continually expanded. The comprehensive program of fundamental and developmental research now under way includes intramural studies at DRH laboratories, extramural projects under contract with universities and medical centers, and independent investigations supported by extramural grants. The general approach is epidemiological, in line with the responsibilities of the Public Health Service to delineate disease patterns in human population groups.

Examples of some of the principal studies now in progress include:

1. A collaborative project with AEC and USDA to study the effectiveness of the ion-exchange process to remove radionuclides from milk.

2. A population exposure study of residents in the San Juan Basin area of New Mexico to measure radium-226 body burden as related to radium exposure from environmental media such as water and food.

3. A multi-state study (Colorado, Michigan, and Minnesota) of congenital malformations to determine if there is a relationship between natural background radiation levels and the incidence of congenital defects.

4. A long-term bone collection program designed to identify and analyze levels of radionuclides, particularly strontium-90, in human bone.

5. A 5-year study of the possible effects from the use of radioactive iodine in the treatment of patients with overactive thyroids.

6. Study in cooperation with the University of Pittsburgh of reactor personnel to determine the level, frequency, and total amount of occupational exposure.

7. Establishment of a Registry of Radiation Pathology in the American Registry of Pathology, Armed Forces Institute of Pathology, Walter Reed Hospital.

State Assistance. With the rapid increase of radiation sources, it is imperative that the states assume increasing responsibilities for radiation protection and control. Particular emphasis is placed on providing technical assistance to bolster radiological health competency at state and local levels.

The Division is using a number of methods in helping start or improve state programs. Technical personnel from the Division are currently assigned as radiological health consultants in each of the DHEW Regional Offices. In addition, by the end of FY 1963 the Division had assigned 50 professional staff members to State health departments.

The states are also being given increased assistance with their radiation problems. Authorized by Public Law 86-373 to take over regulatory authority from the AEC, they are receiving help from the Division in developing programs related to the licensing and regulation of radioactive materials.

The states also receive help in cutting down exposure from x-ray. A nation-wide "Mail Order Survey" (Surpak) for evaluating dental x-ray units by mail has been developed by the Division. Surveys, made either by personal inspection or Surpak method, have now been conducted in 45 states. More than 45,000 dental x-ray units have been inspected.

Training. According to the 1958 estimate of the National Advisory Committee on Radiation, 1,200 radiological health specialists and 4,000 radiation technicians will be needed by 1970 to staff radiation protection programs of health agencies. To help meet this need, the Division of Radiological Health provides grants to universities for the training of radiation health specialists, assistance to junior colleges and other institutions for the training of radiation technicians, graduate-level training of PHS commissioned officers and civil service personnel, and short-course training for public health personnel in government and in industry.

Training grants to universities to improve, expand, or establish radiation health specialist curricula were made available for the first time in 1961 by Congressional approval of an initial $500,000. Congressional support of the program was increased to $1 million in 1962 enabling assistance for 110 trainees and expansion from 15 to 23 in the number of schools participating.

PUERTO RICO NUCLEAR CENTER

A graduate training and research center established in October 1957, primarily to provide graduate-level training for Latin Americans. The Center, with facilities in Rio Piedras and Mayaguez, is operated by the University of Puerto Rico under contract with the USAEC. General activities of the Center are conducted bilingually, but nearly all formal University courses are in Spanish. It has a staff of approximately 200.

The Bio-Medical Building is on the site of the Puerto Rico Medical Center in Rio Piedras. Approximately three-quarters of the 22,000 square foot building is laboratory space. The remaining area includes classrooms, office space, and related facilities. Special equipment includes an 8,000-curie cobalt-60 teletherapy unit and a deep-therapy x-ray unit. Activities include basic research in Chemistry, Clinical Radioisotope Applications, Radiotherapy and Cancer, and Radiobiology. A four-week course in Radioisotope Techniques is offered 5 times a year.

The Reactor and laboratory buildings in Mayaguez house a pool-type Megawatt research reactor, a Model L-77 small training reactor, and a subcritical assembly. Facilities include hot caves, radiation laboratories, counting rooms, glass blowing, machine, and instrument shops, a 1620 computer, an oceanographic vessel, classrooms and offices.

At Mayaguez research activity includes reactor theory and technology, radiation effects in physical, chemical, and living systems, basic physical and biological research employing tracers as related to radiation problems, neutron diffraction, agriculture, biology, and marine biology instrumentation and many related topics. Educational programs are offered at the graduate level in Nuclear Science and Technology, Health Physics, Chemistry, Agriculture, and Marine Biology.

During the academic year 1962 a total of 166 students enrolled in courses supported by the Center.

PULSE

Electrical signal arising from a single event. Various detectors for ionizing radiation events deliver pulses containing different amounts of information: a Geiger-Mueller tube indicates only that an event of a certain kind has occurred; the proportional counter can indicate the size of an event of known kind; the pulse from a scintillation crystal detector may convey accurate information as to the energy or identity of the event.

PULSE HEIGHT

The measure of the strength or signal amplitude of a pulse delivered by a detector; sometimes, the strength of the pulse, after passing through the preamplifier, as it enters an analyzer or counter circuit. Customarily expressed in volts or in millivolts.

See PULSE HEIGHT ANALYZER.

PULSE HEIGHT ANALYZER

Electronic circuit for deriving energy spectrum information from amplified signals originating in a detector such as a crystal scintillator, commonly for the purpose of identifying and measuring the amount of different radioactive nuclides present in a given sample. Important applications of this device are found in activation analysis as well as in the more usual procedures with mixed or unknown radioactive materials.

See WINDOW ANALYZER; KICKSORTER; MULTI-CHANNEL ANALYZER; ENERGY SPECTRUM.

PULSE SHAPING CIRCUIT

Electronic circuit incorporated into radiation detection instruments to permit accurate pulse height analysis information regarding energy absorbed in the detector. This function is to achieve pulses of standard shape, either in terms of pulse height voltage or pulse width time, for delivery to the analyzer circuits.

Q

Q-GAS

A mixture of 98.7% helium and 1.3% butane used in filling Geiger-Mueller counter tubes or in flow counters operating in the Geiger region, compounded to provide dependable pulse formation quenching.

QUANTUM

An elemental unit of energy according to the quantum theory. The quantum theory states that in the emission or absorption of energy by atoms or molecules the process is not continuous but takes place by steps, each step being the emission or absorption of an amount of energy called the quantum. For example, the quantum of energy of electromagnetic radiation of frequency ν is $h\nu$, where h is Planck's constant. The photon is a quantum of the electromagnetic field, and the meson is considered to be the quantum of the nuclear field. Thus, the quantum theory of radiation says that the energy of radiation emitted or absorbed is concentrated in quanta or photons each with an energy in ergs of 6.624×10^{-27} times the frequency of the radiation in cycles per second.

The quantum yield is the number of photon-induced reactions of a specified type per photon absorbed. In the photoelectric effect, the quantum yield is more commonly called the photoelectric efficiency. In plant physiology it is the ratio of the number of reactions of the primary photochemical step of photosynthesis (as yet undetermined) to the number of photons absorbed.

QUARTZ FIBER DOSIMETER

Combined radiation detector and personal measuring instrument of simple and rugged construction, using a small ionization chamber and a simple quartz fiber electrometer built into a structure the size of an ordinary fountain pen, providing a direct reading pocket dosimeter; widely used as a personnel monitor.

QUENCH

To limit the electrical discharge in an ionization detector; can be done by momentarily reducing the voltage on the tube or by incorporating a suitable chemical constituent in the counting gas.

QUENCH CIRCUIT

Input circuit for an amplifier or scaler which is designed to lower the collecting voltage on the tube as soon as it delivers a signal derived from an ionizing event. The purpose is to prepare the tube for the next event in the shortest possible time.

R

Symbol for ROENTGEN.

RAD

An acronym from radiation absorbed dose. A rad is 100 ergs of absorbed energy per gram of absorbing material. The rad is a measure of the energy imparted to matter (i.e., retained by matter) by ionizing radiation per unit mass of irradiated material at the place of interest. Recommended and adopted by the International Commission on Radiological Units at the Seventh International Congress of Radiology, July, 1953.

RADIATION

Emission and propagation of energy through space or through a material medium in the form of waves, for example, electromagnetic radiation, sound waves, and elastic waves.

Energy propagated through space or through a material medium as waves or as energy in the form of electromagnetic waves.

The term radiation, or radiant energy, usually refers to electromagnetic radiation, which is classified, according to frequency, as Hertzian or radiofrequency and microwave, infrared or heat, visible or light, ultraviolet, x-ray, and gamma (γ) ray.

In popular usage, radiation refers to radioactive radiation and is often erroneously solely equated with fallout.

By extension, includes particle emissions, such as alpha and beta radiation and cosmic radiation, sometimes called corpuscular radiation.

Radiation consisting of a beam of particles of a variety of energies, or having different frequencies, or containing different types of particles is called heterogeneous radiation. Homogeneous radiation, on the other hand, consists of an extremely narrow band of frequencies or a beam of monoenergetic particles of a single type.

Monoenergetic radiation is particulate radiation of a given type such as alpha, beta, or neuron, in which all particles have the same energy.

Monochromatic radiation is electromagnetic radiation of a single wave length, or in which all the photons have the same energy.

Secondary radiation consists of particles or photons produced by the interaction of primary radiation with matter. Examples are bremsstrahlung radiation, photoelectrons, Compton recoil electrons, and the secondary cosmic rays.

Primary radiation is sometimes spoken of in referring to the original or first radioactive emissions from a radioactive element. The hard component of cosmic rays is called primary radiation.

See BACKGROUND RADIATION, ENVIRONMENTAL RADIATION, EXTERNAL RADIATION, INTERNAL IRRADIATION HAZARD, NATURAL RADIATION, NUCLEAR RADIATION, RADIATION SOURCES, and TERRESTRIAL RADIATION.

RADIATION ACCIDENTS

Accidents resulting in the spread of radioactive material or in the exposure of individuals to radiation. An overexposure or accident is considered to have occurred when an individual has received more than the maximum permissible dose for the time involved. One of the most serious types of accidents is the CRITICALITY ACCIDENT in which enormous amounts of radiation are released instantaneously. REACTOR ACCIDENTS may be of the criticality type or may result in REACTOR FIRES with the spread of radioactive contamination.

Explosions and fires involving radioactive material account for many radiation accidents. SHIPPING ACCIDENTS usually result in spreading radioactive contamination but rarely result in acute or severe exposure to personnel. (*See* EXPLOSIONS, RADIOACTIVE MATERIAL, and FIRES, RADIOACTIVE MATERIAL.)

Radiation accidents may result in contamination of the environment (*see* CONTAMINATION ACCIDENTS and CONTAMINATION, RADIOACTIVE) by radioactive dust or liquid or in the release of direct radiation from an uncontrolled or improperly shielded source; but are often due to improper handling of radiation sources or radioactive material. Some examples of various types of radiation accidents follow:

An employee inhaled polonium-210 during the handling and counting of a polonium-alpha source and received an estimated $3\frac{1}{2}$ times the maximum permissible body burden. Because the sample was odd-sized, it was being handled in an unorthodox manner.

While unpacking radioactive material an employee allowed it to rest against his leg. He received a radiation burn and lost 36 days from work. Compensation was paid.

Overpressurization of a box for helium cooling at an accelerator installation blew out a thin experimental foil, containing about 0.05 curie of curium-244, causing it to disintegrate. The cost was $58,500 for cleanup and lost operating time.

In a research laboratory a student removed some samples from an irradiator, unaware that a 200-curie cobalt-60 source had become detached and had fallen into the flask holding the samples. In carrying it upstairs to another laboratory he received an estimated 80 to 100 rem exposure, and 11 others received from 200 millirem to 25 rem.

Fifteen to 25 employees working on and around a scaffold received a maximum of 6 roentgens from gamma rays when someone knocked the cap off a pig containing a 32-curie iridium source used in radiographic work.

A film badge exposure of 120 rem occurred while radiographic shots were being made with a faulty camera using a 5.2-curie iridium-192 source. (This type of accident is rather common.)

During the past 15 years there has been a steady improvement in the concepts, techniques, and equipment of radiation dosimetry. But one of the most difficult problems associated with radiation accidents still is in determining accurately the radiation dose received by the exposed individuals, particularly if the dose is very high.

See SAFETY RECORD, USAEC.

RADIATION AREA*

Any area accessible to personnel, in which the level of radiation is such that a major portion of the body could receive in any one hour a dose in excess of 5 millirem, or in any 5 consecutive days a dose in excess of 150 millirem.

If the radiation reaches a level of 100 millirems for a major portion of the body in any one hour, it becomes a high-radiation area.

The conventional RADIATION WARNING SYMBOL must be displayed in any such areas together with the appropriate CAUTION SIGN: Caution, Radiation Area; Caution, High Radiation Area; or Caution, Air-borne Radioactivity Area.

See CONTROLLED AREA.

RADIATION BIOLOGY

That branch of biology which deals with the effects of radiation on biological systems. Closely related to radiation physics and radiation chemistry, which disciplines underlie all thinking about initial mechanisms of radiation biology.

See RADIOBIOLOGY.

---

*Federal Register, Title 10—Atomic Energy; Chapter 1—Atomic Energy Commission, Part 20—Standards For Protection Against Radiation.

RADIATION BURN. See BURNS, RADIATION.

RADIATION CHEMISTRY

The study of the chemical effects (including discomposition) produced by high-energy radiation (x-rays, gamma rays) and particles (alpha, beta) on matter.

RADIATION DAMAGE

A general term for the effects of radiation (x-rays, gamma rays, fission fragments, and neutrons) upon substances. Many types of change may occur in organic and inorganic compounds: dissociation of compounds; evolution of gases; disruption of crystal structure; and changes in mechanical properties and dimensions, thermal conductivity, electrical conductivity, etc. Often applied to biological effects of radiation, in which case the term radiation damage may refer to radiation-induced somatic effects or to genetic damage from radiation. (See SOMATIC EFFECTS, RADIATION INDUCED.)

RADIATION DECOMPOSITION

Radiation may lead to cell death and thus to the formation of decomposition products. The shock-like syndrome which results from high radiation dosage may be due to release of decomposition products into the circulating blood. Decomposition products may be found in labeled organic compounds and one should check for these.

RADIATION DEMOGRAPHY. See DEMOGRAPHY, USE IN STUDY OF RADIATION EFFECTS.

RADIATION DETECTION INSTRUMENTS

Devices which detect and record the characteristics of ionizing radiation fields. They are classified according to the kinds of radiation to which they are sensitive, the levels of radiation they can detect, the kinds of service they can provide, and the nature or extent of the analysis they can perform on the radiations detected. Thus there are instruments for alpha, beta, gamma, and neutron radiations; for low-intensity or high-intensity fields of low- or high-energy radiations; and for purposes of prospecting, protection survey, tracer studies, or radiation treatment in industrial, laboratory, health physics, or medical therapy installations. There are also instruments whose analytical capabilities range from simple indiscriminate counting to complete energy spectrum analysis or the quantitative identification of constituents in a mixture of radioactive isotopes.

The constituent parts of radiation detection instruments must include a detector and an indicator. In the ELECTROSCOPE and the direct reading POCKET DOSIMETER these functions are served in a single component, although means for separate electrical charging must be provided. The more elegant standard FREE-AIR IONIZATION CHAMBER is characterized by highly sensitive electrical measuring circuits but still comprises only the same simple constituents. Instruments which employ pulse-type detectors whether GAS COUNTERS, SCINTILLATORS, or semiconductor elements, generally require more complicated ancillary circuitry. PREAMPLIFIERS, PULSE SHAPING CIRCUITS, AMPLIFIERS, PULSE HEIGHT ANALYZERS, and suitable output count registers or strip chart recorders are combined to provide for whatever functions are necessary in the particular measurement under investigation. In general, the more complex and delicate instrumental assemblies also demand high stability regulation in the high-voltage power supplies.

RADIATION DETECTORS

Any of a wide variety of materials or instruments which provide a signal when stimulated by the passage of ionizing radiation; the sensitive element in RADIATION DETECTION INSTRUMENTS. The most widely used media for the detection of ionizing radiation are photographic film and ionization in gases, followed by scintillation materials.

The earliest studies of ionizing radiations were made by use of photography, fluorescent light, ionization in air, and by studying skin erythema. The discoveries of x-rays and of radioactivity were made through their effects on photographic film. In both fields the early investigations relied heavily on the electroscope and fluorescent screens. Likewise, in both instances, radiation damage was noted in the skin of workers within a few months of the discovery.

For all kinds of ionizing radiations, the fundamental process of detection is the dissipation of energy by a charged particle in a suitable medium. The energy of this initial or secondary charged particle is distributed throughout the detecting material, producing many ionized and excited atomic or molecular units. Some of these units can be observed and collected as ionized atoms or free electrons; those which result in excited states of atoms and molecules may be detected in a variety of ways: color change in transparent media, light quanta emitted on return to a lower-energy state, or the release of stored energy under ultraviolet or thermal stimulation. Ionization in gases has probably been the most widely useful phenomenon for the detection and measurement of ionizing radiation. It has been applied in the IONIZATION CHAMBER, PROPORTIONAL COUNTER, GEIGER-MUELLER COUNTER, and a variety of other special devices. It was of great importance as embodied in the earliest simple ELECTROSCOPE measurements as well as in the extreme sophistication of determinations made with the Wilson CLOUD CHAMBER.

Practical relations which define performance over the range of working voltages is detailed in the discussion on GAS COUNTERS as well as under the specific instruments noted above. Ionization and excitation in liquids provide another group of radiation DETECTOR elements; these include the CHEMICAL DOSIMETERS in which changes of valence state or the production of free radicals result in alterations measurable by colorimetry, densitometry, titration, or the collection of evolved gases. Solid materials display a variety of radiation detector properties. Certain transparent substances respond with scintillations and are classed as FLUORS or PHOSPHORS; those of crystalline nature and of high atomic number provide signals discretely related to the energy absorbed. The plastics are less useful for spectral energy measurement. Transparent substances are also of use in the detection and measurement of Cerenkov radiation. Semiconductor and crystal conduction detectors have been developed for various kinds of radiations. The response of both scintillation and conduction detectors depends on the disturbance by the radiation of impurity centers or other features of the solid-state structures. Certain glassy and crystalline materials are useful as detectors because of their ability to store absorbed radiation for subsequent release under controlled conditions. Silver-activated glass and lithium fluoride in the form of rods or pellets can be made to give quantitative indications through the light released under stimulation by ultraviolet or thermal stimulation, referred to as fluorod and THERMOLUMINESCENT DOSIMETERS. At higher levels of radiation exposure changes in visible light transmission are also usable. Since all radiation energy absorbed in a medium is eventually converted to heat, calorimetry is the one method of detection which can have universal applicability. In comparison with all the other methods noted, however, it is of extremely low sensitivity. In selecting a suitable detector, the range of penetrating ability of the particular radiation must be considered in relation to the absorption and signal-generating capabilities of the detecting material. Thus large scintillation crystals are indicated for high-energy gamma rays while thin crystals serve for alpha particles. For a typical neutron counter a specific material must be provided to give a measurable secondary radiation, either from a nuclear reaction or proton recoil effect.

Other special detectors sometimes utilize a secondary principle to improve response: energetic beta rays can be detected in scintillation crystals through the bremsstrahlung produced in solids or liquids. Conversely, the use of heavy metals in a GEIGER COUNTER CATHODE wall enhances its gamma-ray sensitivity because they release secondary electrons more abundantly.

RADIATION DOSIMETRY

The procedure of determining the quantity of ionizing radiation delivered or the energy absorbed from it in a radiation exposure situation, as, for example, in radiotherapy, radioisotope experimentation, or an occupational radiation environment. Radiation dosimetry is carried out through the use of suitable instrumentation and appropriate calculation. The accurate practice of dosimetry requires careful selection of instruments to detect the particular kind of radiation being measured as well as exact arrangement of conditions to insure proper representation of the exposure situation. The immediate objective of dosimetry is to arrive at a true and reproducible value, in strictly physical terms, for the amount of radiation delivered. The ultimate aim is to achieve a measurement which is equivalent to the response of living tissue to the specific radiation and exposure conditions prescribed. However, because the responses of different living systems vary widely, no simple relationship is possible between biological response and the physically measured quantity of radiation (see RELATIVE BIOLOGICAL EFFECTIVENESS).

Since the concern here relates chiefly to the effects of ionizing radiation in living tissue, it is of historical interest to note that early attempts to establish biological dose parameters utilized such obvious effects as reaction or reddening of the skin and epilation. Thus the unit called SED (skin erythema dose) was used, along with some primitive types of chemical dosimeter, such as the platino-ferrocyanate pastilles which changed from yellow to green after certain exposure levels had been reached. In x-ray work, other attempts to define radiation exposures were based on energy of the radiation characterized in terms of spark-gap measurements of the voltage exciting the x-ray tube, together with time of irradiation and crude or indirect determination of the x-ray tube current. These were eventually supplanted by modern gaseous ionization detectors with refined electrical measurement systems used in current practice.

The ideal dosimeter should respond uniformly to radiations of all kinds and of all energies within its intended field of application. It should be small enough and of such construction that its presence in the radiation field does not interfere with or disturb the radiation pattern in any way. Moreover, its response should be independent of dose rate; it should be convenient to prepare, to use, and to read; and it must be reliable and reproducible at all times. Physical factors which dictate the selection of instruments and modes of procedure in dosimetry include: the kind of radiation (whether electromagnetic or sundry particulate radiations), the quality of the radiation (its energy or energy spectrum), the spatial arrangement of distributed source materials (when interstitial or systemic), the nature of the medium containing or separating the radiation source material and the detector, the distance from source to measuring position, and the rate at which the dose is delivered.

For many routine situations, dosimetry is adequately carried out by the use of a calibrated instrument to measure the amount of ionization released in air at the place of interest. For a considerable further number of standard situations, these measurements can be treated by calculation to give suitable figures for the absorbed energy at that point in a particular substance. But it is essential in many experimental situations to give special attention to the conditions and specific properties of both radiations and materials in designing instruments and procedures which correctly indicate the desired quantities. On this basis, dosimetric methods can provide accurate and reproducible evaluation of the energy delivered under the conditions of radiation exposure in specifically defined situations, in terms of uniformly reproducible quantities which can in turn be measured and defined in terms of fundamental constants.

Absolute standard measurements of x-rays and gamma rays can be made with the FREE-AIR IONIZATION CHAMBER. Since this is not a practical instrument for use in ordinary dosimetry, it is customary to calibrate portable instruments against the standard free-air ionization chamber in the laboratory. The most widely used secondary standard instruments are the thimble chambers. These are small condenser chambers which can be detached from their measuring instruments and established at the desired location in the radiation field. Subsequent to exposure they are made to give a dose reading through simple measurement of their loss of electric charge. They are commonly of the air-equivalent wall type and are used to determine the "air dose" at the point of exposure, representing the situation there as though it simply existed free in air. By calculation, it is possible to convert such information into a more useful form in terms of energy absorbed. To satisfy the variety of situations met in practice, these air-equivalent or TISSUE-EQUIVALENT IONIZATION CHAMBERS can be made in size and dose response ranges for most ordinary situations and even for use within body cavities.

For dosimetric problems which involve mixtures or combinations of radiations, it is necessary to treat the contribution of each distinct constituent individually and to arrive at a summation or an integration of the total effect. The most common situation of this kind is the evaluation of the total dose delivered in the use of most radioactive isotopes in which it is quite common to have both beta-ray and gamma-ray emissions from the source material. Since there is a great difference in the penetration and absorption behavior of these constituent radiations, separate calculation is generally required; in addition, the way the material is distributed throughout the living system under study must be established. It is ordinarily necessary in such problems to give further consideration to that part of the living system which is most susceptible, when differences of radiobiological response are known or are being established.

RADIATION EFFECTS, BIOLOGICAL. *See* BIOLOGICAL EFFECTS OF RADIATION.

RADIATION EFFECTS, CEREBRAL. *See* BRAIN TISSUE, RADIATION EFFECTS ON; CENTRAL NERVOUS SYSTEM, RADIATION EFFECTS ON; and BEHAVIOR AFFECTED BY RADIATION.

RADIATION EFFECTS, GASTROINTESTINAL. *See* GASTROINTESTINAL TRACT, RADIATION EFFECTS ON.

RADIATION EFFECTS, GENETIC. *See* CHROMOSOMES, RADIATION EFFECTS ON; GENETIC DEATH; GENETIC EFFECTS, RADIATION; GONADS, RADIATION EFFECTS ON; MUTATION, RADIATION INDUCED.

RADIATION EFFECTS, HEMATOPOIETIC SYSTEM. *See* HEMATOPOIETIC SYSTEM, RADIATION EFFECTS ON.

RADIATION EFFECTS, ORGANS. *See* ORGANS, RADIATION EFFECTS ON.

RADIATION EXPOSURE

Exposure to radiation may be described and modified by a number of terms. The type of radiation is an important consideration: alpha (α) and beta (β) particles, neutrons, gamma (γ) and x-rays, and cosmic radiation. Radiation exposure may be from an external radiation source, such as gamma rays, x-rays, or neutrons, or it may be from an internal radiation source from radioisotopes retained within the body emitting alpha, beta, or gamma radiation. The exposure may result from penetrating or nonpenetrating radiation in relation to its ability to enter and pass through matter—alpha and beta particles being considered as nonpenetrating and the other types of radiation as penetrating. Exposure may be related to a part of the body or to the whole body.

The terms high-level radiation exposure and low-level radiation exposure are commonly used but are not well defined. High-level generally refers to a heavy exposure which can be easily detected by clinical or laboratory means within a few days after exposure. Low-level usually refers to a small amount of radiation over a long period of time or continuously. Teletherapy treatment for malignant disease would generally be high-level exposure, and the natural radiation to which everyone is exposed is often referred to as low-level exposure.

See ACUTE RADIATION EXPOSURE, and CHRONIC EXPOSURE, RADIATION.

RADIATION EXPOSURE PERSONNEL RECORD

A careful record is kept and reported annually of the external radiation exposure of every individual employed by the USAEC or any of its contractors. This is designed to check on the adequacy of the safeguards and their enforcement. As will be seen in Table R–1, only 0.1% of the 75,611 employees in 1959 received an annual total exposure of 5 rem or over; and only 1 individual received over 15 rem total exposure for the 12 months (*see* MAXIMUM PERMISSIBLE DOSE).

TABLE R–1.   PENETRATING RADIATION EXPOSURE RECORD

RANGE OF ANNUAL TOTAL EXPOSURE IN REM	1959 WORKERS		1960 WORKERS		1961 WORKERS	
	NUMBER	% OF TOTAL	NUMBER	% OF TOTAL	NUMBER	% OF TOTAL
0–1	71,630	94.73	77,522	94.31	90,651	94.55
1–5	3,912	5.17	4,629	5.63	5,174	5.4
5–10	66	0.09	41	0.05	40	.04
10–15	2	0.01	2	0.01	2	.002
15 or over	1	0.01	3	0.01	*8	.008
Total	75,611	100.	82,197	100.	95,875	100.

*Emergency activities SL–1 accident.

RADIATION ILLNESS

An acute, self-limiting organic disorder following radiation and characterized by a group of signs and symptoms called the ACUTE RADIATION SYNDROME varying with the level of dose of whole body irradiation received. Usual agents producing injury are gamma rays, x-rays, and fast and slow neutrons. The following divisions are not exact but will serve to illustrate the variation in this illness.

In the dose range from 0 to 50 roentgens (r), humans normally have no sign or symptoms of radiation illness and no medical problem will be present.

From 50 to 100 r exposure, there may be very mild nausea and VOMITING and some lassitude, but these will be of short duration and will pose no medical problem.

Penetrating radiation in the range of 100 to 200 r causes nausea, vomiting, and fatigue in the majority of those exposed, but the condition is transitory, usually subsiding within 48 hours.

Between 200 and 400 r exposure, the typical hematopoietic form of radiation illness manifests itself (*see* HEMATOPOIETIC SYSTEM). Transient radiation sickness, as noted above, will occur, followed by a 1- to 3-week period of relative well-being, which is usually followed by hemorrhagic disorders, such as gingival bleeding, nose bleed, petechiae of the skin and mucous membrane, and in more serious cases intestinal bleeding (*see* HEMORRHAGE). Profound pancytopenia may be present; in fact, at this level of exposure, destruction of white blood cells and platelets occurs—and recovery of these tissues determines the ultimate recovery of the patient. Figure R–1 depicts the time course of symptoms in a typical case.

From 400 to 600 r, severe prodromal symptoms of nausea and vomiting occur with evidence of the gastrointestinal form of acute radiation illness beginning to show with severe diarrhea and subsequent emaciation. Patients who recover from this may still encounter symptoms resulting from damage to the blood-forming organs.

From 600 to 800 r exposure, the gastrointestinal symptoms are severe with almost continuous vomiting and diarrhea, dehydration, and electrolyte derangements, death occurring at any time from 1 day to 2 weeks following exposure. The earlier the onset of symptoms, the graver the prognosis. From 800 to 1,000 r, death is inevitable, with present-day knowledge of treatment, and is usually the result of gastrointestinal changes.

Above 1,000 r whole body acute exposure, signs and symptoms indicate primary involvement of the central nervous system (*see* CENTRAL NERVOUS SYSTEM), and the radiation illness is said to be of

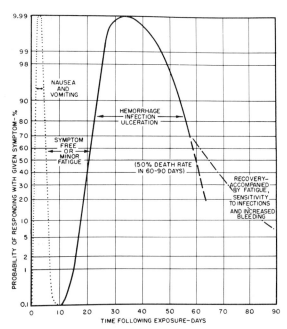

FIGURE R–1. AN IDEALIZED DESCRIPTION OF THE TIME COURSE OF SYMPTOMS OF ACUTE RADIATION ILLNESS FOLLOWING MID-LETHAL EXPOSURE OF WHOLE BODY RADIATION OF 250–500 RAD. (NASA LIFE SCIENCES DATA BOOK.)

the cerebral form. Death is likely to occur within the first 2 days and is associated with convulsions, tremor, ataxia, lethargy, severe apathy, prostration, and unconsciousness.

For exposures over 200 r, hospitalization is necessary with bed rest, nursing care, antibiotics, blood transfusions as indicated, and BONE MARROW GRAFTS for those in the mid-lethal range exposure. (*See* TREATMENT OF RADIATION ILLNESS.) One of the most difficult problems in handling radiation accidents is combating the psychological effects. Radiation accidents bring publicity and visitors, which add to the natural fear and worry of the patient and family. Inevitable rumors add to the psychological problem. The physician's task is to keep the visitors out, to correct false rumors, and to reassure the patient and family.

Table R–2 presents a review of 4 cases and summarizes some of the signs and symptoms of radiation illness that are of diagnostic and prognostic importance.

RADIATION INCIDENTS

Any uncontrolled release of radiation or radioactive material. The incident may involve no exposure of a human being or severe radiation exposure leading to death of one or more workers—but usually involves some measurable external radiation or the internal deposition of radioactive

TABLE R–2. EARLY SIGNS AND SYMPTOMS OF DIAGNOSTIC AND PROGNOSTIC
IMPORTANCE IN RADIATION ILLNESS

	CASE I >300 REM	CASE II 800 REM	CASE III 1,900 REM	CASE IV 12,000 REM
Ataxia and dis- orientation	No	No	No	Prompt
Shock	No	? Mild	No	Severe
Nausea and vomiting, onset	Mild, 2 hr.	Troublesome, 1–1 1/2 hr.	Mild, 1 hr.	Severe, 15 min.
Diarrhea, onset	No	No	Once, 4 hr.	Severe, 45 min.
Erythema, onset	No	3 days	24 hr.	Immediate
Fever	?	Slight and irregular	Moderate and irregular	103.5°, falling to nor- mal in 12 hr.
Hemoconcentration	No	Moderate and gradual	Moderate and gradual	Prompt and severe
WBC, total count	Initial rise, followed by drop, mild	Rise to 16,000 in 24 hr.	Rise to 18,000 in 24 hr.	Rise to 28,000 in 12 hr.
Lymphocytes	Drop to >1,000	Drop to a few hun- dred, 48 hr.	Drop to near 0 in 24 hr.	Complete disappear- ance, in 10 hr.
Renal impairment	No	3 days	24 hr.	Immediate
Death	No	24 days	9 days	35 hr.

material. Property damage, including cost of de-contamination, is always considered in reporting an incident. (*See* ACCIDENTS.)

For USAEC operations, the criteria for reporting are:

"a. A dollar cost of recovery (decontamination, repair, etc.) or damage or loss associated with the incident of $5,000 or more.

b. Radiation exposure to one or more persons of several rems or more, usually delivered in a short time.

c. Potential radiation exposure as in (b) which did not in fact occur (for example, an incident involving the spillage of curie quantities of plutonium).

d. An incident which, for reason of possible public interest, has been reported previously to the public."

For licensee operations, the criteria for reporting are those given in USAEC regulations as stated in 10 CFR Part 20,* which requires immediate reporting of any incident which may have caused or threatened to cause:

"(1) Exposure of the whole body of any individual to 25 rems or more of radiation; exposure of the skin of the whole body of any individual of 150 rems or more of radiation; or exposure of the feet, ankles, hands or forearms of any individual to 375 rems or more of radiation; or

(2) The release of radioactive material in concentrations which, if averaged over a period of 24 hours, would exceed 5,000 times the limits specified for such materials; or

(3) A loss of one working week or more of operation of any facilities affected; or

(4) Damage to property in excess of $100,000."

It is also required by 10 CFR Part 20* that: "Each licensee shall within 24 hours notify the Manager of the appropriate Atomic Energy Commission Operations Office by telephone and telegraph of any incident involving licensed material possessed by him and which may have caused or threatened to cause:

"(1) Exposure of the whole body of any individual to 5 rems or more of radiation; exposure of the skin of the whole body of any individual to 30 rems or more of radiation; or exposure of the feet, ankles, hands, or forearms to 75 rems or more of radiation; or

(2) The release of radioactive material in

*Federal Register. Title 10–Atomic Energy. Chapter 1—Atomic Energy Commission. Part 20—Standard for Protection against Radiation.

concentrations which, if averaged over a period of 24 hours, would exceed 500 times the limits specified for such materials; or

(3) A loss of one day or more of the operations of any facilities affected; or

(4) Damage to property in excess of $1,000."

Thirty-day reports are also required for any overexposure or increase in levels of radiation over the prescribed limits.

RADIATION INJURIES. *See* INJURIES, RADIATION.

RADIATION MONITORING

Also radiological monitoring. Continuous or periodic determination of the amount of radiation present in a given area. MONITORING DEVICES are located in the stack of an air-cooled reactor for continuously recording the radioactivity of the gaseous waste being discharged to the atmosphere. Laboratories handling large amounts of radioactive material are sometimes equipped with devices for continuously monitoring the radiation level which sound an alarm if a hazardous condition develops. Film badges worn by all personnel working in radiation areas are a type of monitoring device. In the MONITORING PROGRAM FOR RADIOACTIVE FALLOUT a number of different types of surveillance and monitoring networks are usually in operation.

RADIATION PRESERVATION. *See* FOOD PRESERVATION.

RADIATION PROTECTION

Protection of the industrial radiation worker and the general public by setting up legislative protective rules and regulations and by taking advantage of the physical characteristics of radiation that affect protection.

Legislative action set up the USAEC's STANDARDS FOR PROTECTION AGAINST RADIATION and the RADIATION PROTECTION STANDARDS of the Federal Radiation Council. There are RADIOLOGICAL SAFETY RULES, and regulations for licensing and INSPECTION, for SAFE HANDLING and use of radioactive material and for waste disposal. Many states have regulations specifically designed to effect radiation protection.

There are 3 physical factors that have a bearing on radiation protection: the first 2, distance from the source and length of exposure, cannot be controlled very practically in an industrial situation, but the third, SHIELDING, is a most practical method of protection—the shield may be a lead apron worn as PROTECTIVE CLOTHING or a 5-foot-thick concrete shield around a hot cell.

But perhaps the most important protective measures are careful planning with a RADIOLOGICAL SURVEY prior to starting a project and careful house-keeping and radiation MONITORING during operation of the project.

RADIATION PROTECTION GUIDES

The radiation dose which should not be exceeded without careful consideration of the reasons for doing so. The following radiation protection guides (RPG) were developed by the Federal Radiation Council and published in the Federal Register on May 18, 1960, for use by all Federal agencies:

TABLE R–3.

TYPE OF EXPOSURE	CONDITION	DOSE (REM)
Radiation worker:		
(a) Whole body, head and trunk, active blood-forming organs, gonads, or lens of eye	Accumulated dose 13 weeks	5 times the number of years beyond age 18 3
(b) Skin of whole body and thyroid	Year 13 weeks	30 10
(c) Hands and forearms, feet and ankles	Year 13 weeks	75 25
(d) Bone	Body burden	0.1 microgram of radium-226 or its biological equivalent
(e) Other organs	Year 13 weeks	15 5
Population:		
(a) Individual	Year	0.5 (whole body)
(b) Average	30 year	5 (gonads)

A number of explanatory points were also published which give additional details concerning the use of the RPG:

1. For the individual in the population, the basic guide for annual whole body dose is 0.5 rem. This guide applies when the individual whole body doses are known. As an operational technique, when the individual whole body doses are not known, a suitable sample of the exposed population should be developed whose protection guide for annual whole body dose will be 0.17 rem per capita per year. It is emphasized that this is an operational technique which should be modified to meet special situations.

2. Considerations of population genetics impose a per capita dose limitation for the gonads of 5 rem in 30 years. The operational mechanism described above for the annual individual whole body dose of 0.5 rem is likely in the immediate future to assure that the gonadal exposure guide (5 rem in 30 years) is not exceeded.

3. These guides do not differ substantially from certain other recommendations, such as those made by the National Committee on Radiation Protection and Measurements (NCRP), the National Academy of Sciences, and the International Commission on Radiological Protection (ICRP).

4. The term "maximum permissible dose" is used by the National Committee on Radiation Protection and the International Commission on Radiological Protection. However, this term is often misunderstood. The words "maximum" and "permissible" both have unfortunate connotations not intended by either the NCRP or the ICRP.

5. There can be no single permissible or acceptable level of exposure without regard to the reason for permitting the exposure. It should be general practice to reduce exposure to radiation, and positive effort should be carried out to fulfill the sense of these recommendations. It is basic that exposure to radiation should result from a real determination of its necessity.

6. There can be different radiation protection guides with different numerical values, depending upon the circumstances. The guides herein recommended are appropriate for normal peacetime operations.

7. These guides are not intended to apply to radiation exposure resulting from natural background or the purposeful exposure of patients by practitioners of the healing arts.

8. It is recognized that our present scientific knowledge does not provide a firm foundation within a factor of 2 or 3 for selection of any particular numerical value in preference to another value. It should be recognized that the radiation

protection guides recommended here are well below the level at which biological damage has been observed in humans.

The Federal Radiation Council staff report No. 2, September, 1961, provides guidance concerning internal deposition of radionuclides occurring in the environment and includes "(1) Radiation Protection Guides for certain organs of individuals in the general population, as well as averages over suitable samples of exposed groups, (2) guidance on general principles of control applicable to all radionuclides occurring in the environment, (3) some general principles by which Federal agencies may establish appropriate concentration values, and (4) specific guidance in connection with exposure of population groups to radium-226, iodine-131, strontium-90 and strontium-89."

The control of the intake of radioactive materials from the environment is considered in relation to "three daily rates of intake by suitable samples of exposed population groups:

"Range I. Intakes falling in this range would not under normal conditions be expected to result in any appreciable number of individuals in the population reaching a large fraction of the RPG." The action required is periodic surveillance to determine the level of radioactivity and the application of routine control.

"Range II. Intakes falling into this range would be expected to result in average exposures to population groups not exceeding the RPG." The action required is quantitative surveillance to determine probable variation in average daily uptake and to detect rising trends. Control includes action to reduce environmental exposure levels.

"Range III. Intakes within this range would be presumed to result in exposures exceeding the RPG if continued for a sufficient period of time." Surveillance as in Range II. More active control designed to reduce levels of radioactivity to levels of Range II or lower.

The Council recommended the adoption of the following guides for daily intake for normal peacetime operations to be applied to the average of suitable samples of an exposed population group:

TABLE R–4. RANGES OF TRANSIENT RATES OF INTAKE FOR USE IN THE GRADED SCALE OF ACTIONS RECOMMENDED.

RADIONUCLIDE	RANGE I	RANGE II	RANGE III
	MICROMICROCURIES PER DAY		
Radium-226	0–2	2–20	20–200
Iodine-131	0–10	10–100	100–1,000
Strontium-90	0–20	20–200	200–2,000
Strontium-89	0–200	200–2,000	2,000–20,000

The radiation protection guides are intended to replace the "maximum permissible dose." But since all the literature and many of the regulations still refer to maximum permissible dose, this older term has been used in this book.

RADIATION PROTECTION STANDARDS

The Federal Radiation Council has issued 2 reports* dealing with background material for the development of radiation protection standards. Report No. 1 presents a general philosophy on RADIATION PROTECTION for use by Federal agencies and introduces the term RADIATION PROTECTION GUIDES (RPG). This report also provides numerical values for RPG's for whole body and certain organs of radiation workers, and whole body for individuals in the general population.

Report No. 2 presents guidance designed to limit exposure of members of population groups to radiation due to internal deposition of radionuclides. In addition to general guidance on control applicable to radionuclides occurring in the environment, the report gives specific guidance for RPG's in connection with exposure of population groups to radium-226, iodine-131, strontium-90, and strontium-89 (see RADIATION PROTECTION GUIDES).

Maximum permissible dose levels for both external radiation and for internal deposition of radioactive materials have been delineated by the National Committee on Radiation Protection and the International Commission on Radiological Protection. These do not have the force of law but are used regularly in any application of radiation protection standards to specific situations. The Federal Radiation Council guides govern in all Federal laboratories.

RADIATION PROTECTIVE COMPOUNDS.
See CHEMICAL PROTECTION AGAINST RADIATION INJURY.

RADIATION SHIELDING
Reduction or stopping the passage of radiation by interposing a shield (absorbing material) between the radioactive source and the person or laboratory area in question.

RADIATION SICKNESS.   See RADIATION ILLNESS.

RADIATION SOURCES
In the usual sense, radiation sources refer to the man-made, sealed sources use in teletherapy,

---

*Federal Radiation Council staff report. Report No. 1, May 13, 1960; and Report No. 2, September, 1961.

radiography, as power sources for batteries, and for industrial activity in gauges of various types.

In the sense of the source or origin of the radiation there are reactors, particle accelerators, x-ray tubes, fission products, natural radionuclides, and activated radionuclides and, of course, the actual process of fission and fusion of the nuclear device with its prompt radiation.

Living material is irradiated constantly and intermittently from many sources. These may be classified under three major headings: natural, man-made, and those from nuclear weapons testing. From the standpoint of the individual human being there are two classifications: external radiation and internal radiation.

NATURAL RADIATION is composed of COSMIC RADIATION coming from outer space and TERRESTRIAL RADIATION from radioactive elements in the crust of the earth, the water areas, and the surrounding atmosphere. Radiation sources have been analyzed from the standpoint of possible genetic hazard, and it has been calculated that the gonads of the average individual living in the United States will be exposed over a 30-year period to 4.3 roentgens of radiation. The term BACKGROUND RADIATION is reserved for use in connection with radiation equipment and the counting of radiation. The term ENVIRONMENTAL RADIATION refers to the local situation, houses, industrial exposure, contamination, and exposure of the operators to medical x-ray equipment, etc.

The largest component in man-made radiation in the United States is the medical use of the x-ray which has been calculated to provide an accumulated gonadal dose of 3.0 roentgens over a 30-year period to the average person living in this country. The developing medical and industrial uses of radioisotopes and the increase in the use of atomic power may add a small component to man-made radiation sources.

FALLOUT from the testing of nuclear weapons adds another component to radiation sources to which the population in the United States is exposed. According to the same criteria of calculation, the accumulated gonadal dose attributable to weapons testing over a 30-year period to the average person living in the United States, if continued for 30 years at the average rate of the years 1950–1955, would amount to 0.1 roentgen. This figure is uncertain by a factor of 5 and thus might be as low as 0.02 or as high as 0.5 roentgen. This does not take into account the Russian, British, or French testing and so another factor of perhaps 2 times may be necessary. This says nothing of a possible all-out nuclear war in which initial nuclear radiation, induced radioactivity, and fallout would be factors of catastrophic proportions.

RADIATION SOURCES, INTERNAL. *See* IN-
TERNAL IRRADIATION HAZARD.

RADIATION STANDARDS

The control of radiation exposure by legislative means; the setting of exposure standards, permissible concentrations, rules of safe handling, regulations for transportation of radioactive materials, and regulations for industrial control.

See RADIATION PROTECTION STANDARDS, STANDARDS FOR PROTECTION AGAINST RADIATION, RADIOLOGICAL SAFETY ORGANIZATION, and RADIOLOGICAL SAFETY RULES.

RADIATION STERILIZATION

Sterilization may be used in two different senses: (1) not fertile—incapable of producing young as the result of exposure to radiation, and (2) rendered free from microorganisms or aseptic by exposure to radiation.

An excellent example of the first use is the eradication of the SCREW WORM FLY in which male flies were made sterile but not impotent by exposure of pupae to about 7,500 roentgens (r) from a cobalt-60 unit (*see* SCREW WORM FLY, ERADICATION). Temporary sterility in the human male has been produced with exposures between 300 and 500 r; above this amount, if death does not occur, sterility may be permanent.

FOOD PRESERVATION usually implies pasteurization in order to delay spoilage and extend shelf life, but actual sterilization is feasible with several types of foods. Fresh meat can normally be sterilized with irradiation to about 2.5×10^6 rad. Many fresh foods, such as milk, cheese, oranges, lettuce, cannot be subjected to such high levels of radiation because unfavorable organic changes are produced which give undesirable flavor, odor, color, or texture.

In pest eradication studies it was found that carpet beetles, cigarette beetles, and rice weevils could be killed fairly rapidly by a dose of 65,000 r. The American cockroach, in all its active stages, died within 24 hours after an exposure to 68,000 r, but body lice required 20,000 r for a complete kill. It has been shown experimentally that the Salmonella group of microorganisms, which are sometimes found in egg products, can be completely destroyed by 300,000 rad of cobalt-60 gamma rays. Flours and grains can be disinfested with 1 to 3×10^5 rad.

Cold sterilization (i.e., irradiation) of drugs (e.g., antibiotics, vaccines) and products such as bandages, gauze, adhesive, and sutures is proving to be economically feasible and desirable for heat-sensitive materials.

RADIATION SURVEY

A special determination of the level of radiation in a given area, building, room, or desk top.

See CONTAMINATION SURVEY, ENVIRONMENTAL SURVEY, RADIOLOGICAL SURVEY, SMEAR SURVEY, and SURVEY.

RADIATION WARNING SYMBOL

Whenever a radiation hazard exists, the symbol prescribed by the USAEC* should always be displayed. The symbol shown in Figure R–2 is the conventional three-bladed design in magenta or purple on a yellow background.

See CAUTION SIGNS, LABELS AND SIGNALS, and RADIATION AREA.

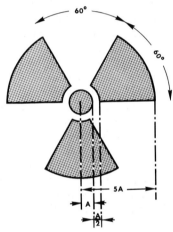

FIGURE R–2. RADIATION WARNING SYMBOL. THE PURPLE OR MAGENTA SYMBOL SHALL BE CENTERED WITHIN A SUFFICIENT AREA OF YELLOW BACKGROUND TO MAKE IT CONSPICUOUS. REGARDLESS OF THE SIZE OF SYMBOL, THE PROPORTION INDICATED MUST BE PRESERVED. APPROPRIATE WORDING MAY BE ADDED, SUCH AS "RADIATION AREA," "RADIOACTIVE SOURCE," ETC. THIS SYMBOL IS REPRODUCED IN THE OFFICIAL COLORS INSIDE THE FRONT COVER.

RADIO-

Prefix or combining form (from the Latin, *radius*, ray) denoting radioactivity or a relationship to it. Affixed to the name of a chemical element to designate a radioactive isotope of that particular element, as radiocarbon, radiogold, radioiodine, etc. Also used in combining forms such as RADIOBIOLOGY, RADIOCHEMISTRY, RADIOECOLOGY, RADIOELEMENT, etc.

RADIOACTIVE

Exhibiting radioactivity, or pertaining to radioactivity. Term used in connection with many

---

*Federal Register, Title 10—Atomic Energy; Chapter 1—Atomic Energy Commission, Part 20—Standards for Protection Against Radiation.

other items: RADIOACTIVE AGE DETERMINATION, RADIOACTIVE DECAY, RADIOACTIVE EMANATIONS, RADIOACTIVE HALF-LIFE, RADIOACTIVE SERIES, RADIOACTIVE STANDARD, RADIOACTIVE TRACER, RADIOACTIVE WASTE, and many others.

RADIOACTIVE AGE DETERMINATION

Determination of the age of an entity by determining its radioactivity. Called by the American chemist W. F. Libby, radioactive dating. The radioactive atom is an absolute and ideal time clock, running along at an immutable rate and readable at any time by the amount of decay products present. For example, the rate at which uranium-238 changes into lead-206 is completely unaffected by changing uranium from the metal form to a compound used to color ceramic pots yellow (the nuclear world is completely isolated from the electronic world). Thus knowing accurately the radioactive half-life of a radioelement, it is possible to determine the age of a rock, for example, by measuring the amount of uranium-238 remaining and the amount formed of its daughter end-product lead-206 as 4.5 billion years. Other radioactive time clocks are rubidium-87 to strontium-87 by electron emission, a process having a half-life of about 50 billion years (4.0 to 6.3×10^{10} years); and potassium-40 to argon-40 by electron capture, half-life 1.16 to 1.61×10^9 years. This has been of inestimable value to the geologists.

See RADIOCARBON DATING.

RADIOACTIVE DECAY

Also called RADIOACTIVE DISINTEGRATION. The spontaneous transformation, with a measurable lifetime, of one nuclide into one or more different nuclides (transmutation). The original radionuclide is the parent, and nuclide or nuclides formed either directly or as later members of a radioactive series are known as daughters. This results in a decrease, with time, of the number of radioactive atoms in a sample. The process involves the emission from the nucleus of alpha particles (α), beta particles (β) or electrons, or gamma rays (γ) or the nuclear capture or ejection of orbital electrons, or fission.

See DECAY CONSTANT, DECAY CURVE, and DECAY PRODUCT.

RADIOACTIVE DISINTEGRATION

Spontaneous nuclear transformation of one radionuclide into one or more different nuclides, characterized by the emission of energy. When large numbers of nuclei are involved, the process is characterized by a definite radioactive half-life. The transformation of one nuclide into one or more different nuclides may also be brought about by

bombardment with high-energy particles such as alpha particles, deuterons, protons, neutrons, or gamma rays.

Nuclear disintegration is a change involving the nuclei, and if spontaneous, is said to be radioactive, but if it results from a collision, it is said to be induced. May also refer to radiative capture, inelastic scattering, beta transformations and isomeric transition.

See RADIOACTIVE DECAY and RADIOACTIVITY.

RADIOACTIVE EMANATIONS

Radioactive gases given off by radium, thorium, and actinium. Radium emanation—radon, Rn^{222}; thorium emanation—thoron, Rn^{220}; and actinium emanation—radon, Rn^{219}.

RADIOACTIVE EQUILIBRIUM

A condition which may exist when the parent element and its daughter element are present together, and a state of equilibrium is attained in which the daughter disintegrates as fast as it is being formed, or in which the ratio of the activity of the parent to that of the descendant is independent of time. This condition can exist only when no activity longer-lived than that of the parent is interposed in the decay chain.

If the radioactive half-life of the parent is very long compared to the succeeding ones when the products attain equilibrium, the condition is known as secular equilibrium. An example in the uranium radioactive series is radium-226 with a half-life of 1.62×10^3 years, while radon has a half-life of 3.82 days and the others following through thalium-210 (radium C'') have half-lives of seconds or a few minutes.

If the lifetime of the parent is relatively short so that there is appreciable decay during the period under consideration, but is still longer than the successive members of the series, a state of transient equilibrium will be reached. This is illustrated by radon mentioned above and the successive radioisotopes through radium C''.

RADIOACTIVE HALF-LIFE

Symbol $T_{\frac{1}{2}}$ or $t_{\frac{1}{2}}$. Often called physical half-life. Time required for disintegration of one-half the atoms of a given radioactive substance. For a single radioactive atom, the time interval over which the chance of survival is exactly one-half. Each radionuclide has a unique half-life, varying from cesium-135m with a half-life of 2.8×10^{-10} second (essentially, decay of xenon-135) to 6×10^{14} years' half-life of indium-115, which is noted as being essentially stable. The half-life for a given nuclide is given by

$$t_{\frac{1}{2}} = \frac{0.693}{\lambda}$$

where λ is the decay constant for the nuclide.

Table R–5 gives the radioactive half-life of many of the biologicaly important radioactive isotopes. *See* MEAN LIFE and DECAY CURVE.

TABLE R–5. RADIOACTIVE HALF-LIFE OF BIOLOGICALLY IMPORTANT RADIOISOTOPES.

Arsenic ($_{33}As^{76}$)	26.8 hours
Bismuth ($_{83}Bi^{210}$)	5.02 days
Bromine ($_{35}Br^{82}$)	35.87 hours
Calcium ($_{20}Ca^{45}$)	164 ± 4 days
Carbon ($_{6}C^{14}$)	5,568 ± 30 years
Cerium ($_{58}Ce^{143}$)	33 hours
Cerium ($_{58}Ce^{144}$)	285 days
Cesium ($_{55}Cs^{137}$)	33 years
Chlorine ($_{17}Cl^{36}$)	$3.03 ± 0.03 × 10^5$ years
Chromium ($_{24}Cr^{51}$)	27.8 ± 0.1 days
Cobalt ($_{27}Co^{60}$)	5.26 ± 0.02 years
Copper ($_{29}Cu^{64}$)	12.80 hours
Gold ($_{79}Au^{198}$)	2.7 days
Iodine ($_{53}I^{131}$)	8.07 ± 0.02 days
Iridium ($_{77}Ir^{192}$)	74.37 days
Iron ($_{26}Fe^{59}$)	45.3 days
Lutecium ($_{71}Lu^{177}$)	6.75 days
Molybdenum ($_{42}Mo^{99}$)	2.85 days
Niobium ($_{41}Nb^{95}$)	35 days
Phosphorus ($_{15}P^{32}$)	14.221 ± 0.005 days
Plutonium ($_{94}Pu^{239}$)	24,000 years
Potassium ($_{19}K^{40}$)	$1.3 × 10^9$ years
Potassium ($_{19}K^{42}$)	12.42 hours
Praseodymium ($_{59}Pr^{143}$)	13.7 days
Promethium ($_{61}Pm^{147}$)	2.6 years
Rubidium ($_{37}Rb^{86}$)	18.66 days
Silver ($_{47}Ag^{111}$)	7.6 days
Sodium ($_{11}Na^{24}$)	14.97 ± 0.02 hours
Strontium ($_{38}Sr^{89}$)	53 days
Strontium ($_{38}Sr^{90}$)	28.0 ± 0.3 years
Sulphur ($_{16}S^{35}$)	87.2 ± 0.1 days
Zinc ($_{30}Zn^{65}$)	244.4 days

RADIOACTIVE ISOTOPE

An isotope which is radioactive may either occur naturally or be made artificially. A radioactive isotope (also called radioisotope) in contrast to a stable isotope, contains atoms that are destined to undergo change and emit radiation of one or more of three types: alpha (α), beta (β- or β+), or gamma (γ). Change may also occur through electron capture, neutron emission, or spontaneous fission. This process is called radioactive decay or disintegration and occurs according to a distinctly different rate for each radioisotope which is measured in terms of half-life ($T_{\frac{1}{2}}$). Variations in half-life are enormous; for example, in the thorium radioactive series, thorium-232 has a half-life of $1.39 × 10^{10}$ years, while polonium-212 has a half-life of only $3 × 10^{-7}$ second. Difference in radioactivity also shows great variation; for example, radium shows radioactivity a million times greater than an equal weight of uranium. The most interesting fact is that in the process of decay,

change from a radioisotope of one element to a radioisotope of another element occurs (transmutation). One also speaks of parent-daughter relationships.

Naturally occurring radioactive isotopes or nuclides may be classified in 4 categories: (1) primary, those having lifetimes longer than 10^8 years, and thus presumably having persisted from the time of nucleogenesis: alpha emitters (U^{238}, U^{235}, Th^{232}, Sm^{147}, Nd^{144}, Gd^{152}, Hf^{174}, Pt^{190}) and the beta disintegrators (K^{40}, Rb^{87}, V^{50}, In^{115}, La^{138}, Lu^{176} and Re^{187}); (2) secondary, those formed in radioactive transformations starting with U^{238} in the uranium radioactive series, with U^{235} in the actinium radioactive series, and Th^{232} in the thorium radioactive series; (3) induced, those formed by nuclear reactions currently occurring in nature, C^{14} by cosmic radiation, and Pu^{239} produced in uranium minerals by neutron capture; (4) extinct, those with lifetimes too short to have survived from the time of nucleogenesis, but long enough to have left measurable effects (I^{129} is the only example).

Artificial radioactive isotopes are those produced by man in splitting the atom in the controlled situation of the nuclear reactor, in the accelerator, or separated as fission products from nuclear fuel. Although not recoverable as commercially available products, artificial radioactive isotopes are also produced in the detonation of a nuclear device (atomic bomb). For commercial production 3 methods are used: bombardment of targets in nuclear reactors; fission of reactor fuels, isotopes of which are then separated out; and bombardment of targets in accelerators. Most radioisotopes available from Oak Ridge are produced in the first way. Two types of nuclear reactions are important in this production: activation and transmutation. A typical example of activation is: cobalt-59 + neutron bombardment ——→ cobalt-60 + gamma rays given off, i.e., $Co^{59}(n,\gamma)Co^{60}$. A typical transmutation reaction results from neutron bombardment of nitrogen-14, which results in carbon-14 plus protons, i.e., $N^{14}(n,p)C^{14}$.

Oak Ridge has in operation a large-scale separation plant for the separation and commercial production of fission product isotopes such as cesium-137 and strontium-90 from spent fuel elements. The cyclotron and other accelerators are also used for the production of radioisotopes unobtainable by other methods.

Table R–6 lists all the radioactive isotopes or nuclides, both natural and artificial.

See RADIOISOTOPE WASTE DISPOSAL; RADIOISOTOPES, ACCELERATOR-PRODUCED; and RADIOISOTOPES AVAILABLE FROM BROOKHAVEN.

TABLE R–6. RADIOACTIVE ISOTOPES OF BOTH NATURAL AND ARTIFICIALLY PRODUCED ELEMENTS

ATOMIC NUMBER	ELEMENT	SYMBOL	MASS NUMBERS REPORTED*
1	Hydrogen	H	3
2	Helium	He	5, 6
3	Lithium	Li	5, 7m, 8, 9
4	Beryllium	Be	7, 8, 10
5	Boron	B	8, 9, 12
6	Carbon	C	10, 11, 14, 15
7	Nitrogen	N	12, 13, 16, 17
8	Oxygen	O	14, 15, 19
9	Fluorine	F	17, 18, 20, 21
10	Neon	Ne	18, 19, 23, 24
11	Sodium	Na	20, 21, 22, 24, 25
12	Magnesium	Mg	23, 27, 28
13	Aluminum	Al	24, 25, 26, 28, 29
14	Silicon	Si	26, 27, 31, 32
15	Phosphorus	P	28, 29, 30, 32, 33, 34
16	Sulfur	S	31, 35, 37
17	Chlorine	Cl	32, 33, 34, 34m, 36, 38, 39, 40
18	Argon	A	35, 37, 39, 41, 42
19	Potassium	K	37, 38, 40m, 41m, 42, 43, 44, 45
20	Calcium	Ca	39, 41, 45, 47, 49
21	Scandium	Sc	40, 41, 42, 43, 44m, 44, 46m, 46, 47, 48, 49, 50
22	Titanium	Ti	43, 45, 51
23	Vanadium	V	45, 46, 47, 48, 49, 50m, 52, 53, 54
24	Chromium	Cr	46, 48, 49, 51, 55
25	Manganese	Mn	49, 50, 51, 52m, 52, 53, 54m, 54, 56, 57
26	Iron	Fe	52, 53, 55, 57m, 59, 60, 61
27	Cobalt	Co	54, 55, 56, 57, 58m, 58, 60, 60m, 61, 62, 64
28	Nickel	Ni	56, 57, 59, 63, 65, 66, 72, 73, 74
29	Copper	Cu	58, 59, 60, 61, 62, 64, 66, 67, 68, 72, 73, 74, 75, 76, 77
30	Zinc	Zn	60, 61, 62, 63, 65, 67m, 69m, 69, 71, 72, 73, 74, 75, 76, 77, 78, 79, 80
31	Gallium	Ga	65, 66, 67, 68, 70, 72, 73, 74, 82
32	Germanium	Ge	66, 67, 68, 69, 71, 72m, 73m, 75m, 75, 77, 77m, 78, 83, 84, 85
33	Arsenic	As	68, 69, 70, 71, 72, 73, 74, 76, 77, 78, 79, 80, 81, 82, 83, 84, 85, 86, 87
34	Selenium	Se	70, 71, 72, 73m, 75, 77m, 79m, 79, 81m, 81, 83m, 83, 84, 85, 86, 87, 88, 89
35	Bromine	Br	74, 75, 76, 77, 78, 78m, 80m, 80, 82, 83, 84, 85, 86, 87, 88, 89, 90, 91, 92
36	Krypton	Kr	76, 77, 78, 79m, 79, 81m, 81, 83m, 85m, 85, 87, 87m, 88, 89, 90, 91, 92, 93, 94, 95, 97
37	Rubidium	Rb	81, 82m, 82, 83, 84m, 84, 85m, 86m, 86, 87, 88, 89, 90, 91m, 91, 92, 93, 94, 95, 96, 97
38	Strontium	Sr	81, 82, 83, 85m, 85, 87m, 89, 90, 91, 92, 93, 94, 95, 97, 98, 99
39	Yttrium	Y	82, 83, 84, 85, 86, 87m, 87, 88, 89m, 90, 91m, 91, 92, 93, 94, 95, 96, 97, 98, 99, 100, 101
40	Zirconium	Zr	86, 87, 88, 89m, 89, 93, 95, 97, 98, 103
41	Niobium (columbium)	Nb	89, 90, 91m, 91, 92, 93m, 94m, 94, 95m, 95, 96, 97m, 97, 98, 99, 107
42	Molybdenum	Mo	90, 91, 93m, 93, 99, 101, 102, 103, 104, 105, 106, 107, 108, 109, 110
43	Technetium	Tc	92, 93, 94, 94m, 95m, 95, 96m, 96, 97m, 97, 98, 99m, 99, 100, 101, 102, 103, 104, 105, 106, 107, 108, 112
44	Ruthenium	Ru	94, 95, 97, 103, 105, 106, 107, 108, 115
45	Rhodium	Rh	97, 98, 99, 100, 101, 102, 103m, 104m, 104, 105m, 105, 106, 107, 108, 109, 119
46	Palladium	Pd	98, 99, 100, 101, 103, 105m, 107, 109m, 109, 111m, 111, 112, 113, 122
47	Silver	Ag	102, 103, 104, 105, 106, 107m, 108, 109m, 110m, 110, 111m, 111, 112, 113, 114, 115, 125
48	Cadmium	Cd	104, 105, 107, 109, 111m, 113m, 115m, 115, 117m, 117, 118, 128
49	Indium	In	107, 108, 109, 110m, 110, 111, 112m, 112, 113m, 114m, 114, 115m, 115, 116m, 116, 117m, 117, 118, 119, 131

*m (metastable). *See* METASTABLE STATE.

Table R–6 continued

ATOMIC NUMBER	ELEMENT	SYMBOL	MASS NUMBERS REPORTED*
50	Tin	Sn	108, 109, 110, 111, 113, 117m, 119m, 121m, 121, 122, 123, 125, 126, 127, 128, 129, 130, 131, 132, 133
51	Antimony	Sb	116m, 116, 117, 118, 119, 120m, 120, 122m, 122, 124, 124m, 125, 126, 127, 128, 129, 130, 131, 132, 133, 134, 135, 136
52	Tellurium	Te	116, 117, 118, 119, 121m, 121, 122, 123m, 123, 125, 125m, 126, 127m, 127, 129m, 129, 131m, 131, 132, 133m, 133, 134, 135, 136, 137, 138
53	Iodine	I	119, 120, 121, 122, 123, 124, 125, 126, 128, 129, 130, 131, 132, 133, 134, 135, 136, 137, 138, 139, 140
54	Xenon	Xe	121, 122, 123, 125, 127, 129m, 131m, 133, 133m, 135, 135m, 137, 137m, 138, 139, 140, 141, 142, 143, 144
55	Cesium	Cs	123, 125, 126, 127, 128, 129, 130, 131, 132, 133m, 134m, 135m, 135, 136, 137, 138, 139, 140, 141, 142, 143, 144, 145
56	Barium	Ba	126, 127, 128, 129, 131, 133m, 133, 135m, 137m, 139, 140, 141, 142, 143, 144, 145, 146, 147, 148
57	Lanthanum	La	131, 132, 133, 134, 135, 136, 137, 138m, 138, 140, 141, 142, 143, 144, 151
58	Cerium	Ce	133, 134, 135, 137, 139, 141, 143, 144, 145, 146, 154
59	Praseodymium	Pr	135, 136, 137, 138, 139, 140, 142, 143, 144, 145, 146, 156
60	Neodymium	Nd	138, 139, 140, 141, 144, 147, 149, 150, 151, 159
61	Promethium	Pm	141, 142, 143, 144, 145, 146, 147, 148, 149, 150, 151, 161
62	Samarium	Sm	143, 145, 146m, 147, 151, 153, 155, 156, 161
63	Europium	Eu	144, 145, 146, 147, 148, 149, 150, 152, 153m, 154, 155, 156, 157, 158, 159, 160, 161
64	Gadolinium	Gd	148, 149, 150, 151, 153, 159, 161
65	Terbium	Tb	149, 150, 151, 153, 154, 155, 156, 157, 160, 161, 162, 163
66	Dysprosium	Dy	153, 157, 159, 160m, 165m, 165, 166
67	Holmium	Ho	157, 160, 161, 162, 163, 164, 166, 167, 169
68	Erbium	Er	160, 161, 163, 165, 166m, 169, 171
69	Thulium	Tm	165, 166, 167, 168, 169m, 170, 171m, 171, 172, 174
70	Ytterbium	Yb	166, 167, 169, 170m, 175, 177
71	Lutetium	Lu	170, 171, 172, 173, 174, 176, 176m, 177, 178, 179
72	Hafnium	Hf	170, 171, 172, 173, 175, 176m, 179m, 180m, 181
73	Tantalum	Ta	176, 177, 178, 179, 180, 181m, 182m, 182, 183, 184, 185, 186
74	Tungsten	W	176, 177, 178, 179, 181, 183m, 183, 185m, 185, 187, 188
75	Rhenium	Re	180, 182, 183, 184, 186, 187m, 187, 188m, 188, 189, 190, 191
76	Osmium	Os	182, 183, 185, 186m, 190m, 191m, 191, 193, 194
77	Iridium	Ir	187, 188, 189, 190, 191, 192m, 192, 193m, 194, 195, 196, 197, 198, 199
78	Platinum	Pt	187, 188, 189, 190, 191, 193m, 195m, 197m, 197, 199
79	Gold	Au	187, 188, 189, 191, 192, 193, 194, 195m, 195, 196, 197m, 198, 199, 200, 201, 202, 203
80	Mercury	Hg	189, 190, 191, 192, 193, 194, 195m, 195, 196m, 197m, 197, 199m, 203, 205
81	Thallium	Tl	195, 196, 197, 198, 199, 200, 202, 204, 206(RaE''), 207(AcC''), 208(ThC''), 209, 210(RaC'')
82	Lead	Pb	197, 198, 199, 200, 201m, 201, 202m, 203, 204m, 205, 207m, 209, 210(RaD), 211m(AcB), 212(ThB), 214(RaB)
83	Bismuth	Bi	198, 199, 200, 201, 202, 203, 204, 205, 206, 207, 208, 210(RaE), 211(AcC), 212(ThC), 213, 214(RaC), 215
84	Polonium	Po	199, 200, 201, 202, 203, 204, 205, 206, 207, 208, 209, 210(RaF), 211(AcC'), 212(ThC'), 213, 214(RaC'), 215(AcA), 216(ThA), 217, 218(RaA)
85	Astatine	At	203, 204, 205, 206, 207, 208, 209, 210, 211, 212, 213, 214, 215, 216, 217, 218, 219
86	Radon (emanation)	Rn	206, 207, 208, 209, 210, 211, 212, 215, 216, 217, 218, 219(An), 220n(Tn), 221, 222(Rn)
87	Francium	Fr	212, 217, 218, 219, 220, 221, 222, 223(AcK)
88	Radium	Ra	213, 219, 220, 221, 222, 223(AcX), 224(ThX), 225, 226, 228(MsTh$_2$), 229, 230
89	Actinium	Ac	221, 222, 223, 224, 225, 226, 227, 228(MsTh$_2$), 229, 230
90	Thorium	Th	223, 224, 225, 226, 227(RdAc), 228(RdTh), 229, 230(Io), 231(UY), 232, 233, 234(UX$_1$), 235
91	Protactinium	Pa	225, 226, 227, 228, 229, 230, 231, 232, 233, 234(UZ), 234m(UX$_2$), 235, 237

*m (metastable). *See* METASTABLE STATE.

ATOMIC NUMBER	ELEMENT	SYMBOL	MASS NUMBERS REPORTED*
92	Uranium	U	227, 228, 229, 230, 231, 232, 233, 234(U_{II}), 235(AcU), 236, 237, 238(U_1), 239, 240
93	Neptunium	Np	231, 232, 233, 234, 235, 236, 237, 237m, 238, 239, 240, 241
94	Plutonium	Pu	232, 234, 235, 236, 237, 238, 239, 239m, 240, 241, 242, 243, 244, 245, 246
95	Americium	Am	237, 238, 239, 240, 241, 242m, 242, 243, 244, 245, 246
96	Curium	Cm	238, 239, 240, 241, 242, 243, 244, 245, 246, 247, 248, 249
97	Berkelium	Bk	243, 244, 245, 246, 247, 248, 249
98	Californium	Cf	244, 245, 246, 247, 248, 249, 250, 251, 252, 253, 254, 255, 256, 257, 258
99	Einsteinium	Es	246, 247, 249, 250, 251, 252, 253, 254, 255, 256
100	Fermium	Fm	250, 251, 252, 253, 254, 255, 256
101	Mendelevium	Mv	256
102	Nobelium	No	?
103	Lawrencium	Lw	257

*m (metastable). *See* METASTABLE STATE.

RADIOACTIVE SERIES

Various radioactive elements have been arranged in series, such as the ACTINIUM RADIOACTIVE SERIES, the THORIUM RADIOACTIVE SERIES, the URANIUM RADIOACTIVE SERIES, and the artificially produced NEPTUNIUM RADIOACTIVE SERIES, showing the decay scheme, i.e., the parent-daughter relationships. In addition there are several COLLATERAL RADIOACTIVE SERIES found associated with both the naturally occurring and the artificially produced series.

RADIOACTIVE SOURCE.   *See* SOURCES OF RADIATION.

RADIOACTIVE STANDARD

A fixed sample of a specified radioactive material in which the number of radioactive atoms was accurately established at a definite reference time; for use in calibrating radiation measuring equipment.

RADIOACTIVE TRACER

A radioactive isotope in minute quantity either as carrier or carrier-free, used to follow biological, chemical, or other processes. It has been shown that the radioactive isotopes have essentially the same chemical properties (for exceptions *see* ISOTOPE EFFECT) and therefore the same reactions as stable isotopes; thus since the radioactive isotopes can be easily detected, the movement and behavior of stable atoms can be traced by following the radioactivity. Radioactive tracing is an extremely sensitive analytical tool. Consider as an example that with phosphorus-32 (6.3×10^{17} disintegrations per minute per gram) and a G-M counter tube with a lower counting limit of 20 counts per minute, it is possible to detect 3.2×10^{-16} gram of P^{32}.

See TRACER TECHNIQUE.

RADIOACTIVE WASTE

Gaseous, liquid, or solid radioactive material which is released or produced from the use of nuclear energy. The mining and processing of uranium releases radioactive gases, and particulate matter that may contaminate the air and water. The preparation of reactor fuels and the reprocessing of the fuel elements produce high-activity waste. The operation of a nuclear reactor produces fission products and induced radioactivity. The use of radioactive isotopes also produces a radioisotope waste disposal problem.

Several characteristics distinguish radioactive waste from the more common industrial type wastes: they are radiotoxic, i.e., their radioactivity is the hazardous feature; their radioactivity cannot be detected by the special senses; instruments must be used to detect radioactive contamination; the radioactivity cannot be immediately destroyed (burning, chemical reactions, etc. have no effect); these wastes become inactive only by the passage of time with natural decay.

Wastes are conveniently classified according to activity level: high, medium, and low activity. High-activity wastes may contain thousands of curies per gallon, and result from reprocessing spent fuel elements. Medium-activity wastes are produced by chemical laboratory processes, aqueous washings from solvent recovery plants, and from water used to cool irradiated fuels before processing. Reactor coolant water, laundry wastes, waste from use of radioactive isotopes, and decontamination-center washing solutions con-

TABLE R-7

RADIONUCLIDE	RADIOACTIVE HALF-LIFE*	APPROXIMATE PER CENT TOTAL ACTIVITY AFTER DECAY OF		
		100 days	3 years	30 years
Strontium-90	28.0 y	2	15	49
Cesium-137	26.6 y	2	15	49
Promethium-147	2.6 y	3	15	1
Cerium-praseodymium-144	290 d	45	50	—
Krypton-85 (gas)	10.3 y	1	1	1
Iodine-131 (gas)	8.1 d	1	—	—
Zirconium-niobium-95	63.3 d	33	—	—
Strontium-89	54.0 d	7	—	—
Ruthenium-rhodium-103	41.0 d	5	—	—
Ruthenium-rhodium-106	1.0 y	2	3	—
Barium-lanthanum-140	12.8 d	1	—	—
Xenon-133 (gas)	5.3 d	1	—	—

*y, year; d, day.

stitute low-activity wastes (usually considered to be in the range of 1 microcurie per gallon). Effluent from tracer-level laboratories, rinse-water from laboratories working at higher levels of activity, and trench water from fuel-rod storage ponds usually have low-level activity.

The volume of waste material varies with the type of work being performed. For example, in the case of most low-level activity, the volume produced may be several million gallons per day; thus billions of gallons are produced per year. In contrast, testimony before the Congressional Joint Committee on Atomic Energy in 1959 indicated that since the beginning of the atomic program only 65 million gallons of high-level wastes have accumulated.

The nature of radioactive wastes varies with the type of operation. The waste product radioactivity may be naturally occurring, or it may be produced by fission or by neutron activation. The naturally occurring radionuclides which may become waste products are uranium-238 (99.28% of uranium waste) with its decay products, uranium-235 (0.71%), uranium-234 (0.005%); thorium-232 with its decay products; and radium and its isotopes.

The principal fission products of interest in waste-disposal operations are listed in Table R-7.

Other radionuclides which must be considered in waste disposal are the activation products formed by neutron activation of the elements making up the coolant or the impurities in the coolant. For example, when the coolant is water, nitrogen-16 is formed by the nuclear reaction $O^{16}(n,p)N^{16}$, by the neutron bombardment of the O^{16} nuclide of the oxygen in the water. In a similar way nitrogen-17 and oxygen-19 are also formed, as is fluorine-18. Neutron activation of the impurities which may be found in the water lead to the formation of such radionuclides as the following: sodium-24, aluminum-28, phosphorus-32, argon-41, manganese-56, cobalt-58, cobalt-60, iron-55, iron-59, chromium-51, copper-64, tantalum-182, and tungsten-187.

In a sodium-cooled reactor, sodium-24, sodium-22, rubidium-86, and antimony-124 are formed by neutron action.

Fission product gaseous waste products discharged to the atmosphere in 1957 from the Hanford Works consisted of the following:

TABLE R-8

RADIONUCLIDE	AMOUNT, CURIES PER DAY
Iodine-131	1
Rare earths plus yttrium	0.02
Niobium-95	0.01
Zirconium-95	0.004
Ruthenium-103	0.004
Ruthenium-106	0.002
Strontium-89	0.004
Strontium-90	0.0005

From the same plant the quantities of radioactive iodine discharged to the atmosphere from the separations plant stacks amounted to the following: 1953—2.0 curies per day of I^{131}; 1954—1.5; 1955—3.2; 1956—1.0; 1957—1.0; and 1958—1.2.

Although it contaminates the biosphere, radioactive fallout from the detonation of a nuclear device is not usually considered as a waste product.

See WASTE DISPOSAL, RADIOACTIVE.

RADIOACTIVITY

Spontaneous disintegration of the nucleus of the atom with the emission of corpuscular or electromagnetic radiations. The phenomenon of natural radioactivity was discovered by French physicist Becquerel in 1896 by the effect produced on a photographic plate by uranium containing mineral pitchblende. According to present-day experimental techniques, for a process to be considered radioactive it must have a measurable lifetime between about 10^{-10} second and about 10^{17} years.

The principal types of radioactivity are ALPHA (α) DISINTEGRATION; BETA DECAY (negatron, β^- emission; positron, β^+ emission); and ELECTRON CAPTURE (EC), GAMMA (γ) RADIATION, and ISOMERIC TRANSITION (IT). Spontaneous FISSION also is considered to be a type of radioactivity.

NATURAL RADIATION, which furnishes the background radiation surrounding us, is furnished largely by cosmic rays; by terrestrial radiation from uranium, thorium, radium and their decay products and potassium-40; and by atmospheric radiation from carbon-14. (See RADIOACTIVE ISOTOPE for the 4 categories of naturally occurring radionuclides and for a complete list of all radioactive isotopes.) There are 3 naturally occurring radioactive series—actinium, radium, and thorium—as well as several collateral radioactive series.

Artificial radioactivity is produced by man in splitting the atom in nuclear reactors or accelerators or as the result of the detonation of a nuclear device.

PROMPT RADIATION or radioactivity given off at the moment of detonation of a nuclear device and by neutron bombardment associated with the detonation; induced radioactivity in biological material and in elements in soil, air, and water.

RADIOACTIVITY CONCENTRATION GUIDE*

The concentration of radioactivity in the environment which is determined to result in whole body or organ doses equal to those prescribed in the RADIATION PROTECTION GUIDE. Any radioactivity concentration guide "is applicable only for the circumstances under which the use of its corresponding Radiation Protection Guide is appropriate."

No specific numerical recommendations were provided and the statement was made that "The Federal agencies, as an interim measure, use radioactivity concentration guides which are consistent with the recommended Radiation Protection Guides. Where no Radiation Protection Guides are provided, Federal agencies continue present practices."

---

*Taken largely from the "Federal Register," May 18, 1960, pages 4402–4403, Federal Radiation Council.

See MAXIMUM PERMISSIBLE BODY BURDENS and MAXIMUM PERMISSIBLE CONCENTRATION, which term will be used in this book.

RADIOAUTOGRAPHY.   See AUTORADIOGRAPHY.

RADIOBIOLOGY

Term used interchangeably with RADIATION BIOLOGY; the science dealing with every step in the action of radiation on living matter from the absorption of energy to injury and repair or death of the cell or the organism. Radiobiology has many facets: energy absorption; ionized and excited molecules; cell changes, biochemical lesions, submicroscopical lesions, visible lesions and cell death; early physiological response to radiation; acute somatic response to radiation; delayed somatic effects; and mutations leading to genetic damage.

RADIOCARBON DATING

A method of estimating the age of carbon-containing materials by measuring the radioactivity of the carbon they contain.

Cosmic rays, in transversing the earth's atmosphere, change atmospheric nitrogen by neutron bombardment into carbon-14 by the following reaction: $N^{14}(n,p)C^{14}$. The radiocarbon formed in this way is soon converted into carbon dioxide ($C^{14}O_2$) and becomes completely mixed in the entire biosphere. In the familiar plant-animal carbon cycle, the plants take up this labeled carbon dioxide and build it into carbohydrates that are eaten by animals, which then return part of it to the atmosphere by respiration. Throughout the years, this $C^{14}O_2$ has been maintained in constant equilibrium and is therefore found in all living matter.

When this living carbonaceous material dies and is thus separated from equilibrium with the plant-animal cycle, the C^{14} will begin to decay with a RADIOACTIVE HALF-LIFE of 5,760 years. Accurate measurement of the radioactivity of the carbon in a given sample allows a calculation of its age up to 50,000 years with an error not much greater than a hundred years.

By this method, specimens of archeological and geological interest have been studied, including textiles, leather, wood, charcoal, peat, and mud from the bottom of the ocean. The original work was done by American scientist Dr. W. F. Libby, for which he received the Nobel prize.

See RADIOACTIVE AGE DETERMINATION.

RADIOCHEMISTRY

Chemistry dealing with radionuclides and their properties; with the use of radionuclides in the study of chemical problems; and with the behavior of minute quantities of radioactive materials detected by means of their radioactivity.

Since radiochemical investigations at all activity levels have the serious problem of preventing contamination of both equipment and personnel, special radiochemical laboratories have been developed; and special procedures called radiochemical asepsis are practiced. A great deal of biochemical as well as chemical work is being performed with radioactive materials. In this experimental work the level of radioactivity may range from less than 1 microcurie to more than 1 curie, and different types of laboratory setup are required. For example, work with material above the curie level is performed in special thick-walled (2 feet) concrete cells called caves, whereas work with material of the microcurie level can be accomplished in an ordinary laboratory. But care must be exercised even with minute quantities, for contamination with even a trace of material of curie-level activity would completely ruin an experiment being carried out at the microcurie level.

See TRACE CHEMISTRY.

RADIOCOLLOIDS.   *See*   COLLOIDS, RADIO-ACTIVE.

RADIOCONTAMINATION

Undesirable contamination of a substance with radioactive material or with an unwanted radioisotope. Term usually used in connection with purity of radioisotope preparations—"Preparation Cd^{115}-P is probably the best for general use, since the others contain appreciable radiocontaminants." Any radioactive atoms that are not in the same valence state or chemical form as the element that is to be followed (in a tracer study) must be considered as radiocontaminants. In the production of radioisotopes, radiocontamination is minimized by selecting a target material which has minimum chemical impurities and which does not contain atomic species prone to activation. In order to achieve radiochemical purity for tracer studies it is essential to eliminate radiochemical contaminants.

RADIOECOLOGY

Study of the effects of radiation on species of plants and animals in natural communities, or ecosystems. All living organisms, from the time of their origin on earth until the present, have been irradiated. Some radiation is unnecessary and some is harmful. Radiation causes an increase in the rate of mutation (hence variation) and is thus one factor affecting the dynamics of an ecosystem.

All members of an ecological community are dependent upon one another. Some species may be modified more than others, and depending on the level of radiation, some may be killed—in either case modifying natural selection and the expected pattern of plant or animal succession.

Radioecology is being intensively studied in a number of places where radiation levels have been changing, including the Nevada Test Site, White Oak Creek in Tennessee, Columbia River in Washington, Lockheed Reactor Site, Dawsonville, Georgia, Savannah River in Georgia, uranium areas of the upper Colorado River basin, east slope of the Front Range in Colorado, and Doe Run, Meade County, Kentucky.

The research program of the USAEC is a varied one, including basic and applied research on both animals and plants in the above-mentioned locations. These studies will help in understanding the possible ecological aftermath of a nuclear war.

RADIOELEMENT

An element containing one or more radioactive isotopes; a radioactive element. Radioelements either occur naturally or are artificially produced. An example of a naturally occurring radioelement is radium, while lawrencium is a radioelement that has been artificially produced recently.

The prefix "radio" before the name of an element indicates the radioactive form, as radiocarbon, radiogold, radiolead. This prefix should not be used to indicate radiogenic; i.e., radiolead should not be used as a synonym for radiogenic lead.

Separation and identification of radioelements are among the problems of radiochemistry.

RADIOGENIC

Of radioactive origin; produced by radioactive transformation. For example, uranium minerals contain radiogenic lead and radiogenic helium.

RADIOGENOL

An emulsion of insoluble radioactive minerals used for injection directly into a tumor or into a body cavity, e.g., colloidal radiogold (gold-198) used for intratumoral injection, or for intrapleural and intraperitoneal application.

See COLLOIDS, RADIOACTIVE.

RADIOGRAPHY

The use of ionizing radiation for the production of shadow images on a photographic emulsion. Some of the rays (gamma or x-ray), directed toward the subject, pass on through, while others are partially or entirely absorbed by the more opaque parts of the subject and cast a shadow on photographic film. Thus the image is the result of the differential absorption of radiation in its passage through the object being radiographed. The film record is called a radiograph. The process is used extensively both in medical diagnosis and in industrial activity. With the advent of the cobalt-60 portable gamma-ray source, the industrial use has increased. It is now much easier to look for defects in a casting or to study a weld than formerly. See INDUSTRIAL RADIOGRAPHY.

The radiography of small objects is called microradiography and is used to study sections of tissue, leaf structure, insect anatomy, seeds, textiles, and artificial fibers.

Stereoradiographs are useful when a three-dimensional image would help in the study of an object or a malformation below the surface.

See AUTORADIOGRAPHY.

RADIOISOTOPE

Any RADIOACTIVE ISOTOPE of an element. Used loosely as a synonym for radionuclide.

See ISOTOPE.

RADIOISOTOPE HAZARD

The hazards from radioisotopes are extremely variable, depending on the amount of radioisotope, the type of radiation emitted, the half-life, and the physicochemical properties. Whether the exposure is internal or external is also a factor.

Of greatest external hazard are the gamma emitters, with radiations that penetrate the deep tissues, such as bone marrow. Alpha emitters do little harm outside the body, and beta emitters are of danger mainly to skin and superficial tissues. (See EXTERNAL RADIATION.)

Internal hazards are very different; radioisotopes may enter the body by way of the gastrointestinal tract, lungs, or other routes. Small amounts may be very dangerous; even alpha emitters may produce great damage, especially the bone-seeking elements of long half-life. (See INTERNAL IRRADIATION HAZARD.)

Two general types of undesirable effects may be seen—acute damage (see ACUTE RADIATION SYNDROME) that is relatively predictable in relation to radiation dose, and late effects such as GENETIC DAMAGE and an increased incidence of cancer, which are much less predictable.

Protection from these hazards is based on avoidance of excessive exposure to internal and external radioisotopes. (See MAXIMUM PERMISSIBLE DOSE and RADIATION PROTECTION STANDARDS.) Radioactive materials must be carefully contained and controlled. Highly sensitive electronic instruments serve admirably to indicate safe levels for those working with these substances. Studies of radioactivity in the urine and whole body radioactivity measurements are also useful in some circumstances. Routine blood counts performed to show evidence of radiation effect are sometimes suitable, but this method is generally too insensitive to be highly useful.

RADIOISOTOPE LICENSE. See LICENSES FOR BYPRODUCT MATERIAL.

RADIOISOTOPE PRODUCTION

Three methods are used for the major production of radioactive isotopes: bombardment of target element in a nuclear reactor; fission of reactor fuels with subsequent separation; and bombardment of target element in an accelerator.

Neutron bombardment of selected target materials in a nuclear reactor is a routine manufacturing operation and supplies the largest variety and quantity of artificial radioactive isotopes. Either radioactive activation of an element or radioactive transmutation of the target element into another element may occur. The most common type of processing is by the (n,γ) nuclear reaction in which a neutron is captured by a target atom and a gamma photon is emitted immediately. This reaction is primarily a thermal-neutron type of reaction and is illustrated by the following: $_{11}Na^{23} + {}_0n^1 \longrightarrow {}_{11}Na^{24} + \gamma$. Sometimes a radioisotope produced by this method decays by beta emission to a radioactive daughter with a different atomic number, which can be separated chemically to obtain high specific activity material. Thus: $_{32}Ge^{76} + {}_0n^1 \longrightarrow {}_{32}Ge^{77} + \gamma$. Then $_{32}Ge^{77}(\beta^-,$ 12-hour radioactive half-life$) \longrightarrow {}_{33}As^{77}$, which can be chemically separated as high specific material. The above reactions can be written $Na^{23}(n,\gamma)Na^{24}$, and $Ge^{76}(n,\gamma)Ge^{77}$. These are examples of radioactive activation of an element.

Neutron bombardment with fast neutrons may result in transmutation of the target element into an element of atomic number lower by 1. For example, $_{16}S^{32} + {}_0n^1 \longrightarrow {}_{15}P^{32} + p$, by the (n,p) nuclear reaction in which a proton is released as a result of a high-energy neutron entering the target nucleus. Very high-energy neutrons may result in the release of an alpha particle by the (n,α) nuclear reaction. Thus $_{13}Al^{27} + {}_0n^1 \longrightarrow {}_{11}Na^{24} + \alpha$.

The fission process results in the formation of a number of intensively radioactive products. These fission products may be utilized as radiation sources without separation or may be separated as an additional step in fuel reprocessing. The Oak Ridge Fission Product Development Laboratory is in operation at the Oak Ridge National Laboratory from which the following separated fission products are available: cerium-144, cesium-137-barium-137m, promethium-147, strontium-90, technetium-99, and zirconium-95–Ce^{144}, Pm^{147}, and Sr^{90} in kilocurie quantities.

The cyclotron and other types of accelerators are used for the production of radioisotopes that cannot be prepared or obtained in concentrated form by other methods. These are listed under RADIOISOTOPES, ACCELERATOR-PRODUCED.

Certain radioisotopes requiring chemical processing are listed under RADIOISOTOPES AVAILABLE FROM BROOKHAVEN NATIONAL LABORATORY.

See tellurium cow under TELLURIUM.

RADIOISOTOPE TECHNIQUES WITH ANIMALS

Radioisotope studies are carried out with almost any species of laboratory or domestic animal. The same procedures are used as for the usual experimental study, with the additional need for prevention of radiation hazard to animals or personnel, avoidance of cross-contamination of animals, and elimination of radioactive dust hazards from diets, shed hair, excreta, and bedding. In general, the experiments are done under controlled conditions with collection of the radioactive excretions for later disposal. Various types of special metabolism cages have been devised for laboratory animals and domestic animals, such as sheep, goat, swine, and cow.

See ANIMAL METABOLISM STUDIES, ANIMAL NUTRITIONAL STUDIES, and ANIMAL PHYSIOLOGICAL STUDIES.

RADIOISOTOPE TECHNIQUES WITH PLANTS

Plant research with radioisotopes may range from laboratory studies with excised roots, through greenhouse work with potted plants, to full-scale field application of labeled fertilizers, in the latter case using short-lived radioisotopes. For studies of carbon fixation it is usually necessary to grow plants in a closed system into which C^{14}O$_2$ can be introduced. The usual methods of plant physiological work are applied with care to avoid dissemination of radioactive materials.

See ISOTOPE FARM, PLANT PHYSIOLOGICAL STUDIES, and PLANT REGULATOR STUDIES.

RADIOISOTOPE TRAINING. See TRAINING, RADIOISOTOPES.

RADIOISOTOPE TRAINING SCHOOL. See OAK RIDGE INSTITUTE OF NUCLEAR STUDIES.

RADIOISOTOPE WASTE DISPOSAL

Radioactive isotopes have been generally available since August 1946, and have found widespread use in research, in medical diagnosis and treatment, in agricultural work, and in industrial processes and operations. The extent of this use may be shown by the fact that from 1946 to 1959 the Oak Ridge National Laboratory, Isotope Division, made 78,598 radioisotope shipments to about 5,200 institutions, amounting to 535,781 curies (c) of activity. Material shipped from all other USAEC installations together amounted to about an equal amount so that in this 13-year period over a million curies have been shipped to licensed users in the United States alone.

Of the Oak Ridge material, fabricated sealed sources accounted for the following amounts: metallic cobalt-60, 430,652 c; sealed source tritium, 33,164 c; metallic iridium-192, 27,844 c; metallic cesium-137, 27,727 c; and sealed sources of krypton-85, 4,678 c; promethium-147, 662 c; and strontium-90, 413 c. Thus 525,140 curies, or 99% of all radioisotopes with a radioactive half-life greater than 30 days, are used in sealed sources and do not present a waste-disposal problem during normal use. These sources are used in teletherapy machines, irradiations, radiography sources, calibrator sources, in therapeutic radiology, and as radiation sources in gauging devices, luminous devices, etc. After these various sources have decayed through several half-lives and are no longer useful as radiation sources, they either are returned to Oak Ridge or are otherwise disposed of as solid waste.

The remaining radioisotopes (less than 1%) with a half-life greater than 30 days are used in research and development work involving applications requiring microcurie, millicurie, or low-curie amounts. The radioactive waste comes primarily from tritium and krypton gaseous waste, which can be filtered and discharged to the atmosphere, and from contaminated laboratory equipment, paper, glassware, and animal carcasses, which can be incinerated and buried on the property of the licensee at a depth of 4 feet in holes 6 feet apart with a limit of 12 burials per year.

Of the approximately 7,910 c shipped from Oak Ridge with a half-life of less than 30 days, 7,733 c were accounted for by iodine-131, phosphorus-32, and gold-198, used primarily in medical research, diagnosis, and therapy. Colloidal gold decays in the patient; the disposal of iodine-131 and phosphorus-32 is discussed below.

The USAEC issues licenses to use radioactive material and maintains the right of inspection.

The disposal methods and procedures used by private users of radioisotopes are: (1) the controlled discharge of laboratory effluents containing low concentrations of radioactivity into streams, sanitary sewerage systems, and the atmosphere; (2) burial of small quantities of waste in soil under controlled conditions; (3) return of radioactive waste to USAEC installations for land burial; (4) treatment by incineration; and (5) disposal of packaged waste at sea.

Disposal requirements for 3 commonly used radioisotopes will be presented in some detail as examples of radioisotope waste disposal techniques: carbon-14, iodine-131, and phosphorus-32.

Carbon is one of the most commonly encountered elements in living matter, and radiocarbon (C^{14}) occurs widely in nature. Carbon-14 is used extensively in research in both medicine and agriculture, and special recommendations have been published in NATIONAL BUREAU OF STANDARDS HANDBOOK 53 for the disposal of waste containing it: (1) C^{14} may be disposed of in any manner provided it is intimately mixed with stable carbon, in the same chemical form, in a ratio that never exceeds 1 microcurie (μc) of C^{14} for every 10 grams of stable carbon; (2) it may be discharged to sewers in amounts that do not exceed 1 millicurie (mc) per 100 gallons of sewage based on the sewage flow available to the disposer within his own institution; (3) combustible material containing C^{14} may be incinerated if the maximum concentration does not exceed 5 μc per gram of carbon; $C^{14}O_2$ from carbonates may be discharged in the exhaust system of a standard chemical laboratory hood that has a linear air flow of at least 50 ft/min, at a rate not to exceed 100 μc/hr/ft^2 of air intake area in the face of the hood as operated; (5) C^{14} may be disposed of with garbage in amounts that do not exceed 1 μc/lb of garbage available to the disposer within his own institution; and (6) C^{14}-containing material may be buried provided it is covered with at least 4 ft of well-compacted earth and does not exceed the following limits: (a) the maximum permissible concentration of C^{14} in biological material (plant or animal) for burial shall not exceed 5 μc/g; and (b) the maximum permissible amount of C^{14} in chemical compounds mixed with 1 ft^3 of soil shall not exceed 10 mc.

"Recommendations for Waste Disposal of Phosphorus-32 and Iodine-131 for Medical Users" is the subject of NATIONAL BUREAU OF STANDARDS HANDBOOK 49; it contains detailed directions for disposal of these 2 radioisotopes in the home, hospital, or laboratory. For example: "In diagnostic and therapeutic uses of P^{32}, in diagnostic use of I^{131}, and in treatment of hyperthyroidism with I^{131}, patients may use the toilet without any instructions or restrictions." But hospital disposal is based on "permissible activities," which are well defined.

RADIOISOTOPES, ACCELERATOR-PRODUCED

Certain radioactive isotopes cannot be prepared or obtained in concentrated form by any method other than bombardment of target materials in a cyclotron or other type of accelerator. The cyclotron was used in early investigations for the production of a radioisotope through the transmutation of a target atom to form a different atom. For example, iron is bombarded by high-energy (80,000 ev to 730 Mev) protons to form cobalt; silver to form cadmium; platinum to form gold; etc. The transformation can also be produced by bombardment with high-energy deuterons. Table R–9 lists a number of accelerator-produced radioisotopes available commercially.

Accelerator-produced radioisotopes, in a number of instances, have distinct advantages over either reactor-produced or fission-separated radioisotopes: high specific activity, appropriate radioactive half-life for the chosen element, and appropriate type of radiation. In many cases they can be prepared carrier-free.

See ISOTOPE.

TABLE R–9. ACCELERATOR-PRODUCED RADIOISOTOPES

PRODUCT ELEMENT	PRODUCT RADIOISOTOPE	RADIOACTIVE HALF-LIFE (*)	RADIATION (†)	PRODUCED BY (‡)
Aluminum	$_{13}Al^{26}$	10^5 y	$\beta+$	Al + p
Arsenic	$_{33}As^{73}$	76 d	EC	Ge + d Ge + p
Arsenic	$_{33}As^{74}$	17.5 d	$\beta-(30\%)$ $\beta+(35\%)$ EC(35%)	Ge + d Ge + p
Beryllium	$_4Be^7$	54.5 d	EC	Li + d Li + p

*y, year; d, day. †$\beta-$, negative beta particle; $\beta+$, positive beta particle; EC, electron capture. ‡p, proton; d, deuteron.

Table R–9 continued

PRODUCT ELEMENT	PRODUCT RADIOISOTOPE	RADIOACTIVE HALF-LIFE (*)	RADIATION (†)	PRODUCED BY (‡)
Cadmium	$_{48}Cd^{109}$	1.3 y	EC	Ag + d Ag + p
Cerium	$_{58}Ce^{139}$	140 d	EC	La + p
Cobalt	$_{27}Co^{56}$	80 d	β^+ EC	Fe + d Fe + p
Cobalt	$_{27}Co^{57}$	270 d	EC	Fe + d Fe + p
Cobalt	$_{27}Co^{58}$	70 d	$\beta^+(14.5\%)$ EC	Fe + d Fe + p
Gold	$_{79}Au^{195}$	180 d	EC	Pt + d Pt + p
Iron	$_{26}Fe^{55}$	2.94 y	EC	Mn + d Mn + p
Manganese	$_{25}Mn^{52}$	6 d	$\beta^+(35\%)$ EC(65%)	Cr + d Cr + p
Manganese	$_{25}Mn^{54}$	310 d	EC	Cr + d Cr + p
Sodium	$_{11}Na^{22}$	2.6 y	β^+ EC	Mg + d
Strontium	$_{38}Sr^{85}$	65 d	EC	Rb + d Rb + p
Tungsten	$_{74}W^{181}$	140 d	EC	Ta + d Ta + p
Vanadium	$_{23}V^{48}$	16 d	β^+ EC	Ti + d Ti + p
Vanadium	$_{23}V^{49}$	330 d	EC	Ti + d Ti + p
Yttrium	$_{39}Y^{88}$	105 d	$\beta^+(0.2\%)$ EC(99%)	Sr + d Sr + p
Zinc	$_{30}Zn^{65}$	250 d	$\beta^+(3\%)$ EC(97%)	Cu + d Cu + p

*y, year; d, day. †β^-, negative beta particle; β^+, positive beta particle; EC, electron capture. ‡p, proton; d, deuteron.

RADIOISOTOPES AVAILABLE FROM BROOKHAVEN

Certain radioactive isotopes requiring special chemical processing are available in the form shown in Table R–10 only from the Hot Laboratory Division, BROOKHAVEN NATIONAL LABORATORY, Upton, Long Island, New York.

RADIOISOTOPES AVAILABLE FROM OAK RIDGE

OAK RIDGE NATIONAL LABORATORY processes and ships more radioactive isotopes than any other supplier. Most of the radioisotopes are produced in the nuclear reactor by neutron bombardment. In the United States a license must be ob-

TABLE R–10. RADIOACTIVE ISOTOPES FROM BROOKHAVEN

RADIOISOTOPE	RADIOACTIVE HALF-LIFE	RADIATION	PRODUCED BY
Fluorine-18	112 minutes	β^+, γ	$O^{16}(t,n)F^{18}$ reactor
Iodine-132*	2.33 hours	β^-, γ	Daughter of separated fission product Te^{132}
Iodine-133	20.8 hours	β^-, γ	Separated fission product
Magnesium-28	21.3 hours	β^-, γ	$Mg^{26}(t,p)Mg^{28}$ reactor
Molybdenum-99	67 hours	β^-, γ	Separated fission product
Technetium-99m	6.0 hours	γ	Daughter Mo^{99}
Tellurium-132	77 hours	β^-, γ	Separated fission product
Yttrium-90	64.2 hours	β^-	Daughter, separated fission product strontium-90

*See TELLURIUM.

tained from the Isotopes Branch, Division of Licensing and Regulation, U.S. Atomic Energy Commission, Washington 25, D.C., in order to use licensed quantities of radioactive isotopes. Correspondence concerning purchase order, specifications, sale, and delivery of radioisotopes should be addressed to Union Carbide Nuclear Company, Oak Ridge National Laboratory, Isotopes Sales Department, P.O. Box X, Oak Ridge, Tennessee. Table R–11 lists according to their radioactive half-life the radioisotopes that are available from Oak Ridge. Oak Ridge also has available fission products, a neutron-activation analysis service, and waste-disposal service.

TABLE R–11. RADIOISOTOPES AVAILABLE FROM OAK RIDGE

RADIOACTIVE* HALF-LIFE	RADIOISOTOPE†	RADIATION‡
24.2 s	Silver-110 (Ag^{110m})	β, γ
30 s	Rhodium-106 (Ru^{106})	β, γ
72 s	Indium-114 (In^{114m})	EC, β, β^+, γ
2.6 m	Barium-137m (Cs^{137})	IT, γ
17.5 m	Praseodymium-144 (Ce^{144})	β, γ
12.7 h	Potassium-42	β, γ
12.8 h	Copper-64	EC, β, β^+, γ
13.6 h	Palladium-109	β, γ
14.2 h	Gallium-72	β, γ
15.0 h	Sodium-24	β, γ
19.0 h	Iridium-194	β, γ
19.3 h	Praseodymium-142	β, γ
24.0 h	Mercury-197m$_2$	EC, IT, γ
24.0 h	Tungsten-187	β, γ

Table R–11 continued

RADIOACTIVE* HALF-LIFE	RADIOISOTOPE†	RADIATION‡
26.6 h	Arsenic-76	β, γ
35.87 h	Bromine-82	β, γ
38.8 h	Arsenic-77	β, γ
40 h	Lanthanum-140	β, γ
47 h	Samarium-153	β, γ
53 h	Cadmium-115	β, γ
64.2 h	Yttrium-90	β
65 h	Gold-198	β, γ
65 h	Mercury-197m	EC, γ
67 h	Molybdenum-99	β, γ
67 h	Antimony-122	β, γ
69.6 h	Ruthenium-97	EC, γ
75.6 h	Gold-199	β, γ
91 h	Rhenium-186	EC, β, γ
4.7 d	Calcium-47	β, γ
5.27 d	Xenon-133	β, γ
5.02 d	Bismuth-210	β
7.5 d	Silver-111	β, γ
8.05 d	Iodine-131	β, γ
11.3 d	Neodymium-147	β, γ
11.6 d	Barium-131	EC, γ
12.8 d	Barium-140	β, γ
13.7 d	Praseodymium-143	β
14.3 d	Phosphorus-32	β
16 d	Osmium-191	β, γ
18.6 d	Rubidium-86	β, γ
27.8 d	Chromium-51	EC, γ
32.5 d	Cerium-141	β, γ
35 d	Argon-37	EC
35 d	Niobium-95	β, γ
41.0 d	Ruthenium-103	β, γ
43 d	Cadmium-115m	β, γ
45.1 d	Iron-59	β, γ
45.8 d	Mercury-203	β, γ
46 d	Hafnium-181	β, γ

*, †, ‡. The footnotes for this table are on page 356.

Table R–11 continued

RADIO-ACTIVE* HALF-LIFE	RADIOISOTOPE†	RADIATION‡
49 d	Indium-114m	IT,γ
50.4 d	Strontium-89	β
58.0 d	Yttrium-91	β,γ
60 d	Antimony-124	β,γ
65 d	Strontium-85	γ
65 d	Zirconium-95	β,γ
72 d	Cobalt-58	EC,β+,γ
74 d	Tungsten-185	β
74.5 d	Iridium-192	EC,β,γ
85 d	Scandium-46	β,γ
87.1 d	Sulfur-35	β
112 d	Tantalum-182	β,γ
115 d	Tin-113	EC,γ
127 d	Selenium-75	EC,γ
164 d	Calcium-45	β
245 d	Zinc-65	EC,β+,γ
270 d	Silver-110m	IT,β,γ
290 d	Cerium-144	β,γ
1.0 y	Ruthenium-106	β
1.3 y	Cadmium-109	EC,γ
2.0 y	Antimony-125	β,γ
2.3 y	Cesium-134	β,γ
2.5 y	Promethium-147	β
2.94 y	Iron-55	EC
4.1 y	Thallium-204	EC,β
5.27 y	Cobalt-60	β,γ
7.2 y	Barium-133	EC,γ
10.27 y	Krypton-85	β,γ
12.46 y	Hydrogen-3	β
12.7 y	Europium-152	EC,β,γ
16 y	Europium-154	β,γ
28 y	Strontium-90	β
30 y	Cesium-137	β
125 y	Nickel-63	β
5.57×10^3 y	Carbon-14	β
2.12×10^5 y	Technetium-99	β
3.2×10^5 y	Chlorine-36	β
1.6×10^7 y	Iodine-129	β,γ

*s, second; m, minute; h, hour; d, day; y, year.

†The radioisotope in parenthesis is the one under which the listed radioisotope is catalogued.

‡β, negative beta; β+, positive beta; EC, electron capture; and IT, isomeric transition.

RADIOISOTOPES IN AGRICULTURE. *See* AGRICULTURE, USE OF RADIOISOTOPES IN.

RADIOISOTOPES IN INDUSTRY. *See* INDUSTRIAL USE OF RADIOISOTOPES.

RADIOISOTOPES IN LIFE SCIENCES RESEARCH. *See* under specific topics, such as AGRICULTURE, USE OF RADIOISOTOPES; ANIMAL METABOLISM STUDIES and ANIMAL NUTRITIONAL STUDIES.

RADIOISOTOPES IN MEDICAL DIAGNOSIS. *See* MEDICAL DIAGNOSIS.

RADIOISOTOPES IN MEDICAL RESEARCH. *See* MEDICAL RESEARCH.

RADIOISOTOPES IN MEDICAL TREATMENT. *See* MEDICAL TREATMENT.

RADIOLOGICAL ASSISTANCE. *See* INTERAGENCY COMMITTEE ON RADIOLOGICAL ASSISTANCE.

RADIOLOGICAL ASSISTANCE PLAN

Since 1957 the USAEC has provided radiological monitoring teams on a nationwide emergency basis to render assistance in connection with incidents believed to involve radioactive materials. The plan is "to make available, upon request from an AEC licensee, AEC contractor, Federal, State or local official, private organization or person cognizant of an incident suspected to involve radioactive material, such advice and radiological assistance from AEC resources as may be appropriate to minimize injury to people, to minimize property damage, to cope with radiological hazards and to protect the public health and safety" (AEC Manual, Chapter 0526, Radiological Assistance Program).

Team capabilities may include alpha, beta, or gamma monitoring; air, water, and food sampling and monitoring; medical advice and assistance; decontamination assistance; and the use of laboratory facilities to perform radiochemical analyses of samples. Through the appropriate Operations Office for the Regional Area (see map and list on page 357) 584 personnel are routinely available —enough for 80 teams of three specialists each, working simultaneously, plus 300 in reserve as needed. During 1960, teams responded to 79 requests, 54 of which were found to involve radioactive materials. Information concerning the plan has been widely disseminated.

See INTERAGENCY COMMITTEE ON RADIOLOGICAL ASSISTANCE.

RADIOLOGICAL DEFENSE

Protection against the effects of radioactive fallout from the detonation of nuclear weapons. One method of defense is to build, stock, and be prepared to occupy FALLOUT SHELTERS or BLAST SHELTERS should the need arise. Thus, protection would be afforded from blast, thermal, and ionizing radiation effects of the nuclear weapon.

Evacuation is another method of defense, but carries with it many inherent risks. Without proper radiation monitoring, evacuees would risk crossing through high-intensity radiation areas. They might be caught in the fallout path if the wind shifts direction. The detonation of additional weapons would present an impossible situation if they were caught in the open.

U.S. ATOMIC ENERGY COMMISSION

REGIONAL OFFICE AREAS

OF RESPONSIBILITY FOR

RADIOLOGICAL ASSISTANCE

IN INCIDENTS INVOLVING

RADIOACTIVE MATERIALS

REGION NO. and OPERATIONS OFFICE	POST OFFICE ADDRESS	TELEPHONE for ASSISTANCE	DDD AREA CODE
① NEW YORK	376 HUDSON STREET NEW YORK 14, NEW YORK	YUKON 9-1000	212
② OAK RIDGE	P. O. BOX E OAK RIDGE, TENNESSEE	483-8611, Ext. 7607 or 483-7486	615
③ SAVANNAH RIVER	P. O. BOX A AIKEN, S.C.	AIKEN, S.C. MIDWAY 9-6211, Ext. 3333 AUGUSTA, GA., PARK 4-6311, Ext. 3333	803 404
④ ALBUQUERQUE	P. O. BOX 5400 ALBUQUERQUE, NEW MEXICO	256-411 Ext. 38267	505
⑤ CHICAGO	9800 S. CASS AVE. ARGONNE, ILLINOIS	CLEARWATER 7-7711 Ext. 2111 or 541	312
⑥ IDAHO	P. O. BOX 2108 IDAHO FALLS, IDAHO	JACKSON 2-6640	208
⑦ SAN FRANCISCO	2111 BANCROFT WAY BERKELEY, CALIFORNIA	THORNWALL 1-5620	415
⑧ RICHLAND	P. O. BOX 550 RICHLAND, WASHINGTON	942-1111 Ext. 6-5441	509

Revised: January 1963

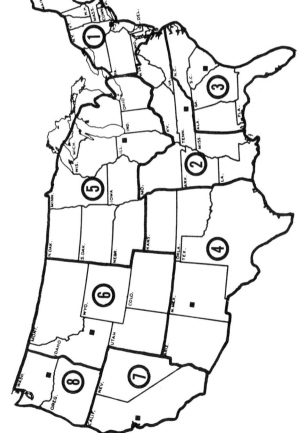

VIRGIN IS.	PUERTO RICO	CANAL ZONE	HAWAII	ALASKA
IN REGION 2	IN REGION 2	IN REGION 3	IN REGION 7	IN REGION 8

357

DECONTAMINATION as soon as possible is also part of radiological defense, but great care must be exercised to avoid undue exposure whenever possible.

Radiological defense monitoring is concerned with locating areas of radioactive contamination and measuring the radiation intensity.

An important part of radiological defense is the education of the civilian population in the proper measures to take should an attack come.

RADIOLOGICAL HEALTH

A new term, used to indicate a special effort, in which particular emphasis is placed on the biological, medical, and public health problems rather than those of HEALTH PHYSICS per se. The only real difference appears to be one of emphasis. Other related terms are INDUSTRIAL HYGIENE, INDUSTRIAL MEDICINE, OCCUPATIONAL MEDICINE, and RADIOLOGICAL PHYSICS.

RADIOLOGICAL LABORATORY, UNIVERSITY OF CALIFORNIA SCHOOL OF MEDICINE, SAN FRANCISCO

This laboratory, supported by the USAEC and managed by the University of California, is concerned with the use of ionizing radiation in the treatment of cancer, in the dosimetry of ionizing radiation, and in certain biological effects of x-rays. The laboratory commenced work on the effects of radiation on the blood in 1942 as a subcontract from the University of Chicago, continuing under the Manhattan Engineer District. It has worked continuously on atomic medicine and radiation biology.

The staff comprises 7 scientific, 10 technical, and 5 nontechnical individuals. The work is performed under 3 main divisions: Clinical Radiology, investigating the value of 70 Mev x-rays in the treatment of cancer; Physics Section, investigating radiation dosimetry, including measurements with ionization chambers, chemical systems, and vacuum calorimeter; and the Biology Section, which emphasizes the study of the delayed and late effects of exposure in mammals, including man, explores their possible relation to certain aging processes, and deals with certain genetic effects postulated to occur in the progeny of irradiated animals.

RADIOLOGICAL PHYSICS

The physical study of radiation and radioactive substances.

RADIOLOGICAL SAFETY ORGANIZATION

Wherever radioactive material or radiation from any source is being used, there must be radiological safety rules and regulations; some individual or group must be responsible for drawing them up and enforcing them. The size of the safety organization depends upon the extent of use of radioactive material and the size of the installation. There may be only a part-time industrial physician or a full-time health physicist; or the organization may be composed of a radiological safety committee, an isotopes committee, an industrial physician, a health physicist, and a complete health physics unit.

The radiological safety committee, usually composed of an industrial physician, a health physicist, a director of research, and an administrator or supervisor, is charged with formulating the rules, regulations, and procedures to be followed when radioactive material is being used. The individual worker and his direct supervisor are responsible for enforcement.

An isotope committee is required by the USAEC for any institution to be eligible for a general authorization for the procurement and use of radioisotopes. This committee reviews and approves all requests for isotopes and determines qualification of applicant, etc.

A health physicist (see HEALTH PHYSICS), an industrial hygienist, or a radiological health technician is necessary as a member of any organization when radioactive material is used in quantities above the licensing exempt levels.

RADIOLOGICAL SAFETY RULES

The fundamental purposes of safety rules are to prevent the inhalation, ingestion, or other modes of entry of radioactive material into the body; reduce the amount of external radiation to levels as far below the maximum permissible concentration (or the RADIATION PROTECTION GUIDES) as is reasonably possible; and prevent the spread of radioactive contamination to uncontrolled areas. Rules must be drawn up for each different situation but the following are general considerations:

1. Careful planning with a careful survey should precede inauguration of any new activity.

2. Arrange for maximum practical distance and shielding along with minimum practical personnel exposure time.

3. Experiments using more than the exempt levels of spreadable activity should be conducted in a properly ventilated hood or glove box. High-level radiation sources should be handled with remote control equipment from behind an adequate barrier or barricade shield or in a hot room. Sealed radiation sources should be stored in properly shielded containers (pigs) or caves when not in use.

4. All procedures employing special handling

tools or equipment should be rehearsed and problems worked out prior to actual operation with radioactive material. Any equipment used in a radiation area where spreadable activity is present will be regarded as contaminated and not released until a survey has indicated that it is clean.

5. Immaculate housekeeping procedures are required wherever radioactive material is being used. Milk bottles or other reusable food containers should not be used to store radioactive materials. No eating, smoking, or preparation of food or drink should be allowed in any radiation area where spreadable activity is handled or stored.

6. Personal cleanliness is essential at all times, particularly where spreadable activity is present. This means: check body for any exposed skin breaks and either stay out of the area or appropriately protect the skin area before entering; monitor hands, hair, face, and all exposed areas of the body with appropriate instruments at the end of each work period; if any part of the body is contaminated, wash and recheck until decontamination is complete; wash hands and face before eating or smoking at the end of work period; monitor personal clothing before leaving controlled radiation area, and if contaminated, remove and send to laundry for clothing decontamination.

7. Protective clothing such as respirators, gloves, laboratory coats or special suits should be worn when conditions indicate the need.

8. Responsibility for drawing up and enforcing the safety rules must be established. The organization required to accomplish this will depend upon the size of the laboratory or activity. A single individual may handle the program or there may be a large radiological safety organization.

RADIOLOGICAL SURVEY

Also known as protection survey. Evaluation of the radiation hazards incident to the production, use, or existence of radioactive materials or other sources of radiation, in relation to a specific condition. Such an evaluation includes measurement or estimate of the level of radiation that may occur, a survey of equipment and materials to be used, and a prediction of the hazards which may result.

RADIOLOGICAL WARFARE

The deliberate use of radioactive material as an offensive weapon. Contamination of areas (see CONTAMINATION, RADIOACTIVE) of land, industrial complexes, and equipment makes their use impossible or extremely hazardous even without inflicting any other damage.

Before the advent of high-fission energy yields, use of radiation as a contaminating agent posed too many problems. For example, material which depended upon a gamma emitter with a radiological half-life of a few weeks or months would be too difficult to produce and store. Now, however, high-fission energy nuclear weapons are really, in effect, weapons of radiological warfare. They can cause radioactive contamination of areas far beyond the radius of physical damage. The material does not have to be produced and stockpiled in advance, since the radioactive substances (fission products) are produced by fission at the time of detonation. Thus high-yield weapons have the offensive capability for radiological warfare. In addition, material can be added to provide additional radioactive fallout of appropriate half-life for contaminating the environment.

RADIOLOGY

Science of radioactive substances, x-rays, and other ionizing radiations. The medical application of the principles of this science is used in diagnosis and treatment of disease.

RADIOLUCENCY

A radiological term meaning the property of being nearly, but not entirely, transparent to x-ray, i.e., permitting the passage of radiant energy, yet offering enough resistance to produce contrasting shadows on x-ray film.

See RADIOPACITY and RADIOPARENCY.

RADIOLYSIS

The dissolution of cells (e.g., bacteria or red blood cells) or their breakdown from structural form to structureless fluid, as a result of irradiation. The decomposition of water and organic chemical solutions by bombardment with electrons or particles.

In radiation chemistry the cyclotron has been used to study the rate of production of formic acid and of other more complex organic molecules from the radiolysis of water and of other organic substances. Heavy-particle irradiation of acetic acid, oxygenated formic acid, and glycine has yielded detailed knowledge of the radiolysis of these compounds; and heavy particles from a cyclotron have been employed in studies of the mechanism of radiolysis of aqueous protein solutions. Thus light is being shed on the origin of organic substances. Labeling with carbon-14 helps to trace the chemical mechanisms.

RADIOMIMETIC SUBSTANCES

Chemical substance which simulates the BIOLOGICAL EFFECTS OF RADIATION. The biological activity of certain chemical substances which produce the same biological end-effects as those observed following exposure to ionizing radiation.

TABLE R–12. COMPARISON OF GENETIC EFFECTS PRODUCED IN DROSOPHILA

EFFECT	X-RAYS	SULFUR MUSTARD	NITROGEN MUSTARD	FORMAL-DEHYDE	URETHANE
Recessive lethals	+	+	+	+	+
Dominant lethals	+	+	+	+	?
Visible mutations	+	+	+	+	+
Minor deficiencies	+	+	+	+	+
Gross deletions	+	+	+	+	+
Inversions	+	+	?	+	?
Translocations	+	+	+	+	?
Gynandromorphs	+·	+	?	+	?

+ Observed
? Not observed or only very infrequently observed.

To be classed as radiomimetic the substance must simulate all the end-effects of radiation: cause genetic damage, i.e., produce gene-mutations, chromosome abnormalities, arrest mitosis; kill cells (lymphocytes); induce tumors, i.e., be carcinogenic. Substances which exhibit these effects at the cellular level give rise to an acute syndrome in mammals which shows the same characteristics as the ACUTE RADIATION SYNDROME.

The most characteristic group of chemicals are the biological alkylating agents, all of which are closely related in chemical reactivity to mustard gas and peroxides. The similarity between the genetic effects produced by radiation and chemical mutagens is clearly shown in Table R–12.

RADIOMUTATION

A permanent, transmissible change in form, quality, or some other characteristic of a cell or offspring from its parent, due to radiation exposure.

See MUTATION, RADIATION INDUCED.

RADIONECROSIS

Death or destruction of a cell or a group of cells (in contact with living tissue) as a result of exposure to radiant energy.

See NECROSIS.

RADIONUCLIDE

A condensation for radioactive nuclide. There are over 50 or 60 naturally occurring radionuclides; those produced artificially number well over 900. See RADIOACTIVE ISOTOPE for a complete listing.

See ISOTOPE.

RADIONUCLIDES OF BIOLOGICAL INTEREST (BOMB)

Many radionuclides are formed as FISSION PRODUCTS from the detonation of a nuclear device. Also, as the result of neutron bombardment and the associated induced radioactivity, there are additional quantities of radionuclides produced in air, water, and soil.

Identification of the radioactive nuclides of biological importance from among the hundreds produced depends upon a number of factors, some of which are:

1. Bomb characteristics
   Fission-to-fusion ratio
   NEUTRON FLUX
   Weapon or bomb constituents
   YIELD
2. Rate or frequency of testing
3. Type of detonation
   HEIGHT OF BURST
     Dropped from plane
     Balloon shot
     Tower shot
     Over or in the sea
     Over, on, or under land
       Type of soil
4. Type of fallout
   LOCAL FALLOUT
   TROPOSPHERIC FALLOUT
   STRATOSPHERIC FALLOUT
5. Physical characteristics of debris
   Size of particles
   Chemical structure
6. Abundance of the radionuclide as a function of time after detonation
7. Biological factors
   Mode of entry
     INHALATION OF RADIOACTIVE MATERIAL
     INGESTION OF RADIOACTIVE MATERIAL
     EXTERNAL RADIATION
   Metabolism of the element in the body (bone seeker, etc.)
   EFFECTIVE HALF-LIFE

Taking all these factors into consideration and considering as significant only those radionuclides that have an abundance one month after detonation of 1,000 curies per megaton of yield, the following have biological importance: strontium-89; strontium-90–yttrium-90; yttrium-91; zirconium-95–niobium-95; iodine-131; cesium-137–barium-137m; barium-140–lanthanum-140; cerium-143–praseodymium-143; cerium-144–praseodymium-144; and neodymium-147–promethium-147.

Although it does not meet all the requirements, we should add carbon-14 formed in the air, because of its possible genetic effect (*see* GENETIC EFFECTS, RADIATION). Also, under certain circumstances, iron-55, iron-59, and plutonium-239 may be of interest, as well as isotopes of cobalt (Co^{57}, Co^{58}, Co^{60}).

RADIONUCLIDES PRODUCED IN AIR, WATER, AND SOIL (BOMB)

Radionuclides are produced in the elements of the air, sea water, and soil as the result of neutron bombardment from a nuclear explosion. The INDUCED RADIOACTIVITY results from a nuclear reaction of either the activation or transmutation type.

Of the various radionuclides formed in air, carbon-14 is of the greatest biological significance. Neutron interaction with nitrogen-14 (80% constituent of air) changes it to carbon-14 by the neutron, proton (n,p) nuclear reaction. Carbon is an intimate part of all living material, and since radiation is known to be deleterious it follows that radioactive carbon is a potential hazard to man. Other induced radionuclides in air which have been identified and measured are: hydrogen-3, nitrogen-16, oxygen-19, and argon-37, -39, -41. Other radionuclides are probably produced, but their concentrations are too low to produce significant radioactivity levels.

Fifty-seven radionuclides have been found to be formed in sea water as the result of induced radioactivity in various elements by neutrons formed in a nuclear explosion. These radionuclides range in atomic number (Z) from 3 (lithium-8) to 91 (protactinium-232). Only 3 are found at the end of the year with estimated activities of more than 1 curie per megaton (MT) of fission: sulfur-35 with 0.00215 megacurie (MC) per MT; calcium-45 with 0.0002 Mc/MT; and chlorine-36 with 0.00019 Mc/MT. It should be borne in mind, however, that some of the shorter-lived radionuclides may be concentrated by algae and thus enter the food chain (*see* AQUATIC ORGANISMS UPTAKE OF RADIONUCLIDES).

When a nuclear device is detonated close enough to the earth's surface so that neutrons can react with soil constituents, an appreciable amount of induced radioactivity results. The primary nuclear reaction is that of neutron capture with the ejection of a gamma ray. Differences in soil composition will produce wide variations, but in general

the significant contributors to the residual radiation in the soil are the isotopes: sodium (Na^{24}), manganese (Mn^{56}), silicon (Si^{31}), aluminum (Al^{28}), iron ($Fe^{55, 59}$), and calcium (Ca^{45}).

RADIOPACITY

A radiological term meaning the property of being radiopaque or prohibiting the passage of radiant energy; the opposite of RADIOPARENCY. It is important in both industrial and medical use of x-rays or gamma rays for diagnostic purposes; e.g., a fracture of a bone can be "seen" with x-ray because bone is relatively radiopaque compared with the surrounding soft tissue.

RADIOPARENCY

A radiological term meaning the property of being transparent to or permitting the passage of x-rays. The use of x-rays or gamma rays in both industrial activity and medical practice rests upon the fact that certain materials are radioparent or relatively so while others are radiopaque or relatively so.

See RADIOPACITY.

RADIOPROTECTION

Protection of the body against damaging effects of ionizing radiation is afforded by physical means in SHIELDING part or all of the body by some substance which absorbs some of the radiation (*see* ABSORPTION).

Protection, in a more general sense of reducing the radiation effect, can be provided by the addition of a protective agent such as AET, which combines with the damaging free radicals that would otherwise attack the "target molecule" (*see* CHEMICAL PROTECTION AGAINST RADIATION DAMAGE). AET administered orally before exposure, 200 milligrams per kilogram of body weight, has protected mice against lethal doses of radiation of as much as 900 roentgens.

RADIORESISTANCE

Relative resistance of cells, tissues, organs, or organisms to the injurious action of radiation. The opposite of RADIOSENSITIVITY. The term may be applied to chemical compounds and other non-living substances.

RADIOSENSITIVITY

Relative susceptibility of various substances, such as cells, tissues, organs, and organisms, to the injurious action of radiation. RADIORESISTANCE and radiosensitivity are at present employed in a qualitative or comparative sense, rather than in a quantitative or absolute one. Every degree of radiosensitivity is to be found among various living organisms, ranging from 300,000 roentgens (r) necessary to kill infusoria, down to 0.01 r which is required to modify the growth of a fungus (Phycomyces blakesleeanus). Table R–13 gives examples of the MEDIAN LETHAL DOSE within 30 days ($LD_{50}/30$) in rems for various species of living organisms exposed to x-rays.

TABLE R–13. $LD_{50}/30$ FOR X-RAY IRRADIATION

ORGANISM	REM
Guinea pig	250 (175 to 400)
Pig	350 to 400
Dog	335
Goat	350
Monkey	about 600
Man	400 to 450
Mouse	550 to 665
Rat	665 (590 to 970)
Rabbit	750 to 825
Hamster	610
Chicken	600 to 800
Goldfish	670
Frog	700
Tortoise	1,500
Snail	8,000 to 20,000
Yeast	30,000
Amoeba	100,000
B. mesentericus	150,000
Paramecium and Infusoria	300,000 to 350,000

It is not well understood why there should be such a wide spread of response to radiation, with some organisms being highly resistant while others are sensitive; but the following general statements clarify the situation somewhat:

1. There is a species specificity, although there may be variation within the species due to other factors.

2. Among the vertebrates, mammals are more sensitive to radiation than birds, fish, amphibians, or reptiles.

3. Warm-blooded organisms (mammals and birds) are usually more sensitive to radiation than cold-blooded organisms.

4. Age is an important factor, the adult organism being in general much more resistant than the embryo or organisms in early developmental stages.

5. Temperature is a physical factor having an important influence upon radiosensitivity. (See TEMPERATURE AND RADIATION EFFECTS.)

6. Oxygen tension is directly related to sensitivity with anoxia enhancing radioresistance. (See OXYGEN, RADIATION SENSITIVITY.)

7. Unicellular organisms are generally very resistant to radiation.

8. Insects are much more resistant than mammals but not as resistant as unicellular organisms.

Drosophila (fruit fly), which has been studied extensively, is resistant to 64,000 r in the form of gamma rays from cobalt-60.

9. The number of chromosomes is important—diploid races of yeast are much less sensitive to ionizing radiation than are the haploid yeasts.

In a general sense, mammalian tissues can be arranged in the order of increasing resistance to radiation as follows: spermatogonia, lymphocytes, erythroblasts, the rest of the classical hemopoietic tissues, lining of the small intestinal tract, stomach, colon, skin, central nervous system, muscle, bone, and collagen.

Stated in another way, the progenitive tissues of mammalian body are the most susceptible to radiation, i.e., those tissues whose function is to proliferate cells needed for maintenance and function of the organism, such as the blood-forming components, the alimentary tract mucosa, the germinal epithelium of the testes, the skin and skin elements (hair follicles and pigment cells), and the lens of the eye. Mature cells of cartilage, bone, muscle, and central nervous system are comparatively much less susceptible to radiation.

RADIOSTERILIZATION. *See* RADIATION STERILIZATION

RADIOTHERAPY

The treatment of disease by means of radiation. The use of external beams from radioisotope sources (TELETHERAPY) and the use of x-ray machines are the most typical examples, but the term radiotherapy also includes BRACHYTHERAPY, INTRACAVITARY, and INTERSTITIAL insertion of radioisotopes, treatment with radioisotopes that are internally absorbed, and the use of special types of beams such as those of protons. Most radiotherapy is used for the treatment of cancer, but some nonmalignant diseases are also treated.

Radiotherapy is one of 3 major forms of treatment for cancer, the other 2 being surgery and drug therapy. The success of radiotherapy depends greatly on the type and stage of the disease. For some situations it is the best treatment, yielding a high percentage of complete cures; for others it is of temporary or palliative value only, and for still others it is of no value.

RADIOTHORIUM

A thorium isotope of mass number 228 occurring in the thorium radioactive series: Actinium

(mesothorium II) $(_{89}Ac^{228})$ $\xrightarrow[\beta]{6.13 \text{ hrs}}$ thorium

(radiothorium) $(_{90}Th^{228})$ $\xrightarrow[\alpha]{1.91 \text{ yr}}$ radium (thorium X) $(_{88}Ra^{224})$.

RADIUM

Symbol Ra; atomic number 88; atomic weight 226. Radioactive half-life 1,622 years; alpha emitter. Radium metal is brilliant white, shows luminescence, alters rapidly in contact with air, decomposes water, and is highly radioactive. Discovered by M. and Mme. Curie in 1898 in the form of the salt $RaBr_2$, from pitchblende. Isolated in 1911 by Mme. Curie and Debierne. Named from Latin, *radius*, ray. The richest deposit is in the Great Bear Lake region of Canada. It is commercially obtained as the bromide or chloride. Chemically related to barium although somewhat more volatile.

Radium is formed from thorium (ionium in the uranium radioactive series) ($_{90}Th^{230}$) by alpha-particle emission, and in turn emits an alpha particle to form radon (radium emanation). Isotope radium-223 (actinium X) ($_{88}Ra^{223}$), half-life 11.7 days, alpha emitter, appears in the actinium radioactive series. Isotope radium-228 (mesothorium I) ($_{88}Ra^{228}$), half-life 6.7 years, beta emitter, appears in the thorium radioactive series. Isotope radium-224 (thorium-X) ($_{88}Ra^{224}$), half-life 3.64 days, alpha emitter, also appears in the thorium radioactive series. Radium-225 ($_{88}Ra^{225}$), half-life 14.8 days, beta emitter, appears in the neptunium radioactive series. Radium-226 ($_{88}Ra^{226}$), radioactive half-life 1,622 years; with bone as the critical organ, biological half-life 44.9 years, effective half-life 44.8 years; 56% of equilibrium would be reached in the body within 50 years; alpha emitter. Eight other radioactive isotopes have been identified.

Used industrially in radiography, gamma density gauging, pipewall thickness gauging, and in self-luminous paints. Mesothorium I (Ra^{228}) is mixed with radium to make these paints. Used in medicine in the treatment of certain types of cancer. Toxic to a marked degree. Constitutes one of the important internal emitters from natural sources. Taken up from the environment through ingestion of radium-containing water or food and deposited, together with calcium, in bone structure. The average annual dose to the bone is about 38 millirems, but may easily be 10 times as much in certain geographical areas.

Some figures for radium content are: rocks, 10^{-11} to 10^{-12} gram of radium per gram of rock; soil, 0.9 to 8.0×10^{-13} gram of radium per gram of soil; ocean water, 0.7 to 7×10^{-17} gram of radium per cubic millimeter of water (g/cm^3); rivers in the United States, 7×10^{-17} g/cm^3; tap water average, 0.42×10^{-16}; Joliet, Illinois, tap water, 7×10^{-15}; spring water in Boulder, Colorado, 3×10^{-10} g/cm^3.

None of the above levels constitutes a hazard.

However, in cases of industrial exposure or of early-1900 misguided medical treatment, resulting in the accumulation of 12 to 100 micrograms of radium in the body (largely in bones), osteogenic sarcoma and carcinoma have developed. Evidence of the hazard is furnished by the girls who were painting luminous watch dials and who pointed their radium-laden brushes with the tongue and lips. (*See* RADIUM-DIAL PAINTER CASES.) Great care is now taken to prevent inhalation or ingestion of radium or any of its daughters. The maximum permissible body burden for bone is set at 0.1 microcurie. The maximum permissible concentration for occupational exposure for a 40-hour week for soluble material with bone as the critical organ is 4×10^{-7} microcurie per cubic centimeter ($\mu c/cc$) in water and 3×10^{-11} in air; for 168-hour week (continuous exposure), 10^{-7} $\mu c/cc$ in water and 10^{-11} $\mu c/cc$ in air.

Standards of exposure are based on total body radium content and its known effects. It was known almost from the beginning that skin burns leading to cancer of the skin could result from overexposure to radium. And as noted above, malignant disease may result from heavy internal deposition.

RADIUM-DIAL PAINTER CASES

During the period from 1914 to 1925 it was the habit of the girls who painted luminous watch dials (in New Jersey, Connecticut, and Illinois) to put a fine point on their brushes by shaping them with their lips. In this way, small amounts of radium, mesothorium, and radiothorium were ingested.

In 1922, 1923, and 1924, 9 girls who had worked for a few years as dial painters died with severe anemia and destructive lesions of the mouth and jaw. By 1925 an industrial etiology was clearly demonstrated, and the practice of shaping the brush with the lips was stopped. Continuing studies on this group of women have yielded valuable information on the DOSE-EFFECT RELATIONSHIP. Several research laboratories have conducted detailed medical, radiographic, and physical studies on over 500 of those exposed who are now between 50 and 70 years of age.

Symptoms attributable to chronic radiation exposure arise largely as the result of pathologic changes of the bones in which radium becomes concentrated: necrosis and bone destruction especially in joints, pathological fractures, bone tumors, and tumors of the paranasal or mastoid sinuses. Radiographic signs range from barely detectable coarsening of trabeculation and osteoporosis, to those of advanced severity such as aseptic necrosis, pathological fracture, and malignant disease.

Among those whose residual radium body burden (about 35 years after ingestion) is 0.1 microgram (μg) of radium-226 or less, there is no case in which any significant symptom or sign of a possible radiation effect has been observed. If the residual radium burden is 1.0 μg or greater, symptoms show and signs of radium damage are found in some individuals. However, it is remarkable that so many are symptom-free in spite of demonstrated heavy doses of radium. Of particular significance is the fact that no anemia, leukemia, or other blood dyscrasia has been demonstrated in the chronic radium and mesothorium cases, even though the residual body burdens have been as high as 23 μg of radium 10 to 48 years after exposure.

A residual retention of 0.1 μg at 35 years corresponds to an earlier burden of 0.6 μg one year after exposure or 2.3 μg at one month after exposure. The "average" skeletal radiation dose rate from a 35-year retained 0.1 μg radium-226 body burden would be 5.4 rad per year for the 35-year period. In addition there will be hot spots or bone areas of radium concentration which may be as much as 100 times as radioactive as the average.

RADON

Symbol Rn; atomic number 86; atomic weight 222. One of the heaviest gases known. It is radioactive, odorless, and colorless. Discovered in 1900 by Dorn in the radioactive transformation of radium and named radium emanation. Isolated in 1908 by Ramsay and Gray, who named it niton. Since 1923, has been called radon to indicate its origin from radium.

Thirteen radioactive isotopes have been identified. Rn^{222} appears in the URANIUM RADIOACTIVE SERIES. Isotope Rn^{219} (actinon) appears in the ACTINIUM RADIOACTIVE SERIES, and Rn^{220} (thoron) appears in the THORIUM RADIOACTIVE SERIES.

About 100 cubic millimeters of radon gas are spontaneously generated per day by 1 kilogram of radium. This gas is present in the atmosphere in concentrations depending on the radium content of the soil and on meteorological conditions. In addition, as a result of radioactive decay, particulate gamma-emitting daughters are present: lead (radium-B) ($_{82}Pb^{214}$); bismuth (radium-C) ($_{83}Bi^{214}$); and polonium (radium-C') ($_{84}Po^{214}$).

The average (a tenfold variation is found) radon concentration in outdoor air is about 10^{-13} to 10^{-14} curie per liter of air. The external gamma dose rate is calculated to be about 0.17 microroentgen per hour, or about 1 to 2% of the total natural external gamma dose.

Analyzing the exhaled breath for radon (breath samples) is one method of determining the human body content of radium. Two or more years after injection or ingestion of radium the ratio (Rn/Ra) of body radium detectible as exhaled-breath radon to total-body radium remains fairly constant at about 0.45. Values ranging from 0.32 to 0.55 were found in subjects who had ingested radium 8 to 25 years previously as radium watch-dial painters.

Radon seeds, although extensively used in the past for implantation BRACHYTHERAPY of malignant disease, are now quite largely replaced by gold-198, cobalt-60, and other radioactive isotopes.

The maximum permissible concentration for a 40-hour week industrial exposure, with the lung as the critical organ, is 3×10^{-7} microcurie per cubic centimeter (μc/cc) in air for Rn^{220} and 3×10^{-8} μc/cc in air for Rn^{222}. For a 168-hour (continuous exposure) week, the MPC in air for Rn^{220} is 10^{-7} μc/cc, and for Rn^{222} is 10^{-8} μc/cc.

RADON BREATH ANALYSIS

Examination of exhaled air for the presence of radon has been shown to be a method of determining the presence and quantity of radium in the human body. The radioactive gas, radon ($_{86}Rn^{222}$, half-life 3.825 days) is the daughter of radium ($_{88}Ra^{226}$, half-life 1,622 years) and appears in the uranium radioactive series. The rate of production of radon by 10^{-10} gram of radium is 12.6×10^{-15} curie per minute, and approximately 70% of the radon produced in the human body is eliminated in the breath.

Drinking water at the Stateville Penitentiary near Joliet, Illinois, contains 3.4×10^{-12} gm Ra per liter and that of the city of Lockport, 8×10^{-12} gm Ra per liter. To determine the retention of radium by these groups, radon breath analyses were done and compared with a control group from Chicago where drinking water contains only 0.03×10^{-12} gm Ra per liter.

The air in the Chicago area contains about 1 to 2×10^{-12} curie Rn per liter. Thus, to determine such small amounts as those held in the body from the drinking water, it was first necessary to breathe pure or radon-free air for 12 hours and then collect all the exhaled air for a 30-minute period. The amount of radon expired in 30 minutes by a subject containing 10^{-10} gm Ra would be 0.264×10^{-12} curie for 70% elimination, and this is enough for a satisfactory measurement. Table R–14 gives the results.

RANGE

The distance that a particle will penetrate a given substance before its kinetic energy is reduced to a value below which it can no longer produce ionization. For a heavy ion such as an alpha particle, in which little straggling occurs, the range

TABLE R–14. MEAN VALUES OF BODY RADIUM FOR GROUPS OF SUBJECTS*

| GROUP | NO. OF SUBJECTS | YEARS | | MEAN BODY CONTENT UNITS OF 10^{-10} gm Ra |
		MEAN AGE	MEAN TIME STATEVILLE	
Stateville				
New	11	27	0.32	1.00
Intermediate	8	38	7.6	2.02
Long term	11	44	19.7	2.36
Chicago boys	7	16.6	—	0.36
Lockport boys	8	16.6	—	3.68

*Work performed at Argonne National Laboratory.

usually refers to the component of displacement in the initial direction and is only slightly shorter than the path length or the distance measured along the track of the particle. For a meson, whose track shows moderate deflections near the end, the range usually refers to the path length. For a beta particle (electron), with a tortuous track due to frequent deflections, the range usually refers to the greatest distance of penetration in a specified direction, although this distance usually is considerably shorter than the path length. The range of beta particles is very short, as will be seen in Table R–15, showing the range in centimeters of water for the pure beta emitters commonly used in medical activity.

Obviously the range depends upon two factors: the initial maximum energy of the particles in the beam and the type of matter being penetrated.

The extrapolated range is the value of the range in matter for a given type of charged particle obtained by an extrapolation of the absorption curve according to some prescription, for example, the intercept on the range-axis of a straight line drawn through the descending portion of a numbers-versus-range curve for initially monoenergetic particles. For heavy charged particles (protons, deuterons, helium ions) the usual prescription involves tangential extrapolation to the zero

ordinate from the point of half-reduction of the beam intensity.

The linear range is the range expressed in units of length.

The mass range is the range expressed in units of surface density; thus it is the mass per unit area of a layer of thickness equal to the linear range and is equal to the product of the linear range and the density of the substance being traversed.

The mean range is the range that is exceeded by half the particles.

The residual range is the distance over which the particle can still produce ionization after having lost some of its energy in passing through matter.

The visual range is the value of the range of beta particles in an absorber, usually aluminum, estimated by visual inspection of the breaks in the aluminum absorption curve.

See IONIZATION PATH.

RARE EARTHS

A group of 16 metallic elements: yttrium, atomic number 39; lanthanum, 57; cerium, 58; praseodymium, 59; neodymium, 60; promethium, 61; samarium, 62; europium, 63; gadolinium, 64; terbium, 65; dysprosium, 66; holmium, 67; erbium, 68; thulium, 69; ytterbium, 70; and lutecium, 71. Some add scandium, 21. All have

TABLE R–15

ELEMENT	RADIOISOTOPE	TYPE	ENERGY (Mev)	RANGE IN WATER (cm)
Hydrogen	$_1H^3$	β^-	0.0180	0.0006
Carbon	$_6C^{14}$	β^-	0.156	0.029
Phosphorus	$_{15}P^{32}$	β^-	1.710	0.79
Sulfur	$_{16}S^{35}$	β^-	0.1673	0.032
Calcium	$_{20}Ca^{45}$	β^-	0.256	0.061
Strontium	$_{38}Sr^{90}$	β^-	0.544	0.18
Yttrium	$_{39}Y^{90}$	β^-	2.25	1.09

almost identical chemical properties, and all except yttrium (by some chemists not classified with the rare earths) are grouped together in position IIIB of the periodic table under lanthanum, and this group is called lanthanides or the lanthanide series. All but promethium (reactor-produced) occur naturally in the form of oxides and are found in various minerals but most important in monazite. They are really not "rare," although originally considered so, for they are more abundant than copper or zinc, and cerium is even more abundant than tin.

They have achieved industrial importance and are used in such diversified ways as in cigarette-lighter flints, motion picture projectors, precision lenses, alloy steels, colored glass, paint driers, and color television picture tubes.

Nine of the rare earths (atomic numbers 57 through 65) have been identified as fission products and would therefore need to be considered in connection with fallout, fuel reprocessing, and radioactive waste disposal. Lanthanum and cerium (atomic numbers 57 and 58) are also listed as possible nuclides induced in sea water following a nuclear detonation on the surface of or under the sea.

Isotopes of lanthanum, cerium, praseodymium, neodymium, promethium, samarium, and europium have been studied in animals for their metabolic and toxic properties. None of the rare earths is found naturally in significant quantities in biological material.

RATE METER. *See* COUNT RATE METER.

RBE. *See* RELATIVE BIOLOGICAL EFFECTIVENESS.

REACTION, NUCLEAR. *See* NUCLEAR REACTION.

REACTOR

In the field of nuclear science and technology, a short form for NUCLEAR REACTOR. *See* POWER REACTOR and MEDICAL RESEARCH REACTOR.

REACTOR ACCIDENTS

Accidents have occurred in the operation and upkeep of nuclear reactors in spite of all the effort and planning that has gone into reactor safety. But reactors have been in operation for about 20 years, with well over 100 in operation at present. Until 1961 there had been no fatal reactor accidents in the United States.

However, a nuclear excursion is possible and occurred in the SL-1 REACTOR ACCIDENT, with the loss of 3 lives, on January 3, 1961.

An uncontrolled power surge in a reactor being operated in Vinca, Yugoslavia, on October 15, 1958, heavily irradiated 8 men, one of whom died in spite of treatment, including bone-marrow therapy.

A number of reactor accidents have been caused by malfunction of the control rod mechanism or improper handling of the control rod. An example of this is the June 2, 1952, accident at the Argonne National Laboratory, where during an experiment, the manual withdrawal of a control rod caused an accidental supercriticality. Four persons received 190, 160, 70, and 12 rem respectively, but although they were hospitalized for over 3 weeks, no injury could be clinically demonstrated.

Ruptured fuel elements have been noted on a number of occasions, and a fuel corrosion leak was found in an experimental reactor. Fuel melt-down has also occurred. None of these accidents has been associated with injury to personnel.

One of the most common types of accident involving exposure of personnel to radiation is illustrated by the accident in which 6 employees were working on the top of a reactor which was shut down. A highly radioactive component was placed in a position in which it was not adequately shielded because of lowered water level in the reactor tank. Eight workers received radiation exposure to gamma rays of 2.5 r to 21.5 r.

One hazard which has not materialized, except in the WINDSCALE REACTOR ACCIDENT, is the release of radioactivity in sufficient quantity to contaminate the surrounding countryside.

The USAEC has an Advisory Committee on Reactor Safeguards whose duties deal with the problems of reactor safety and reactor accidents.

See REACTOR FIRES.

REACTOR FIRES

Fires in and around a reactor are always a possibility. The extent of the hazard depends to a large degree on the type of reactor: (1) Water-cooled or nonflammable gas-cooled reactors offer a low fire hazard. (2) Air-cooled reactors are considered a moderate fire hazard owing to the oxygen content of the air stream, while (3) reactors using liquid pyrophoric metals, or organic liquids above the flash point, are definitely a fire hazard. For example, a leak in the primary cooling system allowing liquid sodium to come in contact with air may cause a spontaneous fire.

Uranium is pyrophoric and is subject to possible burning and release of fission products.* Even graphite can ignite if the temperature is high

---

*Fission product self-heating can produce a major fire or meltdown, and lead to contamination spread, if reactor coolant flow is lost or interrupted.

enough as was the case in the reactor fire in the WINDSCALE REACTOR ACCIDENT.

Charcoal filters have burned, fires have occurred in shielding material, and combustible materials around a reactor are always a hazard.

There is also the possibility of a chemical blast or explosion associated with a fire or with a "runaway" nuclear excursion, as in the case of the SL-1 reactor accident. But reactor design and containment is such that, even though the release of energy for the production of heat is accomplished through a chain reaction, it is impossible for an atomic bomb type of explosion to occur. If all the safety devices failed, the most that could occur is a nuclear runaway or excursion, a chemical blast, or a fire—none of these remotely resemble an atomic explosion.

In reactor fires the normal fire-fighting principles must be modified by consideration of the possibility of spreading radioactive contamination.

REACTOR SAFETY

Safety of the general public in the operation of a stationary power reactor is of prime importance and is achieved by the following measures:

1. The USAEC Advisory Committee on Reactor Safeguards carefully reviews and passes upon the plans for every new reactor installation to insure that it meets all safety requirements.

2. The USAEC staff inspects reactors for compliance with safety regulations.

3. A site away from centers of heavy population is chosen for the location of a reactor. Careful ecological surveys are made for comparison purposes to determine the effects of any possible accidental dispersal of radioactivity.

4. Power reactors designed for use in a populated area are contained in a steel and reinforced concrete pressure vessel so that a runaway reaction could not spread to the surrounding environment.

5. All reactors are built with many safety factors designed to automatically shut down the reactor if a dangerously high power level develops.

6. The USAEC continuously conducts an experimental reactor safety program investigating all aspects of possible reactor accidents.

During operation of the over 100 reactors in the world during the past several years, 4 serious reactor accidents have occurred: the SL-1 reactor accident; the Windscale reactor accident; the Chalk River accident and an accident in Vinca, Yugoslavia.

REACTOR TRAINING

The USAEC sponsors several training programs in the field of reactor technology.

The Oak Ridge School of Reactor Technology is designed to instruct college graduates who have had previous experience in nuclear science in a 1-year, graduate-level course in reactor technology.

The School of Nuclear Science and Engineering at Argonne National Laboratory offers a graduate-level course of 7 months for scientists and engineers on an international basis. Instruction includes courses in design, construction, and operation of reactors for nuclear research, principles of design of nuclear power reactors, and handling of irradiated materials.

The Shippingport Supervisory Training Course offers a 4-month nuclear training course designed to give domestic and foreign supervisory personnel and engineers a practical background in the operation of a nuclear power reactor.

In addition to these sponsored courses concentrating on reactor technology, degree programs in "nuclear engineering" are developing at many universities. These courses include information on the general principles of reactor technology, and some include specific consideration of reactor design, construction, and operation.

See EDUCATION AND TRAINING, USAEC.

RECOMBINATION. *See* CELL DIVISION, RADIATION EFFECTS ON.

RECORDER, GRAPHIC STRIP CHART

Mechanical device which prepares a continuous graphical presentation of data received from an instrument such as count rate meter or spectrum analyzer. Used to give an immediate and permanent record of an observed function, such as a constantly changing level of radioactivity, in relation to time or the variation of some other variable, by gearing the chart drive to a clock motor or to an instrumental parameter such as the discriminator setting of a pulse height analyzer. In the simpler devices of this kind, the writing element is frequently driven by a simple electrical meter movement; more precise and more sensitive recorders are based on the self-balancing potentiometer circuit in which the motor that provides the balancing action also carries the pen or other writing component.

RECORDER, TABULATING

Machine built on electromagnetic principles which delivers a printed columnar arrangement of data accumulated from counters or other instruments. Such machines can be arranged to make a correlated presentation of items such as the sample number, counting time, count interval, and counts received from one or more detecting channels.

RECOVERY FROM IRRADIATION

Return to normal function following exposure to radiation. Restoration, repair, and regeneration all have a direct relationship to recovery from irradiation. The many other factors having a bearing upon the recovery process may be conveniently divided into 4 groups: (1) physical factors relating to radiation—type, dose rate, total dose, fractionation; (2) environmental factors—relationship to other organisms, temperature, oxygen supply, available nutrition, shielding, irradiation of the whole body or of a part; (3) preventative measures taken and treatment given; (4) the organism itself—condition at the time of irradiation, radiosensitivity of the tissue, organ, or part of the body irradiated, vital need for the function of the part irradiated, and most important, the sign, symptom, or function that is being measured to determine recovery from irradiation.

If the dose is not too large, the organism will recuperate from acute effects of radiation, but because of the long latent period for some of the delayed effects, it is difficult to say at any given time that complete recovery has occurred. In general it may be taken for granted that there is some residual or irreparable damage.

In man, if death does not intervene, the acute clinical signs and symptoms will begin to abate in the 5th or 6th week, and by the 7th or 8th week, the individual will appear healthy. The blood picture shows slow recovery—the peripheral neutrophil count usually begins to recover during the 5th week, the platelet count a week or so later, and the peripheral lymphocyte return is even slower. Many months or even a year or two may be necessary for complete recovery of all peripheral blood elements.

A recovery factor is shown in that divided or fractionated doses produce less biological damage than the same amount of radiation given in a single dose. For example, rats were given 6 equal x-ray doses of 131 roentgens (r) at various intervals, with each fraction requiring 1 minute to give. At the zero interval (6 minutes continuous at a dose rate of 131 r per minute) the mortality was 95%, whereas when the total amount of x-ray was given at 30-minute intervals (156 minutes elapsed time), the mortality was only 50%.

In split-dose studies (single dose compared with the same dose of radiation given in 2 doses) the findings show that the combined lethal effect of the 2 doses decreases steadily as the time interval between the doses increases. Let us assume that with a given quality of x-rays, skin erythema of a certain degree is produced by a skin dose of 700 r administered in 1 hour. It has been found that with 2 short exposures separated by 24 hours, each dose must be 525 r, or a total of 1,070 r to achieve the same degree of erythema (for shorter time intervals the difference is less and for longer intervals it is greater). Evidently some type of recovery from the effects of the first 535 r occurred in the 24-hour interval. Since 700 r given at one time produced the erythema in question, the effective dose remaining from the first exposure of 535 r must have been 165 r; i.e., recovery in the 24-hour period overcame the effect of 370 r.

Continuous repair during irradiation and recovery after irradiation are shown by studies of radiation effects on luminous bacteria, Achromobacter fischerii. If the organism is cultivated under proper conditions, light will be emitted at a constant intensity. Figure R–3 shows that during irradiation the emission of light decreases with the slope of response being sharper with the higher dose rate (repair during irradiation); and recovery commences immediately upon cessation of irradiation (some of the biochemical alterations induced by the radiation are apparently repaired instantly). The intensity of light did not, in this

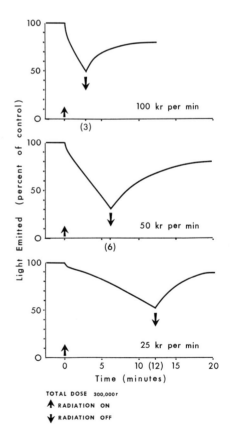

FIGURE R–3. CONTINUOUS REPAIR DURING IRRADIATION AND RECOVERY AFTER IRRADIATION DEMONSTRATED BY IRRADIATION OF LUMINOUS BACTERIA.

experiment, return to the original normal level, indicating some irreparable damage.

Recovery from temporary sterility is the rule if the male receives less than 500 r. A number of individuals who have been exposed in criticality accidents at dose levels sufficient to cause severe acute radiation illness have remained fertile and subsequently have produced children. Temporary sterility has lasted for a few months in some cases.

Prevention of radiation damage and treatment of radiation illness are closely related to recovery but are discussed separately: BONE MARROW GRAFTS; CHEMICAL PROTECTION AGAINST RADIATION INJURY; and TREATMENT OF RADIATION ILLNESS. Recovery from genetic damage and the problem of natural selection are closely related to recovery.

RED CELL LIFE SPAN MEASUREMENT

Patients may become anemic because of failure of red cell formation, loss of blood by hemorrhage, or abnormal breakdown of red cells in the body (hemolysis). It is particularly to determine the presence of hemolysis that radioisotopic studies of red cell survival are of value. These studies are of 2 general types: one in which the label is built into new cells during their formation, and another in which cells already formed and of all ages are labeled either in vivo or in vitro.

Examples of the first type of study are those using radioiron (iron-59) or amino acids labeled with carbon-14 or nitrogen-15. If a tracer of radioiron is injected intravenously, most of it normally will be incorporated during a few days in new red cells formed during that period. As these young red cells enter the circulation the amount of radioactivity in the blood will increase rapidly. Subsequently it will remain stationary (except for physical decay) for over 100 days. Then there will be a decline in blood radioactivity corresponding with the destruction of the labeled red cells at the end of their life span. Reutilization of some of the radioiron in a second crop of red cells may make this part of the curve difficult to interpret. The normal life span of the human red cell is shown to be about 120 days. (See Figure R–4.)

The second type of study involves the labeling of red cells already formed. These cells will be of all ages—on the average about half through their life span when labeled; this is in contrast to the previously described situation in which only newly formed cells are tagged. Prominent labels for cells already formed are radiochromium (chromium-51) and di-isopropylfluorophosphonate (DFP) containing phosphorus-32. When radiochromium is used, the cells are usually labeled out-

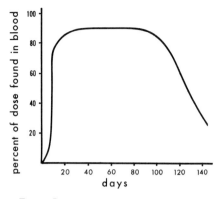

FIGURE R–4. IRON-59 STUDY OF RED CELL SURVIVAL. AVERAGE LIFE SPAN ABOUT 120 DAYS.

side the body by incubating them with the isotope in the form of sodium chromate. The cells are reinjected and blood samples are radioassayed at intervals for several days. When the results (corrected for physical decay) are plotted, they usually do not give a straight line on either linear or semilogarithmic graph paper. There usually is a rapid early decrease in radioactivity of the blood and then a more gradual fall. Some of the radiochromium leaves the red cells while they are still intact (elution), but the main fall in activity is due to red cell destruction. Experience has shown that in normal patients the blood radioactivity reaches 50% of its initial level in about 25 to 30 days. If this level is reached more rapidly, there is evidence of abnormal destruction or loss of red cells. (See Figure R–5).

DFP also labels cells already formed, but its best use involves injection of the labeled material into the body to avoid handling the red cells. The P32-labeled DFP is difficult to obtain with suitable specific activity. It labels the red cells by combin-

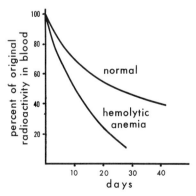

FIGURE R–5. CHROMIUM-51 STUDY OF RED CELL SURVIVAL IN A NORMAL SUBJECT AND IN ONE WITH HEMOLYTIC ANEMIA.

ing with choline esterase. Under ideal conditions it eliminates some of the defects of the chromium-51 method, and a plot of the blood radioactivity yields a nearly straight line on linear graph paper.

RED CELL MASS MEASUREMENT

The measurement of the red cell (erythrocyte) volume or mass is based on labeling of the red cells with a radioisotope. Phosphorus-32 was first used to tag red blood cells isotopically, but chromium-51 is much more stable and is largely used today— less than 1% of the chromium is lost from the red cells per day, compared with 6% per hour for the P^{32} label.

A patient's blood is drawn and the red cells are incubated in a solution containing radiochromium; then the cells are washed several times with normal saline, measured for radioactivity, returned to the patient by injection into a vein, and then a blood sample drawn after time has been allowed for mixing. The radioactivity of this sample is determined and the volume of the red cells determined by the classic dilution formula:

$$\begin{matrix} V\text{ (volume to be} \\ \text{determined)} \end{matrix} = \frac{A\text{ (counts/min of injected cells)}}{S\text{ (counts/min/ml blood sample)}}$$

See BLOOD VOLUME, MEASUREMENT; ISOTOPE DILUTION; and PLASMA VOLUME MEASUREMENT.

RED CELL SURVIVAL. *See* RED CELL LIFE SPAN MEASUREMENT.

REFLECTOR

A layer or structure of material surrounding the core of a reactor to reduce the escape of neutrons. A reflecting material must have a low cross section for neutron capture and a high scattering cross section. Beryllium and its oxide, graphite (carbon), and natural uranium are used as reflecting materials. Neutrons entering the reflector are scattered randomly, some of them many times. It is possible to design a reflector so that 90% of the neutrons that would otherwise be lost are returned to the core.

REGENERATION

The recovery process by which damaged cells are replaced by new ones of the same type. When skin is damaged by radiation to the extent of cell destruction, healing takes place by replacement, in kind, of destroyed cells.

See RECOVERY FROM IRRADIATION.

REGISTER, COUNT

Electromechanical or electronic display device which totalizes and presents a number representing the data accumulated from a pulse-counting instrument.

See RECORDER, TABULATING.

REGULATION

The control and stabilization of voltage or power supply provided for an instrument or other device and necessary to insure uniformly reliable performance and constant sensitivity.

REGULATOR CIRCUIT

Electronic sensing and controlling circuitry built into a power supply to stabilize the voltage it provides for operation of radiation detectors or other sensitive circuits. Typically, such a circuit functions by sensing the deviation of its delivered voltage from a standard comparison signal, automatically developing a correcting stimulus which operates instantaneously through related elements in the circuit.

RELATIVE BIOLOGICAL EFFECTIVENESS

RBE is a factor which is used to compare the biological effectiveness of absorbed radiation doses (i.e., rad) due to different types of ionizing radiation. A term used to indicate that different types of radiation result in different effects in biological materials or systems. More specifically, it is the ratio of an absorbed dose of x-rays or gamma rays to the absorbed dose of a certain particulate radiation required to produce an identical biological effect in a particular experimental organism or tissue. The relative biological effectiveness may be defined as follows:

$$RBE = \frac{\text{Biological efficiency of radiation under investigation}}{\text{Biological effectiveness of therapy x-rays or gamma rays}}$$

$$= \frac{\text{Dose in rad to produce effect with therapy x-rays or gamma rays}}{\text{Dose in rad to produce effect with radiation under investigation}}$$

Thus if an absorbed dose of 0.2 rad of slow neutron radiation produced the same biological effect as an absorbed dose of 1 rad of x- or γ-radiation, the RBE for slow neutrons would be:

$$RBE = \frac{1 \text{ rad}}{0.2 \text{ rad}} = 5$$

Typical values of RBE for radiations of several types are given in Table R–16.

TABLE R–16

RADIATION	RBE
X or gamma	1
Beta	1
Proton	10
Alpha	20
Fast neutron	10
Slow neutron	5

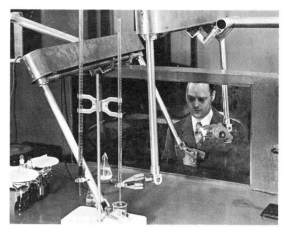

FIGURE R–6. REMOTE CONTROL EQUIPMENT FOR HANDLING EQUIPMENT IN A HOT CELL. (COURTESY OF THE ARGONNE NATIONAL LABORATORY.)

Thus it is seen that although all ionizing radiations are capable of producing similar biological effects, the absorbed dose, measured in rad, which will produce a given effect varies from one type of radiation to another. Actually the RBE of different ionizing radiations depends solely on the ionization density or LINEAR ENERGY TRANSFER and not on the different physical characteristics of the radiations.

In addition, the RBE of a particular radiation depends upon the effect being studied, the dose, the dose rate, the presence or absence of oxygen, and the postirradiation conditions.

REM

The term rem is an acronym for ROENTGEN EQUIVALENT, MAN.

REMOTE-CONTROL EQUIPMENT

Highly radioactive materials and intense radiation sources are frequently controlled and manipulated remotely to insure safety of the workers and to avoid contaminating the environment. To carry out procedures involving radiation hazards of such nature that the direct presence of an operator is prescribed, remote control equipment has been employed ranging widely in degree of complexity from the simplest "long tongs" to fully automatic machine tools equipping entire laboratory and shop arrangements for production, analysis, or fabrication of dangerous materials. The essential components of remote manipulators may employ simple and direct mechanical linkages, self-synchronized pairs of electric motors or their hydraulic or pneumatic equivalents, or may run through the full gamut of automated equipment

used for robot operation, much of it invented specifically for these purposes. Thus remote controls may and do range from the simplest hand-held instruments and tools to master-slave manipulators of complexity exceeding even that of a remotely controlled pair of prosthetic hands (Fig. R–6). At the scale of "hot lab" operations, some maneuvers are carried out in the depths of a pool of water and others are set up in "hot cells." The pool provides a shielding medium which is penetrable and permits observation during transfer and assembly of active materials. The design of a hot cell permits it to be opened to assemble and adjust apparatus and to carry out cold runs; the actual hot operation takes place after the cell is closed, when the radioactive substance can be safely introduced by delivery apparatus through access overhead or beyond other protective barriers. On an even grander scale, large tractors and Diesel locomotives have been modified for use under radiocontrol to explore and to effect manipulations through truly remote signals at radio beam range.

Simple procedures can be carried out with small-scale laboratory arrangements resembling a glove box, in which the hand ports are fitted with long-stemmed manipulators operated entirely from outside the enclosure while valves and switches are operated electrically. Equipment and methods for use under more stringent conditions should provide shielding. In addition, containment or separate ventilation is frequently necessary for the space surrounding substances or equipment which must be kept at a distance from the person of the worker, and with procedures which must be carried out under full-scale protective measures.

Television monitors may be employed to observe

operations under these conditions, especially in geographically remote locations. But in many situations it is entirely adequate and may even be preferable to use direct optical means utilizing mirrors or periscopes and such transparent materials as heavy glass or liquid-filled tanks.

RENAL CLEARANCE TIME. *See* KIDNEY FUNCTION MEASUREMENT.

REP

The term rep is an acronym for ROENTGEN EQUIVALENT, PHYSICAL.

REPRODUCTION, ANIMAL, RADIATION EFFECTS ON

Most of the data on the effects of radiation on reproduction have been obtained on laboratory animals and dogs, with fewer observations on domestic animals. Mammalian gonads contain several gametogenic stages of varying sensitivity to radiation. For example, spermatocytes, spermatids, sperm, Sertoli cells, and interstitial tissue are relatively insensitive, whereas spermatogonia are quite sensitive to radiation. The importance of this differential response lies in the fact that germ cells which survive to form gametes can transmit radiation-induced genetic changes. After an initial high dosage (300 roentgens or more), males are fertile for a matter of weeks because of development of gametes irradiated as the insensitive forms; they then become temporarily sterile because of destruction of some spermatogonia and their precursors; and then regain fertility because of repopulation by a few surviving spermatogonia.

Observations on male beagle dogs subjected to daily exposure to x-rays from a 1,000 kvp x-ray machine or to neutrons from a cyclotron, 5 or 6 days per week, are shown in Table R–17.

In contrast to males, females may be permanently sterilized by low acute radiation doses, since the supply of oöcytes, if once destroyed, is not replaced. In females, irradiation can cause profound atrophy of the ovary with either temporary or permanent sterility, depending on the dose. The ova and follicular cells are the most radiation-sensitive cells in the mammalian ovary, but the sensitivity varies with their functional states. In addition, changes in the ovaries may be followed by secondary hormonal disturbances and atrophic changes in accessory genitalia. Prevention of development of primary follicles of the ovary causes complete sterility.

Studies of irradiated ovaries of mice have indicated that nearly all early oöcytes are destroyed by 50 r, but that sensitivity is less with increased maturity of the follicle.

Embryos are especially sensitive to radiation. Exposure at a very early stage may cause death but at a later time may produce malformations, especially of the central nervous system, eye, or skeleton, depending upon the stage of organo-

TABLE R–17. MALE BEAGLE DOGS EXPOSED DAILY (5 OR 6 DAYS PER WEEK) TO X-RAYS OR NEUTRONS

DOSE/WK.	APPROXIMATE TOTAL DOSE	DURAT. OF EXPOSURE	OBSERVATIONS
0.3r	125r	8 yr	No signif. change in sperm count
0.6r	250r	8 yr	No signif. change in sperm count
0.6r	62r	2 yr	Little change in germinal epithelium
0.6n	31n	1 yr	Little change in germinal epithelium
3.0r	156r	1 yr	80% sterile, 20% reduc. sperm
3.0r	312r	2 yr	Substantial atrophy of germinal epithelium
6.0r	312r	1 yr	Aspermia
6.0r	624r	2 yr	Marked atrophy of germinal epithelium 100% sterile
10.2n	398–561n	39–55 wk	Extreme atrophy of germinal epithel. 100% sterile
15.4r	477r	31 wk	Aspermia, after 375 r still sterile 5 yr after irradiation
15.4r	634r	41 wk	Aspermia, after 375 r still sterile 5 yr after irradiation
15.4r	375r	25 wk	Still aspermic 1 yr post-irradiation

*One n = approximately 2 rad.

genesis at the time of irradiation. Doses as low as 30 to 50 r may cause abnormalities.

It is obvious that fertility is depressed by exposure to radiation. The degree of the loss of fertility depends upon the total dose and, possibly also, upon the dose rate. A typical result, following exposure of the gonads of male mice to 500 r, is for fertility to decline rapidly in the first few weeks after irradiation, followed by a sterile period of several weeks, and this in turn followed by a period of increasing fertility. This result is accounted for by the differential killing of cells in various stages of spermatogenesis. Fertility returns, if at all, because of a repopulation of the germinal epithelium by surviving spermatogonia. The effect of radiation on fertility varies from species to species and from animal to animal within species.

See GONADS, RADIATION EFFECT ON.

RESIDENCE TIME

The time during which radioactive material is held in the atmosphere following injection by the detonation of a nuclear device, usually expressed as residence half-time since the time for all such material to leave the atmosphere is not known.

In the immediate area of detonation the heavier particles will return to earth as LOCAL FALLOUT with a short residence time and with a rate of fall related to their size. For example, assuming that all particles start to fall when they reach 80,000 feet and that the meteorological conditions are stable, the time required to reach the earth is as shown in Table R–18.

TABLE R–18. APPROXIMATE TIMES FOR PARTICLES TO FALL FROM 80,000 FEET

PARTICLE DIAMETER (microns)	TIME OF FALL (hours)
340	0.75
250	1.4
150	3.9
75	16
33	80
16	340
8	1,400
5	3,400

The residence half-time for radioactive material carried from the site of detonation in the TROPOSPHERIC air is on the order of 3 to 4 weeks, but this time may be shortened by the SCAVENGING effect of rain and snow.

There is a great deal of uncertainty about the residence time of the radioactive material coming down as STRATOSPHERIC FALLOUT, but the present estimated mean residence time of material in the stratosphere is from 1 to 5 years with the shortest

time for debris from Arctic shots, and a period of about 3 years' residence half-time rather than the earlier predicted half-time of 7 years.

RESIDUAL CONTAMINATION

Radioactive contamination which remains after decontamination steps have been taken (*see* WEAPON DEBRIS, FISSION PRODUCTS, and INDUCED RADIOACTIVITY). Radioactive fallout is frequently spoken of as residual contamination.

See RADIONUCLIDES PRODUCED IN AIR, WATER, AND SOIL (BOMB); and RESIDUAL NUCLEAR RADIATION.

RESIDUAL NUCLEAR RADIATION

Residual radiation, lingering radiation, or radiation (gamma rays, beta particles, alpha particles) emitted by radioactive material remaining after a nuclear explosion. About 10% of the energy formed by the detonation of a nuclear device (fission) is residual nuclear radiation, which is that radiation emitted later than 1 minute from the instant of the nuclear explosion. The radioactive residue is in the form of fission products, unfissioned material (uranium and plutonium), and constituents of earth, air, water, and bomb materials in which radioactivity has been induced by neutron bombardment.

The primary hazard of residual radiation results from the creation of fallout particles which may be dispersed over large areas.

Both the total and relative contributions to residual nuclear radiation of fission product and induced radioactivity will depend on the total and fission yield of the weapon, the height of burst, the nature of the surface at ground zero, and the length of time after the explosion.

RESISTOR

Component used in an electric circuit to provide control of current or to establish a desired voltage gradient. Characterized by its ability to limit the passage of electricity, the resistance normally being measured in ohms.

RESOLVING TIME

The minimum time interval between events which can be resolved or reported separately by a radiation detector or by a radiation detection instrument; related to the dead time.

RESPIRATION STUDIES

Radioisotopes offer great advantages in the study of respiration and function of the lungs, but only limited application has been made of these possibilities. One approach uses xenon-133, a rare radioactive gas that is not significantly absorbed into the blood stream. The patient takes several breaths of this radioisotope along with a mixture of stable xenon and oxygen. Several scintillation detectors previously placed at various points over the chest are used to supply a continuous recording of the levels of radioactivity. Normally the counting rates increase symmetrically and simultaneously over all areas of the lung. When the radioactive gas is no longer inhaled, the counting levels normally fall nearly to zero within 70 seconds. If part of the lung is diseased and is aerating poorly, the counting rate over it rises less than normally; in such areas there may also be a delayed clearing after the intake of the labeled gas is discontinued.

RESPIRATORS

Breathing devices worn as RESPIRATORY PROTECTION against radioactive aerosols, dusts, fumes, or smoke. There are 2 general classes of respirators: filter and supplied air. The MSA Comfo half mask (Fig. R–7) and the MSA full-face mask (Fig. R–8) are typical examples of the many different types of filter masks. Most masks of a given manufacturer have interchangeable canisters or cartridges to filter out and absorb particulate matter. Half masks are difficult to fit snugly to the face, and in normal routine use are considered to allow about 20% penetration. It therefore follows that such masks can be used only in an atmosphere in which the concentration of the radioactive contaminant does not exceed 5 times the MAXIMUM PERMISSIBLE

FIGURE R–8. FULL-FACE MASK RESPIRATOR. (COURTESY OF MINE SAFETY APPLIANCES CO.)

CONCENTRATION for air (MPC_a) during the time the mask is worn. The full-face filter-type mask allows only about 1 to 2% penetration and can therefore be worn when the concentration of contaminant is no more than 50 times the MPC_a. With either type it is important to remember that in general the mask does not protect against toxic or radioactive gases and definitely does not protect against atmospheres deficient in oxygen.

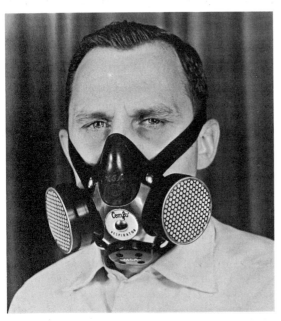

FIGURE R–7. MSA COMFO HALF MASK RESPIRATOR. (COURTESY OF MINE SAFETY APPLIANCES CO.)

FIGURE R–9. SUPPLIED AIR HOOD. (COURTESY OF MINE SAFETY APPLIANCES CO.)

FIGURE R–10. PLASTIC AIR SUIT. AIR SUPPLIED THROUGH HOSE. (COURTESY OF MINE SAFETY APPLIANCES Co.)

FIGURE R–11. PLASTIC AIR SUIT. AIR SUPPLIED THROUGH LARGE SLEEVE. (COURTESY OF MINE SAFETY APPLIANCES Co.)

Either of the above masks can be supplied with air from a compressed-air tank or from an air compressor and used with a constant flow or demand regulator valve. In addition there are several types of oxygen-breathing apparatus of the self-contained demand type. Compressed air can also be supplied to a plastic hood with a transparent window (Fig. R–9) or to a completely enclosed suit closed with a double zipper and acceptable for use when whole body protection is desired. (See Figures R–10 and R–11.)

See PROTECTIVE CLOTHING.

RESPIRATORY PROTECTION

Inhalation of radioactive material in industrial activity is considered to be the most important route of entry for potentially hazardous air-borne radioactivity. Respiratory protection is therefore important and consists of careful housekeeping to keep dust down, adequate ventilation for the general working area, the use of HOODS and GLOVE BOXES for potentially dusty operations, continuous AIR MONITORING in known dusty areas, AIR SAMPLING in potentially dusty areas, and the wearing of RESPIRATORS whenever indicated.

REST MASS

Symbol m_0. The mass of a particle at rest. It is mass in the classical, or Newtonian, sense; i.e., it does not include the additional mass which, according to the relativistic mass equation, is acquired by a particle or body when set in motion.

RESTORATION AFTER IRRADIATION. *See* RECOVERY FROM IRRADIATION.

RETINAL BURNS

Burns of the retina of the eye can result from exposure to thermal radiation from the detonation of a nuclear device. The lens of the eye has a focusing action, and retinal burns have been experienced, from accidental exposure during nuclear tests, at a distance of 10 miles from a 20-kiloton energy yield explosion. Thirty-five per cent of the energy of a typical air burst of a nuclear device is released as thermal radiation which reaches the eye in a few milliseconds. Blinking and pupilary contractile reflexes of the eye are too slow to offer complete protection. There is a loss of visual acuity in all cases, the severity of which depends upon the degree of the burn and its location relative to the center of the visual field. If the eye is focused directly on the fireball (up to 10 miles, depending on the yield), it is possible that a permanent scotoma (blind spot) may be produced by the retinal burn. However, in a group of 1,000 Japanese survivors who were in the open within 6,600 feet of ground zero, there was no case of permanent central scotoma, although several of the survivors stated that they were looking in the direction of the bomb at the time of explosion.

See FLASH BLINDNESS.

RHENIUM

Symbol Re; atomic number 75; atomic weight 186.22. A platinum-white, very hard metal. Discovered in 1925 by Noddack, Tacke, and Berg in the minerals tantalite, wolframite, and columbite. Named for Rhine Province, Germany. (Its existence was predicted by Mendelyeev in 1871.) Natural abundance by 1 stable isotope, Re^{185}, 37.07%; and 1 long-lived (5×10^{10} years half-life) radioactive isotope, Re^{187}, 62.93%. Very rare element (relative occurrence in the earth's crust estimated at 10^{-12}) with little known of naturally occurring levels in biological material.

Eleven radioactive isotopes have been identified. Re^{186} (half-life 92.8 hours, β^- and γ emitter) is commercially available. None has been shown to have biological, medical, or agricultural significance.

RHODIUM

Symbol Rh; atomic number 45; atomic weight 102.91. A white metal occurring in nature in platinum ores (2% at times). Discovered by the English physician Wollaston in 1803. Named from Greek rhodon, rose, since its salts form red solutions. Abundance 100% in the stable isotope Rh^{103}.

Used as a plating finish for silverware, as a mirror surface in searchlights, and as an alloy with platinum. No biological, medical, or agricultural uses.

There are 22 radioactive isotopes. Seventeen may be produced as fission products in the detonation of a nuclear device: Rh^{103m}, Rh^{105m}, and Rh^{105} through Rh^{119}. Two are significant in radioactive fallout: Rh^{103m}, half-life 57 minutes, isomeric transition to stable Rh^{103}; and Rh^{106}, half-life 30 seconds, beta (β^-) and gamma emitter. As a fission product, 11.0 Mc/MT (megacuries per megaton of fission) of Rh^{103m} is found at the end of 1 month and 0.0316 Mc/MT at the end of 1 year; 0.148 Mc/MT of Rh^{106} is left at the end of a year.

r-METER. *See* CONDENSER R-METER.

ROCHESTER ATOMIC ENERGY PROJECT

The University of Rochester Atomic Energy Project was organized in 1943 within the School of Medicine and Dentistry at the request of the Manhattan Engineer District to provide research, consultation, and other services on the health hazards expected to arise in the Oak Ridge plants and other installations contributing to the development of the atomic bomb. Supervised by the office of the Medical Director of the Manhattan District, it was closely coordinated with work being done at the universities of California, Chicago, and Columbia.

A particular responsibility of the Rochester Project at that time was the collection and analysis of data from periodic medical examinations of personnel in plants involved in atomic energy production all over the country. In addition to this, certain plants were surveyed periodically to determine radiation and other hazards, and recommendations were made for safe operation. Film badge and analytical services were provided for plant personnel. Research programs were established in 2 broad fields, the biological effects of external radiation and the toxicity of radioactive and chemical materials.

The Project was transferred to the jurisdiction of the newly formed USAEC and placed under the supervision of the New York Operations Office of the Commission. A Department of Radiation Biology was created to administer the Project locally and to provide it with academic status. Outside services to operating plants were gradually reduced as these were assumed by the Health and Safety Laboratory. Of the original functions of the Project, this left only research and consultation. These were later amplified by an educational program which got fully under way when additional space for the purpose was completed by the Commission in 1950.

The Project administers for the AEC a fellowship in industrial medicine, which is tenable at schools approved for residencies in occupational health. The objective of the program is to provide a supply of industrial physicians with orientation toward the special problems of atomic energy development. Consultation with industry and agencies of the government is extensive.

Most of the research of the Project is concerned with the biological effects of external radiation of internally deposited radioactive materials and of toxic chemicals, and with studies ancillary to these. The inhalation laboratory is well equipped to study the relation of various particle sizes to the inhalation, retention, and distribution of aerosols and dusts. There is some work on the beneficial uses of radioactive materials especially in the field of cancer.

The Division of Biology and Medicine of the USAEC relies heavily on the laboratory for toxicological data. The division of radiation chemistry and toxicology conducts studies on the toxicity, retention, excretion, and movement within the body of materials in the atomic energy industry suspected of chemical or radiological toxicity or other detrimental effects. Such materials as the following have been investigated: uranium, thorium, radium, radon, beryllium, polonium, thallium, indium, and mercury.

Curricula have been developed for 1- or 2-year programs in health physics and radiological health. The department collaborates with the Department of Preventive Medicine and Community Health in a curriculum in industrial medicine. Masters and doctorate degrees are offered in radiation biology and in biophysics. The total registration of graduate students in the department since 1948 has been 479, of whom 33 were foreign nationals. During the period, about 70 Ph.D. and 200 M.S. degrees were awarded.

TABLE R–19

TYPE OF ROCK	RA^{226} g/g $\times$ 10^{12}	Th^{232} g/g $\times$ 10^6	K^{39} g/g $\times$ 10^2
Igneous rocks:			
Acid rocks >65% SiO$_2$ Granites	3.1	20	3.4
Young granites (Max. level) (Granodiorite)	6.5 2.7	59 18	5.1 2.5
Intermediate rocks 65–55% SiO$_2$ (Diorite)	1.4	6	1.7
Basic rocks <55% SiO$_2$ (Gabbro)	0.87	5.1	0.7
Ultrabasic rocks: (Peridotite)	0.52	3.3	0.8

ROCKS, RADIOACTIVE

Several types of rocks contain radioactive elements. Acid igneous rocks are richer in radioactive elements than basalts as seen in Table R–19. Here the radium, thorium, and potassium content of various rocks is expressed in grams per grams of rock.

Shales, which contain organic substances, are more highly radioactive than other sedimentary rocks. Radioactive elements tend to be highest in igneous rock (e.g., granite) and lowest in sedimen-

tary rock (e.g., limestone), but considerable variation exists, with dunite yielding an exposure rate of less than 1 millirad per year (mrad/yr), while uranium or thorium ores give several thousand mrad/yr.

Table R–20 gives the average radium, uranium, thorium, and potassium content of various rocks and the dose rates of external gamma irradiation from the contained radioactive elements.

See TERRESTRIAL RADIATION.

TABLE R–20.   AVERAGE CONTENT.

TYPE OF ROCK	Ra^{226} g/g $\times$ 10^{12}	U^{238} g/g $\times$ 10^6	Th^{232} g/g $\times$ 10^6	K^{39} g/g $\times$ 10^2
Igneous	1.3	4.0	12	2.6
Sedimentary rocks:				
Sandstones	0.71	1.2	6	1.1
Shales	1.08	1.2	10	2.7
Limestones	0.42	1.3	1.3	0.27
	Ra^{226}	DOSE RATES IN mrad/year U^{238} Th^{232}		K^{40}
Igneous rocks	24	25.8	36.8	34.6
Sedimentary rocks:				
Sandstones	13	7.7	18.4	14.6
Shales	20	7.7	30.6	30
Limestones	7.7	8.4	4	3.6

ROENTGEN

Symbol r. The quantity of x- or gamma radiation such that the associated corpuscular emission per 0.001293 gram of air produces, in air, ions carrying 1 electrostatic unit of quantity of electricity of either sign.

The energy gained by the absorption of 1 r of x-rays in 1 gram of air is 86 ergs. Named for the German physicist W. C. Roentgen, who discovered x-rays in 1895.

Other related terms are: RAD; ROENTGEN EQUIVALENT, MAN (rem); ROENTGEN EQUIVALENT, PHYSICAL (rep); and MILLIROENTGEN.

The roentgen is considered as a unit of exposure dose.

Some interesting equivalents to 1 roentgen are: 2.083×10^9 ion pairs (1 esu) created per cubic centimeter (0.00129 gram) of air; 1.161×10^{12} ion pairs created per gram of air; 83 ergs of energy absorbed per gram of air; 93 ergs of energy absorbed per gram of soft tissue; 5.23×10^{13} electron volts of energy absorption per gram of air; and 6.77×10^{10} electron volts of energy absorption per cubic centimeter (0.00129 gram) of air.

ROENTGEN EQUIVALENT, MAN

Abbreviated to rem. The quantity of any ionizing radiation such that the energy imparted to a biological system (cell, tissue, organ, or organism) per gram of living matter by the ionizing particles present in the region of interest, has the same biological effectiveness as an absorbed dose of 1 rad of x-radiation with average specific ionization of 100 ion pairs per micron of water in the same region. A unit of human biological dose as a result of exposure to one or many types of ionizing radiation. Equal to the absorbed dose in rad times the RELATIVE BIOLOGICAL EFFECTIVENESS (RBE) of the particular type of radiation being absorbed:

Dose in rem = dose in rad × RBE

The roentgen is considered as a unit of exposure dose; the rad is a unit of absorbed radiation dose; and the rem as a unit of biological dose.

The RBE for x-rays and gamma rays may be taken as unity. Hence, for gamma rays, the biological dose in rem is equal to the absorbed dose in rad. Table R–21 shows the relations among radiation units, with the values applying particularly to cataract formation by neutrons and production of tumors by alpha-particle sources within the body. Rem equals the RBE in each case. Rad refers to absorption in soft tissue.

ROENTGEN EQUIVALENT, PHYSICAL

The rep is rapidly becoming obsolete and is being replaced by the more easily defined RAD unit. Absorbed dose representing 93 to 97 ergs per gram of soft animal tissue. Quantity of corpuscular radiation which produces per gram of tissue an ionization equivalent to the quantity of ionization of 1 roentgen of gamma radiation in air.

ROENTGENOGRAPHY

Photography by means of roentgen rays, i.e., x-rays. RADIOGRAPHY by means of x-rays. The photographic image is called a roentgenogram or a roentgenograph (also radiogram). The first radiogram made in the United States was in 1896, either by Thomas A. Edison or by M. I. Pupin of Columbia University.

Roentgenography is used extensively in medical diagnosis and also in various industrial activities. Special techniques have been developed for roentgenography of different parts of the human body and have been given different names: angiography, angiocardiography, pyelography, etc.

RONGELAP NATIVES, EXPOSURE. See MARSHALL ISLANDERS, RADIATION EXPOSURE.

ROOTING PATTERN STUDIES. See FERTILIZER STUDIES.

ROVER PROJECT

Investigations in the United States of the application of nuclear energy to space flight are divided into 2 main fields: the Rover project, which is concerned with the generation of the propulsive power to lift spacecraft off the earth, and Project Snap, which is concerned with the generation of electrical power and ion propulsion. Tests of propulsion reactors began in July 1959 at Jackass Flats, Nevada. The heat generated by controlled fission is used to heat hydrogen gas, the expansion and escape of which through an exhaust nozzle at high velocity creates the thrust which propels the rocket.

RUBIDIUM

Symbol Rb; atomic number 37; atomic weight 85.48. A soft, silver-white, rare element of the alkali metals group. Discovered by German scientists Bunsen and Kirchhoff in 1861. Named

TABLE R–21

TYPE OF RADIATION	r	rad	rem or RBE
X-rays and gamma rays	1	1	1
Beta particles		1	1
Fast neutrons		1	10
Thermal neutrons		1	4–5
Alpha particles		1	10–20

from Latin, *rubidius*, dark red. Occurs in lepidolite (lithium aluminosilicate). Natural abundance furnished by 1 stable isotope, Rb^{85}, 72.15%; and 1 radioactive isotope of long radioactive half-life $(5 \times 10^{10}$ years) Rb^{87}, 27.85%.

Rubidium is of limited use in manufacturing of photoelectric cells. It also has been used in tracing underground streams. Toxicity of minor importance in industry. Found widespread in nature, with some plants showing levels of 3.4 to 5.7 parts per million. Found in animal and human tissues but not considered an essential element.

Twenty-one radioactive isotopes have been identified. Twelve may occur as fission products following the detonation of a nuclear device. None have significance in radioactive fallout.

Rubidium-86 ($_{37}Rb^{86}$). Radioactive half-life, 18.66 days; biological half-life, 80 days, effective half-life, 15.1 days; beta (β^-) and gamma emitter. Usually produced by the neutron bombardment of Rb^{85}, (n,γ) reaction. Used in agricultural research to study absorption, transport, and concentration in plants and trees. Used in medical research in such studies as the permeability of the blood–cerebrospinal fluid barrier to the passage of ions. The maximum permissible concentration for a 168-hour (continuous exposure) period for soluble material, with the pancreas as the critical organ, is 7×10^{-4} microcurie per cubic centimeter ($\mu c/cc$) in water and 10^{-7} $\mu c/cc$ in air.

RUTHENIUM

Symbol Ru; atomic number 44; atomic weight 101.1. A hard, brittle, gray metal belonging to the platinum group. Discovered by Klaus in 1844, more than a century after the discovery of platinum. Named for Ruthenia, Ukraine. Occurs native in platinum ores, at times to the extent of 2%. Natural abundance furnished by 7 stable isotopes.

No practical commercial uses known. Little known about naturally occurring levels in biological material. Toxicity not known.

Fifteen radioactive isotopes have been identified. Twelve may be formed as fission products following the detonation of a nuclear device or in the operation of a nuclear reactor. The fission product radioisotopes of ruthenium are a complicating factor in fuel reprocessing, for they form products that are soluble in the organic solvents used in aqueous fuel reprocessing operations. Two are significant in radioactive fallout: Ru^{103} and Ru^{106} with 0.0316 and 0.148 megacurie per megaton of fission still remaining at the end of 1 year. Because it is a significant fission product, the following radioisotopes have been prepared for experimental studies of metabolism: Ru^{97} (half-life, 2.8 days, gamma emitter); Ru^{103} (half-life, 39.8 days, beta and gamma emitter); and $Ru^{106} + Rh^{106}$ (half-life, 1.0 year, pure beta emitter; rhodium daughter, half-life 30 seconds, beta and gamma emitter).

S

SAFE HANDLING

The handling of radioactive material and radio-active isotopes in such a manner as to protect individuals from overexposure to ionizing radiation.

The following items are pertinent: AUTOPSY ON BODIES CONTAINING RADIOACTIVITY; CADAVERS, RADIOACTIVE, HANDLING OF; HANDLING TECHNIQUES; HOT LABORATORY; LABORATORY DESIGN; MONITORING; PROTECTIVE CLOTHING; RADIATION PROTECTION; RADIATION PROTECTION STANDARDS; RADIOLOGICAL SAFETY ORGANIZATION; RADIOLOGICAL SAFETY RULES; REMOTE CONTROL EQUIPMENT; RESPIRATORS; SHIELDS; STANDARDS FOR PROTECTION AGAINST RADIATION; and TRANSPORTATION OF RADIOACTIVE MATERIALS.

The IAEA* has put out 3 booklets which nicely summarize safe handling of radioisotopes.

SAFETY RECORD, USAEC

Because of the seriousness of radiation injuries both from the standpoint of immediate and long-range somatic effects and that of genetic damage, steps were taken at the very beginning of the program of the Atomic Energy Commission (USAEC) to prevent radiation accidents. Licenses to use radioactive material are required, and licensing for radioisotope use is part of the USAEC program. Rules and regulations for safe use have been promulgated, and any type of accident involving release of radioactive material must be reported. The USAEC also has the right of inspection. The excellent record of the USAEC and its contractors and licensees is in large measure due to this foresight in careful planning. In industrial practice generally, safety regulations result only after serious accidents have occurred. (*See* LICENSING AND REGULATING, USAEC.)

Over an 18-year period of work by USAEC and its contractors there were 6,498 reportable injuries from all causes, of which only 35, or 0.6%, were radiation injuries. In the "time-lost" category the results are even more impressive for of 283,153,896 man-days of potential exposure there were only 800,517 (0.4%) days lost from work injuries for all causes and of these 0.01% or 19,124 days resulted

from radiation exposure (note that a fatality is charged as 6,000 man-days lost, and there were 3 fatalities charged to radiation).

The USAEC has established a Managers Best Safety Record Award for the contractors or operations offices achieving the best all-time Commission record, i.e., the largest number of injury-free man-hours. As of September, 1961 the Dow Chemical Company received the Award, and holds the trophy, having accumulated over 15,000,000 injury-free man-hours since September 17, 1957. The following USAEC contractors have achieved over 5,000,000 injury-free man-hours and at one time held the award:

Dow Chemical Co.*	9/17/57–(9/17/61)	15,000,000
Sandia Corp.	7/16/59–9/6/60	14,936,169
General Electric Co., Richland	1/12/60–10/3/60	11,270,000
General Electric Co., NFPD, Lockland	1/1/53–1/31/57	11,175,509
Union Carbide, NC-Y12	10/11/59–10/16/60	10,307,137
General Electric Co., Richland	2/24/54–9/27/54	9,437,211
Dupont-SRP	8/29/59–4/4/60	7,830,130
Dupont-SRP	1/10/55–8/9/55	7,538,447
General Electric Co., Richland	1/28/55–6/21/55	6,824,173
General Electric Co., Richland	8/14/58–12/31/58	5,671,390
Westinghouse-APD	3/28/58–9/19/58	5,302,910
Argonne National Lab.	7/15/58–5/7/59	5,171,481
Phillips Petroleum	7/20/56–4/27/58	5,000,000

SALTED WEAPON. *See* CLEAN WEAPON.

SAMARIUM

Symbol Sm; atomic number 62; atomic weight 150.35. A member of the cerium subgroup of the rare earth metals. Discovered by the French chemist Boisbaudran in 1879. Named for a Russian, Samarski. Its natural abundance is furnished by 6 stable isotopes and 1 long half-life radioactive isotope; and there are 12 other radioactive isotopes.

Ten radioisotopes of samarium are formed in the atomic fission process. Samarium-151 ($_{62}Sm^{151}$,

---

*International Atomic Energy Agency. No. 1, Safe Handling of Radioisotopes; No. 2, Health Physics Addendum; and No. 3, Medical Addendum. May be purchased from National Agency for International Publications, Inc., 801 Third Avenue, New York 22, N. Y.

---

*Dow Chemical Co.	9/17/57–12/31/60	11,871,495
Dow Chemical Co.	9/17/57–12/31/59	8,067,014

(Both of these Awards were for hours included within the same period for which they received the Award trophy in September, 1961.)

half-life 73 years, β⁻ emission) has biological significance as a fallout hazard, for at the end of 1 year a measurable amount of radioactivity remains. The biological half-life for the total body is 656 days, but for the critical organ, bone, the biological half-life is 1,500 days. The redeeming feature is that only 0.00003% of the samarium taken orally and 0.05% of that inhaled reaches the bone.

Samarium-153, with an activation index of 3,445, was selected as of possible medical therapeutic value but to date none of the radioisotopes of samarium has been found to have any biological, medical or agricultural significance.

SAMPLE CHANGER

A machine, usually controlled by an automatic programming device, which successively selects and places a series of prepared radioactive samples in position for counting by a radiation detector. Generally used in conjunction with an assembly which carries through the entire counting procedure and produces a printed record of the sample number, counting interval, and counts accumulated.

SAMPLING

Collecting and analyzing samples for the presence of radioactivity.

See AIR SAMPLING; BONE SAMPLING; FOOD SAMPLING; MONITORING; SAMPLING PROGRAM FOR RADIOACTIVE FALLOUT; and SURVEY.

SAMPLING PROGRAM FOR RADIOACTIVE FALLOUT

The United States program of research, measurement, analysis, interpretation and reporting of fallout sampling has 4 main components: (1) development of stratospheric and ground-level sampling devices; (2) collection and analysis of stratospheric and surface air samples; (3) measurement of fallout deposition on the earth's surface and of fallout on and in plants and animals, including man; and (4) compilation and meteorological interpretation of fallout data.

This program, inaugurated in 1948 and recently conducted cooperatively with other Federal agencies, is directed toward a complete understanding of radioactive contamination throughout both the United States and the world. Samples are collected and analyzed from the upper air and from surface air. Fallout deposition is studied with a variety of programs; biospheric contamination is carefully investigated on a continuing basis; man is studied by human bone collection, by examination of urine and by whole-body counting.

Air samples are collected by the high-altitude sampling program; by collection of samples from the radioactive cloud at the time of the test "shot"; and from surface air samples from the USPHS National Surveillance Net, the Naval Research Laboratory 80th Meridian Net, the USAEC Site Net, and from many research and development programs.

Fallout deposition was for several years collected and studied from a world-wide network of gum paper collectors and analyzed by the USAEC Health and Safety Laboratory. Precipitation is collected, also on a world-wide basis, in the "pot" and "funnel" network, and in the "washtub" collection network. The National Surveillance Net and the 80th Meridian Net are active in sampling fallout deposition as well as in surface air sampling.

Snow acts as a scavenging agent carrying fallout down with it. This is particularly true if it falls through a radioactive cloud, producing radioactive or "hot" snow. For example, in Cincinnati in a testing year (March 1958) the range in radioactivity of 4 snowfalls was 1,081 to 2,187 micro-microcuries per liter ($\mu\mu c/l$), while the radioactivity of cistern water (8 samples) was 126–197 $\mu\mu c/l$, and 5 samples of surface water were only 4 to 70 $\mu\mu c/l$.

Rain water sampling is also important because of the scavenging effect of rain in bringing radioactive fallout down. Again during the testing year of 1958, rain water samples taken at the same location as the snow samples varied from 258 $\mu\mu c/l$ one time to 21,924 $\mu\mu c/l$ when a known cloud was passing.

Working with the Department of Agriculture for collection, and with the USAEC Health and Safety Laboratory for analysis, soil samples are collected on a world-wide basis for analysis for strontium-90. The first network includes collections from 17 sites in the United States each year since 1955; and the second network includes samples from 64 sites in most countries of the world in 1956 and repeat samples from about the same places in 1958, 1959 and 1960. The northern hemisphere showed a definitely higher amount of strontium-90 than did the southern—the highest in the southern was 13 millicuries of strontium-90 per square mile found in New Zealand in 1958, while 55 millicuries was found in the soil from Norway for the same year.

Ocean water contamination is of interest because of the uptake of radionuclides by aquatic organisms. Samples have been taken of water from the Atlantic Ocean, but most of the sampling of ocean or sea water has been related to underwater detonation, or to contamination by local fallout. Of the 3 fission products with long radioactive half-life, strontium-90, cesium-137 and cerium-144, only the last is found in marine organisms.

A food sampling program was started years ago by the USAEC and is being continued by the Public Health Service and the Food and Drug Administration. This includes sampling of milk and dairy products, marine foods, and meats and vegetables.

In fact, sampling patterns have been developed by the USAEC to define relations between quantities of strontium-90 in the stratosphere and rates of fallout; relations between rainfall and fallout; occurrence in soil and in plants and animals raised on the soil; uptake from the soil as affected by the nature of the soil; behavior of fallout reaching vegetation directly from the air; variation in soils, plants, animals and food products in relation to location on the earth's surface; and effect of age and diet upon uptake by humans.

But probably the most important of the programs of the USAEC is human bone sampling, under which bone samples were collected for several years (through 1960) on a world-wide basis and analyzed for their strontium-90 content.

See AIR SAMPLING, BONE SAMPLING, FOOD SAMPLING, and HIGH-ALTITUDE SAMPLING PROGRAM.

SARCOMAS DUE TO RADIATION

A large, heterogeneous group of new growths, usually malignant, having elements resembling embryonic connective tissue and composed of densely packed cells embedded in a fibrillar or homogeneous matrix. Osteogenic sarcomas have been shown to develop in animals following a single injection of such long-lived radioactive isotopes as plutonium-239, radium-226, mesothorium (radium-228), radiothorium (thorium-228) and strontium-90. Human osteogenic sarcomas developed in some of the RADIUM-DIAL PAINTER CASES 12 to 30 years following ingestion of the radium from the luminous paint. Metastatic spreading occurs mainly through transportation by the bloodstream.

As a whole, the sarcomas are considerably more resistant to the effects of ionizing radiation than their epithelial and lymphoid counterparts.

SATURATION CURRENT

The amount of electrical charge collected per unit time when the voltage is high enough to sweep in all the ions formed by a given source of ionizing radiation in a given detector.

SATURATION VOLTAGE

In an ionization chamber, the voltage required to achieve collection of all ions formed by the passage of ionizing radiation.

SCALER

Electronic circuit or other device which accepts signal pulses from a radiation detector, counting them and delivering an output signal to a register when a fixed number of events have accumulated. Scalers provide for rapid counting or high-counting capacity, and permit wide flexibility in preset count or elapsed time counting procedures. The number of counts required to produce an output signal is called the scaling factor. Scalers are made up of a series of binary scaler or decimal scaler sections; scaling factors are thus commonly expressed as a power of 2 or as a power of 10. A principal purpose of scaling tube circuits is to allow accurate counting of events occurring at a rapid rate. It is therefore customary to give the first scaling stages a very quick response characteristic, that is, a short resolving time, in order to assure the best counting efficiency and to reduce dead time losses.

A second important use for scalers is in timing circuits, where accurate counting intervals can be controlled by a scaling circuit which counts to any preset number of signals from a standard frequency source such as a crystal or vacuum tube oscillator.

SCALING LAW

A mathematical relationship which permits the effects of a nuclear explosion of given energy yield to be determined as a function of distance from the explosion (or from ground zero), provided the corresponding effect is known as a function of distance for a reference explosion, e.g., of 1-kiloton energy yield.

See blast scaling laws in BLAST PHYSICAL PHENOMENA; and CUBE ROOT LAW.

SCANDIUM

Symbol Sc; atomic number 21; atomic weight 44.96. By some classed as a member of the cerium subgroup of rare earth metals. Predicted by Mendelyeev in 1871, who called it "ekaboron." Discovered by Nilson in 1879. Named for Scandinavia. Occurs in a few uncommon minerals such as wolframite, and in traces in several types of rocks. Natural abundance furnished 100% by the stable isotope Sc[45]. No industrial uses. No information in regard to occurrence in biological material.

Nine radioactive isotopes have been identified. Scandium-46, β^- and γ emitter; radioactive half-life, 85 days; with liver as the critical organ, biological half-life, 36 days, and effective half-life, 25 days; is available commercially but little biological, medical or agricultural use has been found. Scandium-47, β^- and γ emitter; radioactive half-life, 3.43 days; with liver as the critical organ, biological half-life, 36 days, and effective half-life 3.1 days; may be found among the nuclides induced in soil following detonation of a nuclear device, as a result of calcium-47 decay.

SCANNING, RADIOISOTOPE

A method of determining the location of radioactive isotopes within the body by measurements taken from outside the body. A number of different types or techniques of scanning have been developed in order to answer such questions as: what radioisotope is being measured; where is it distributed; how is it localized; when does it appear in the area of concentration; and how much is present? These types of scanning are:

a. Point scanning used to locate tumors and metastases by moving a small ''point'' detector from place to place (sometimes at the time of operation, within the body) to determine the location of a hot spot.

b. Area scanning to determine the localization of a radioisotope in a given organ, e.g., phosphorus-32 localized in the liver, or iodine-131 localized in the thyroid.

c. Depth scanning attempts to combine point scanning and area scanning and is used largely for localizing brain tumors.

d. Linear scanning is a scan over the entire body and furnishes a profile of radioactivity distributed in the body.

e. Spectral scanning is designed to determine the type of radioisotope in the total body by making a rapid spectrometric determination (*see* WHOLE-BODY COUNTERS).

f. Temporal scanning, which studies the distribution and movement of radioactive material through the body as illustrated by Figure S–1, which presents a linear scan of an individual

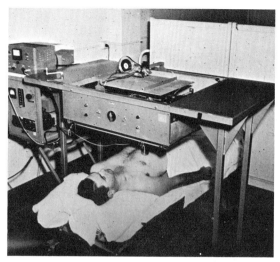

FIGURE S–2. TYPICAL DEVICE FOR LINEAR SCANNING OF THE ENTIRE BODY.

shortly after receiving a dose of iodine-131 by mouth, a scan some hours later and then one 48 hours later when the radioiodine has been taken up by the areas of metastatic thyroid cancer.

A number of different types of instruments are on the market designed to produce various kinds of scans and to answer the diagnostic questions. Figure S–2 pictures a typical device for linear scanning of the entire body. A diagram of the same type of scanner with a sample scan is shown in Figure S–3. The scan is the same as that shown in Figure S–1.

Since most types of equipment have similar features and relationships to the body it is practical to have a standard nomenclature for describing a scanner and these relationships (see Figure S–4). Note isoresponse lines—*see* ISODOSE CURVES.

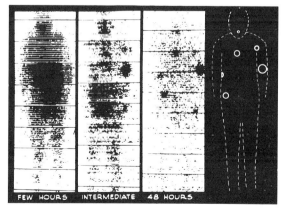

FIGURE S–1. STUDY OF THE DISTRIBUTION AND MOVEMENT OF IODINE-131 THROUGH THE BODY BY THE TECHNIQUE OF TEMPORAL SCANNING. THE LINEAR SCAN ON THE LEFT WAS TAKEN A FEW HOURS AFTER THE IODINE-131 WAS GIVEN. THE MIDDLE SCAN SOME 10 HOURS LATER, AND RIGHT SCAN 48 HOURS LATER SHOW THE RADIOIODINE TAKEN UP BY AREAS OF METASTATIC THYROID CANCER.

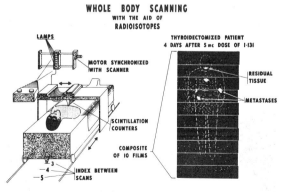

FIGURE S–3. DIAGRAM OF A LINEAR SCANNING DEVICE WITH A SAMPLE SCAN (48-HOUR SCAN SHOWN IN FIGURE S–1).

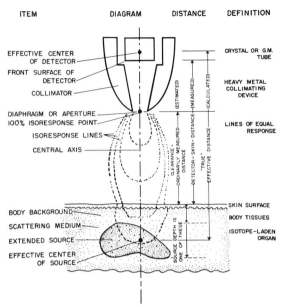

ITEM	DIAGRAM	DISTANCE	DEFINITION

FIGURE S–4. STANDARD NOMENCLATURE FOR DESCRIB-
ING A SCANNER AND ITS RELATIONSHIPS TO THE HUMAN
BODY.

A visual record is prepared by most of the
standard scanning devices which consists of a dot
or mark made on paper after a certain number of
counts have been integrated by the scaling system.
Figure S–5 shows the writing arm in action. There
are a large number of factors to be considered in
developing a scan in order to insure satisfactory
definition for accurate diagnosis: size of the dot—
small dots best; shape of dot—round or very short
line; shade or color of dot—all dots must have
identical shade; speed of movement of scanning

FIGURE S–5. SCANNER WRITING ARM IN ACTION.

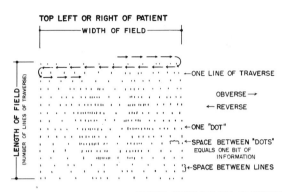

FIGURE S–6. STANDARD NOMENCLATURE FOR DESCRIB-
ING A SCAN.

head—dose and uptake determine speed but as
slow as possible is best; number of counts per dot—
dose is determining, but fewer dots better than
heavy accumulation; the effect of dosage—the
amount of activity will determine dial settings for
satisfactory scan; the effect of line spacing—
widely spaced usually better than very narrow;
and the effect of distance—the distance from
counting head to the body must be kept constant
if scans are to be comparable. A standard nomenclature has been developed for describing all these
factors and is shown in Figure S–6.

The interpretation of the scan depends upon the
factors enumerated and the doctor should never
attempt to make a diagnosis from a scan without
knowing exactly how the scan was made.

SCATTERED RADIATION

Radiation which, during its passage through a
substance, has been deviated in direction. It may
also have been modified by an increase in wave
length. The first object struck by the useful beam
of radiation is the principal source of scattered
radiation; the amount depends upon the size of
the irradiated area, the amount absorbed in the
object, the angle of scattering, and the incident
exposure dose. Scattered radiation is a potential
exposure risk and protection must be provided
either by an appropriate shield or by the use of
distance maintained by physical barriers and
warning signs.

See SCATTERING.

SCATTERING

Change of direction of a subatomic particle or
photon as a result of a collision or interaction with
the atoms of the material through which it is passing. The first scattering studies were done by the
New Zealand-born physicist Ernest Rutherford
when he studied the scattering of alpha particles

allowed to fall on a thin foil of gold and counted the scintillations produced on a zinc sulfide screen.

There are a number of types of scattering in atomic energy reactions which will be discussed briefly here:

Elastic scattering is one of the simplest of nuclear reactions and is effected through the agency of elastic collisions and therefore with conservation of the kinetic energy of the system. For example, when a neutron as the projectile strikes a target nucleus, it is deprived of some of its energy, but it appears as kinetic energy, i.e., energy of motions of the target nucleus. The neutron then recoils and travels with less energy than it had before the impact. This is an elastic or billiard-ball type of collision.

The other principal type is inelastic scattering in which the collision of a subatomic particle results in the nucleus being left in an excited state, and the total kinetic energy being decreased. The kinetic energy which the particle has lost has been converted into excitation or potential energy of the target nucleus. A neutron, not being electrically charged, cannot cause nuclear excitation by electrostatic interaction but if it has sufficient energy it can produce excited nuclei by inelastic scattering. Here the target nucleus captures a fast neutron, forms a compound nucleus, and then expels a neutron of lower energy, leaving the original nucleus in an excited or high-energy state. With the lighter elements, i.e., with low atomic number, elastic scattering of neutrons is more probable than inelastic scattering unless the neutron energy exceeds 1 Mev. But with increasing atomic number the minimum excitation energy of the nucleus decreases to about 0.1 Mev, so neutrons with energy in excess of this amount interacting with the heavier elements will show inelastic as well as elastic scattering.

Coherent scattering refers to scattering of photons or particles in which there are definite phase relationships between the incoming and the scattered waves.

In incoherent scattering the scattering elements act independently of one another so that there are no definite phase relationships among the different parts of the scattered beam.

Compton scattering is the inelastic scattering of a photon through interaction with atomic electrons, accompanied by ejection of a recoil electron from the atom with which the interaction occurred.

Single scattering is the deflection of a particle from its original path as the result of a single encounter with one scattering center in the material traversed.

Multiple scattering is scattering of a photon or a particle in which the final displacement is the vector sum of many, although usually small, displacements.

In plural scatter the final deflection of a particle or photon is the vector sum of a small number of displacements.

The angle between the initial and final lines of motion of the scattered particle is termed the scattering angle.

SCAVENGING

Removal of radionuclides from the atmosphere by rain, snow or dew. An important process in the deposition of tropospheric fallout is the scavenging effect of rain or other moisture precipitation.

SCHILLING TEST. *See* PERNICIOUS ANEMIA, DIAGNOSIS.

SCINTILLATION

Flash of light emitted by a fluor or phosphor when it absorbs a particle or quantum of ionizing radiation. Energy taken up from the incident radiation by the electronic or molecular structure of the phosphor substance is re-emitted as quanta of visible or ultraviolet light.

See SPINTHARISCOPE and SCINTILLATION DETECTOR.

SCINTILLATION COUNTER. *See* SCINTILLATION DETECTOR.

SCINTILLATION DETECTOR

Sensitive element used to detect ionizing radiation by observing the SCINTILLATION induced in a phosphor, which may be crystal, plastic, gas or liquid. The simplest application is in the spinthariscope, using direct visual observation; scintillation detection is now customarily used in conjunction with a photomultiplier tube in most counting applications, as in Figure S–7. This principle is also widely employed in fluoroscopic and intensifying screens for diagnostic x-ray practice.

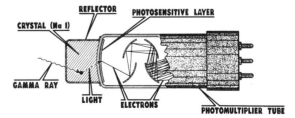

FIGURE S–7. SCINTILLATION DETECTOR. TOTAL LIGHT TO THE TUBE IS NEARLY PROPORTIONAL TO GAMMA-RAY ENERGY. IF 1 ELECTRON EJECTS 5 FROM A DYNODE, 11 DYNODES RESULT IN 5^{11} OR ABOUT 50 MILLION ELECTRONS OUTPUT. (USAEC-1D-193A.)

SCINTILLATION SCANNER

Mechanical and electronic device which automatically moves a scintillation detector over the body of a subject, measuring the radiation counting rate as it travels and producing a diagram of the relative activity throughout the area covered. Used to evaluate uptake or localization of specific materials in certain organs, as thyroid, liver or brain, especially to establish the functional status or the presence of malignancy. The diagram which results is a scintigram or SCINTISCAN; if recorded on photographic film by a counting-rate controlled light source, it is called a PHOTOSCAN. (See Figure S–8.)

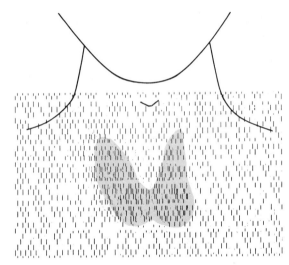

FIGURE S–8.   GAMMAGRAM OF NORMAL THYROID GLAND IN VIVO.

SCINTILLATOR

Component of a system for detecting ionizing radiations; made from a class of substances known as fluors or phosphors, which emit a light flash when struck by a radiation particle or photon.

See SCINTILLATION DETECTOR.

SCINTISCAN

Distribution pattern of radioactive uptake determined by systematically passing collimator and scintillation detector over the area of interest, usually by automatically programmed equipment.

See SCINTILLATION SCANNER.

SCREW-WORM FLY ERADICATION

Insect control or eradication through the use of males made sexually sterile by irradiation has been shown to be feasible in the case of the screw-worm fly, Callitroga hominivorax. The female lays eggs in wounds of warm-blooded animals; the eggs hatch into flesh-burrowing larvae, which feed upon cattle and sheep causing losses formerly amounting to over $20,000,000 annually in southeastern United States alone. These flies can cause the death of a full-grown steer in 10 days. After extensive ecological studies and laboratory experiments, a field test was run on the island of Curaçao, where male flies were sterilized but not made impotent by exposure to about 7,500 roentgens from a cobalt-60 unit and were released by airplane at the rate of about 400 per square mile per week over a period of several months. The natural population of male flies on the island was about 100 to 200 per square mile, and the sterile males caused a rapid decline of the flies, with the ratio of sterile to fertile males increasing with each successive release. The fact that the female mates but once made the task easier but within 5 months the flies had been completely eradicated and 6 years later had not returned. The fly was also successfully eradicated in Florida where it normally wintered.

Other types of flies and insects may be amenable to the same type of treatment.

SECONDARY RADIATION.   *See* RADIATION.

SELENIUM

Symbol Se; atomic number 34; atomic weight 78.96. A nonmetal occurring as selenide in many sulfide ores, especially those of copper, silver, lead and iron. Natural abundance furnished by 6 stable isotopes. Discovered in 1817 by Swedish chemist Berżelius. Named from Greek *Selene*, moon, for it was found associated with tellurium which was named for the earth.

Used commercially in glass, ceramic and enamel industry and to a lesser extent in rubber manufacture. Recent evidence indicates that it may be an essential element.

Selenium is of agricultural importance because it occurs in some soils in amounts sufficient to cause toxic effects in animals feeding on plants. The limit of toxicity to animals under ordinary conditions is 3 to 4 parts per million (ppm) in the diet. The minimum lethal dose for horses is about 3 milligrams per kilogram (mg/kg) body weight, for cattle 9 mg/kg, and for pigs 12 mg/kg. About 10 ppm in the food of rats was fatal. Toxic effects on human beings have been reported, from ingestion of food grown in seleniferous areas. Acute toxic effects have been noted in workers following inhalation of selenium fumes. There was early recovery, with no fatalities.

Seventeen radioactive isotopes have been identified, of which 13 may occur as fission products following the detonation of a nuclear device. None have significance as components of radioactive fallout. Selenium-75 (half-life 127 days, γ emitter) is available commercially and used for tracer studies in determining absorption, movement, distribution and elimination of selenium.

SELF-ABSORPTION

Absorption of radiation by the matter in which the atoms emitting the radiation are located. It reduces the radiation level, and cuts down slightly on the amount of shielding necessary. Self-absorption is most important in the measurement of activity in a given sample, where the sample thickness becomes most important, with a thick sample significantly reducing the activity recorded by the counting instrument. It is also an important factor in beta-particle counting, requiring a correction factor for the weight of the sample.

See ABSORBER and ABSORPTION.

SENSITIVE VOLUME

In instrumentation, that portion of a counter tube or ionization chamber which responds to a specific radiation. In radiobiology, the part or region of a cell particularly sensitive to radiation. Also, in studying the target theory, attempts have have made to determine sensitive volumes particularly for viruses and enzymes.

SENSITIVITY

A measure of the limit of a detector's ability to sense radiation expressed in terms of the lowest level to which the instrument can respond, either as the least quantity or the least energy of the radiation for which it can provide reliable indication.

When applied to other instrumentation associated with detectors, sensitivity commonly refers to strength of the electrical signal required, as to operate the input of an amplifier or scaler.

SENSITIVITY TO RADIATION. *See* RADIO-SENSITIVITY.

SHELTERS. *See* BLAST SHELTERS and FALLOUT SHELTERS.

SHERWOOD PROJECT

The U.S. Atomic Energy Commission's effort to attain continuous, controlled THERMONUCLEAR REACTIONS. Practical controlled fusion would provide a practically unlimited source of power, as each volume of sea water contains enough deuterium (fusion fuel) to supply the energy equivalent of 300 volumes of gasoline. Fusion reactions require temperatures measured in millions of degrees centigrade. The principal efforts to achieve such

high temperatures involve the generation of plasmas, or high temperature, high density, ionized, conducting gases. Magnetic fields are usually used to confine the plasma, but plasma and magnetic field instabilities and loss of energy by various radiative mechanisms have thus far thwarted efforts to maintain the required temperatures long enough to produce a significant number of fusion reactions. At present the only fusion reactions known to occur are the uncontrolled reactions in thermonuclear weapons and in stars. Controlled fusion energy has potential applications in chemical synthesis, metal working, and propulsion of space vehicles.

SHIELD

A body of material used to prevent or reduce the passage of radiation. The handling of radioactive materials usually requires shielding to insure safety of personnel. A shield may also be necessary to reduce the radiation sufficiently to allow use of counting equipment; or for locating contamination or air-borne radioactivity.

A radiation shield may be designed according to what is to be absorbed. The thickness and type of shielding depend on the energy and quantity of radiation. For alpha emitters shielding is no problem as the particles do not penetrate human skin. Beta particles can be stopped by 1/4 inch of plastic or wood. X-rays may be stopped by lead gloves or a lead apron, but depending upon their energy may require a heavy CONCRETE SHIELD. Gamma rays usually require thick shields of concrete, iron or lead for protection. NEUTRON SHIELDS are also usually quite heavy.

Shields are also classified according to the location of the shield. In general they are either portable or fixed. The shielding worn by the individual consists of protective clothing; lead gloves or lead aprons are often worn for radiation protection. A CLOSE SHIELD fits around the radioactive object and may either be portable around a bottle of radioactive isotopes or fixed around a nuclear reactor. An entire space may be shielded or a simple lead brick barricade may be constructed around a bottle of radioactive material. Fixed BARRIER SHIELDS are often constructed; but the portable barricade is the most commonly relied upon in a radioisotope laboratory.

A shield may be designated according to the kind of protection it is intended to give: a radiation shield to prevent or reduce the passage of radiation; a thermal shield for protection against heat; or a blast shield (blast shelter) to protect against the force of a blast of air. A background shield is used to protect delicate counting instruments from background radiation (*see* WHOLE-

BODY COUNTER); and if human beings are to be protected a BIOLOGICAL SHIELD is constructed.

The material used to construct a shield varies with the type of radiation, its energy and quantity, and whether the shield is to be permanently fixed or portable. A concrete shield is a common permanent, fixed variety but even here large concrete blocks are often used which may be moved from place to place. Lead is used in sheets for lining and in the form of bricks to make BARRICADE SHIELDS. Plastic is frequently used for close shields for low-level radioactive sources. Transparent plastic and water are commonly used for a window shield (liquid window) even for high-level activity shielding.

SHIELDING

The use of SHIELDS and their arrangement for any particular circumstances or establishment.

SHIPPING ACCIDENTS

It is of vital importance to avoid accidents in the transportation of radioactive material, particularly when a single unescorted shipment may contain over a million curies of radioactivity. To guard against environmental contamination in the case of an accident, special containers are required and careful rigging is practiced. For many shipments special escorts are provided to take care of radiological safety interests. Interstate Commerce Commission regulations control packaging, labeling, handling and shipping, and a Bureau of Explosives permit must be obtained for certain levels of curie-content.*

There have been train wrecks in which the car containing scrap uranium was demolished and the uranium had to be recovered piece by piece. There have been accidents to trucks carrying radioactive waste. There have been fires and explosions of material being transported, but fortunately human exposure has been very slight, recovery of the material has been accomplished, and decontamination has been effective.

SHOE-FITTING FLUOROSCOPES

A special type of fluoroscope unit, operating in the range of 50 to 65 kv, designed to visualize the feet in the shoes to obtain a proper fit. Popular in fitting children's shoes, it presents a hazard in unnecessary radiation exposure to both children and parents as well as the clerk. These machines have

---

*Shipping Radioactive Material at the National Reactor Testing Station. Safety and Fire Protection Bulletin 6. USAEC, Washington, D.C. For sale by Superintendent of Documents, U.S. Government Printing Office, Washington 25, D.C.

been outlawed in many states and put under specific regulations in others. The regulation to keep the dose to the feet below the recommended 2 roentgens for a single exposure requires a time limit of less than 5 seconds, which is quite unsatisfactory for visualization of a fit, and is thus invariable exceeded. Three exposures in a day per customer and not over 12 fittings per year are equally difficult to control. All such machines should be banned.

SILICON

Symbol Si; atomic number 14; atomic weight 28.09. A nonmetallic crystalline solid, or an amorphus brown powder. Not found free in nature, but in combination, usually as silica (silicon dioxide, SiO_2). Second in abundance to oxygen as a constituent of the earth's crust (27.7% of the solid crust). First isolated by the Swedish chemist Baron J. J. Berzelius in 1823. Named from Latin *silex*, flint. Natural abundance furnished by 3 stable isotopes. Glass, cement and clay working are called the silicate industries. Found as a trace element in the biochemical standard man but not considered essential. Inhalation of silicon-bearing dust leads to lung involvement, called silicosis. Other than silicosis no toxicity, and no biological, medical or agricultural significance.

The detonation of a nuclear device in contact with the earth's surface produces Si^{31} (half-life 2.62 hours, pure β^- emitter) by induced radioactivity in proportion to the amount of silicon present. Not, however, an important long-term component of residual contamination. Si^{27} (half-life 4.9 seconds, β^+ emitter) is the only other radioactive isotope.

SILVER

Symbol Ag; atomic number 47; atomic weight 107.880. A white metal, softer than copper and harder than gold. Found native in Peru and in ores in combination with nonmetallic elements, as argentite (Ag_2S) and horn silver (AgCl) in many other parts of the world. Natural abundance furnished by 2 stable isotopes, Ag^{107}, 51.35%, and Ag^{109}, 48.65%. Known to the ancients. Named from Anglo-Saxon *soelfor*, silver. Symbol Ag from Latin *argentum*, silver.

Used in coins, tableware, ornaments, deposited on glass for mirrors, in alloys, in the photographic industry, in dental and medical supplies; and silver iodide crystals and smoke are used in rainmaking. Colloidal silver and some insoluble compounds used in medicine for antiseptic and antibacterial action on skin and mucous membranes.

Almost completely nontoxic except that ingestion or inhalation of large amounts (industrial exposure) of silver salts leads to deposition in the skin and underlying tissues. On exposure to light these silver salts darken and lead to the condition known as argyria which is permanently disfiguring. Not biologically essential.

Daily intake in foods may amount to 0.06 to 0.08 milligram. As much as 0.3 part per million has been found in wheat flour.

Twenty-eight radioactive isotopes of silver have been identified. Seventeen of these may be produced as fission products from the detonation of a nuclear device. Ag^{111} is significant in radioactive fallout with 0.0292 megacurie per megaton of fission yield, remaining at the end of 1 month and a measurable amount remaining at the end of 1 year. Ag^{106}, Ag^{108}, Ag^{110} and Ag^{110m} may occur in sea water as the result of induced radioactivity from neutron bombardment associated with the detonation of a nuclear device.

Silver-111 ($_{47}Ag^{111}$). Radioactive half-life 7.5 days; with total body as the critical organ, biological half-life 5 days; effective half-life 3.0 days; beta (β^-) and gamma emitter. Used in metabolic and distribution studies, and in detecting abscesses and tumors; also in treating cancer, in the form of radioactive silver colloids put into body cavities, and into the lung through the bronchial tree. Also used as a coating for radioactive gold, thus increasing the amount of gold that gets into the lymph nodes (gold does not move into the lymph channels as rapidly as silver does).

The maximum permissible concentration for a 168-hour week (continuous exposure) for soluble Ag^{111} with the gastrointestinal tract as the critical organ is 4×10^{-4} microcurie per cubic centimeter ($\mu c/cc$) in water and 10^{-7} $\mu c/cc$ in air.

SINGLE-CHANNEL ANALYZER

A radiation-measuring circuit which is made to respond only to 1 section of the radiation energy spectrum through the use of discriminators, to provide for the study of signals whose pulses vary in amplitude or signal height (voltage). The device can be used to determine the energy distribution of radiation sources by passing on to the output only those pulses whose peaks fall between 2 preset levels, rejecting all larger and smaller pulses. Controls are included to permit the selection of admitted energy range to suit the purposes of a particular experiment. The simplest device of this kind can be adjusted to receive and count radiation by only one or two or more radioactive materials which may be present in the same experimental sample, thus facilitating multiple tracer study procedures. The selector controls may be fitted with a motor drive which moves the discriminator settings across the spectrum range, as

in analyzing or searching for purity of a particular material. This type is sometimes referred to as a window analyzer or spectrum scanner. The selectivity of response is obtained by the use of a pair of discriminators which are controlled to set upper and lower limits of energy or pulse size (amplitude) which the counter circuits may accept; the region delimited by these discriminators is commonly called the "window."

SINGLE SCATTERING

Deflection of a particle from its original path owing to one encounter with a single scattering center in the material traversed.

SKIN, RADIATION EFFECTS ON

The most readily observable effects of radiation are seen in the skin and its appendages (hair, nails). Radiation burns of the skin (BURNS, RADIATION) may be merely ERYTHEMA or third degree, depending on the dose. BETA BURNS of the skin were seen among the Marshall Islanders and the Japanese fishermen as the result of fallout deposition of fission products on the skin. Figure S–9 shows the histological picture of normal skin, and the histopathology of skin exposed to a low-level dose [5,000 roentgens (r)]; and the destruction of tissue associated with a high-level dose of 30,000 r. Epilation may be spotty if due to fallout beta particle irradiation or complete if due to whole body irradiation of 300 rad or more.

Skin irradiation of sufficient amount induces radiodermatitis with 2 frequently overlapping stages—acute (early) and chronic (late). The acute phase may be divided into a 6- to 14-day latent period and a variable period of sustained erythema. Early histologic changes include edema, beginning degeneration of epidermis, skin appendages and collagen, and a predominantly mononuclear inflammatory infiltrate. Ulceration

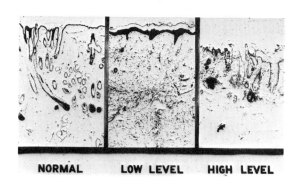

NORMAL   LOW LEVEL   HIGH LEVEL

FIGURE S–9. BETA RADIATION EFFECTS ON SKIN. NORMAL HISTOLOGY, HISTOPATHOLOGY OF RADIATION EFFECT OF 5,000 R, AND OF 30,000 R EXPOSURE.

may occur early and atrophy frequently occurs as a late manifestation.

With higher dosages the acute phase continues irregularly into the chronic phase with gross induration, depigmentation, telangiectasia and ulceration. Underlying this radiodermatitis is occlusive fibrotic hyalinization and thickening of the dermal blood vessels. Variably present also are epidermal dyskeratosis and atrophy, bizarre fibroblasts with dense collagen, and atrophy of skin appendages. Carcinoma, usually epidermoid, may develop any time from 2 to 30 or more years after exposure to ionizing radiation (see CANCER, DUE TO RADIATION).

The accompanying pictures show beta burns on the feet of one of the Marshall Islanders. Figure S–10 shows open lesions with second-degree burns. Figure S–11 shows complete healing without scarring 5 months later.

Certain biological factors influence the effect of radiation on the skin: species differences; thinner-skinned flexor surfaces of the body more sensitive than thicker-skinned extensor surfaces; highly pigmented skin (Negro) more resistant than light-colored skin (blondes); and areas of the body where perspiration is profuse so that fallout can cling, burn more frequently.

Treatment for skin contamination consists of prompt, thorough decontamination of skin and hair with use of detergents and copious amounts of water. Treatment of the actual burn lesions is very similar to the treatment of thermal burns: daily cleansing and application of antipruritic ointments to reduce itching; if painful, analgesic and

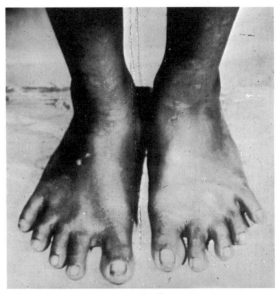

FIGURE S–11. BURNS ON THE FEET OF THE SAME MARSHALLESE COMPLETELY HEALED 5 MONTHS LATER.

anesthetic ointments; and antibiotics applied locally if secondary infection occurs. Severe lesions may require surgical cleaning, wet dressings, immobilization, and, if scarring results, early skin grafting. Some experts think all radiation burns should be excised and skin grafted.

See FLASH BURN and THERMAL BURN.

SLIT

A term that refers to the range of energy or other function accepted by a detector or spectrum analyzer, adopted through analogy with the slit width aperture control used in optical spectrographic procedures.

SLOPE. See PLATEAU SLOPE.

SL-1 REACTOR ACCIDENT

The first fatal accident in the history of United States reactor operation occurred January 3, 1961, at the USAEC National Reactor Testing Station near Idaho Falls, Idaho, when the Stationary Low Power Reactor No. 1 (SL-1) underwent a nuclear excursion and explosion.

The SL-1 was designed for the Department of Defense as a prototype of a low-power, boiling-water reactor plant to be used in geographically remote locations, and to operate at 3 megawatts gross thermal capacity to produce 200 kilowatts of net electricity and 400 kilowatts of net energy in the form of space heat.

It had been operating successfully for over two years as part of the experimental activity of the

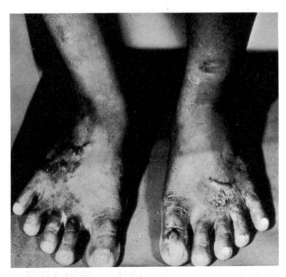

FIGURE S–10. SECOND-DEGREE BETA RADIATION BURNS ON THE FEET OF A MARSHALL ISLAND WOMAN EXPOSED TO FALLOUT FROM THE TESTING OF A NUCLEAR WEAPON AS SHE WAS WALKING BAREFOOT IN THE SAND.

Army Reactors Branch of the USAEC. It was housed as shown in Figure S–12, in a cylindrical steel building, resting on dummy piles as it would in the perma-frost area for which it was intended. It is important to note that there was no containment vessel as there would have been if this were to be operated in a populated area.

The reactor was shut down on December 23, 1960 for maintenance work on certain components. Most of the work had been completed and the 3-man military crew on the 4:00 P.M. to midnight shift on January 3, 1961 had the task of reassembling the control rod drives and preparing the reactor for startup. The first indication of trouble was when the alarm rang at 9:01 P.M. When the fire department personnel could not arouse the SL-1 crew they started to enter the reactor support building but immediately detected radiation levels up to 25 roentgens per hour, with increase up to 200 r/hr near the stairway to the reactor building. Entry was made by health physics personnel to locate the crew, all of whom were found on the floor near the reactor in a radiation field of about 1,000 r/hr. Two were dead; one was still living, although he died a few minutes after he was removed. Over 100 people were engaged in recovery operations during the first 24 hours and several hundred during the first week, but by limiting the time in the reactor building to one minute per man, only 22 persons received radiation exposures in the range of 3 to 27 r total body exposure, and these were during the rescue period.

The evidence points to a nuclear excursion as the initial event, caused by rapid removal of the central control rod. There is no question but that this was associated with an explosion, for there was ample evidence of blast effects. The energy release was estimated as total fission during the excursion of 1.5×10^{18} which is approximately equivalent to 50 megawatt-seconds. Thermal neutron doses determined from induced radioactivity in various samples may have been from 1×10^8 to 2×10^{10}.

The explosive blast was generally upward from the ports in the top of the reactor. Structural damage to the building was slight and due principally to objects projected from the nozzles on the top of the reactor. The reactor core was extensively damaged although there was no evidence of gross melting.

The three-man reactor crew was evidently engaged in the reassembly of control rod mechanisms and housings on top of the reactor when the nuclear excursion and associated explosion occurred. The results of postmortem examinations of the 3 deceased persons show that 2 died instantly as a direct or indirect result of blast damage. The third man lived for about 2 hours after the accident but had a fatal wound in the head which precluded any possibility of survival.

Direct radiation from the reactor building as determined by both ground and aerial monitoring indicated that most of the activity was contained within the reactor building, in spite of its being an ordinary and not a containment-type building.

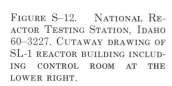

FIGURE S–12.   NATIONAL RE-ACTOR TESTING STATION, IDAHO 60–3227. CUTAWAY DRAWING OF SL-1 REACTOR BUILDING INCLUDING CONTROL ROOM AT THE LOWER RIGHT.

The readings remained relatively constant for many weeks: 1,000 roentgens per hour (r/hr) in the immediate vicinity of the reactor; 200 r/hr near the stairway to the reactor building; 10 r/hr outside near the base of the reactor building; 1.1 r/hr at 100 feet; .037 r/hr at 500 feet; .009 r/hr at 1,000 feet and .002 r/hr at 2,000 feet.

Some gaseous fission products, including iodine-131, escaped to the atmosphere outside the building and were carried downwind in a narrow plume, but air-borne radioactivity was largely confined to the immediate vicinity. Some low-level off-site activity from iodine-131 was found in sagebrush, but was not of any significance. By April, measured iodine-131 was essentially background. Some strontium-90 as determined by 5 soil samples collected 10 days after the accident ranged from 1018 ± 18 disintegrations per minute per 20 grams (d/m/20 gm) near the building to 65 ± 8 d/m/20 gm about 20 feet from the guard house (about 1,000 feet) along the perimeter fence. The most remarkable finding is that even in an ordinary building the particulate fission material was largely confined within the reactor building—if the building had been the pressure type containment vessel as would have been used for a reactor located in a populated area there would have been no radioactivity released to the environment.

Since this accident the USAEC has conducted a survey of all reactor operations at 36 locations, including industrial organizations, research laboratories and universities, to insure the utmost safety in operating procedures.

SMEAR SURVEY

The smear test is a method of determining the level of radioactive contamination of a surface (desk, floor, or piece of equipment). Particularly important in assessing removable activity. A piece of filter paper (5 cm in diameter) is rubbed lightly but firmly over an area about 10 cm radius—this area of about 300 cm² would give, for example, about 3×10^{-5} microcurie (μc), or roughly 1 disintegration per second if the filter paper picked up removable contamination of 10^{-7} μc per cm². The smear paper can be roughly checked or counted to establish the level of surface contamination, or the effectiveness of surface decontamination. Surfaces of desks, hoods, or other places where active materials are handled may need a smear every day as a method of monitoring for surface contamination.

See WIPE TEST.

SNAP PROJECT

SNAP is an acronym for Systems for Nuclear Auxiliary Power. The first approach to the prob-

lem, called SNAP-I, uses the heat from a radioactive isotope to operate electrical power conversion equipment. The second approach, called SNAP-II, uses a nuclear reactor as a heat source to operate a generator. Such compact nuclear power sources may be used for a number of in-orbit operations such as operating the communications gear, navigational transmitters, MIDAS/-SAMDS gear, etc.

The SNAP project is also concerned with ion engines. Ion propulsion involves the use of accelerated-charged particles for the generation of thrust. This method is not expected to produce sufficient thrust for take-off from the earth (the Rover project is working on this problem), but has a high efficiency suitable for providing a small sustained thrust after the spacecraft is in space. Over a prolonged period of time the acceleration imparted by a low thrust can lead to very high velocities.

Compact nuclear power sources will have many other uses in addition to power for space operations. Use as a power source for Navy underwater sonar installations has been suggested.

SODIUM

Symbol Na; atomic number 11; atomic weight 22.991. A silvery-white alkali metal, can be molded and cut by a knife, oxidizes instantly on exposure to air, and reacts violently with water. Compounds long recognized, but first isolated by English chemist Sir Humphry Davy in 1807. Named from English, soda. Symbol from Latin, *natarium*. Occurs as sodium chloride in the ocean (1.14% Na), in salt deposits and in common rocks; as sodium nitrate; as sodium borate; and as sodium sulfate. Natural abundance furnished 100% by Na^{23}.

Hundreds of sodium compounds are used in various ways. Sodium is essential for life in both plants and animals. Approximate daily intakes for various species are as follows: man, 4 grams (g); sheep, 5 g; swine, 3 g; cattle, 8 g; poultry, 0.5 g and rats 50 milligrams. Sodium content of the biochemical standard man is 0.15% or 105 grams per 70 kilograms of body weight. Blood serum contains about 330 mg/100 ml, and red cells, about 23. Crop plants range from 0.1 to 3% on a dry-matter basis. Toxicity has been determined on 77 different sodium compounds and varies according to the type of compound.

Five radioactive isotopes have been identified. Sodium-22 and sodium-24 are both available commercially for biological research.

Sodium-24 ($_{11}Na^{24}$). Radioactive half-life 14.97 hours with total body as the critical organ, biological half-life, 11 days, effective half-life 14.6 hours. Beta and gamma emitter. Usually produced by neutron bombardment of Na^{23} in a reactor by the following reaction: $Na^{23}(n,\gamma)Na^{24}$. Na^{24} may be formed in sea water or soil as a result of induced radioactivity resulting from neutron bombardment of Na^{23} associated with the detonation of a nuclear device in contact with the land or water surface of the earth. If sodium is present in any quantity in the soil Na^{24} may contribute to the radiation picture at about 10–20 hours after the detonation, but it is not significant as a long-term residual radiation component.

Radioactive sodium is used in man to measure circulation times and circulation efficiency for detecting normal and restricted blood flow or arterial constriction. Na^{24} also used to study sodium metabolism and transport in the body. Used to measure exchangeable sodium, and for clearance studies. In animal research used to study kidney function and excretory mechanisms, distribution and determination of extracellular space.

Maximum permissible concentration for soluble material for a 168-hour week (continuous exposure) with the total body as the critical organ is 4×10^{-3} microcuries per cubic centimeter ($\mu c/cc$) in water, and 6×10^{-7} $\mu c/cc$ in air.

Cyclotron-produced sodium-22, beta and gamma emitter, radioactive half-life 2.6 years; with total body as the critical organ, biological half-life 11 days, and effective half-life 11 days; is useful for long-term studies of sodium metabolism.

SOIL STUDIES

Radiation procedures are coming into wide use for determination of soil moisture content and soil density. The primary advantages are: (a) the soil can be studied in its natural undisturbed state, (b) repeated measurements in one location can be made, (c) high precision, (d) speed of measurement, (e) general application, and (f) independence of the physical and chemical properties of the soil.

Determination of soil moisture content is based on neutron moderation. From a neutron source, such as a mixture of radium and beryllium, fast neutrons are emitted in all directions: when these collide with atoms in the vicinity of the source they are usually scattered with little loss in energy, unless the collisions are with light atoms. In colliding with light atoms, such as hydrogen, fast neutrons give up some of their kinetic energy to the nuclei of the light atoms, and become slow neutrons. In actual practice, a source of fast neutrons is placed on the soil surface or in a well in the soil. The fast neutrons radiate out into the soil, and those that strike hydrogen nuclei (present

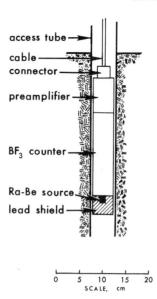

FIGURE S–13.   SOIL MOISTURE NEUTRON PROBE.

mainly in water) are converted to slow neutrons and deflected back towards a sensing agent, which is close to the neutron source. From the measurement by this sensing agent, the amount of hydrogen and thus the moisture in the soil can then be directly determined (Fig. S–13) and calibrated (Fig. S–14).

Estimation of soil density is based on gamma scattering which is somewhat analogous to that of neutron scattering. A gamma source enveloped by a material will be the focus of a field of low-energy gammas which will result from the backscatter of the originally emitted gammas. Generally, the secondary intensity close to the source will be

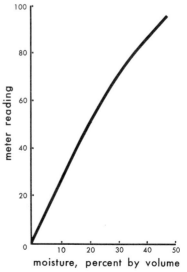

FIGURE S–14.   SOIL MOISTURE CALIBRATION CURVE.

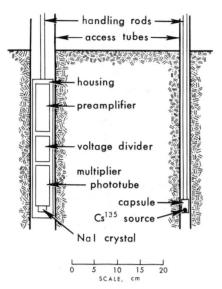

FIGURE S–15. SOIL DENSITY GAMMA PROBE FOR MEASUREMENT BY TRANSMISSION.

greater as the density of the surrounding material increases.

It is also possible to measure soil density by means of gamma transmission, which is different in principle from the two other methods. In this procedure, the detector and source of radiation are separated by the body of material under investigation, as illustrated in Figure S–15 (calibration curve, Figure S–16). The gamma transmission method measures the total density, including moisture.

See FERTILIZER STUDIES.

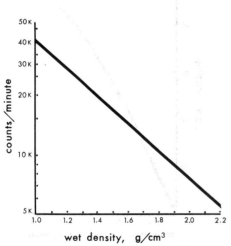

FIGURE S–16. CALIBRATION CURVE FOR MEASUREMENT OF SOIL DENSITY WITH A GAMMA PROBE.

SOLAR RADIATION

Radiations from the sun comprise a wide range of wave lengths in the electromagnetic spectrum, ranging from the short ultraviolet radiation at one end to the long infrared radiation at the other end. Fortunately for man, much of the energy toward either end of the spectrum is absorbed by the atmosphere, with the solar radiation on earth being confined largely to the visible and near infrared. The intensity of solar radiation is known as the solar constant and averages about 1.34×10^6 ergs per sq. cm. per sec.; or, in more familiar terms, and neglecting atmospheric absorption, this amounts to 1.8 horsepower falling upon each square meter of the earth. If solar energy cost the earth only 1 cent per kilowatt hour, the bill would be $478,000,000 per second!

Absorption of ultraviolet wave lengths in the higher atmosphere probably contributes to atmospheric ionization. Cosmic rays account for part of the natural radiation man receives, and in their passage through the atmosphere the heavy particles are responsible for the transmutation of some of the atoms of stable nitrogen-14 into radioactive carbon-14.

SOLID WASTE

Solid radioactive waste consists of the following types of material: contaminated equipment, tools, ion exchange resins, animal carcasses, broken glassware, ashes, insulation, paper, cloth, and wiping waste. Solid waste from nuclear submarines includes ion exchange resins, metal scrap, pieces of insulation, rags, sheet plastic, and paper.

In order to make routine laboratory collection easier, solid wastes are usually separated according to their activity levels. Low-level wastes are placed in receptacles lined with paper or plastic bags, which are collected and reduced in volume by incineration or baling. If incineration is employed the low-level material must be separated into combustible (paper, clothing, rags, etc.) and non-combustible (equipment, glassware, metal, etc.) items. Baling also requires sorting for compressibility. Solid wastes of high activity are placed in shielded receptacles that are monitored and collected when full or when intensities exceed maximum permissible levels. These high-activity solid wastes are then usually held in decay storage or handled by LAND BURIAL or OCEAN DISPOSAL.

Commercial concerns are licensed by the USAEC to collect, process and dispose of solid waste.

SOMATIC CELLS

All cells of an organism other than the germ cells. Specifically they are those cells having paired or diploid chromosomes, in contrast to those with unpaired or haploid chromosomes. Somatic cells are generally more resistant to the effects of ionizing radiation than germ cells. When damaged, they cannot engender genetic alterations in the organism's progeny. Damage to somatic cells leads to organic damage and loss of function of tissues and organs, and may result in death.

See SOMATIC EFFECTS, RADIATION-INDUCED.

SOMATIC EFFECTS, RADIATION-INDUCED

The totality of biochemical, physiological and morphological alterations induced by radiation in the nonhaploid (i.e., diploid) cells of an organism. Somatic effects are differentiated from GENETIC EFFECTS in that somatic effects are limited to the life span of the individual.

Severity of alteration is a function of the radiation's duration, intensity, nature, and of the individual properties of the irradiated tissue. In general, poorly differentiated tissue is more susceptible to radiation-induced change than well differentiated tissue. Acute whole-body irradiation in sufficient quantity produces an acute radiation syndrome which is called radiation illness.

The term somatic effects is often used to refer to chronic effects due to radiation.

See CHRONIC EFFECTS, RADIATION.

SOMATIC MUTATIONS

Mutations in the cells of the body as distinguished from mutations in reproductive cells. Such mutations cannot be transmitted sexually, and so disappear with the death of the individual. They may sometimes be propagated asexually, e.g., a bud mutation on a tree can be propagated and produce a new line. Spontaneous or radiation-induced somatic mutations have resulted in changes in plants and animals: color mosaics in petals of flowers, and fleece mosaicism in sheep. Some scientists consider induction of leukemia and cancer by ionizing radiation to be the result of one or several somatic mutations. Plant breeding or crop improvement by mutation, as a method of asexually improving crops, is being tried experimentally.

See MUTATION, RADIATION-INDUCED.

SOURCE MATERIALS

Term used to designate materials, other than special nuclear materials, containing by weight one-twentieth of 1% or more of uranium and/or thorium. These elements constitute the source of the fissionable materials, U^{235}, U^{233} and plutonium-239. Source materials are subject to USAEC regulations and a license (*see* LICENSING AND REGULATING, USAEC) must be obtained before source materials can be mined, bought or sold, imported or exported, or otherwise transferred.

See BYPRODUCT MATERIAL and SPECIAL NUCLEAR MATERIAL.

SOURCES OF RADIATION

An element or substance from which radiation emanates; or a device which generates radiation. Usually used in the sense of a source of radiation for use in biological research, and in medical or industrial activity. For example, in medical treatment, sealed sources containing radium, gold-198, cobalt-60, etc., are used in brachytherapy, while x-ray and cobalt-60 are used in teletherapy. Sources may be collimated as in the use of x-ray, or noncollimated as in the brachytherapy use of interstitial implants. Nonsealed radioactive sources are usually radioisotopes used as chemicals or drugs rather than as discrete sources of radiation.

In a broader sense, sources of radiation may be: (1) natural radiation; (2) all radioactive isotopes and their products; (3) electrical sources, e.g., x-ray; (4) particle accelerators; (5) nuclear reactors; and (6) nuclear weapons.

SPECIAL NUCLEAR MATERIAL

Term referring to plutonium, uranium enriched in the U^{235} or U^{233} isotopes, or any material containing plutonium or enriched uranium. By definition, source materials are not special nuclear materials. Licenses must be obtained to use special nuclear material as the USAEC has all rights and title to it (*see* LICENSING AND REGULATING, USAEC).

See BYPRODUCT MATERIAL and SOURCE MATERIALS.

SPECIFIC ACTIVITY

Ratio of the number of atoms of a given radioactive isotope to the total number of atoms of the same element, or the fraction of the given element that is present in the form of the particular radioisotope. In tracer experimental and diagnostic work the carrier may be stable isotopes of the same element; and since their separation is extremely difficult it is satisfactory and much simpler to express the proportion of the active species in terms of the specific activity of the material.

May also be defined as the activity per unit mass of a pure radionuclide. For commercially available radioactive isotopes the specific activity is usually given for 1200 Eastern Standard Time (E.S.T.) the day following shipment, in terms of activity per unit mass, expressed as millicuries per gram of element (mc/g), or per milliliter of solution (mc/ml). For example, gold-198 for medical use is described as: "Radiogold Solution, U.S.P., Sterile. Provides 30 to 50 mc/ml. (γ) Au¹⁹⁸ with a specific activity of 4 to 5 mc./mg. Au. Contains benzyl alcohol, 0.9% as preservative. Calibrated for 1200 E.S.T. day following shipment." May also be the activity per unit weight of any sample of radioactive material.

Commonly, though perhaps unfortunately, specific activity is also used to express the rate at which unit weight of radioactive material decays, i.e., the rate at which it emits charged particles. This gives a useful measure since the detection of the radionuclide depends on counting these particles. It can be illustrated by considering phosphorus-32, quoted as available with a specific activity of 50 millicuries per gram. Since a curie gives 3.70×10^{10} disintegrations per second, a millicurie would be 3.7×10^7 disintegrations per second. Thus for every gram of phosphorus there would be $50 \times 3.7 \times 10^7 = 1.85 \times 10^9$ disintegrations taking place per second, or 1.85×10^9 beta particles expelled per second from the P³². It is known that the specific activity of pure P³² is 2.7×10^5 curies per gram, and since in the example above there is 0.05 curie (50 millicuries) of P³² per gram of phosphorus, the actual weight of P³² would be 1.8×10^{-7} gram per gram of total phosphorus, $(0.05/2.7 \times 10^5)$. This is a very small quantity but since modern instruments can detect as low as 4 particles per second there is plenty of activity for tracer experiments. The smallest weight of P³² which can be conveniently measured in an ionization counter is about 4×10^{-16} gram. It is interesting to note that the specific activity of pure phosphorus-32, expressed in curies per gram, because of its short radioactive half-life $(1.3 \times 10^6$ seconds) is greater than that of radium itself; but because of its longer radioactive half-life pure carbon-14 is only 5 curies per gram.

SPECIFIC IONIZATION

The number of ion pairs formed per centimeter along the track of a moving charged particle through matter, i.e., the intensity of ionization. For particles of the same mass the specific ionization increases with the magnitude of the charge, and for particles of the same energy it increases with the mass, that is, with decreasing speed. The specific ionization of charged particles is proportional to the square of their charge and inversely proportional to their velocity. The slower moving particle has a greater chance of causing ionization for it spends more time in the vicinity of an atom or molecule of the matter through which it is passing. For example, an alpha particle from a radioactive source would produce 50,000 to 100,000 ion pairs per centimeter of ordinary air;

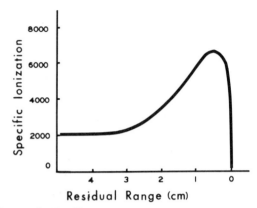

FIGURE S–17. NUMBER OF ION PAIRS FORMED PER CENTIMETER ALONG THE TRACK OF AN ALPHA PARTICLE AS A FUNCTION OF RESIDUAL RANGE.

while a beta particle of similar energy but higher speed and smaller charge would produce only a few hundred per centimeter. However, the total ionization would be about the same, for the beta particle would travel about a hundred times as far as the alpha particle. In the case of an individual alpha particle, as it moves away from its source and slows down the specific ionization increases steadily. Ultimately, however, a point is reached where electrons attach themselves to the particle and convert it into a neutral atom incapable of ionization.

The relative specific ionization is the specific ionization for a particle in a given medium relative either to that for (1) the same particle and energy in a standard medium, such as air at 15°C at 1 atmosphere; or (2) the same particle and medium at a specified energy.

A specific ionization curve shows the average specific ionization of an ionizing particle of a particular kind as a function of either its kinetic energy, velocity, range or residual range, as illustrated in Figures S–17 and S–18.

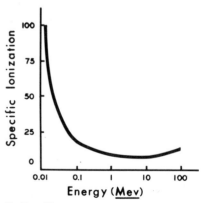

FIGURE S–18. NUMBER OF ION PAIRS FORMED PER CENTIMETER ALONG THE TRACK OF A BETA PARTICLE AS A FUNCTION OF ITS ENERGY.

SPECTROMETER

Any device which analyzes the radiation received to classify it according to the intensity or amount of radiation having different specific energies, providing an energy spectrum of the source.

SPECTRUM

A visual display, a photographic record, or a plot of the distribution of the intensity of a given type of radiation as a function of its wave length, energy, frequency, momentum, mass, or any related quantity.

The most familiar is the ELECTROMAGNETIC SPECTRUM, which includes radiation from the following sources: cosmic rays, gamma rays, x-rays, ultraviolet, visible light, infrared, radiowaves and electric waves.

The ALPHA-PARTICLE SPECTRUM represents the distribution of energy or momentum of alpha particles emitted by a radionuclide. Each radionuclide has one or more discrete lines.

The BETA-RAY SPECTRUM consists of the distribution of energy or momentum of beta particles. This is a continuous distribution up to a maximum energy.

The GAMMA-RAY SPECTRUM is a part of the electromagnetic spectrum representing the intensity of gamma radiation given off during the process of disintegration of a radionuclide.

The x-ray spectrum is also part of the electromagnetic spectrum and represents different characteristics of x-rays as produced in various ways.

A line spectrum represents the energy values which are clustered about one or more discrete values, as contrasted to a continuous spectrum. The alpha-particle spectrum is of the line spectrum type.

In contrast, the continuous spectrum presents no detailed structure but rather a gradual variation of intensity between the two extremes. For example, the continuous x-ray spectrum or the spectrum of light from an incandescent solid. The beta-ray spectrum represents a continuous variation of momentum or energy.

The mass spectrum shows the distribution in mass or in mass-to-charge ratio of ionized atoms, molecules or molecular fragments. The mass spectrum of an element shows the abundance ratio of the isotopes of an element: determined by the use of a mass spectrometer.

When radiation with a continuous spectrum is passed through a selectively-absorbing medium an absorption spectrum results, which shows spaces or dark lines for the wave lengths for which the emission spectrum of the medium itself would be bright.

Emission spectrum is a broad term referring to any spectrum from a given source.

The term fine spectrum is used in connection with atomic emission spectra in referring to the resolution of an apparently single line into two or more lines close together. The term hyperfine spectrum refers to a further more detailed resolution.

There are many other types of spectra not as closely related to atomic energy activities: arc, flame, infrared absorption, magnetic resonance, microwave, Raman, ultraviolet and visible.

SPERMATOGENESIS, RADIATION EFFECTS ON. See GONADS, RADIATION EFFECTS ON.

SPILL

Accidental contamination of a small area by the release of radioactive material. Term usually used only for minor incidents.

SPINAL CORD TUMORS, LOCALIZATION

Certain spinal cord tumors can be localized by the injection of a solution of a gamma-emitting radioisotope into the spinal canal. The isotopic preparation usually used is radioiodine attached to albumin; a dose in the neighborhood of 100 microcuries is usually adequate. This material does not quickly leave the spinal canal but tends to move by gravity to the most dependent area where there is a free flow. It will be stopped at the point where a tumor produces a block in the normal passage around the spinal cord. The location of the radioisotope and its pattern of distribution are demonstrated by means of a detector outside the body that produces a scintiscan record. As compared with an x-ray examination using a nonradioactive contrast medium (myelography), this isotopic method generally gives less detailed information but it has the advantage of eliminating the irritating effects sometimes produced by the contrast medium.

SPINTHARISCOPE (HISTORICAL)

A simple scintillation detector, consisting only of a phosphor screen and magnifying eyepiece; important in early studies of radioactivity, especially in counting alpha particle events from natural radioactive substances.

SPLEEN, RADIATION EFFECTS ON

The spleen is extremely radiosensitive, showing inhibition of mitosis less than an hour after midlethal doses of radiation, with evidence of severe damage to the lymphocytes following shortly. Loss in splenic weight (experimental animals) is a sensitive indicator with the threshold dose being about 40 roentgens (r). The percentage of splenic weight loss as a function of the dose of radiation is shown in Figure S–19, which indicates a dose-effect relationship. Minimum weight is seen about the fourth day after exposure. For example, on the fourth day following an exposure to 300 rep, the spleen of the experimental animal weighed only about 40% as much as that of a control.

In the mid-lethal range of exposure one of the earliest observations is the cessation of the production of both red blood cells and white blood cells in the spleen (mouse and rat). During this period the precursor cells may atrophy so that only stromal cells and the central arteriole are left. If the animal goes into the hemorrhagic phase of radiation illness, bleeding into the spleen may be marked.

Shielding of the spleen to prevent radiation damage protects the experimental animal re-

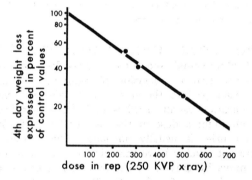

FIGURE S–19. SPLENIC WEIGHT LOSS DUE TO RADIATION.

markably from permanent damage to the hematopoietic system. Acceleration of regeneration, and in some cases complete restoration of the function of blood-forming organs, follow injection of splenic homogenate containing living cells.

SPLEEN HOMOGENATE THERAPY

Acceleration of regeneration and often complete restoration of function of the blood-forming organs in mice has been shown to follow injection of homogenates of mouse spleen given from 1 to 45 hours (usually 2 or 3 hours) after irradiation. This type of treatment leading to cellular grafts is closely related to bone marrow grafts.

See SPLEEN, RADIATION EFFECTS ON.

SPURIOUS COUNT

Extra count delivered by radiation counting equipment resulting from a pulse of extraneous origin in the radiation detector, not arising from the activity of the sample being counted or from background radiation. Common sources of spurious counts are failure of the quenching mechan-

ism, pitted electrode surfaces, leakage over unclean insulators, improper operating conditions and noisy electrical power conditions traceable to poor electrical connections, malfunctioning fluorescent lights, or rough commutators on nearby electrical motors.

STABLE ISOTOPE

An isotope or nuclide that is incapable of spontaneous change. An isotope of an element which is not radioactive. Stability is in a sense a relative property depending upon our present scientific ability to measure very weak activities and very long lifetimes; thus suspected radioactive nuclides with lifetimes exceeding about 10^{15} to 10^{18} years cannot be detected and are considered stable at present. Of over 1,000 different known isotopes, only about 25% are stable. Radioactive isotopes always decay toward stable isotopes. It is interesting that over half the stable nuclei contain even numbers of protons (Z) and even numbers of neutrons (N) and are called even-even nuclei. About 20% have even Z and odd N and are called even-odd nuclei; and another 20% have odd Z and even N (odd-even nuclei); but only four ($_1H^2$, $_3Li^6$, $_5B^{10}$ and $_7N^{14}$) are odd-odd with an odd number of protons and of neutrons. Of the 83 naturally occurring elements 21 have only one stable isotope; tin, with 10 stable isotopes has the greatest number. However, regardless of how many different stable isotopes make up the natural abundance of the element, the isotopes almost always occur in approximately the same proportion no matter where the element is found. Table S–1 lists all the stable isotopes of naturally occurring elements.

TABLE S–1. STABLE ISOTOPES* OF NATURALLY OCCURRING ELEMENTS

ATOMIC NUMBER	ELEMENT	SYMBOL	MASS NUMBER OF ISOTOPE	PER CENT ABUNDANCE
1	Hydrogen	H	1	99.98
			2	0.02
2	Helium	He	4	100
3	Lithium	Li	6	7.4
			7	92.6
4	Beryllium	Be	9	100
5	Boron	B	10	18.83
			11	81.17

*Strongly radioactive elements and radioactive isotopes of all elements are presented in Table R–6 RADIOACTIVE ISOTOPES.

ATOMIC NUMBER	ELEMENT	SYMBOL	MASS NUMBER OF ISOTOPE	PER CENT ABUNDANCE	ATOMIC NUMBER	ELEMENT	SYMBOL	MASS NUMBER OF ISOTOPE	PER CENT ABUNDANCE
6	Carbon	C	12	98.9	23	Vanadium	V	50	0.25
			13	1.1				51	99.75
7	Nitrogen	N	14	99.64	24	Chromium	Cr	50	4.49
			15	0.36				52	83.78
								53	9.43
8	Oxygen	O	16	99.76				54	2.30
			17	0.04					
			18	0.20	25	Manganese	Mn	55	100
9	Fluorine	F	19	100	26	Iron	Fe	54	5.81
								56	91.64
10	Neon	Ne	20	90.51				57	2.21
			21	0.28				58	0.34
			22	9.21					
					27	Cobalt	Co	59	100
11	Sodium	Na	23	100	28	Nickel	Ni	58	67.8
12	Magnesium	Mg	24	78.6				60	26.2
			25	10.1				61	1.2
			26	11.3				62	3.7
								64	1.1
13	Aluminum	Al	27	100					
14	Silicon	Si	28	92.28	29	Copper	Cu	63	69.09
			29	4.67				65	30.91
			30	3.05					
					30	Zinc	Zn	64	48.87
15	Phosphorus	P	31	100				66	27.62
								67	4.12
16	Sulfur	S	32	95.06				68	18.71
			33	0.74				70	0.69
			34	4.18					
			36	0.02	31	Gallium	Ga	69	60.0
								71	40.0
17	Chlorine	Cl	35	75.4	32	Germanium	Ge	70	20.45
			37	24.6				72	27.41
								73	7.77
18	Argon	A	36	0.34				74	36.58
			38	0.06				76	7.79
			40	99.6					
					33	Arsenic	As	75	100
19	Potassium	K	39	93.1	34	Selenium	Se	74	0.96
			40	0.01				76	9.12
			41	6.9				77	7.50
								78	23.61
20	Calcium	Ca	40	96.92				80	49.96
			42	0.64				82	8.84
			43	0.13					
			44	2.13	35	Bromine	Br	79	50.6
			46	0.0032				81	49.4
			48	0.179					
					36	Krypton	Kr	78	0.354
21	Scandium	Sc	45	100				80	2.27
								82	11.56
22	Titanium	Ti	46	7.94				83	11.55
			47	7.75				84	56.90
			48	73.45				86	17.37
			49	5.52					
			50	5.34	37	Rubidium	Rb	85	72.15

TABLE S–1—*Continued*

TABLE S–1—*Continued*

ATOMIC NUMBER	ELEMENT	SYMBOL	MASS NUMBER OF ISOTOPE	PER CENT ABUNDANCE	ATOMIC NUMBER	ELEMENT	SYMBOL	MASS NUMBER OF ISOTOPE	PER CENT ABUNDANCE
38	Strontium	Sr	84	0.55	51	Antimony	Sb	121	57.25
			86	9.75				123	42.75
			87	6.96	52	Tellurium	Te	120	0.09
			88	82.74				122	2.47
39	Yttrium	Y	89	100				123	0.89
40	Zirconium	Zr	90	51.46				124	4.74
			91	11.23				125	7.03
			92	17.11				126	18.72
			94	17.40				128	31.75
			96	2.80				130	34.27
41	Niobium	Nb	93	100	53	Iodine	I	127	100
42	Molybdenum	Mo	92	15.05	54	Xenon	Xe	124	0.095
			94	9.35				126	0.088
			95	15.78				128	1.91
			96	16.56				129	26.24
			97	9.60				130	4.053
			98	24.60				131	21.24
			100	9.65				132	26.92
44	Ruthenium	Ru	96	5.68				134	10.52
			98	2.22				136	8.93
			99	12.81	55	Cesium	Cs	133	100
			100	12.70	56	Barium	Ba	130	0.10
			101	16.98				132	0.09
			102	31.34				134	2.39
			104	18.27				135	6.56
45	Rhodium	Rh	101	0.08				136	7.74
			103	100				137	11.25
46	Palladium	Pd	102	0.8				138	71.83
			104	9.3	57	Lanthanum	La	139	99.911
			105	22.6	58	Cerium	Ce	136	0.19
			106	27.2				138	0.26
			108	26.8				140	88.45
			110	13.5				142	11.10
47	Silver	Ag	107	51.35	59	Praseodymium	Pr	141	100
			109	48.65	60	Neodymium	Nd	142	27.13
48	Cadmium	Cd	106	1.21				143	12.20
			108	0.87				145	8.30
			110	12.40				146	17.18
			111	12.75				148	5.72
			112	24.07	62	Samarium	Sm	144	2.87
			113	12.26				148	11.24
			114	28.86				149	13.85
			116	7.58				150	7.36
49	Indium	In	113	4.16				152	26.90
50	Tin	Sn	112	1.01				154	22.84
			114	0.68	63	Europium	Eu	151	47.77
			115	0.35				153	52.23
			116	14.28	64	Gadolinium	Gd	152	0.20
			117	7.67				154	2.15
			118	23.84				155	14.78
			119	8.68				156	20.59
			120	32.75				157	15.71
			122	4.74				158	24.78
			124	6.01				160	21.79

ATOMIC NUMBER	ELEMENT	SYMBOL	MASS NUMBER OF ISOTOPE	PER CENT ABUNDANCE
65	Terbium	Tb	159	100
66	Dysprosium	Dy	156	0.05
			158	0.09
			160	2.29
			161	18.88
			162	25.53
			163	24.97
			164	28.19
67	Holmium	Ho	165	100
68	Erbium	Er	162	0.136
			164	1.56
			166	33.41
			167	22.94
			168	27.07
			170	14.88
69	Thulium	Tm	169	100
70	Ytterbium	Yb	167	0.002
			168	0.14
			170	3.03
			171	14.34
			172	21.88
			173	16.18
			174	31.77
			176	12.65
71	Lutecium	Lu	175	97.5
72	Hafnium	Hf	174	0.18
			176	5.15
			177	18.38
			178	27.08
			179	13.78
			180	35.44
73	Tantalum	Ta	181	99.98
74	Tungsten (Wolfram)	W	180	0.126
			182	26.31
			183	14.28
			184	30.64
			186	28.64
75	Rhenium	Re	185	37.07
76	Osmium	Os	184	0.018
			186	1.59
			187	1.64
			188	13.3
			189	16.1
			190	26.4
			192	41.0
77	Iridium	Ir	191	38.5
			193	61.5
78	Platinum	Pt	192	0.8
			194	32.8
			195	33.7
			196	25.4
			198	7.3

ATOMIC NUMBER	ELEMENT	SYMBOL	MASS NUMBER OF ISOTOPE	PER CENT ABUNDANCE
79	Gold	Au	197	100
80	Mercury	Hg	196	0.16
			198	10.02
			199	16.92
			200	23.10
			201	13.22
			202	29.72
			204	6.84
81	Thallium	Tl	203	29.52
			205	70.48
82	Lead	Pb	204	1.37
			206	26.26
			207	20.82
			208	51.55
83	Bismuth	Bi	209	100
90	Thorium	Th	232	100
92	Uranium	U	234	0.006
			235	0.71
			238	99.28

STABLE STATE

Term applied to an element, a nuclide or an isotope that is not radioactive. The stable isotopes furnish the natural abundance of the elements. A stable atomic or nuclear system is incapable of spontaneous change. Nuclides with lifetimes over 10^{15} to 10^{18} years are usually considered stable. The term may be applied to indicate a specific stability, as beta stable, i.e., incapable of ordinary beta disintegration, although possibly capable of some other type of disintegration: alpha disintegration, isomeric transition, or even spontaneous fission. The GROUND STATE as distinguished from the EXCITED and METASTABLE STATE. The opposite of unstable.

STACK DISPOSAL

Disposal of radioactive gaseous material through a chimney, the stack of a reactor, or some other ventilating device. GASEOUS WASTES from peaceful uses of atomic energy are released from relatively low altitudes (few stacks are higher than 500 feet) and except under extremely turbulent conditions practically all mixing takes place below 3,000 meters (m), i.e., 10,000 feet. The total volume of the atmosphere below 3,000 m is calculated to be 1.55×10^{18} cubic meters (m^3), which is remarkably close to the volume of the oceans, 1.37×10^{18} m^3. Thus on a volumetric basis it would seem that the biosphere and the hydrosphere would have the same ultimate diluting capacity. However, the maximum permissible concentrations for water are quite consistently 10^4 times those for air, and thus for the same rate of waste discharge and rate of mixing the atmosphere becomes contaminated to the maximum permissible level 10^4 times faster than the oceans. The only cleansing system for the atmosphere is the gradual precipitation of particulate matter by gravity or by rainout, but for particles of small size this is very slow.

The possibility of world-wide air pollution has received a great deal of attention and some interesting calculations have been made. A 500 MW reactor operating on a fuel reprocessing cycle of 180 days will contain 4.1×10^8 curies (c) of fission products of which 5×10^7 c are iodine isotopes, 3.4×10^7 c are noble gases, 1.7×10^7 c are Sr^{89} and 3×10^5 c are Sr^{90}. If one assumes that by the year 2000, nuclear reactors will supply 2.5×10^6 MW of power throughout the world it is easy to calculate that the fission product concentration in the atmosphere if all were released and evenly distributed would be 200 times the maximum permissible level for off-site personnel. Of course, normally operating reactors emit very little stored fission products and hence represent no real world-wide hazard.

Even though a release from a reactor did occur, very little would be deposited on a global scale—most of the radioactivity would be deposited within a very few miles of the site. The actual deposition of the released material depends quite largely on meteorological conditions but these and other variables can be predicted sufficiently accurately to make useful predictions at least of the order of magnitude of anticipated atmospheric pollution from normal plant operations and even from serious accidents.

The important measures for the prevention of atmospheric pollution are limiting the generation of such possible air-borne wastes and effective air cleaning of radioactive gaseous waste prior to release. In order to properly select air-cleaning equipment it is necessary to know the characteristics of the gases; their solubility, vapor pressure, reaction rates, adsorption characteristics, specific activity, half-life, nature of radioactive emission, combustibility and concentration. For particulates or aerosols it is necessary to have much the same data plus information as to particle size, size distribution, shape, surface area and nature. The type of element is important for with some radioisotopes only 10 curies per year can be released safely from a 300-foot stack; but with a chemically inert gas, e.g., argon-41 or krypton-85, 10,000 curies might be safely released from the same stack.

Knowing the type of material and its characteristics makes it possible to select the proper mechanical device to trap the particles, or the proper type of filter to absorb the radioactive gases. For particle removal one of the following would be suitable: mechanical centrifugal collectors (cyclones), baffle chambers, cyclone scrubbers, spray washers, viscous air-conditioning filters, dry spun-glass filters, high-efficiency cellulose-asbestos filters, all-glass web filters, conventional fabric filters and electrostatic precipitators. For radioactive gaseous contaminants one of the following should be considered: detention chamber, spray tower, packed tower, absorbent beds, limestone beds, liquefaction column, stripping column, wet filter or activated charcoal filter. In order not to exceed the limit of one-tenth of the maximum permissible concentrations for occupational exposure, which is the maximum for the general public, it is frequently necessary to remove $99+\%$ of the radioactive material, and a combination of the above devices may be necessary. On the other hand, it may be that all that is required is an enormous volume flow of air to dilute the radioactive material.

The cost of stack disposal of radioactive gaseous wastes to the atmosphere is high. For example, the tall stacks employed for radioactive operations range in cost from $300 to $1,000 per foot and many are 200 to 400 feet high. The total cost of the filter house and its elements is about $350 per 1,000 cubic feet per minute (cfm). And the flow may be as high as 300,000 cfm passing through the final filters. Changing "AEC filters" for a single cell costs about $2,500 plus 24.5 man-days labor.

At any rate, gaseous wastes must be monitored (see AIR MONITORING) continuously during release, and in addition filters and samples of scrubbing solutions should be analyzed, counted and recorded. A regional monitoring program is necessary for complete safety control.

STANDARD MAN

Term applied to certain average or standard measurements of physiological function, anatomy and composition of the adult human body. When the early work was being done to establish body burdens and concentration values for the various radionuclides, it became evident that it would be impossible to compare suggested values from different laboratories unless everyone used the same basic assumptions relative to the average man. As a consequence certain characteristics of the so-called standard man were agreed upon. The chemical standard man is shown in Table S–2, Element Distribution in Total Body of the

TABLE S–2. ELEMENT DISTRIBUTION IN TOTAL BODY OF THE STANDARD MAN

ELEMENT	SYMBOL	PER CENT BY WEIGHT	APPROXIMATE AMOUNT IN 70-KG MAN (grams)
Oxygen	O	65.0	45,500
Carbon	C	18.0	12,600
Hydrogen	H	10.0	7,000
Nitrogen	N	3.0	2,100
Calcium	Ca	1.5	1,050
Phosphorus	P	1.0	700
Sulfur	S	0.25	175
Potassium	K	0.2	140
Sodium	Na	0.15	105
Chlorine	Cl	0.15	105
Magnesium	Mg	0.05	35
Iron	Fe	0.0057	4
Zinc	Zn	0.0033	2.3
Rubidium	Rb	0.0017	1.2
Strontium	Sr	2×10^{-4}	0.14
Copper	Cu	1.4×10^{-4}	0.1
Aluminum	Al	1.4×10^{-4}	0.1
Lead	Pb	1.1×10^{-4}	0.08
Tin	Sn	4.3×10^{-5}	0.03
Iodine	I	4.3×10^{-5}	0.03
Cadmium	Cd	4.3×10^{-5}	0.03
Manganese	Mn	3×10^{-5}	0.02
Barium	Ba	2.3×10^{-5}	0.016
Arsenic	As	1.4×10^{-4}	0.1
Antimony	Sb	1.3×10^{-4}	0.09
Lanthanum	La	7×10^{-5}	0.05
Niobium	Nb	7×10^{-5}	0.05
Titanium	Ti	2.1×10^{-5}	0.015
Nickel	Ni	1.4×10^{-5}	0.01
Boron	B	1.4×10^{-5}	0.01
Chromium	Cr	8.6×10^{-6}	0.006
Ruthenium	Ru	8.6×10^{-6}	0.006
Thallium	Tl	8.6×10^{-6}	0.006
Zirconium	Zr	8.6×10^{-6}	0.006
Molybdenum	Mo	7×10^{-6}	0.005
Cobalt	Co	4.3×10^{-6}	0.003
Beryllium	Be	3×10^{-6}	0.002
Gold	Au	1.4×10^{-6}	0.001
Silver	Ag	1.4×10^{-6}	0.001
Lithium	Li	1.3×10^{-6}	9×10^{-4}
Bismuth	Bi	4.3×10^{-7}	3×10^{-4}
Vanadium	V	1.4×10^{-7}	10^{-4}
Uranium	U	3×10^{-8}	2×10^{-5}
Cesium	Cs	1.4×10^{-8}	10^{-5}
Gallium	Ga	3×10^{-9}	2×10^{-6}
Radium	Ra	1.4×10^{-13}	10^{-10}

Standard Man. Table S–3, Organs of the Standard Man, records the mass in grams of the various organs and their effective radius. Careful analyses have been made of the amount of each element of the body which is contained in each organ.* Because the gastrointestinal tract is of prime importance from the standpoint of ingestion, absorption and elimination, its characteristics are presented as Table S–4, Gastrointestinal Tract of the Standard Man. This table also notes the movement of material from the lung to the gastrointestinal tract.

Two physiological processes are important in internal deposition: Intake and Excretion of the Standard Man (Table S–5); and Air Balance (Table S–6). The total water in the body is taken as 4.3×10^4 grams.

*Report of ICRP Committee II on Permissible Dose for Internal Radiation (1959), with Bibliography for Biological, Mathematical and Physical Data Journal of Health Physics, Volume 3, June, 1960.

TABLE S-3. ORGANS OF THE STANDARD MAN

	MASS (grams)	PER CENT OF TOTAL BODY*	EFFECTIVE RADIUS (cm)
Total body*	70,000	100	30
Muscle	30,000	43	30
Skin and subcutaneous tissue†	6,100	8.7	0.1
Fat	10,000	14	20
Skeleton			
Without bone marrow	7,000	10	5
Red marrow	1,500	2.1	
Yellow marrow	1,500	2.1	
Blood	5,400	7.7	
Gastrointestinal tract*	2,000	2.9	30
Contents of gastrointestinal tract			
Lower large intestine	150		5
Stomach	250		10
Small intestine	1,100		30
Upper large intestine	135		5
Liver	1,700	2.4	10
Brain	1,500	2.1	15
Lungs (2)	1,000	1.4	10
Lymphoid tissue	700	1.0	
Kidneys (2)	300	0.43	7
Heart	300	0.43	7
Spleen	150	0.21	7
Urinary bladder	150	0.21	
Pancreas	70	0.10	5
Salivary glands (6)	50	0.071	
Testes (2)	40	0.057	3
Spinal cord	30	0.043	1
Eyes (2)	30	0.043	0.25
Thyroid gland	20	0.029	3
Teeth	20	0.029	
Prostate gland	20	0.029	3
Adrenal glands or suprarenal (2)	20	0.029	3
Thymus	10	0.014	
Ovaries (2)	8	0.011	3
Hypophysis (pituitary)	0.6	8.6×10^{-6}	0.5
Pineal gland	0.2	2.9×10^{-6}	0.04
Parathyroids (4)	0.15	2.1×10^{-6}	0.06
Miscellaneous (blood vessels, cartilage, nerves, etc.)	390	0.56	

*Does not include contents of the gastrointestinal tract.
†The mass of the skin alone is taken to be 2,000 grams.

TABLE S-4. GASTROINTESTINAL TRACT OF THE STANDARD MAN

PORTION OF GASTROINTESTINAL TRACT THAT IS THE CRITICAL TISSUE	MASS OF CONTENTS (grams)	TIME FOOD REMAINS (hours)	FRACTION FROM LUNG TO GASTROINTESTINAL TRACT (sol.)	(insol.)
Stomach (S)	250	1	0.50	0.625
Small intestine (SI)	1,100	4	0.50	0.625
Upper large intestine (ULI)	135	8	0.50	0.625
Lower large intestine (LLI)	150	18	0.50	0.625

TABLE S–5.   INTAKE AND EXCRETION OF THE
STANDARD MAN (WATER BALANCE)

	INTAKE (cm³/day)		EXCRETION (cm³/day)
Food	1,000	Urine	1,400
Fluids	1,200	Sweat	600
Oxidation	300	From lungs	300
		Feces	200
Total	2,500	Total	2,500

Retention of particulate matter in the lungs depends on many factors, such as size, shape and density of the particles, their chemical form, and also on whether or not the person is a mouth breather. However, when specific data are unavailable it is assumed that distribution is as shown in the table accompanying inhalation of radioactive material.

Various standards recorded in these 5 tables are used in all calculations of maximum permissible concentration, maximum permissible body burden, maximum permissible dose and critical organ. In the calculations 70 years is taken as the average life span of man, and his occupational exposure time = 8 hours per day, 40 hours per week, 50 weeks per year, and 50 years total employment time. For example, maximum permissible concentration values in water and in air are based on the values given in Tables S–5 and S–6, together with the standards for the maximum permissible dose to the total body or critical organ.

Manikins are available which duplicate man's body reactions to radiation hazards—plastic man-equivalent stand-ins. They may be equipped to function in the study of absorption of radiation, with a skeleton and a versatile system of ports and ducts for insertion of dosimeters within the long bones, spinal column and in soft tissue regions. This set-up is suitable for depth-dose studies, accident re-creation, testing shielding and protective clothing and equipment, and background studies in health physics. See Figure S–20 which shows the "plastic man" being used for studies of internal radiation with a crystal detector in an iron-room whole-body counter.

Manikins may be fitted with any desirable combination of organs, such as thyroid, liver, stomach, spleen, kidneys, testes; and each organ may be separately filled with any desired radioactive solution or the body as a whole may be given a separate generalized burden. With such an arrangement it is possible to track the movement of tracers in physiological research, study the amount of interorgan irradiation; or calibrate various types of radiation detection instruments. Hence, if one wished to find the average radiation dose to the human head as the result of the decay of one millicurie of iodine-131 in the thyroid he could use a compartmentalized standard-man phantom filled with tissue equivalent solution: a thyroid phantom containing the desired amount of iodine-131 would be placed in the neck compartment and the head compartment would be filled with an aqueous chemical dosimeter. After a

TABLE S–6.   AIR BALANCE

	O_2 (vol. %)	CO_2 (vol. %)	N_2 + OTHERS (vol. %)
Inspired air	20.94	0.03	79.03
Expired air	16	4.0	80
Alveolar air (inspired)	15	5.6	—
Alveolar air (expired)	14	6.0	—

Vital capacity of lungs 3–4 liters (men)
2–3 liters (women)

Air inhaled during 8-hr work day	10^7 cm³/day
Air inhaled during 16 hr not at work	10^7 cm³/day
Total	2×10^7 cm³/day

Interchange area of lungs	50 m²
Area of upper respiratory tract, trachea, bronchi	20 m²
Total surface area of respiratory tract	70 m²

FIGURE S–20. MANIKIN OR PLASTIC MAN BEING COUNTED WITH A CRYSTAL COUNTER IN AN IRON ROOM WHOLE-BODY COUNTER. (LOS ALAMOS SCIENTIFIC LABORATORY.)

sufficient decay period, a sample removed from the head compartment would yield information on the irradiation effect from the thyroid.

PHANTOMS may be developed for any organ and do not have to be too elaborate. Granulated cork and even Grape Nuts cereal have been successfully used to simulate lung tissue. Closely related to organ phantoms is the development of isodose curves or patterns with the use of tissue-equivalent plastic organ phantoms.

STANDARDIZATION

Procedure to establish the exact absolute quantity of radioactivity present in a given sample or source. The methods used depend on the kind of radiations emitted by the particular isotope being measured. The simplest standardization procedures, where high accuracy is not required, rely on direct comparison of the test sample with a known sample of the same isotope. In some cases it is possible to use mock-standards for this purpose, made of combinations of other isotopes giving nearly the same radiations but having longer half-life.

Proper standardization can be achieved by appropriate methods, however. Pure beta emitters can be standardized in a carefully designed beta counting system, which can be operated at 100% efficiency. Correction factors must be worked out for geometry, back scatter, self-absorption, and for the presence of other radiations which may co-exist.

Standardization of gamma-ray sources requires that the energy of the radiation be known, because of the dependence of detector response on energy. It is required to delete any accompanying beta rays by a suitable screen or absorber, usually of lead (Pb). The standardization is then accomplished by comparing the response of the unknown with that of a standard, such as cobalt-60 or radium, of which the disintegration rate and gamma energy have been established.

An absolute counting technique useful for beta-gamma emitters utilizes coincidence counting between 2 detectors responding to the beta particle and the gamma ray respectively. The decay scheme of the isotope must be known in order to allow use of this procedure.

STANDARDS FOR PROTECTION AGAINST RADIATION

This is the title of Part 20* of the regulation promulgated by the USAEC which, with its various amendments, has established standards for protection of industrial workers and the public against radiation hazards. The regulation establishes permissible doses (see MAXIMUM PERMISSIBLE DOSE) to which workers may be exposed, and levels and concentrations (see MAXIMUM PERMISSIBLE CONCENTRATION) of radioactivity both in restricted areas and in unrestricted areas, access to which is not controlled by the licensee. This regulation also contains provisions regarding personnel monitoring; caution signs, labels and signals; the radiation warning symbol; radiation areas; storage of licensed material; instruction of personnel in safe handling procedures; waste disposal; and records, reports and notification.

The radiation standards of these regulations are based on the work of the National Committee on Radiation Protection and Measurements (NCRP), as published in the National Bureau of Standards Handbooks. The International Commission on Radiological Protection (ICRP), and the International Commission on Radiological Units and Measurements (ICRU) have also exercised a role in setting protection standards.

See RADIATION PROTECTION STANDARDS.

---

*Federal Register. Title 10–Atomic Energy. Chapter 1–Atomic Energy Commission. Part 20–Standards for Protection Against Radiation.

STARTING POTENTIAL

The lowest voltage at which a Geiger counter or Geiger-Mueller tube will show consistent pulse formation. See the characteristic curve for the GEIGER-MUELLER COUNTER.

STATE DEPARTMENT, U.S.

A department of the Federal government, concerned in atomic energy matters with international, intelligence and world opinion aspects. For example, the Department of State is responsible for providing information to the United Nations Scientific Committee on the Effects of Atomic Radiation on the effects of atomic weapons, including fallout data. Maintains liaison with both United States and international organizations responsible for various aspects of atomic energy, e.g., the USAEC, the Department of Defense, EURATOM, and the International Atomic Energy Agency.

STERILITY DUE TO RADIATION

One of the important aspects of the acute radiation syndrome is the production of sterility in man by exposure to ionizing radiation. Temporary (up to 6 months) sterility in the human male may occur following exposure to 200 roentgens or more, but experience (Marshall Islanders, Hiroshima and Nagasaki survivors, and accident cases) indicates that up to about 50% of the lethal dose will have no permanent effect on FERTILITY of either male or female.

See GONADS, RADIATION EFFECTS ON.

STERILIZATION. *See* RADIATION STERILIZATION.

STEROID STUDIES

The steroids are a large group of chemically related compounds that have important functions in nature; they include, among others, cholesterol and the hormones of certain endocrine glands—the adrenals, ovaries and testes. Tracer research with carbon-14 has helped to clarify mechanisms of their formation and degradation. Such work has been especially extensive on cholesterol. Metabolic studies on adrenal and sex hormones by this method have been handicapped by the fact that, since these are naturally very potent substances, effective in minute amounts, and since carbon-14 has a large number of atoms per microcurie (associated with its long half-life), it is difficult or impossible to give enough labeled hormone for adequate measurement without greatly exceeding the natural concentrations.

Nevertheless, useful data have been obtained. They are of a complex sort and reference to original publications is needed for an adequate summary.

After labeled hydrocortisone and testosterone are injected it is found that rapid biochemical transformations take place, and labeled excretion products quickly begin to appear. Studies after oral ingestion of these suggested that the portal venous system is important in absorption; no significant amount is found in the lymph of the thoracic duct. It appears that these products are effectively absorbed from the gastrointestinal tract and not broken down by intestinal bacteria. The liver plays an important role in their metabolism, but only small amounts are found in the bile of human beings.

STIBIUM. *See* ANTIMONY.

STOPPING POWER

Rate of loss of energy by a charged particle per unit distance as it travels through a medium; or a measure of the effect of a substance upon kinetic energy of a charged particle passing through it; a quantity called the stopping power of the medium.

The relative stopping power is a more convenient and practical term and is defined as the ratio of the stopping power of a given substance to that of a standard substance, commonly air or aluminum. Thus for alpha particles traversing any material

$$\text{relative stopping power} = \frac{\text{range of alpha particle in air}}{\text{range of alpha particle in material}}$$

the same source of alpha particles being used in both instances. The relative stopping power of mica and thin metal foils has been determined: mica, 2,000; aluminum, 1,700; copper, 3,800; gold, 4,900 and silver 3,700. (See the closely related subject of absorption for a discussion of equivalent thickness which is frequently used in considering relative stopping power.)

Linear stopping power (S_1) is the energy loss per unit distance (d), and is given by $S_1 = -dE/dx$, where E is the kinetic energy of the particle and x is the distance traversed in the medium.

The mass stopping power (S_m) is the energy loss per unit surface density traversed, and is given by $S_m = S_1/p$, where p is the density of the substance.

The atomic stopping power (S_a) of an element is the energy loss per atom, per unit area normal to the particle's motion, and is given by $S_a = S/n = S_m A/N$, where n is the number of atoms per unit volume, N is the Avogadro number and A is the atomic weight.

The stopping equivalent for a given thickness of a substance is that thickness of a standard substance capable of producing the same energy loss. Frequently this is an air equivalent, i.e., using air at 15 °C and 1 atmosphere as the standard substance.

See ABSORBER and HALF-THICKNESS.

STRAGGLING

The random fluctuation or variation of a property associated with ions of a particular type as they pass through matter.

Range straggling is the variation in the range of particles that all start with the same initial energy. Assume a number of alpha particles all starting with the same energy. They do not lose exactly the same amount of energy in their encounters with molecules in their path and therefore do not all lose their ionizing power at exactly the same difference from the source. This slight variation is called straggling. It may be partly due to the attachment of one electron to some of the alpha particles with the formation of $He+$, which still has some ionizing power and will therefore cause a slight extension of the range before taking up a second electron and becoming a neutral helium atom.

Angle straggling is the variation in the direction of motion of particles after passing through a certain thickness of matter, the paths of the particles being parallel initially.

STRATOSPHERIC FALLOUT

The stratosphere is that part of the earth's atmosphere above the troposphere, from which it is separated by the tropopause. In the stratosphere temperature changes little with altitude, and there are none of the weather phenomena seen in the troposphere.

In the detonation of nuclear devices in the megaton energy range, much of the fine particle (under 1 micron) radioactive material is carried by the atomic cloud up into the stratosphere. Here, owing to the fineness of the particles and the absence of any weather phenomena, the residence time is from 1 to 5 years with a probable residence half-time of 3 years. Because of this time factor, stratospheric fallout is often spoken of as delayed fallout. Thus the radioactive particles are in effect stored in the stratosphere where much of the short radioactive half-life material decays (decay, radioactive). During the long residence time these atomic bomb residues diffuse slowly but widely, so that when they do return to earth it may be at a point remote from the point of burst; for this reason the fallout is often called "world-wide fallout."

There is still uncertainty as to the method of re-entry into the troposphere but there are 2 possibilities: (1) simple uniform re-entry due to gravitational settling; and (2) slow poleward movement of air from the equatorial region carry-

ing some of the material and bringing it down through a break in the tropopause or with a jet stream.

HIGH-ALTITUDE SAMPLING PROGRAMS are conducted by the Department of Defense and USAEC, in order to study theoretical problems and as a practical monitoring measure.

STRAY RADIATION

Radiation not serving any useful purpose. It includes LEAKAGE RADIATION and secondary radiation from irradiated objects.

STRIPPABLE PAINT

Frequently used areas such as bench tops, hood interiors and walls behind benches are usually painted with special strippable coatings to facilitate decontamination in the case of a spill.

See LABORATORY DESIGN.

STRONTIUM

Symbol Sr; atomic number 38; atomic weight 87.63. Silver-white metal belonging to the calcium group; soft as lead, malleable, ductile, and oxidizes rapidly on exposure to air. Discovered by a Scotsman, Crawford, in 1790 and independently by Hope and by Klaproth in 1793; isolated by Sir Humphry Davy in 1808. Named for Strontian, Scotland. Found widely distributed but in small concentration chiefly as the sulfate in celestite and as the carbonate in strontianite. Natural abundance furnished by 4 stable isotopes. Used in tracer bullets, in fireworks, and in red signal flares. Strontium salts are also used in beet sugar refining. Occurs in traces in biological material, but is not essential. Strontium and calcium have similar biological behavior and metabolism. Nontoxic.

Twenty-one radioactive isotopes have been identified of which 11 may be produced as fission products associated with the operation of a nuclear reactor or with the detonation of a nuclear device. A strontium radionuclide appears as a possible biological hazard in radioactive fallout at each of the 5 time periods as follows: 1 hour to 1 day after detonation, Sr^{92} and Sr^{91}; 1 day to 1 week, Sr^{91} and Sr^{89}; 1 week to 1 month, Sr^{89}; 1 month to 1 year, Sr^{89} and Sr^{90}; and 1 year to 70 years, Sr^{90}. Sr^{89} is among those radionuclides presenting the major hazard in the third and fourth periods, Sr^{90} being considered the greatest hazard in the 1 to 70 year (fifth) period. Ce^{144}, Cs^{137} and Ru^{106} follow Sr^{90} as hazards in the same time period. Both Sr^{89} and Sr^{90} are used in biological, medical and industrial activity.

Strontium-85 $(_{38}Sr^{85})$. Radioactive half-life 65 days; with bone as the critical organ, biological half-life 1.8×10^4 days (49.3 years), effective half-life 64.8 days. One of the accelerator-produced

radioisotopes recently coming into use because of
its shorter half-life. A pure gamma emitter with
energy of 0.513 Mev it can be readily assayed in
the presence of a pure beta emitter such as cal-
cium-45. It is thus well suited for human in vivo
studies of bone metabolism, for example in measurement of the rate of bone healing shortly after
the production of a lesion.

Strontium-89 ($_{38}$Sr^{89}). Radioactive half-life
50.5 days; with bone as the critical organ, biological half-life 1.8×10^4 days, effective half-life
50.4 days. A pure beta emitter (β^-). Sr^{89} is one of
the radionuclides presenting the major biological
hazard from fallout in the period 1 week to 1
month, and in the period 1 month to 1 year. Because of its shorter half-life it is mainly significant
in tropospheric fallout, although it is 1 of the 6
radionuclides routinely monitored in the U.S.
Atomic Energy stratospheric air sampling program. Available commercially.

Strontium-90 ($_{38}$Sr^{90}). Radioactive half-life
10^4 days; with bone as the critical organ, biological
half-life 1.8×10^4 days, effective half-life 6.4×10^3
days. A pure beta (β^-) emitter with a maximum
energy of 0.544 Mev and a range in water of 0.18
centimeter. Yttrium-90 (Y^{90}), the daughter of
Sr^{90}, has a half-life of 64.03 hours, and is thus constantly being created and decaying in a Sr^{90}
source. Most sources have reached equilibrium
with the number of Y^{90} nuclei decaying per second
equal to the number being created. The number of
disintegrations in such a source is equal to twice
the number of Sr^{90} disintegrations, and the maximum energy for Y^{90} beta particles is 2.25 Mev,
and its range in water is 1.09 centimeters.

Sr^{90} is now available in kilocurie quantities as a
separated fission product. The most important industrial use of radioisotopes is probably the use of
Sr^{90} to activate beta gages, which are used to
measure and control the thickness of coatings and
of materials (paper, textiles, linoleum); to control
the density of material (tobacco in a cigarette).
Together with its yttrium daughter it makes an
excellent power source. Has been used in micro-
watt batteries, and in 5-watt power sources, used,
for example, to power automatic weather stations.
Also used as a luminescence source by beta activation of a phosphor.

Sr^{90}–Y^{90} is used extensively in biological and
medical research. Its metabolism has been ex-
haustively studied because of its biological significance in fallout. Used in animal experimental
work to study bone accretion and resorption, bone
fractures and tumors. Used in medical practice as
a small teletherapy device for beta radiation in the
treatment of skin disease, benign and malignant
lesions of the eye and for diseases of the nose and
upper air passages.

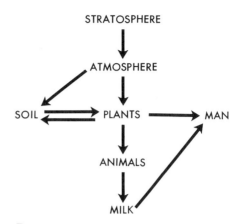

FIGURE S–21.   FOOD CHAIN CONTAMINATION.

Considered the biologically most important of
all fission products in stratospheric fallout. This is
because of the amount of Sr^{90} in fallout and its
long half-life, but particularly because it is
metabolized by the body and deposited in bone
tissue in the same way calcium is.

The USAEC, the U.S. Public Health Service
and the Department of Agriculture working
together have maintained an extensive worldwide
sampling program to determine the Sr^{90} (and
other radionuclides) content of water, milk, food
and human bones. There is in addition the stratospheric balloon monitoring program and the atmospheric air sampling program in which the
U.S. Weather Bureau participates.

Since Sr^{90} is a weak beta emitter, it is important
as an internal emitter and therefore the food chain
is important. Figure S–21 illustrates the main
pathways in the food chain.

The strontium/calcium relationship is important
because the movement of strontium from soil to
man is interrelated and to some extent governed
by the simultaneous movement of calcium (*see*
STRONTIUM—CALCIUM RATIO). The contribution
of dietary constituents in the United States of
calcium and strontium to man is estimated as follows: calcium—4% from cereals, 16% from other
plant products, 75% from dairy products, and 5%
from meat, fish, eggs, etc.; and strontium-90—
10% from cereals, 40% from other plant products,
45% from dairy products, and 3% from meat,
fish, eggs, etc.

There are a number of body processes that discriminate against strontium in favor of calcium
taken into the animal or human body (*see* DIS-
CRIMINATION FACTOR). There is a much greater
amount of calcium absorbed from the alimentary
canal compared with the amount of strontium
absorbed when equal amounts are ingested at the
same time. Strontium is discriminated against in
urinary excretion as a result of very efficient kidney tubular reabsorption of calcium and somewhat

less reabsorption of strontium. There is a marked difference in the calcium and strontium secretion from blood into milk. On a diet which contains 100 strontium-90 per 100 calcium fed to a lactating cow or goat, the milk will contain 11 strontium-90 per 100 calcium.

Although strontium and calcium are chemically similar there is a difference in their use by the body. The actual extent of the over-all calcium-strontium discrimination from the diet of man to his skeleton has not been firmly established, but values ranging from 2 to 8 have been suggested with a value of 4 being an acceptable compromise. The reduction in strontium-calcium ratio from vegetation to the human body is also quite uncertain but is considered to be about a factor of 10 with a slight chance that it could be as low as 5 or as high as 20. A factor of 15 has been suggested for dairy products.

An accident in which persons were exposed to contamination by inhalation of $Sr^{90}-Y^{90}$ was carefully studied from the standpoint of urinary elimination. On the first day the radioactivity was 20,300 disintegrations per minute, which dropped to 130 disintegrations per minute on the 27th day and leveled off after a few weeks to 16. This rapid and copious elimination indicated that only a very small portion of the inhaled material was permanently deposited in the bone.

The final criterion of most importance is the actual amount of strontium-90 in the bone (*see* BONE SAMPLING). Human bone ash studies indicate that the average skeletal concentration for most of the world's population at the end of 1959 was 0.30 micromicrocurie (μμc) (a millionth of a millionth of a curie) of Sr^{90} per gram of calcium. In 1959 the maximum strontium-90 concentration was found in one-year-olds; 2.1 μμc per gram of calcium for Western culture areas. This will drop rapidly to 0.9 μμc per gram of calcium by 1970.

The maximum permissible burden of Sr^{90} in the total body for occupational exposure is 2 microcuries, which corresponds to 2,000 μμc per gram of calcium in the skeleton and to a dose rate in bone of 5.6 rad per year. The maximum permissible body burden for an individual of the population is then $(1/30 \times 2)$ 0.067 microcurie, which is equivalent to 67 μμc per gram of calcium in the bone and which delivers a lifetime (75 years) dose of 15 rem to the bone. The maximum for a large population would be perhaps one-fifth of 15 rem, which would make the lifetime dose to the bone 3 rem as an average for the population. This takes into consideration the genetic burden.

The maximum permissible concentration for a 168-hour week (continuous exposure) for soluble material with bone as the critical organ is 10^{-6} microcuries per cubic centimeter (μc/cc) in water and 10^{-10} μc/cc in air.

STRONTIUM-90 APPLICATORS, USE IN THERAPY

Strontium-90 is an isotope of long half-life (about 28 years) with a weak beta emission. It has a daughter isotope, yttrium-90 with a short half-life (65 hours) and a strong beta emission. Sources of Sr^{90}, by continuously providing a supply of Y^{90}, make available the desirable beta radiation without a rapid change in dose rate. Such sources prepared in suitable applicators yield a form of radiation useful for the treatment of certain surface lesions. They are most commonly applied to the eye for the treatment of diseases (e.g., benign tumors) of the cornea. (See Figure S–22.)

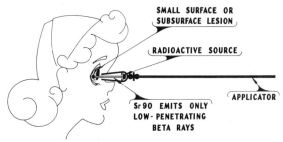

FIGURE S–22. APPLICATOR FOR USE OF STRONTIUM-90 IN TREATING SMALL SUPERFICIAL LESIONS. BY THIS TECHNIQUE BENIGN TUMORS CAN BE REMOVED WITHOUT SURGERY. (USAEC-1D-200.)

STRONTIUM UNIT

Defined as 1 micromicrocurie of strontium-90 per gram of calcium. Used in connection with deposition of strontium-90 in bones as the result of fallout. For example, the average strontium-90 body burden of young children was observed to be about 2 strontium units early in 1958. Term is used infrequently at present.

STRONTIUM-CALCIUM RATIO

The ratio of strontium retained in the body compared with the amount of calcium retained. Strontium and calcium are chemically similar and are metabolized by the body in the same way, both being taken up by bone. However, the animal and human bodies show a definite preference for calcium, i.e., there is a discrimination factor (or a series of factors) operating against the absorption of strontium, and in favor of calcium when both are available. For example, when the diet of the mother rat contains 100 strontium and 100 calcium units, there is a Sr/Ca ratio developed in her body of 28 strontium-100 calcium, and a further reduction in the ratio in the fetus to about 17 strontium-100 calcium. A survey of human still-births confirms the figure that the fetus will have about one-half the Sr/Ca ratio of the mother.

See STRONTIUM UNIT.

SUBMARINES, ATOMIC POWERED. *See* POWER-REACTORS.

SUBSURFACE BURST. *See* UNDERGROUND BURST and UNDERWATER BURST.

SULFHYDRYL COMPOUND

A compound containing the univalent radical, SH, found to offer CHEMICAL PROTECTION AGAINST RADIATION INJURY, when given shortly before irradiation. An example is cysteine which, when injected or ingested in large amounts before irradiation, protects mice and rats against x-rays or gamma rays.

SULFUR

Symbol S; atomic number 16; atomic weight 32.066. A pale yellow, odorless, brittle solid, insoluble in water. Discovery prehistoric, used by the ancients. Named from Latin, *sulfur*, brimstone. Widely distributed in nature in free form; in sulfides, and in sulfates. It occurs in two crystalline forms, alpha-rhombic sulfur and beta-monoclinic sulfur, and an allotropic form known as plastic sulfur. Natural abundance furnished by 4 stable isotopes.

Several million tons of sulfur are used each year in industrial activity. Three-fourths of the sulfur mined is burned and converted to sulfuric acid; the remainder is used in fertilizer, insecticides, pulp and paper, explosives, paint and varnish, dyes, rubber, and in food products. Sulfur itself is inert and nontoxic. Some of its compounds are slightly toxic. Both animals and plants require sulfur for growth and development. Daily intake for man is approximately 1.3 grams. The biochemical standard man contains 0.25% or 175 grams per 70 kilograms of body weight. A recommended nutrient solution for plants contains about 64 parts per million.

Only three radioactive isotopes have been identified. S^{35} and S^{37} may be produced in soil or sea water as induced radioactivity from neutron bombardment associated with the detonation of a nuclear device. Not significant in residual contamination.

Sulfur-35 $(_{16}S^{35})$. Radioactive half-life 87.1 days; with skin as the critical organ, biological half-life 1,530 days, effective half-life 82.4 days, pure beta (β^-) emitter. Maximum energy 0.1673 Mev, 0.032 centimeter range in water. Usually produced by bombarding stable chlorine-35 with neutrons in a nuclear reactor. The reaction is Cl^{35} (n,p)S^{35}. S^{35} decays back to stable Cl^{35}. Third most extensively used (P^{32} and C^{14} being first and second) radioisotope in agricultural research. Some of the areas of use: metabolism of sulfur; kidney function and excretory mechanisms; determination of extracellular space; milk formation; egg formation; correlation with production characteristics; dietary requirements of sulfur; and cause or treatment of disease.

The maximum permissible concentration for 168-hour week (continuous exposure) for soluble material with testes as the critical organ is 6×10^{-4} microcuries per cubic centimeter ($\mu c/cc$) in water and 9×10^{-8} $\mu c/cc$ in air.

SUNSHINE PROJECT

All the studies and programs of the USAEC directed toward the study of world-wide fallout were at one time considered as the "Sunshine Project." Initiated in 1953 to study fallout from testing of atomic weapons, it became limited later to the study of the relationships between the production of strontium-90 in testing of nuclear devices and its uptake and deposition in human bone, and included the occurrence of radiostrontium in and movement through all phases of the environment. The term is no longer used, although the work is still being done.

See MONITORING PROGRAM FOR RADIOACTIVE FALLOUT.

SUNSHINE UNIT

An obsolete term, replaced by STRONTIUM UNIT.

SUPERCRITICAL STATE

Term used to describe the state of a given fission system when the quantity of fissionable material is greater than the CRITICAL MASS under the existing conditions. A highly supercritical system is essential for the production of energy at a rate rapid enough so that a nuclear explosion will occur.

SURFACE BURST

The detonation of a nuclear device at the surface of land or water or at a height above the surface less than the radius of the fireball at maximum luminosity in the second pulse.

If over land, because of the intense heat (thermal radiation), a large amount of rock, soil and other material will be vaporized and carried up with the fireball. It is estimated that if only 5% of a 1-megaton bomb's energy is spent in this manner, about 20,000 tons of vaporized soil elements will be added to the fireball. This is graphically illustrated in Figure S–23.

FIGURE S–23.   FORMATION OF DIRT CLOUD IN SURFACE BURST.

A surface burst forms an atomic cloud much more heavily loaded with radioactive debris than an air burst. For example, in the Hiroshima and Nagasaki bombings with the detonation at 1,850 feet above the surface there was very little radioactive fallout, whereas in the detonation on March 1, 1954 of the thermonuclear weapon near the coral surface of Bikini Atoll fallout was heavy over an area of more than 7,000 square miles.

If a nuclear device is detonated above but near the surface of the water, and if only 5% of the energy of a 1-megaton bomb is expended in the process, about 100,000 tons of water will be converted into vapor and carried up into the radioactive cloud.

Contact surface burst.   An explosion in which the weapon is detonated actually on the surface, or within $5W^{0.3}$ feet above or below the surface, where W is the explosion yield in kilotons.

Surface zero.   See GROUND ZERO.

True surface burst.   Term used interchangeably with contact surface burst.

SURFACE CONTAMINATION

The deposition and attachment of radioactive materials to a surface. An amount of material which would otherwise be inconsequential becomes important if it is radioactive. Thus control of surface contamination is important and routine monitoring, or at least an occasional survey, should be done on all surfaces likely to become contaminated. This can be done either by the use of a probe detector, by a wipe test or by a smear survey.

Usual sources of contamination are: any dust-producing operation, such as handling powders, or grinding a solid; evaporation or aeration of a liquid which may produce a mist; chemical reactions or heating radioactive material which may produce fumes; spills; and transfer by shoes, clothing or hands from any of the listed sources.

The condition of the surface is important with such factors as the following being significant: porosity, roughness, breaks or cracks, wetability and chemical affinity. The selection of surfacing materials is important; the final surface should be a material with a low susceptibility to contamination.

SURFACE DECONTAMINATION

Removal of radioactive material from a surface. Control of surface contamination is important for it is a source of skin contamination, clothing contamination, and of the production of dusts and mists which may be inhaled or ingested.

The first step in surface decontamination if dust is present is using an industrial-type vacuum cleaner with suitable exhaust filter, followed by dusting with a wet cloth or mop. For loose contamination a strippable lacquer can be applied, allowed to dry and then removed together with the contamination. For large areas, hosing with large quantities of water may be the only possible approach. For small spills, local sponging and hand scrubbing (using rubber gloves) with detergents and complexing agents may be satisfactory. Hot-liquid-jet cleaning using a steam injector, detergents and floor brushes followed by hosing with large quantities of water (boots and face shield) may be necessary for an extensive contamination of a floor surface. For high-level penetrating contamination, paint stripping, and scraping coupled with scrubbing and hosing may be necessary.

SURVEY

Examining and determining a condition, a situation, a radiation value, or the presence of radioactive contamination. An evaluation of the actual or potential radiation hazard is a survey for radiation protection. Before the location is selected for a nuclear reactor, a careful area or site survey is conducted to determine levels of radiation present, type of drainage, etc. Before an x-ray or cobalt-60 teletherapy unit is used it should be carefully surveyed to determine the adequacy of shielding, beam-defining devices, and tube enclosure, and a written report submitted (see National Bureau of Standards Handbooks 50, 51, 73 and 76). A survey should be distinguished from the more routine, continuous or periodic monitoring.

See special types of surveys: CONTAMINATION SURVEY, ENVIRONMENTAL SURVEY, RADIATION SURVEY, RADIOLOGICAL SURVEY and SMEAR SURVEY.

SURVEY INSTRUMENTS. *See* SURVEY METER.

SURVEY METER

Any complete and portable radiation detection instrument especially adapted for surveying or inspecting an area to establish the existence and amount of radiation present, usually from the standpoint of radiological protection or to evaluate radiation hazards. Survey instruments are customarily powered by self-contained batteries and are designed to respond quickly and to indicate directly the exposure conditions at the point of interest. Figure S–24 shows a variety of standard types. In general, such instrumentation is either sensitive to a specific type of radiation or it incorporates discrimination means for separate or combined evaluation of various radiation components. Discrimination is achieved in some through use of adjustable screens or selective filters, in others by the use of alternative radiation detector tubes and phosphors, or sometimes by adjustment of electric and electronic parameters in the circuitry. Since survey meters measure the dosage rate of a radiation field, the calibration of scale readings on survey meters of ionization chamber type indicates milliroentgens per hour (mr/hr). Geiger or proportional types indicate counts per minute. When the latter type reads

mr/hr there is an implied compromise, in view of their nonuniform sensitivity toward different energies and kinds of radiation. A further compromise is indicated in those instruments which give "rem/hour," in this case utilizing an assumed standard RBE (relative biological effectiveness). Note that functions similar to those of survey meters are served by monitoring devices.

Survey meters are also made for other purposes, such as reconnoitering for deposits of radioactive materials and minerals containing elements which act as natural radioactive tracers, or in exploring subterranean strata along a bore hole by detecting radiation backscatter or neutron-induced activity effects.

See CUTIE PIE, JUNO, ZEUTO and ALPHA SURVEY METER.

SURVIVAL CURVE

Curve obtained by plotting the number or percentage of organisms surviving at a given time against the dose of radiation; or the number surviving at different intervals after a particular dose of radiation.

In Figure S–25 mortality of mice at 30 days is plotted against a single exposure dose of x-ray. It will be noted that no mouse died following a dose less than 300 roentgens (r); a few animals died within the 30-day period following 400 r; then an increasing number died with increased dosage, until at about 700 r all died within a month's time. This is a sigmoid, threshold curve, but death at 30 days is an all-or-none effect. If we plot survival time as the number of days the mice live, the curve becomes more nearly a straight line, for even doses of the order of 100 r decrease the life span.

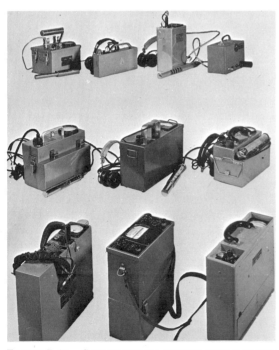

FIGURE S–24. SURVEY METERS, ILLUSTRATING VARIOUS TYPES UTILIZING GEIGER, SCINTILLATION OR ION CHAMBER DETECTORS; SUITABLE FOR PURPOSES OF RADIATION PROTECTION OR PROSPECTING FOR RADIOACTIVE ORES. (COURTESY OAK RIDGE, TENNESSEE.)

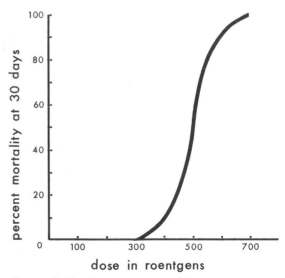

FIGURE S–25. SURVIVAL CURVE. MORTALITY OF MICE AT 30 DAYS PLOTTED AGAINST A SINGLE DOSE OF X-RAY.

Survival is expressed in terms of radiation as a lethal dose, median lethal dose (MLD) (LD_{50}) or, with time considered, as LD/50/30 with the 30 representing days within which half of the exposed animals will die.

Clinical signs and symptoms following human exposure to ionizing radiation yield enough information to group individuals into three classes: survival being improbable, survival being possible, and probable survival, although observed responses are not sufficiently exact for the construction of a survival curve.

See DOSE-EFFECT RELATIONSHIP.

SYMBOL

A letter or character used instead of or to represent a word or words. In physics and chemistry, for example, all elements are identified by symbols: Ac for actinium, O for oxygen, S for sulfur, Th for thorium, etc. (*See* ATOMIC WEIGHTS table.) In atomic energy: α for alpha, β for beta, γ for gamma, n for neutron. T 1/2 for half-time.

An acronym is a shortened form using the first letter of each word; for example, amu for atomic mass unit, Bev for billion electron volts, RBE for relative biological effectiveness.

See RADIATION WARNING SYMBOL.

SYNCHRO-CYCLOTRON

Particles accelerated in the smaller cyclotrons stay in phase because, as they spiral outward, their path lengths increase in proportion to their velocities, and the gap-to-gap time remains a constant. At relativistic velocities, however, the path length increases faster than the velocity does and the particles tend to get out of phase. This dif-

ficulty is overcome in the synchro-cyclotron by pulsing the output beam and constantly modulating the RF frequency so that the polarity alternations keep in step with the accelerated particles. The magnet of the 184-inch diameter synchro-cyclotron at the University of California at Berkeley weighs about 4,000 tons. This machine will accelerate deuterons to 200 Mev or alpha particles to 400 Mev. The deuteron beam has sufficient energy to penetrate several centimeters of tissue, and has been used experimentally to produce radiation hypophysectomies. Figure S–26 presents schematically the Berkeley synchro-cyclotron, while Figure S–27 is a photograph.

SYNCHROTRON

A particle accelerator in which the accelerated particles (usually protons or electrons) maintain

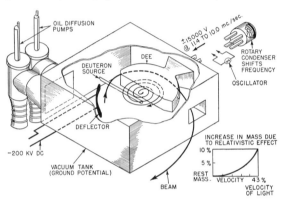

FIGURE S–26. SCHEMATIC REPRESENTATION OF PRINCIPAL FEATURES OF 184-INCH SYNCHRO-CYCLOTRON. THE ACCELERATED PARTICLES FOLLOW THE PATH INDICATED BY THE SPIRAL. (COURTESY LAWRENCE RADIATION LABORATORY, UNIVERSITY OF CALIFORNIA.)

FIGURE S–27. VIEW OF 184-INCH SYNCHRO-CYCLOTRON BEFORE INSTALLATION OF SHIELDING. DIFFUSION PUMPS, VACUUM TANK AND THE MAGNET YOKE ARE AMONG THE PROMINENT FEATURES SHOWN. (COURTESY RADIATION LABORATORY, UNIVERSITY OF CALIFORNIA.)

an orbit of approximately constant radius, as different from a cyclotron, in which the accelerated particles spiral outward from an injection point near the center. The 6-Bev Bevatron at the University of California at Berkeley, and the 3-Bev Cosmotron and the 30-Bev Alternating Gradient Synchrotron (AGS) at the Brookhaven National Laboratory are examples of proton accelerators of this type in the United States.

Synchrotrons consist of a vacuum chamber of relatively small cross section (measured in inches) and long length (measured in tens or hundreds of feet) arranged in a roughly circular configuration, and with the vacuum chamber in the opening of a ring of "C"-shaped laminated magnets, which serve to constrain the particles within the desired orbit. The strong focusing method, using alternately magnets having faces shaped to promote vertical convergence and those having faces shaped to promote horizontal convergence, has made it possible to maintain the orbits within narrow limits, with consequent great savings in the number of tons of steel needed for the magnets of the most powerful machines. Acceleration is achieved by having the particles fall through electrical gradients across one or more accelerator gaps, which are straight sections between magnets. The beam of particles is pulsed so that, as their energy increases, the magnetic field can be increased as is necessary to keep the particles in the desired orbit, and so that their time of arrival at the accelerating gap can be kept in phase with the polarity changes. The circumference of the AGS is approximately 1/2 mile. The protons are first injected into a linear accelerator from a Cockroft-Walton machine, and are pre-accelerated to some 50 Mev. They are then injected tangentially into the main vacuum chamber for acceleration up to 33 Bev, with a 3.2 second repetition period. Intensities as high as 3×10^{11} protons/pulse have been recorded. (See Figure S–28.)

SYNDROME, RADIATION

See ACUTE RADIATION SYNDROME and RADIATION ILLNESS.

FIGURE S–28.   INSIDE THE TUNNEL OF THE ALTERNATING GRADIENT SYNCHROTRON (AGS) AT THE CONJUNCTION OF THE LINEAR ACCELERATOR, OR LINAC, AND THE MAIN MAGNET ENCLOSURE. THE 50-MEV PROTON BEAM LEAVES THE LINAC, WHICH IS LOCATED BEHIND THE SHIELDING WALL (LEFT REAR), AND TRAVELS ALONG THE 4-INCH PIPE TO THE LOWER RIGHT, PASSING THROUGH A SERIES OF FOCUSING LENSES AND STEERING MAGNETS INTO THE ORBIT OF THE SYNCHROTRON MAGNET RING. JUST ABOVE THE HEAD OF THE MAN IN THE FOREGROUND IS A SET OF STEERING MAGNETS FOR HORIZONTAL AND VERTICAL DEFLECTIONS. IN THE FOREGROUND IS A VIEWING BOX WITH LUCITE COVERS OVER THE DRIVE MECHANISMS. INSIDE IT ARE LOCATED ADJUSTABLE SLITS, DEFINED BY 1/4-INCH COPPER PLATES, WHICH ARE USED TO ALIGN THE PROTON BEAM AND TO EXAMINE ITS SPATIAL AND ANGULAR DISTRIBUTION IN ORDER THAT THE CORRECT FOCUSING ADJUSTMENTS CAN BE DETERMINED. INSIDE THE VIEWING BOX THERE IS ALSO A QUARTZ PLATE WHICH CAN BE ROTATED INTO THE BEAM FOR VISUAL OBSERVATION OF THE BEAM POSITION AND DIMENSIONS; THE PROTONS IMPINGING UPON THE QUARTZ PRODUCE LIGHT, WHICH IS OBSERVED BY MEANS OF THE TV CAMERA IN FRONT OF THE MAN IN THE FOREGROUND. THE EXPERIMENTAL AREA, IN WHICH THE BEAM IS EXTRACTED FROM THE MAIN ORBIT, IS LOCATED DIAMETRICALLY OPPOSITE THE INJECTION AREA. THE TUNNEL IS UNDERGROUND, WITH EARTH SERVING AS SHIELDING MATERIAL FOR MOST OF THE LENGTH. (COURTESY BROOKHAVEN NATIONAL LABORATORY.)

T

TAGGED ATOM

The atomic position in a molecule which is distinguished by an isotopic tracer, either radioactive or stable.

See LABELED COMPOUND, LABELED MOLECULE, RADIOACTIVE TRACER and TRACER STUDIES.

TANK STORAGE, RADIOACTIVE WASTE

All intermediate-level or high-level radioactive LIQUID WASTES should be held in some type of container for monitoring and any necessary mixing, pH adjustment, cooling or decay. The storage container may vary from a 5-gallon laboratory glass bottle to a carbon steel, concrete-encased 1,300,000-gallon storage tank buried in the ground.

Bottle disposal is used in RADIOISOTOPE WASTE DISPOSAL of small quantities of low-level activity used in research and medical diagnosis and treatment.

Retention tanks are a necessary part of any active radioisotope laboratory where larger quantities of radioisotopes are used. These tanks are for temporary cooling and decay storage to allow for the reduction of radioactivity to a level at which dilution and slow, carefully monitored disposal into the regular sewer line may be safely carried out. There should be 2 tanks—one for holding the waste and the other for receiving the daily material. The size and number of these tanks are determined by the type and extent of the laboratory operations.

One present method of processing high-level RADIOACTIVE WASTES is through storage in large tanks grouped together in a tank "farm" (Fig. T–1) of 6 to 18 tanks. The primary tank, about 75 feet in diameter and 20 to 40 feet high, is built of carbon steel and rests in a steel saucer designed to retain leakage. As shown in the accompanying diagram (Fig. T–2), the tank and saucer are enclosed in a reinforced-concrete structure with annular space to permit inspection of the primary tank. Cooling coils are provided to prevent boiling and cut down on corrosion. A ventilation system draws in fresh air and filters the effluent prior to release to the atmosphere. Openings through the the concrete to the primary tank permit monitoring of radioactivity, liquid level, temperature and pressure. Monitoring wells are placed at various levels around the tank farm to detect any leaks and seepage.

At the Hanford Works over 52,000,000 gallons of high-level wastes were being stored in 1960 in tanks with a construction cost per gallon varying from $0.266 to $0.831. Considering the original construction cost, the amortization, maintenance and operating costs, the 1-year storage cost could conceivably range from $0.41 to $3.00 per gallon,

FIGURE T–1. VIEW OF TANK FARM DURING CONSTRUCTION. THE STEEL LINER COVERS THE BOTTOM AND SIDES OF THE REINFORCED CONCRETE TANK.

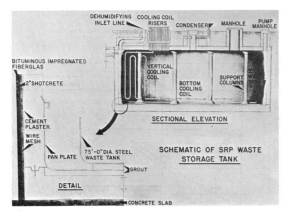

FIGURE T–2. GENERAL DETAILS OF A LIQUID WASTE STORAGE TANK.

with a proportionate increase for 20- and 30-year storage. It is obvious that the research and development program must find a less expensive and more permanent method.

TANTALUM

Symbol Ta; atomic number 73; atomic weight 180.95. A metal found in tantalite and samarskite. Discovered by Ekeberg in 1802. Named from Greek mythology, *Tantalus*. Natural abundance is furnished by the stable isotope Ta[181], 99.98%, and by the radioactive isotope Ta[180], 0.02%.

Many industrial uses: in radar and other electronic tubes, neon tubes, lamp filaments, electrolytic cathodes, dental instruments, electrical contacts; the oxide used in optical glass; the carbide used in cutting tools; and in the chemical industry. Used for wire, pins, screws and plates for the surgical fixation of bone fragments.

No toxic properties demonstrated. Not important from a biological or agricultural standpoint.

Fifteen radioactive isotopes identified. Ta[182] (half-life 115 days, β- and γ emitter) available commercially. Ta[182] used for interstitial implants, and experimentally as a possible gamma-ray source for teletherapy.

TARGET THEORY

Also hit theory. Theory explaining some biologic effects of radiation on basis of ionization occurring in a very small sensitive region within the cell.

The cell can be inactivated or changed in some way by single events. The basic concept is that the biological end-effect which is measured stands in a precise relation to the initial physical events which occur on irradiation, or that the exact site where an anatomical lesion, such as a chromosome break, is seen must also be the place where the primary ionizations responsible for these effects occurred. An in-vivo reaction may be assumed to be of the single-hit target type if it is independent of dose rate, if the inactivation dose curve is exponential, and if the relative biological effectiveness for different radiations is as expected. Although the bactericidal effects of radiation appear to be explained by the target theory, the work with mammalian species is not so clear-cut.

There are 2 general concepts of action of radiation on chemical systems. The target theory postulates direct action as ionization or excitation in the target molecule. The indirect action postulates a transfer of energy through the universal protoplasmic solvent, water, by the production of free radicals. The indirect action of radiation through the solvent is now widely accepted as contributing a large proportion of the effects seen in complex biological material.

TECHNETIUM

Symbol Tc; atomic number 43; atomic weight 99; radioactive element, not of natural occurrence. Discovered in 1937 by Italian chemists C. Perrier and E. Segrè in molybdenum which had been bombarded with deuterons in the Berkeley, California, cyclotron. Named from Greek, *technetos*, artificial, because it was the first element, previously unknown, to be artificially made. Twenty-one radioactive isotopes have been found. Thirteen, Tc[99m], and Tc[99] through Tc[111], may be formed in fission products associated with the detonation of a nuclear device; or in uranium fission in a nuclear reactor.

Tc[99] (half-life 2.1×10^5 years, β- emitter) was discovered by G. T. Seaborg and E. Segrè in the United States in 1939. Tc[99] can be formed by neutron bombardment of molybdenum, but is also formed in uranium fission, starting with a fission fragment of Mo[99] as follows:

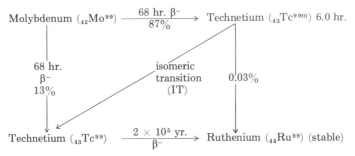

Available in quantity as a separated fission product from atomic waste.

Commercially interesting, for corrosion of iron can be significantly inhibited by the addition of 5 parts per million to circulating water in water-cooled engines.

TECHNICAL INFORMATION DIVISION, USAEC

Division of Technical Information (DTI) plans and directs a comprehensive technical information program to meet the needs to the USAEC, its contractors, other Government agencies, industry, and the worldwide scientific community. It is composed of 2 parts, a Headquarters staff, located in Washington, D.C., and the Division of Technical Information Extension (DTIE), located at Oak Ridge, Tennessee. The Washington staff administers special programs and develops technical information policies and procedures. DTIE maintains a master collection of technical reports and other literature, prepares and disseminates bibliographic and reference tools, serves as a clearing house for the acqustion and distribution of non-AEC literature, and provides a centralized publishing service.

Information in the field of atomic energy may be found in scientific articles, books, monographs, technical reports, engineering drawings, patents, publications of universities and learned societies, and in translations of foreign articles. The DTIE scans this material for the purpose of selecting, abstracting, indexing and disseminating information about the science of nuclear energy.

The following are some of the forms in which scientific material is made available:

Technical reports. These reports may be progress reports on research under way, or final reports at the completion of the research project. They may be AEC contractor reports, domestic non-AEC reports or foreign reports.

Technical books, reviews, and conferences. Reviews of important research areas are covered in a series of monographs produced in conjunction with interested professional societies. Proceedings of technical meetings and conferences are also published. A catalog is available.

Translations. Selected information within the atomic energy field is translated and sent to the Office of Technical Services, where it is available for sale.

Engineering materials. Such materials as drawings, specifications, bills of materials, design criteria, photographs and parts lists are also made available.

Nuclear science abstracts. Abstracts of the unclassified literature of nuclear science and engineering issued since 1947 semimonthly by the USAEC. NSA provides coverage of (1) technical reports of the USAEC and its contractors; (2) technical reports of government agencies, universities, and industrial and independent research organizations in the United States and abroad; and (3) the book, patent and journal literature, and translations thereof, on a worldwide basis.

Bibliographies and reference lists. These are prepared for numerous subject areas of interest to the USAEC. They are available in the USAEC depository libraries and at the Office of Technical Services.

Special booklets are published by the USAEC which list the availability of all types of information and information services. All correspondence regarding informational materials should be directed to:

U.S. Atomic Energy Commission
Division of Technical Information Extension
P.O. Box 62
Oak Ridge, Tennessee

TEETH SURVEY

During the years 1959, 1960 and 1961 an extensive program of collecting deciduous teeth and analyzing them for their strontium-90 content was conducted in the greater St. Louis, Missouri, area. It was demonstrated that with cooperative community effort, collection of a large number (14,500 in 1959, 27,000 in 1960, and 19,500 in the first 6 months of 1961) of deciduous teeth is possible. Analysis showed that there was a close correlation in the concentration of strontium-90 in bones and in teeth, and deviations from a one-to-one ratio appeared to be random. It was also shown that analysis of deciduous teeth provided valuable information about strontium-90 deposition in bone as the result of fallout from the testing of nuclear devices. The strontium-90, in micromicrocuries per gram of calcium, in the teeth of children born in 1951 ranged from 0.155 to 0.193; in 1952, 0.188 to 0.204; in 1953, 0.260 to 0.400; and in 1954 from 0.500 to 0.725 $\mu\mu c$/g Ca.

TELETHERAPY

Radiation treatment administered at a distance from the body. Usually treatment of disease by means of external gamma-ray beams from radioisotope sources. The availability of cobalt-60 and cesium-137 in high specific activity has made possible the development of teletherapy machines that are highly effective for clinical use. The machine is simply a container for the source, shielding it in most directions and providing an aperture from which a controlled beam can be directed toward the patient. By moving the source in relation to

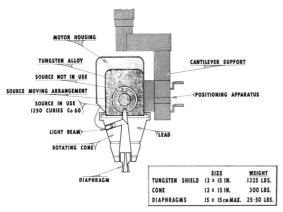

	SIZE	WEIGHT
TUNGSTEN SHIELD	13 x 15 IN.	1325 LBS.
CONE	13 x 15 IN.	300 LBS.
DIAPHRAGMS	15 x 15 cm MAX.	25-50 LBS.

FIGURE T–3. HEAD OR HOUSING FOR COBALT-60 TELE-THERAPY SOURCE. (USAEC-1D-481.)

the shielding material it is possible to turn the instrument "off," i.e., to have the sources shielded on all sides (see Figure T–3).

These teletherapy machines (see Figure T–4) are used chiefly in the treatment of cancer, usually of the deeper tissues. They produce an effect similar to that of x-ray therapy, but their high-energy gamma rays allow a more effective depth dose and less skin damage than are produced by the usual hospital x-ray therapy machines.

The advent of teletherapy has not greatly increased the percentage of patients with cancer suitable for radiotherapy, nor has it dramatically changed the cure rates, but it has improved results significantly and has reduced undesirable side effects.

See BRACHYTHERAPY.

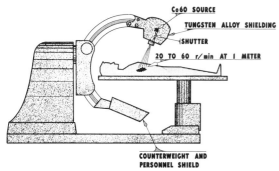

FIGURE T–4. ROTATIONAL TELETHERAPY UNIT USING COBALT-60 GAMMA RAYS FOR TREATMENT OF DEEP-SEATED TUMORS. (USAEC-1D-155a.)

TELEVISION, RADIATION

All cathode-ray tubes may give off x-rays, but with conventional metal or glass direct-viewing picture tubes, the standard home television receivers do not give off significant amounts of x-radiation. The genetically significant annual mean dose to the population of the United States from these sources is calculated to be less than 1 millirem.

See CATHODE-RAY TUBE HAZARDS.

TELLURIUM

Symbol Te; atomic number 52; atomic weight 127.61. A brittle silver-white semimetallic element of the sulfur group. Discovered by Muller von Reichenstein in 1782. Named by Klaproth in 1798 from Latin, *tellus*, earth. May occur naturally, but usually as telluride in gold, silver, copper, lead and nickel ores. Natural abundance furnished by 8 stable isotopes.

Used commercially as a hardener for lead, and in the rubber industry. Soluble salts are highly toxic. Otherwise not of importance to biology, medicine or agriculture.

Twenty-two radioactive isotopes have been identified, of which 15 may be formed as fission products in the detonation of a nuclear device. Five of these are significant in radioactive fallout, having the following amounts in megacuries per megaton of fission at the end of 1 year after detonation: Te^{125m}, 7.56×10^{-4}; Te^{127m}, 0.00775; Te^{127}, 0.00486; Te^{129m}, 4.54×10^{-4}; and Te^{129}, 4.7×10^{-4}.

Tellurium-132 ($_{52}Te^{132}$). Radioactive half-life 3.2 days (77 hours); with thyroid as the critical organ, biological half-life 9 days, and effective half-life 2.4 days. Beta (β^-) and gamma emitter. A fission product of uranium-235; yield 4 to 5%. Of particular interest in biomedical work since it is the parent of iodine-132, and constitutes a continuing fresh source of this radioiodine. A simple system has been developed by the Brookhaven National Laboratory so that iodine-132 can be extracted (milked) repeatedly during the 77-hour half-life of tellurium-132. By shipping the longer-lived parent, tellurium-132, scientists are able to have immediately available in their own laboratories the desirable short-lived (2.3-hour half-life) iodine-132, which now, in effect, has a useful half-life of 77 hours.

This so-called tellurium cow is actually a special I^{132} generator (Fig. T–5), shipped to the scientist, which is set up as shown in Figure T–6, and can be milked over and over. A study of the parent-daughter relationship shows, as seen in Figure T–7, that I^{132} rises to a maximum and reaches transient equilibrium 12.4 hours after the parent sample of Te^{132} has been milked, and is thus ready to be milked again.

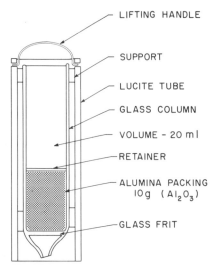

FIGURE T–5. IODINE-132 GENERATOR, SHOWING DETAIL OF CONSTRUCTION. THE CARRIER-FREE PARENT TELLURIUM-132 IS ABSORBED ON THE 10G OF ALUMINA (Al_2O_3), PACKING READY FOR MILKING BY THE ADDITION OF THE REAGENT, AQUEOUS AMMONIA SOLUTION. THE GENERATOR IS ONLY 4 INCHES HIGH. (COURTESY OF BROOKHAVEN NATIONAL LABORATORY.)

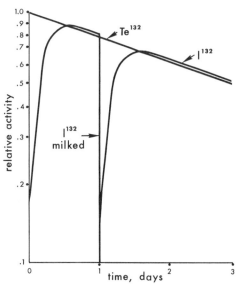

FIGURE T–7. RELATIVE ACTIVITIES OF TELLURIUM-132 AND IODINE-132, SHOWING GROWTH OF IODINE-132 FROM FRESHLY MILKED TELLURIUM-132 AND EFFECT OF MILKING 1 DAY LATER.

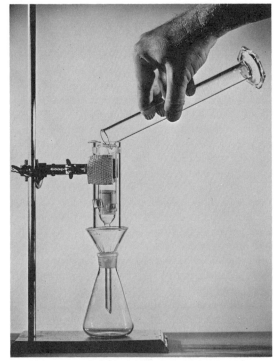

FIGURE T–6. TYPICAL SETUP FOR MILKING IODINE-132 GENERATOR. THE GENERATOR IS CLAMPED OVER THE FUNNEL AND PRODUCT-RECEIVING FLASK. THE REAGENT, 15 ml OF 0.01 M AQUEOUS AMMONIA SOLUTION, IS ADDED, AND THE IODINE-132 IS GENERATED FROM THE TELLURIUM-132 HELD IN THE ALUMINA PACKING. (COURTESY OF BROOKHAVEN NATIONAL LABORATORY.)

TEMPERATURE AND RADIATION EFFECTS

Temperature is a physical factor which is considered to have an important influence upon radiosensitivity. Changes in environmental temperature have been studied as a method of modifying the effect of radiation on living material.

In studies of the effect of postirradiation incubation temperature on ability of E. coli to form colonies, it is seen (Fig. T–8) that survival as measured by colony production goes through a maximum response (18 °C) as a function of the temperature, the over-all effect being independent of dose.

Seasonal variation associated with temperature changes appear to be directly related to radioresistance within an ecosystem or natural plant-animal community. For example, in the winter in temperate latitudes nearly all the community is in hibernation or is dormant, and radioresistance is at a maximum. With spring and warmer weather, growth and reproductive activity begin and continue throughout the summer and into the fall, and radioresistance is minimal.

Metabolic rate is related to temperature, and warm-blooded organisms (birds and mammals) are usually more sensitive to radiation than are cold-blooded organisms: LD_{50} for the dog is about 375 roentgens and for the turtle 1,500 roentgens. There is evidence that for the same organism low temperature is protective for bacteria as well as yeast;

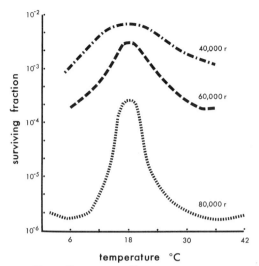

FIGURE T–8. SURVIVAL OF E. COLI TO X-RAY EXPOSURE AS A FUNCTION OF INCUBATION TEMPERATURE.

they are more resistant in the frozen state than in suspension.

There is evidence, however, in the mammalia, at least, that lowering the temperature during irradiation does not inherently increase resistance to radiation. For if one irradiates a hibernating mammal and keeps it hibernating, the cytological evidence of radiation injury does not develop, but when the animal is warmed to its normal ambient temperature, the entire sequence of histological events takes place in response to the previously given radiation. It is as if the radiation had simply been stored or held at the low temperature, awaiting warming and the increased metabolic rate. There appears to be no evidence of a temperature relation to recovery from irradiation.

TENNESSEE-AEC AGRICULTURAL RESEARCH LABORATORY

An agricultural laboratory at Oak Ridge, Tennessee, supported by the USAEC and operated by the University of Tennessee. The research program has 3 main objectives: to conduct agricultural research programs of interest to the USAEC; to provide a facility for graduate and postgraduate study for the University of Tennessee; and to provide a tie with other universities and colleges for the purpose of special studies for staff and graduate students. Many different metabolic studies are conducted, using beef and dairy cattle, sheep, swine and small laboratory animals. Radiation physiology, including growth and reproductive physiology, is studied on all types of farm animals. Radiation pathology has been extensively studied. Some studies are also conducted in plant genetics and plant growth.

The laboratory started in 1948, the first experimental animals being the 60 head of cattle exposed to radioactive fallout at the time of the Alamogordo nuclear weapons tests. Metabolic studies (1962) require an average of 8 to 12 dairy cows, 12 to 16 calves, 50 to 60 sheep, 8 to 12 beef steers and 20 to 30 swine. The radiation physiology studies utilize a steady population of 200 cows and 10 bulls on a life-time breeding program, 150 cows and 20 sows for prenatal studies, 70 bulls and 25 boars on spermatogenesis studies, and 90 swine, 250 burros and 50 cattle on long-term effects and clinical studies.

The research staff comprises a group of 20 investigators, all of whom have professional appointments with the University. The technical staff at graduate or equivalent training level numbers 17. Subtechnical-level staff numbers 11, plus 43 to handle the farm and the animals and an additional 40 to care for the maintenance and administration activities.

The buildings housing the staff, animals and plants consist of the main laboratory building, 3 buildings for metabolic studies, a surgery and associated isolation barn, 10 buildings principally for reproductive studies in cattle and swine, 8 buildings for studies on long-term radiation effects, 2 greenhouses and 2 buildings for handling and storing plants and plant materials.

Facilities are available for visiting scientists and for graduate students. During the first 14 years of its operation the laboratory has had the association of 39 staff members from 31 educational institutions, and 16 graduate students have been trained.

TERBIUM

Symbol Tb; atomic number 65; atomic weight 158.93. A member of the yttrium subgroup of rare earth metals. Discovered in 1843 by Mosander and named for the town of Ytterby, Sweden. It occurs in gadolinite and in other minerals. All the natural abundance is stable isotope Tb[159].

There are 10 radioactive isotopes of terbium, of which Tb[161] is a fission product with some fallout significance, since it is present in measurable amounts at the end of one month. No biological, medical or agricultural value has been demonstrated.

TERRESTRIAL RADIATION

Radiation from naturally occurring radioactive elements which are widely distributed over the earth's surface. There is variability in the distribution of radioactive elements in the ground, some rocks such as dunite yielding less than 1 millirad per year (mrad/yr), while uranium and thorium

TABLE T–1.   SKELETAL DOSE RATE IN MRAD/YR

ROCK	URANIUM	THORIUM	POTASSIUM	TOTAL
Igneous	17	22	27	66
Sandstone	5	12	11	28
Shale	5	20	28	53
Limestone	6	21	3	30

ores give several thousand mrad/yr. An example of high radioactivity is the monazite sand regions of India and Brazil. These extreme conditions are rare, however, and only a small part of the world's population is exposed to ground radioactivity more than a factor of 2 outside the range of the typical skeletal dose rates attributable to the uranium radioactive series, the thorium radioactive series, and potassium-40, as shown in Table T–1. (In this table a factor of 0.7 has been applied to the surface dose rate to account for body shielding, in obtaining the skeletal dose rate.)

The radium concentration in the soil in various parts of the United States has been found to vary from 0.9 to 8.0×10^{-13} gram of radium per gram of soil, with the average radium content in the soil estimated at 2×10^{-12} gram of radium per gram of soil. Radium is also found in water, which is thus made radioactive.

An extensive survey was made of NATURAL RADIATION at 154 locations in 19 states of the United States between New York and Utah. Readings ranged from a low of 8.4 microroentgens per hour ($\mu r/hr$) along the Pennsylvania Turnpike to a high of 38.6 $\mu r/hr$ at the summit of Pike's Peak (altitude 14,110 feet—COSMIC RAYS were counted with the terrestrial radiation in this study). Of the major cities surveyed, Denver had a level of 18.5 $\mu r/hr$, which was almost twice that found in eastern and midwestern cities.

A preliminary feasibility study was conducted to determine the relation between the incidence of congenital malformation death as taken from USPHS mortality statistics and geologic terrestrial environments characterized by concentrations of radioactive material in rock, soil, water and air. Data suggest that mortality incidence from malformation may be higher in those geologic provinces of the United States that contain large uranium ore deposits, uraniferous waters or helium concentrations and thus a higher than average level of radiation.

TESTES, RADIATION EFFECTS ON. *See* GONADS, RADIATION EFFECTS ON.

TESTING AREAS

The United States, the USSR, the United Kingdom and the Republic of France have all conducted test detonations of nuclear devices. The names and the approximate latitudes and longitudes of the various test sites are as follows:

United States
    Nevada test site, U.S.A. . . . . 31° N. 116° W.
    Eniwetok Proving Grounds, Pacific:
        Eniwetok . . . . 11° N. 162° E.
        Bikini . . . . 11° N. 165° E.
    Johnston Island, Pacific . . . . 17° N. 169° W.
    Christmas Island, Pacific (also U.K.) 2° N. 157° W.
United Kingdom
    Monte Bello Islands, Australia . . . . 20° S. 115° E.
    Woomera, Australia . . . . 31° S. 137° E.
    Maralinga proving ground,
      Australia . . . . 30° S. 131° E.
USSR
    Arctic test site (Novaya Zemlya) . . . 75° N. 55° E.
    Siberian test site . . . . 52° N. 78° E.
Republic of France
    Reggan, Sahara Desert . . . . 27° N. 0°.

See PACIFIC TESTING AREA.

TESTS, ATOMIC, NUCLEAR OR WEAPONS.
See NUCLEAR WEAPONS TESTING.

THALLIUM

Symbol Tl; atomic number 81; atomic weight 204.39. A bluish-gray metal, soft enough to be cut with a knife, and malleable. Discovered by English chemist Sir William Crookes in 1861, and isolated by him in 1862. Named from Greek *thallos*, budding twig. Occurs in small amounts in pyrite, zinc blende and hematite. Is prepared from flue dust of sulfuric acid works. Its natural abundance is furnished by 2 stable isotopes: Tl[203], 29.50%; and Tl[205], 70.50%.

Principal uses are as a rodenticide, insecticide and fungicide. Used in the optical glass industry because of high refracting power. Highly toxic when inhaled, ingested or even painted on the skin. Cases of suicide, murder and accidental death have been verified. The lethal oral dose for mammals is about 25 mg per kilogram of body weight. Also poisonous to plant life at about 5 parts per million in the soil.

Eleven radioactive isotopes have been identified. Thallium-204, radioactive half-life 1.1×10^3 days (3.0 years); with kidney as the critical organ, biological half-life 7 days and effective half-life 7 days; beta (β−) emitter; is available commercially for biological research, in which it has been chiefly used to study the absorption, distribution and elimination of thallium.

THERMAL BURNS

Burns of the skin (or other organic material) due to thermal radiation produced by the detonation of a nuclear device. About a third of the total energy of a nuclear explosion is emitted in the form of thermal radiation. This means that for a 1-kiloton explosion, about 3.3×10^{11} calories are released. This is enough energy to convert over a million pounds of room-temperature water into steam. The energy required to produce a first-degree burn would be 2 calories per square centimeter (cm²), for a second-degree burn 4, and for a third-degree burn 6 calories/cm². In Nagasaki first-degree burns were experienced at 2.5 miles from ground zero. Skin burns due to thermal energy are usually described as FLASH BURNS.

THERMAL NEUTRONS

Neutrons whose speed or energy has been reduced by a number of collisions with nuclei to approximately the average kinetic energy of the atoms (or molecules) of the medium in which the neutron is undergoing elastic scattering. At normal room temperature, 293° absolute, or 20 °C, the thermal neutron energy is usually taken as 0.025 electron volt (ev). This slowing down or reducing the energy of a neutron to the thermal region by elastic scattering is called thermalization or slowing down. The material used to slow down fast neutrons in a nuclear reactor is called a moderator.

The property possessed by neutrons of having their energies reduced from millions of electron volts to thermal values of a fraction of an ev, and still being capable of producing nuclear reactions, is very remarkable.

THERMAL NOISE. *See* SPURIOUS COUNT.

THERMAL PHYSICAL DAMAGE

Physical damage resulting from thermal radiation from a nuclear explosion; consisting of scorching, charring, and possible ignition of combustible organic substances such as wood, fabrics, forest fuels, household material, paper, etc. Heavy fabrics, plastics, and wood more than 1/2 inch thick char, but usually do not burn, as illustrated by tests at the Nevada test site, in which a white-painted house front became covered with thick black smoke (Fig. T–9, A), which within 2 seconds (before arrival of the blast wave) died out, leaving only a charred surface (Fig. T–9, B). Thin, light-weight or porous materials such as dried grass or leaves, newspaper, dry rotted wood, etc., may flame and continue to support combustion with the possibility of spreading and developing into a fire storm.

The ignition of materials by thermal radiation depends upon the following factors: the level of thermal radiation and the resulting temperature; the rate of delivery—damage is greater if energy is delivered rapidly; the thickness of the object—a thin piece of material ignites more easily than a thick piece; moisture content—dry sample is more easily damaged; the temperature of the object—cold material is less likely to ignite; color of the object—black absorbs heat, white reflects; and highly reflecting materials are resistant.

Table T–2 gives experimentally determined ignition energy in calories per square centimeter for various materials. It will be noted that almost double the amount of energy (cal/sq cm) is re-

| A | B |

FIGURE T–9. *A*, THERMAL EFFECT ON WOOD-FRAME HOUSE ALMOST IMMEDIATELY AFTER EXPLOSION (ABOUT 25 CAL/SQ CM). *B*, SAME HOUSE AS IN *A*, 2 SECONDS LATER.

TABLE T–2. IGNITION ENERGY FOR VARIOUS MATERIALS

MATERIAL	WEIGHT OZ/PER SQ YD	IGNITION EXPOSURE CAL/SQ CM	
		20 KILOTONS	10 MEGATONS
Fabrics			
Rayon twill lining (black)	3	1	2
Cotton bedspread (light blue)		4	8
Cotton sheeting, washed (cream)	3	15	30
Doped fabric, aluminized		18	35
Household Materials			
Newspaper, shredded	2	2	4
Dust mop (oily gray)		3	5
Paper, bristol board (dark)	10	8	15
Paper, bristol board (white)	10	12	25
Paper, bond typing, new (white)	2	15	30
Forest Fuels			
Dry rotted wood (punk)		4	9
Fine grass		5	10
Coarse grass		7	16
Spruce needles		8	17

quired to produce the same effect by the 10-megaton burst, because the energy required for ignition is delivered over a much longer period of time.

Very high temperatures are attained at the surface from an air burst; e.g., it is estimated that in the nuclear explosions over Japan, which were at some 1,850 feet, the temperature at ground zero was probably from 3,000 to 4,000 °C.; hence the total thermal exposure was great. Since atmospheric attenuation is effective in absorbing thermal energy, the amount of damage decreases rapidly with distance, but there is evidence that even at 4,000 feet from the zero point (*see* GROUND ZERO) the temperature exceeded 1,600 °C.

FIGURE T–10. PAINT ON A GAS TANK SCORCHED BY THERMAL RADIATION, EXCEPT WHERE PROTECTED BY THE VALVE SHADOW.

Thermal radiant energy travels in a straight line; thus only the exposed surface (in line of sight) of an object is charred or ignited. For example, in Hiroshima and Nagasaki telephone poles were charred only on the side facing the point of burst. The fact that any opaque object will protect a surface where its shadow falls is illustrated in the well known picture (Fig. T–10) of the gas tank, the shadow of the valve of which was the only area where the paint was not scorched (1.33 miles from ground zero in Hiroshima).

THERMAL RADIATION (BOMB)

Electromagnetic radiation emitted from the fireball produced by the detonation of a nuclear device. The temperature of the fireball is several tens of million degrees, and of the total energy produced in a nuclear explosion, 35% is transmitted as thermal radiation, essentially as ultraviolet, visible and infrared radiations. The fireball literally resembles the sun in the large amount of energy emitted as thermal radiation. For every 1 kiloton of energy of the nuclear explosion, approximately 3.3×10^{11} calories (equivalent to nearly 400,000 kilowatt hours) is released as thermal energy yield within the first few seconds.

For a surface or air burst the thermal radiation is emitted in 2 pulses from the fireball. (For a high-altitude burst there is but 1 pulse.) The first pulse, lasting about 1/10 second for a 1-megaton explosion, carries only about 1% of the thermal radiation. In contrast, the second pulse may last for 10 seconds and carry 99% of the total thermal radiation energy. This is graphically illustrated in

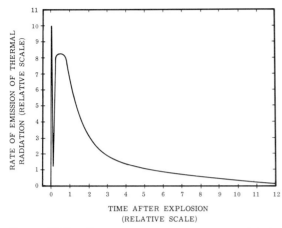

FIGURE T–11. EMISSION OF THERMAL RADIATION IN 2 PULSES IN AN AIR BURST.

Figure T–11. Radiation from the second pulse causes most of the skin burns of persons exposed up to 12 miles or more from the 1-megaton bomb, and of eye damage at even greater distances.

Thermal radiation travels in a straight line and with the speed of light (186,000 miles per second), but is attenuated by the atmosphere and by distribution in all directions. Thus, if atmospheric attenuation is disregarded, the amount of thermal radiation received per unit area varies inversely with the square of the distance from the explosion; e.g., at 2 miles the thermal energy received would be one-fourth of that received at 1 mile from the same explosion. Atmospheric attenuation by absorption and scattering does occur, and increases with fog, rain, or atmospheric contamination with dust or smoke particles.

Shielding is afforded by any solid, opaque material; even white or light-colored clothing offers some protection. But for any combustible material there will be scorching, charring and possible ignition, depending upon the "thermal exposure."* Thermal physical damage with the associated destruction by fire and sometimes fire storms constitutes one of the important destructive aspects of the nuclear weapon.

Exposure of lightly protected or unprotected skin of a person will result in a thermal burn or FLASH BURN; this was the principal cause of death on the first day among the exposed population of Hiroshima.

---

*Thermal exposure is the total normal component of thermal radiation impinging on a given surface throughout the course of a nuclear detonation. It is expressed as calories per square centimeter.

THERMOLUMINESCENT DOSIMETER

A new form of solid-state radiation dosimeter has come forth in the last few years to compete with photographic film. This is known as the thermoluminescent dosimeter, since the energy released in the crystal by the ionizing radiation is largely stored and only liberated upon subsequent heating of the material. As the temperature reaches a characteristic value, the energy is released in the form of light of a particular color. One material for which this technique has been carried to a high degree of development is calcium fluoride with manganese activation.

See LUMINESCENCE.

THERMONUCLEAR REACTION

Nuclear fusion reaction in which the energy necessary for the reaction is furnished by colliding particles that have the necessary kinetic energy due to enormously high temperature. In fact, temperatures of millions of degrees and higher are necessary for thermonuclear reactions to occur at appreciable rates; the rate increases rapidly as the temperature increases.

See THERMONUCLEAR WEAPON.

THERMONUCLEAR WEAPON

A nuclear weapon in which energy is produced by nuclear interactions of the fusion type. The fusion process takes place with some of the lightest (low atomic number) nuclei, i.e., hydrogen, which exists in 3 isotopic forms: (H^1) with a nucleus having a mass number of 1, containing no neutrons; deuterium (H^2 or D^2), atomic number 1, mass number 2, having 1 neutron; and tritium (H^3 or T^3), mass number 3, having 2 neutrons. Under suitable conditions 2 deuterium nuclei may combine (unite or fuse together) to form a nucleus of a heavier element, helium, a neutron, together with the release of energy:

$$_1D^2 + {}_1D^2 \longrightarrow {}_2He^3 + {}_0n^1 + 3.22 \text{ Mev}$$

Nuclear fusion reactions can be brought about only in the presence of very high temperatures; thus the process is called thermonuclear. The way to achieve the million-degree temperature necessary is by means of a nuclear fission reaction in a nuclear explosion. A quantity of deuterium or tritium (or a mixture) is combined with a fission or atomic weapon, and upon detonation a combined fission and fusion reaction takes place with the release of enormous energy. Weight for weight, the fusion of deuterium nuclei produces over 3 times as much energy as the fission of uranium or plutonium; e.g., 1 pound of uranium produces as much energy as 8,000 tons of TNT, while 1 pound of deuterium releases roughly the explosive energy equivalent to 26,000 tons of TNT.

The reactions involving tritium are of particular interest, for they add additional neutrons which contribute to the more thorough fission of uranium. Thus,

$$H^3 + H^3 \longrightarrow He^4 + 2n + 11.3 \text{ Mev}$$
or the more common
$$H^3 + H^2 \longrightarrow He^4 + n + 17.6 \text{ Mev}$$

produces neutrons of high energy that can cause the fission of the most abundant isotope (U^{238}) in uranium as well as of U^{235}. It is possible to make use of these neutrons by surrounding the fusion material in the weapon with a blanket of ordinary uranium.

In general, the energy released in the explosion of thermonuclear weapons is roughly half fusion and half fission.

The first experimental thermonuclear weapon was the Bravo shot of the Castle series of 1954 at the Eniwetok Proving Ground. The fallout from this shot involved Japanese fishermen and the Marshall Islanders. The first experimental thermonuclear device was tested in 1952—the Mike shot of the Ivy series.

THICKNESS GAGING

Radioactive isotopes are used in gages to determine and control thickness of material being rolled out, or of a coating being applied. Thickness gages are used in the manufacture of paper and paper products, foam rubber, tires, plastics, coated abrasives and sheet metals. These gages assure more uniform thickness, thus reducing the amount of raw material used in meeting the minimum thickness requirement, and reduce or eliminate scrap and time waiting for the finished product to be inspected. The radioactive source can be selected to suit the material being processed. For control of thickness of a material on a continuous basis the type of arrangement shown in Figure T–12 is typical. The absorption of radiation by the material passing between the source and the counter is measured and reported to the meter

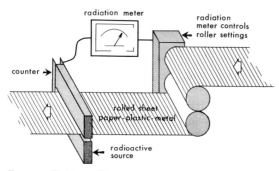

FIGURE T–12.   RADIOACTIVE SOURCE FOR GAGING THICKNESS.

controlling the roller settings. In measuring and controlling the uniformity of a coating being applied, the amount of radiation reflected from the material is used to activate the control mechanisms.

The pharmaceutical industry uses thickness gaging for many tasks: detection of the number of individual medicament containers inside a quantity package; determination of the placement of the label; continuous measurement and control of percentage of solids in suspensions; and determination of wall thickness of gelatin capsules.

THIMBLE CHAMBER

An INTEGRATING IONIZATION CHAMBER used in the CONDENSER R-METER. This radiation dosimeter is patterned after the original "fingerhutkammer," which was developed to measure quantity of ionizing radiation by determining the loss of electrical charge while irradiating the ion chamber. The modern instrument is commonly known as the condenser r-meter.

THORIUM

Symbol Th; atomic number 90; atomic weight 232.05. A heavy, slightly radioactive, metallic element. Named for Thor, Scandinavian god of war. Although there are 13 radioactive isotopes of thorium with mass numbers 223 through 235, the natural source for 100% of the abundance is Th^{232}, which occurs in monazite sand and in other rock formations.

Thorium-232, with a half-life of 1.39×10^{10} years, is the precursor for, and eventually decays to, lead-208, through the so-called thorium decay series. (See THORIUM RADIOACTIVE SERIES.)

This element is of primary interest as a source of the fissionable material uranium-233, a possible fuel material for sustaining a chain reaction in a power-producing nuclear reactor. It is used in the manufacture of gas mantles and in other commercial processes, the most notable of which is the use of mesothorium in the painting of watch and clock dials to produce luminescence.

Thorium and its salts are only slightly poisonous. Because of their radioactivity there is a danger of continued contact. Dermatitis of the hands has been reported from handling thorium nitrates used in manufacturing gas mantles. The use of mesothorium to paint watch and clock dials produced malignancy in the girls who "licked the brushes." Also Thorotrast, widely used in the 1930's as a contrast medium for x-ray visualization, has been shown to have carcinogenic effects.

Animal experiments on the toxicity of thorium compounds have shown that the LD_{50} for subcutaneous injection of thorium chloride in mice is

4,000 milligrams per kilogram (mg/kg); the lethal dose (LD) for intravenous injection in rats is 24.2 to 32.2 mg/kg; and in rabbits the LD for intravenous injection is 50 mg/kg. For thorium nitrate the LD subcutaneous dose in frogs is 600 mg/kg; the LD for intravenous dose in rabbits is 50 mg/kg; and the LD_{50} for intraperitoneal injection in rats is 68 ± 12 mg/kg. For thorium sodium citrate the LD subcutaneous dose for frogs is 600 mg/kg. Thorium dioxide was widely used as an experimental carcinogen before the discovery of the artificial radioisotopes and the carcinogenic hydrocarbons. Carcinomas were produced with it in rats, guinea pigs and rabbits.

Th^{230}, radioactive half-life 8.0×10^4 years, and Th^{232}, radioactive half-life of 1.39×10^{10} years; with bone as the critical organ, each has a biological half-life of 200 years, effective half-life 200 years, and would reach only 16% equilibrium in the body in the first 50 years. Thus thorium and some of its radioisotopes and compounds constitute important internal emitter hazards. For Th^{232} the maximum permissible body burden for the critical organ, bone, is 0.04 microcurie (μc), and the maximum permissible concentration for continuous exposure for a 40-hour week is 5×10^{-5} μc/cc for water and 2×10^{12} μc/cc for air.

THORIUM RADIOACTIVE SERIES

The thorium series shown in Table T–3 depicts the decay disintegration chain, and parent-daughter transmutation from radioactive thorium (Th^{232}) to stable lead (Pb^{208}). This series is named after its long-lived precursor thorium-232 (half-life of 1.39×10^{10} years). Thus, even though the earth is assumed to be 4.5×10^9 years old, over half the thorium-232 still remains to feed the disintegration chain.

The table details the disintegration, the nature of the radiations given off, and the half-life of each radioisotope, and in parentheses below each radioisotope is the colloquial name.

It will be noted that in the disintegrations in which an alpha (α) particle is emitted, the atomic weight of the daughter element is 4 units less than that of the parent. This is because an alpha particle on the atomic weight scale has a mass of 4, and thus the loss of 1 alpha particle would reduce the weight by 4. On the other hand, since a beta (β) particle is an electron, the mass of which is negligible on the atomic weight scale, the parent and daughter elements have virtually the same atomic weights when there is a disintegration accompanied by the emission of a beta particle. Thus it is evident that the atomic weights of all members of the thorium series may be represented by 4n, where *n* is an integer varying from 58 for thorium ($4 \times 58 = 232$, the atomic weight of thorium) to 52 for lead ($4 \times 52 = 208$).

A branched disintegration occurs with two-

TABLE T–3.   FLOW CHART—THE THORIUM RADIOACTIVE SERIES (Simplified Form)

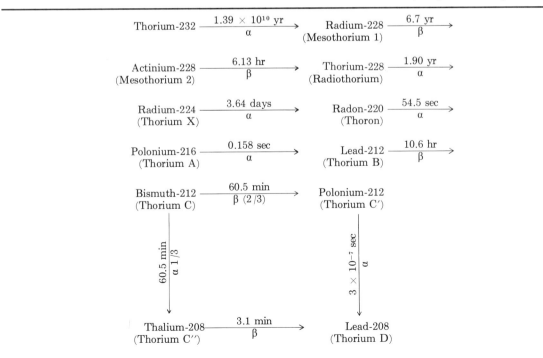

TABLE T-4. FIRST COLLATERAL THORIUM RADIOACTIVE SERIES

Protactinium $(_{91}Pa^{228})$ $\xrightarrow[\alpha]{22 \text{ hr}}$ Actinium $(_{89}Ac^{224})$ $\xrightarrow[\alpha]{2.9 \text{ hr}}$

Francium $(_{87}Fr^{220})$ $\xrightarrow[\alpha]{27.5 \text{ sec}}$ Astatine $(_{85}At^{216})$ $\xrightarrow[\alpha]{3 \times 10^{-4} \text{ sec}}$

Bismuth $(_{83}Bi^{212})$ (ThC) $\longrightarrow$ Thorium radioactive series

TABLE T-5. SECOND COLLATERAL THORIUM RADIOACTIVE SERIES

Plutonium $(_{94}Pu^{232})$ $\xrightarrow[\alpha]{36 \text{ min}}$ Uranium $(_{92}U^{228})$ $\xrightarrow[\alpha]{9.3 \text{ min}}$

Thorium $(_{90}Th^{224})$ $\xrightarrow[\alpha]{1 \text{ sec}}$ Radium $(_{88}Ra^{220})$ $\xrightarrow[\alpha]{3 \times 10^{-2} \text{ sec}}$

Radon $(_{86}Rn^{216})$ $\xrightarrow[\alpha]{10^{-4} \text{ sec}}$ Polonium $(_{84}Po^{212})$ (Th C') $\longrightarrow$

Thorium radioactive series

thirds the thorium C atoms giving off beta particles to form C', and one-third giving off alpha particles to form C'', but both decaying to thorium D or lead. The significance of this, which occurs also in other decay series, is probably explained quantum mechanically.

By careful research it has been found that the naturally occurring radioelements of high atomic weight, at the end of the periodic system, fall into 3 distinct series. Thus, in addition to the thorium series, there are the URANIUM RADIOACTIVE SERIES and the ACTINIUM RADIOACTIVE SERIES.

There are 2 collateral 4n series. The first, shown in Table T-4, starts with protactinium-228, produced by irradiating thorium-232 with deuterons; and the second collateral thorium series, shown in Table T-5, begins with plutonium-232 resulting from bombardment of uranium-235 with alpha particles.

THORON

An isotope of radon; atomic number 86; mass number 220. Formerly called thorium emanation, and sometimes given the symbol Tn. Thoron is a radioactive nuclide occurring in the thorium radioactive series:

Discovered by British physicist Ernest Rutherford in 1900.

This gaseous radioactive isotope diffuses from thorium-bearing ground and is present in the earth's atmosphere. As a result of radioactive decay, particulate (attached to particles in the air) gamma-emitting daughters are also present: lead (thorium-B) $(_{82}Pb^{212})$, bismuth (thorium-C) $(_{83}Bi^{212})$, thallium (thorium-C'') $(_{81}Tl^{208})$.

Because of the short half-life, measurement is difficult, but it appears that the average concentration of thoron in outdoor air is about 10^{-13} to 10^{-14} curie per liter of air, and that the external gamma dose rate is about 0.17 microroentgen per hour. Substantial variation may be found, due to the level of thorium content of the soil, seasonal changes and meteorological conditions.

THOROTRAST

Proprietary, stabilized suspension of the white, amorphous, insoluble powder, thorium dioxide. Formerly used in roentgen visualization of the liver and spleen after intravenous administration. Also used in arteriography and cystography, and in retrograde pyelography. It was shown that radioactive elements in the thorium series were present in the feces, urine and breath of 2 patients

Radium $(_{84}Ra^{224})$ (Thorium X) $\xrightarrow[\alpha]{3.64 \text{ days}}$ Radon $(_{86}Rn^{220})$ (Thoron) $\xrightarrow[\alpha]{52 \text{ sec}}$ Polonium $(_{84}Po^{216})$ (Thorium A)

TABLE T–6. THRESHOLD DETECTORS FOR NEUTRON SPECTRUM MEASUREMENTS

DETECTOR MATERIAL	THRESHOLD ENERGY	TYPE OF REACTION	CROSS SECTION	ACTIVITY PRODUCED	HALF-LIFE OF PRODUCT
P^{31}	2.5 Mev	n,p	0.075 barn	Si^{31}	2.6 hours
S^{32}	2.9 Mev	n,p	0.30 barn	P^{32}	14.3 days
Ni^{58}	5.0 Mev	n,p	1.23 barn	Co^{58}	72 days
Al^{27}	5.3 Mev	n,p	0.08 barn	Mg^{27}	9.8 min
Si^{28}	6.1 Mev	n,p	0.19 barn	Al^{28}	2.3 min
Mg^{24}	6.3 Mev	n,p	0.048 barn	Na^{24}	15.0 hr
Al^{27}	8.6 Mev	n,α	0.11 barn	Na^{24}	15.0 hr
Ag^{107}	9.6 Mev	n,2n	. . .	Ag^{106}	. . .
I^{127}	10 Mev	n,2n	. . .	I^{126}	13 days
C^{12}	20 Mev	n,2n	. . .	C^{11}	20.4 min

6 and 7 years after intravenous injections of "Thorotrast." It was also shown that lung cancer and other types of malignancy were associated with the use of "Thorotrast." Nine cases of leukemia have also been authenticated. In 1937 The Journal of the American Medical Association editorially pointed out the potential hazards of the diagnostic use of thorium dioxide, and its use has been discontinued.

THRESHOLD DETECTORS

For detecting and measuring neutrons, substances are used which become radioactive through nuclear reactions which can occur only with neutrons having energies in specifically limited regions. In general, these substances react when the neutron energy exceeds a value called the threshold; typical examples are listed in Table T–6. Foils of materials listed in the first column, upon exposure to neutrons with energies above those in column 2, undergo the reactions indicated in column 3 with relative efficiencies in column 4 to produce the radioactive materials and half-lives shown in the right-hand columns. In using threshold detectors to establish the energies and the quantities of neutrons making up a radiation field, the methods sometimes use selective filters to further define the range of response; in fact, it is usually necessary to exclude all thermal neutrons from the foils during exposure.

THRESHOLD DOSE

The dose of radiation below which effects are not observable. A true threshold implies that below a certain dose there is no damage and therefore no danger—a safe dose. In biological experiments there is often no observable effect until the dose passes a certain value, but it is frequently impossible to distinguish between a true threshold dose-response curve (curve 3 on Figure T–13) and a hyperbolic relation (curve 2). Curve 1 represents linearity.

If we assume that any amount of radiation will produce some damage, and further assume that there is no repair, then there will be no threshold dose, and the only threshold will depend upon the sensitivity of methods for detecting tissue or organ damage.

Since, however, in SOMATIC EFFECTS there is usually regeneration, restoration, repair, i.e., RECOVERY FROM IRRADIATION, there is a threshold dose for manifestation of a change in a living system. This type of threshold is the lowest dose which produces damage more severe or extensive than the system is immediately capable of compensating for.

In considering the concept of threshold dose it is imperative that the same responses be compared, for because of the extremes in susceptibility of mammalian tissue, amounts of radiation required to produce a given type of observable damage may vary by a factor of 10^5.

In a complex living organism the determination of a threshold for a given effect is difficult. For example, the smallest dose for which a statistically significant shortening of life can be demonstrated is about 100 roentgens. This is probably not a true

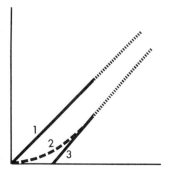

FIGURE T–13. THRESHOLD DOSE, REPRESENTED BY CURVE 3. CURVE 2 IS A HYPERBOLIC RELATIONSHIP, AND CURVE 1 REPRESENTS LINEARITY.

threshold below which there is no damage leading to life shortening, for repair and recovery are undoubtedly occurring, and further experimental work may demonstrate a lower or nonexistent threshold.

Simple systems observed in tissue culture studies have indicated that a definite threshold exists for radiation damage. For example, hamster cells in tissue culture showed a dose-response curve threshold corresponding to 5 hits by target theory. Recovery from a sublethal number of hits (less than 5) was complete; and 5 or more hits had to be accumulated during a single irradiation before death of the cell occurred.

The threshold concept of a safe dose, or a tolerance dose as once used, has changed to the concept of PERMISSIBLE DOSE, MAXIMUM PERMISSIBLE DOSE and RADIATION PROTECTION GUIDES. This concept recognizes the possibility that there is no safe or threshold dose, but that it is necessary to find a dose which balances the possible damage against the need for exposure, thus arriving at an acceptable risk level of exposure.

See DOSE and DOSE-EFFECT RELATIONSHIP.

THRESHOLD VOLTAGE

The beginning of the counting plateau of a Geiger-Mueller counter, being the lowest voltage at which the passage of an ionizing ray produces pulses uniformly, regardless of the incident energy.

THULIUM

Symbol Tm; atomic number 69; atomic weight 168.94. A member of the yttrium subgroup of rare earth metals. Discovered by Cleve in 1879 and found in such minerals as xenotime, fergusonite, gadolinite and euxonite. Named for Thule, Greenland. All the natural abundance is furnished by the stable isotope Tm[169]. There are 9 radioactive isotopes. Medical interest lies in the possible use of Tm[170] (half-life 129 days, β^- and γ emitter) in teletherapy when a high degree of penetration is not required. None of the isotopes has been shown to have any biological or agricultural value.

THYMUS, RADIATION EFFECTS ON

The thymus gland shows a rapid response to irradiation because of its large and radiosensitive lymphocyte content (*see* LYMPHOCYTES, RADIATION DAMAGE). The threshold dose for decrease in thymic weight is below 30 roentgens (r); 90 r will reduce the weight by 50% in mice. In the early 1920's many children were given x-ray treatment for an enlarged thymus gland in order to reduce its size and activity. Although the retrospective studies of these children leave much to be desired, there is evidence of increased incidence of leukemia and of thyroid cancer.

THYROID, RADIATION EFFECTS ON

In whole-body irradiation the thyroid gland rarely shows any histopathology other than an occasional small hemorrhage. No serious late local effects of external radiation of the normal thyroid in adults have been recorded; e.g., cancer of the thyroid has not occurred after irradiation for carcinoma of the larynx. Cancer has been shown to develop in adult nodular goiters treated with x-ray. In children receiving x-ray therapy for an enlarged thymus gland there is a significant increase in the thyroid cancer, due to scattered radiation of, or improper shielding of, the thyroid.

A single injection of 400 microcuries of iodine-131 has produced thyroid cancer in rats; but a careful survey of hundreds of human cases of hyperthyroidism treated with iodine-131 has failed to reveal a single case of thyroid cancer.

See TOXICITY, RADIATION.

THYROID CANCER, LOCALIZATION

In patients with known or suspected cancer of the thyroid gland, test doses of radioiodine are given, after which studies are made with external detectors or scanners. (*See* SCANNING, RADIOISOTOPE.) Early, untreated cancers may appear as zones of decreased or absent radioactivity contrasting with the generally high concentration in the rest of the thyroid gland. Such zones may not be distinguishable from those produced by benign nodules. More clear-cut results, of great clinical usefulness, may be obtained after removal or destruction of most or all of the normal thyroid gland. Now the cancer, if reasonably well differentiated, may show considerable radioiodine-concentrating ability, and extensions or metastases of the tumor will reveal themselves to the radiation detector as hot spots. (See Figure T–14.)

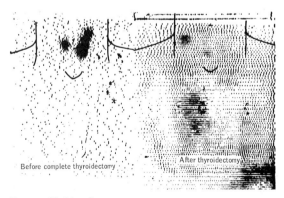

FIGURE T–14. SCAN OF THE THYROID SHOWING INCREASE IN IODINE UPTAKE BY THE LEFT LOBE BEFORE THYROIDECTOMY (LEFT). AFTER COMPLETE REMOVAL OF THE THYROID (LEFT LOBE CANCER) THE SCAN ON THE RIGHT SHOWS THE IODINE-131 TAKEN UP BY METASTATIC CANCER AREAS.

THYROID CANCER, TREATMENT

Radioiodine (iodine-131) has proved an effective form of treatment for certain cases of cancer of the thyroid—those that are too extensive for complete surgical removal and that are enough like normal thyroid tissue to concentrate the radioisotope effectively. When a high concentration is present in the malignant tissue, the local radiation causes damage to or death of the cancerous cells and gives rise to scar tissue. In many cases, however, the treatment fails because of insufficient ability of the tumor to concentrate iodine. Certain drugs and clinical maneuvers may be used to increase this concentrating ability. The first stage in treatment is usually the removal of the remaining normal thyroid gland by surgery. The doses of radioiodine required are generally much higher than those used in nonmalignant thyroid disease (as much as 100 millicuries). Repeated treatment may be given over a period of months or years. Soft-tissue lesions generally respond better than those in bone. In the most favorable cases the disease has been suppressed and has remained clinically quiescent for 10 or more years after treatment. (See Figure T–15.)

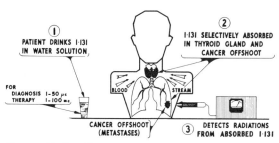

FIGURE T–15. DIAGRAM SHOWING METHOD OF TREATING THYROID CANCER WITH IODINE-131. THE SAME TECHNIQUE IS USED FOR DIAGNOSIS, BUT WITH SMALLER AMOUNTS OF RADIOIODINE. (USAEC-1D-234.)

THYROID FUNCTION STUDIES

Iodine-131 is extensively used for the clinical and research study of thyroid function. The most common test is the measurement of the percentage of the dose to be found in the thyroid gland at 6, 12 and 24 hours after oral administration. At 24 hours a normal "uptake" is between 20 and 45% of the dose. Higher values suggest overactive thyroid function; lower values, subnormal function. (See Figure T–16.) The urinary excretion of the radioisotope, which may also be measured, tends to approximate 100% of the dose minus the amount in the thyroid, but it is an unsatisfactory index of thyroid function because of the retention of significant amounts in nonthyroidal tissues. Additional tests used in selected cases include

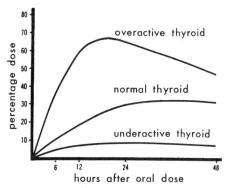

FIGURE T–16. THYROID FUNCTION MEASURED IN TERMS OF IODINE-131 UPTAKE.

measurement of the free and bound fractions of the radioisotope in the plasma; these yield information on the rate of removal by the thyroid gland and on the amount of organic thyroid hormone iodine released. For these diagnostic tests doses of 10 to 300 microcuries of I^{131} are usually used. Drugs containing iodine and drugs that alter thyroid function interfere with results.

Triiodothyronine Suppression Test for Hyperthyroidism. A method for clarifying the significance of a borderline high uptake of radioiodine by the thyroid gland. When such a result is obtained on the first test, the patient is given a series of daily doses of triiodothyronine by mouth for a week, and the test is repeated. In hyperthyroidism the uptake is likely to be as high or nearly as high as on the first test, but in the absence of hyperthyroidism the uptake is usually reduced greatly. (See Figure T–17.) The test is believed to be based on the fact that the hyperfunctioning thyroid gland does not have its activity altered much by suppression of TSH (thyroid-stimulating

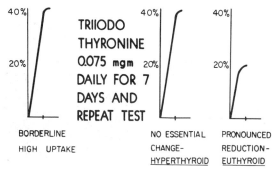

FIGURE T–17. TEST FOR HYPERTHYROIDISM BY MEASURING UPTAKE OF TRIIODOTHYRONINE. (COURTESY OF MEDICAL DIVISION, OAK RIDGE INSTITUTE OF NUCLEAR STUDIES.)

hormone) output by the pituitary gland. On the other hand, the normal thyroid gland is highly dependent on TSH stimulation.

THYROID HORMONES. *See* HORMONE STUDIES.

THYROID SCANNING

A special technique for study of thyroid disease, emphasizing size, shape and location of abnormal tissue rather than over-all thyroid function. The detector of the scanning instrument is designed to be sensitive to only a small area of tissue at a time as it moves over the part of the body under investigation and makes a density pattern of the distribution of radioactivity. The resulting record after a suitable test dose of radioiodine shows the

size and shape of the thyroid gland and may reveal nodules that take up more or less of the radioisotope than does the surrounding tissue. In some patients, especially after removal of most or all of the thyroid gland, scanning may reveal foci of functioning thyroid cancer remaining in the neck or having spread to other sites in the body.

Figure T–18 shows the usual pattern of movement of the detector over the thyroid region of the neck. Figure T–19 is the writing arm of the scanning instrument which is recording the radioactivity information being picked up and transmitted from the detector. Figure T–20 shows a scan of a normal thyroid gland which is superimposed over the thyroid gland in the neck.

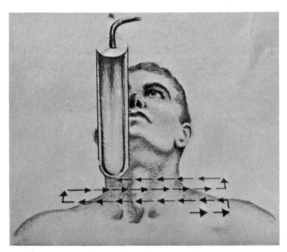

FIGURE T–18. PATTERN OF MOVEMENT OF DETECTOR OVER THE THYROID REGION. (COURTESY OF OAK RIDGE INSTITUTE OF NUCLEAR STUDIES.)

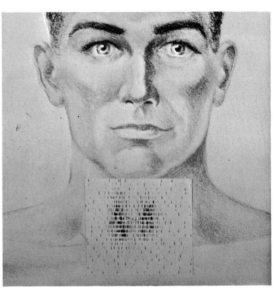

FIGURE T–20. SCAN OF A NORMAL THYROID SUPERIMPOSED IN ANATOMICAL POSITION. (COURTESY OF OAK RIDGE INSTITUTE OF NUCLEAR STUDIES.)

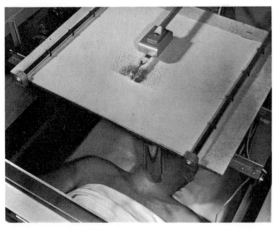

FIGURE T–19. WRITING ARM OF THE SCANNING INSTRUMENT RECORDING THE INFORMATION TRANSMITTED FROM THE DETECTOR. (COURTESY OF OAK RIDGE INSTITUTE OF NUCLEAR STUDIES.)

TIME CONSTANT

The characteristic of the integrating and averaging circuit of a rate-meter which determines the time interval over which the summation of the incoming signals is taken. A short time constant is selected when the expected counting rate is high; for slower counting, a longer time constant is appropriate. Time constant is selected on the basis of compromising the desire for rapid response of the instrument with the necessity for greater total counts in the interest of statistical accuracy in the resultant data.

TIMER

A device for controlling the interval during which a counter is allowed to count. This may be a simple clock-type mechanism or an electronic frequency generator-counter. In its simplest use it is a device that functions to terminate the count over a selected interval. In more refined measurements it may provide several functions, each of a time-controlled nature, to select the moment of starting, to begin and end the count, and to program other operations which may be part of the counting protocol. The timer normally effects its control functions through acting as an electric or electronic switch, connected into the appropriate part of the scaler or rate-meter circuit.

TIN

Symbol Sn; atomic number 50; atomic weight 118.70. A silver-white, malleable metal, softer than zinc and harder than lead. Discovery prehistoric. Symbol Sn from Latin *stannum*, Anglo-Saxon tin. Found chiefly in the mineral cassiterite, associated with granite rocks. Natural abundance furnished by 10 stable isotopes.

Tin is practically an indispensable metal, being used in tin plate for cans, for solder, for tin foil, and as an alloy with other metals. It is one of the least toxic of the common metals. Traces occur naturally in biological material, but it is not considered an essential element.

Eighteen radioactive isotopes have been identified. Twelve may occur as fission products associated with the detonation of a nuclear device. Sn^{123} is significant in radioactive fallout, 0.0043 megacurie per megaton of fission remaining at the end of 1 year. Sn^{113}—radioactive half-life 112 days; with bone as the critical organ, biological half-life 100 days, effective half-life 53 days; electron capture and gamma decay—is available commercially, but has not found significant medical or agricultural usefulness.

TISSUE EQUIVALENT IONIZATION CHAMBER

An ionization chamber in which the walls, the electrodes and the gas consist of materials which closely match the composition and structure of a particular tissue. Such chambers are used to provide radiation intensity measurements directly corresponding to the radiation effect experienced by the actual tissue. For use with ordinary x-ray or gamma-ray fields, the physical characteristics of the materials, which must be close to those of the tissue, are the average atomic number and the electron density; for neutron radiations it is also of great importance to maintain the correct ratios of atomic or nuclide species, because of the induced and other secondary radiation processes which occur.

This instrument is an elaboration of the cavity ionization chamber based on the Bragg-Gray principle. It may take whatever form the purposes of the immediate application demand. Most frequently it is built along the lines of the thimble chamber or condenser r-meter. Although a cavity ionization chamber with walls of air-equivalent material is appropriate for measuring the exposure dose in roentgen units, the tissue equivalent chamber attempts to establish in addition all the special attributes of energy absorption for any radiation and all energies, by providing the detecting volume with an environment which responds exactly as tissue would. Materials which have been used in this kind of instrument include especially treated plastics and gelatin compositions. The collecting gas has also been compounded of suitable mixtures. It is further possible, in particular instances, to contrive these instruments to include or exclude the contributions of reactions characteristic of specific atomic species of interest.

TISSUE EQUIVALENT MATERIAL

Material made up of the same elements and in the same proportions as they occur in some particular biological tissue. But in the development of phantoms, in some cases equivalence may be approximated with sufficient accuracy, using materials readily available, on the basis of effective atomic number. For example, a mixture of granulated cork and Grape-Nuts cereal (*see* PHANTOM) makes a perfectly satisfactory equivalent material for lung tissue. Tissue equivalent fluids and plastics are in constant use in radiation biology and health physics research, and in roentgenology.

See TISSUE EQUIVALENT IONIZATION CHAMBER.

TITANIUM

Symbol Ti; atomic number 22, atomic weight 47.90. A white metal occurring in practically all rocks, estimated as ninth in abundance of the elements of the earth's crust (0.58%). Discovered by English chemist William Gregor in 1791. Named from Latin *Titanes*, Titans, the first sons of the Earth. Natural abundance furnished by 5 stable isotopes: Ti^{46} through Ti^{50}.

Used industrially as pigment for paints, welding-rod coating, and in alloys and cemented carbides.

Careful study has revealed it to be completely nontoxic. It is not a normal constituent of living material.

Only 3 radioactive isotopes have been identified: Ti^{43} (half-life 0.6 second); Ti^{45} (half-life 3.09 hours, beta (β^+), orbital-electron capture and weak gamma); and Ti^{51} (half-life 5.82 minutes, β^- and γ). The latter two may be formed both in the soil and in sea water as induced radionuclides after contact detonation of a nuclear device. No biological, medical or agricultural significance.

TNT EQUIVALENT

A measure of energy released in the detonation of a nuclear (or atomic) weapon, or in the explosion of a given quantity of fissionable material, expressed in terms of the weight of TNT which would release the same amount of energy when exploded. The basis of TNT equivalence is that the explosion of 1 ton of TNT releases 10^9 calories of energy. The TNT equivalent is usually stated in kiloton energy, or megaton energy.

See YIELD.

TOXIC SUBSTANCES DUE TO RADIATION

An exhaustive search has been made over the years for some specific toxic substance responsible for the effects of radiation. Blood plasma has been studied, tissues have been extracted, urine has been examined, and respiratory gases have been analyzed for the presence of some specific toxin or toxins, but it can be stated that there is no known specific toxin.

Nevertheless toxins may be liberated from heavily damaged or dying cells which affect the irradiated organism. It is probable that a mixture of polypeptides, amines, potassium and histamine-like substances leaves the tissues damaged by irradiation and is circulated in the blood and body fluids. It is likely that these and other toxic products may kill or injure a cell not directly damaged by radiation. There is evidence that damage to proliferative cells may occur as the result of indirect toxic action as well as direct cellucidal action of radiation. Some of the symptoms of radiation illness are likely due to circulating toxins produced by necrosis of radiosensitive tissues. It is possible that the shocklike syndrome appearing shortly after a high radiation dose may be due, in part at least, to such toxins released into the circulation. These toxins cannot be considered unique, however, for shock can be produced by toxic products

released after removal of a tourniquet that had been applied to an arm for an extended period of time.

FREE RADICALS, produced in body water as the result of irradiation, have a damaging toxic effect on biological objects, and probably account for further damage to cells and tissues after radiation exposure in addition to direct cell damage from the ionizing event occurring within the cell.

TOXICITY, RADIATION

Radiotoxicity is the damaging and destructive effects of ionizing radiation upon biological material. The degree of toxicity depends upon such physical factors as the type and dose of radiation; the route of delivery, i.e., internal deposition or external radiation; and upon many biological factors covered in detail under RADIOSENSITIVITY.

The toxic effect of ingestion of radioiodine (iodine-131) is graphically illustrated by the work performed at the Biology Operation of the Hanford Works, where radioiodine was fed to lambs in doses of 0.15, 0.5, 1.5 and 5 microcuries per day (μc/day) during their entire life (the mother was on a similar regimen). Figure T–21 shows the growth retardation with the smallest animal on 5 μc/day, the intermediate size on 1.5 μc/day, and the large animal on the left the control. The hair loss shown by the animal on the right is the result of radioiodine ingestion of 5 μc/day. Figure T–22 shows the destruction of the thyroid gland associated with the ingestion of 5 μc/day of iodine-131.

See THYROID, RADIATION EFFECTS ON.

TRACE CHEMISTRY

The chemical behavior of a substance present in a system in imponderable amount or in very minute concentration. Trace chemical behavior is observable with radioactive nuclides free or nearly free of nonradioactive isotopes, and may be much

GROWTH RETARDATION   HAIR LOSS

FIGURE T–21. LAMBS SHOWING GROWTH RETARDATION (LEFT) AND HAIR LOSS (RIGHT) RESULTING FROM INGESTION OF RADIOIODINE. (COURTESY OF BIOLOGY OPERATION, HANFORD WORKS.)

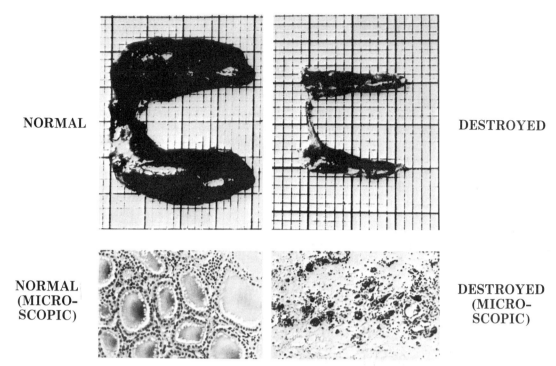

NORMAL

DESTROYED

NORMAL
(MICRO-
SCOPIC)

DESTROYED
(MICRO-
SCOPIC)

FIGURE T–22. DESTRUCTION OF THYROID GLAND TISSUE OF LAMBS AS A RESULT OF INGESTION OF RADIOIODINE. A
SINGLE DOSE OF 3 mc OF IODINE-131 OR CONTINUOUS INGESTION OF 5 µC PER DAY FOR SEVERAL YEARS HAS BEEN FOUND
TO CAUSE SUCH DESTRUCTION. (COURTESY OF BIOLOGY OPERATION, HANFORD WORKS.)

different from the behavior of the same material in ordinary amounts and concentrations. Knowledge of trace chemical behavior may therefore be of great importance in the handling of radioactive materials. Characteristic features of trace chemical behavior include the prominence of surface effects due to adsorption, incorporation of trace material in bulk precipitates (*see* CARRIER), and dissociation (e.g., the stability of bromine atoms in aqueous solutions of trace bromine).

See TRACER and TRACER, ISOTOPIC.

TRACE CONCENTRATION

Concentration of a substance below the usual limits of chemical detection. Extremely dilute solutions are used, 10^{-10} molar, or less. If radioactive material of a reasonably strong activity is used, it is possible to trace quantities as small as 10^{-10} gram. For example, 1 milligram (mg) of carbon-14 in a drug, vitamin or hormone injected into a 1,000-pound cow can be identified and measured in 10-mg samples of blood, milk or tissue subsequently taken from the injected cow.

See TRACER and TRACER TECHNIQUE.

TRACER

A foreign substance mixed with or attached to a given substance to facilitate the determination of

the distribution or location of the latter. A physical tracer is one that is attached by purely physical means to the substance being traced. A CHEMICAL TRACER has similar chemical properties to those of the substance being traced and with which it is mixed homogeneously. A RADIOACTIVE TRACER has radioactivity as the property used in tracing and may be either physical or chemical. An isotopic tracer (TRACER, ISOTOPIC) is a radionuclide or an allobar used as a chemical tracer for the element with which it is isotopic. Indicator was formerly used as a synonym for tracer.

TRACER, ISOTOPIC

An isotope or an allobar of an element which may be incorporated into a sample to facilitate observation of the course of that element through a chemical, biological or physical process. If the tracer is radioactive, the observations consist in measuring the radioactivity; if the tracer is stable, the isotopic composition is determined by mass spectrographic, density measurement, or neutron activation.

TRACER CHEMISTRY

The use of isotopic tracers in chemical studies.

See TRACE CHEMISTRY, TRACER STUDIES and TRACER TECHNIQUE.

TRACER DOSE

The amount or medical dose of an element or substance administered to a patient or an experimental subject or animal which is extremely small compared with the normal intake of the substance or that normally present in the system. For example, in one experiment "the radioactive yttrium was prepared free of carrier from a mixture of strontium-90 and yttrium-90. The concentration was approximately 10^{-11} molar." Ability to use effectively such minute amounts of radioactive material permits human experimental work with no harm from chemical toxicity.

See TRACE CONCENTRATION.

TRACER INDUSTRIAL APPLICATIONS

Industrial use of radioactive tracers ranks third in number of licensed users of radioisotopes. Two important characteristics make radioisotopes useful in tracer studies: exhibition of the same chemical behavior as a stable species of the same element, and the emitted radiation allows location and identification even in minute quantities. Industrial applications are wear and corrosion studies, flow and location determinations, chemical reaction studies and chemical analysis. For example, irradiated piston rings containing iron-59 can be studied for wear by analyzing the crankcase oil for radioactive particles; automobile tires can be studied for wear by adding phosphorus-32 to the tread compound, and testing the material worn from the tire for radioactivity; and the blending of hydrocarbons can be achieved by incorporating a radioisotope in one component of the blend, and monitoring until a constant activity level is reached.

TRACER STUDIES

Studies using the tracer technique as a method of operation. The use of an isotopic tracer to study the role of an element, a group of elements, or a compound in a biological, chemical or physical process. Either stable or radioactive isotopes can be used, in any desirable chemical form. The following items should be read to see the type of activity in which tracer studies are used: AGRICULTURE STUDIES, BIOLOGICAL RESEARCH, INDUSTRIAL USE, MEDICAL DIAGNOSIS, MEDICAL RESEARCH and MEDICAL TREATMENT.

TRACER TECHNIQUE

The use of radioactive isotopes as tracers in the study of biological, medical and agricultural problems is of the greatest significance. It is made possible because a radioactive atom, before disintegration, has the same chemical behavior as the corresponding stable atom.

Radioactive tracing is simple in principle, but most difficult in practice. The radioactive tracer desired is produced by neutron bombardment of a suitable target in a nuclear reactor or by suitable bombardment in a nuclear particle accelerator. The desired tracer is next separated chemically from the other elements in the target. The active element is then incorporated into the desired molecular configuration by chemical synthesis, the proper dose is administered by the desired route, and appropriate samples are taken and analyzed by standard techniques.

The choice of the radioactive tracer isotope depends upon factors such as radioactive half-life, chemical synthesis and chemical exchange. Nature has been most unkind so far as tracers for organic molecules are concerned. Carbon, hydrogen, oxygen and nitrogen constitute the elements of most organic molecules, and satisfactory radioisotopes are available for only carbon (usually C^{14}, half-life 5,760 years, and occasionally C^{11}, half-life 20.5 minutes) and recently tritium (H^3, half-life 12 years). But tritium illustrates another general problem in that its radiations are not sufficiently energetic to be easily counted. Chemical synthesis is time-consuming and presents a number of problems. The chemical exchange of 1 atom bonded to a molecule with similar atoms in other molecules adds to the difficulty of selecting the proper isotope for the experiment.

The specific activity or the disintegration rate per gram of the element chosen is also important, for it must be detectable in quantities so small as not to alter the normal physiological functions. The material may be used carrier-free, or an appropriate carrier may be added to facilitate proper reactions.

The selection of the target material and the choice of internal or external placement for bombardment are matters for the nuclear engineer. The selection of the appropriate animal for experimental work and the selection of the appropriate dose rate for either animal or human use require careful consideration involving matters of safety of use, such as total dose, biological half-life and effective half-life.

Scanning and localization techniques for determining distribution and concentration of the radioactive tracer in the intact body leave room for improvement.

In spite of the difficulties, tracer studies are extensively used in industrial and chemical activities as well as in biological, medical and agricultural work.

TRACK

Visual manifestation of the path of an ionizing

particle in a CLOUD CHAMBER, a BUBBLE CHAMBER or a NUCLEAR EMULSION. In addition to visualization at the time of the event, the tracks can be photographed by appropriate techniques.

See RANGE.

TRAINING, RADIOISOTOPES

Some training is carried out in all the USAEC laboratories, but the Oak Ridge Institute of Nuclear Studies (ORINS) is the principal contractor providing training in the use of radioactive isotopes. The first course in basic radioisotope technology was given in 1948, and similar courses have continued to be presented. At present ORINS offers 6-week sequences of 2-week courses, 6 times each year; 72 participants are accepted for the first 2-week course in basic radiation physics. During the next 2 weeks, participants select one of 2 concurrent courses—one in basic radioisotope research techniques, and the other in industrial radioisotope techniques. For a final option, up to 24 participants may elect to remain for the third 2-week period for an advanced course in specialized industrial and research techniques. This course sequence gives flexibility in selecting subject material desired. In addition to the basic research and industrial courses, special and advanced courses are offered for specialized training in the use of radioisotopes in medicine, biochemistry, radiation chemistry, radiography, and a series of special courses in veterinary radiological activity. Formal courses in general medical uses of radioisotopes are supplemented by seminars in teletherapy, brachytherapy, thyroid uptake, autoradiography, scanning or hematology, designed for physicians, pathologists or technicians.

ORINS designed and operates a Mobile Radioisotope Laboratory which provides faculty members and advanced science majors at undergraduate institutions with specialized training in the techniques and applications of radioisotopes. During the usual 2-week visit to a campus, a series of lectures is given by ORINS staff members, and laboratory experiments are conducted in the well equipped mobile laboratory.

The Division of Biology and Medicine (DBM) of the USAEC developed and continues to handle an equipment grant program (now under Division of Education and Training—DET) in which requests are granted for funds to be used for the purchase of radiation equipment to be used as demonstration apparatus, student laboratory equipment and training aids. The funds have gone to nonprofit institutions, college departments of biology, medical and dental schools, and schools of pharmacy, public health, agriculture and veterinary medicine.

DBM, jointly with the National Science Foundation, has been sponsoring high school and college faculty training in radioisotope techniques through summer institutes and academic year institutes (now under DET). Other courses for high school science teachers are given at ORINS, and for several years they have sponsored a successful Traveling Science Demonstration Lecture Program to high schools throughout the Southeast.

TRAINING, USAEC. *See* EDUCATION AND TRAINING, USAEC.

TRANSIENT EQUILIBRIUM

If the lifetime of the parent is sufficiently short, so that the quantity present decreases appreciably during the time of observation, but is still longer than the lifetime of the successive members of the series, a stage of transient equilibrium will be reached, after which all members of the series decrease in amount exponentially with the period of the parent. An example is radon seen in the uranium radioactive series with a radioactive half-life of 3.82 days, while the successive members of the series through thallium (radium C″) have a half-life of a few seconds to a few minutes. When transient equilibrium exists between a parent, A, and a daughter, B, then

$$N_A \lambda_A = N_B (\lambda_B - \lambda_A),$$

when N_A and N_B are the number of atoms and λ_A and λ_B the respective decay constants.

See RADIOACTIVE EQUILIBRIUM.

TRANSLOCATION IN PLANTS. *See* PLANT PHYSIOLOGICAL STUDIES.

TRANSMUTATION

The conversion of one element into another. More specifically, the transformation of a nuclide of one element into a nuclide of a different element by a nuclear reaction.

For many hundreds of years the ancient alchemists vainly tried to change common metals into gold, but all their attempts to bring about transmutation met with complete failure. It was not until 1914 that the English scientist Rutherford predicted, and in 1919 accomplished, the first controlled disintegration of an atomic nucleus: the transmutation of nitrogen atoms into hydrogen atoms by bombardment with alpha particles. Another example is the fission of uranium producing krypton-90, which is the parent of rubidium-90, which is the parent of strontium-90, which is the parent of yttrium-90.

Fission $\longrightarrow$ $_{92}U^{226}$ $\longrightarrow$ $_{36}Kr^{90}$ $\longrightarrow$ $_{37}Rb^{90}$ $\longrightarrow$ $_{38}Sr^{90}$ $\longrightarrow$ $_{39}Y^{90}$.

Now, thanks to the accumulated knowledge of the years, the deliberate change of one element into another is a daily occurrence in many laboratories.

TRANSPORTATION OF RADIOACTIVE MATERIALS

Because of the hazard of contamination or exposure of personnel to radiation, the movement, transfer or shipment of any radioactive material is carefully controlled.

The USAEC issues a booklet* which covers the Interstate Commerce Commission regulations; the Civil Air regulations; the U.S. Coast Guard regulations; the U.S. Postal regulations; and additional information for shippers of radioactive material.

Some general precautions are the following:

1. No movement of radioactive materials should be made without specific authorization in writing.

2. All radioactive material must be properly labeled.

3. All radioactive material must be carefully packed in approved containers and shielded before it is moved.

4. It is wise for all assignments of active material to be from person to person, and not from a person to a location.

5. Personnel meters are worn as appropriate by employees handling or transferring radioactive material, except when boxed and certified safe.

6. All shipments shall be posted with the radiation symbol so as to alert personnel approaching.

7. In all cases, materials shall be packaged so as to eliminate the possibility for spread of contamination.

8. Vehicles loaded with radioactive materials should not be left unattended en route.

TRANSURANIUM ELEMENTS

Elements that lie beyond uranium in the periodic table, i.e., elements with atomic numbers greater than 92. All have been produced by artificial means, and the following are known: neptunium, atomic number 93; plutonium, 94; americium, 95; curium, 96; berkelium, 97; californium, 98; einsteinium, 99; fermium, 100; mendelevium, 101; nobelium, 102; and lawrencium, 103. It is believed possible to produce elements with higher atomic numbers, but they have not yet been identified or obtained.

TRAPPING

Term used to denote the removal of inorganic

iodine from the blood by the thyroid gland. This process is an active movement against a gradient and requires energy. The fact that the iodine in the gland reaches concentrations many times those of the blood leads to the concept that it is "trapped." This can be readily demonstrated by the use of the radioisotope iodine-131.

TREATMENT OF RADIATION ILLNESS

The treatment of radiation illness and injury depends on the nature, dose and distribution of the radiations, and on the duration of exposure.

The acute total body radiation syndrome is the typical injury produced by penetrating radiations directed to the whole body such as might occur in a criticality accident or in direct exposure to an atomic weapon. Similar effects are produced by internal radioisotopes that are widely distributed in the body and that deliver their radiation over a short period of time.

At doses of 100 rad or less there is no known treatment. Early effects may consist of mild gastrointestinal disturbance and some changes in laboratory results, but these do not require therapy.

At higher doses—in the range from 200 to 800 rad—a hematologic syndrome is produced; i.e., a sequence of symptoms based chiefly on damage to blood-forming tissues. It is in this group that treatment is most important and effective. The disease picture has a characteristic pattern of events over a period of weeks, and the most severe aspect may not occur until 3 to 6 weeks after exposure; with the higher doses in this range, serious symptoms may begin somewhat earlier. Spontaneous recovery generally occurs if the patient can be carried through the temporary phase of depression of the bone marrow.

During the earliest, prodromal, phase, characterized by nausea and vomiting, treatment consists of sedatives and symptomatic measures with intravenous fluids to correct dehydration and loss of body salts. During the subsequent latent period the patient should avoid excessive activity, and efforts should be made to avoid exposure to infections. During the next phase, which is one of marrow depression, most intensive treatment is needed to combat hemorrhage and infection.

The tendency to hemorrhage is due chiefly to a deficiency of thrombocytes (platelets) in the blood. Bleeding may occur at many sites—in the skin, in the eyes, around the teeth, from the nose and into the genitourinary and gastrointestinal passages; the most serious single site of hemorrhage is the brain. Certain general measures have some value: rest, avoidance of high blood pressure, and the use of a bland diet. Efforts to stop bleeding

---

*Handbook of Federal Regulations applying to Transportation of Radioactive Materials. Superintendent of Documents, U.S. Government Printing Office, Washington 25, D.C. 25 cents.

by local pressure are largely ineffectual except on the skin and in the nose. The most important form of treatment for all the hemorrhagic manifestations is the use of fresh thrombocytes obtained from donor blood. Special methods may be needed to obtain maximum numbers of thrombocytes, and large volumes of blood may be necessary to supply enough.

About the same time that the bleeding tendency becomes a problem, susceptibility to infection looms as an additional hazard. A lack of white cells in the blood and impairment of antibody formation contribute to poor resistance. One useful measure is the establishment and maintenance of a sterile environment. The patient is placed in a special room where measures such as those used in operating rooms are used to prevent the introduction of infection from outside. Some effort to control the patient's own natural bacterial inhabitants may also be made.

Antibiotics are the strongest weapon against infection, but their use in radiation casualties requires special skill. Their routine prophylactic use may do harm; on the other hand, infections are difficult to diagnose in these patients and may require prompt therapy. So far as possible, antibiotic treatment should be based upon culture of specific bacteria and upon sensitivity tests. Infections with fungi are also prominent in patients with marrow depression, and the prophylactic use of an oral antibiotic active against these organisms in the gastrointestinal tract may be advisable and does not have the dangers of prophylactic use of broad-spectrum antibiotics. Injections of gamma globulin may also have some value in combating the infections that follow radiation injury. In the past it was not practical to give enough white blood cells from donors to be of much value; newer techniques give promise that this approach may be an additional means of treatment.

A treatment that may combat the marrow depression in a more basic way is the injection of living blood-forming cells (i.e., bone marrow) from healthy donors. (See BONE MARROW GRAFTS.)

Certain treatment measures are of less importance than those already described, but may have usefulness in certain situations. Adrenocorticotropic hormone and cortisone have some effects that may be desirable, but they also tend to increase the susceptibility to infection. They should probably not be used in the treatment of radiation illness except in special circumstances. Androgens, the male sex hormones, may be useful to suppress menstruation during the hemorrhagic syndrome in women. Estrogens given before exposure have been shown in experimental animals to have a definite protective effect. When given

after exposure, inconsistent results are reported. They probably have no place in the clinical management of radiation injury. Conflicting reports are available on the effects of diet and nutrition on radiation injury. Malnourished animals with multiple vitamin deficiencies are more susceptible to radiation damage. Fat-free diets and those of very high fat content are both reported to be deleterious. In practical management, a well balanced diet should be recommended, with intravenous feedings during periods of poor intake by mouth. For patients who have a hemorrhagic tendency, a bland diet is advisable.

At still higher doses of total body radiation— 800 to 2,000 rad—the gastrointestinal manifestations predominate. Vomiting and diarrhea lead to severe dehydration and salt depletion. Direct damage to the lining of the intestine impairs its function and provides a site for bleeding and invasion by bacteria. Replacement therapy with fluids, salts and nutrients has some value, but this syndrome is usually fatal within a few days. Should it be survived, the occurrence of the hematologic syndrome in severe form could be anticipated.

With exceedingly high acute radiation doses— above 3,000 rad—it is believed that the principal manifestations in man would be those seen in other mammals, i.e., chiefly in the nervous system, with convulsions, coma, and death within a few hours. No effective treatment is known.

In addition to total body exposures, one may encounter radiation injury to limited parts of the body and various combinations of total body exposure with higher doses to particular areas. If a significant part of the functioning bone marrow of the body is protected, this greatly lessens the severity of over-all hematopoietic damage and the likelihood of death from infection and bleeding. Treatment for local areas of skin damage is generally conservative; early removal of apparently necrotic tissue is not recommended. Late treatment may involve amputation and skin grafting. A very late complication is the development of skin cancer at heavily irradiated sites.

Patients subjected to large doses of radiation, particularly total body radiation, and surviving the acute effects, are subject to certain ill effects that may develop long after exposure. Delayed hematopoietic disorders are seen in a few cases, and the late development of leukemia occurs in a small percentage of those exposed. Cataracts, and changes in skin and hair, are recorded. Premature aging is postulated chiefly on the basis of work in experimental animals. There is no general treatment or preventative for these effects after radiation. Specific therapeutic measures are available for some effects after they have appeared; i.e., surgery for cataracts, the usual medical treatment for leukemia.

When radiation injury is incurred chronically over a period of years, the acute radiation syndrome is not seen, and the effects are more like those delayed manifestations that have been discussed. Treatment must be individualized. Blood transfusions may be needed for chronic marrow depression; marrow grafts have not been shown to be useful here. Careful observations should be made for early manifestations of skin cancer. The specific measures needed for treatment are combined with a program to avoid additional excessive radiation exposure.

See ACUTE RADIATION SYNDROME, and RADIATION ILLNESS.

TREES, STUDIES. *See* PLANT PHYSIOLOGICAL STUDIES.

TRIAGE

Means culling or sorting. As applied to radiation injuries suffered by a large number of people, as in the explosion of a nuclear weapon, it refers to the process of determining which casualties need urgent treatment, which ones are well enough to go untreated, and which ones are beyond hope of benefit from treatment. In a situation with many casualties and limited medical facilities, it obviously would be important to use the available resources in caring for those patients most likely to be saved; the selection would depend on knowledge of the ACUTE RADIATION SYNDROME (*see* TREATMENT OF RADIATION ILLNESS). In most situations of this type that can be anticipated, however, injuries due to trauma and burns would be so plentiful that triage would not be based chiefly on evidences of radiation injury.

TRITIUM

Tritium ($_1H^3$) is a radioactive isotope of hydrogen, with a mass number 3, and an atomic weight of 3.0221 on the chemical scale. One of the rarest of the atomic species discovered in nature, it exists in the atmosphere in a concentration of 3×10^{-18} gram of tritium per gram of hydrogen-1 (PROTIUM), which constitutes 99.98+% of the natural abundance; DEUTERIUM or heavy hydrogen ($_1H^2$) furnishes about 2% of the natural abundance.

Tritium is formed in nature by cosmic-ray fast neutrons bombarding nitrogen-14 with the following reaction:

$$_7N^{14} + {_0}n^1 \longrightarrow (_7N^{15}) \longrightarrow {_6}C^{12} + {_1}H^3.$$

May also be formed by neutron bombardment of nitrogen-14 after the detonation of an atomic device. Tritium is one of the nuclides measured in the USAEC stratospheric sampling program.

Tritium is the only direct radioactive product resulting from the fusion reaction: $D + D \longrightarrow T + H$ with the production of 4 Mev energy (D = deuterium, T = tritium, and H = hydrogen-1). Tritium may be used in the production of the controlled thermonuclear reaction: $D + T \longrightarrow He^4 + n$, with the production of 18 Mev energy (He = helium, n = neutron).

Tritium has a radioactive half-life of 12.26 years; with body water as the critical organ, a biological half-life of 12 days, and an effective half-life of 12 days. It is a pure beta emitter (β^-) with a maximum energy of 0.0180 Mev, with a RANGE in water of 0.0006 cm. It decays to the stable isotope helium (He^3).

Even though it is a weak beta emitter, it is a potential hazard as an internal emitter, since it is an intimate part of the body chemistry, being part of the DNA. The natural tritium concentration in the biosphere may be calculated to result in a dose rate of 1.8×10^{-3} millirad per year to the soft tissues. The maximum permissible concentration (MPC) for soluble material, with the total body as the critical organ, for a 40-hour work week is 0.2 microcurie per cubic centimeter ($\mu c/cc$) in water and 2×10^{-5} $\mu c/cc$ in air; for a 168-hour week (continuous exposure) the MPC is 0.05 $\mu c/cc$ in water and 7×10^{-6} $\mu c/cc$ in air. The maximum permissible burden in the total body is 2×10^3 microcuries.

For commercial use tritium is usually produced by the action of low-energy neutrons in a nuclear reactor, using a stable isotope of lithium (Li^6), by the nuclear reaction (n,α), with the emission of an alpha particle as follows:

$$_3Li^6 + {_0}n^1 \longrightarrow {_1}H^3 + {_2}He^4.$$

The USAEC made over a million curies available in order to stimulate its use.

It has been used in ground-water studies, in sediment-movement studies and in large-scale hydrology experiments with the labeling of an entire lake (Lake McMillan in New Mexico). Used in oil well logging and in studies of frozen hydrocarbons. Approved for watch and clock dial painting. It is also made by Oak Ridge National Laboratory as tritium-zirconium targets, used for neutron production in particle accelerators.

Used extensively in agricultural research (fifth most frequently used radioisotope); and stands third in frequency in medical research on human subjects (iodine-131, chromium-51, tritium). The following examples, selected from over a hundred tritium-labeled compounds listed for sale, give a picture of the value of tritium labeling in biomedical activity: acetic acid, adenine, benzene, cortisone, estradiol, folic acid, glycerol, methanol, L-noradrenaline, progesterone, stearic acid, thymidine, uracil and water. Such tritium-labeled compounds are used in biomedical research for tracer and metabolic studies, basic studies of cell function, gene functions, chromosome reduplication and genetic studies. Tritiated thymidine has been used to study the effect of irradiation on the incorporation of this specific pyrimidine into DNA both in vitro and in vivo. Its content has been determined in body fluids, in urine, in tissues and in other biological materials. There is an almost unlimited number of possible tracer uses in the biomedical field. Also, since tritium can be attached strongly to carbon, it can serve as a tracer for carbon and in many instances is used in preference to carbon-14 in biomedical research.

TROPOSPHERIC FALLOUT

The troposphere is that part of the atmosphere closest to the earth in which occur all weather phenomena: jet streams, winds, clouds, rain and snow. In the middle latitudes it extends up to about 30,000 to 40,000 feet, being lower at the poles and higher at the equator. Above the troposphere is the stratosphere (see STRATOSPHERIC FALLOUT), and the area dividing the two is called the tropopause.

Tropospheric fallout is composed of bomb debris of relatively small particle size (a few microns to a fraction of a micron in diameter) which has not been carried up to the stratosphere, but which is carried as a radioactive cloud (see CLOUD, RADIO-ACTIVE) in the troposphere. The heavier particles of radioactive material have already descended from the atomic cloud as local fallout in the area where the nuclear device was detonated.

Simple gravitational settling accounts for the deposition of much of the particulate material, but the scavenging effect of moisture precipitation washes out particulate material, and a heavy rain through a cloud produces a hot spot of contamination. Significant tropospheric fallout from a single shot does not continue longer than 3 to 4 weeks, and thus the residence time is relatively short. Because of this time factor, tropospheric fallout is often called intermediate fallout.

The radionuclides of biological interest from tropospheric fallout are strontium-89, iodine-131, barium-140 and cerium-144.

TUMORS DUE TO RADIATION

Irradiation of almost any part of the mammalian body, if it is in sufficient amount, appears to be able to induce tumors. The mechanism of induction is by no means clear, although tumors appear to develop only in tissue extensively damaged by radiation. These "precancerous" areas go through changes over many years before becoming malig-

nant. The theory of somatic mutation as a result of radiation events (see TARGET THEORY) altering a cell has many adherents who believe that very small doses of radiation may induce tumors. Others are convinced that there is a threshold dose below which no tumors will develop. In this controversy the National Academy of Sciences* said, "In view of the many uncertainties, the Committee does not consider it justifiable to predict human tumor incidences from small radiation doses based on extrapolation from the observed incidences following high dosage."

See BONE TUMORS RESULTING FROM RADIATION, CANCER DUE TO RADIATION, LEUKEMIA DUE TO RADIATION and SARCOMA DUE TO RADIATION.

TUNGSTEN

Symbol W (also known as wolfram); atomic number 74; atomic weight 183.86. Discovered by the d'Elhujar brothers in 1783. Occurs as the oxide in wolframite, hubnerite and scheelite. Natural abundance furnished by 5 stable isotopes. Its name in Swedish means heavy stone.

Used industrially as ferrotungsten introduced into steel, for other alloys, in incandescent lamps, and in the manufacture of cemented tungsten carbide-cutting tools.

Ten radioactive isotopes have been identified. Five radioisotopes, W^{180}, W^{181}, W^{182m}, W^{185} and W^{187}, may be produced in sea water as a result of induced activity from the detonation of a nuclear device in contact with the sea. W^{185} is one of 7 radionuclides analyzed for in the stratospheric monitoring program. W^{185} (half-life 73.2 days, β^- and γ emitter) and W^{187} (half-life 24.1 hours, β^- and γ emitter) are both available commercially. Used in tool-wear studies. Tungsten does not usually occur in biological materials. None of the isotopes appear to have any biological, medical or agricultural significance.

TURNOVER TIME

Many of the body constituents continually undergo simultaneous formation and degradation, and the net change in the concentration of the constituent will depend upon the relative rates of synthesis and degradation. In the adult organism, in which many constituents are characterized by constancy of composition, their synthesis and degradation must be equal. Isotope techniques can be used to estimate the rates of such opposing reactions.

The term "turnover" refers to the renewal of a

---

*NAS–NRC. The Biological Effects of Atomic Radiation. Summary Reports. 1960.

substance, and the term "turnover rate" or "renewal rate" is used to indicate the amount of a substance renewed in a given time. Turnover time is the time required to renew completely the amount of substance present in the tissue. The turnover rate or turnover time can be estimated most conveniently by measurement of the rate of disappearance of a radioisotope label from the substance of interest. If the precursor is known, it is also possible to calculate the turnover rate from the time specific activity curves of the precursor and product. (*See* PRECURSOR IDENTIFICATION.) In some cases it is possible to determine the turnover rate by the appearance of the label in the product, without having to identify the precursor. This can be done by administration of the radioactive label over a long time, so that the specific activity of the product approaches a plateau, and in this instance the specific activity of the precursor at such a time will be equal to the specific activity of the product.

This method was used to determine the turnover rate of fibrinogen in the dog. Animals were fed daily with sulfur-labeled methionine for about 3 weeks, at which time the specific activity of the

fibrinogen reached an equilibrium level. The equation for calculation was as follows:

$$2.3 \log \frac{S_{eq}}{S_{eq} - S} = kt$$

where S_{eq} was the specific activity of the fibrinogen at equilibrium, S the specific activity of fibrinogen at time t, and k the fraction renewed per unit of time. It was found in this experiment that the half-turnover time for the fibrinogen in dogs averaged about 4 days.

202 HEARINGS

Hearings conducted by the JOINT COMMITTEE ON ATOMIC ENERGY, during the first 60 days of each session of Congress, to obtain the latest information on the problems relating to the development, use and control of atomic energy. 202 refers to Section 202. Authority and Duty; Chapter 17. Joint Committee on Atomic Energy; Atomic Energy Act of 1954 as amended. The Section also provides that the members of the Joint Committee shall report to their respective bodies as to matters within the jurisdiction of the Joint Committee.

UCLA LABORATORY OF NUCLEAR MEDICINE AND RADIATION BIOLOGY

The Laboratory of Nuclear Medicine and Radiation Biology supported by USAEC is a laboratory of the Department of Biophysics and Nuclear Medicine of the University of California Medical Center, Los Angeles. From 1947 through 1960 the research effort was known as "UCLA Atomic Energy Project." The change to the present name came July 1, 1958, and a new building providing 60,000 square feet of adequate laboratory facilities was provided in July, 1961.

The laboratory staff consisting of over 200 scientists, technicians and supporting personnel includes: physicians, pathologists, zoologists, physicists, plant physiologists, physical chemists, biochemists, soil chemists, animal and plant ecologists, toxicologists, electron microscopists, spectroscopists, physiologists and radiologists.

The program encompasses a wide scope of research interest including areas of Somatic Effects of Radiation, Combating Detrimental Effects of Radiation, Molecular and Cellular Level Studies, Environmental Radiation Studies, Radiological and Health Physics Instrumentation, Chemical Toxicity, Cancer Research, and Selected Beneficial Applications. The over-all objectives of the Laboratory may be summarized as follows:

1. Investigation of the effects of ionizing radiation on systems of biological significance and on living organisms, and investigation of methods of minimizing or preventing the detrimental effects of ionizing radiation.

2. The assessment and study of the immediate and long-term consequences of the detonation or operation of nuclear devices on the environment, on flora, fauna and man.

3. The development of beneficial uses of ionizing radiation and radioactive substances in medicine and biology.

4. Investigation of the dynamic aspects of physiological and biochemical processes in man, animals and plants and how these processes are modified by radiation and related pathological states.

5. Research and development of new and more efficient radiation detection instruments.

6. Research, including field studies and operational assistance in connection with the conduct of weapons tests and biomedical and civil effects experiments at such tests conducted at either the Nevada Test Site or the Pacific testing areas.

7. The conduct of training and educational activities in the biological and medical aspects of radiation and related fields.

One of the distinctive programs of the Laboratory is the radioecology field study of the Nevada Test Site and the immediate environs. It is particularly important that this work be carried out vigorously as planned. The Laboratory, as an addition to its program of basic research plans progressively increased emphasis on molecular biology.

In addition to research, the Laboratory has a strong education and training program, with both graduate and postdoctoral education and training in research provided for United States and foreign physicians and scientists.

ULCERS, RADIATION-INDUCED

Heavy doses of radiation may lead to destruction of tissue or loss of substance (i.e., an ulcer) on a skin surface or on mucous membrane, causing gradual disintegration and death of damaged tissues. A radiation-induced ulcer may be precancerous, e.g., some of the early x-ray skin ulcers later developed into cancer of the skin. (See SKIN, RADIATION EFFECTS ON.)

Of the more heavily exposed Marshall Island group on Rongelap (175 roentgens [r] total gamma dose in air and probably 2,000 r beta particle radiation), about 90 per cent of the 64 people developed multiple, spotty, pigmented lesions on exposed parts of the body; of these, 20 per cent developed ulcerating lesions, and secondary infection occurred in a few. These ulcerating burns are very painful, are likely to develop secondary infection, require longer to heal, may result in atrophy and scarring of the skin, and may require skin grafting. All the skin lesions in the Marshall Islanders healed spontaneously.

In experimental animals (swine) and in man following heavy WHOLE BODY IRRADIATION ulcers frequently develop in the mucous membranes around the gingival margins, buccal mucosa and the tonsils. These ulcers do not ordinarily penetrate deeper than the submucosal layer but are very slow in healing.

In those individuals with the gastrointestinal form of acute RADIATION ILLNESS ulceration may appear in the walls of the gastrointestinal tract anywhere, but it is more likely in the large intestine and stomach. These ulcers usually extend no deeper than the submucosa or the muscularis mucosae and do not perforate. Ulcers do tend to hemorrhage, however, and may be a major contributing factor in death. The intestinal ulcers tend to be elongated in the longitudinal axis of the intestine, and the ulcers in the stomach tend to have margins that are elevated, roughly circular and clearly demarcated. These ulcers may lead to bacterial invasion of the blood stream.

ULTRAVIOLET RADIATION

Electromagnetic radiation from the ultraviolet region, i.e., about 4,000 Å (angstroms or 10^{-8} centimeters) to 400 Å. This range has pronounced ionizing effects. Rapidly absorbed in most forms of matter. Not visible.

UNDERGROUND BURST

A nuclear explosion with its center or zero point more than $5W^{0.3}$ feet below the ground surface, where W is the explosive yield in kilotons. An underground burst may be shallow and break through to the surface, or may be deep and fully contained underground.

Shallow Underground Burst. If a nuclear device were dropped from the air and penetrated loose or sandy soil to a depth of 50 feet before exploding, the following phenomena would be observed (assuming an energy yield of 100 kilotons):

The usual fireball forms and breaks through the surface of the earth, carrying large quantities of soil, rock and debris up into the air in a hollow column (see Figure U–1) similar to that formed in an underwater burst. The amount of earth moved in the first 2 seconds is fantastic—over a million

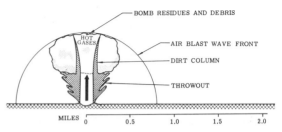

FIGURE U–2. CHRONOLOGICAL DEVELOPMENT OF A 100-KILOTON SHALLOW UNDERGROUND BURST: 2.0 SECONDS AFTER DETONATION.

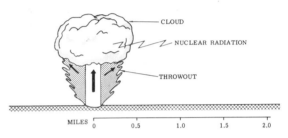

FIGURE U–3. CHRONOLOGICAL DEVELOPMENT OF A 100-KILOTON SHALLOW UNDERGROUND BURST: 9.0 SECONDS AFTER DETONATION.

tons in the case of a 100-kiloton device, leaving a crater 120 feet deep and 720 feet across; for a 1-megaton device the crater would be 190 feet deep and 1,400 feet across and about 10 million tons of soil and rock would be hurled upward from the earth's surface. The development of the 100-kiloton burst at the end of the first 2 seconds is shown schematically in Figure U–2.

A highly radioactive atomic cloud, containing large quantities of radioactive debris, is formed above the center of detonation as the hot gases begin to cool and condense. A shock wave (see **BLAST PHYSICAL PHENOMENA**) or 'ground wave'* is generated in the earth, and a blast wave is formed in the air.

By the end of 9 seconds (Fig. U–3) the larger pieces of rock and other material are falling back to the earth, but the atomic cloud is continuing to rise and to give off intense initial nuclear radiation.

As the 'throwout' particles descend to earth they join the outward movement at the base and by 45 seconds (Fig. U–4) a definite base surge (see **UNDERWATER BURST**) is being formed. The extent of this radioactive base surge depends upon the energy yield of the explosion, the depth of the burst and the nature of the soil—sandy soil being most conducive to movement.

FIGURE U–1. SHALLOW UNDERGROUND BURST, NEVADA TEST SITE, 1951.

*Terms in single quotes, plus other related terms not treated separately will be defined later in this item.

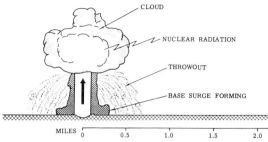

FIGURE U–4. CHRONOLOGICAL DEVELOPMENT OF A 100-KILOTON SHALLOW UNDERGROUND BURST: 45 SECONDS AFTER DETONATION.

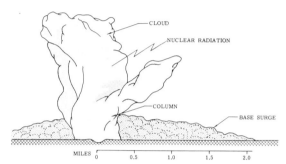

FIGURE U–5. CHRONOLOGICAL DEVELOPMENT OF A 100-KILOTON SHALLOW UNDERGROUND BURST: 4.5 MINUTES AFTER DETONATION.

At 4.5 minutes (Fig. U-5) the base surge has increased in height and area and is beginning to merge with the atomic cloud. Radioactive fallout over a large area can be expected from this type of detonation.

Almost all the thermal radiation and most of the initial nuclear neutron radiation will be absorbed by the soil, causing extensive induced radiation in various elements of the soil. (See RADIONUCLIDES PRODUCED IN AIR, WATER AND SOIL.)

Deep Underground Burst. A nuclear explosion at such a depth that there is little or no venting of weapon debris through the surface of the ground. The phenomena are illustrated by a description of a 1.7-kiloton detonation 790 feet below the surface in a chamber 6 feet × 6 feet × 7 feet, hollowed out of a geological "tuff" medium.

First, the energy was released in less than 1 microsecond, the pressure in the chamber rose to several million atmospheres within a few microseconds and the temperature reached about a million degrees. In the second, or hydrodynamic stage, lasting a few hundredths of a second, the chamber expanded as a result of the terrific pressure to produce a spherical cavity 62 feet in radius. The shock crushed the rock to a radius of 130 feet and fractured it out to 180 feet and continued outward until it became attenuated. Seismic signals

were detected at a distance of several hundred miles and could be described as a "minor" earthquake. At the end of this phase the cavity was lined with a shell of molten rock about 4 inches thick which in the third stage, lasting a minute or so, flowed down and collected at the bottom of the cavity. Here it "froze" to form a glassy mass which contained 65 to 80 per cent of the total fission product radioactivity. The third stage ended with the collapse of the roof, enlarging the chamber upward by about 400 feet, and with dropping temperature. In the final long-term or fourth stage the remaining heat gradually diffused outward, and the radioactive material began to decay.

The following additional terms are related to the subject of underground burst:

Base Surge. *See* UNDERWATER BURST.

Contained Underground Burst. An underground detonation at such a depth that none of the radioactive residues escape through the surface of the ground.

Crater. See separate item.

Free Earth Measurements. Measurements of acceleration, velocity, displacement, impulse, and pressure produced in the earth by an explosion. Quantitative determinations can be made without being influenced by geological changes in ground structure.

Ground Roll. Surface waves propagated radially from the point of detonation, following an underground explosion.

Ground Wave. A wave formed in the ground by the blast from a nuclear explosion. Three types of waves are formed: longitudinal waves (compression), transverse waves (shear), and surface waves (similar to ripples in water).

Shock Wave. *See* BLAST PHYSICAL PHENOMENA.

Throwout. Pieces of rock, soil, and other debris thrown out or falling out as dust or water droplets following the shallow underground detonation of a nuclear device. Similar to rainout following an underwater burst.

UNDERWATER BURST

The detonation of a nuclear device with its center or zero point below the surface of the water. Such a burst produces certain unique responses. If the detonation of a 100-kiloton yield device occurs at a depth of about 100 feet the bubbles of intensely hot gases will burst through the surface of the water, carrying a 'dome'* of water over it (Fig. U–6). Prior to breaking through the surface, the

---

*Words enclosed by single quotes are defined at the end of this item.

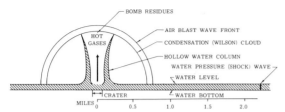

FIGURE U–6. CHRONOLOGICAL DEVELOPMENT OF A
100-KILOTON SHALLOW UNDERWATER BURST: 2 SECONDS
AFTER DETONATION.

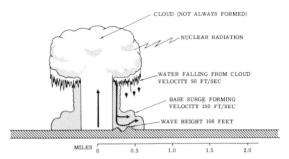

FIGURE U–8. CHRONOLOGICAL DEVELOPMENT OF A
100-KILOTON SHALLOW UNDERWATER BURST: 20 SECONDS
AFTER DETONATION.

shock wave moving outward produces a 'slick' on
the surface. The dome soon collapses, but the
hollow 'column' of water and spray are shot up to
a height of more than a mile in 2 seconds. A direct
shock wave (see BLAST PHYSICAL PHENOMENA) results from the terrific force of the explosion and
travels through the water at such speed that it is 2
miles from surface zero in the first 2 seconds. The
shock wave which is formed in air moves more
slowly, traveling only 0.8 mile in the first 2 seconds. Sometimes a condensation cloud (see FIRE-
BALL) of condensed water droplets is formed which
lasts only a second or two.

At about 12 seconds after the detonation (see
Figure U–7) the column of water has reached its
maximum height of a little more than a mile and is
about 3,300 feet in diameter with the wall of water
500 feet in thickness. The water is beginning to fall
back from the column and this highly radioactive
mist together with the outward moving water near
the base of the column forms the ring-shaped 'base
surge' moving at an initial speed of 200 feet per
second. The bomb residue vents through the
column forming the typical highly radioactive
atomic cloud. The enormous force of the explosion
causes waves to form, the first of which may be 176
feet in height (crest to trough) and at 12 seconds
will have traveled about 1,800 feet from surface
zero.

Figure U–8, showing events at 20 seconds after
detonation, indicates that the column is beginning

to collapse, producing a massive water 'rainout.'
The base surge is now about 1,000 feet high and a
half mile from ground zero, traveling out in an
ever widening circle at about 150 feet per second.
The first water wave is about 2,000 feet from the
zero point and its height has decreased to a little
over 100 feet, but other waves are forming and
following it.

By the end of the first minute (Fig. U–9) the
water rainout or fallout is beginning to reach the
surface and the radioactive base surge cloud has
moved away from the bottom of the column, its
height now 1,300 feet and outward motion slowed
to 75 feet per second. The atomic cloud is enlarging
and moving upward, and several waves have
formed on the surface of the water.

Figure U–10 shows events at the end of 2.5
minutes. The leading face of the base surge is now
more than 2 miles from zero and its height about
2,000 feet and rising from the surface. The greatest
spread is about 2 1/2 miles (5 miles across) reached
in 4 minutes. Because of decay and dilution the
radioactivity of the base surge is now only 1/20

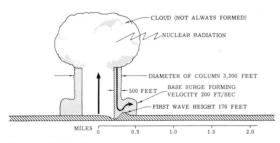

FIGURE U–7. CHRONOLOGICAL DEVELOPMENT OF A
100-KILOTON SHALLOW UNDERWATER BURST: 12 SECONDS
AFTER DETONATION.

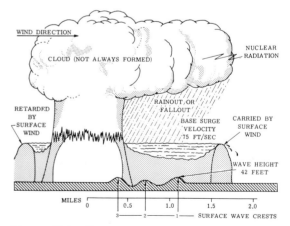

FIGURE U–9. CHRONOLOGICAL DEVELOPMENT OF A
100-KILOTON SHALLOW UNDERWATER BURST: 1 MINUTE
AFTER DETONATION.

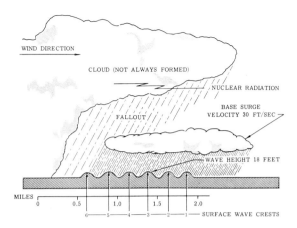

FIGURE U–10. CHRONOLOGICAL DEVELOPMENT OF A 100-KILOTON SHALLOW UNDERWATER BURST: 2.5 MINUTES AFTER DETONATION.

the amount it was at the end of 1 minute. A continuous cloud is formed by the water fallout and condensation which ultimately is dispersed by air movement. In an underwater burst almost all the thermal radiation and most of the initial nuclear radiation is absorbed by the water, resulting in the formation of many different radionuclides (see RADIONUCLIDES PRODUCED IN AIR, WATER, AND SOIL [BOMB]).

The following terms are related to the subject of underwater burst:

Base Surge.   The cloud which rolls out from the bottom of the column produced by the subsurface detonation of a nuclear device. For underwater bursts, the base surge is, in effect, a cloud of water droplets which has the flowing properties of a homogenous liquid. For shallow underground bursts, the base surge is made up of small solid particles but behaves like a fluid. Soft earth favors base surge formation.

Column (or Plume).   A cylinder of water and spray ascending from an underwater burst in which the hot gases under very high pressure, formed in the detonation, are vented to the atmosphere. An underground burst causes a column of dirt which ascends the same way.

Dome.   The mound of water and spray pushed ahead of the hot gas bubbles and thrown up into the air over the point of detonation of an underwater burst of a nuclear device when the shock wave reaches the surface. Frequently called the 'spray dome.'

Rainout.   Large quantities of water descending from the dome and column (and from the atomic cloud, if formed) formed by the underwater detonation of a nuclear device. Sometimes referred to as the "massive water fallout."

Slick.   A circular, rapidly advancing and increasing in size patch of water whiter than the surrounding water. The sign of an advancing shock wave from an underwater burst which can be seen on the water surface when it is calm. This phenomenon is caused by small droplets of water at the surface being hurled short distances into the air; the resulting entrainment of air makes the shocked water surface look white.

Spray Dome.   Same as 'dome.'

Surge or Surge Phenomena.   Same as 'base surge.'

UNITED NATIONS

The United Nations has a number of specialized agencies interested in various aspects of atomic energy. The principal ones are:

Food and Agriculture Organization (FAO).

International Atomic Energy Agency (IAEA). The IAEA has been established by the UN as the principal agency for conducting and coordinating the program relating to peaceful uses of atomic energy.

International Civil Aviation Organization (ICAO).

International Labor Organization (ILO).

Inter-Governmental Maritime Consultative Organization (IMCO).

United Nations Education, Scientific, and Cultural Organization (UNESCO).

United Nations Scientific Committee on the Effects of Atomic Radiation (UNSCEAR).

World Health Organization (WHO).

World Meteorological Organization (WMO).

UNITED NATIONS SCIENTIFIC COMMITTEE ON THE EFFECTS OF ATOMIC RADIATION (UNSCEAR)

A committee of the United Nations, established by the General Assembly on 3 December 1955 by resolution 913 (X). The committee was requested to receive, assemble in useful form, review and evaluate reports on environmental levels of radioactivity and on reports dealing with scientific observations and experiments relevant to the effects of ionizing radiation upon man (somatic and genetic). It was requested to recommend uniform standards for all activities concerned with sample collection (see SAMPLING PROGRAM FOR RADIOACTIVE FALLOUT). Yearly reports are required and interim reports are suggested as material becomes available. A special report* was submitted to the

_____

*Report of the United Nations Scientific Committee on the Effects of Atomic Radiation. General Assembly, Official Records, Thirteenth Session, Supplement No. 17 (A3838), New York, 1958.

General Assembly in 1958, which reviewed detailed facts concerning the effects of ionizing radiation upon man and his environment. A second report* brought the facts up to date.

UNSTABLE STATE

Capable of undergoing spontaneous change or disintegration. The nucleus of an atom is unstable when it is capable of spontaneous disintegration (radioactivity). The excited state of a system, decaying by isomeric transition to the ground state.

See STABLE STATE and METASTABLE STATE.

UPTAKE

The amount of an element or radioactive isotope absorbed into a plant or animal body, compared with the amount available. The amount of uptake depends largely upon the solubility of the chemical form in which the element or radioisotope is presented. A completely insoluble form would not be absorbed by the plant; e.g., plutonium deposited in the soil is very weakly taken up by the plant, whereas phosphorus compounds are usually readily absorbed. The same is true in the human body; e.g., elemental gold is almost insoluble and therefore the uptake from the intestine would be very low, whereas iodine would be almost completely and immediately absorbed into the body. Another factor affecting uptake is the discrimination factor, whereby the plant or animal body tends to absorb one element in preference to another when both are chemically similar and equally available.

See AQUATIC ORGANISMS, UPTAKE OF RADIONUCLIDES.

URANIUM

Symbol U; atomic number 92; atomic weight 238.07. A hard, white metal, ductile, malleable and radioactive. Discovered by Klaproth in pitchblende in 1789. Named for the planet Uranus. In addition to pitchblende (75–90%) U_3O_8, occurs in carnotite (62–65%), which is found in Colorado and Utah, the Republic of the Congo (Leopoldville), and Great Bear Lake region of Canada. Abundance furnished by 3 naturally occurring radioactive isotopes: U^{238} (U_1) 99.28%; U^{235} (AcU or actinouranium) 0.715%; and U^{234} (U_{11}) 0.0058%.

U^{234}, radioactive half-life 2.48×10^5 years; with bone as the critical organ, biological half-life 300 days, effective half-life 300 days; alpha emitter, is nonfissionable, nonfertile, and not of practical

importance in nuclear energy. Occurs in the URANIUM RADIOACTIVE SERIES.

U^{235} radioactive half-life 7.13×10^8 years; biological and effective half-life the same as U^{234}; alpha emitter, is the only one of the 3 primary fission materials that occurs naturally. Used as a fuel in nuclear reactor operation and as fissionable material in the manufacture of nuclear weapons. Progenitor of the ACTINIUM RADIOACTIVE SERIES.

U^{238}, radioactive half-life 4.49×10^9 years; biological and effective half-life the same as U^{234}; alpha emitter, of importance for it is a fertile† material from which is obtained the primary fissionable material, plutonium. It will also undergo fission under fast neutron bombardment. Progenitor of the uranium radioactive series.

Eleven radioactive isotopes have been made artificially. U^{233}, radioactive half-life 1.62×10^5 years, alpha emitter, is of importance as the third primary fissionable material. Is formed from the fertile thorium. Occurs in the neptunium radioactive series. U^{230}, half-life 20.8 days, alpha emitter, occurs in the COLLATERAL URANIUM RADIOACTIVE SERIES.

None of the uranium radioactive isotopes is significant in biological, medical or agricultural activity. Uranium and its salts are highly toxic and great care is exercised in mining, milling, refining and conversion, and in metal production to prevent inhalation or ingestion of dust or particles. Uranium is a definite kidney poison. Determination of the amount of uranium excreted in the urine is a valuable index of previous exposure to uranium. The USAEC safety record in handling uranium is an excellent one with no serious cases of poisoning among the many thousands of employees working over the years.

The maximum permissible concentration (MPC) has been determined for 8 uranium radioisotopes. For the 168-hour week (continuous exposure to soluble material), with the gastrointestinal tract as the critical organ, 3×10^{-4} microcuries per cubic centimeter ($\mu c/cc$) in water is the MPC for U^{232}, U^{233}, U^{234}, U^{235} and U^{236}. With the critical organ bone, 2×10^{-10} $\mu c/cc$ in air is the MPC for U^{233}, U^{234}, U^{235} and U^{236}; 3×10^{-11} $\mu c/cc$ for U^{232}.

URANIUM RADIOACTIVE SERIES

Table U–1 depicts the decay disintegration chain of the uranium series and parent-daughter transmutation from uranium-238 (uranium I) to lead-206 (Radium G). Named for uranium, the first member of the series.

The table details the name of the element, the

---

*Report of the United Nations Scientific Committee on the Effects of Atomic Radiation. General Assembly, Official Records, 17th Session. Supplement 16 (A5216) United Nations, New York, 1962. Available, Sales Office, United Nations, New York, New York, for $5.00.

---

†Capable of being transformed into fissionable substance by capture of a neutron.

TABLE U–1.   URANIUM RADIOACTIVE SERIES

Uranium (Uranium I) $(_{92}U^{238})$ $\xrightarrow[\alpha]{4.5 \times 10^9 \text{ yr}}$

Thorium (Uranium X_1) $)_{90}Th^{234}$ $\xrightarrow[\beta]{24.1 \text{ days}}$

Protactinium (Uranium X_2) $(_{91}Pa^{234})$ $\xrightarrow[\beta]{1.14 \text{ min}}$

Uranium (Uranium II) $(_{92}U^{234})$ $\xrightarrow[\alpha]{2.35 \times 10^5 \text{ yr}}$

Thorium (Ionium) $(_{90}Th^{230})$ $\xrightarrow[\alpha]{8.0 \times 10^4 \text{ yr}}$

Radium $(_{88}Ra^{226})$ $\xrightarrow[\alpha]{1.62 \times 10^3 \text{ yr}}$

Radon (Ra Emanation) $(_{86}Rn^{222})$ $\xrightarrow[\alpha]{3.82 \text{ days}}$

Polonium (Radium A) $(_{84}Po^{218})$ $\xrightarrow[\alpha \text{ and } \beta]{3.05 \text{ min}}$

α β
99.96%   0.04%

Lead (Radium B) $(_{82}Pb^{214})$ $\xrightarrow[\beta]{26.8 \text{ min}}$

Astatine (Astatine-218) $(_{85}At^{218})$ $\xrightarrow[\alpha]{2 \text{ sec}}$

Bismuth (Radium C) $(_{83}Bi^{214})$ $\xrightarrow[\beta \text{ and } \alpha]{19.7 \text{ min}}$

β α
99.96%   0.04%

Polonium (Radium C′) $(_{84}Po^{214})$ $\xrightarrow[\alpha]{1.5 \times 10^{-4} \text{ sec}}$

Thallium (Radium C″) $(_{81}Tl^{210})$ $\xrightarrow[\beta]{1.32 \text{ min}}$

Lead (Radium D) $(_{82}Pb^{210})$ $\xrightarrow[\beta]{22 \text{ yr}}$

Bismuth (Radium E) $(_{83}Bi^{210})$ $\xrightarrow[\beta \text{ and } \alpha]{5.0 \text{ days}}$

β α
100% 10^{-5}%

Polonium (Radium F) $(_{84}Po^{210})$ $\xrightarrow[\alpha]{140 \text{ days}}$

Thallium (Thallium-206) $(_{81}Tl^{206})$ $\xrightarrow[\beta]{4.23 \text{ min}}$

Lead (Radium G) $(_{82}Pb^{206})$ Stable end product.

TABLE U–2. COLLATERAL URANIUM RADIOACTIVE SERIES

Protactinium	$(_{91}Pa^{230})$	$\xrightarrow[\beta^-]{17.7\ days}$	Uranium	$(_{92}U^{230})$	$\xrightarrow[\alpha]{20.8\ days}$
Thorium	$(_{90}Th^{226})$	$\xrightarrow[\alpha]{30.9\ min}$	Radium	$(_{88}Ra^{222})$	$\xrightarrow[\alpha]{38\ sec}$
Radon	$(_{86}Rn^{218})$	$\xrightarrow[\alpha]{0.02\ sec}$	Polonium (Radium C′)	$(_{84}Po^{214})$	$\longrightarrow$

Uranium Radioactive Series.

Protactinium	$(_{91}Pa^{226})$	$\xrightarrow[\alpha]{1.8\ min}$	Actinium	$(_{89}Ac^{222})$	$\xrightarrow[\alpha]{5.5\ sec}$
Francium	$(_{87}Fr^{218})$	$\xrightarrow[\alpha]{5\ \times\ 10^{-3}\ sec}$	Astatine	$(_{85}At^{214})$	$\xrightarrow[\alpha]{2\ \times\ 10^{-6}\ sec}$

Bismuth $(_{86}Bi^{210})$ (Radium E) $\longrightarrow$ Uranium Radioactive Series.

corresponding radioelement, the symbol, the radioactive half-life, and the type of radiation given off. In disintegrations in which an alpha (α) particle is emitted, the atomic weight of the daughter element is 4 units less than that of the parent, because an alpha particle on the atomic weight scale has a mass of 4 and thus the loss of 1 alpha particle would reduce the weight by 4. On the other hand, since a beta (β) particle is an electron with a negligible mass, the daughter element in this disintegration has the same weight as the parent. It was found in the THORIUM RADIOACTIVE SERIES that the atomic weights of all members of the series could be represented by 4n, where n is an integer varying from 58 for thorium ($4 \times 58 = 232$, the atomic weight of thorium) to 52 for lead ($4 \times 52 = 208$). In the same way it can be shown that the formula for the uranium series is 4n + 2. For example, uranium-238 is $4 \times 59 + 2 = 238$, and lead-206 is $4 \times 51 + 2 = 206$.

Two collateral radioactive series of uranium are presented in Table U–2. These have different parents from the main series, but they become identical when, in the course of disintegration, they have a member in common.

URINALYSIS FOR RADIOACTIVITY

Since many radionuclides are excreted according to a fairly definite pattern, it is possible to estimate the amount of a radionuclide in the organism by the amount excreted in the urine. Radiochemical techniques usually consist of the following: sample preparation (total 24-hour sample desirable); chemical isolation of radionuclides; quantitative determination by measurement of radioactivity;

and identification of the radionuclide. Chemical separation is effected by physio-chemical methods of coprecipitation, adsorption, ion exchange, etc. Quantitative determination is accomplished by counting the alpha-, beta- or gamma-activity. To identify and measure the amount of each radionuclide, modes of RADIOACTIVE DECAY; ABSORPTION (for beta emitters); SPECTROMETRY (for gamma emitters); and TRACKS in nuclear emulsions (for alpha emitters) are carried out.

Experimental work has demonstrated that radionuclides are eliminated by several routes: Uranium and plutonium are excreted primarily in urine; strontium in feces and urine; radon in breath (RADON BREATH ANALYSIS); tritium in perspiration and urine. These studies are frequently referred to as bio-assays. All major laboratories have the capability of determining the presence of radionuclides in the urine and many have available special techniques for the other determinations.

The excretion pattern varies somewhat at early times according to the route of administration; at a long time after administration excretion rate is less affected by the route of entry.

URINARY BLADDER, RADIATION EFFECTS ON

The epithelium lining the bladder is relatively radiosensitive. The cells often appear vacuolated and desquamated. Hemorrhage into the mucous membrane of the urinary tract is often extensive and may lead to death of the superficial epithelium with subsequent erosion. This may account for the hematuria in the last few days of life following exposure to a lethal dose of radiation, and for the blood clots in the bladder found at autopsy.

USAEC

Used throughout this encyclopedia for United States Atomic Energy Commission.

See ATOMIC ENERGY COMMISSION.

USAEC DEPOSITORY LIBRARIES

Collections of USAEC reports available for use by the general public. Also available are atomic energy reports of countries other than the United States that are abstracted in Nuclear Science Abstracts. The following list gives the libraries or organizations where collections of reports are maintained.

ALABAMA
Auburn, Auburn University
Birmingham, Public Library

ARIZONA
Tucson, University of Arizona

ARKANSAS
Fayetteville, University of Arkansas

CALIFORNIA
Berkeley, University of California
Los Angeles, University of California
Menlo Park, Stanford Research Institute
San Diego, Public Library

COLORADO
Denver, Public Library

CONNECTICUT
New Haven, Yale University

DELAWARE
Newark, University of Delaware

DISTRICT OF COLUMBIA
Washington, Library of Congress

FLORIDA
Coral Gables, University of Miami
Gainesville, University of Florida

GEORGIA
Atlanta, Georgia Institute of Technology

HAWAII
Honolulu, University of Hawaii

ILLINOIS
Chicago, John Crerar Library
Chicago, University of Chicago
Evanston, Northwestern University
Urbana, University of Illinois

INDIANA
Indianapolis, Public Library
Lafayette, Purdue University

IOWA
Ames, Iowa State University

KANSAS
Manhattan, Kansas State University

KENTUCKY
Lexington, University of Kentucky
Louisville, University of Louisville

LOUISIANA
Baton Rouge, Louisiana State University
New Orleans, Tulane University

MARYLAND
Baltimore, Johns Hopkins University
College Park, University of Maryland

MASSACHUSETTS
Cambridge, Harvard University
Cambridge, Massachusetts Institute of Technology

MICHIGAN
Ann Arbor, University of Michigan
Detroit, Public Library

MINNESOTA
Minneapolis, University of Minnesota

MISSOURI
Kansas City, Linda Hall Library
Rolla, University of Missouri School of Mines and Metallurgy
St. Louis, Washington University

MONTANA
Bozeman, Montana State College

NEVADA
Reno, University of Nevada

NEW JERSEY
Princeton, Princeton University

NEW MEXICO
Albuquerque, University of New Mexico

NEW YORK
Buffalo, University of Buffalo
Ithaca, Cornell University
New York, Atomic Industrial Forum, Inc.
New York, Columbia University
New York, Public Library
Rochester, University of Rochester
Schenectady, Union College
Syracuse, Syracuse University
Troy, Rensselaer Polytechnic Institute

NORTH CAROLINA
Charlotte, Charlotte and Mecklenburg County Public Library
Durham, Duke University
Raleigh, North Carolina State College

NORTH DAKOTA
Grand Forks, University of North Dakota

OHIO
Cincinnati, University of Cincinnati
Cleveland, Public Library
Columbus, Ohio State University
Toledo, University of Toledo
Youngstown, Youngstown University

OKLAHOMA
Stillwater, Oklahoma State University

OREGON
Corvallis, Oregon State College
Portland, Reed College

PENNSYLVANIA
Philadelphia, University of Pennsylvania
Pittsburgh, Carnegie Library
University Park, Pennsylvania State University

PUERTO RICO
Rio Piedras, University of Puerto Rico

RHODE ISLAND
Providence, Brown University

SOUTH CAROLINA
Columbia, University of South Carolina

TENNESSEE
Knoxville, University of Tennessee
Memphis, Public Library
Nashville, Joint University Libraries

TEXAS
Austin, University of Texas
College Station, Agricultural and Mechanical College
of Texas
Dallas, Southern Methodist University
Houston, Rice Institute
San Antonio, Public Library

UTAH
Salt Lake City, University of Utah

VIRGINIA
Blacksburg, Virginia Polytechnic Institute
Charlottesville, University of Virginia

WASHINGTON
Pullman, Washington State University
Seattle, University of Washington

WEST VIRGINIA
Morgantown, West Virginia University

WISCONSIN
Madison, University of Wisconsin
Milwaukee, Public Library

WYOMING
Laramie, University of Wyoming

See USAEC DEPOSITORY LIBRARIES, FOREIGN.

USAEC DEPOSITORY LIBRARIES, FOREIGN

Collections of USAEC reports are maintained for public use in 86 libraries and organizations located in 60 different countries as follows:

ARGENTINA
Buenos Aires, Comisión Nacional de Energía Atómica

AUSTRALIA
Canberra, Australian National Library
Sutherland, New South Wales, Australian Atomic
Energy Commission

AUSTRIA
Vienna, Zentral Bibliothek der Physikalischen Institute der Universität

BELGIUM
Mol-Donk, Centre d'Etude de l'Energie Nucleaire

BRAZIL
Rio de Janeiro, Instituto Brasileiro de Bibliografia e
Documentacao
São Paulo, Instituto de Energia Atomica, Cidade
Universitaria São Paulo

BURMA
Rangoon, Union of Burma Applied Research Institute, Atomic Energy Center Library

CANADA
Hamilton, McMaster University
Ottawa, National Research Council Library
Vancouver, University of British Columbia

CEYLON
Colombo, University of Ceylon

CHILE
Santiago, Instituto de Fisica y Matematicas, Universidad de Chile

CHINA
Hsinchu, Taiwan, Free China, National Tsing Hua
University

COLOMBIA
Bogota, Instituto De Asuntos Nucleares

COSTA RICA
San Pedro, University of Costa Rica Library

DENMARK
Risö, Danish Atomic Energy Commission

DOMINICAN REPUBLIC
Santo Domingo, National Palace

ECUADOR
Quito, Escuela Politécnica Nacional

EGYPT
Cairo, Atomic Energy Commission

EL SALVADOR
San Salvador, Universidad de El Salvador, Biblioteca
de Energia Nuclear

ENGLAND
Birmingham, Central Library
Bristol, Central Library
Kingston upon Hull, Central Library
Leeds, Central Library
Liverpool, Central Library
London, Central Library, Acton
London, Science Museum Library, South Kensington
Manchester, Central Library
Newcastle upon Tyne, Central Library
Nottingham, Public Libraries
Sheffield, Central Library

FINLAND
Helsinki, Teknillisen Korkeakoulun Kirjasto

FRANCE
Gif-sur-Yvette, Centre d'Etudes Nucléaires de Saclay
Paris, Academie des Sciences

GERMANY
Berlin, Hahn-Meitner-Institut für Kernforschung
Berlin
Frankfurt/Main, Gmelin-Institut
Munich, Technische Hochschule, Bibliothek

GHANA
Accra, University College of Ghana

GREECE
Athens, Greek Atomic Energy Commission

GUATEMALA
  Guatemala, Comisión Nacional de Energía Nuclear

HAITI
  Port au Prince, University of Haiti

HONDURAS
  Tegucigalpa, Comisión Hondureña de Energía Atómica

ICELAND
  Reykjavik, University of Iceland, Atomic Energy Library

INDIA
  Bombay, Department of Atomic Energy

INDONESIA
  Bandung, Java, Bandung Institute of Technology
  Djogjakarta, Java, Science Faculty, Gadjah Mada University

IRAN
  Tehran, Tehran University Center for Nuclear Studies

IRAQ
  Baghdad, Iraqi Atomic Energy Commission

IRELAND
  Dublin, University College

ISRAEL
  Rehovoth, Israel Atomic Energy Commission

ITALY
  Casella, Centro di Studi Nucleari di Ispra del C.N.R.N.
  Rome, Comitato Nazionale per le Ricerche Nucleari

JAPAN
  Tokyo, Science Section, Diet Library

KOREA
  Seoul, Office of Atomic Energy

LEBANON
  Beirut, American University

LUXEMBOURG
  Luxembourg, Ministry of Transport and Electricity

MEXICO
  Mexico, D.F., Comisión Nacional de Energía Nuclear

NETHERLANDS
  The Hague, Reactor Centrum Nederland

NEW ZEALAND
  Wellington, Department of Scientific and Industrial Research

NORTHERN IRELAND
  Belfast, City Library

NORWAY
  Lilleström, Institutt för Atomenergi

PAKISTAN
  Lahore, West Pakistan, Atomic Energy Centre

PERU
  Lima, Junta de Control de Energia Atomica

PHILIPPINE REPUBLIC
  Manila, Philippine Atomic Energy Commission

POLAND
  Warsaw, Biura Pelnomocnika Rzadu do Spraw Wykorzystania Energii Jadrowej

PORTUGAL
  Lisbon, Junta de Energia Nuclear

REPUBLIC OF SOUTH AFRICA
  Pretoria, Atomic Energy Board Library

REPUBLIC OF THE CONGO
  Leopoldville, Université Lovanium

SCOTLAND
  Glasgow, Mitchell Library

SPAIN
  Madrid, Junta de Energía Nuclear, Bibliotaca Documentación y Publicaciones, Ciudad Universitaria

SWEDEN
  Stockholm, Aktiebolaget Atomenergi

SWITZERLAND
  Zurich, Institut für Physik, Eidg. Technische Hochschule

THAILAND
  Bangkok, Office of the Thai Atomic Energy Commission, Department of Science

TURKEY
  Ankara, Turkish Atomic Energy Commission, Atomic Energy Library

URUGUAY
  Montevideo, Comision Nacional de Energia Atomica

VENEZUELA
  Caracas, Instituto Venezolano de Investigaciones Científicas

VIET-NAM
  Saigon, Office of Atomic Energy

YUGOSLAVIA
  Belgrade, Federal Commission for Nuclear Energy

In International Agencies

AUSTRIA
  Vienna, International Atomic Energy Agency

BELGIUM
  Brussels, La Bibliotheque EURATOM

FRANCE
  Paris, European Nuclear Energy Agency, O.E.C.D.

ITALY
  Ispra, EURATOM Research Center

SWITZERLAND
  Geneva, United Nations Library

UNITED STATES
  Washington, D.C., Inter-American Nuclear Energy Commission

  See USAEC DEPOSITORY LIBRARIES.

UTAH UNIVERSITY RADIOBIOLOGY PROJECT

A program to compare the effects of radium-226, plutonium-239, radium-228 (mesothorium), thorium-228 (radiothorium) and strontium-90 in adult beagle dogs by observing both biological changes and radiation dose rates, and making correlations between them. In 1950 the Radiobiology Laboratory was established at the University of Utah, supported by the USAEC. In 1955 the study became the Radiobiology Division of the Department of Anatomy of the College of Medicine.

Each dog (other than normal or x-ray controls) is given a single injection of one of the radionuclides at one of several dose levels. The toxicity animals are kept for a life-time, the test animals may be sacrificed as needed for special studies. The 1962 census of the beagle colony was 408 dogs.

Data indicate that the highest levels of bone retention lead to spontaneous fractures and to tumors of the bone, which result in death. Early hematologic changes, largely leukopenia, are seen in the higher levels within the first 2 weeks, and a drop in the platelet count usually occurs at the end of 1 month: complete recovery from acute symptoms. There is some evidence of early aging, but the most common pathological manifestations are in bone. Accurate retention levels are being determined for the various radionuclides.

V

VANADIUM

Symbol V; atomic number 23; atomic weight 50.95. A silver-white, very hard metal. Discovered by Del Rio in 1801. Also credited to Sefström in 1830. Wohler and J. J. Berzelius also worked on it about 1830. Isolated by Roscoe in 1869. Named for the Scandinavian goddess, Vanadis. Relatively rare but occurs in a variety of minerals; patronite, carnotite and vanadinite are most common sources. Natural abundance furnished by 1 stable isotope: V^{51}, 99.76%; and by V^{50}, 0.24%, which has a radioactive half-life of 4×10^{14} years.

Used in manufacturing special rust-resistant alloy steels; in the preparation of aniline black and for coloring glass. Present in biological materials but not important in biological, medical or agricultural activity. Inhaled dusts are highly toxic.

Eight radioactive isotopes have been identified. V^{49} and V^{52} may occur as the result of induced radioactivity produced by neutron bombardment associated with the detonation of a nuclear device.

VAN de GRAAFF ELECTROSTATIC GENERATOR

One of the earliest types of particle accelerators to be invented, the electrostatic generator remains a relatively common "atom smasher." The classical version consists of a large hollow sphere (Fig. V–1) insulated from the ground and to which a charge is delivered by a rapidly moving belt. The belt picks up its charge from a source at about 50,000 volts and delivers it to the inside of the sphere. With this arrangement, charges of up to 5,000,000 volts can be built up on the sphere, and this voltage can be used to accelerate charged particles. The sphere is charged negatively to accelerate electrons or positively to accelerate positive particles, such as protons, deuterons, alpha particles and He^3 ions. The machine can be pulsed at radio frequencies. The accelerated particles can be injected into more powerful accelerators or may be used directly to bombard targets. When deuterons are accelerated and strike appropriate targets, beams of high-energy neutrons are produced. These have been used in studies of the effects of radiation on mice.

VASCULAR SYSTEM, RADIATION EFFECTS ON

Functional and morphological abnormalities ranging from transient changes in permeability of blood and lymphatic vessels to rupture with

FIGURE V–1. THE BROOKHAVEN VAN DE GRAAFF ACCELERATOR, WHICH PRODUCES BEAMS OF PROTONS, DEUTERONS OR ALPHA PARTICLES AT UP TO 3 MILLION-ELECTRON-VOLT ENERGIES. THE ACCELERATOR ITSELF IS HOUSED INSIDE THE PRESSURE TANK IN THE BACKGROUND; IN THE FOREGROUND ARE PIPES THROUGH WHICH THE BEAMS OF CHARGED PARTICLES ARE GUIDED OUT MAGNETICALLY TO EXPERIMENTAL SET-UPS. THIS MACHINE IS USED MAINLY FOR SERVICE IRRADIATIONS FOR THE MEDICAL, NUCLEAR ENGINEERING AND HEALTH PHYSICS DEPARTMENTS, IN PHYSICS EXPERIMENTS ON PRECISION SCATTERING, AND IN THE DETERMINATION OF NUCLEAR ENERGY LEVELS. A SIMILAR VAN DE GRAAFF ACCELERATOR IS USED FOR INJECTION OF PARTICLES TO BE ACCELERATED FURTHER IN THE COSMOTRON. (COURTESY OF BROOKHAVEN NATIONAL LABORATORY.)

hemorrhage into the extravascular spaces have been observed in many organs as the result of heavy irradiation. Skin lesions (*see* SKIN, RADIATION EFFECTS ON) are usually associated with damage to the vascular system. Impairment of blood flow due to damage to the vascular system can cause secondary metabolic changes and damage to the organ receiving the blood supply; e.g., in the kidneys nephrosclerosis may be a late result of radiation vascular damage. Endarteritis, calcareous deposits and obliteration of vessels are late manifestations.

In radionecrosis of the human brain (*see* BRAIN TISSUE, RADIATION EFFECTS ON) there is always associated vascular damage. The possibility exists that the brain damage is secondary to vascular damage and failure.

See BLOOD VESSELS, RADIATION EFFECTS ON.

VIRUS STUDIES

Radioisotopes—for example, phosphorus-32 as soluble phosphate or sulfur-35 as the amino acid methionine—have been introduced into the tissue culture media or fertilized eggs in which viruses are grown; under these conditions labeling of the virus is achieved. The tagged virus particles, after they have been separated and purified by special methods, can be introduced into host cells where their later fate can be followed by radioassay techniques. These studies have had limitations, particularly because it has not been possible to introduce optimal amounts of the radioisotope without killing the cells of the culture medium.

VITAMIN B$_{12}$, RADIOACTIVE, IN DIAGNOSTIC TESTS

See PERNICIOUS ANEMIA DIAGNOSIS.

VITAMIN STUDIES

Because vitamins are active at extremely low concentrations, the use of radioisotopes has been of particular advantage in study of their metabolic role. Many of the vitamins have been prepared with a radioisotope label; in addition, studies of

vitamin action have been undertaken by use of a radionuclide which is affected by the vitamin, as for instance the influence of vitamin D on calcium-45 absorption and metabolism.

Labeled vitamin B$_{12}$ is widely used for medical purposes. Radioactive cobalt is incorporated into the vitamin B$_{12}$ molecule biosynthetically, and the product is purified by paper chromatography and recrystallization. Studies on human patients can then be carried out to determine the degree of vitamin B$_{12}$ absorption by measurement of fecal or urinary excretion, or by liver uptake by the use of directional scintillation counting. The urinary excretion test appears to be most convenient, and is especially useful in diagnosis of the early stages of pernicious anemia.

VOMITING DUE TO RADIATION

The classic prodromal symptoms of the ACUTE RADIATION SYNDROME are anorexia (loss of appetite), nausea and vomiting (*see* GASTROINTESTINAL TRACT, RADIATION EFFECTS ON). A careful analysis of the clinical signs and symptoms of 31 human radiation injury cases indicates:

Group I: 14 cases with doses ranging from 10 rad to 159 rad. 4 patients had some anorexia and nausea but only 2 vomited (not protracted).

Group II: 8 patients, doses 236 to 365 rad, had mild anorexia and nausea, 6 vomited.

Group III: 6 patients, doses 500 to 640 rad, experienced anorexia, nausea and vomiting within 6 hours which continued intermittently for about 2 days.

Group IV: 2 patients, doses 640 and 1,350 rad, vomited within the first hour, continued vomiting intermittently until death.

Group V: 1 patient, dose 9,200 rad, had violent retching and vomiting almost at once, continued vomiting intermittently until death 35 hours later.

In RADIATION ILLNESS, vomiting is of diagnostic importance, early onset being an indication of a heavy dose of radiation, carrying a poor prognosis. Psychosomatic causation and malingering must be ruled out.

WASHINGTON UNIVERSITY LABORATORY OF RADIATION BIOLOGY

The Fisheries Center, Laboratory of Radiation Biology, University of Washington at Seattle, is an aquatic radiobiology research and graduate training unit administratively responsible to the Graduate School, but with major research support from the USAEC. The Laboratory is one of the oldest now engaged in nuclear studies, having been organized in August 1943 as the Applied Fisheries Laboratory to perform experiments on the effects of x-radiation on fish and other aquatic forms. This work was conducted with the Manhattan Engineer District to determine the possible effects on aquatic life in the Columbia River from operation of the proposed Hanford Works at Richland, Wash.

The Laboratory's interest in aquatic radiobiology was expanded after 1946 when members of the staff performed surveys on and near the nuclear weapon test atolls of Bikini and Eniwetok. The Laboratory continued and is continuing to study the radiobiological effects of radiation of nuclear weapons testing in the Pacific. Long-term studies are being conducted of Rongelap Atoll, accidentally contaminated by fallout in 1954. The Laboratory coordinated the marine aspects of the survey of the northwest coast of Alaska in connection with the proposed harbor digging by use of a nuclear explosion (*see* PLOWSHARE PROGRAM).

Basic research is being conducted at Fern Lake, in cooperation with the Washington State Department of Game involving the use of radioisotopes to determine the metabolic patterns of a natural watershed. Studies are also being conducted on the effects on successive generations of salmon of the exposure of eggs during their developmental stages to chronic low-level irradiation.

The Laboratory is active in graduate training. In addition, it has conducted since 1959 annual Summer Institutes in Radiobiology for 20 college and 20 high school science teachers. In-Service Institutes have also been held.

WASTE DISPOSAL, ECONOMICS

The cost of disposing of reactor fission-product waste must be considered in developing a nuclear-power economy. It has been estimated that by the year 2000, the accumulated fission-product activity may be greater than 3×10^{11} curies. Disposal costs are dependent upon: reactor operating and design characteristics, the radiochemical separation process employed, the cost of tank storage for decay and cooling, the transportation costs to the tank farm and to the final disposal site, and the cost of ocean disposal or land burial. Taking everything into consideration, it has been estimated that a cost of from $1.60 to as much as $64.00 per gallon of high-level activity waste would be permissible for the predicted nuclear-power economy, a range of from $5 to $20 per gallon being a reasonable basis on which to determine the direction of waste-disposal research.

Actual bids for disposal of the radioactive wastes from the Berkeley and Livermore, California, laboratories for ocean disposal of concreted, 55 gallon, 750-pound steel drums were from $7.48 to $8.00 per drum from one commercial concern; $8.53 (1,850 drum load) to $20.47 (500 drum load) from another; $14.50 per drum (regardless of the number) from another; and using Military Sea Transport Service about $5.28 per drum. The cost of land burial at regular burial sites ranged from $14.05 to $15.89 per drum if rail transportation were used; and from $14.90 to $19.25 per drum if through-truck transportation were used. Drums are normally not concreted for land burial and can therefore contain 3 to 4 times the volume of waste.

The cost of waste disposal should be materially lowered by further research, particularly in chemical separation and commercial utilization of fission products.

WASTE DISPOSAL, NUCLEAR-POWERED SHIPS

The principal source of radioactive waste from the operation of nuclear-powered ships is the reactor coolant water, which contains small quantities of activated impurities (*see* ACTIVATION), and may contain trace amounts of fission products. All nuclear-powered United States naval or merchant ships in operation or planned and in construction are powered by pressurized water reactors. The pressurized water circulates through the reactor core and picks up the heat from the nuclear reaction; it then passes through heat exchangers, which transfer the heat from the pressurized water to water in a steam system. The resulting steam is then used as a source of power for the propulsion plant and for the auxiliary machinery. In bringing the reactor plant up to

TABLE W–1. CONCENTRATIONS OF RADIONUCLIDES IN REACTOR COOLANT

NUCLIDE	HALF-LIFE	MAXIMUM	AVERAGE	DUMPING TOLERANCE
Manganese-56	2.5 hours	9.3×10^{-2}	2.2×10^{-2}	15
Cobalt-60	5.2 years	2.5×10^{-2}	5.7×10^{-6}	2
Iron-59	45 days	2.8×10^{-3}	1.5×10^{-4}	1×10^{-2}
Nickel-65	2.56 hours	1.3×10^{-3}	1.6×10^{-4}	19
Chromium-51	27.8 days	5.5×10^{-3}	1.0×10^{-5}	50
Sodium-24	14.97 hours	2.0×10^{-2}	8.0×10^{-5}	8.0×10^{-1}
Copper-64	12.8 hours	9.1×10^{-3}	1.5×10^{-4}	8
Tantalum-182	112 days	5.6×10^{-2}	7.3×10^{-3}	10
Fluorine-18	1.87 hours	6.8×10^{-2}	1.2×10^{-2}	90
Tungsten-187	24 hours	9.0×10^{-3}	3.3×10^{-4}	9.0×10^{-2}
Gross activity measured 15 min. after sampling		1.5×10^{-1}	5.0×10^{-2}	3.0
Gross activity measured 120 hours after sampling		3.6×10^{-2}	3.1×10^{-3}	1.0×10^{-1}

TABLE W–2. CONCENTRATIONS OF FISSION PRODUCTS IN REACTOR COOLANT

NUCLIDE	HALF-LIFE	CONCENTRATION	DUMPING TOLERANCE
Total iodine	variable	5×10^{-4}	1×10^{-3} used
Iodine-131	8 days	1×10^{-5}	3×10^{-3}
Total strontium	variable	5×10^{-5}	1×10^{-4} used
Strontium-90	28 years	5×10^{-8}	8×10^{-5}
Strontium-89	53 days	5×10^{-6}	7×10^{-3}
Barium-140	12.8 days	1×10^{-6}	2×10^{-1}
Cerium-144	285 days	1×10^{-7}	4.0
Cesium-137	33 years	1×10^{-8}	1.5×10^{-1}

operating temperature in a submarine the coolant water expands so that an average of 500 gallons of water is discharged to sea with each heat-up. The reactor coolant water has been carefully analyzed; the activated impurities that are of any importance are listed in Table W–1. Dumping tolerance for restricted waters for each radionuclide is listed in the last column. All figures are in microcuries per cubic centimeter (μc/cc).

Fission products may occur in reactor coolant water because of uranium impurity in core structural materials. The concentrations of fission products from this source are shown in Table W–2; again the last column shows the tolerance for waste disposal, and the figures are in μc/cc.

The basic criterion adopted by the United States Navy for disposal of coolant water is that disposal should not increase the average concentration of radionuclides in the surrounding water by more than 1/10 of the maximum permissible concentration for continuous exposure listed in the National Bureau of Standards Handbook 69. By equally scaling up the activities of all the individual nuclides until the first nuclide reaches its dumping tolerance, it is determined that when the gross coolant activity is 3 μc/cc all nuclides are below their respective dumping tolerances. This gross activity then becomes the Navy standard for discharge in port. In addition, the fission product iodine-131 must be below 10^{-3} μc/ml. This assumes a dilution factor of at least 1,000, which would require mixing with a volume of water approximately equal to the displacement of the submarine. Measurement alongside the dock indicated an immediate dilution factor of about 100,000.

Liquid wastes may also be produced from sampling, from laboratory and decontamination activity and from the reactor shield water. Some particulate and gaseous air-borne activity may also be associated with radiolytic dissociation of water due to irradiation; from direct activation of the constituents of the air in the containment vessel; and from collection, handling and storing of radioactive liquids. The principal source of solid waste is the ion exchange resins used in the by-pass purification system for the reactor coolant water. These resin beds are changed at the end of 6 months of operation and may be dumped at sea; if on shore, the used resin is placed in sealed tanks and buried in the land or sea. Other solid wastes include material from maintenance operations: metal scrap, pieces of insulation, rags, plastic, paper, etc., which are monitored and then handled according to the level of radioactivity.

The fission products in the reactor core are sealed in and so present no operating hazard. The fuel elements are removed and taken ashore for reprocessing, where there is the usual fission product waste disposal problem.

The present philosophy for the first United States nuclear-powered merchant ship, the N.S. Savannah, is based on complete containment of all liquid and solid wastes—nothing will be discharged or dumped into the sea. With favorable weather conditions, controlled release of radioactive gas at the top of the forward mast will be permitted.*

WASTE DISPOSAL, RADIOACTIVE

Radioactive wastes from the nuclear energy industry vary so much that there is no single solution to their management or disposal. The solution depends upon such factors as the specific nature (radioactive half-life, biological half-life, type of radiation, etc.), concentration, and quantity of radioactive materials involved; and on the specific environment in which disposal is being considered. As in every other industry, the disposal of wastes has posed problems and added hazards. The problem of disposal of radioactive waste is that there is no way of immediately destroying the radioactivity; time alone and radioactive decay serve to render the waste stable or of very low radioactivity and therefore nontoxic.

There are 2 general methods of disposal—storage or release to the environment. Storage is associated with concentration, packaging, LAND BURIAL, TANK STORAGE of liquid material, and OCEAN DISPOSAL of either liquid or packaged material. Release to the environment is used only for low-level radioactive wastes with the aim of achieving sufficient dilution during and following release to the environment that the amount of radioactivity likely to reach man will be so low as to be unlikely to produce harmful effects.

Physically the radioactive material may be fine air-borne particulate matter or GASEOUS WASTE, LIQUID WASTE, or SOLID WASTE.

Radioactive waste may be handled by the following general methods: STACK DISPOSAL of gaseous material, river or ocean disposal of liquid material or sealed packaged material, and land burial of either solid or packaged liquid waste. Tank storage is used for containment of all high-level liquid waste to allow time for decay. Various forms of waste processing, including chemical processing, are also being used or experimented with, in an attempt to find a more economical and satisfactory method.

---

*Kramer, A. W.: Nuclear Propulsion for Merchant Ships, 1962. Superintendent of Documents, U.S. Government Printing Office, Washington 25, D.C.

Low-level radioactive wastes, defined as having a radioactivity concentration in the range of 1 microcurie per gallon, are usually disposed of by the method of dilution and release in the environment, in air, land or water. Gaseous waste is usually handled by stack disposal; liquid waste by direct discharge into a river with sufficient flow to provide for adequate dilution, or by discharge into the ground or by release into the ocean; solid waste is baled or otherwise packaged and given land burial or is burned and the ashes buried.

Medium-level radioactive wastes are usually held in trenches, in artificial ponds or in tanks to allow for radioactive decay to a level at which they may be discharged to the environment. Some wastes with radioisotopes of reasonably short radioactive half-lives (weeks or months) are discharged directly into the ground. Some medium-activity wastes have been incorporated into concrete in steel drums, which have then been buried in trenches. One such "monolith" is reported to contain 420 curies of strontium-90 and 32 grams of plutonium. Ion exchange treatment (see CHEMICAL PROCESSING) is also used for this medium-level activity material and the contaminated resins may then be placed in containers and buried underground. As with low-level wastes the quantities here may be large and the cost of "absolutely" processing or containing the material would be prohibitive; it will always be necessary to use the diluting power of the environment to some extent in handling medium-level radioactive wastes.

High-level radioactive wastes must be handled by containment in tank storage to allow time for radioactive decay. Suggestions for final disposal of high-level wastes include: conversion of liquid wastes to solids by one of several methods; permanent storage of solids in geological strata with major emphasis on salt beds; disposal of liquids directly into geological strata, either deep wells or salt beds; and disposal of liquids or solids into the sea. In the hearings on Industrial Radioactive Waste Disposal before the Congressional Joint Committee on Atomic Energy in 1959, the conversion to solids and storage of these solids in salt formations was the most favored method of disposal; the least favored was disposal of high-level wastes in the sea.

The disposal of radioactive waste generated in the use of radioisotopes is discussed under RADIOISOTOPE WASTE DISPOSAL.

FISSION PRODUCT DISPOSAL is presented as a separate item.

State, national and international considerations of the health, safety and legal aspects of waste disposal are very involved and are presented under LEGAL ASPECTS, WASTE DISPOSAL.

As examples of methods, the waste disposal plans of 3 AEC installations will be briefly presented: the General Electric Hanford Works, Richland, Washington; the Idaho Chemical Processing Plant; and the Commonwealth Edison power plant at Dresden, Illinois.

The Hanford plant area is well suited for ground disposal because of its favorable hydrology and geology. Direct ground disposal of low-activity wastes has been practiced for more than 12 years, more than a million cubic meters of liquid waste, containing about 10^6 curies of radioactivity, having been so disposed of. Because of the porosity of the soil, the hydraulic retention time and the chemical reactions within the soil, it is possible to consider ground "storage" rather than ground "disposal," until natural decay has reduced the levels to those compatible with discharge into the biological environment. For medium-level activity waste the practice is to chemically remove cesium and strontium because of their longer half-lives, and to discharge the remaining liquid waste to a "crib." Low-level liquid waste is discharged directly to the crib, which consists of a shallow hole ($12 \times 12 \times 5$ feet) filled with stones and covered with soil from the excavation. Pipes discharge the liquid waste to it and lead to the surface as vents. Each crib is surrounded by a series of monitoring wells to follow the migration of activity. The volume which a crib can take without detectable "contamination" of ground water depends largely upon the acidity and inert salt content of the waste. One site received 8,000 curies of low salt-content waste without detectable contamination, but an identical site receiving high salt-content waste showed appreciable contamination after only 800 curies had been discharged into it. Large volumes of reactor coolant water are fed to dyked ponds or "swamps" situated in natural ground depressions. The policy at Hanford is to: minimize volumes discharged by avoiding dilution wherever possible, separate out long half-life radionuclides before discharge, and evaluate each waste on its merits before discharge to the selected site. Even in the isolated and geologically favorable situation of the Hanford site, ground disposal is complex and costly, but not as costly as sea disposal from an inland site.

The principal activity of the Idaho Chemical Processing Plant (ICPP) is the recovery of enriched uranium from spent reactor fuel elements. The recovery process involves dissolution of the fuel elements in acid followed by extraction of essentially all the enriched uranium from the resulting solutions. The sources of radioactive liquid wastes are the 3 cycles of liquid extraction by which the enriched uranium is recovered from the dissolved fuel elements. The first-step aqueous

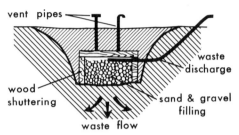

FIGURE W–1. CRIB INTO WHICH LOW-LEVEL RADIOACTIVE LIQUID WASTE IS DISCHARGED.

waste contains most of the fission products and must be stored for several years in water-cooled tanks to eliminate boiling and to reduce corrosion of tank materials. The second-and third-stage cycle wastes contain few heat-generating fission products and are stored together in uncooled tanks. The volume of waste produced varies from 50 to 150 gallons per pound of uranium recovered. The total investment in storage tanks for the ICPP operation is $7,700,000. There are nine 300,000-gallon permanent storage tanks for aluminum wastes, of which 6 are cooled. The average cost is $789,000 per tank, which amounts to a storage cost of $2.63 per gallon. Four 30,000-gallon tanks are provided for storage of zirconium wastes, at a total cost of $580,000, which amounts to a per gallon cost of $4.90. The storage of high-level radioactive waste in tanks is not considered a permanent solution to the problem. The search for better methods is taking many forms. One of the most promising is converting liquid wastes to solid form, thus making storage much easier, safer and more economical.

The Commonwealth Edison plant at Dresden, Illinois, typifies the waste disposal problem of an atomic energy electric power plant. A comparison of its radioactive waste disposal with the disposal of waste from fossil fuels (coal, oil and gas) used to generate power in most electric plants is of interest. Solids consumed as fossil fuels in one year amounted to the equivalent of 4,500,000 railroad car loads of 50-ton capacity of coal; and the resulting solid waste (slag, fly ash or cinders) would require 400,000 railroad car loads to haul it away. By contrast, if the entire electrical power output had been obtained from heterogeneous reactor plants with a burnup of 10,000 megawatt days per ton of uranium used, the total amount of nuclear fuel would have been about 50 car loads, and the volume of waste from the nuclear fuel would have been less than .01% as much as from fossil fuels. Although the spent fuel elements would be chemically processed at another site, it would be possible to store the accumulating volume of fission products for 100 years on a fraction of the area of the Dresden site. Liquid wastes are not very large for either the fossil-fueled plants or the nuclear plants, but the disposal of the radioactive wastes presents a greater problem, which can be handled by either dilution and dispersion or concentration and storage. Gaseous waste presents a very interesting contrast, for tremendous volumes of gaseous waste are produced from burning of fossil fuels. The nuclear power plant produces minute amounts of gaseous waste which can normally be dispersed to the atmosphere with safety. The waste disposal equipment for handling all types of radioactive waste at the Dresden plant cost about $2,400,000 or $13.25 per KW of capacity. Equipment for handling fossil fuel waste costs about $5.50 per KW capacity. If the cost of all waste control activities, including monitoring the environs is considered, the cost of handling radioactive waste from the Dresden plant is about 2.4 times that of a conventional plant. However, with the normal development of nuclear power, waste disposal should be no more, and perhaps less, of a problem than disposal of wastes from fossil fuels.

See WASTE DISPOSAL, NUCLEAR-POWERED SHIPS.

WASTE PROCESSING

The handling and treatment of radioactive waste prior to disposal. Gaseous waste may be put through a precipitator or various types of filters for removal of particulate matter prior to release, or it may be collected and stored. Liquid waste may be diluted and dispersed, or the liquid may be concentrated by boiling or allowing it to evaporate, and then it may be stored in tanks or put into sealed drums and buried. Liquids may also be held in various types of open tanks or ponds to allow for settling, evaporation and decay. Chemical processing of liquid waste for converting it to solid form, or for removal of long-lived radionuclides, is also common practice. Solid waste may be burned or pressed and baled to cut down on the volume, or it may be buried directly. Solid waste may also be chemically converted to liquid waste and then processed.

See WASTE DISPOSAL, RADIOACTIVE.

WATCH, LUMINOUS DIAL, RADIATION

The hands and figures on the faces of watches and clocks are often painted with radium so that they will be luminous (*see* LUMINESCENCE) and thus easily seen in the dark. A watch face may contain 1 microgram of radium, and clocks range from 10 to 100 micrograms. The skin of the wrist may receive a dose of radiation of 10 milliroentgens (mr) in 12 hours, or a total of 7.0 roentgens in a year. The wearing of a luminous-dial radium wrist watch gives a whole body dose of from 10 to 40 mr per year. With 3 million men's luminous dial watches being worn, plus 1 million women's and children's watches and 10 million luminous clocks,

the total population gonadal dose is equivalent to about 1 per cent of the natural radiation.

Tritium-painted dials would be just as satisfactory to read and would be a much smaller potential hazard; there would be no external dose to the whole body, and the weak beta energy would produce negligible radiation to the wrist.

Some watches appeared with strontium-90 luminous paint which would have given a dose to the skin of the wrist of from 35 to 150 rem per year. The USAEC immediately ordered them recovered from the owners and returned to the manufacturer (they had been imported).

WATER BALANCE

Water balance, electrolyte balance and plasma volume are found to change significantly as a result of acute radiation exposure. Severe damage to the gastrointestinal tract is frequently associated with the acute radiation syndrome. Such damage results in severe vomiting and diarrhea with associated loss of fluids and electrolytes. Hemorrhage resulting from radiation injury also causes changes in the plasma volume and electrolytes.

Radioactive isotopes, particularly tritium, have been used extensively to study water metabolism and fluctuation of body water associated with various disease states, as well as with radiation damage.

WATER, RADIOACTIVE

Natural radioactivity of water is usually due to radium-226 and results from leaching of radium-

TABLE W–3

TYPE OF WATER	CONCENTRATION IN GRAMS PER CUBIC CENTIMETER
Ocean	0.7 to 7 $\times$ 10^{-17}
U. S. A. rivers	
Mississippi	1 to 3 $\times$ 10^{-15}
Average of several	7 $\times$ 10^{-17}
Public water supplies	
U. S. A. (tap water)	
Average for 41 towns	0.42 $\times$ 10^{-16}
Maximum—Joliet, Illinois	7 $\times$ 10^{-15}
Sweden (tap water)	2 to 10 $\times$ 10^{-16}
USSR mean value (fresh water)	10 $\times$ 10^{-16}
Germany, Frankfurt-am-Main	1.4 to 3.1 $\times$ 10^{-16}
Austria, Bad Gastein	6.2 $\times$ 10^{-16}
Springs in special areas	
Boulder, Colorado, U. S. A.	3 $\times$ 10^{-10}
Hot Springs, Japan	7 $\times$ 10^{-10}
Jachymov, Czechoslovakia	5 $\times$ 10^{-10}
Bad Gastein, Austria	1 $\times$ 10^{-10}
France	0.3 to 1.4 $\times$ 10^{-13}

containing rocks. Water containing calcium, barium and stable strontium is particularly likely also to contain radium. Radioactive spring water is bottled and sold in some parts of the world for its supposed medicinal value. Table W–3 gives the concentration of radium in various types of water.

See ACTIVATED WATER.

WEAPON, ATOMIC, NUCLEAR OR THERMONUCLEAR. *See* ATOMIC WEAPON, NUCLEAR WEAPON, and THERMONUCLEAR WEAPON.

WEAPON DEBRIS

The residue of a nuclear device after it has been detonated. It includes products of neutron capture in material used for the casing and other components of the weapon or device, plus unexpended plutonium or uranium together with FISSION PRODUCTS.

WEAPONS EFFECTS

Effects of a nuclear explosion may be divided into 2 broad categories: immediate and delayed. The immediate effects are those occurring within a few minutes of the explosion: air BLAST, ground SHOCK, THERMAL RADIATION and INITIAL NUCLEAR RADIATION. The delayed effects are associated with radioactive FALLOUT, RESIDUAL NUCLEAR RADIATION.

As a general summary, the effects associated with the different types of burst are briefly as follows:

High-Altitude Burst. (*See* AIR BURST.) The most significant biological effect is FLASH BLINDNESS and RETINAL BURNS in persons looking at the explosion; other effects are relatively unimportant.

Air Burst. Blast causes physical and biological damage; burns to exposed skin occur. Initial nuclear radiation is a hazard at closer distances, but early fallout hazard is negligible.

Ground Surface Burst. Virtual complete destruction near GROUND ZERO; but otherwise effects of blast, thermal radiation, and initial nuclear radiation are less extensive than for air burst. Early fallout is a very serious hazard over a large area.

Shallow Underground Burst. Thermal radiation and initial nuclear radiation are less than for a ground surface burst. Early fallout may be significant. Near the explosion the base surge may be an important hazard.

Water Surface Burst. Effects are similar to those for ground surface burst, except that the shock wave in water extends farther, and water waves of great height can cause serious damage.

Shallow Underwater Burst. Thermal and initial nuclear radiation and blast effects are less than for surface burst. Early fallout is significant. Radioactive base surge is an important hazard.

Confined Subsurface Burst. The only hazard is from ground shock, and at a distance this is negligible.

The distances from ground zero within which various degrees of destruction may occur are presented in Figure W–2 for weapons yields from 10 kilotons to 10 megatons, TNT equivalent. The height of burst is such as to give the greatest ranges at which the indicated thermal radiation,

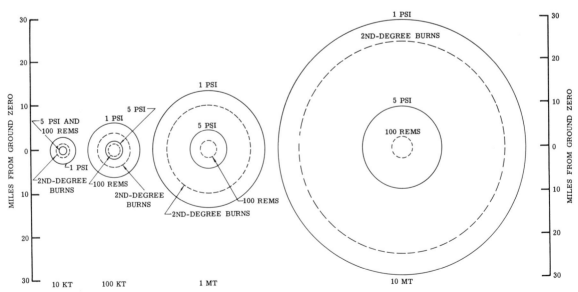

FIGURE W-2. IDEALIZED RANGES FOR EFFECTS OF AIR BURST WITH THE HEIGHTS OF BURST OPTIMIZED TO GIVE THE MAXIMUM RANGE FOR EACH INDIVIDUAL EFFECT.

initial nuclear radiation, and overpressure levels will occur.

WEAPONS TESTING.   *See* NUCLEAR WEAPONS TESTING.

WELL COUNTER

Radioisotope measuring device usually having a scintillation crystal detector formed with a central well into which the samples can be inserted. Major advantages of this arrangement are the simplicity of sample preparation and the increased counting efficiency which results from surrounding the sample by the detector, as in Figure W–3. This method excels in the counting of gamma radioactivity; it is also used for measuring energetic beta radiation through the bremsstrahlung produced within the sample container or detector. These devices are now built in sizes to accommodate samples ranging from the smallest of test tubes to a full-size living human subject (*see* WHOLE BODY COUNTER). Whereas scintillating crystals are suitable for the smaller varieties, the larger instruments utilize detector scintillators made of suitable liquid or plastic materials. In the smaller instruments, a single photomultiplier tube can be used to observe the light flashes which occur when an ionizing event occurs in the detector proper; the larger well counters require extended arrays of photomultiplier tubes in order to pick up the scintillations from wherever they take place in the

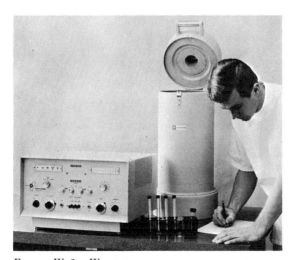

FIGURE W–3. WELL COUNTER AND TYPICAL SYSTEM FOR IN-VITRO MEASUREMENT OF GAMMA RADIATION IN RED CELL MASS AND RED CELL SURVIVAL STUDIES. AT LEFT, CLINICAL SPECTROMETER, COMBINING SCALER, PULSE HEIGHT ANALYZER, AND COMPUTING CIRCUIT. CENTER, WELL DETECTOR WITH LARGE, 3-INCH DIAMETER CRYSTAL; WELL ACCOMMODATES SAMPLES UP TO 20 ml. (COURTESY OF NUCLEAR-CHICAGO.)

large detecting volume. The additional auxiliary equipment generally includes preamplifier, amplifier, scaler or rate meter, and an appropriate recording register or chart.

WESTERN RESERVE UNIVERSITY PROJECT

The Division of Radiation Biology, Department of Radiology, Western Reserve University School of Medicine, operates a radiation biology research program under contract with the USAEC. Historically, in 1946 the University entered into a contract with the Manhattan Engineer District to initiate studies on thorium toxicity. The original research staff was organized around a group of established investigators representing the various disciplines of physics, biochemistry, pharmacology, pathology and clinical radiology, who held faculty appointments in the departments representing their fields of special training. This interdisciplinary approach has continued. In 1962 there were 2 Ph.D.'s in physics, 3 in biochemistry, 3 radiologists and a pathologist, plus 16 technical assistants. A new building furnishes ample space.

This group has stimulated cooperative research within the medical school and has been active in the use of radioactive elements as tracers in metabolic studies and for a variety of clinical applications. More recently research has centered on the study of the mechanism of action of ionizing radiation in living systems and of factors which modify radiation effects. The principal emphasis is placed on those immediate and early physical and chemical events which occur between the initial deposition of energy and the biochemical lesions that subsequently lead to observable biological effects.

WHITE BLOOD CELL STUDIES.   *See* LEUKOCYTE STUDIES.

WHITE BLOOD CELLS, RADIATION DAMAGE.   *See* HEMATOPOIETIC SYSTEM, RADIATION EFFECTS ON; LYMPHOCYTES, RADIATION DAMAGE; and NEUTROPHIL LEUKOCYTE, RADIATION DAMAGE.

WHOLE BODY COUNTERS

Also known as human counters since they are large enough to scan an entire adult male. Essentially there are 2 types of human counters: (1) the multicrystal arrays of solid crystals developed at the Argonne National Laboratory by Marinelli, Miller and Rose; and (2) the four-pi liquid scintillation counter developed at the Los Alamos Scientific Laboratory by Anderson, Van Dilla and Langham. At present (1962) the solid crystal arrays are slower and less sensitive but have much higher resolution of primary gamma rays that reach the detector of the crystal instrument, thus allowing much sharper identification of different isotopes; whereas the liquid counter has higher efficiency in terms of counts detected per gamma ray emitted in the body and also has an apparent inherent superiority in geometry. Continuing research will undoubtedly increase the resolution of the liquid scintillators and the sensitivity of solid scintillators. Both are effective in the micromicrocurie (10^{-12}) level of detection and measurement.

The solid crystal Argonne whole body counter uses large sodium iodide (NaI) crystals (8×4 inches) arranged about 40 centimeters from the body and housed in an iron room $2.4 \times 2.1 \times 1.8$ meters. The room is assembled with iron plates (Navy battleship steel) 0.63 cm thick weighing about 72 kg each. The plates are staggered, bolted together and supported by angle irons, so as to make a wall 8 inches thick. Figure W–4 illustrates both the room and the position of the subject being counted. Figure W–5 illustrates the Brookhaven whole body counter, which is being used extensively in clinical research studies. The potassium-40 (K^{40}) normally in the human body emits about 28,000 gamma rays per minute. The human body may also contain other radioactive isotopes such as cesium-137 (Cs^{137}) shown in the spectrum of

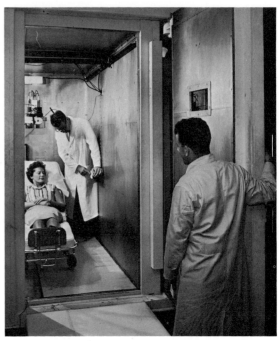

FIGURE W–5. WHOLE BODY COUNTER USED IN LONG-TERM METABOLIC TURNOVER STUDIES WITH MINUTE QUANTITIES OF RADIOACTIVE ISOTOPES IN HUMANS. (COURTESY OF MEDICAL DEPARTMENT, BROOKHAVEN NATIONAL LABORATORY.)

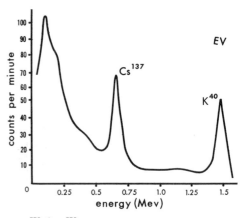

FIGURE W–6. WHOLE BODY COUNTER MEASUREMENT OF CESIUM-137 AND POTASSIUM-40 CONTENT OF A NORMAL ADULT, UNCONTAMINATED.

FIGURE W–4. WHOLE BODY COUNTER. BY MEANS OF A CUTAWAY, THIS PHOTO SHOWS THE EXTERIOR AND INTERIOR OF THE ARGONNE NATIONAL LABORATORY WHOLE BODY COUNTER. THE COUNTER ROOM IS CONSTRUCTED OF LEAD AND STEEL TO EXCLUDE ANY BACKGROUND RADIOACTIVITY SO THAT THE SCANNING HEAD (CIRCULAR OBJECT ABOVE MODEL) CAN ACCURATELY DETERMINE THE RADIOISOTOPIC CONTENT OF THE SUBJECT'S BODY. THE TERM "WHOLE BODY" IS USED IN THE SENSE THAT THE DEVICE CAN DIFFERENTIATE AMONG THE WHOLE SPECTRUM (BODY) OF GAMMA-RAY EMITTING RADIOISOTOPES.

Figure W–6, the measurement of an uncontaminated subject. The scintillation caused by gamma rays striking the NaI crystals is picked up by photomultiplier tubes and is carried through amplifying and scaling circuits, recorded and visually displayed on an oscilloscope.

The Los Alamos counter operates on the same principle except that the subject is surrounded by a tank of liquid scintillation solution surrounding

FIGURE W–7. WHOLE BODY
COUNTER (HUMCO I) ROLLED
OUT OF ITS LEAD SHIELD TO
MOUNT PHOTOMULTIPLIER TUBES.
(COURTESY OF LOS ALAMOS
SCIENTIFIC LABORATORY.)

a well 18 inches in diameter and 72 inches in length. The 108 photomultiplier tubes are arranged outside the scintillation tank and the entire array is housed in a lead shield (see Figure W–7). Figure W–8 shows this counter in operation about to assay a new-born boy for radioactive iron which had been fed to the mother 2 months before his birth. It was found that the iron-59 had passed through the placenta and had been taken up by the baby.

A great deal of research is done using small animals, and an animal whole body counter such as the one shown in Figure W–9 is often used. This same type of counter is often used to count a hand or individual arm, e.g., for the presence of radioactive contamination in a wound. Larger whole body animal counters have been made, e.g., the counter developed by the Hanford Works for counting the strontium-90 content of small swine fed 25 microcuries a day for 2 years, which resulted in a bone concentration 250 times the radioactivity concentration guide levels for occupational exposure in man. The offspring of the first generation all appear normal, but the experiment will continue through 2 more generations.

The use of low-level scintillation spectroscopy in the evaluation of radioactive contamination of the human body has been shown to be a valuable medical tool. Natural body content of potassium-40, cesium-137, radium, and other radionuclides has been determined on many subjects as well as accidental contamination with such radioactive substances as uranium, thorium dioxide, and

plutonium. Such measurements increase the precision of the estimation of the concentration, the topical distribution, and the dose rate from internally deposited radioactive materials.

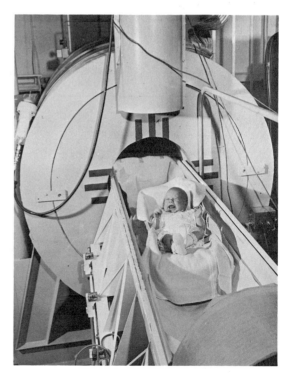

FIGURE W–8. WHOLE BODY COUNTER IN USE TO MEASURE RADIOACTIVE IRON IN AN INFANT. (THE BABY CAME OUT HAPPIER THAN HE WENT IN.) (COURTESY OF LOS ALAMOS SCIENTIFIC LABORATORY.)

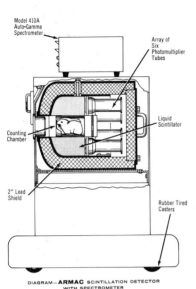

FIGURE W-9. WHOLE BODY COUNTER FOR SMALL ANIMALS. (COURTESY OF PACKARD INSTRUMENT COMPANY.)

WHOLE BODY IRRADIATION

Exposure of the entire body to ionizing radiation from external radiation sources. Irradiation of the body from internal emitters is not usually considered to be whole body irradiation. Prior to the use of nuclear weapons on Hiroshima and Nagasaki any heavy irradiation of humans had been

PARTIAL BODY IRRADIATION given in the treatment of malignancy or polycythemia by x-ray therapy.

Since the development of nuclear energy there have been numerous cases of whole body irradiation from which biological and medical information has been or can be gained. In addition to the Japanese exposed in Hiroshima and Nagasaki

TABLE W-4.   ANALYSIS OF RADIATION INJURY CASES

GROUP*	NUMBER OF CASES	EXPOSURE (RAD)	CLINICAL SIGNS AND SYMPTOMS†
I.	13	10, 20, 22, 27, 28, 36, 55, 60, 68, 126, 142, 159, and one low case (incomplete information)	Almost completely without symptoms or signs in most cases.
II.	8	236, 242, 270, 300, 327, 350, 365, and 369	Mild nausea and vomiting. Mild clinical and laboratory evidence of damage to hematopoietic system.
III.	6	420, 500, 580, 590, 600, and one high case (incomplete information)	Marked prodromal symptoms of nausea and vomiting. Marked evidence of damage to hematopoietic system. Damage to gastrointestinal tract. 590 rad exposure patient died.
IV.	2	640 and 1,350	Marked acceleration of all signs and symptoms of acute radiation syndrome. Both patients died.
V.	1	9,200	Central nervous system involvement. Shock. Fulminating course. Death.

*Same groups as in vomiting due to radiation.

†For details *see* ACUTE RADIATION SYNDROME; CENTRAL NERVOUS SYSTEM; GASTROINTESTINAL TRACT; HEMATOPOIETIC SYSTEM; and RADIATION ILLNESS.

there were the Marshall Islanders, the American servicemen and the Japanese fishermen exposed to fallout radiation during the atomic bomb tests conducted at the Pacific Proving Ground in 1954. There have also been radiation accidents which have been carefully studied. Animal experimental work has provided the basis for our knowledge of the details of acute effects and chronic effects of exposure to ionizing radiation, and human experience has served to compare the similarities and differences between man and laboratory animals.

Whole body ACUTE EXPOSURE, if of sufficient dosage (200 rad or more), may result in the development of RADIATION ILLNESS and in the manifestation of the ACUTE RADIATION SYNDROME. Whole body irradiation (experimental animals and human experience) has been shown to result in such chronic effects as early AGING, CANCER and LIFE SHORTENING.

One of the most comprehensive studies of 31 known human radiation injury cases grouped and defined the clinical signs and symptoms shown in Table W–4.

The possibility of the use of nuclear weapons in warfare brings with it the need to know the loss in ability to carry on physical and mental effort following different levels of irradiation. Determining such military fitness is most difficult, so the figures in Table W–5 should be considered only as approximations.

TABLE W–5.　RADIATION EXPOSURE AND EFFECTIVENESS

DOSE IN RAD (WHOLE BODY)	COMBAT EFFECTIVENESS
50	No casualties. No reduction in effectiveness.
100	2% may be casualties (nausea and/or vomiting for short period of time). No evacuation necessary. No significant reduction in effectiveness.
150	25% casualties in a few hours. First definite reduction in effectiveness. Half of the 25% casualties in this group will have to be evacuated.
200	All should be evacuated as soon as possible. 50% will be noneffective.
300	Approximately 20% deaths. All should be evacuated immediately. All are noneffectives.
450	50% deaths. All others are noneffectives.
Over 650	Lethal dose, but with treatment some survivors.

A summary of the effects and conditions caused by whole body irradiation are given in Table W–6. The predictions are for human beings and

TABLE W–6.　EFFECTS TO BE EXPECTED FROM RADIATION DOSES

DOSE, SINGLE (ROENTGENS)	EFFECTS AND CONDITIONS
100,000 r	Death within seconds with spastic seizures.
10,000 r	Death within minutes or hours with central nervous system damage evident.
1,000 r	Death of all exposed within 30 to 60 days. Evidence of damage to hematopoietic system and gastrointestinal system.
100 r	No deaths. Mild radiation illness symptoms in a few cases.
10 r	Few or no detectable effects.
DOSE, MULTIPLE, INFINITE	
10 r/day	Death in 3 to 6 months, debilitation in 3 to 6 weeks.
1 r/day	Death in 3 to 6 years, debilitation in 3 to 6 months.
0.1 r/day	No effect. Permissible dose range 1930 to 1950.
0.01 r/day	No effect. Permissible dose range 1957.
0.001 r/day	No effect. Natural radiation level.

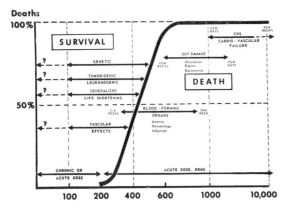

FIGURE W–10. POSSIBLE BIOLOGICAL EFFECTS OF WHOLE BODY RADIATION EXPOSURE.

may be inaccurate within a factor of 2 or 3. Similar possible biological effects of radiation exposure of human beings are graphically presented in Figure W–10. There is a large variation in individual response, plus a degree of uncertainty.

WILZBACH TECHNIQUE

A simple method for labeling organic compounds with tritium (H^3). The compound to be labeled is sealed in a container with tritium gas. Over a period of time some of the tritium atoms exchange places with some of the stable hydrogen atoms of the compound, which thus becomes labeled and can be used for tracer studies. Depending on the nature of the functional group, some hydrogen atoms are more easily replaced by tritium than others, and so the degree of labeling is not uniform for different compounds or for different hydrogen positions in any one compound.

WINDOW ANALYZER

Mechanically driven single-channel pulse height analyzer in which the "window" or region of signal acceptance is traversed across the range of input signal voltage strengths. The amount of radiation detected at any moment is limited to that which lies between the upper and lower DISCRIMINATOR levels defining the window position at that time. When coupled with a strip chart recorder, it can be made to present its data in the form of a completed energy spectrum graph. This device allows a complete scan of the energy spectrum in a sequential manner, avoiding the complication and expense of a multichannel pulse height analyzer. Since it can detect radiation in only one energy channel at a time, there is a consequent loss of counting economy which reduces its usefulness in short-term or low-level studies.

WINDSCALE REACTOR ACCIDENT

The air-cooled, uranium-loaded, graphite-moderated reactor at Windscale, England, on the morning of October 10, 1957, developed a fire which ultimately ruined the reactor and spread contaminated radioactive material over the surrounding countryside. The accident occurred during a controlled release of stored Wigner energy (energy in the graphite due to neutron bombardment) by the application of nuclear heating. Too rapid heating caused the graphite to swell, obstructing the coolant air-flow, which resulted in overheating sections of the reactor, causing the fuel element jackets to split, the graphite to ignite and the uranium to burn. The air circulating through the reactor carried the radioactive material up the stack, and although the filters used in the regular stack disposal took out some of it, much was carried to the atmosphere and the surrounding environment.

Air contamination in the stack and in the immediately surrounding area rose rather rapidly, a 3-hour sample between 1,100 and 1,200 hours on the 10th giving a count of 3,000 beta disintegrations per minute per cubic meter compared with a normal level of 200 to 300 β d.p.m. /m³. On subsequent samples the values were patchy and varied with time; and by ICRP standards for lifetime breathing, the values recorded varied from 2 times the maximum permissible concentration on the afternoon of the 10th of October to 5 or 10 times during the night, with a few peaks as high as 150 times on the following morning. By noon on October 11th the values were dropping rapidly, and the readings were about 1/4 or less, the value of 2 never being reached again.

Standard radiological health control was immediately instituted: special protective clothing, gas masks personal dosimeters were worn, and monitoring and decontamination teams were called to duty. A review of the effectiveness of these measures indicates that only 14 workers concerned with the accident exceeded the maximum permissible body burden of 3.0 r in a 13-week period, the highest figure being only 4.66 r. During the accident 2 workers received 4.5 r, one 3.3 r and 4 others in excess of 2 r. External decontamination of all workers was successful and none had to be detained after the accident.

By noon of the 12th the first milk samples were reported to have an iodine-131 contamination, indicating that iodine vapor had come through the stack filter, had been carried by the wind and deposited on the grass eaten by the cows and had been eliminated in their milk. (This nicely illustrates food chain contamination.) Depending upon the downwind location of the pasture, the first samples showed iodine-131 contents ranging from traces to 0.48 microcurie (μc)/liter. Subsequent samples rose to 0.8 μc/liter, and since 0.1 μc/liter was considered to be the highest concentration allowed for young children, the milk had to be "dumped." At first only 12 milk producers within a 2-mile radius were involved, but the restrictions had to be extended until by the 14th an area approximately 30 miles along the sea coast was involved, 10 miles broad at the southern end and 6 miles broad at the northern end. No other nearby land masses showed contamination. No other sources, such as vegetables, eggs, meat or water supplies, were found to exceed allowable levels; and because of the radioactive half-life for iodine-131 of 8.07 days the contamination of the milk soon dropped to acceptable levels. The highest thyroid activity measured among adults and children was 0.28 μc in the gland of a child (the ICRP safe continuous level for adults is considered to be 0.1 μc in the thyroid gland).

Strontium-89, strontium-90 and cesium-137 concentrations never rose to a level constituting hazard at any time. The entire accident was handled in such a way that it is extremely unlikely that any harm was done to the health of any person.

See REACTOR FIRES, REACTOR ACCIDENTS and REACTOR SAFETY.

WIPE TEST

A test for radioactive surface contamination, usually of a bench top or some piece of equipment, done as part of a contamination survey and to determine the effectiveness of decontamination procedures, especially after a spill. Some of the details of conducting the test are as follows: Use a single piece of filter paper (the diameter depends upon the counting equipment but 5.5 cm is the usual size); record the place and time taken; place between the fingers and wipe a 12-inch strip once with firm but not heavy pressure; count the paper for 3,000 counts or for 2 minutes. Action to be taken will depend upon level of activity and safety regulations. The wipe test is similar to the SMEAR SURVEY.

WOLFRAM. *See* TUNGSTEN.

WORLD HEALTH ORGANIZATION (WHO)

The WHO is a specialized agency of the United Nations whose interests and activities encompass the entire field of international public health.

WHO was first proposed at the United Nations Conference in San Francisco in 1945. In 1946 representatives of 61 governments met at the International Health Conference in New York, drafted and signed the WHO Constitution, and established an Interim Commission. Following ratification by 26 member states of the United Nations the Constitution of WHO came into force in April 1948. In September 1948 the permanent Organization was established.

Expert Committee on Radiation. Essential to the operation of WHO are expert advisory panels and committees. Members of these bodies serve in their personal scientific capacity and not as representatives of governments. The Committee on Radiation met in Geneva in the summer of 1958 and produced its first report, "Effect of Radiation on Human Heredity: Investigations of Areas of High Natural Radiation," which was published in 1959 as No. 166 of the World Health Organization Technical Report Series. The Committee works closely with the United Nations Scientific Committee on the Effects of Atomic Radiation and with other international bodies having an interest in radiation effects.

WOUND CONTAMINATION

Abrasions, cuts, puncture wounds or any destruction of the integrity of the skin associated with radioactive contamination present a most difficult problem. Careful and extensive cleansing of the wound and surrounding area and removal of damaged tissue must be done before the wound is closed. In spite of great care a general body burden may result from even small wounds if the material is soluble in body fluid. For example, a technician broke a flask containing a low-level plutonium solution and sustained a cut 2 centimeters long at the base of her left thumb. In spite of immediate cleansing with soap and water and of profuse bleeding, evidence indicated that she received a general body burden at a level of from 25,000 to 30,000 disintegrations per minute.

An explosion in a dry box caused 3.2 millicuries of plutonium to be lodged in a finger, necessitating amputation.

General skin contamination, even without a break in the skin, also requires careful scrubbing to remove radioactivity.

XENON

Symbol Xe; atomic number 54; atomic weight 131.30. A colorless, odorless gas occurring in air as 1 part in about 11,000,000 by volume. Formerly considered to be chemically inert, but the Argonne National Laboratory in 1962 succeeded in combining xenon with fluorine to form xenon tetrafluoride, thus opening a new area for the study of chemical bonding. Discovered by Scottish chemists Ramsay and Travers in 1898. Named from Greek *xenos*, strange. Nine stable isotopes furnish the natural abundance.

No industrial, biological, medical or agricultural interest.

Twenty-two radioactive isotopes have been identified. Twelve may be produced as fission products from the detonation of a nuclear device. None have any fallout significance. Induced radioactivity may result in trace quantities of 5 xenon radioisotopes being produced in air.

The maximum permissible concentration for a 168-hour week (continuous exposure) with the total body as the critical organ is 4×10^{-6} microcurie per cubic centimeter ($\mu c/cc$) in air for Xe^{131m}; 3×10^{-6} $\mu c/cc$ for Xe^{133}; and 10^{-6} $\mu c/cc$ for Xe^{135}.

X-RAYS

Also called roentgen rays. Penetrating electromagnetic radiation of wave length 10^{-6} to 10^{-12} centimeters, frequency 3×10^{16} to 3×10^{22} cycles per second, and photon energy of 10^2 to 10^8 electron volts. Discovered by German physicist Wilhelm Conrad Roentgen in 1895 while studying the operation of a Crookes vacuum tube. He noted fluorescence on a barium platinocyanide-coated sheet of paper and concluded that whatever was responsible for this originated in the vacuum tube. He also found that the x-rays, as he called them, which emanated from the tube could cause darkening or fogging of photographic plates, even when wrapped in paper and enclosed in a box. This led Roentgen almost at once to take x-ray photographs of normally opaque bodies, such as the hand, and he noted that differential absorption allowed different structures such as bones to stand out prominently.

X-rays are usually produced by bombarding, in a high vacuum, a metallic target called an anticathode with a stream of fast electrons from the anode. In general, any stream of high-energy elec-trons, no matter how formed, will produce x-rays when slowed down by striking suitable target material. By varying the target material and the speed of the cathode particles (targets of high atomic weight yield more x-rays, and the greater the speed of the cathode rays the harder the resulting x-rays), it is possible to vary the wave length of the x-rays and thus their hardness or ability to penetrate matter; in general, the shorter the wave length the harder and therefore the more penetrating the radiation. Filters may also be used to remove the soft rays and allow the more penetrating rays to pass.

In the usual x-ray machine, the target is made of tungsten. Voltages used in diagnostic and x-ray therapy are in the range of 50 to 200 kilovolts (kev), but high-energy machines for deep therapy develop up to 2,000 kilovolts. In a betatron, x-ray energies of several million volts have been achieved. X-rays are also produced by INTERNAL CONVERSION in the radioactive transition from one nuclear isomer to another of lower energy, i.e., ISOMETRIC TRANSITION. X-ray radiation is also produced in the BREMSSTRAHLUNG process. GAMMA RAYS and x-rays are identical in their physiological action, but it is customary to refer to photons originating in the nucleus as gamma rays, and to those originating in the extranuclear part of the atom as x-rays.

X-rays, like gamma rays, produce ionization as a secondary effect. These radiations are without electrical charge and are thus much less likely to interact when they pass in the vicinity of an electron. But they penetrate very deeply into matter (may pass completely through the human body) and can interact with electrons in the atomic shells by the following processes: the PHOTOELECTRIC EFFECT, in which the x-ray photon disappears and a single energetic electron is ejected; the COMPTON EFFECT, in which the initial x-ray photon energy is shared between two products, a photon having less energy and an ejected electron; and PAIR PRODUCTION, in which the x-ray photon disappears and a positron-electron pair appears. Electrons ejected by the above processes produce ionization and are responsible for the bulk of the biological damage from x-ray exposure. All the relative biological effectiveness (RBE) values are related to an assumed RBE = 1 for x-rays having energy commonly used diagnostically.

Biological damage as a result of exposure to

x-rays may take a number of forms depending on the cumulative or total dose: local skin reactions, ERYTHEMA, ULCERS, EPILATION and CARCINOMA of the skin; general manifestations, ACUTE RADIATION SYNDROME, STERILITY, early AGING, LIFE SHORTENING, LEUKEMIA, CANCER, and death due to the direct effects of a single dose of whole-body radiation. Irradiation may also cause mutations leading to genetic death or to the development of subnormal offspring.

The use of x-rays and the fluoroscope in medical and dental practice is a radiation source which accounts for a gonadal (ovaries or testes) exposure to the average individual living in the United States of 3.0 roentgens over a 30-year period. Obviously the gonadal dose to the individual varies with the type of examination; for example, a diagnostic roentgenogram of the head would give a gonadal dose of only 0.2 millirem (one thousandth of a rem), whereas an x-ray salpingography (roentgenologic visualization of the oviduct after injection of an opaque medium) would result in a gonadal dose to the female patient of as much as 10,000 millirem. However, in spite of the slight risk entailed, the continued use of x-ray for diagnosis and treatment is essential in modern medicine and dentistry. It is necessary to balance the need against the risk; but it is doubly necessary to reduce the risk (exposure dose) to a minimum consistent with good results.

It follows that when x-ray, fluoroscope or photofluoroscope is used, the exposure should be held to a minimum. This may be accomplished by controlling the scatter of rays from the machine by proper collimation and shielding; by limitation of exposure time; and by individual shielding with a lead apron or lead jockstrap for the male to reduce gonadal dose and therefore genetic hazard.

The installation of the x-ray machine should be carefully planned in accordance with the recommendations of the National Bureau of Standards Handbook 76, "Medical X-ray Protection up to 3 Mev" (for sale by the Superintendent of Documents, Washington 25, D.C., price 25 cents), and

particular care should be exercised in assuring proper shielding. Although an alpha particle can be stopped by a sheet of paper and a beta particle by an inch of wood, it takes a great amount of lead or cement to stop high-energy x-rays.

Characteristic x-rays are produced when cathode rays are allowed to fall on a given metal element. These are superimposed on the continuous spectrum, and are uniquely characteristic of the element used as the target in the x-ray tube. It has been shown that wave lengths of characteristic x-rays change in a regular manner with increasing atomic numbers of the elements.

X-ray analysis by the diffraction of x-rays by crystalline solids is a well-known technique for identification and solution of crystal structures.

It is possible to utilize the diffraction-grating effect of a crystal to analyze the various wave lengths of a BEAM of nonhomogeneous x-rays and to measure the relative intensities of the various components of this spectrum which has been formed.

An X unit (Xu) is sometimes used in expressing the wave lengths of x-rays or gamma rays. It is about 10^{-11} centimeter or 10^{-3} angstrom.

Dosage units were first set for x-ray use on the basis of erythema of the skin and were called HED units (from either human erythema dose or Hauteinheitsdosis). Other early units of x-ray dosage used were "German R units" and "French R units," Bordier units, Sabouraud units, and Holzknecht units. However, by international agreement the roentgen (r) was adopted in 1928 and soon became used universally.

X-RAY DIFFRACTION UNIT

Apparatus comprising a source of x-rays together with a camera or other means for recording angles and intensities of x-rays diffracted by the regular array of atoms in crystalline substances; also applied in the determination of long-range order in large organic molecules and other materials whose lattice symmetry is not perfect or of long range.

Y

YIELD

Also "energy yield." The total effective energy released in the detonation of a nuclear device, manifested as NUCLEAR RADIATION, THERMAL RADIATION and BLAST ENERGY. Yield is usually expressed in terms of TNT EQUIVALENT tonnage required to produce the same energy release in an explosion, and is rated in kiloton energy or megaton energy. In nuclear weapons testing the reported yields have varied from about 0.1 kiloton to 15 or more megatons. (USSR series of 1961, yields of 56 to 58 megatons.)

Fission yield is that portion of the total explosive yield attributable to nuclear fission, as opposed to fusion. In an atomic weapon the energy is entirely from fission and therefore the total yield and fission yield are the same. In the detonation of a thermonuclear weapon the fission yield is usually roughly 50 per cent of the total yield. The interest in fission yield stems from the interest in fission product formation and its relationship to radioactive fallout.

Blast yield is that portion of the total energy of a nuclear detonation that is identified as the blast or shock wave.

Thermal energy yield is the total quantity of thermal radiation emitted by a nuclear detonation; it is expressed in calories, ergs or joules.

YTTERBIUM

Symbol Yb; atomic number 70; atomic weight 173.04; a member of the yttrium subgroup of rare earth metals. Separated by Marignac in 1878. In 1907 Urbain and in 1908 von Welsbach separately showed that ytterbium and lutetium are found in the same earth metals. Named for Ytterby, in Sweden. Its natural abundance is furnished by 7 different stable isotopes; in addition, there are 7 radioactive isotopes. None has been shown to have any significance for biological, medical or agricultural activity.

YTTRIUM

Symbol Y; atomic number 39; atomic weight 88.92. A rare earth metal occurring as Y_2O_3 in such uncommon minerals as gadolinite, xenotine and fergusonite. Discovered by Gadolin in 1794; isolated by Mosander in 1843. Named for Ytterby, in Sweden. Stable isotope Y^{89} accounts for 100% of the natural abundance. The yttrium subgroup of rare earth metals consists of the elements yttrium, gadolinium, terbium, dysposium, holmium, erbium, thulium, ytterbium and lutetium.

There are 18 radioactive isotopes but only Y^{90} and Y^{91} are important biologically and medically. Yttrium-90 ($_{39}Y^{90}$, half-life 2.54 days, β^- emitter) is important because it is the radioactive daughter of strontium-90 produced in fission and thus is significant in radioactive fallout. A total of 14 radionuclides of yttrium are formed as fission products, appreciable amounts of Y^{90} and Y^{91} remaining at the end of 1 year. Both Y^{90} and Y^{91} are available commercially for biological study, Y^{91} being the preparation of choice for radioassay studies. Some interest has been shown in using Y^{90} colloids for medical treatment. Small spheric Y^{90} beads with an activity of 0.08 microcurie have been inserted by transnasal implantation to successfully destroy the hypophysis; 400,000 rad are delivered at 1-millimeter distance.

The parent-daughter Sr^{90}–Y^{90} combination is highly radiotoxic. LD_{50} values for 3 yttrium compounds ranged from 117 to 395 milligrams per kilogram, administered intraperitoneally to rats. The maximum permissible concentration has been worked out for 5 yttrium radionuclides. Soluble compounds of Y^{91} (radioactive half-life 61 days; with bone as the critical organ, biological half-life 1.8×10^4 days; effective half-life 51 days; beta and gamma emission): for a 40-hour work week, 0.8 microcurie per cubic centimeter ($\mu c/cc$) in water, and 4×10^{-8} $\mu c/cc$ in air; for a 168-hour week (continuous exposure), 0.3 $\mu c/cc$ in water, and 10^{-8} $\mu c/cc$ in air.

Z-DEPENDENCE

Efficiency of certain interactions between ionizing radiations and matter depends upon the number of electrons (Z) associated with atoms of the absorber. For example, electromagnetic radiation of a particular energy or wave length interacts with absorbing media by the photoelectric process in proportion to Z^3, the pair production process increases uniformly with Z, and the Compton (modified scattering) process is nearly independent of Z; the total energy exchange from radiation to medium is the sum of each of these effects. This property must be considered when dealing with interaction of radiations with matter, as in the absorption of radiation or in the design of detectors used in dosimetry.

ZERO POINT. *See* GROUND ZERO.

ZEUS

Portable air IONIZATION CHAMBER SURVEY METER, similar to the JUNO.

ZEUTO

Portable survey meter of nondiscriminating type, incorporating AIR IONIZATION CHAMBER and RATE METER circuit. This instrument does not have internal means of discriminating between radiations, but it is especially sensitive for alpha-ray detection, with ranges to 4,000 or 40,000 disintegrations per minute; also detects gamma rays to 4 mr/hr or 40 mr/hr, and beta rays according to individual calibration based on the specific energies and geometrical arrangement of the source and detector.

ZINC

Symbol Zn; atomic number 30; atomic weight 65.38. A bluish white malleable metal. Discovery prehistoric. Used for making brass for centuries before it was recognized as a separate metal in 1746 by German chemist Marggraf. Named for German, Zink. Occurs as sulfide, carbonate or oxide. Natural abundance furnished by 5 stable isotopes.

Among its varied uses are: in galvanizing, in brass products, in alloys, in chemical manufacturing and as a paint pigment. Zinc compounds have antiseptic properties and are used in medicine, e.g., zinc acetate, zinc chloride and zinc oxide

ointment. It is an essential element for both animal and plant growth and development. Normal intake for human beings is 12 to 20 milligrams per day (mg/day). Rats require at least 0.04 mg/day. Zinc content in animal tissues: liver, 40 to 140 parts per million (ppm); blood, 6 to 9 ppm; milk, 3 to 5 ppm. Crop plants may contain 10 to 200 ppm. A nutrient solution for plants contains 0.02 ppm. Low order of toxicity; 60 ppm nutrient solution is toxic for plants; fatal dose for rabbits was 34 mg/kg daily for 11 days.

Seventeen radioactive isotopes have been identified. Nine may occur as fission products associated with the detonation of a nuclear device. Zn^{72} is slightly significant in radioactive fallout, 1.21×10^{-5} megacurie per megaton of fission remaining at the end of 1 month. Zn^{65} has biomedical usefulness.

Zinc-65 $(_{30}Zn^{65})$. Radioactive half-life 244 days; with prostate as the critical organ, biological half-life 14 days; effective half-life 21 days; beta (β^+), electron-capture (EC), and gamma (γ). Usually produced by irradiation of zinc with reactor neutrons; thus, Zn^{64} (n,γ) Zn^{65}. If high specific activity is desired, cyclotron deuterons are used, Cu^{65} $(d,2n)$ Zn^{65}. Used extensively (stands sixth among radioisotopes used) in biological and agricultural research to study zinc uptake, distribution and metabolism. Used to study absorption, distribution, metabolism and excretion of zinc in animals and man. Maximum permissible concentration for 168-hour week (continuous exposure), soluble material with total body and prostate as the critical organs: 10^{-3} microcurie per cubic centimeter ($\mu c/cc$) in water and 4×10^{-8} $\mu c/cc$ in air.

ZIRCONIUM

Symbol Zr; atomic number 40; atomic weight 91.22. Occurs in baddeleyite and zircon ores and is present in the earth's crust in larger amounts than lead, copper or zinc. Discovered in zircon by Klaproth in 1789; isolated by Swedish chemist Berzelius in 1824. The natural abundance is furnished by 5 stable isotopes.

A valuable structural material for nuclear reactors because of its heat resistance, resistance to corrosion and damage from neutron radiation, and its very low thermal-neutron cross section (0.18 barn). Also used as an alloy with other metals, as an igniter for flash bulbs, in arc lamps, and in the preparation of glass and enamel.

It is not an important naturally occurring constituent of biological materials and has limited biological and agricultural interest. Has only a mild pharmacological action.

Of primary medical interest as a chelating agent in increasing and speeding up the removal of bone-seeking radioisotopes from the body. For example, zirconium salts chemically bind plutonium while it is in the blood stream and the bound particles are deposited in the liver and spleen, where they can be eliminated. They are thus blocked from the bone, where plutonium (Pu^{239}) has a biological half-life of 7.3×10^4 days and an effective half-life of 7.24×10^4 days. Zr^{95} (plus its daughters Nb^{95m} and Nb^{95}), on the other hand, has a biological half-life of 1,000 days in bone and only 320 days in liver. (Because of the short physical half-life of 63.3 days for Zr^{95} alone, the effective half-life in bone is 60 days and in liver 53 days.)

Of additional medical interest because 8 of the 15 radioactive isotopes of zirconium may be pro-duced as fission products in the detonation of a nuclear device. Zr^{95} at the end of 1 year is found to be present in 0.432 megacurie per megaton of fission. Zirconium and its daughter niobium (Zr^{95}–Nb^{95}) are among the 10 most important components of radioactive fallout because of their abundance and their bone-seeking quality. They dominate the picture of residual radiation at the site of the shot, being most prominent about 2 months after detonation. In addition, they are components of both stratospheric and tropospheric fallout, and are among the 7 radioisotopes routinely analyzed for in the stratospheric filter sampling program.

Zr^{95}, a fission product in the operation of a nuclear reactor, is now being separated from the fission product waste and is available in megacurie quantities.

The maximum permissible concentration for soluble zirconium (Zr^{95}) with total body as the critical organ is 1 microcurie per cubic centimeter ($\mu c/cc$) in water and 4×10^{-8} $\mu c/cc$ in air for a 168-hour week (continuous exposure).

UNITED STATES ATOMIC ENERG

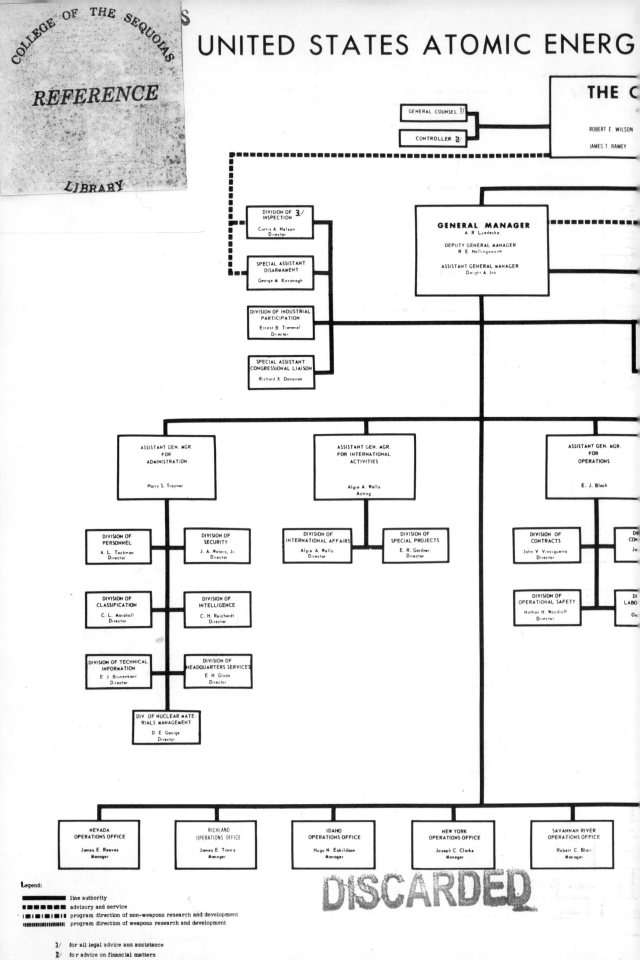

THE C

GENERAL COUNSEL 1/

CONTROLLER 2/

ROBERT E. WILSON

JAMES T. RAMEY

DIVISION OF INSPECTION 3/
Curtis A. Nelson
Director

SPECIAL ASSISTANT DISARMAMENT
George M. Kavanagh

DIVISION OF INDUSTRIAL PARTICIPATION
Ernest B. Tremmel
Director

SPECIAL ASSISTANT CONGRESSIONAL LIAISON
Richard X. Donovan

GENERAL MANAGER
A. R. Luedecke

DEPUTY GENERAL MANAGER
R. E. Hollingsworth

ASSISTANT GENERAL MANAGER
Dwight A. Ink

ASSISTANT GEN. MGR.
FOR
ADMINISTRATION

Harry S. Traynor

ASSISTANT GEN. MGR.
FOR INTERNATIONAL
ACTIVITIES

Algie A. Wells
Acting

ASSISTANT GEN. MGR.
FOR
OPERATIONS

E. J. Bloch

DIVISION OF
PERSONNEL
A. L. Tackman
Director

DIVISION OF
SECURITY
J. A. Waters, Jr.
Director

DIVISION OF
INTERNATIONAL AFFAIRS
Algie A. Wells
Director

DIVISION OF
SPECIAL PROJECTS
E. R. Gardner
Director

DIVISION OF
CONTRACTS
John V. Vinciguerra
Director

DI
CON
Jo

DIVISION OF
CLASSIFICATION
C. L. Marshall
Director

DIVISION OF
INTELLIGENCE
C. H. Reichardt
Director

DIVISION OF
OPERATIONAL SAFETY
Nathan H. Woodruff
Director

DI
LABO
Os

DIVISION OF TECHNICAL
INFORMATION
E. J. Brunenkant
Director

DIVISION OF
HEADQUARTERS SERVICES
E. H. Glade
Director

DIV OF NUCLEAR MATE-
RIALS MANAGEMENT
D. E. George
Director

NEVADA
OPERATIONS OFFICE
James E. Reeves
Manager

RICHLAND
OPERATIONS OFFICE
James E. Travis
Manager

IDAHO
OPERATIONS OFFICE
Hugo N. Eskildson
Manager

NEW YORK
OPERATIONS OFFICE
Joseph C. Clarke
Manager

SAVANNAH RIVER
OPERATIONS OFFICE
Robert C. Blair
Manager

DISCARDED

Legend:

▬▬▬▬ line authority
▪▪▪▪▪▪ advisory and service
▪▬▪▬▪▬ program direction of non-weapons research and development
▥▥▥▥▥ program direction of weapons research and development

1/ for all legal advice and assistance
2/ for advice on financial matters
3/ inspects both regulatory and operational activities